ENGAGING VIDEOS

Active learning opportunities in the form of short, interactive pieces or videos within an assignment pique your interest and motivate you to learn more about the concept. Aplia™ integrates your textbook, art, and media to give you a comprehensive, visual, and interactive experience.

▶ Multimedia material reinforces key concepts and ties the homework to the textbook, helping you visualize dynamic biological processes.

▶ Sequential parts of a question provide incremental explanations for complex concepts.

P9-DOF-312

Determine whether the following statements about DNA replication are true or false.

RNA primers are left intact in the DNA and are not replaced until after DNA replication.	▼
DNA polymerases attach free nucleotides to the 3' end of a growing strand.	▼
Nucleotides are added according to complementary base-pairing rules.	▼
DNA polymerases can only add DNA nucleotides to the end of an existing DNA chain.	▼

We wish to put forward a radically different structure for the salt of deoxyribose nucleic acid. This structure has two helical chains each coiled round the same axis (see diagram). We have made the usual chemical assumptions, namely, that each chain consists of phosphate diester groups joining deoxyribose residues with linkages.[1] Both chains follow right-handed helices, but the sequences of the atoms in the two chains run in _____.[2] Each chain loosely resembles Furberg's model No. 1; that is, the _____ are on the inside of the helix and the _____ on the outside. ...

[1][This sentence] describes the sugar–phosphate backbone.

[2][This sentence] describes the
[dropdown ▼]

[Clear this section's highlighting]

The novel feature of the structure is the manner in which the two chains are held together by the purine and pyrimidine bases. The planes of the bases are perpendicular to the fibre axis. They are joined together in pairs, a single base from one chain being _____ to a single base from the other chain, so that the two lie side by side.[3] ... One of the pair must be a purine and the other a pyrimidine for bonding to occur. ...

It is found that only specific pairs of bases can bond together.

[3][This sentence] describes the
[dropdown ▼]

KEY CONCEPTS

Interactive assignments and tools ensure that you grasp and can apply fundamental course concepts.

◀ The optional highlighting tool makes it easy to interact with the text on the screen the way you would on a page.

Greenish warblers live throughout Asia, as shown on the distribution map on the left. Although they share a broad range in central Siberia, the eastern Siberian greenish warblers (range represented in red) and western Siberian greenish warblers (range represented in purple) do not interbreed.

Source: D. E. Irwin, S. Bensch, J. H. Irwin, and T. D. Price, "Speciation by distance in a ring species," Science 307, no. 5708 (January 2005): 414-416. Copyright © 2005 by the American Association for the Advancement of Science. Reprinted by permission.

On the map, a graduated transition in color from one geographic region to another represents gene flow between adjacent populations. Notice that, despite the physical distance between them, the eastern Siberian population does exchange genes with the populations to the south. Based on the information provided, the greenish warblers consist of _____

EMPIRICAL RESEARCH

Aplia's text-specific problems offer a variety of question types and styles and encourage you to think critically.

▶ Aplia™ helps you analyze primary research data with questions that are varied to accommodate different learning styles.

In 2000, Dr. Darren E. Irwin traveled all over Asia and collected data about local green warbler populations. The symbols on the map above refer to locations he visited. These locations are represented on the graphs below by a two-letter designation (for example, MN, which stands for Mongolia). At each site, he quantified characteristics of the local greenish warbler song and properties of the local environment that would have a strong influence on bird song. For example, the density of the forest has direct effects on the acoustics of bird song, or how it is heard.

Source: Darren E. Irwin, "Song variation in an avian ring species," Science 54, no. 3 (2000): 998-1010, Figure 5. Copyright © 2000. Reprinted by permission of John Wiley & Sons, Inc.

▶ Graph-based questions test your qualitative understanding.

As he moved farther north (increase in latitude), what observations did he make about how the environment changed?

○ The habitat becomes less open.
○ The habitat becomes more open.

As he moved farther north (increase in latitude), what observations did he make about how song behavior changed?

○ The warblers repeat themselves more.
○ The warblers repeat themselves less.

BIOLOGY

Exploring the Diversity of Life

Second Canadian Edition

Volume Three

Peter J. Russell

Paul E. Hertz

Beverly McMillan

M. Brock Fenton
University of Western Ontario

Heather Addy
University of Calgary

Denis Maxwell
University of Western Ontario

Tom Haffie
University of Western Ontario

Bill Milsom
University of British Columbia

NELSON / EDUCATION

NELSON / E D U C A T I O N

Biology: Exploring the Diversity of Life, Second Canadian Edition, Volume Three

by Peter J. Russell, Paul E. Hertz, Beverly McMillan, Brock Fenton, Heather Addy, Denis Maxwell, Tom Haffie, Bill Milsom

Vice President, Editorial Higher Education:
Anne Williams

Publisher:
Paul Fam

Executive Marketing Manager:
Sean Chamberland

Senior Developmental Editor:
Mark Grzeskowiak

Photo Researcher:
Kristiina Paul

Permissions Coordinator:
Kristiina Paul

Content Production Manager:
Christine Gilbert

Production Service:
Integra Software Services Pvt. Ltd.

Copy Editor:
Julia Cochrane

Proofreader:
Integra Software Services Pvt. Ltd.

Indexer:
Jin Tan

Production Coordinator:
Ferial Suleman

Design Director:
Ken Phipps

Managing Designer:
Franca Amore

Interior Design:
Dianna Little

Cover Design:
Jennifer Stimson

Cover Image:
Sea slug: Dr. Mary Tyler & Dr. Mary Rumpho, University of Maine, (2008). "Horizontal gene transfer of the algal nuclear gene psbO to the photosynthetic sea slug Elysia chlorotica," *PNAS*, 105 (46), 17868, Copyright 2008 National Academy of Sciences, U.S.A. Generic DNA code: kentoh/Shutterstock

Compositor:
Integra Software Services Pvt. Ltd.

Printer:
RR Donnelley

COPYRIGHT © 2013, 2010 by Nelson Education Ltd.

Adapted from Biology: The Dynamic Science, Second Edition, by Peter J. Russell, Paul E. Hertz, and Beverly McMillan, published by Brooks/Cole, Cengage Learning. Copyright ©2011 Brooks/Cole, Cengage Learning.

Printed and bound in the United States of America
2 3 4 15 14 13 12

For more information contact Nelson Education Ltd., 1120 Birchmount Road, Toronto, Ontario, M1K 5G4. Or you can visit our Internet site at http://www.nelson.com

Statistics Canada information is used with the permission of Statistics Canada. Users are forbidden to copy this material and/or redisseminate the data, in an original or modified form, for commercial purposes, without the expressed permissions of Statistics Canada. Information on the availability of the wide range of data from Statistics Canada can be obtained from Statistics Canada's Regional Offices, its World Wide Web site at <http://www.statcan.gc.ca>, and its toll-free access number 1-800-263-1136.

ALL RIGHTS RESERVED. No part of this work covered by the copyright herein may be reproduced, transcribed, or used in any form or by any means—graphic, electronic, or mechanical, including photocopying, recording, taping, Web distribution, or information storage and retrieval systems—without the written permission of the publisher.

For permission to use material from this text or product, submit all requests online at www.cengage.com/permissions. Further questions about permissions can be emailed to permissionrequest@cengage.com

Every effort has been made to trace ownership of all copyrighted material and to secure permission from copyright holders. In the event of any question arising as to the use of any material, we will be pleased to make the necessary corrections in future printings.

Interior Images: Closeup of girl looking into a microscope: Yuri Arcurs/Shutterstock; Pickleweed Growing from Cracked Landscape: © DLILLC/Corbis

ISBN-13: 978-0-17-665133-6
ISBN-10: 0-17-665133-0

For, and because of, our generations
of students.

About the Canadian Authors

M.B. (BROCK) FENTON received his Ph.D. from the University of Toronto in 1969. Since then, he has been a faculty member in biology at Carleton University, then at York University, and then at the University of Western Ontario. In addition to teaching parts of first-year biology, he has also taught vertebrate biology, animal biology, and conservation biology, as well as field courses in the biology and behaviour of bats. He has received awards for his teaching (Carleton University Faculty of Science Teaching Award; Ontario Confederation of University Faculty Associations Teaching Award; and a 3M Teaching Fellowship, Society for Teaching and Learning in Higher Education) in addition to recognition of his work on public awareness of science (Gordin Kaplan Award from the Canadian Federation of Biological Societies; Honourary Life Membership, Science North, Sudbury, Ontario; Canadian Council of University Biology Chairs Distinguished Canadian Biologist Award; The McNeil Medal for the Public Awareness of Science of the Royal Society of Canada; and the Sir Sanford Fleming Medal for public awareness of Science, the Royal Canadian Institute). He also received the C. Hart Merriam Award from the American Society of Mammalogists for excellence in scientific research. Bats and their biology, behaviour, evolution, and echolocation are the topics of his research, which has been funded by the Natural Sciences and Engineering Research Council of Canada (NSERC).

HEATHER ADDY is a graduate of the University of Alberta and received her Ph.D. in plant–soil relationships from the University of Guelph in 1995. During this training and in a subsequent post-doctoral fellowship focusing on mycorrhizas and other plant–fungus symbioses at the University of Alberta, she discovered a love of teaching. In 1998, she joined the Department of Biological Sciences at the University of Calgary in a faculty position that emphasizes teaching and teaching-related scholarship. In addition to teaching introductory biology classes and an upper-level mycology class, she has developed investigative labs for introductory biology courses and introduced peer-assisted learning groups in large biology and chemistry classes. She received the Faculty of Science Award for Excellence in Teaching in 2005 and an Honourable Mention for the Students' Union Teaching Excellence Award in 2008.

DENIS MAXWELL received his Ph.D. from the University of Western Ontario in 1995. His thesis, under the supervision of Norm Hüner, focused on the role of the redox state of photosynthetic electron transport in photoacclimation in green algae. Following his doctorate, he was awarded an NSERC post-doctoral fellowship. He undertook post-doctoral training at the Department of Energy Plant Research Laboratory at Michigan State University, where he studied the function of the mitochondrial alternative oxidase. After taking up a faculty position at the University of New Brunswick in 2000, he moved in 2003 to the Department of Biology at the University of Western Ontario. His research program, which is supported by NSERC, is focused on understanding the role of the mitochondrion in intracellular stress sensing and signalling. In addition to research, he is passionate about teaching biology and science to first-year university students.

TOM HAFFIE is a graduate of the University of Guelph and the University of Saskatchewan in the area of microbial genetics. Tom has devoted his 20-year career at the University of Western Ontario to teaching large biology classes in lecture, laboratory, and tutorial settings. He led the development of the innovative core laboratory course in the biology program; was an early adopter of computer animation in lectures; and, most recently, has coordinated the implementation of personal response technology across campus. He holds a UWO Pleva Award for Excellence in Teaching, a UWO Fellowship in Teaching Innovation, a Province of Ontario Award for Leadership in Faculty Teaching (LIFT), and a national 3M Fellowship for Excellence in Teaching.

Bill Milsom

BILL MILSOM (Ph.D., University of British Columbia) is currently the Head of the Department of Zoology at the University of British Columbia, where he has taught a variety of courses, including first-year biology, for over 30 years. His research interests include the evolutionary origins of respiratory processes and the adaptive changes in these processes that allow animals to exploit diverse environments. He examines respiratory and cardiovascular adaptations in vertebrate animals in rest, sleep, exercise, altitude, dormancy, hibernation, diving, and so on. This research contributes to our understanding of the mechanistic basis of biodiversity and the physiological costs of habitat selection. His research has been funded by NSERC, and he has received several academic awards and distinctions, including the Fry Medal of the Canadian Society of Zoologists, the August Krogh Award of the American Physiological Society, and the Izaak Walton Killam Award for Excellence in Mentoring. He has served as the President of the Canadian Society of Zoologists and as President of the International Congress of Comparative Physiology and Biochemistry.

About the U.S. Authors

PETER J. RUSSELL received a B.Sc. in Biology from the University of Sussex, England, in 1968 and a Ph.D. in Genetics from Cornell University in 1972. He has been a member of the biology faculty of Reed College since 1972; he is currently a Professor of Biology. He teaches a section of the introductory biology course, a genetics course, an advanced molecular genetics course, and a research literature course on molecular virology. In 1987, he received the Burlington Northern Faculty Achievement Award from Reed College in recognition of his excellence in teaching. Since 1986, he has been the author of a successful genetics textbook; current editions are *iGenetics: A Mendelian Approach, iGenetics: A Molecular Approach, and Essential iGenetics.* He wrote nine of the BioCoach Activities for The Biology Place. Russell's research is in the area of molecular genetics, with a specific interest in characterizing the role of host genes in pathogenic RNA plant virus gene expression; yeast is used as the model host. His research has been funded by agencies including the National Institutes of Health, the National Science Foundation (NSF), and the American Cancer Society. He has published his research results in a variety of journals, including *Genetics, Journal of Bacteriology, Molecular and General Genetics, Nucleic Acids Research, Plasmid,* and *Molecular and Cellular Biology.* He has a long history of encouraging faculty research involving undergraduates, including cofounding the biology division of the Council on Undergraduate Research (CUR) in 1985. He was Principal Investigator/Program Director of an NSF Award for the Integration of Research and Education (AIRE) to Reed College, 1998–2002.

PAUL E. HERTZ was born and raised in New York City. He received a bachelor's degree in Biology at Stanford University in 1972, a master's degree in Biology at Harvard University in 1973, and a doctorate in Biology at Harvard University in 1977. While completing field research for the doctorate, he served on the biology faculty of the University of Puerto Rico at Rio Piedras. After spending two years as an Izaac Walton Killam Postdoctoral Fellow at Dalhousie University, Hertz accepted a teaching position at Barnard College, where he has taught since 1979. He was named Ann Whitney Olin Professor of Biology in 2000, and he received The Barnard Award for Excellence in Teaching in 2007. In addition to his service on numerous college committees, Hertz was Chair of Barnard's Biology Department for eight years. He has also been the Program Director of the Hughes Science Pipeline Project at Barnard, an undergraduate curriculum and research program funded by the Howard Hughes Medical Institute, since its inception in 1992. The Pipeline Project includes the Intercollegiate Partnership, a program for local community college students that facilitates their transfer to four-year colleges and universities. He teaches one semester of the introductory sequence for biology majors and preprofessional students as well as lecture and laboratory courses in vertebrate zoology and ecology. Hertz is an animal physiological ecologist with a specific research interest in the thermal biology of lizards. He has conducted fieldwork in the West Indies since the mid-1970s, most recently focusing on the lizards of Cuba. His work has been funded by the National Science Foundation (NSF), and he has published his research in such prestigious journals as *The American Naturalist, Ecology, Nature, Oecologia,* and *Proceedings of the Royal Society.* In 2010, he received funding from NSF for a project designed to detect the effects of global climate warming on the biology of Anolis lizards in Puerto Rico.

BEVERLY McMILLAN has been a science writer for more than 20 years and is coauthor of a college text in human biology, now in its seventh edition. She has worked extensively in educational and commercial publishing, including eight years in editorial management positions in the college divisions of Random House and McGraw-Hill. In a multifaceted freelance career, McMillan has also written or coauthored six trade books and numerous magazine and newspaper articles, as well as story panels for exhibitions at the Science Museum of Virginia and the San Francisco Exploratorium. She has worked as a radio producer and speechwriter for the University of California system and as a media relations advisor for the College of William and Mary. She holds undergraduate and graduate degrees from the University of California, Berkeley.

Brief Contents

Contents

lavigne herve/Shutterstock

Sebastian Kaulitzki/Shutterstock

Preface

Welcome to an exploration of the diversity of life. The main goal of this text is to guide you on a journey of discovery about life's diversity across levels ranging from molecules to genes, cells to organs, and species to ecosystems. Along the way, we will explore many questions about the mechanisms underlying diversity as well as the consequences of diversity for our own species and for others.

At first glance, the riot of life that animates the biosphere overwhelms the minds of many who try to understand it. One way to begin to make sense of this diversity is to divide it into manageable sections on the basis of differences. In this book, we highlight the divisions between plants and animals, prokaryotic organisms and eukaryotes, protostomes and deuterostomes, but we also consider features found in all life forms. We examine how different organisms solve the common problems of finding nutrients, energy, and mates on the third rock from our Sun. What basic evolutionary principles inform the relationships among life forms regardless of their different body plans, habitats, or life histories? Unlike many other first-year biology texts, this book has chapters integrating basic concepts such as the effects of genetic recombination, light, nutrition, and domestication across the breadth of life from microbes to mistletoe to moose. As you read this book, you will be referred frequently to other chapters for linked information that expands the ideas further.

Evolution provides a powerful conceptual lens for viewing and understanding the roots and history of diversity. We will demonstrate how knowledge of evolution helps us appreciate the changes we observe in organisms. Whether the focus is the conversion of free-living prokaryotic organisms into mitochondria and chloroplasts or the steps involved in the domestication of rice, selection for particular traits over time can explain the current condition.

We hope that Canadian students will find the subject of biology as it is presented here accessible and engaging because it is presented in familiar contexts. We have highlighted the work of Canadian scientists, used examples of Canadian species, referred to Canadian regulations and institutions, and highlighted discoveries made by Canadians.

Although many textbooks use the first few chapters to introduce and/or review background information, we have used the first chapters to convey the excitement and interest of biology itself. Within the centre of the book, we have placed important background information about biology and chemistry in the reference section entitled *The Chemical, Physical, and Environmental Foundations of Biology*. With their purple borders, these pages are distinct and easy to find and have become affectionately known as *The Purple Pages*. These pages enable information to be readily identifiable and accessible to students as they move through the textbook rather than being tied to a particular chapter. This section keeps background information out of the mainstream of the text, allowing you to focus on the bigger picture.

In addition to presenting material about biology, this book also makes a point of highlighting particular people, important molecules, interesting contexts, and examples of life in extreme conditions. Science that appears in textbooks is the product of people who have made careful and systematic observations that led them to formulate hypotheses about these observations and, where appropriate, design and execute experiments to test these hypotheses. We illustrate this in each chapter with boxed stories about how particular people have used their ingenuity and creativity to expand our knowledge of biology. We have endeavoured to show not just the science itself but also the process behind the science.

Although biology is not simply chemistry, specific chemicals and their interactions can have dramatic effects on biological systems. From water to progesterone, amanitin, and DDT, each chapter features the activity of a relevant chemical.

To help frame the material with an engaging context, we begin each chapter with a section called "Why It Matters." In addition, several chapters include boxed accounts of organisms thriving "on the edge" at unusual temperatures, pressures, radiation dosages, salt concentrations, and so on. These brief articles explain how our understanding of "normal" can be increased through study of the "extreme."

Examining how biological systems work is another theme pervading this text and underlying the idea of diversity. We have intentionally tried to include examples that will tax your imagination, from sea slugs that steal chloroplasts for use as solar panels, to hummingbirds fuelling their hovering flight, to adaptive radiation of viruses. In each situation, we examine how biologists have explored and assessed the inner workings of organisms from gene regulation to the challenges of digesting cellulose.

Solving problems is another theme that runs throughout the book. Whether the topic is gene therapy to treat a disease in people, increasing crop production, or conserving endangered species, both the problem and the solution lie in biology. We will explore large problems facing planet Earth and the social implications that arise from them.

Science is by its nature a progressive enterprise in which answers to questions open new questions for consideration. Each chapter presents questions for discussion to emphasize that biologists still have a lot to learn—topics for you to tackle should you decide to pursue a career in research.

Study Breaks occur after most sections in the chapters. They contain questions written by students to identify some of the important features of the section. At the end of each chapter is a group of multiple-choice self-test questions, the answers to which can be found at the end of the book. Questions for Discussion at the end of each chapter challenge you to think more broadly about biology. You are encouraged to use these in discussions with other students and to explore potential answers by using the resources of the electronic or physical library.

To maximize the chances of producing a useful text that draws in students (and instructors), we sought the advice of colleagues who teach biology (members of the Editorial Advisory Board). We also asked students (members of the Student Advisory Boards) for their advice and comments. Both groups read draft chapters and provided valuable feedback, but any mistakes are ours. The members of the Student Advisory Boards also wrote the Study Break questions found throughout the text.

We hope that you are as captivated by the biological world as we are and are drawn from one chapter to another. But don't stop there—use electronic and other resources to broaden your search for understanding.

M. Brock Fenton
Heather Addy
Denis Maxwell
Tom Haffie
Bill Milsom

London, Calgary, and Vancouver
November 2011

New to This Edition

This section highlights the changes we made to enhance the effectiveness of *Biology: Exploring the Diversity of Life,* Second Canadian Edition. Every chapter has been updated to ensure currency of information. We made organizational changes to more closely link related topics and reflect preferred teaching sequences. New features in the text have been developed to help students actively engage in their study of biology. Enriched media offerings provide students with a broad spectrum of learning opportunities.

Organizational Changes

We divided "Origins of Life and Cells" into two chapters: "The Cell: An Overview" with expanded coverage of cell biology and the emergent properties of life, and "Defining Life and Its Origins," which builds on the content from the First Canadian Edition with more in-depth coverage of multicellularity, key experiments into the origins of life, and a discussion on the probability of extraterrestrial life.

In response to reviewers' comments, we integrated the topics from Chapter 3 Selection, Biodiversity, and Biosphere from the First Canadian Edition into other chapters to strengthen those sections and enhance the flow of topics in the first section of the textbook.

The chapter sequence in Unit 5 Evolution and Classification from the First Canadian Edition was rearranged to improve the flow of topics and include the section on evolution of humans, which was in Chapter 27 Deuterostomes: Vertebrates and Their Closest Relatives in the First Canadian Edition.

New Features

A priority for the Second Canadian Edition was improved illustrations throughout the book; many figures have been redrawn in response to feedback from reviewers, colleagues, and students, and new photographs have been added, such as the photomicrographs provided by Dr. E.C. Yeung, a plant anatomist at the University of Calgary. Another priority was to reorganize some animal biology chapters and to integrate new material (e.g., the discovery of a new species of *Australopithecus* and the presence of photoreceptors in the tube feet of echinoderms).

Our new Concept Fixes **CONCEPT FIX** draw on the extensive research literature dealing with misconceptions commonly held by biology students. Strategically placed throughout the text, these short segments help students identify—and correct—a wide range of misunderstandings. ⬡

Major revisions to selected chapters are listed below:

Chapter 2 The Cell: An Overview
- Combination of the fundamentals of eukaryotic and prokaryotic cell structure and function into a single chapter
- Addition of a detailed figure describing the major types of light and electron microscopy

Chapter 3 Defining Life and Its Origins
- New dedicated chapter addressing fundamental questions such as: What is life? How did life arise? What drove the evolution of the eukaryotic cell and multicellularity?
- Addition of a section on astrobiology and the search for extraterrestrial life

Chapter 4 Energy and Enzymes
- Clarification of the role of ATP breakdown as distinct from ATP hydrolysis in biochemical reactions

Chapter 5 Cell Membranes and Signalling
- Integration of membrane structure and function along with fundamentals of signal transduction into one chapter

Chapter 6 Cellular Respiration
- Improved figures illustrating electron transport

Chapter 7 Photosynthesis
- Improved figures illustrating light absorption and photosynthetic electron transport

Chapter 8 Cell Cycles
- New information and figure about prokaryotic cell cycle
- Modernized immunofluorescence photomicrographs illustrating stages of mitosis
- Clarification of cell cycle controls

Chapter 12 DNA Structure, Replication, and Organization
- Clarification of enzymology of DNA replication, particularly the action of telomerase

Chapter 13 Gene Structure and Expression
- Addition of a figure to illustrate charging of tRNA molecules with amino acids

Chapter 14 Control of Gene Expression
- Addition of figures to illustrate DNA-binding motifs and breast cancer genes

Chapter 15 DNA Technologies and Genomics
- Expanded treatment of comparative genomics and microarrays

Chapter 18 Classification, Evolution, and Phylogeny
- New information about phylogenetic analysis
- Expanded section on human evolution, including latest (2011) findings

Chapter 19 Species
- New information about variation in giraffes, connection appearance, and genetic distinctiveness
- New information about speciation via hybridization

Chapter 20 Bacteria and Archaea
- Title change from "Prokaryotes" to better reflect the content, and updated terminology throughout this chapter and the rest of the book
- Rewrite of section on metabolic diversity for greater clarity
- Redrawn figures comparing cell wall structure of Gram-positive and Gram-negative bacteria

Chapter 22 Protists
- Some figures and photographs replaced or revised to increase clarity, for example, figure showing life cycle of organism that causes malaria
- Rewrite of section on primary and secondary endosymbiosis for greater clarity

Chapter 24 Plants
- Updates to numerous figures
- Revision of material relating to comparisons of bryophytes and vascular plants to clarify the key differences and similarities

Chapter 26 Diversity of Animals 2: Deuterostomes: Vertebrates and Their Closest Relatives
- Streamlined
- Human evolution moved to chapter on evolution and phylogeny

Chapter 27 The Plant Body
- Update of numerous figures
- New photomicrographs from Dr. E.C. Yeung, a plant anatomist at the University of Calgary, for many figures
- Descriptions of structures and processes rewritten to help students understand the most important general principles without overwhelming them with too much terminology and too many details

Chapter 28 Transport in Plants
- Several sections rewritten to provide better clarity on key concepts (e.g., water potential)
- Topics related to the Canadian forest industry and to forestry research in Canada added to the chapter

Chapter 31 Introduction to Animal Organization and Physiology
- Revised section on homeostasis

Chapter 33 Reproduction in Animals
- More emphasis on energy partitioning as a function of reproductive strategy

Chapter 34 Animal Development
- Discussion of epigenetics

Chapter 36 Control of Animal Processes: Neural Control and Chapter 37 Control of Animal Processes: Neural Integration
- New Chapter 36 covering the basics of the nervous system (including afferent sensory neurons) and new Chapter 37 covering neural integration, both at the level of the sensory receptors and within the central nervous system

Chapter 38 Muscles, Skeletons, and Body Movements
- Serious errors in crossbridge cycling during muscle contraction corrected

Chapter 39 Animal Behaviour
- New information about migration, including flight paths of Arctic Terns

Chapter 44 Population Ecology
- New section on challenges to population biologists

Chapter 46 Ecosystems
- New information about nitrogen fixation
- New information about impact of salmon on riparian forests

Chapter 48 Putting Selection to Work
- Added information about human evolution and domestication of other species

Enhanced Art Program
Helping today's students understand biological processes requires effective visual learning support. In preparation for this edition, we undertook a rigorous review of all of the art in the text.

The effective integration of text and illustration has also been a top priority for the development of the art.

Enriched Media
New to the second Canadian edition is Aplia™ for *Biology*, an automatically graded homework management system tailored to this edition. Aplia™ courses are customized to fit with each instructor's syllabus and provide automatically graded homework with detailed, immediate feedback on every question. Aplia's interactive tools serve to increase student engagement and understanding. New interactive 3-D

animations have been developed that help students visualize processes in a more dynamic way. These animations promote in-depth understanding of key biological topics, including cellular respiration, photosynthesis, DNA replication, and evolutionary processes. Embedded assessments in the animations ensure that students have the necessary foundation for understanding these important concepts. Also new to the second Canadian edition are clips from the BBC Motion Gallery. This diverse and robust library of high-quality videos features clips from well-respected scientists and naturalists, including Sir David Attenborough. The clips can be used in conjunction with the text to spark discussion and help students connect the material to their lives outside the classroom.

We now invite you and your students to preview the many exciting features that will help them think and engage like scientists.

THE BIG PICTURE

Each chapter of *Biology: Exploring the Diversity of Life*, **Second Canadian Edition**, is carefully organized and presented in digestible chunks so you can stay focused on the most important concepts. Easy-to-use learning tools point out the topics covered in each chapter, show why they are important, and help you learn the material.

Study Plan The Study Plan provides a list of the sections and subsections in the chapter. Each section breaks the material into a manageable amount of information, building on knowledge and understanding as you acquire it.

Why It Matters For each chapter we provide a brief overview, outlining the main points that follow.

a. b.

Paintings by Claude Monet (1840–1926). Compared to his early works, including "The Water-Lily Pond" **(a)**, his later paintings, including "The Japanese Footbridge" **(b)**, bordered on the abstract with almost complete loss of light blue. Monet suffered from vision degenerative disease cataracts, diagnosed in 1912.

STUDY PLAN

1.1 The Physical Nature of Light
1.1a What Is Light?
1.1b Light Interacts with Matter

1.2 Light as a Source of Energy

1.3 Light as a Source of Information
1.3a Rhodopsin, the Universal Photoreceptor
1.3b Sensing Light without Eyes
1.3c The Eye
1.3d Darwin and the Evolution of the Eye

1.4 The Uniqueness of Light

1.5 Light Can Damage Biological Molecules
1.5a Damage Is an Unavoidable Consequence of Absorption
1.5b Ultraviolet Light Is Particularly Harmful
1.5c Melanin, Suntanning, and Vitamin D

1.6 Using Light to Tell Time
1.6a Circadian Rhythms Are Controlled by a Biological Clock
1.6b Biological Clocks Track the Changing Seasons
1.6c Jet Lag and the Need to Reset Biological Clocks

1.7 The Role of Light in Behaviour and Ecology
1.7a Using Colour as a Signal: Animals
1.7b Using Colour as a Signal: Plants
1.7c Camouflage
1.7d Ecological Light Pollution

1.8 Life in the Dark

1.9 Organisms Making Their Own Light: Bioluminescence

1 Light and Life

WHY IT MATTERS

Claude Monet (1840–1926), a French painter, is considered by many to be the master of the impressionist form that rose to prominence in the late nineteenth century. Other well-known impressionists include Edgar Degas and Paul Cézanne. Impressionism as an art movement was characterized by the use of small visible brush strokes that emphasized light and colour, rather than lines, to define an object. The artists used pure, unmixed colour, not smoothly blended, as was the custom at the time. For example, instead of physically mixing yellow and blue paint, they placed unmixed yellow paint on the canvas next to unmixed blue paint so that the colours would mingle in the eye of the viewer to create the impression of green. The impressionists found that they could capture the momentary and transient effects of sunlight and the changing colour of a scene by painting *en plein air*, in the open air, outside the studio, where they could more accurately paint the reflected light of an immediate scene.

Interestingly, compared with his early works, which included "The Water-Lily Pond" (1899), Monet's later paintings verge on the abstract, with colours bleeding into each other and a lack of rational

1

Study Breaks The Study Breaks encourage you to pause and think about the key concepts you have just encountered before moving to the next section. The Study Break questions are written by Canadian students for their peers across the country and are intended to identify some of the important features of the section.

STUDY BREAK

1. Define light.
2. What structural feature is common to all pigments?

MOLECULE BEHIND BIOLOGY 3.1
L1 Ligase Ribozyme

In the RNA world, RNA served as the molecule of information storage as well as structure and catalysis. To replicate RNA, individual nucleotide triphosphate monomers need to be joined, or ligated, together to form the RNA polymer. Today, this ligation reaction, carried out by a group of protein enzymes called polymerases, can result in RNA strands being many thousands of nucleotides in length. How this polymerization reaction would have been catalyzed in an RNA-only world stumped scientists for years.

Using what is called *in vitro* evolution and selection, scientists recently produced a range of synthetic ribozymes that do not currently exist in nature. One of these synthetic ribozymes is called the L1 ligase ribozyme, and it has been shown to catalyze the joining of two RNA monomers together. This finding clearly suggests that, although not currently found in nature, a ribozyme capable of ligating nucleotides together may have existed on primitive Earth.

Molecule behind Biology "Molecule behind Biology" boxes give students a sense of the exciting impact of molecular research. From water to progesterone, amanitin, and DDT, each chapter features the activity of a relevant chemical.

People behind Biology "People behind Biology" boxes in each chapter contain boxed stories about how particular people have used their ingenuity and creativity to expand our knowledge of biology. The purpose of these boxes is to recognize that advances in biology are accomplished by people.

PEOPLE BEHIND BIOLOGY 3.2
Lyle Whyte, Astrobiologist—McGill University

The heightened research interest into extremophiles coupled with technological advances that are driving the robotic exploration of Mars and other planets has spurred the development of the multidisciplinary science of astrobiology. Broadly defined, astrobiology is the study of the origin, evolution, distribution, and future of life in the universe. The field encompasses the search for habitable environments within and outside our solar system and the search for evidence of prebiotic chemistry and life on Mars and elsewhere. As well, astrobiology includes laboratory and field research into the origins and early evolution of life on Earth and studies of the potential for life to adapt to challenges on Earth and in space.

Canada is at the forefront of astrobiology research, as the government has recently established the Canadian Astrobiology Training Program. The program will create the first cross-disciplinary, multi-institutional undergraduate, graduate, and postdoctoral training program in astrobiology. This initiative brings together researchers at five institutions (McGill University, McMaster University, University of Western Ontario, University of Winnipeg, and University of Toronto) with expertise in fields as diverse as geology, chemistry, physics, astronomy, microbiology, and robotics.

The head of the Canadian Astrobiology Training Program is Lyle Whyte of McGill University. Whyte is a Canada Research Chair in Environmental Microbiology. His research examines microbial biodiversity and ecology in unique Canadian high Arctic ecosystems and is contributing significantly to the knowledge of the diversity, abundance, and critical roles played by microorganisms in polar regions. His research is providing new insights into microbial life at subzero temperatures and their role in global biogeochemical cycling. Whyte and his colleagues do considerable field research in the Canadian Arctic, which is considered by NASA and the Canadian Space Agency to be one of the best sites around the globe to mimic conditions on Mars.

LIFE ON THE EDGE 23.3
Cryptoendolithic Lichens

We tend to think of Antarctica as completely covered in ice, but some valleys of this continent are completely lacking in ice **(Figure 1a)**. These dry valleys may look barren, but they are home to many endoliths—organisms that live in a narrow band under the surface of porous rocks. Predominant among these endoliths are cryptoendo-lithic lichens ("crypto" = hidden; "endo" = inside; "lith" = rock) **(Figure 1b)**. These lichens lack the stratified layers typical of most other lichens; instead, hyphae and clusters of photobiont cells grow around and between the rock crystals, and the lichen that forms is embedded inside the rock. Enough light penetrates the translucent surface layer of rock to allow photosynthesis. Studying endolithic organisms not only helps us understand the diversity of life on Earth but may also be a model for life on other planets. If some organisms can live in such extreme conditions here on Earth, could similar kinds of organisms also exist elsewhere in the universe?

FIGURE 1
(a) Antarctic dry valley. **(b)** Cryptoendolithic lichen.

Life on the Edge "Life on the Edge" boxes provide accounts of organisms thriving "on the edge" at unusual temperatures, pressures, radiation dosages, salt concentrations, and so on. These boxes explain how our understanding of "normal" can be increased through study of the "extreme."

Chemical, Physical, and Environmental Foundations of Biology
While many textbooks use the first few chapters to introduce and/or review, we believe that the first chapters should convey the excitement and interest of biology itself. We therefore placed important background information about biology and chemistry in the reference section entitled Chemical, Physical, and Environmental Foundations of Biology, in the centre of the book. With their purple borders, these pages are distinct and easy to find and have become affectionately known as *The Purple Pages*. *The Purple Pages* enable information to be readily identifiable and accessible to students as they move through the textbook, rather than tied to one particular chapter. *The Purple Pages* keep background information out of the main text, allowing you to focus on the bigger picture.

CONCEPT FIX **Concept Fix Icons** Concept Fixes draw on the extensive research literature dealing with misconceptions commonly held by biology students. Strategically placed throughout the text, these short segments help students identify—and correct—a wide range of misunderstandings. ⬢

PURPLE PAGES

The Chemical, Physical, and Environmental Foundations of Biology

The Scientific Basis of Biology

The information contained in this textbook represents the culmination of hundreds of years of research involving a huge number experiments carried out by countless scientists. The entire content of this book—every observation, experimental result, and generality—is the product of **biological research**, the collective effort of individuals who have worked to understand every aspect of the living world. This section describes how biologists working today pose and find answers to questions.

The Scientific Method
Beginning about 500 years ago in Europe, inquisitive people began to understand that direct observation is the most reliable and productive way to study natural phenomena. By the nineteenth century, researchers were using the **scientific method**—an investigative approach to acquiring knowledge in which scientists make observations about the natural world, develop working explanations about what they observe, and then test those explanations by collecting more information.

Application of the scientific method requires both curiosity and skepticism: successful scientists question the current state of our knowledge and challenge old concepts with new ideas and new observations. Explanations of natural phenomena must be backed up by objective evidence rooted in observation and measurement. Most importantly, scientists share their ideas and results by publishing their work.

Testing a Hypothesis Is Central to the Scientific Method
A **hypothesis** can be defined as a tentative explanation for an observation, phenomenon, or scientific problem that can be tested by further investigation. Scientific hypotheses have two fundamental elements. First a hypothesis must be testable. That is, there must be some set of observations or experiments that can be undertaken to support the hypothesis. For example, you may be studying a gene in yeast that you find is activated when cells are placed under conditions of heat stress. You may hypothesize that the protein encoded by this gene is essential for the yeast to survive short-term exposure to high temperature. Using modern molecular techniques, you can test this hypothesis by inactivating the gene in a population of yeast cells and observing if there is a change in heat tolerance. Today, this hypothesis is easily testable. A scientist may have had a similar idea 30 years ago, but given the lack of molecular techniques, the hypothesis would not have been testable at that time.

The second key to a scientific hypothesis is that it must be *falsifiable*. That is, through observation or experimentation you must be able to show that the original hypothesis may not be correct. Getting back to the yeast analogy, it is very possible that through analysis you would find that inactivation of the gene does not change the ability of yeast cells to survive high temperatures.

Scientists test the predictions that come from hypotheses with experimental or observational tests that generate relevant data. And if data from just one study refute a scientific hypothesis (that is, demonstrate that its predictions are incorrect), the scientist must modify the hypothesis and test it again or abandon it altogether. However, no amount of data can prove beyond a doubt that a hypothesis is correct; there may always be a contradictory example somewhere on Earth, and it is impossible to test every imaginable example. That is why scientists say that positive results are consistent with, support, or confirm a hypothesis.

F-2 THE CHEMICAL, PHYSICAL, AND ENVIRONMENTAL FOUNDATIONS OF BIOLOGY   NEL

THINK LIKE A SCIENTIST

Your study of biology focuses not only on *what* scientists now know about the living world but also on *how* they know it. Use these unique features to learn through example how scientists ask scientific questions and pose and test hypotheses.

Throughout the book, we identify recent discoveries made possible by the development of new techniques and new knowledge. In "Using the Genome as an Investigative Tool," Box 37.2, page 916, for example, learn how the photoreceptors of sea urchins were found in their tube feet.

USING THE GENOME AS AN INVESTIGATIVE TOOL 37.2
Seeing with Your Feet

It is one thing to demonstrate that an animal responds behaviourally to external stimuli, but it may be more challenging to determine how the stimuli were detected. For example, there is evidence of animals such as garden toads (*Bufo bufo*) changing their behaviour in advance of an earthquake, but we do not know what cues trigger the response.

For some time, it has been clear that echinoderms such as sea urchins respond to changing light conditions, but nobody had found photoreceptors in these animals (see Chapter 1 for a discussion of the significance of light and light sensing). The publication of

the genome of purple urchins (*Strongylocentrotus purpuratus*) **(Figure 1)** provided biologists with a means of investigating photoreception in these animals.

Specifically, data in the genome showed that sea urchins possess several genes that code for a widely occurring eye protein, opsin. Discovering this, the researchers designed antibodies against different opsin proteins and performed *in situ* hybridization (see Chapter 15 for a discussion of DNA technologies and genomics). They found that the urchins possess *Sp-opsin4* and *Sp-pax6*, two proteins that regulate

phototaxis. This approach also allowed them to visualize where the photoreceptor cells were located—in the urchin's tube feet. The sea urchin photoreceptive cells are microvillar r-opsin, previously known only from protostomes. Since tube feet are found all over the body of the sea urchin, it appears that the entire adult sea urchin acts as a huge compound eye!

There are many other mysteries about the sensory world of animals. We know that many animals show a magnetic sense, but in most cases we do not know the details of the receptor.

FIGURE 1
(a) The purple sea urchin Strongylocentrotus purpuratus. *(b) Close-up showing the tube feet between the spines. The photoreceptors are located at the tips of the tube feet.*

of light that enters. In dim light, radial muscles contract and enlarge the pupil, increasing the amount of light that enters the eye. Muscles move the lens forward and back with respect to the retina to focus the image. This is an example of **accommodation**, a process by which the lens changes to enable the eye to focus on objects at different distances. A neural network lies under the retina, meaning that light rays do not have to pass through the neurons to reach the photoreceptors. The vertebrate eye has the opposite arrangement. This and other differences in structure and function indicate that cephalopod and vertebrate eyes evolved independently.

37.4c Vertebrate Eyes Have a Complex Structure

The human eye **(Figure 37.15)** has similar structures—cornea, iris, pupil, lens, and retina—to those of the cephalopod eye just described. Light entering the eye

through the cornea passes through the iris and then the lens. The lens focuses an image on the retina, and the axons of afferent neurons originating in the retina converge to form the optic nerve leading from the eye to the brain. A clear fluid called the **aqueous humour** fills the space between the cornea and the lens. This fluid carries nutrients to the lens and cornea, which do not contain any blood vessels. The main chamber of the eye, located between the lens and the retina, is filled with the jellylike **vitreous humour** (*vitrum* = glass). The outer wall of the eye contains a tough layer of connective tissue (the *sclera*). Inside it is a darkly pigmented layer (the *choroid*) that prevents light from entering except through the pupil. It also contains the blood vessels nourishing the retina.

Two types of photoreceptors, rods and cones, occur in the retina along with layers of neurons that carry out an initial integration of visual information before it is

H_3N^+ — | Phe | Val | Asn | Gln | His | Leu | Cys | Gly | Ser | His | Leu | Val | Glu | Ala | Leu | Tyr | Leu | Val | Cys | Gly | Glu | Arg | Gly | Phe | Phe | Tyr | Thr | Pro | Lys | Ala | — COO^-

Ball-and-stick model of α helix

Amino acid side group

Hydrogen bond

Cylinder representation of α helix

Hydrogen bond

Peptide bond

Hydrogen bond

The Chemical, Physical, and Environmental Foundations of Biology. Also known as *The Purple Pages,* these distinct and easy-to-find pages contain readily identifiable and accessible information in one place, rather than tied to a particular chapter, allowing you to focus on the bigger picture.

Special boxes in most chapters present research topics in more depth.

Molecule Behind Biology boxes give students a sense of the exciting impact of molecular research.

People Behind Biology boxes profile Canadian and international researchers and discoveries, and their impact on research in biology.

Life on the Edge boxes explain how our understanding of "normal" can be increased through study of the "extreme" through accounts of organisms thriving "on the edge" at unusual temperatures, pressures, radiation dosages, salt concentrations, and so on.

Research Figures throughout the book contain information about how biologists formulate and test specific hypotheses by gathering and interpreting data.

Research Method

Observational Research

a. *Eurytoma gigantea,* a parasitic wasp

b. *Picoides pubescens,* a predatory bird

Experimental Research

VISUAL LEARNING

Spectacular illustrations—developed with great care—help you visualize biological processes, relationships, and structures.

Illustrations of complex biological processes are annotated with numbered step-by-step explanations that lead you through all the major points. Orientation diagrams are inset on figures and help you identify the specific biological process being depicted and where the process takes place.

From Macro to Micro: Multiple views help you visualize the levels of organization of biological structures and how systems function as a whole.

Electron micrographs are keyed to selected illustrations to help clarify biological structures.

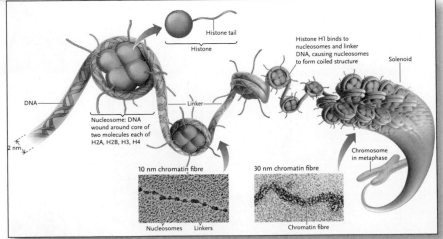

End-of-chapter material encourages you to review the content, assess your understanding, think analytically, and apply what you have learned to novel situations.

Review Key Concepts This brief review often references figures and tables in the chapter and provides a summary of important ideas developed in the chapter.

Review

CourseMate Access an interactive eBook, chapter-specific interactive learning tools, including flashcards, quizzes, videos, and more in your Biology **CourseMate**, accessed through NelsonBrain.com **Aplia™** is an online interactive learning solution that helps you improve comprehension—and your grade—by integrating a variety of mediums and tools such as videos, tutorials, practice tests, and an interactive eBook.

12.1 Establishing DNA as the Hereditary Molecule
- Griffith found that a substance derived from killed virulent *Streptococcus pneumoniae* bacteria could transform nonvirulent living *S. pneumoniae* bacteria to the virulent type (Figure 12.2).
- Avery and his coworkers showed that DNA, and not protein or RNA, was the molecule responsible for transforming *S. pneumoniae* bacteria into the virulent form.
- Hershey and Chase showed that the DNA of a phage, not the protein, enters bacterial cells to direct the life cycle of the virus. Taken together, the experiments of Griffith, Avery and his coworkers, and Hershey and Chase established that DNA is the hereditary molecule (Figure 12.3).

...ture

...discovered that a DNA molecule consists of ... chains twisted around each other into a ...le helix. Each nucleotide of the chains ...bose; a phosphate group; and one of adenine, ...and cytosine. The deoxyribose sugars are ...e groups to form an alternating sugar–phos-...he two strands are held together by hydrogen ...hymine (A·T) and guanine–cytosine (G·C) ...ll turn of the double helix involves 10 base ... and 12.6).

... the DNA double helix are antiparallel.

...ation

... by semiconservative replication, in which the ...rental DNA molecule unwind and each ...e for the synthesis of a complementary copy ...).

...talyze DNA replication. Helicase unwinds ...synthesizes an RNA primer used as a starting ...e assembly by DNA polymerases. DNA poly-...nucleotides into a polymer, one at a time, in a ...entary to the sequence of bases in the tem-...polymerase removes the primers and fills in ...DNA ligase closes the remaining single-...res 12.10–12.12 and 12.15).

...unwinds, only one template runs in a direc-...new DNA strand to be made continuously in ...winding. The other template strand is copied ...at run in the direction opposite to unwinding.

The short lengths produced by this discontinuous replication are then linked into a continuous strand (Figures 12.14 and 12.15).
- DNA synthesis begins at sites that act as replication origins and proceeds from the origins as two replication forks moving in opposite directions (Figures 12.16 and 12.17).
- The ends of eukaryotic chromosomes consist of telomeres: short sequences repeated hundreds to thousands of times. These repeats provide a buffer against chromosome shortening during replication. Although most somatic cells show this chromosome shortening, some cell types do not because they have a telomerase enzyme that adds telomere repeats to the chromosome ends (Figure 12.18).

12.4 Mechanisms That Correct Replication Errors
- In proofreading, the DNA polymerase reverses and removes the most recently added base if it is mispaired as a result of a replication error. The enzyme then resumes DNA synthesis in the forward direction (Figure 12.19).
- In DNA mismatch repair, enzymes recognize distorted regions caused by mispaired base pairs and remove a section of DNA that includes the mispaired base from the newly synthesized nucleotide chain. A DNA polymerase then resynthesizes the section correctly, using the original template chain as a guide (Figure 12.20).

12.5 DNA Organization in Eukaryotes and Prokaryotes
- Eukaryotic chromosomes consist of DNA complexed with histone and nonhistone proteins.
- In eukaryotic chromosomes, DNA is wrapped around a core consisting of two molecules each of histones H2A, H2B, H3, and H4 to produce a nucleosome. Linker DNA connects adjacent nucleosomes. The chromosome structure in this form is the 10 nm chromatin fibre. The binding of histone H1 causes the nucleosomes to package into a coiled structure called the 30 nm chromatin fibre (Figure 12.21).
- Chromatin is distributed between euchromatin, a loosely packed region in which genes are active in RNA transcription, and heterochromatin, densely packed masses in which genes, if present, are inactive. Chromatin also folds and packs to form thick, rodlike chromosomes during nuclear division.
- Nonhistone proteins help control the expression of individual genes.
- The bacterial chromosome is a closed, circular double helix of DNA; it is packed into the nucleoid region of the cell. Replication begins from a single origin and proceeds in both directions. Many bacteria also contain plasmids, which replicate independently of the host chromosome (Figure 12.22).
- Bacterial DNA is organized into loops through interaction with proteins. Other proteins similar to eukaryotic nonhistones regulate gene activity in prokaryotic organisms.

Questions

Self-Test Questions

1. Working on the Amazon River, a biologist isolated DNA from two unknown organisms, P and Q. He discovered that the adenine content of P was 15% and the cytosine content of Q was 42%. Which of the following conclusions can be drawn?
   a. The amount of adenine in Q is 42%.
   b. The amount of guanine in P is 15%.
   c. The amount of guanine and cytosine combined in P is 70%.
   d. The amount of thymine in Q is 21%.

2. The Hershey and Chase experiment involved infecting bacterial cells with radioactively labelled viruses. What did this experiment show?
   a. ^{35}S-labelled DNA ended up inside the virus progeny.
   b. ^{32}P-labelled DNA entered bacterial cells.
   c. ^{35}S-labelled protein was incorporated into bacterial cells.
   d. ^{32}P-labelled protein was incorporated into virus coats.

3. Which of the following would appear on a list of pyrimidines?
   a. cytosine and thymine
   b. cytosine and guanine
   c. adenine and thymine
   d. adenine and guanine

4. Which of the following statements about DNA replication is TRUE?
   a. DNA polymerase III extends an RNA primer.
   b. Some DNA polymerases can add new bases to the 5′ end of a growing strand.
   c. Each eukaryotic chromosome has a single origin of replication.
   d. Okazaki fragments are made only of RNA.

5. Which of the following statements about DNA structure is TRUE?
   a. Each DNA strand has a 3′ OH on one end and a 5′ OH on the other end.
   b. Each strand of the double helix runs parallel to the other.
   c. The binding of adenine to thymine is through three hydrogen bonds.
   d. Bonds between components of the backbone (i.e., sugar–phosphate) are stronger than those between one strand and the other.

6. In the Meselson and Stahl experiment, the DNA in the parental generation was all ^{15}N^{15}N, and after one round of replication, the DNA was all ^{15}N^{14}N. What ratio of DNA would be seen after three rounds of replication?
   a. one ^{15}N^{14}N : one ^{14}N^{14}N
   b. one ^{15}N^{14}N : two ^{14}N^{14}N
   c. one ^{15}N^{14}N : three ^{14}N^{14}N
   d. one ^{15}N^{14}N : four ^{14}N^{14}N

7. Since DNA is synthesized in the 5′ → 3′ direction, which of the following must be true?
   a. The template must be read in the 5′ → 3′ direction.
   b. Polymerase must add successive nucleotides to the 3′–OH end of the newly forming chain.
   c. Ligase must unwind the two DNA strands in opposite directions.
   d. Primase must add RNA nucleotides to the growing 5′ end.

8. Which of the following is a characteristic of telomerase?
   a. It is active in cancer cells.
   b. It is more active in adult than in embryonic cells.
   c. It has telomeres made of RNA.
   d. It shortens the ends of chromosomes.

9. What does the process of mismatch repair accomplish?
   a. It seals Okazaki fragments with ligase into a continual DNA strand.
   b. It removes RNA primers and replaces them with the correct DNA.
   c. It restores DNA sequence that is lost during the replication of the ends of chromosomes.
   d. It replaces incorrect bases that escape proofreading by DNA polymerase.

10. The DNA of prokaryotic organisms differs from that of eukaryotes. In what way?
    a. Prokaryotic DNA is surrounded by densely packed histones; eukaryotic DNA is not.
    b. Prokaryotic DNA has many sites for the initiation of DNA replication; eukaryotic DNA does not.
    c. Prokaryotic DNA is typically single stranded; eukaryotic DNA is typically double stranded.
    d. Prokaryotic DNA is rarely packaged in linear chromosomes, eukaryotic DNA is commonly packaged in linear chromosomes.

Questions for Discussion

1. Chargaff's data suggested that adenine pairs with thymine and guanine pairs with cytosine. What other data available to Watson and Crick suggested that adenine–guanine and cytosine–thymine pairs normally do not form?

2. Exposing cells to radioactive thymidine can label eukaryotic chromosomes during the S phase of interphase. If cells are exposed to radioactive thymidine during the S phase, would you expect both or only one of the sister chromatids of a duplicated chromosome to be labelled at metaphase of the following mitosis (see Section 8.3)?

3. If the cells in question 2 finish division and then enter another round of DNA replication in a medium that has been washed free of radioactive label, would you expect both or only one of the sister chromatids of a duplicated chromosome to be labelled at metaphase of the following mitosis?

4. During replication, an error uncorrected by proofreading or mismatch repair produces a DNA molecule with a base mismatch at the indicated position:

   AATTCCGACTCCTATGG
   TTAAGGTTGAGGATACC
   ↑

   This DNA molecule is received by one of the two daughter cells produced by mitosis. In the next round of replication and division, the mutation appears in only one of the two daughter cells. Develop a hypothesis to explain this observation.

5. Strains of bacteria that are resistant to an antibiotic sometimes appear spontaneously among other bacteria of the same type that are killed by the antibiotic. In view of the information in this chapter about DNA replication, what might account for the appearance of this resistance?

Self-Test Questions These end-of-chapter questions focus on factual content in the chapter while encouraging you to apply what you have learned. These questions have been revised as per Nelson Education's NETA program, as described in detail in the Ancillaries section on page xxviii.

Questions for Discussion

1. Chargaff's data suggested that adenine pairs with thymine and guanine pairs with cytosine. What other data available to Watson and Crick suggested that adenine–guanine and cytosine–thymine pairs normally do not form?

2. Exposing cells to radioactive thymidine can label eukaryotic chromosomes during the S phase of interphase. If cells are exposed to radioactive thymidine during the S phase, would you expect both or only one of the sister chromatids of a

Questions for Discussion These questions enable you to participate in discussions on key questions to build your knowledge and learn from others.

ANCILLARIES

An extensive array of supplemental materials is available to accompany *Biology: Exploring the Diversity of Life,* Second Canadian Edition. These supplements are designed to make teaching and learning more effective. For more information on any of these resources, please contact your local Nelson Education sales representative or call Nelson Education Limited Customer Support at 1-800-268-2222.

Instructor Ancillaries

The **Nelson Education Teaching Advantage (NETA)** program delivers research-based instructor resources that promote student engagement and higher-order thinking to enable the success of Canadian students and educators.

Instructors today face many challenges. Resources are limited, time is scarce, and a new kind of student has emerged: one who is juggling school with work, has gaps in his or her basic knowledge, and is immersed in technology in a way that has led to a completely new style of learning. In response, Nelson Education has gathered a group of dedicated instructors to advise on the creation of richer and more flexible ancillaries that respond to the needs of today's teaching environments.

The members of our editorial advisory board, listed below, have experience across a variety of disciplines and are recognized for their commitment to teaching:

> **Norman Althouse,** Haskayne School of Business, University of Calgary
> **Brenda Chant-Smith,** Department of Psychology, Trent University
> **Scott Follows,** Manning School of Business Administration, Acadia University
> **Jon Houseman,** Department of Biology, University of Ottawa
> **Glen Loppnow,** Department of Chemistry, University of Alberta
> **Tanya Noel,** Department of Biology, York University
> **Gary Poole,** Director, Centre for Teaching and Academic Growth and School of Population and Public Health, University of British Columbia
> **Dan Pratt,** Department of Educational Studies, University of British Columbia
> **Mercedes Rowinsky-Geurts,** Department of Languages and Literatures, Wilfrid Laurier University
> **David DiBattista,** Department of Psychology, Brock University
> **Dr. Roger Fisher,** Ph.D.

In consultation with the editorial advisory board, Nelson Education has completely rethought the structure, approaches, and formats of our key textbook ancillaries. We've also increased our investment in editorial support for our ancillary authors. The result is the Nelson Education Teaching Advantage (NETA) and its key components: *NETA Engagement, NETA Assessment,* and *NETA Presentation.* Each component includes one or more ancillaries prepared according to our best practices and a document explaining the theory behind the practices.

NETA Engagement presents materials that help instructors deliver engaging content and activities to their classes. Instead of Instructor's Manuals that regurgitate chapter outlines and key terms from the text, NETA Enriched Instructor's Manuals (EIMs) provide genuine assistance to teachers. The EIMs answer questions such as *What should students learn? Why should students care?* and *What are some common student misconceptions and stumbling blocks?* EIMs not only identify the topics that cause students the most difficulty but also describe techniques and resources to help students master these concepts. Dr. Roger Fisher's *Instructor's Guide to Classroom Engagement (IGCE)* accompanies every EIM. (Information about the NETA EIM prepared for *Biology: Exploring the Diversity of Life,* Second Canadian Edition, is included in the description of the Instructor's Resource DVD (IRDVD) below.)

NETA Assessment relates to testing materials: not just Nelson's Test Banks and Computerized Test Banks, but also in-text self-tests, Study Guides, and web quizzes, and homework programs like CNOW. Under *NETA Assessment,* Nelson's authors create multiple-choice questions that reflect research-based best practices for constructing effective questions and testing not just recall but also higher-order thinking. Our guidelines were developed by David DiBattista, a 3M National Teaching Fellow whose recent research as a professor of psychology at Brock University has focused on multiple-choice testing. All Test Bank authors receive training at workshops conducted by DiBattista, as do the copy editors assigned to each Test Bank. A copy of *Multiple Choice Tests: Getting beyond Remembering,* DiBattista's guide to writing effective tests, is included with every Nelson Test Bank/Computerized Test Bank package. (Information about the NETA Test Bank prepared for *Biology: Exploring the Diversity of Life,* Second Canadian Edition, is included in the description of the IRDVD on the next page.)

NETA Presentation has been developed to help instructors make the best use of PowerPoint in their classrooms. With a clean and uncluttered design developed by Maureen Stone of StoneSoup Consulting, *NETA Presentation* features slides with improved readability, more multimedia and graphic materials, activities to use in class, and tips for instructors on the Notes page. A copy of *NETA Guidelines for Classroom Presentations* by Maureen Stone is included with each set of PowerPoint slides. (Information about the NETA PowerPoint prepared for *Biology: Exploring the Diversity of Life*, Second Canadian Edition, is included in the description of the IRDVD below.)

Instructor's Resource DVD (IRDVD)

Key instructor ancillaries are provided on the *Instructor's Resource DVD (IRDVD)* (ISBN 0-17-661837-6), giving instructors the ultimate tool for customizing lectures and presentations. (Downloadable web versions are also available at **http://biologyedl2e.nelson.com.**) The IRD includes the following components:

- **NETA Engagement:** The Enriched Instructor's Manual was written by Tanya Noel and Tamara Kelly from York University. It is organized according to the textbook chapters and addresses eight key educational concerns, such as typical stumbling blocks students face and how to address them. Other features include tips on teaching using cases as well as suggestions on how to present material and use technology and other resources effectively, integrating the other supplements available to both students and instructors. This manual doesn't simply reinvent what's currently in the text; it helps the instructor make the material relevant and engaging to students.

- **NETA Assessment:** The Test Bank was written by Ivona Mladenovic of Simon Fraser University and Ian Dawe of Selkirk College. It includes over 2500 multiple-choice questions written according to NETA guidelines for effective construction and development of higher-order questions. Also included are true/false, essay, short answer, matching, and completion questions. Test Bank files are provided in Word format for easy editing and in PDF format for convenient printing, whatever your system.

  The ExamView Computerized Test Bank includes all the questions from the Test Bank. The easy-to-use ExamView software is compatible with Microsoft Windows and Mac. Create tests by selecting questions from the question bank, modifying these questions as desired, and adding new questions you write yourself. You can administer quizzes online and export tests to WebCT, Blackboard, and other formats.

- **NETA Presentation:** Microsoft PowerPoint lecture slides for every chapter have been created by Dr. Jane P. Young, University of Northern British Columbia. There is an average of 80 slides per chapter, many featuring key figures, tables, and photographs from *Biology: Exploring the Diversity of Life, Second Canadian Edition*. NETA principles of clear design and engaging content have been incorporated throughout.

- **Image Library:** This resource consists of digital copies of figures, short tables, and photographs used in the book. Instructors may use these JPEGs to create their own PowerPoint presentations.

- **DayOne:** DayOne—ProfInClass is a PowerPoint presentation that you can customize to orient your students to the class and their text at the beginning of the course.

- **TurningPoint:** Another valuable resource for instructors is **TurningPoint classroom response software** customized for *Biology: Exploring the Diversity of Life*, Second Canadian Edition by Dr. Jane P. Young, University of Northern British Columbia. Now you can author, deliver, show, access, and grade, all in PowerPoint, with no toggling back and forth between screens! JoinIn on TurningPoint is the only classroom response software tool that gives you true PowerPoint integration. With JoinIn, you are no longer tied to your computer. You can walk about your classroom as you lecture, showing slides and collecting and displaying responses with ease. There is simply no easier or more effective way to turn your lecture hall into a personal, fully interactive experience for your students. If you can use PowerPoint, you can use JoinIn on Turning-Point! (Contact your Nelson publishing representative for details.) These have been adapted by Dr. Jane P. Young, University of Northern British Columbia, and contain poll slides and pre- and post-test slides for each chapter in the text.

Student Ancillaries

CourseMate The more you study, the better the results. Make the most of your study time by accessing everything you need to succeed in one place. Your Biology CourseMate includes the following components:

- An interactive eBook with highlighting, note taking, and an interactive glossary
- Interactive learning tools, including:
  - Quizzes
  - Design an Experiment, Interpret the Data, and Apply Evolutionary Concepts exercises
  - Flashcards
  - Videos
  - BioExperience 3D Animations

The CourseMate for *Biology: Exploring the Diversity of Life*, Second Canadian Edition, was prepared by Dora Cavallo-Medved, University of Windsor and Reehan Mirza, Nipissing University.

 Founded in 2000 by economist and Stanford professor Paul Romer, Aplia™ is an educational technology company dedicated to improving learning by increasing student effort and engagement. Currently, Aplia™ products have been used by more than 650 000 students at over 750 institutions.

For students, Aplia™ offers a way to stay on top of coursework with regularly scheduled homework assignments. Interactive tools and additional content are provided to further increase engagement and understanding.

For instructors, Aplia™ offers high-quality, auto-graded assignments that ensure students put forth effort on a regular basis throughout the term. These assignments have been developed for a range of textbooks and are easily customized for individual teaching schedules. The Aplia course for *Biology: Exploring the Diversity of Life,* Second Canadian Edition, was prepared by Anna Hicks, Memorial University, and Todd Nickle and Alexandria Farmer, Mount Royal University.

Study Guide

The Study Guide (ISBN: 0-17-663368-5) from the First Canadian Edition has been adapted for the Second Canadian Edition by Colin Montpetit of the University of Ottawa, Julie Smit of the University of Windsor, and Wendy J. Keenleyside of the University of Guelph. The Study Guide contains unique case studies to integrate the concepts within the text, study strategies, interactive exercises, self-test questions, and more.

Students and Instructors

Visit the website accompanying *Biology: Exploring the Diversity of Life,* Second Canadian Edition, at **http://biologyedl2e.nelson.com.** This website contains flashcards, weblinks, and much more.

Prospering in Biology

Using This Book

The following are things you will need to know in order to use this text and prosper in biology.

Names

What's in a name? People are very attached to names—their own names, the names of other people, the names of flowers and food and cars and so on. It is not surprising that biologists would also be concerned about names. Take, for example, our use of scientific names. Scientific names are always italicized and Latinized.

Castor canadensis Kuhl is the scientific name of the Canadian beaver. *Castor* is the genus name; *canadensis* is the specific epithet. Together they make up the name of the species, which was first described by a person called Kuhl. "Beaver" by itself is not enough because there is a European beaver, *Castor fiber,* and an extinct giant beaver, *Castoides ohioensis*. Furthermore, common names can vary from place to place (*Myotis lucifugus* is sometimes known as the "little brown bat" or the "little brown myotis").

Biologists prefer scientific names because the name (Latinized) tells you about the organism. There are strict rules about the derivation and use of scientific names. Common names are not so restricted, so they are not precise. For example, in *Myotis lucifugus, Myotis* means "mouse-eared" and *lucifugus* means "flees the light"; hence, this species is a mouse-eared bat that flees the light.

Birds can be an exception. There are accepted "standard" common names for birds. The American Robin is *Turdus migratorius*. The common names for birds are usually capitalized because of the standardization. However, the common names of mammals are not capitalized, except for geographic names or patronyms (*geographic* = named after a country, e.g., Canadian beaver; *patronym* = named after someone, e.g., Ord's kangaroo rat).

Although a few plants that have very broad distributions may have accepted standard common names (e.g., white spruce, *Picea glauca*), most plants have many common names. Furthermore, the same common name is often used for more than one species. Several species in the genus *Taraxacum* are referred to as "dandelion." It is important to use the scientific names of plants to be sure that it is clear exactly which plant we mean. The scientific names of plants also tell us something about the plant. The scientific name for the weed quack grass, *Elymus repens,* tells us that this is a type of wild rye (*Elymus*) and that this particular species spreads or creeps (*repens* = creeping). Anyone who has tried to eliminate this plant from their garden or yard knows how it creeps! Unlike for animals, plant-naming rules forbid the use of the same word for both genus and species names for a plant; thus, although *Bison bison* is an acceptable scientific name for buffalo, such a name would never be accepted for a plant.

In this book, we present the scientific names of organisms when we mention them. We follow standard abbreviations; for example, although the full name of an organism is used the first time it is mentioned (e.g., *Castor canadensis*), subsequent references to that same organism abbreviate the genus name and provide the full species name (e.g., *C. canadensis*).

In some areas of biology, the standard representation is of the genus, for example, *Chlamydomonas*. In other cases, names are so commonly used that only the abbreviation may be used (e.g., *E. coli* for *Escherichia coli*).

Units

The units of measure used by biologists are standardized (metric or SI) units, used throughout the world in science.

Definitions

The science of biology is replete with specialized terms (sometimes referred to as "jargon") used to communicate specific information. It follows that, as with scientific names, specialized terms increase the precision with which biologists communicate among themselves and with others. Be cautious about the use of terms because jargon can obscure precision. When we encounter a "slippery" term (such as species or gene), we explain why one definition for all situations is not feasible.

Time

In this book, we use CE (Common Era) to refer to the years since year 1 and BCE (Before the Common Era) to refer to years before that.

Geologists think of time over very long periods. A geological time scale (see *The Purple Pages,* pp. F-50–F-51) shows that the age of Earth could be measured in years, but it's challenging to think of billions of years expressed in days (or hours, etc.). With the advent of using the decay rates of radioisotopes to measure the age of rocks, geologists adopted 1950 as the baseline, the "Present," and the past is referred to as BP ("Before Present"). A notation of 30 000 years BP (^{14}C) indicates 30 000 years before 1950 using the ^{14}C method of dating.

Other dating systems are also used. Some archaeologists use PPNA (PrePottery Neolithic A, where A is the horizon or stratum). In deposits along the Euphrates River, 11 000 PPNA appears to be the same as 11 000 BP. In this book, we use BCE or BP as the time units, except when referring to events or species from more than 100 000 years ago. For those dates, we refer you to the geological time scale (see *The Purple Pages,* pp. F-50–F-51).

Sources

Where does the information presented in a text or in class come from? What is the difference between what you read in a textbook or an encyclopedia and the material you see in a newspaper or tabloid? When the topic relates to science, the information should be based on material that has been published in a scholarly journal. In this context, "scholarly" refers to the process of review. Scholars submit their manuscripts reporting their research findings to the editor (or editorial board) of a journal. The editor, in turn, sends the manuscript out for comment and review by recognized authorities in the field. The process is designed to ensure that what is published is as accurate and appropriate as possible. The review process sets the scholarly journal apart from the tabloid.

There are literally thousands of scholarly journals, which, together, publish millions of articles each year. Some journals are more influential than others, for example, *Science* and *Nature*. These two journals are published weekly and invariably contain new information of interest to biologists.

To collect information for this text, we have drawn on published works that have gone through the process of scholarly review. Specific references (citations) are provided, usually in the electronic resources designed to complement the book.

A citation is intended to make the information accessible. Although there are many different formats for citations, the important elements include (in some order) the name(s) of the author(s), the date of publication, the title, and the publisher. When the source is published in a scholarly journal, the journal name, its volume number, and the pages are also provided. With the citation information, you can visit a library and locate the original source. This is true for both electronic (virtual) and real libraries.

Students of biology benefit by making it a habit to look at the most recent issues of their favourite scholarly journals and use them to keep abreast of new developments.

M. Brock Fenton
Heather Addy
Denis Maxwell
Tom Haffie
Bill Milsom

London, Calgary, and Vancouver
November 2011

Acknowledgements

We thank the many people who have worked with us on the production of this text, particularly Paul Fam, Publisher, whose foresight brought the idea to us and whose persistence saw the project through. Thanks go to those who reviewed the First Canadian Edition text to provide us with feedback for the Second Canadian Edition, including Dora Cavallo-Medved, University of Windsor; Anna Hicks, Memorial University; Heather Roffey, McGill University; and Todd Nickle, Mount Royal University. We are also grateful to the members of the Editorial Advisory Board and the Student Advisory Boards, who provided us with valuable feedback and alternative perspectives (special acknowledgements to these individuals are listed below). We also thank Richard Walker at the University of Calgary and Ken Davey at York University, who began this journey with us but were unable to continue. We thank Carl Lowenberger for contributing Chapter 43 Defences against Disease. We are especially grateful to Mark Grzeskowiak, Senior Developmental Editor, who kept us moving through the chapters at an efficient pace, along with Sreejith Govindan, Project Manager, and Christine Gilbert, Content Production Manager. We thank Kristiina Paul, our photo researcher, for her hard work with the numerous photos in the book, Julia Cochrane for her careful and thoughtful copy editing, and Sandra Peters, who did a cold read as a further check on our presentation. Finally, we thank Sean Chamberland, Executive Marketing Manager, for making us look good.

Brock Fenton would like to thank Allan Noon, who offered much advice about taking pictures; Laura Barclay, Jeremy McNeil, Tony Percival-Smith, C.S. (Rufus) Churcher, and David and Meg Cumming for the use of their images; and Karen Campbell for providing a critical read on Chapter 48 Putting Selection to Work.

Heather Addy would like to thank Ed Yeung for generously providing many images and assistance with revision of figures, and Cindy Graham, David Bird, Fengshan Ma, and William Huddleston for providing feedback and valuable suggestions for improving several chapters.

Tom Haffie would like to acknowledge the cheerful and insightful editorial work of Jennifer Waugh on Chapter 16. The authors are all indebted to Johnston Miller whose extensive background research anchored our Concept Fixes in the education literature.

It is never easy to be in the family of an academic scientist. We are especially grateful to our families for their sustained support over the course of our careers, particularly during those times when our attentions were fully captivated by bacteria, algae, fungi, parasites, snakes, geese, or bats. Saying "yes" to a textbook project means saying "no" to a variety of other pursuits. We appreciate the patience and understanding of those closest to us that enabled the temporary reallocation of considerable time from other endeavours and relationships.

Many of our colleagues have contributed to our development as teachers and scholars by acting as mentors, collaborators, and, on occasion, "worthy opponents." Like all teachers, we owe particular gratitude to our students. They have gathered with us around the discipline of biology, sharing their potent blend of enthusiasm and curiosity and leaving us energized and optimistic for the future.

Editorial and Student Advisory Boards

We were very fortunate to have the assistance of some extraordinary students and instructors of biology across Canada who provided us with feedback that helped shape this textbook into what you see before you. As such, we would like to say a very special thank you to the following people:

Editorial Advisory Board

Declan Ali, University of Alberta
David Creasey, University of Victoria
Ken Davey, York University
Mark Fitzpatrick, University of Toronto Scarborough
Wendy Keenleyside, University of Guelph
Tamara Kelly, York University
Paul Marino, Memorial University
Yves Maufette, Université du Québec à Montréal
Iain McKinnell, Carleton University
Todd Nickle, Mount Royal University
Carol Pollock, University of British Columbia
Ken Wilson, University of Saskatchewan

Depicted above are the author team, Nelson Education representatives, and the members of the Student and Editorial Advisory Boards at the Royal Ontario Museum on January 20, 2011. Top row (l-r): Brock Fenton, Tamara Kelly, Todd Nickle, Ken Wilson, Mark Fitzpatrick, Wendy Keenleyside, Yves Maufette, Paul Fam, Mark Grzeskowiak. Bottom row [l-r]: Bill Milsom, Heather Addy, Tom Haffie, Denis Maxwell, Ken Davey, Laura Anne Aubrey, and Leah Blain.

Student Advisory Boards

University of Calgary

Jason Abboud
Jessica Hann
Carolyn Gratton
Jennifer Mikhayel
Emily Mitic
Simon Sun
Bhavisha Thankey
Anita Tieu
Sahar Zaidi

Depicted above are members of the Student Advisory Board at Mount Royal University. Top row (l-r): Todd Nickle; Sean Davis; Nathan Scherger; Matthew Bell; Annabelle Stratton. Bottom row (l-r): Bayli Law; Samantha Mann; Jennifer Corbin; Erin Froome; Kristina Lindsay. Not shown: Christina Bruce, Danielle Gronnestad, Melodie Lough, Brittney Morgan

University of Western Ontario

Alexandra Katz
Chanelle Ramsubick
Laura Anne Aubrey
Anam Islam
Elissa Pendergast
Samira Khajehi
Samuel Joshua Rothman
Eden Amber
Iva Lucic

Depicted above are members of the University of Calgary Student Advisory Board. Top row (l to r): Jason Abboud, Simon Sun, Jessica Hann, Carolyn Gratton. Bottom row (l to r): Sahar Zaidi, Jennifer Mikhayel, Emily Mitic, Bhavisha Thankey

Mount Royal University

Todd Nickle
Sean Davis
Nathan Scherger
Matthew Bell
Annabelle Stratton
Bayli Law
Samantha Mann
Jennifer Corbin
Erin Froome
Kristina Lindsay
Christina Bruce
Danielle Gronnestad
Melodie Lough
Brittney Morgan

Depicted above are members of the Student Advisory Board at the University of Western Ontario. (l-r) Samuel Joshua Rothman, SAB member, Chanelle Ramsubick, Laura Anne Aubrey, Alexandra Katz, SAB member. Not shown: Anam Islam, Elissa Pendergast, Samira Khajehi, Eden Amber, Iva Lucic.

Carleton University

Andres Acero
Shawna Reddie
Jaime Graham

THIERRY BERROD, MONA LISA PRODUCTION/SCIENCE PHOTO LIBRARY

Magnetic resonance image (MRI) of a dolphin. Various organs can be seen in the scan: the whitish skeleton throughout the body, the brain within the skull, and the lungs (dark) in the chest.

31 Introduction to Animal Organization and Physiology

WHY IT MATTERS

When winter sets in across Canada, different species of animals begin to prepare for the cold in different ways. Many species begin to slow body processes and prepare their cells to withstand freezing as a way of surviving until the spring. Others undergo changes that will allow them to remain fully active throughout the cold snowy months. Yet other species cannot tolerate the cold and migrate to warmer climates for the winter **(Figure 31.1)**. To fully understand the factors that determine species tolerances and distributions requires a detailed knowledge of the organization and physiology of animal tissues, organs, and organ systems.

In multicellular organisms, cells differentiate to form different tissues. In animals, tissues combine in different ways to form organs and organ systems. Each organ system has a unique function. This specialization allows multicellular organisms to establish an internal environment around their cells that can be maintained relatively independent of the external environment through a process called **homeostasis** (*homeo* = the same; *stasis* = standing or stopping). The processes and activities responsible for homeostasis are called **homeostatic mechanisms.** This greatly broadens the geographic range over which animals can live actively. Organ systems can be highly adapted to enable

Photos.com

© Rolf Nussbaumer Photography/Alamy

Figure 31.1
Ways of surviving the winter include avoidance (migratory birds), cold adaptation (small mammals), and freeze tolerance (many insects).

some species to perform better in select habitats, usually at the cost of restricting their ability to inhabit others. Understanding biodiversity and species distribution ultimately requires an understanding of the form and function of the organs and organ systems within each species, which in turn requires an understanding of the specialized cells and tissues that compose them. **Anatomy** is the study of the structures of organisms, and **physiology** is the study of their functions.

In this chapter, we begin with the organization of individual cells into tissues, organs, and organ systems, the major body structures that carry out animal activities. Our discussion continues with the coordination of the processes and activities of organ systems that accomplish homeostasis. The other eight chapters in this unit discuss the individual organ systems that carry out major body functions such as digestion, movement, and reproduction. Although we emphasize vertebrates throughout the unit (including humans), we also make comparisons with invertebrates, to keep the structural and functional diversity of the animal kingdom in perspective and to understand the evolution of the structures and processes involved.

31.1 Organization of the Animal Body

31.1a In Animals, Specialized Cells Are Organized into Tissues, Tissues into Organs, Organs into Organ Systems, and Organ Systems into Organisms

The individual cells of multicellular animals have the same requirements as cells of any kind, including single-celled organisms. They must be surrounded by an aqueous solution that contains ions and molecules required by the cells, including complex organic molecules that can be used as energy sources. The concentrations of these molecules and ions must be balanced to keep cells from shrinking or swelling excessively due to osmotic water movement. Most animal cells also require oxygen to serve as the final acceptor for electrons removed in oxidative reactions. Animal cells must be able to release waste molecules and other by-products of their activities, such as carbon dioxide, to their environment. The physical conditions of the cellular environment, such as temperature, must also remain within tolerable limits.

The evolution of multicellularity (see Section 3.5) made it possible for organisms to create an *internal fluid environment* that supplies all the needs of individual cells, including nutrient supply, waste removal, and osmotic balance. By regulating this internal environment despite changes in the external environment, multicellular organisms can occupy diverse habitats, including dry terrestrial habitats that would be lethal to single cells. While multicellular organisms can become very large, their individual cells remain small enough to exchange ions and molecules easily with the internal fluid.

The evolution of multicellularity also allowed specialized groups of cells to differentiate and take on major life functions, with each group concentrating primarily on a single activity. Specialization greatly increases the efficiency by which animals carry out these functions. In most animals, these specialized groups of cells are organized into tissues, the tissues into organs, and the organs into organ systems **(Figure 31.2, p. 758)**. A **tissue** is a group of cells with the

Organ system:
A set of organs that interacts to carry out a major body function. The digestive system coordinates the activities of organs, including the mouth, esophagus, stomach, small and large intestines, liver, pancreas, rectum, and anus, to convert ingested nutrients into absorbable molecules and ions, eliminate undigested matter, and help regulate water content of the body.

Organ:
Body structure that integrates different tissues and carries out a specific function. For the stomach, this function is processing food.

Stomach

Epithelial tissue:
Protection, transport, secretion, and absorption of nutrients released by digestion of food

Connective tissue:
Structural support

Muscle tissue:
Movement

Nervous tissue:
Communication, coordination, and control

Figure 31.2
Organization of animal cells into tissues, organs, and organ systems as exemplified here by the digestive system.

same structure and function, working together as a unit to carry out one or more activities. Four types of tissue are shown in Figure 31.2: epithelial, connective, muscle, and nervous tissue. An **organ** integrates two or more different tissues into a structure that carries out a specific function. The eye, liver, and stomach are examples of organs. An **organ system** coordinates the activities of two or more organs to carry out a major body function such as digestion, excretion, or reproduction. The organ system carrying out digestion, for example, coordinates the activities of organs, including the mouth, stomach, pancreas, liver, and small and large intestines. Some organs contribute functions to more than one organ system. For instance, the pancreas forms part of the endocrine system as well as the digestive system.

STUDY BREAK

1. What are the differences among tissues, organs, and organ systems?
2. Why must multicellular organisms have organs and organ systems?

31.2 Animal Tissues

Although the most complex animals may contain hundreds of distinct cell types, all can be classified into one of only four basic tissue groups: *epithelial, connective, muscle,* and *nervous* (see Figure 31.2). Each tissue type is assembled from individual cells. The properties of these cells determine the structure and, therefore, the function of the tissue. More specifically, the structure and function of a tissue depend on the structure and organization of the cytoskeleton within the cell, the type and organization of the extracellular matrix surrounding the cell, and the junctions holding the cells together. The **extracellular matrix** (ECM) is a nonliving material secreted by cells consisting of a variety of proteins and glycoproteins. The ECM provides support and shape for tissues and organs. The cell walls of plants and the cuticle of arthropods are examples of specialized ECM.

Junctions of various kinds link cells into tissues (see **Figure 31.3**). *Anchoring junctions* form buttonlike spots or belts that weld cells together. They are most abundant in tissues subject to stretching, such as skin and heart muscle. *Tight junctions* seal the spaces

Cells

Plaque Intermediate filaments

Anchoring junction:
Adjoining cells adhere at a mass of proteins (a plaque) anchored beneath their plasma membrane by many intermediate filaments (adherens junction) or microfilaments (desmosome) of the cytoskeleton.

Tight junction:
Tight connections form between adjacent cells by fusion of plasma membrane proteins on their outer surfaces. A complex network of junction proteins makes a seal tight enough to prevent leaks of ions or molecules between cells.

Channel in a complex of proteins

Gap junction:
Cylindrical arrays of proteins form direct channels that allow small molecules and ions to flow between the cytoplasm of adjacent cells.

Figure 31.3

Anchoring junctions, tight junctions, and gap junctions, which connect cells in animal tissues. Anchoring junctions reinforce the cell-to-cell connections made by cell adhesion molecules, tight junctions seal the spaces between cells, and gap junctions create direct channels of communication between animal cells.

between cells, keeping molecules and even ions from leaking between cells. For example, tight junctions in the tissue lining the urinary bladder prevent waste molecules and ions from leaking out of the bladder into other body tissues. *Gap junctions* are open channels between cells in the same tissue, allowing ions and small molecules to flow freely from one cell to another. For example, gap junctions between muscle cells help muscle tissue to function as a unit.

31.2a Epithelial Tissue Forms Protective, Secretory, and Absorptive Coverings and Linings of Body Structures

Epithelial tissue (*epi* = over; *thele* = covering) consists of sheetlike layers of cells that are usually joined tightly together, with little ECM material between them **(Figure 31.4, p. 760)**. Also called *epithelia* (singular, *epithelium*), these tissues cover body surfaces and the surfaces of internal organs and line cavities and ducts within the body. They protect body surfaces from invasion by bacteria and viruses and secrete or absorb substances. For example, the epithelium covering a fish's gill structures serves as a barrier to bacteria and viruses and exchanges oxygen, carbon dioxide, and ions with the aqueous environment.

The epithelium of the external surface of arthropods secretes the tough cuticle that, in addition to acting as a barrier to the environment, functions as their skeleton. Some epithelial cells in the epidermis of vertebrates also contain a network of fibrous proteins (keratin) that form such protective structures as scales, nails, claws, hooves, and horns as well as hair and feathers.

Some epithelia, such as those lining the capillaries of the circulatory system, act as filters, allowing ions and small molecules to leak from the blood into surrounding tissues while barring the passage of blood cells and large molecules such as proteins.

Because epithelia form coverings and linings, they have a free (or outer) surface and an inner surface. The outer **apical surface** may be exposed to water, air, or fluids within the body. In internal cavities and ducts, the apical surface is often covered with *cilia*, which beat like oars to move fluids through the cavity or duct. The epithelium lining the oviducts in mammals, for example, is covered with cilia that generate fluid currents to move eggs from the ovaries to the uterus. In free-living flatworms, the ventral epithelium of the animal is frequently ciliated, allowing the worm to glide over surfaces. In some epithelia, including the lining of the small intestine, the free surface is crowded

a. Simple squamous epithelium

Ray Simmons/Photo Researchers, Inc.

b. Stratified squamous epithelium

Dr. Cladden Willis/Getty Images

c. Cuboidal epithelium

Ed Reschke/Peter Arnold/ Photolibrary

d. Columnar epithelium

Don Fawcett/Visuals Unlimited, Inc.

Description: Layer of flattened cells

Common locations: Blood vessel walls; air sacs of lungs

Function: Diffusion

Description: Several layers of flattened cells

Common locations: Skin and other surfaces subject to abrasion, such as the mouth, esophagus, and vagina

Function: Protection against abrasion; typically not involved in secretion or absorption

Description: Layer of cubelike cells; free surface may have microvilli

Common locations: Glands and tubular parts of nephrons in kidneys

Function: Secretion, absorption

Description: Layer of tall, slender cells; free surface may have microvilli

Common locations: Lining of gut and respiratory tract

Function: Secretion, absorption

Figure 31.4
Principle types of epithelia.

with *microvilli*, fingerlike extensions of the plasma membrane that increase the area available for secretion or absorption.

The inner, **basal surface** of an epithelium adheres to a layer of ECM secreted by the epithelial cells called the **basal lamina** (see Figure 31.4). In many cases, such as the intestinal epithelium of vertebrates, a further layer of fibres is secreted by underlying connective tissue, but this is lacking in most invertebrate epithelia. The entire assemblage is the **basement membrane.**

Types of Epithelia. Epithelia are classified as *simple*—formed by a single layer of cells—or *stratified*—formed by multiple cell layers (see Figure 31.4). The shapes of cells within an epithelium may be *squamous* (mosaic, flattened, and spread out), *cuboidal* (shaped roughly like dice or cubes), or *columnar* (elongated, with the long axis perpendicular to the epithelial layer). Four principle types of epithelia are found in the body (see Figure 31.4).

The cells of some epithelia, such as those forming the skin and the lining of the intestine, divide constantly to replace worn and dying cells. New cells are produced through division of stem cells in the basal (lowest) layer of the skin. *Stem cells* are undifferentiated (unspecialized) cells in the tissue that divide to produce more stem cells as well as cells that differentiate (that is, become specialized into one of the many cell types of the body). Stem cells are found in both adult organisms and embryos. Besides the skin, adult stem cells are found in tissues of the brain, bone marrow, blood

vessels, skeletal muscle, and liver ("People behind Biology," Box 31.1, describes the discovery of stem cells in the brain). Stem cells are important for development in many invertebrates. In some cases, the stem cells may already be programmed for a specific cell type, as in the eye or wing disks of insect pupae, whereas in others, the stem cells may be totipotent, as in flatworms (Chapter 25). A totipotent cell has the capacity to form an entire organism.

Glands Formed by Epithelia. Epithelia typically contain or give rise to cells that are specialized for secretion. Some of these secretory cells are scattered among non-secretory cells within the epithelium. Others form structures called **glands**, which are derived from pockets of epithelium during embryonic development.

Some glands, called **exocrine glands** (*exo* = external; *crine* = secretion), remain connected to the epithelium by a duct, which empties their secretion at the epithelial surface. Exocrine secretions include mucus, saliva, digestive enzymes, sweat, earwax, oils, milk, and venom (**Figure 31.5a,** shows an exocrine gland in the skin of a poisonous tree frog). Other glands, called **endocrine glands,** may not be composed of epithelial cells. They have no ducts but secrete their products, hormones, into the interstitial fluid to be picked up by the blood for circulation to the organs and tissues of the body (**Figure 31.5b).** The endocrine glands are considered in detail in Chapter 35.

Some glands contain both exocrine and endocrine elements. The pancreas, for example, has an exocrine

PEOPLE BEHIND BIOLOGY 31.1
Samuel Weiss, University of Calgary

Through much of the twentieth century, one of the dogmas of developmental biology held that the number of neurons in an adult brain was fixed. Once adulthood was reached, no new neurons appeared. Those neurons lost in the normal aging process or by trauma or disease could not be replaced.

In the early 1990s, Samuel Weiss at the University of Calgary, together with his graduate student, Brent

Reynolds, was exploring how growth factors (see Chapter 8) might be used to protect the brain. When they applied the growth factors to mouse brain cells in culture, they discovered some cells that were capable of division and that could differentiate into both neurons and glial cells. They realized that they had found adult neural stem cells. The publication of their results in 1992 generated enormous excitement as

scientists explored the possibility that brains damaged by trauma or disease might be stimulated to repair themselves.

This extraordinary discovery, as is so often the case, was accidental. But it required a receptive and agile mind to appreciate its significance and to explore what was previously considered to be impossible.

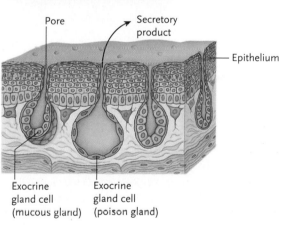

Pore · Secretory product · Epithelium · Exocrine gland cell (mucous gland) · Exocrine gland cell (poison gland)

a. Examples of exocrine glands: The mucus- and poison-secreting glands in the skin of a blue poison frog

Thyroid · Epithelium · Endocrine gland cell · Blood vessel

b. Example of an endocrine gland: The thyroid gland, which secretes hormones that regulate the rate of metabolism and other body functions

Figure 31.5
Exocrine and endocrine glands. **(a)** The poison secreted by the blue poison frog (*Dendrobates azureus*) is one of the most lethal glandular secretions known. **(b)** the hormones secreted by the thyroid gland are vital for growth, development, maturation and metabolism in all vertebrates.

function of secreting pancreatic juice through a duct into the small intestine, where it plays an important role in food digestion (see Chapter 40), and different cells provide an endocrine function by secreting the hormones insulin and glucagon into the bloodstream to help regulate glucose levels in the blood (see Chapter 35).

Some epithelial cells, particularly in the epidermis of vertebrates, contain a network of fibres of keratin, a family of tough proteins. Keratin forms the scales of

fish and reptiles (including the shells of turtles); the feathers of birds; and the hair, claws, hooves, horns, and fingernails of mammals.

31.2b Connective Tissue Supports Other Body Tissues

Most animal body structures contain one or more types of **connective tissue.** Connective tissues support other body tissues, transmit mechanical and other forces, and in some cases act as filters. They consist of cells that form networks or layers in and around body structures and that are separated by nonliving material, specifically the ECM secreted by the cells of the tissue. Many forms of connective tissue have more nonliving ECM material (both by weight and by volume) than living cellular material.

The mechanical properties of a connective tissue depend on the type and quantity of its ECM. The consistency of the ECM ranges from fluid (as in blood and lymph), through soft and firm gels (as in tendons), to the hard and crystalline (as in bone). In most connective tissues, the ECM consists primarily of the fibrous glycoprotein **collagen** embedded in a network of proteoglycans—glycoproteins that are very rich in carbohydrates. Collagen is the most abundant family of proteins in animals. More than 25 different forms have been described, and some form of collagen occurs in all Metazoa, including Porifera (sponges). The collagen molecule is thus an ancient one that has been modified during evolution. In bone, the glycoprotein network surrounding the collagen is impregnated with mineral deposits that produce a hard, yet still somewhat elastic, structure. Another class of glycoproteins, **fibronectin**, aids in the attachment of cells to the ECM and helps hold the cells in position.

In some connective tissues, another rubbery protein, **elastin**, adds elasticity to the ECM. It is able to return to its original shape after being stretched, bent, or compressed. Elastin fibres, for example, help the skin return to its original shape when pulled or stretched and give the lungs the elasticity required for their alternating inflation and deflation. Resilin is a protein related to elastin that occurs only in insects and some Crustacea. It is the most elastic material known and is the basis for the jumping of fleas and locusts (see "Molecule behind Biology," Box 31.2).

Vertebrates have six major types of connective tissue: *loose connective tissue, fibrous connective tissue, cartilage, bone, adipose tissue,* and *blood.* Each type has a characteristic function correlated with its structure **(Figure 31.6)**.

Loose Connective Tissue. **Loose connective tissue** consists of sparsely distributed cells surrounded by a more or less open network of collagen and other glycoprotein fibres (see Figure 31.6a). The cells, called **fibroblasts**, secrete most of the collagen and other proteins in this connective tissue.

In vertebrates, loose connective tissues support epithelia and form a corsetlike band around blood vessels, nerves, and some internal organs; they also reinforce deeper layers of the skin. Sheets of loose

MOLECULE BEHIND BIOLOGY 31.2

Resilin: An Insect Rubber with Amazing Properties

While Torkel Weis-Fogh, a young Danish comparative physiologist, was conducting his groundbreaking studies on insect flight in the Zoological Laboratory in Cambridge, U.K., in 1960, he discovered patches of highly elastic cuticle in the wing joints of locusts. Subsequently, the same elastic protein proved to be important to other insect movements. For example, it is involved in the movements of the membrane that produce the song of cicadas. Fleas are able to jump very large distances because muscle contractions store energy in pads of resilin in the hind legs **(Figure 1).** The sudden release of this energy, in less than a millisecond, propels the jump with an instantaneous acceleration greater than that of the space shuttle.

Resilin belongs to the same family of proteins as elastin, an elastic protein in many animals, but it is restricted to insects and a few crustacea. Resilin's elastic properties have proven to be astonishing. It can be stretched to four times its length without breaking (elastin only manages two). It is 97% efficient, so that when energy stored in it by stretching is released, only 3% is released as heat. It survives huge numbers of cycles of stretch and relaxation. The membrane producing the song of cicadas vibrates several thousand times per second. Like other elastic proteins, resilin is composed of coiled protein molecules cross-linked to one another, and stretching involves uncoiling.

In 2005, a gene coding for *Drosophila* resilin was cloned in *E. coli*

by a team led by Christopher Elvin of the Commonwealth Scientific and Industrial Research Organisation in Australia. That lab is now able to produce significant quantities of resilin. Ultimately, this insect rubber should find application, for example, as replacements for spinal disks in humans or as artificial blood vessels.

FIGURE 1 *The pad of resilin (blue) in the coxa (part of the thigh) of the hind leg of a flea.*

Courtesy of Dr. David Merritt

a. Loose connective tissue

- Collagen fibre
- Fibroblast
- Elastin fibre

Ed Reschke

Description: Fibroblasts and other cells surrounded by collagen and elastin fibres forming a glycoprotein matrix

Common locations: Under the skin and most epithelia

Function: Support, elasticity, diffusion

b. Fibrous connective tissue

- Collagen fibres
- Fibroblast

Ed Reschke

Description: Long rows of fibroblasts surrounded by collagen and elastin fibres in parallel bundles with a dense extracellular matrix

Common locations: Tendons, ligaments

Function: Strength, elasticity

c. Cartilage

- Collagen fibres embedded in an elastic matrix
- Chondrocyte

Fred Hossier/Visual Unlimited, Inc.

Description: Chondrocytes embedded in a pliable, solid matrix of collagen and chondroitin sulphate

Common locations: Ends of long bones, nose, parts of airways, skeleton of vertebrate embryos

Function: Support, flexibility, low-friction surface for joint movement

d. Bone tissue

- Fine canals
- Central canal containing blood vessel
- Osteocytes

Ed Reschke

Description: Osteocytes in a matrix of collagen and glycoproteins hardened with hydroxyapatite

Common locations: Bones of vertebrate skeleton

Function: Movement, support, protection

Figure 31.6
The six major types of connective tissues in vertebrates.

e. Adipose tissue

- Nucleus
- Fat deposit

Ed Reschke

Description: Large, tightly packed adipocytes with little extracellular matrix

Common locations: Under skin; around heart, kidneys

Function: Energy reserves, insulation, padding

f. Blood

- Leukocyte
- Erythrocyte
- Platelet
- Plasma

Ed Reschke

Description: Leukocytes, erythrocytes, and platelets suspended in a plasma matrix

Common locations: Circulatory system

Function: Transport of substances

connective tissue, covered on both surfaces with epithelial cells, form the **mesenteries**, which hold the abdominal organs in place and provide lubricated, smooth surfaces that prevent chafing or abrasion between adjacent structures as the body moves. In insects, and perhaps some other invertebrates, the loose connective tissues suspending organs and providing support for epithelia are the products of specialized cells circulating in the blood.

Fibrous Connective Tissue. In **fibrous connective tissue**, fibroblasts are sparsely distributed among dense masses of collagen and elastin fibres that are lined up in highly ordered, parallel bundles (see Figure 31.6b). The parallel arrangement produces maximum tensile strength and elasticity. Examples include **tendons**, which attach muscles to bones, and **ligaments**, which connect bones to each other at a joint. The cornea of the eye is a transparent fibrous connective tissue formed from highly ordered collagen molecules.

In some invertebrates, fibrous connective tissue provides shape to the animal, as in many sponges (see Chapter 25) and echinoderms. In sea cucumbers (see Chapter 26), the rigidity of the connective tissue can be changed quickly by the animal, resulting in a loss or change of shape. This acts as an escape response.

Cartilage. Cartilage consists of sparsely distributed cells called **chondrocytes**, surrounded by networks of collagen fibres embedded in a tough but elastic matrix of the glycoprotein *chondroitin sulfate* (see Figure 31.6c). Elastin is also present in some forms of cartilage.

The elasticity of cartilage allows it to resist compression and stay resilient, like a piece of rubber. Bending your ear or pushing the tip of your nose, which are supported by cores of cartilage, will give you a good idea of the flexible nature of this tissue. Cartilage also supports the larynx, trachea, and smaller air passages in the lungs. It forms the disks cushioning the vertebrae in the spinal column and the smooth, slippery capsules around the ends of bones in joints such as the hip and knee. Cartilage also serves as a precursor to bone during embryonic development; in sharks and rays and their relatives, almost the entire skeleton remains as cartilage in adults.

Bone. The densest form of connective tissue, **bone**, forms the skeleton, which supports the body, protects softer body structures such as the brain, and contributes to body movements by forming levers for muscle to pull on.

Mature bone consists primarily of cells called **osteocytes** (*osteon* = bone) embedded in an ECM containing collagen fibres and glycoproteins impregnated with *hydroxyapatite*, a calcium–phosphate mineral (see Figure 31.6d). The collagen fibres give bone tensile strength and elasticity; the hydroxyapatite resists compression and allows bones to support body weight. Cells called **osteoblasts** (*blast* = bud or sprout) produce the collagen and mineral of bone—as much as 85% of the weight of bone is mineral deposits. Osteocytes, in fact, are osteoblasts that have become trapped and surrounded by the bone materials they themselves produce. **Osteoclasts** (*clast* = break) remove the minerals and recycle them through the bloodstream. Bone is not a stable tissue; it is reshaped continuously by the bone-building osteoblasts and the bone-degrading osteoclasts.

Although bones appear superficially to be solid, they are actually porous structures consisting of a system of microscopic spaces and canals. The structural unit of bone is the **osteon**. It consists of a minute central canal surrounded by osteocytes embedded in concentric layers of mineral matter (see Figure 31.6d). A blood vessel and extensions of nerve cells run through the central canal, which is connected to the spaces containing cells by very fine, radiating canals filled with interstitial fluid. The blood vessels supply nutrients to the cells with which the bone is built, and the nerve cells innervate the blood vessels as well as the connective tissue (periosteum) surrounding the bone.

Adipose Tissue. The connective tissue called **adipose tissue** mostly contains large, densely clustered cells called *adipocytes* that are specialized for fat storage (see Figure 31.6e). It has little ECM. Adipose tissue also cushions the body and, in mammals, forms an especially important insulating layer under the skin.

The animal body stores limited amounts of carbohydrates, primarily in muscle and liver cells. Unlike plants, in animals excess carbohydrates are converted into the fats stored in adipocytes. The storage of chemical energy as fats offers animals a weight advantage. For example, the average human would weigh about 45 kg more if the same amount of chemical energy were stored as carbohydrates instead of fats. Adipose tissue is richly supplied with blood vessels, which move fats or their components to and from adipocytes.

In invertebrates, fat storage may occur in a variety of tissues. Insects have a fat body, an organ that functions both for storage and as an important structure for metabolism, much like the vertebrate liver.

Blood. Blood is considered to be a connective tissue because the fluid portion is essentially a fluid form of ECM. Blood functions as the principal transport vehicle to carry nutrients, oxygen (in most animals), and hormones to the tissues and to remove metabolic wastes for transport to the organs specialized for waste removal. It is also frequently involved in defence against disease (Chapter 43) and may be important in wound healing.

Vertebrates have two basic types of cells suspended in a straw-coloured fluid, the plasma (see Figure 31.6f). Erythrocytes (*erythros* = red), or red blood cells, contain hemoglobin, a protein to which O_2 binds; these are specialized for O_2 transport. Several types of leukocytes (*leukos* = white), or white blood cells, protect the body against foreign elements such as viruses and bacteria. These are considered in Chapter 32. Vertebrate blood also contains platelets (often called thrombocytes), which are membrane-bound fragments of specialized leukocytes. They play an essential role in the formation of blood clots to heal wounds.

In invertebrates, the oxygen-carrying pigments, such as hemoglobin, may be present either within special cells, as in some annelids, or free in the plasma. Blood cells in insects are also known to take part in wound healing and protection against foreign bodies.

31.2c Muscle Tissue Produces Movement

Muscle tissue consists of cells that have the ability to contract (shorten). The contractions, which depend on the interaction of two proteins—*actin* and *myosin*—move body limbs and other structures, pump the blood, and produce a squeezing pressure in organs such as the intestine and uterus. Three types of muscle tissue, *skeletal*, *cardiac*, and *smooth*, produce body movements in vertebrates (**Figure 31.7**).

Skeletal Muscle. Skeletal **muscle** is so called because most muscles of this type are attached by tendons to the skeleton. Skeletal muscle cells are also called **muscle fibres** because each is an elongated cylinder (see Figure 31.7a). These cells contain many nuclei and are packed with actin and myosin molecules arranged in highly ordered, parallel units that give the tissue a banded or striated appearance when viewed under a microscope. Muscle fibres packed side by side into parallel bundles surrounded by sheaths of connective tissue form many body muscles.

Skeletal muscle contracts in response to signals carried by the nervous system. The contractions of skeletal muscles, which are characteristically rapid and powerful, move body parts and maintain posture. The contractions also release heat as a by-product of cellular metabolism. This heat helps mammals, birds, and some other vertebrates maintain their body temperatures, particularly through the process of shivering when environmental temperatures fall. (Skeletal muscle is discussed further in Chapter 38.)

Cardiac Muscle. **Cardiac muscle** is the contractile tissue of the heart (see Figure 31.7b). Cardiac muscle has a striated appearance because it contains actin and myosin molecules arranged like those in skeletal muscle. However, cardiac muscle cells are short and branched, with each cell connecting to several neighbouring cells; the joining point between two such cells is called an *intercalated disk*. Cardiac muscle cells thus form an interlinked network, which is stabilized by anchoring junctions and gap junctions. The gap junctions transmit electrical signals through the movement of ions that make cardiac muscles contract as a unit. This network makes heart muscle contract in all directions, producing a squeezing or pumping action rather than the lengthwise, unidirectional contraction characteristic of skeletal muscle.

Smooth Muscle. **Smooth muscle** is found in the walls of tubes and cavities in the body, including blood vessels, the stomach and intestine, the bladder, and the uterus. Smooth muscle cells are relatively small and spindle shaped (pointed at both ends), and their actin and myosin molecules are arranged in a loose network rather than in bundles (see Figure 31.7c). This loose network makes the cells appear smooth rather than striated when viewed under a microscope. Smooth muscle cells are connected by gap junctions and enclosed in a mesh of connective tissue. As in cardiac muscle, the gap junctions transmit signals that make smooth muscles contract as a unit, typically producing a squeezing motion. Although smooth muscle contracts more slowly than skeletal and cardiac muscles do, its contractions can be maintained at steady levels for a much longer time. These contractions move and mix the stomach and intestinal contents, constrict blood vessels, and push the infant out of the uterus during childbirth.

a. Skeletal muscle

b. Cardiac muscle

c. Smooth muscle

Ed Reschke

Ed Reschke

Bio Photo Associates/Photo Researchers, Inc.

Figure 31.7
Structure of skeletal, cardiac, and smooth muscle.

Width of one muscle cell (muscle fibre)

Cell nucleus

Cell nucleus

Intercalated disk

Cell nucleus

(cells separated for clarity)

Description: Bundles of long, cylindrical, striated, contractile cells called muscle fibres

Typical location: Attached to bones of skeleton

Function: Locomotion, movement of body parts

Description: Cylindrical, striated cells that have specialized end junctions

Location: Wall of heart

Function: Pumping of blood within circulatory system

Description: Contractile cells with tapered ends

Typical location: Wall of internal organs, such as stomach

Function: Movement of internal organs

Invertebrate Muscle. In general, most invertebrates have striated muscles throughout, even muscles involved with structures such as the intestine or reproductive ducts. In insects, the striated muscles that control the movements of some of the viscera, such as the ovaries and parts of the digestive system, are frequently branched and interconnected to form a lattice.

31.2d Nervous Tissue Receives, Integrates, and Transmits Information

Nervous tissue contains cells called **neurons** (also called *nerve cells*) that serve as lines of communication and control between body parts. Billions of neurons are packed into the human brain; others extend throughout the body. Nervous tissue also contains **glial cells** (*glia* = glue), which physically support and provide nutrients to neurons, provide electrical insulation between them, and scavenge cellular debris and foreign matter.

A neuron consists of a *cell body,* which houses the nucleus and organelles, and two types of cell extensions, dendrites and axons **(Figure 31.8).**

Figure 31.8

Neurons and their structure. The micrograph shows a network of motor neurons, which relay signals from the brain or spinal cord to muscles and glands. (Micrograph: Lennart Nilsson from *Behold Man,* © 1974 Albert Bonniers Forlag and Little, Brown and Company, Boston.)

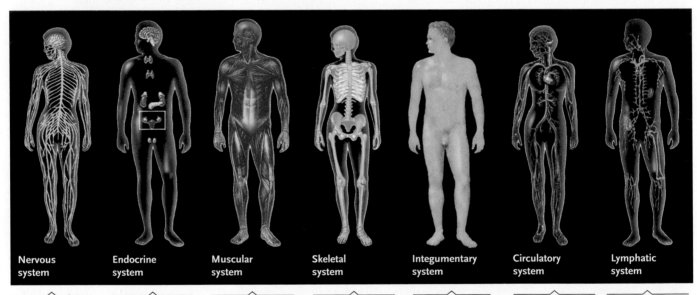

Nervous system	**Endocrine system**	**Muscular system**	**Skeletal system**	**Integumentary system**	**Circulatory system**	**Lymphatic system**
Main organs: Brain, spinal cord, peripheral nerves, sensory organs	**Main organs:** Pituitary, thyroid, adrenal, pancreas, and other hormone-secreting glands	**Main organs:** Skeletal, cardiac, and smooth muscle	**Main organs:** Bones, tendons, ligaments, cartilage	**Main organs:** Skin, sweat glands, hair, nails	**Main organs:** Heart, blood vessels, blood	**Main organs:** Lymph nodes, lymph ducts, spleen, thymus
Main functions: Principal regulatory system; monitors changes in internal and external environments and formulates compensatory responses; coordinates body activities. Nervous systems are present in all metazoans except sponges.	**Main functions:** Regulates and coordinates body activities through secretion of hormones. Endocrine systems are also present in most metazoans.	**Main functions:** Moves body parts; helps run bodily functions; generates heat. Specialized muscle cells do not appear in evolution until triploblastic animals.	**Main functions:** Supports and protects body parts; provides leverage for body movements. An internal skeleton composed of bone and/or cartilage occurs only in the vertebrates. Similar functions in invertebrates are carried out by an external skeleton or by internal hydrostatic pressure.	**Main functions:** Covers external body surfaces and protects against injury and infection; helps regulate water content and body temperature. All Metazoa except sponges have an integument of some sort.	**Main functions:** Distributes water, nutrients, oxygen, hormones, and other substances throughout body and carries away carbon dioxide and other metabolic wastes; helps stabilize internal temperature and pH. Specialized circulatory systems occur in all vertebrates and in the annelids, molluscs, and arthropods.	**Main functions:** Returns excess fluid to the blood; defends body against invading viruses, bacteria, fungi, and other pathogens as part of immune system. Invertebrates do not have a specialized lymphatic system.

Dendrites receive chemical signals from other neurons or from body cells of other types and convert them into an electrical signal that is transmitted to the cell body of the receiving neuron. Dendrites are usually highly branched. *Axons* conduct electrical signals away from the cell body to the axon terminals, or endings. At their terminals, most axons convert the electrical signal to a chemical signal that stimulates a response in nearby muscle cells, gland cells, or other neurons (direct electrical connections are discussed further in Chapter 32). Axons are usually unbranched except at their terminals. Depending on the type of neuron and its location in the body, its axon may extend from a few micrometres or millimetres to more than a metre (the cell body of a neuron innervating the foot of a giraffe is in its spinal cord). (Neurons and their organization in body structures are discussed further in Chapter 36.)

All four major tissue types—epithelial, connective, muscle, and nervous—combine to form the organs and organ systems of animals. The next section depicts the major organs and organ systems of vertebrates and outlines their main tasks.

STUDY BREAK

1. Embryonic stem cells can differentiate into any tissue. How many major tissue types are there in vertebrates and what are the differences between them in terms of their structure and function?
2. Distinguish between exocrine and endocrine glands. What do they have in common? What makes them different?

31.3 Coordination of Tissues in Organs and Organ Systems

31.3a Organs and Organ Systems Function Together to Enable an Animal to Survive

In the tissues, organs, and organ systems of an animal, each cell engages in the basic metabolic activities that ensure its own survival and performs one or more functions of the system to which it belongs. All vertebrates have 12 major organ systems, which are summarized in **Figure 31.9.** Most invertebrates have

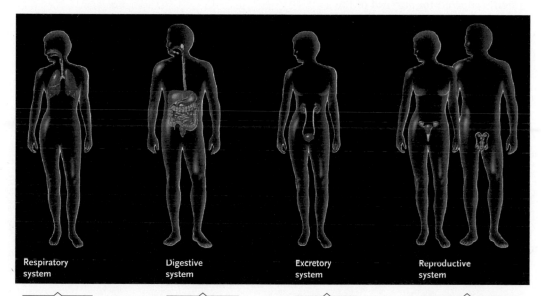

Respiratory system

Digestive system

Excretory system

Reproductive system

Figure 31.9
Organ systems of the human body. The immune system, which is primarily a cellular system, is not shown. The functions performed by these organ systems are performed by all animals, although different organs and systems may be involved.

Main organs:
Lungs, diaphragm, trachea, and other airways

Main functions:
Exchanges gases with the environment, including uptake of oxygen and release of carbon dioxide. Fish have a respiratory system that involves gills. Some form of specialized respiratory system occurs in most invertebrates.

Main organs:
Pharynx, esophagus, stomach, intestines, liver, pancreas, rectum, anus

Main functions:
Converts ingested matter into molecules and ions that can be absorbed into body; eliminates undigested matter; helps regulate water content. Most metazoans, with the exception of some parasitic forms, have a digestive system.

Main organs:
Kidneys, bladder, ureter, urethra

Main functions:
Removes and eliminates excess water, ions, and metabolic wastes from body; helps regulate internal osmotic balance and pH. All animals perform these functions. All vertebrates have kidneys, and most invertebrates have specialized excretory organs and systems.

Main organs:
Female: ovaries, oviducts, uterus, vagina, mammary glands
Male: testes, sperm ducts, accessory glands, penis

Main functions:
Maintains the sexual characteristics and passes on genes to the next generation. Most triploblastic animals have specialized reproductive organs and systems.

the same systems but do not have a separate system of lymphatic ducts.

The functions of all these organ systems are coordinated and integrated to collectively accomplish a series of tasks that are vital to all animals, whether a flatworm, a salmon, a moose, or a human. These tasks include

1. acquiring nutrients and other required substances, such as oxygen; coordinating their processing; distributing them throughout the body; and disposing of wastes;
2. synthesizing the protein, carbohydrate, lipid, and nucleic acid molecules required for body structure and function;
3. sensing and responding to changes in the environment, such as temperature, pH, and ion concentrations;
4. protecting the body against injury or attack from other animals and from viruses, bacteria, and other disease-causing agents; and
5. reproducing and, in many instances, nourishing and protecting offspring through their early growth and development.

Together these tasks maintain homeostasis, preserving the internal environment required for survival of the body. Homeostasis is the topic of the next section.

CONCEPT FIX While each organ system has a major role to perform for the body (e.g., the circulatory system moves essential materials around the body and remove wastes from tissues, and the integumentary system provides mechanical protection), *it is not true that most organ systems serve only one role.* Many have minor supporting roles in other functions, and none of these systems work in isolation.

STUDY BREAK

1. What are the major functions of each of the 12 organ systems? What are the key organs in each?
2. What are the major organ systems in a duck? In a shark? In an insect? In an earthworm?

31.4 Homeostasis

To live, cells of all organisms must take in nutrients and O_2 from the external environment and eliminate wastes such as CO_2 and nitrogenous wastes to the external environment. A single-celled organism such as an amoeba is in direct contact with the external environment. Although most cells of a multicellular animal are isolated from direct contact with the external environment, these cells have the same needs for nutrient and O_2 input and waste

Figure 31.10
Nature of the extracellular fluid (ECF).

elimination. These needs are met by the specialized tissues of the different organ systems that establish an internal environment in the form of the extracellular fluid (ECF) **(Figure 31.10)**. The ECF has two components:

- **plasma**, the fluid portion of the blood, and
- **interstitial fluid** (*inter* = between; *stitial* = that which stands), the fluid that surrounds the cells.

The ECF connects all cells to the external environment. Thus, no matter where a cell is within the body, it can make the exchanges essential to its life with the interstitial fluid. Particular organ systems enable these exchanges between the external and internal environments. The digestive system processes incoming food and transfers absorbed nutrients into the plasma of the blood. The nutrients reach all parts of the body by the action of the circulatory system, along with O_2 that enters the blood by the action of the respiratory system. The nutrients and O_2 in the plasma reach the interstitial fluid through the capillaries, and, from there, they enter the cells as needed. Waste moves in the opposite direction: from the cells into the interstitial fluid and then into the plasma. The respiratory system handles the removal of CO_2, and the excretory system handles the metabolic wastes.

For optimal function of these systems, the composition and state of the ECF must be maintained within a narrow range so that cells have available the necessary nutrients and O_2 and wastes can be eliminated. Further, other aspects of the internal environment that are important for cellular (and therefore organismal) life, such as temperature, must also be regulated within a tolerable range.

Animals fall into two major categories in this regard: **regulators** maintain factors of the internal environment in a relatively constant state, and **conformers** have internal environments that match the external environment. Any given animal may regulate some factors and conform to others. For instance, animals such as fishes, reptiles, and insects are thermoconformers. Their body temperatures match that of the external environment. They are also osmoregulators, meaning that they maintain the ionic composition of their ECF relatively constant regardless of the composition of the external environment. Homeostasis is the process by which animals regulate their internal environment to maintain a relatively stable state. Homeostasis is a dynamic process, in which internal adjustments are made continuously to compensate for changes in the internal or external environment.

31.4a Many Factors of the Internal Environment Are Homeostatically Regulated

Factors of the internal environment that are regulated homeostatically include the following:

1. *Nutrient concentration.* Energy production by cells requires a constant supply of nutrient molecules. The energy generated by catabolizing the nutrients is used for basic cellular processes and any specialized activities of the cell.
2. *Concentration of O_2.* Cellular respiration (see Chapter 6), the process that generates energy from catabolic reactions, requires a constant supply of O_2 for optimal productivity.
3. *Concentration of CO_2.* The CO_2 produced by the catabolic reactions of cellular respiration must be removed as waste or else the ECF would become increasingly acidic.
4. *Concentration of waste chemicals.* Particular biochemical reactions in the cell generate products that would be toxic to the cell if not removed as waste.
5. *Concentration of water and NaCl.* The relative concentrations of water and NaCl in the ECF affect how much water enters or leaves a cell and hence the cell's volume. These concentrations must be regulated to maintain a cell volume that is optimal for function; swollen or shrunken cells are typically functionally impaired.
6. *pH.* Changes in the pH of the ECF can adversely affect enzymatic activities within cells, as well as the functions of all other functional proteins (ion channels, receptors, etc.).
7. *Volume and pressure of the plasma.* Both the volume and the pressure in blood vessels must be maintained at adequate levels to distribute the fluid throughout the body. This circulation is vitally important for supplying cells with their needs and removing wastes.
8. *Temperature.* Body cells function optimally within a specified temperature range. Outside that range, chemical reactions change their rates and may be completely inhibited. If cells become too cold, the rates of enzymatic reactions decrease too much,

and, if cells become too hot, structural and enzymatic proteins can be denatured and become inactive.

31.4b Homeostasis Is Accomplished by Negative Feedback Control Systems

The primary mechanism of homeostasis is **negative feedback**, in which a stimulus resulting from a change in the external or internal environment triggers a response that compensates for the environmental change **(Figure 31.11, p. 770)**. The components of a negative feedback control system are as follows:

- A **stimulus** is an environmental change (external or internal) that triggers a response.
- A **sensor** is a tissue or organ that detects the environmental change (such as external temperature, or the internal concentration of a molecule such as glucose).
- An **integrator** is a control centre that compares the detected environmental change with a **set point**, the level at which the condition controlled by the pathway is to be maintained. In most animals, the integrator is part of the central nervous system or the endocrine system.
- An **effector** is a system, activated by the integrator, that returns the condition to the set point if it has strayed away. Effectors may include parts of any body tissue or organ.

The Thermostat as a Negative Feedback Mechanism. The concept of negative feedback may be most familiar in systems designed by human engineers. The thermostat maintaining temperature at a chosen level in a house provides an example. In the thermostat, the following are the components of the negative feedback system:

- The stimulus is a change in room temperature of a few degrees (up or down) from the temperature set on the thermostat.
- The sensor is the thermometer within the thermostat that measures the temperature.
- The integrator is the electrical circuit in the thermostat that activates the effectors.
- The effector returns the room temperature to the set point. If the temperature has fallen below the set point, the effector is the furnace, which adds heat to the house until the temperature rises to the set point. If the temperature has risen above the set point, the effector is the air conditioner, which removes heat from the room until the temperature falls to the set point.

Thermostats and Negative Feedback Mechanisms in Animals. Mammals and birds also have a homeostatic mechanism that maintains body temperature within a

Figure 31.11

Components of a negative feedback mechanism maintaining homeostasis. The integrator coordinates a response by comparing the level of an environmental condition with a set point that indicates where the level should be.

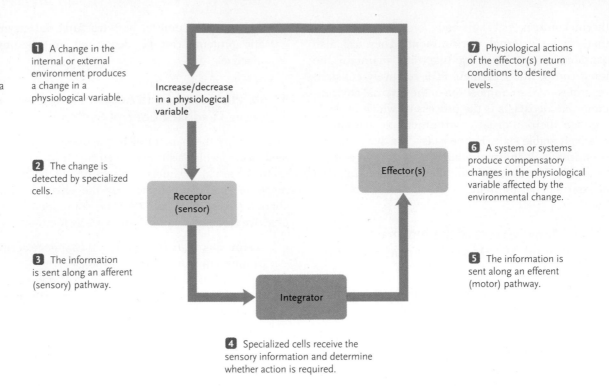

1 A change in the internal or external environment produces a change in a physiological variable.

Increase/decrease in a physiological variable

2 The change is detected by specialized cells.

Receptor (sensor)

3 The information is sent along an afferent (sensory) pathway.

4 Specialized cells receive the sensory information and determine whether action is required.

Integrator

7 Physiological actions of the effector(s) return conditions to desired levels.

6 A system or systems produce compensatory changes in the physiological variable affected by the environmental change.

Effector(s)

5 The information is sent along an efferent (motor) pathway.

relatively narrow range around a set point. The components of the negative feedback system are as follows:

- The stimulus is a change in body temperature beyond normal levels.
- The sensors are groups of neurons that detect changes in the temperature throughout the body.
- The integrator is the temperature control centre in a region of the brain called the *hypothalamus* that compares the changes in temperature of the brain and the rest of the body with the set point. For most mammals, including humans, the set point has a relatively narrow range centred at about 37°C.
- The effectors are physiological or behavioural responses that function to return the body temperature to desired levels (the set point).

All birds and mammals regulate their body temperature around a relatively narrow set point. If the temperature falls below the lower limit, the hypothalamus activates effectors that constrict the blood vessels in the skin. The reduction in blood flow means that less heat is conducted from the blood through the skin to the environment; in short, heat loss from the skin is reduced. Small muscles may be activated to cause the fur or feathers to stand up, increasing the thickness of the animal's insulation. Other effectors may induce shivering, a physical mechanism to generate body heat. Some animals are capable of nonshivering heat production using specialized fat cells (brown fat). Also, integrating neurons in the brain, stimulated by signals from the hypothalamus, initiate behavioural responses such as moving to a warmer area (see Chapter 42 for details).

Conversely, if the blood temperature rises above the set point, the hypothalamus triggers effectors that dilate the blood vessels in the skin, increasing blood flow to the skin and heat loss from it. Other effectors cause fur and feathers to flatten, reducing the insulation layer. Yet other effectors can induce sweating on bare patches of skin, which cools the skin and the blood flowing through it as the sweat evaporates. And again, through integrating neurons in the brain, animals may consciously sense being overheated, which may be counteracted by moving to cooler locations, or taking a dip in a pool of water. **Figure 31.12** illustrates how a dog responds to activity at high environmental temperatures.

CONCEPT FIX It is commonly believed that *all physiological variables that are homeostatically regulated are always held more or less constant.* This is not always the case. For instance, sometimes the temperature set point changes, and the negative feedback mechanisms then operate to maintain body temperature at the new set point. Thus, when animals become infected by certain viruses and bacteria, the temperature set point increases to a higher level, producing a fever to help overcome the infection. Once the infection is combated, the set point is readjusted down again to its normal level.

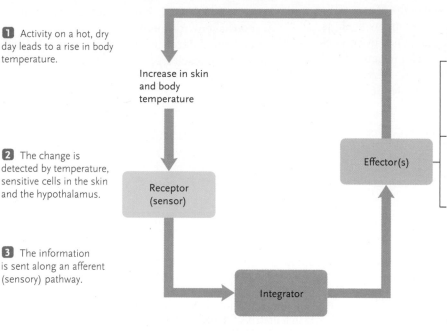

7 Physiological actions of the effector(s) lead to cooling and return body temperature to normal levels.

1 Activity on a hot, dry day leads to a rise in body temperature.

Increase in skin and body temperature

2 The change is detected by temperature, sensitive cells in the skin and the hypothalamus.

Receptor (sensor)

3 The information is sent along an afferent (sensory) pathway.

Integrator

4 Neurons in the hypothalamus receive the sensory information and determine whether action is required.

Effector(s)

6 Panting is produced by respiratory muscles to produce evaporative heat loss from the respiratory passages.

Blood vessels dilate, conducting meabolically generated heat to evaporative surfaces (lungs, throat, mouth, tongue, feet).

Salivary glands secrete fluid to increase evaporation from the tongue, mouth, and throat.

5 The information is sent along an efferent (motor) pathways.

Figure 31.12
Homeostatic mechanisms maintaining the body temperature of a husky when environmental temperatures are high.

Fred Bruemmer

Whereas mammals and birds regulate their internal body temperature within a narrow range around a set point, certain other vertebrates regulate over a broader range. These vertebrates use other negative feedback mechanisms for their temperature regulation. Snakes and lizards, for example, respond behaviourally to compensate for variations in environmental temperatures and use other, less precise negative feedback mechanisms for their temperature regulation. They may absorb heat by basking on sunny rocks in the cool early morning and move to cooler, shaded spots in the heat of the afternoon.

Many insects employ similar mechanisms to raise their body temperature. Some caterpillars group together, increasing their body temperatures by a degree or two and shortening the time of development by as much as three days. Flight requires energy, and the flight muscles operate best at higher temperatures. Some insects bask in the sun to warm the muscles. Many, such as dragonflies, bumblebees, butterflies, and moths, contract the flight muscles rapidly in a process similar to shivering in order to warm them. This is particularly important in moths that fly at night, when the environmental temperature is lower. Honeybees form masses in the winter and maintain the temperature by contracting the wing muscles. Once insects are in flight, however, the energy production is so high that they must dissipate the heat produced. In bees, the most important method is evaporative cooling by regurgitation of some of the intestinal contents onto the mouthparts, a process equivalent to panting in vertebrates.

31.4c Animals Also Have Positive Feedback Mechanisms That Do Not Result in Homeostasis

Under certain circumstances, animals respond to a change in internal or external environmental condition by a **positive feedback** mechanism that intensifies or adds to the change. Such mechanisms, with some exceptions, do not result in homeostasis. They operate when the animal is responding to life-threatening conditions (an attack, for instance), or as part of reproductive processes, and produce sudden explosive events.

The birth process in mammals is a prime example. During human childbirth, initial contractions of the uterus push the head of the fetus against the cervix, the opening of the uterus into the vagina. The pushing causes the cervix to stretch. Sensors that detect the stretching signal the hypothalamus to release a hormone, oxytocin, from the pituitary gland. Oxytocin increases the uterine contractions, intensifying the squeezing pressure on the fetus and further stretching

CHAPTER 31 INTRODUCTION TO ANIMAL ORGANIZATION AND PHYSIOLOGY the cervix. The stretching results in more oxytocin release and stronger uterine contractions, repeating the positive feedback circuit and increasing the squeezing pressure until the fetus is pushed entirely out of the uterus.

Because positive feedback mechanisms such as the one triggering childbirth do not result in homeostasis, most occur less commonly than negative feedback in animals. Others, such as the nerve action potential that will be discussed in Chapter 36, are very regular events.

STUDY BREAK

1. Describe how animals are able to maintain homeostasis despite changes in their external or internal environments.
2. What is the difference between a positive and a negative feedback loop? Describe an example of each, listing the major components of each system.

Review

  Access an interactive eBook, chapter-specific interactive learning tools, including flashcards, quizzes, videos, and more in your Biology **CourseMate**, accessed through NelsonBrain.com **Aplia™** is an online interactive learning solution that helps you improve comprehension—and your grade—by integrating a variety of mediums and tools such as videos, tutorials, practice tests, and an interactive eBook.

31.1 Organization of the Animal Body

- Multicellularity permits organisms to maintain an internal environment, allowing them to exploit a greater variety of external environments. It allows organisms to become larger but requires cells to differentiate and become specialized to perform specific functions. Since not all cells perform all functions, the extracellular fluid (ECF) serves to ensure that the net results of the specialized cells are relayed to every single cell in the organism.

- In most animals, cells are specialized and organized into tissues, tissues into organs, and organs into organ systems. A tissue is a group of cells with the same structure and function, working as a unit to carry out one or more activities. An organ is an assembly of tissues integrated into a structure that carries out a specific function. An organ system is a group of organs that carry out related steps in a major physiological process.

31.2 Animal Tissues

- Animal tissues are classified as epithelial, connective, muscle, or nervous. The properties of the cells of these tissues determine the structures and functions of the tissues.

- Various kinds of junctions link cells in a tissue. Anchoring junctions "weld" cells together. Tight junctions seal the cells into a leakproof layer. Gap junctions form direct avenues of communication between the cytoplasm of adjacent cells in the same tissue.

- Epithelial tissue consists of sheetlike layers of cells that cover body surfaces and the surfaces of internal organs and line cavities and ducts within the body.

- Exocrine glands are secretory structures derived from epithelia. Exocrine glands are connected by a duct that empties onto the epithelial surface. Endocrine glands are ductless. Not all endocrine glands are derived from epithelia.

- Connective tissue consists of cell networks or layers and a prominent extracellular matrix (ECM) that separates the cells. It supports other body tissues and transmits mechanical and other forces.

- Loose connective tissue consists of sparsely distributed fibroblasts surrounded by an open network of collagen and other glycoproteins. It supports epithelia and organs of the body and forms a covering around blood vessels, nerves, and some internal organs.

- Fibrous connective tissue contains sparsely distributed fibroblasts in a matrix of densely packed, parallel bundles of collagen and elastin fibres. It forms high-tensile-strength structures such as tendons and ligaments.

- Cartilage consists of sparsely distributed chondrocytes surrounded by a network of collagen fibres embedded in a tough but highly elastic matrix of branched glycoproteins. Cartilage provides support, flexibility, and a low-friction surface for joint movement.

- In bone, osteocytes are embedded in a collagen matrix hardened by mineral deposits. Osteoblasts secrete collagen and minerals for the ECM; osteoclasts remove the minerals and recycle them into the bloodstream.

- Adipose tissue consists of cells specialized for fat storage. It also cushions the body and provides an insulating layer under the skin.

- Blood in most animals consists of a fluid matrix, the plasma, in which cells may be suspended. In vertebrates, the erythrocytes carry oxygen to body cells and the leukocytes produce antibodies and initiate the immune response against disease-causing agents.

- Muscle tissue contains cells that have the ability to contract forcibly. Skeletal muscle, containing long cells called muscle fibres, moves body parts and maintains posture.

- Cardiac muscle, which contains short contractile cells with a branched structure, forms the heart.

- Smooth muscle consists of spindle-shaped contractile cells that form layers surrounding body cavities and ducts.

- Nervous tissue contains neurons and glial cells. Neurons communicate information between body parts in the form of electrical and chemical signals. Glial cells support the neurons or provide electrical insulation between them.

31.3 Coordination of Tissues in Organs and Organ Systems

- Organs and organ systems are coordinated to carry out vital tasks, including maintenance of internal body conditions; nutrient acquisition, processing, and distribution; waste disposal; molecular synthesis; environmental sensing and response; protection against injury and disease; and reproduction.

- In all vertebrates, the major organ systems that accomplish these tasks are the nervous, endocrine, muscular, skeletal, integumentary, circulatory, lymphatic, immune, respiratory, digestive, excretory, and reproductive systems. Many invertebrates also have these organ systems, with the exception of a lymphatic system.

31.4 Homeostasis

- Homeostasis is the process by which animals maintain their internal environment at conditions their cells can tolerate. It is a dynamic state in which internal adjustments are made continuously to compensate for environmental (external or internal) changes.

- Homeostasis is accomplished by negative feedback mechanisms that include a sensor, which detects a change in an external or internal condition; an integrator, which compares the detected change with a set point; and an effector, which returns the condition to the set point if it has varied.

- Animals also have positive feedback mechanisms, in which a change in an internal or external condition triggers a response that intensifies the change and typically does not result in homeostasis.

Questions

Self-Test Questions

Any number of answers from a to e may be correct.

1. Which structure has the highest level of organization (i.e., contains the other structures)?
   a. the liver
   b. the epithelium
   c. mitochondria
   d. the hepatic (liver) cell

2. What is a muscle, such as the biceps muscle, composed of?
   a. similar tissues
   b. different tissues
   c. similar cells
   d. different organs
   e. similar organs

3. Which tissue is a constant source of adult stem cells in a mammal?
   a. kidneys
   b. pancreas
   c. basal lamina
   d. heart muscle
   e. bone marrow

4. The bones of an elderly woman break more easily than those of a younger person. Which cell type would you surmise diminishes in activity with aging?
   a. osteocyte
   b. osteoblast
   c. osteoclast
   d. fibroblast
   e. chondrocyte

5. Where is interstitial fluid found in organisms?
   a. in the cytoplasm
   b. in the cell membrane
   c. in the cell walls
   d. between cells

6. What type of junction allows ions and molecules to flow between cells by way of channels?
   a. tight junction
   b. gap junction
   c. anchoring junction

7. What type of a cell can a chemical signal be passed to after leaving a neuron?
   a. gland cell
   b. muscle cell
   c. another neuron
   d. all of the above

8. Which of the following is NOT a homeostatic response?
   a. The basketball players are dripping sweat at halftime.
   b. The pupils in the eyes constrict when looking at a light.
   c. The brain is damaged when a fever rises above 40.5°C.
   d. Slower breathing in sleep changes carbon dioxide and oxygen levels in the blood, which affect blood pH.
   e. In a contest, a student eats an entire chocolate cake in 10 minutes. Due to hormonal secretions, his blood glucose level does not change dramatically.

9. A decrease in body temperature causes the pituitary gland to release a hormone that stimulates the release of thyroxine from the thyroid gland. Thyroxine increases metabolism, generating heat. As the body temperature increases, the release of the pituitary hormone decreases and less thyroxine is released. What is this an example of?
   a. integration
   b. osmolarity
   c. positive feedback
   d. negative feedback
   e. environmental sensing

10. Which system coordinates other organ systems?
   a. the skeletal system
   b. the muscular system
   c. the nervous system
   d. the reproductive system
   e. the endocrine system

Questions for Discussion

1. Astronauts lose bone mass during space travel. Why do you think this happens? To test your hypothesis, can you devise an experiment that does not involve space travel?

2. There are at least 25 known collagens. What information would you need to have and how would you use that information to propose a hypothesis that explains the way that evolution has acted to produce so many versions of the same molecule?

3. Positive feedback mechanisms are rarer in animals than negative feedback mechanisms. Why do you think this is so?

4. Name four important functions of epithelial tissue. Provide an example of one tissue for each function.

5. Why was the discovery of neural stem cells so important?

Confocal image of red blood cells in a small arteriole in muscle. In 1628, William Harvey published the first account of the circulation of the blood with a clear account of the action of the heart and the movement of blood around the body in blood vessels such as this, forming a continuous circuit.

32 Transport in Animals: The Circulatory System

WHY IT MATTERS

Jimmie the bulldog stood on the stage of a demonstration laboratory at a meeting of the Royal Society in London in 1909, with one front paw and one rear paw in laboratory jars containing salt water (**Figure 32.1**). Wires leading from the jars were connected to a galvanometer, a device that can detect electrical currents.

Jimmie's master, Dr. Augustus Waller, a physician at St. Mary's Hospital, was relating his experiments in the emerging field of *electrophysiology*. Among other discoveries, Waller found that his apparatus detected the electrical currents produced each time the dog's heart beat.

Waller had originally experimented on himself. He already knew that the heart produces an electrical current as it beats; other scientists had discovered this by attaching electrodes directly to the heart of experimental animals. Looking for a painless alternative to that procedure, Waller reasoned that because the human body can conduct electricity, his arms and legs might conduct the currents generated by the heart if they were connected to a galvanometer. Accordingly, Waller set up two metal pans containing salt water and connected

a. Jimmie the bulldog

From A. D. Waller, Physiology, The Servant of Medicine, Hitchcock Lectures, University of London Press, 1910.

b. Electrocardiogram

Figure 32.1
The first electrocardiograms.
(a) Jimmie the bulldog standing in laboratory jars containing salt water, with wires leading to a galvanometer that recorded the electrical currents produced by his heartbeat. **(b)** One of Waller's early electrocardiograms.

wires from the pans to a galvanometer. He put his bare left foot in one pan and his right hand in the other. The technique worked; the indicator on the galvanometer jumped each time his heart beat. And it worked with Jimmie, too.

Waller also invented a method for recording the changes in current, which became the first electrocardiogram (ECG). He constructed a galvanometer by placing a column of mercury in a fine glass tube, with a conducting salt solution layered above the mercury. Changes in the current passing through the tube caused corresponding changes in the surface tension of the mercury, which produced movements that could be detected by reflecting a beam of light from the mercury surface. By placing a moving photographic plate behind the mercury tube, Waller could record the movements of the reflected light on the plate (Figure 32.1b shows one of his records). These were the first ECGs.

As discussed in Chapter 31, with the evolution of multicellularity came the evolution of specialized tissues with specific functions. In this chapter, we discuss how the circulatory system is designed to allow these specialized tissues to exchange important molecules, and often cells, between tissues. Examples of transported molecules are oxygen (O_2), nutrients, hormones, and wastes.

The circulatory system consists of a fluid and a pump (usually a heart) and vessels for moving the fluid. It also consists of an accessory system, a lymphatic system consisting of its own vessels and organs, that balances the distribution of fluid between the blood and the extracellular fluid (ECF) surrounding tissues and participates in the body's defences against invading disease organisms.

32.1 Animal Circulatory Systems: An Introduction

Protostomes with simple body plans, including sponges, cnidarians, flatworms, and nematodes, function with no specialized circulatory system. Nearly all of these animals are aquatic or, like parasitic flatworms, live surrounded by the body fluids or intestinal contents of a host animal. Their bodies are structured as thin sheets of cells that lie close to the fluids of the surrounding environment **(Figure 32.2a, p. 776).** The products of digestion diffuse among the cells via the interstitial fluids, and O_2 and CO_2 are exchanged with the medium through the surface of the animal. Nematodes have a fluid-filled body cavity but no special mechanism for circulating that fluid.

32.1a Animal Circulatory Systems Share Basic Elements

In larger and more complex animals, most cells lie in cell layers too deep within the body to exchange substances directly with the environment via diffusion. Instead, the animals have a circulatory system, composed of tissues and organs, that conducts O_2, CO_2, nutrients, and the products of metabolism among the cells and tissues. The circulatory system connects specialized regions of the animal where substances are exchanged with the external environment. For example, oxygen is absorbed from the environment in the gills or lungs of many animals and is carried by the blood to all parts of the body; CO_2 released from body cells is carried by the blood to the lungs or gills, where it is released to the environment. Soluble wastes are conducted from body cells to the kidneys or other excretory organs, which remove wastes from circulation and excrete them into the environment.

Animal circulatory systems carrying out these roles share certain basic features:

- A specialized fluid medium, usually containing at least some cells, carries nutrients from the digestive system, the products of metabolism, and soluble wastes. With the conspicuous exception of the insects, it also transports O_2 and CO_2.
- The fluid is usually contained in tubular vessels that distribute it to the various organs. Animal circulatory systems take one of two forms, either *open* or *closed*. In an **open circulatory system,** vessels leaving the heart release fluid, usually

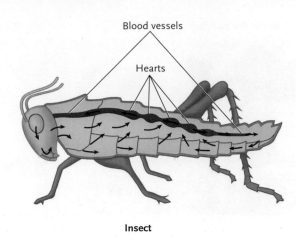

Sponge	Cnidarian		Insect

a. Circulation of external fluid through an open body cavity

b. Circulation of internal fluid through an open circulatory system

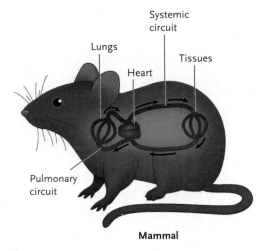

Fish

Mammal

c. Circulation of internal fluid through a closed circulatory system

d. Circulation of internal fluid through a closed circulatory system with a double circuit

Figure 32.2
The general plan of the circulatory system in different animals. **(a)** Multicellular organisms such as sponges and cnidarians use the external medium to transport molecules between cells. **(b)** Most invertebrates circulate an internal fluid through an open circulatory system. **(c)** Some invertebrates and all vertebrates move an internal fluid through a closed circulatory system in which blood is separated from the interstitial fluid. **(d)** In birds and mammals, two separate circuits serve the lungs and all other tissues of the body.

termed **hemolymph**, directly into body spaces or into sinuses surrounding organs **(Figure 32.2b; Figure 32.3a).** Thus, the organs and tissues are directly bathed in the hemolymph. The hemolymph re-enters the heart through valves in the heart wall that close each time the heart pumps, thereby maintaining a unidirectional flow. In a **closed circulatory system**, the blood is confined to blood vessels and is distinct from the interstitial fluid **(Figure 32.2c, d; Figure 32.3b).** Substances are exchanged between the blood and the interstitial fluid and then between the interstitial fluid and cells.

- A muscular heart pumps the fluid through the circulatory system. Words associated with the heart often include *cardio,* from *kardia,* Greek for heart.

32.1b Most Invertebrates Have Open Circulatory Systems

Among the protostomes, arthropods and most molluscs have open circulatory systems with one or more muscular hearts (Figure 32.2b, **Figure 32.4**). The blood is not conveyed directly to all cells by tubes but is ejected from the open ends of the blood vessels and directly bathes the body tissues. In an open system, most of the fluid pressure generated by the heart dissipates when the blood is released from vessels into body spaces. Although the pressure remains low, the rate at which the blood circulates can be increased by an increase in the rate of beating of the heart. Because of one-way valves in the heart and vessels, the beating heart draws hemolymph in from the tissue spaces as they expand and pushes it out through the vessels as

a. Open circulatory system: no distinction between haemolymph and interstitial fluid

b. Closed circulatory system: blood separated from interstitial fluid

Figure 32.3

(a) Open circulatory system: hemolymph bathes the organs and body tissues. **(b)** Closed circulatory system: blood is confined in tubes that lie among the cells of all tissues.

the heart contracts. In highly active invertebrates, such as flying insects, the heart rate may rise to three or more times the resting rate, increasing the circulation of the hemolymph among the tissues. In addition, most insects have accessory hearts associated with the wings and each leg, which experience the same increases in rate during periods of high metabolic activity. In insects and molluscs, heart rate is controlled in some cases by nerves but largely by a variety of amine and peptide hormones (see Chapter 36).

32.1c Some Invertebrates and All Vertebrates Have Closed Circulatory Systems

Annelids, cephalopod molluscs such as squids and octopuses, most deuterostome invertebrates, and all vertebrates have closed circulatory systems (Figure 32.2c, Figure 32.4). In these systems, vessels called **arteries** conduct blood away from the heart at relatively high pressure. From the arteries, the blood enters highly branched networks of microscopic, thin-walled vessels called **capillaries** that are well adapted for diffusion of substances. Nutrients and wastes are exchanged between the blood and body tissues as the blood moves through the capillaries. The blood then flows at relatively low pressure from the capillaries to larger vessels, the **veins**, which carry the blood back to

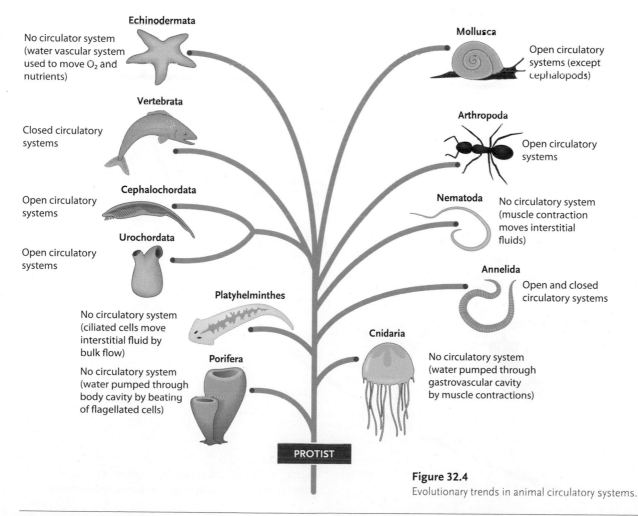

Figure 32.4

Evolutionary trends in animal circulatory systems.

the heart. Typically, the blood is maintained at a higher pressure and moves more rapidly through the body in closed systems than in open systems. In many animals, closed systems allow precise control of the distribution and rate of blood flow to different body regions by means of muscles that contract or relax to adjust the diameter of the blood vessels. Contraction leads to reduced blood vessel diameter, while relaxation increases the blood vessel diameter.

32.1d Vertebrate Circulatory Systems Have Evolved from Single to Double Blood Circuits

A comparison of the different vertebrate groups reveals several evolutionary trends that accompanied the invasion of terrestrial habitats. Among the most striking are the changes that occurred in the major vessels of the body and the heart. These changes converted the single-circuit system of sharks and bony fish, in which the gills are in the same circuit as the rest of the blood vessels, to a double-circuit system in which the circulation to the lungs parallels the circulation to the rest of the body (Figure 32.2d, p. 776).

There were two major developments. In one, the blood vessels supplying the gills were reorganized to accommodate the appearance of lungs. There is an evolutionary progression to an increasing separation of blood flow to the gas exchange organs (pulmonary circuit) and to the rest of the body (systemic circuit) **(Figure 32.5).**

The second involved developments in the structure of the heart. In a shark or bony fish **(Figure 32.6a)**, venous, deoxygenated blood from the tissues enters the first chamber, the atrium. The atrium contracts, forcing open flaplike valves leading into the ventricle and closing valves that prevent backflow into the veins.

Figure 32.5

Evolution of the circulatory system. The single circulation of most fishes gives rise to the double circulation of tetrapods.

Contraction of the ventricle propels the blood forward into the ventral aorta leading to the blood vessels going to the gills (the aortic arches); the gill capillaries; and the dorsal aorta, which carries blood to the tissues. In amphibians, the atrium is divided, with one side (left atrium) receiving oxygenated blood from the lungs and the other side (right atrium) receiving deoxygenated blood from the body and skin **(Figure 32.6b)**. In the single ventricle, some separation of the two streams is achieved by the spongy nature of the ventricle that prevents open mixing, and by a flaplike structure in the vessel leaving the heart that can direct blood into the arteries going to the skin and lungs or into the arteries going to the rest of the body. In modern reptiles, such as lizards and snakes, the ventricle is partially divided **(Figure 32.6c)**.

CONCEPT FIX *The partially divided ventricle of most reptiles* is often referred to as incompletely divided, with the inference that this *is a phylogenetic artefact and less than ideal*. The cardiovascular systems of reptiles, however, are extraordinarily flexible and no less adaptive for their lifestyles than the systems found in birds and mammals. Evolution of the cardiovascular system does not represent a progressive improvement in design but rather different adaptive alternatives for meeting the different demands that different lifestyles place on the circulatory system. In the case of the reptiles, the amount of mixing of blood returning from the two atria that occurs in the ventricles can be carefully regulated. ⬡

Full separation of the blood supply to the lungs occurs in mammals, birds, and crocodilians (alligators and crocodiles share ancestry with birds) by complete division of the ventricle **(Figure 32.6d)**. There are thus two separate circuits. One circuit delivers oxygenated blood from the lungs into the left atrium, which then propels it into the left ventricle. The contraction of the left ventricle sends blood to the body circulation via the carotid arteries to the head and the dorsal aorta, which supplies the remainder of the body. In the second circuit, deoxygenated blood from the body and head enters the right atrium and, via the right ventricle, is propelled to the lungs in the pulmonary artery.

This progressive separation of the body and lung circulation (illustrated in Figure 32.5), and the accompanying changes in the architecture of the heart (illustrated in Figure 32.6), demonstrate that although

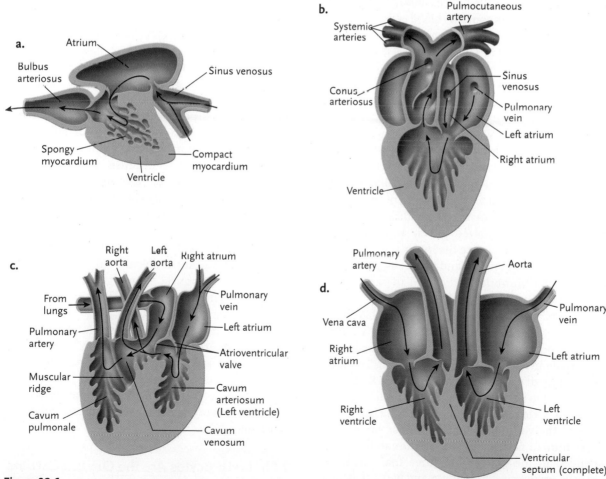

Figure 32.6

Major steps in the evolution of the heart leading to separate circulation for the lungs. **(a)** The two-chambered heart in a shark or a bony fish, **(b)** two atria in an amphibian, **(c)** partial division of the ventricle in modern reptiles, and **(d)** complete separation into two ventricles in crocodilians, birds, and mammals.

evolution happens by changes in existing structures, changes in one set of structures (the aortic arches) are correlated with changes in other structures (the heart).

STUDY BREAK

1. What are the differences between open and closed circulatory systems? Has the closed system evolved only once? What are the advantages of a closed system over an open one?
2. Which vertebrates have a separate pulmonary circulation? Compare and contrast the circulatory systems of a fish, a frog, and a beaver and describe the changes in the structure of the heart that accompany them. What might be the advantages or disadvantages of the differences?

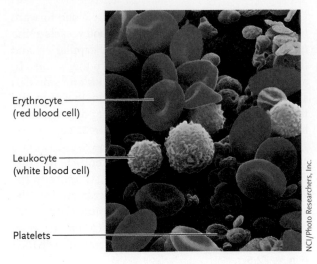

Erythrocyte (red blood cell)

Leukocyte (white blood cell)

Platelets

NCI/Photo Researchers, Inc.

Figure 32.7

Typical components of human blood. The colourized scanning electron micrograph shows the three major cellular components.

32.2 Blood and Its Components

In both vertebrates and invertebrates, blood is a complex connective tissue that may contain blood cells suspended in a liquid called the *plasma*. Although the blood of all vertebrates contains blood cells, the blood of some invertebrates may consist exclusively of plasma with few or no suspended cells, as in the Nematoda. In other invertebrates, such as the arthropods, blood cells or hemocytes of various recognizable types may occur in large numbers (up to 275 000 per μL in crickets) that can vary with activity and developmental stage. Whereas some hemocytes circulate with the hemolymph, others may attach temporarily to various tissues. These hemocytes can be mobilized rapidly and enter the circulation, for example, to take part in wound healing or in defence against disease and parasites. In addition to transporting nutrients, dissolved gases, and metabolic wastes, blood helps stabilize the internal pH and salt composition of body fluids and serves as a highway for cells of the immune system and the antibodies produced by some of these cells.

In vertebrates, blood also helps regulate body temperature by transferring heat between warmer and cooler body regions and between the body and the external environment (see Chapter 42). The total blood volume of most vertebrates is 5 to 8% of body mass (about 4 to 5 L in an average-sized adult human). The *plasma*, a clear, straw-coloured fluid, is about 45 to 55% of the volume of blood in most vertebrates (55% in human males and 58% in human females). Suspended in the plasma are three main types of blood cells, *erythrocytes, leukocytes,* and *platelets,* which account for the remainder of the blood volume. The typical components of human blood are shown in **Figure 32.7.**

32.2a Plasma Is an Aqueous Solution of Proteins, Ions, Nutrient Molecules, and Gases

Plasma is complex, and its composition varies depending on many factors. Its average composition in humans is given in **Table 32.1.** The plasma proteins of vertebrates fall into three classes: the albumins, the globulins, and fibrinogen. The **albumins**, the most abundant proteins of the plasma, are important for osmotic balance and pH buffering. They also transport a wide variety of substances through the circulatory system, including hormones and metabolic wastes. Because of their similar chemical composition to hormones, many therapeutic drugs are designed to be transported this way. The **globulins** transport lipids (including cholesterol) and fat-soluble vitamins; a specialized subgroup of globulins, the *immunoglobulins,* includes antibodies and other molecules that contribute to the immune response. Some globulins are also enzymes. **Fibrinogen** plays a central role in the clotting mechanism of the blood.

The ions of the plasma include Na^+, K^+, Ca^{2+}, Cl^-, and HCO_3^- (bicarbonate). The Na^+ and Cl^- ions are the most abundant and are present in concentrations similar to those of seawater, reflecting evolutionary ancestry. Some of the ions, particularly the bicarbonate ion, help maintain arterial blood at its characteristic pH (see Chapter 42).

32.2b Erythrocytes Are the Oxygen Carriers of Vertebrate Blood

Erythrocytes, or red blood cells, carry O_2 from the lungs to body tissues. Each microlitre of human blood

Table 32.1 | The Composition of Human Blood

The sketch of the test tube shows what happens when you centrifuge a blood sample. The blood separates into three layers: a thick layer of straw-coloured plasma on top, a thin layer containing leukocytes and platelets, and a thick layer of erythrocytes. The table shows the relative amounts and functions of the various components of blood.

Plasma Portion (55–58% of total volume)

Components	Relative Amounts	Functions
1. Water	91–92% of plasma volume	Solvent
2. Plasma proteins (albumin, globulins, fibrinogen, etc.)	7–8%	Defence, clotting, lipid transport, roles in ECF volume, and so on
3. Ions, sugars, lipids, amino acids, hormones, vitamins, dissolved gases, urea and uric acid (metabolic wastes)	1–2%	Roles in ECF volume, pH, eliminating waste products, and so on

Cellular Portion (42–45% of total volume):

	Relative Amounts	Functions
1. Erythrocytes (red blood cells)	4 800 000–5 400 000 per microlitre	Transport oxygen, carbon dioxide
2. Leukocytes (white blood cells)		
Neutrophils	3000–6750	Phagocytosis during inflammation
Lymphocytes	1000–2700	Immune response
Monocytes/macrophages	150–720	Phagocytosis in all defence responses
Eosinophils	100–360	Defend against parasitic worms
Basophils	25–90	Secrete substances for inflammatory response and for fat removal from blood
3. Platelets	250 000–300 000	Roles in clotting

Plasma

Leukocytes and platelets

Packed cell volume, or hematocrit

Erythrocytes

normally contains about 5 million erythrocytes, which are small, flattened, and disklike. They measure about 7 µm in diameter and 2 µm in thickness. Microtubules of the cytoskeleton (see Chapter 2) are arranged beneath the surface of the cell so that they are *biconcave*—thinner in the middle than at the edges (see Figure 32.7). The proteins of the cytoskeleton that determine their shape also give them the flexibility to squeeze through narrow capillaries.

Like all blood cells, erythrocytes arise from stem cells (see Chapter 31) in the red bone marrow. As they mature, mammalian erythrocytes lose their nucleus, cytoplasmic organelles, and ribosomes. Because they are no longer capable of synthesizing new proteins, this limits their metabolic capabilities and their lifespan (as short as 35 days in a chicken but 120 days in a human). The remaining cytoplasm contains enzymes, which carry out glycolysis, and large quantities of *hemoglobin,* the O_2-carrying protein of the blood. The erythrocytes of nearly all other vertebrates retain a nucleus.

Hemoglobin, the molecule that gives erythrocytes, and thus blood, their red colour, consists of four polypeptides, each linked to a nonprotein *heme* group (see "Molecule behind Biology," Box 32.1, p. 782) that contains an iron atom in its centre. The iron atom binds O_2 molecules as the blood circulates through the lungs and releases the O_2 as the blood flows through

other body tissues. This is described in more detail in Chapter 41. It is the oxygenation of the iron that gives arterial blood its bright red colour (and red blood cells their name), just as the oxygenation of iron in nature gives rust its colour. When hemoglobin releases its oxygen, the venous blood changes to a much darker colour.

Some 2 to 3 *million* erythrocytes are produced in the average human each second. The lifespan of an erythrocyte in the circulatory system is about 120 days. At the end of their useful life, erythrocytes are engulfed and destroyed by *macrophages* (*macro* = big; *phagein* = to eat), a type of large leukocyte, in the spleen, liver, and bone marrow.

A negative feedback mechanism keyed to the blood's O_2 content stabilizes the number of erythrocytes in blood. If the O_2 content drops below the normal level, the kidneys synthesize **erythropoietin**, a peptide hormone that stimulates stem cells in bone marrow to increase erythrocyte production. Erythropoietin is also secreted after blood loss and when mammals move to higher altitudes. As new red blood cells enter the bloodstream, the O_2-carrying capacity of the blood rises. If the O_2 content of the blood rises above normal levels, erythropoietin production falls and red blood cell production drops. Erythropoietin has been used in "blood doping" by some athletes to improve their performance.

Heme

Heme is a member of a family of chemicals called porphyrins **(Figure 1)**. Among the properties of porphyrins is their ability to bind metals. In heme, the metal bound is iron. The complex attracts O_2, which binds to the iron. Heme is a cofactor of several important animal proteins and, as such, is an important carrier of O_2 in biological systems. Because these protein molecules are coloured, they are often referred to as oxygen-carrying pigments.

Hemoglobin is a protein that includes four heme molecules. In the lungs, the higher concentration of O_2 loads the hemoglobin in the erythrocytes with O_2 (oxidizing the iron and turning the blood bright red), and in the tissues, the low concentration leads to unloading (deoxidizing the iron and turning the blood a darker colour). The process of unloading the O_2 is assisted by higher concentrations of CO_2 in the tissues. Slight changes in the structure of the hemoglobin molecule lead to changes in the ability of the protein to bind oxygen. Animals that live in oxygen-poor environments possess hemoglobins with stronger binding affinities for oxygen than those that live in oxygen-rich environments. The mammalian fetus, for example, lives in a relatively oxygen-poor environment and has a special embryonic hemoglobin with a very strong binding affinity.

Myoglobin in muscle, neuroglobin in nervous tissue, and cytoglobin in all tissues are proteins that bind oxygen with an affinity higher than that of hemoglobin. They facilitate diffusion of oxygen through tissues, scavenge nitric oxide or reactive oxygen species, or serve a protective function by increasing oxygen availability during oxidative stress. The oxygen that is bound to myoglobin also serves as a reservoir that can be called on during periods of high metabolic demand resulting from increased muscle activity.

a.

b.

c.

Cytochrome oxidase, the terminal enzyme in the complex that transfers electrons to molecular O_2 (see Chapter 6), also contains a heme molecule.

d.

FIGURE 1

(a) *The heme molecule.* Animals with heme-containing hemoglobins that bind oxygen readily include those that live in oxygen-poor environments such as **(b)** *the llama at altitude;* **(c)** *fish, such as the carp, in hypoxic waters; and* **(d)** *mammalian fetuses such as that of an elephant shown here.*

Other oxygen-carrying pigments, such as hemocyanin, which occurs in molluscs and some arthropods, and hemerythrin, found in a variety of invertebrates, also function as O_2 carriers. They do not, however, contain heme as the functional group.

32.2c Leukocytes Provide the Body's Front Line of Defence against Disease

Leukocytes eliminate dead and dying cells from the body, remove cellular debris, and provide the body's first line of defence against invading organisms. They are called white cells because they are colourless, in contrast to the red blood cells. Because leukocytes retain their nuclei, cytoplasmic organelles, and ribosomes, they are fully functional cells.

Like red blood cells, leukocytes arise from the division of stem cells in red bone marrow. As they mature, they are released into the bloodstream, from which they enter body tissues in large numbers. Some types of leukocytes are capable of continued division in the blood and body tissues. The specific types of leukocytes and their functions in the immune reaction are discussed in Chapter 43.

32.2d Platelets Induce Blood Clots that Seal Breaks in the Circulatory System

Blood **platelets** are oval or rounded cell fragments, 2 to 4 μm in diameter, each enclosed in its own plasma membrane. They are produced in red bone marrow by the division of stem cells. Platelets contain enzymes and other factors that take part in blood clotting. When blood vessels are damaged, collagen fibres in the extracellular matrix are exposed to the leaking blood. Platelets in the blood stick to the collagen fibres and release signalling molecules that induce additional platelets to stick to them. The process continues, forming a plug that helps seal off the damaged site. As the plug forms, the platelets release other factors that convert the soluble plasma protein, fibrinogen, into long, insoluble threads of **fibrin**. Cross-links between the fibrin threads form a meshlike network that traps blood cells and platelets and further seals the damaged area **(Figure 32.8).** The entire mass is a blood clot.

STUDY BREAK

1. Why is blood considered a tissue? What are its three main cellular components and what are their functions?
2. Hemoglobin occurs in the blood of many animals, but in many invertebrates, it occurs free in the plasma. What advantages can you think of that might have led to its incorporation in erythrocytes during the evolution of vertebrates? The nonvertebrate chordates do not have hemoglobin in their blood, but they do have cells in their blood that have a role in defence, suggesting that erythrocytes may have originated from such cells. What evidence could be used to examine this hypothesis?

32.3 The Heart

The vertebrate heart is composed of cardiac muscle cells (see Chapters 31 and 38). In mammals, we have seen (Figures 32.5, 32.6) that the heart is a four-chambered pump, with two atria (singular, atrium) and two ventricles **(Figure 32.9).** The atria pump blood into the ventricles, and then powerful contractions of the ventricles push the blood at relatively high pressure into arteries leaving the heart. This arterial pressure is responsible for blood circulation. Valves between the atria and the ventricles, and between the ventricles and the arteries leaving the heart, keep the blood from flowing backward.

Figure 32.8
Red blood cells caught in a meshlike network of fibrin threads during formation of a blood clot.

© Professor P. Motta/Department of Anatomy/ University La Sapienza, Rome/SPL/Photo Researchers, Inc.

Figure 32.9
Cutaway view of a mammalian heart showing its internal organization.

The mammalian heart pumps the blood through two completely separate circuits of blood vessels: the systemic circuit and the pulmonary circuit (Figure 32.10). The right atrium (toward the right side of the body) receives blood returning from the entire body, except for the lungs. The *superior vena cava* conveys blood returning from the head and forelimbs, and the *inferior vena cava* conveys blood returning from the abdominal organs and hindlimbs. This blood is depleted of O_2 and has a high CO_2 content. The right atrium pumps the blood into the right ventricle, which contracts to push the blood into the *pulmonary arteries* leading to the lungs. In the capillaries of the lungs, the blood releases CO_2 and picks up O_2. The oxygenated blood completes this pulmonary circuit by returning to the heart in *pulmonary veins*.

Blood returning from the pulmonary circuit enters the left atrium, which pumps it into the left ventricle. This ventricle, the most thick-walled and powerful chamber, contracts to send the oxygenated blood into a large artery, the **aorta**, which branches into arteries leading to all body regions except the lungs.

The arteries divide into smaller and smaller arteries and then into capillary networks, in which the blood releases O_2 and picks up CO_2. The O_2-depleted blood collects in veins, which complete the systemic circuit. The blood from the veins enters the right atrium. The amount of blood pumped by the two halves of the heart is normally balanced so that neither side pumps more than the other.

The heart also has its own circulation, called the *coronary circulation*. Two small *coronary arteries* branch off the aorta and then branch extensively over the heart, leading to dense capillary beds that serve the cardiac muscle cells. The blood from the capillary networks collects into veins that empty into the right atrium. If a coronary artery becomes blocked, the muscle cells it supplies can die and the person can suffer a heart attack (see "People behind Biology," Box 32.2).

32.3a The Heartbeat Is Produced by a Cycle of Contraction and Relaxation of the Atria and Ventricles

Average heart rates vary among mammals (and among vertebrates generally), depending on body size and the overall level of metabolic activity. An adult human heart beats 72 times each minute, on average, with each beat lasting about 0.8 second. The heart rate of a trained endurance athlete is typically much lower. In infants and young children it beats 120 to 160 times each minute. The heart of a flying bat may beat 1200 times a minute, whereas that of an elephant beats only 30 times a minute. **Systole** is the period of contraction and emptying of the heart, and **diastole** is the period of relaxation and filling of the heart between contractions. The systole–diastole sequence of the heart is called the **cardiac cycle (Figure 32.11)**. The following discussion goes through one cardiac cycle.

Starting when both atria and ventricles are relaxed in diastole, the atria begin to fill with blood (step 1 in Figure 32.11). At this point, the **atrioventricular (AV) valves** between each atrium and ventricle and the **semilunar (SL) valves** between the ventricles and the aorta and pulmonary arteries are closed. As the atria fill, the pressure pushes open the AV valves and begins to fill the relaxed ventricles (step 2). When the ventricles are about 80% full, the atria contract and completely fill the ventricles with blood (step 3).

SYSTEMIC CIRCUIT

Capillary networks of head and forelimbs

PULMONARY CIRCUIT

Superior vena cava

Pulmonary artery

Pulmonary vein

RA

Pulmonary vein

Capillary network of right lung

Inferior vena cava

PULMONARY CIRCUIT

Aorta

Pulmonary artery

LA

Pulmonary vein

LV

RV

To lower body parts

Capillary network of left lung

Capillary networks of abdominal organs and lower limbs

SYSTEMIC CIRCUIT

KEY

RA Right atrium
LA Left atrium
RV Right ventricle
LV Left ventricle

Figure 32.10

The pulmonary and systemic circuits of a typical mammal (a human). The right half of the heart pumps blood into the pulmonary circuit, and the left half of the heart pumps blood into the systemic circuit.

PEOPLE BEHIND BIOLOGY 32.2

Lorrie Kirshenbaum, University of Manitoba

Cardiac muscle cells do not divide after birth; the growth of the heart is the result of an increase in the size of the muscle cells. When the cells are damaged in a heart attack, they cannot repair themselves, nor can they be replaced.

Lorrie Kirshenbaum, Canada Research Chair in Molecular Cardiology at the University of Manitoba, explores the molecular events controlling the growth and death of cardiac muscle. *BNIP3* is one of a family of genes that initiate cell death. In particular, it initiates cardiac cell death when there is a lack of oxygen.

Kirshenbaum's lab has been active in describing the pathways that activate the *BNIP3* gene and the intracellular pathways that the protein product of the gene uses to kill the cells. Kirshenbaum is exploring how this information might be used to prevent the activation of the gene or its effects and thus prevent the death of cardiac cells when deprived of oxygen. He is also studying whether the gene could be activated to kill cancer cells in other tissues.

A different approach involves exploring ways to replace damaged heart cells. Cardiac muscle cells,

which do not divide, have the normal cell division pathway blocked. Kirshenbaum's lab is using growth factors, delivered as genes in viruses, to activate the cell division pathway. However, it turns out that adult myocytes that have the cell division pathway turned on enter a pathway leading to death. To get around this difficulty, Kirshenbaum also delivers growth factors that block the self-destructive pathway together with the growth factors that stimulate cell division. This is a promising alternative to using stem cells to replace damaged heart cells.

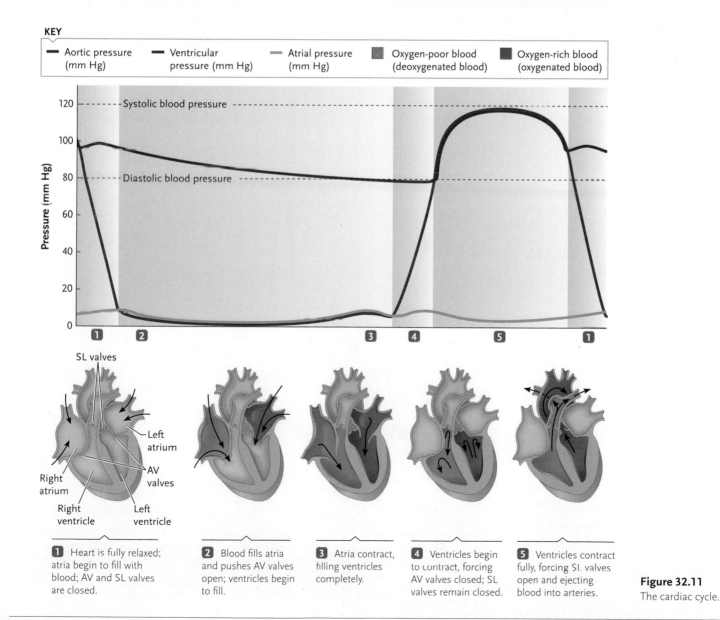

KEY

- Aortic pressure (mm Hg)
- Ventricular pressure (mm Hg)
- Atrial pressure (mm Hg)
- Oxygen-poor blood (deoxygenated blood)
- Oxygen-rich blood (oxygenated blood)

1. Heart is fully relaxed; atria begin to fill with blood; AV and SL valves are closed.

2. Blood fills atria and pushes AV valves open; ventricles begin to fill.

3. Atria contract, filling ventricles completely.

4. Ventricles begin to contract, forcing AV valves closed; SL valves remain closed.

5. Ventricles contract fully, forcing SL valves open and ejecting blood into arteries.

Figure 32.11
The cardiac cycle.

Although there are no valves where the veins open into the atria, the atrial contraction compresses the openings, sealing them so that little backflow occurs into the veins.

As the ventricular muscles begin to contract, rising pressure in the ventricular chambers forces the AV valves shut (step 4). As they continue to contract, the pressure in the ventricular chambers rises above that in the arteries leading away from the heart, forcing open the SL valves. Blood now rushes from the ventricles into the aorta and the pulmonary arteries (step 5).

Completion of the contraction squeezes about two-thirds of the blood in the ventricles into the arteries. Now the ventricles relax, lowering pressure in the ventricular chambers below that in the arteries. This reversal of the pressure gradient reverses the direction of blood flow in the regions of the SL valves, causing them to close. For about half a second, both the atria and the ventricles remain in diastole and blood flows into the atria and ventricles. Then the blood-filled atria contract, and the cycle repeats.

In most vertebrates at rest, each minute a ventricle pumps roughly an amount equivalent to the entire volume of blood in the body; that is, blood leaving the heart takes roughly one minute to complete a single circulation. At maximum rate and strength, the hearts of most vertebrates pump about 10 times the resting amount. The human heart is only capable of about half this increase.

32.3b The Cardiac Cycle Is Initiated within the Heart

Contraction of cardiac muscle cells is triggered by action potentials that spread across the muscle cell membranes. Recall that cardiac muscle cells are connected to one another by gap junctions (see Chapters 31 and 38). As a result, electrical activity can pass rapidly from one cell to its neighbours. Crustaceans, such as crabs and lobsters, have **neurogenic hearts,** that is, hearts that beat under the control of signals from the nervous system. Each contraction is initiated by signals from a cardiac ganglion located in the heart, and the heart will continue to beat and respond to some environmental signals in isolation from the central nervous system, as long as the ganglion is intact. Other animals, including all insects and all vertebrates, have **myogenic hearts** that maintain their contraction rhythm with no requirement for signals from the nervous system. Isolated cardiac myocytes contract rhythmically when grown in a suitable medium. Both neurogenic and myogenic hearts can also be influenced by signals from the central nervous system and by hormones.

The rate and timing of the contraction of individual cardiac muscle cells in a mammalian myogenic heart are coordinated by a region of the heart called the **sinoatrial node (SA node).** The SA node consists of **pacemaker cells,** which are specialized cardiac muscle cells in the upper wall of the right atrium (**Figure 32.12,** step 1).

Figure 32.12

The electrical control of the cardiac cycle. The bottom part of the figure shows how a signal originating at the SA node leads to ventricular contraction. The top part of the figure shows the electrical activity for each of the stages as seen in an ECG. The colours in the hearts show the location of the signal at each step and correspond to the colours in the ECG.

1 Pacemaker generates a wave of signals to contract.

2 Signals are delayed in the region between the atria and ventricles.

3 AV node cells are stimulated to produce a signal, which travels along Purkinje fibres to the bottom of the heart.

4 Signals spread from the bottom of the heart upward, causing the ventricles to contract.

Ion channels in these cells open in a cyclic, self-sustaining pattern that alternately depolarizes and repolarizes their plasma membranes. The regularly timed depolarizations spread to neighbouring cells, causing them to contract and initiating waves of contraction that travel over the entire heart.

A layer of connective tissue separates the atria from the ventricles, acting as a layer of electrical insulation between the two sets of chambers of the heart. The insulating layer keeps a contraction signal from the SA node from spreading directly from the atria to the ventricles (step 2). Instead, the atrial wave of contraction excites cells of the **atrioventricular (AV) node**, located in the heart wall between the right atrium and the right ventricle, just above the insulating layer of connective tissue. The signal produced travels from the AV node to the bottom of the heart via *Purkinje fibres* (step 3). These fibres follow a path downward, through the insulating layer, to the bottom of the heart, where they branch through the walls of the ventricles. The signal carried by the Purkinje fibres induces a wave of contraction that begins at the bottom of the heart and spreads from cell to cell upward, squeezing the blood from the ventricles into the aorta and pulmonary arteries (step 4). The transmission of a signal from the AV node to the ventricles takes about 0.1 second; this delay gives the atria time to finish their contraction before the ventricles contract.

As Augustus Waller found in experiments with Jimmie the bulldog, the electrical signals passing through the heart can be detected by attaching electrodes to different points on the surface of the body. The signals change in a regular pattern corresponding to the electrical signals that trigger the cardiac cycle, producing what is known as an **electrocardiogram** (**ECG**; also EKG, from the German *Elektrokardiogramm*). The highlighted region of the ECG above each stage of the cardiac cycle in Figure 32.12 indicates the electrical activity measured in those stages.

32.3c Arterial Blood Pressure Cycles between a High Systolic and a Low Diastolic Pressure

The pressure exerted by a fluid in a confined space is called *hydrostatic pressure*. That is, fluid in a container exerts some pressure on the wall of the container. Blood vessels are essentially tubular containers that are part of a closed system filled with fluid. Hence, the blood in vessels exerts hydrostatic pressure against the walls of the vessels. *Blood pressure* is the measurement of that hydrostatic pressure on the walls of the arteries as the heart pumps blood through the body. Blood pressure is determined by the force and amount of blood pumped by the heart and the size and stiffness of the arteries. In any animal, blood pressure changes in response to activity, temperature, body position, behaviour, time of day, and diet.

As the ventricles contract, a surge of high-pressure blood moves outward through the arteries leading from the heart. This peak of high pressure, called the *systolic blood pressure*, can be felt as a *pulse* by pressing a finger against an artery that lies near the skin, such as the arteries of the neck or the artery that runs along the inside of the wrist. Between ventricular contractions, the arterial blood pressure reaches a low point called the *diastolic blood pressure*. In healthy humans at rest, the systolic pressure, measured in the large artery in the forearm, is equivalent to between 90 and 120 mm of mercury (mm Hg) and the diastolic to between 60 and 80 mm Hg. These pressures are illustrated in Figure 32.11, p. 785.

The blood pressure in the systemic and pulmonary circuits is highest in the arteries leaving the heart and drops as the blood passes from the arteries into the capillaries. By the time the blood returns to the heart, its pressure has dropped to 2 to 5 mm Hg, with no differentiation between systolic and diastolic pressures. The reduction in pressure occurs because the blood encounters resistance as it moves through the vessels, primarily due to the friction created when blood cells and plasma proteins move over each other and over vessel walls.

STUDY BREAK

1. Distinguish between systolic and diastolic blood pressure. Why are these two values different? Why doesn't pressure fall to zero during diastole when the heart is not contracting?
2. What is the function of the sinoatrial node? What is the function of the AV node? How do their roles differ?

32.4 Blood Vessels of the Circulatory System

Both the systemic and the pulmonary circuit consist of a continuum of different blood vessel types that begin and end at the heart (**Figure 32.13, p. 788**). From the heart, large arteries carry blood and branch into progressively smaller arteries, delivering blood to the various parts of the body. When a small artery reaches the organ it supplies, it branches into yet smaller vessels, the **arterioles**. Within the organ, arterioles branch into capillaries, the smallest vessels of the circulatory system. Capillaries form a network in the organ, where they exchange substances between the blood and the surrounding interstitial fluid. Capillaries rejoin to form small **venules**, which merge into the small veins that leave the organ. The small veins progressively join to form larger veins that eventually become the large veins that enter the heart.

Figure 32.13

The structure of arteries, capillaries, and veins and their relationship in blood circuits.

32.4a Arteries Transport Blood Rapidly to the Tissues and Serve as a Pressure Reservoir

Arteries have relatively large diameters and therefore provide little resistance to blood flow. They are structurally adapted to the relatively high pressure of the blood passing through them. The walls of arteries consist of three major tissue layers (see Figure 32.13):

*   an outer layer of connective tissue containing collagen fibres mixed with fibres of the protein elastin, making the vessel elastic and giving it the ability to recoil;
*   a relatively thick middle layer of vascular smooth muscle cells also mixed with elastin fibres; and
*   an inner layer of flattened cells only one cell in thickness, forming an endothelium.

In addition to being conduits for blood travelling to the tissues, arteries also act as a pressure reservoir for blood movement when the heart is relaxing. When contraction of the ventricles pumps blood into the arteries, a greater volume of blood enters the arteries than leaves them to flow into the smaller vessels downstream because of the higher resistance to blood flow in these smaller vessels. Arteries accommodate the excess volume of blood because of their elastic walls, which allow the arteries to expand in diameter. When the heart relaxes and blood is no longer being pumped into the arteries, the arterial walls recoil passively back to their original state and the pressure in them falls from systolic to diastolic levels. The longer the interval between heartbeats, the more the diastolic pressure

falls. The recoil pushes the excess blood from the arteries into the smaller downstream vessels. As a result, blood flow to tissues is continuous during systole and diastole even though the heart is relaxing and not contracting during diastole.

32.4b Capillaries Are the Sites of Exchange between the Blood and Interstitial Fluid

Capillaries thread through nearly every tissue in the body and are arranged in networks bringing them within 0.01 mm of most body cells. In humans, they are estimated to have a surface area of about 2600 km² for the exchange of gases, nutrients, and wastes with the interstitial fluid. Capillary walls consist of a single layer of endothelial cells, resting on a thin basement membrane. They do not contain smooth muscle (see Chapter 31).

Control of Blood Flow through Capillaries. Blood flow through capillary networks is controlled by contraction of smooth muscle in the arterioles that feed them **(Figure 32.14)**. In addition to the normal layer of smooth muscle, some arterioles have circular rings of smooth muscle at the entrance to the capillary bed, called *precapillary sphincter muscles*. When the arteriole and sphincter smooth muscles are relaxed, blood flows readily through the arterioles and capillary networks. When they are contracted, blood flow through the arterioles and capillary networks is limited. By varying the contraction of the arteriole and sphincter smooth muscles, the rate of flow through the capillary networks of individual organs can be adjusted. For example, during exercise, the flow of blood through the capillary networks of the intestines is decreased while that through the muscles of the legs is increased.

The Velocity of Blood Flow through Capillaries. Although their total surface area is astoundingly large, the diameter of individual capillaries is so small that red blood cells must squeeze through most of them in single file **(Figure 32.15)**. As a result, each capillary presents a high resistance to blood flow. In addition, there are so many billions of capillaries in the networks that their combined diameter is about 1300 times the cross-sectional area of the aorta. As a result of the resistance and the vastly increased diameter of the combined tubes, blood slows considerably as it moves through capillaries, maximizing opportunities for exchange between the blood and the interstitial fluids. As they leave the tissues, capillaries rejoin to form venules and veins. Veins have a total cross-sectional area that is smaller than the total cross-sectional area of the capillaries, so the velocity of flow increases as blood returns to the heart.

The Exchange of Substances across Capillary Walls. In most body tissues, narrow spaces between the capillary

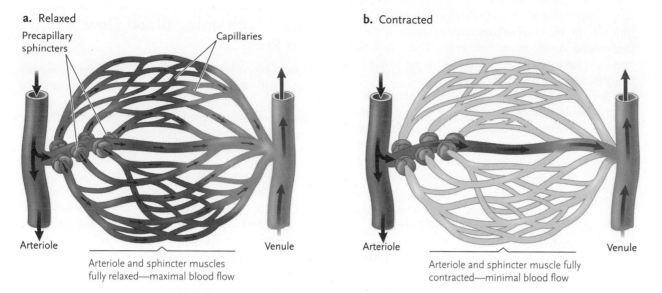

a. Relaxed

Precapillary sphincters

Capillaries

Arteriole

Venule

Arteriole and sphincter muscles fully relaxed—maximal blood flow

b. Contracted

Arteriole

Venule

Arteriole and sphincter muscle fully contracted—minimal blood flow

Figure 32.14

Control of blood flow through capillary networks. **(a)** Maximal blood flow when arteriole and sphincter muscles are fully relaxed. **(b)** Minimal blood flow when the arteriole and sphincter muscles are fully contracted.

a.

Dennis Kunkel Microscopy, Inc./Visuals Unlimited, Inc.

b.

Dennis Kunkel Microscopy, Inc./Visuals Unlimited, Inc.

c.

Erythrocytes

Endothelial cell of capillary wall

Capillary

10 μm

Lennart Nilsson/SCANPIX

Figure 32.15

Erythrocytes moving through a capillary that is just wide enough to admit the cells in single file as seen by **(a)** confocal microscopy, **(b)** cross section and staining using light microscopy, and **(c)** sagittal section through muscle fibres.

endothelial cells allow water, ions, and small molecules such as glucose to pass freely between blood and interstitial fluid. Erythrocytes, platelets, and most plasma proteins are too large to pass between the cells and are retained inside capillaries, except for molecules that are transported through epithelial cells by specific carriers. Leukocytes, however, can squeeze actively between the cells and pass from the blood to the interstitial fluid.

There are exceptions to these general properties. In the brain, endothelial cells are tightly sealed together, preventing all molecules and ions from passing between them. The tight seals set up the *blood–brain barrier* (Chapter 37). This limits the exchange between capillaries and brain tissues to molecules and ions that are specifically transported through the capillary endothelial cells. At the other

extreme are capillaries in the liver, in which the spaces between endothelial cells are wide enough to admit most plasma proteins (most plasma proteins are synthesized in the liver), and in the small intestines, where wide spaces between capillary endothelial cells allow many nutrient molecules to pass into the bloodstream. In bone marrow and other sites of erythrocyte production, spaces are large enough to admit red blood cells.

32.4c Venules and Veins Serve as Blood Reservoirs in Addition to Conduits to the Heart

Because of the high resistance in the capillaries, the pressure remaining in the blood is low as it enters the venules and veins. Accordingly, the walls of venules and veins are thinner than those of arteries and contain little elastin. Many veins have flaps of connective tissue that extend inward from their walls. These flaps form one-way valves that keep blood flowing toward the heart (see Figure 32.13, p. 788).

Because of the differences in their structure, the relatively thin walls of venules and veins can expand over a relatively wide range without developing much recoil. This allows them to act as blood reservoirs as well as conduits. At times, venules and veins may contain from 60 to 80% of the total blood volume of the body. The stored volume is adjusted by skeletal muscle contraction and the valves, in response to metabolic conditions and signals carried by hormones and neurotransmitters.

Although blood pressure in the venous system is relatively low, several mechanisms assist the movement of blood back to the heart. The contraction of skeletal muscles compresses nearby veins, increasing their internal pressure **(Figure 32.16)**. The one-way valves in the veins, especially numerous in the larger veins of the limbs, keep the blood from flowing backward when the muscles relax. Respiratory movements also force blood from the abdomen toward the chest cavity.

STUDY BREAK

1. Why must arterial walls be thick and elastic?
2. During strenuous exercise, more capillary beds open up to receive blood flow. Where does the extra blood that it takes to fill them come from?
3. How do skeletal muscles assist in the circulation of blood?

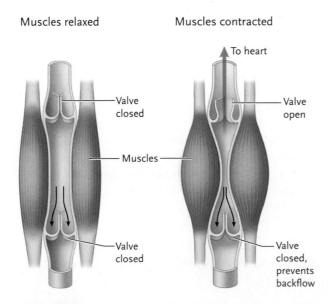

Figure 32.16
How skeletal muscle contraction and the valves inside veins help move blood toward the heart.

32.5 Maintaining Blood Flow and Pressure

Arterial blood pressure is the principal force moving blood to the tissues. Blood pressure must be regulated carefully so that the brain and other tissues receive adequate blood flow, but it must not be so high that the heart is overburdened, risking damage to blood vessels. The three main regulators of blood pressure are

- *cardiac output,* the amount of blood pumped by the left and right ventricles combined, which is a product of the rate at which the heart beats (*heart rate*) and the amount of blood pumped with each beat (*stroke volume*);
- the degree of constriction of the blood vessels (primarily the arterioles); and
- the total blood volume.

The autonomic nervous system and the endocrine system interact to coordinate the mechanisms controlling these factors. The system effectively counteracts the effects of constantly changing internal and external conditions, such as movement from rest to physical activity or ending a period of fasting by eating a large meal. In humans, for example, moderate physical activity results in an increase in blood flow to the heart itself by 360%, to the muscles of the skin by 370% (increases loss of heat), and to the skeletal muscles by 1060%. Flow is decreased to the digestive tract and liver by 60%, to the kidneys by 40%, and to the bone and most other tissues by 30%. Only the blood flow to the brain remains unchanged. These changes are the result of changes in cardiac output together with adjustments to the muscles in the arterioles supplying the various organs.

32.5a Cardiac Output Is Controlled by Regulating the Rate and Strength of the Heartbeat

Regulation of the strength and rate of the heartbeat starts at stretch receptors called *baroreceptors* (a type of mechanoreceptor; see Chapter 37), located in the walls of blood vessels. The baroreceptors in the cardiac muscle, aorta, and carotid arteries (which supply blood to the brain) are the most crucial. By detecting the amount of stretch of the vessel walls, baroreceptors constantly provide information about blood pressure, sending signals to the medulla within the brain stem. In response, the brain stem sends signals to the heart (primarily the SA node) and muscles of the blood vessels via the autonomic nervous system (see Chapter 36). The sympathetic system, using norepinephrine, stimulates the heart, whereas the parasympathetic system uses acetylcholine to slow the rate. These signals adjust the rate and force of the heartbeat: the heart beats more slowly and contracts less forcefully (pumping less blood with each heartbeat) when arterial pressure is above normal levels, and it beats more rapidly and contracts more forcefully (pumping more blood with each heartbeat) when arterial pressure is below normal levels.

The O_2 content of the blood, detected by chemoreceptors in the aorta and carotid arteries, also influences cardiac output. If O_2 concentration falls below normal levels, the brain stem integrates this information with the baroreceptor signals and issues signals that increase the rate and force of the heartbeat. Too much O_2 in the blood has the opposite effect, reducing cardiac output.

32.5b Hormones Regulate Both Cardiac Output and Arteriole Diameter

Hormones secreted by several glands contribute to the regulation of blood pressure and flow. For example, as part of the stress response, the adrenal medulla reinforces the action of the sympathetic nervous system by secreting epinephrine and norepinephrine into the bloodstream (see Chapter 35). Epinephrine in particular raises cardiac output by increasing the strength and rate of the heartbeat. It also stimulates vasoconstriction (decrease in diameter) of arterioles in some parts of the body, including the skin, gut, and kidneys, and induces vasodilation (increase in diameter) of arterioles that deliver blood to the heart, skeletal muscles, and lungs. Thus, epinephrine increases blood flow to the structures essential for dealing with stress and reduces blood flow to those structures that are not necessary at that time.

32.5c Local Controls Also Regulate Arteriole Diameter

Several automated mechanisms also operate locally to increase the flow of blood to body regions engaged in increased metabolic activity. Repeated contraction of the muscles of the legs during the escape response of an antelope produces low O_2 and high CO_2 concentrations in the legs because of the increased oxidation of glucose and other fuels. This increases vasodilation of the arterioles and hence the blood supply serving the muscles. At least part of the vasodilation is caused by nitric oxide (NO) produced by arterial endothelial cells. NO is broken down quickly after its release, ensuring that its effects are local.

CONCEPT FIX The interaction between blood pressure, cardiac output, and blood vessel resistance is complex. *People often believe that heart rate is the key regulated variable in the circulatory system.* This is because heart rate changes, but the changes maintain constant blood pressure, which is the true controlled variable. The reason that a constant blood pressure is so important is that each capillary bed is capable of controlling its

own blood flow (as just described). The job of the heart is to ensure that the total blood flow, that is, the cardiac output, is equal to the local demands of all the tissues. The way this occurs is by monitoring blood pressure and altering cardiac output to keep it constant (increasing cardiac output when blood pressure falls and dropping cardiac output when it increases). Since the local tissues alter their flow by constricting and dilating blood vessels, which alters resistance and hence blood pressure, if the heart can maintain blood pressure constant, then the total flow will equal all the local demands. ⬡

"Life on the Edge," Box 32.3, p. 792, discusses aquatic animals and their specialized circulatory systems, which allow deep and prolonged dives by the careful regulation of blood flow and blood pressure.

STUDY BREAK

1. What are the three factors by which blood pressure and flow are controlled? Why is it so important to control blood pressure?
2. How do O_2 and CO_2 concentrations affect local blood flow?
3. How do changes in local blood flow alter blood pressure?
4. What are baroreceptors, and how do they affect circulation?
5. In some people, the pressure of the blood pooling in the legs leads to a condition called *varicose veins*, in which the veins stand out like swollen, purple knots. Explain why this might happen and why veins closer to the leg surface are more susceptible to the condition than those in deeper leg tissues.

32.6 The Lymphatic System

Under normal conditions, a little more fluid from the blood plasma in the capillaries enters the interstitial fluid than is reabsorbed into the plasma. The **lymphatic system** is an extensive network of vessels that collect excess interstitial fluid and return it to the venous blood **(Figure 32.17a, p. 793)**. Interstitial fluid picked up by the lymphatic system is called **lymph**. This system also collects fats that have been absorbed from the small intestine and delivers them to the blood circulation. The lymphatic system is also a key component of the immune system (see Chapter 43).

32.6a Vessels of the Lymphatic System Extend throughout Most of the Body

Vessels of the lymphatic system collect lymph and transport it to *lymph ducts*, which empty into the veins of the circulatory system. *Lymph capillaries*, the

Taking a Long Dive—How Do They Do It?

Reptiles, birds, and mammals evolved as land animals, but many species (e.g., snakes, turtles, penguins, loons, otters, seals, and whales; see **Figure 1**) have taken up life in freshwater or marine environments and feed under water. This may involve prolonged dives, sometimes to considerable depths and for extended times. Among the champion divers are marine turtles, emperor penguins, elephant seals, and some species of whales. For example, sperm whales, *Physeter macrocephalus*, grow up to 18 m in length and weigh up to 40 tonnes. They feed on schools of deep-water squid and other animals that live near the bottom of the ocean. The whales can dive to depths of 2 km (but typically less than 1000 m) and remain submerged for as long as 90 minutes. Most species, however, do not dive to great depths and remain submerged for a relatively brief period. The time they spend submerged, however, still exceeds the abilities of land dwellers. The supply of oxygen to the muscles, the brain, and some other tissues needs to be maintained throughout the dive, which raises the question, "How do these animals remain submerged for so long (particularly in the case of the champion divers!) while swimming actively?"

To begin with, most diving species possess increased oxygen stores. Diving mammals often have large blood volumes with more erythrocytes per unit of blood than other animals, and these erythrocytes are larger. The muscles of many divers also contain far more myoglobin (see "Molecule behind Biology," Box 32.1) than terrestrial mammals. Weddell seals can store five times as much oxygen in the blood as humans can and sperm whales store four times as much oxygen in muscle as humans do. The lungs of most divers are not large and do not store much oxygen. This is largely because these animals either exhale before they dive (reducing buoyancy) or because the lungs are severely compressed by the increase in pressure at depth.

For many species, diving is a brief event, for feeding or avoiding predation. Other species spend their entire life underwater, returning to the surface only to breathe. In infrequent divers, and in all species during prolonged dives, metabolic rate is reduced (often assisted by reducing body temperature), and the *diving reflex* is invoked. All birds and mammals (including humans) possess a diving reflex, a defensive reflex that inhibits breathing while an animal is underwater and produces changes in blood flow designed to conserve oxygen for the tissues that need it most. The diving reflex is particularly well developed in marine mammals. It involves a reduction in metabolic rate (reducing the need for oxygen), and a redirection of blood flow, by adjustment of arteriole muscles, away from skin, skeletal muscles, and digestive organs and toward the heart and brain. During these dives, heart rate slows, sometimes by as much as 90%. This *bradycardia* is required to prevent blood pressure from rising due to the profound vasoconstriction of the blood vessels in all of the nonessential organs. The extent of this diving bradycardia depends on dive duration in voluntary dives so that short dives involve little or no bradycardia, while long dives involve a profound bradycardia.

When the animals return to the surface, the air in the lungs expands and circulation returns to the surface condition. CO_2 accumulated during the dive is exhaled during the familiar "blow," and the animal breathes on the surface to restore depleted oxygen and excrete CO_2 before diving again.

a.

pix2go/Shutterstock

b.

rebvt/Shutterstock

c.

Natapong Ratanavijittakorn/Shutterstock

d.

Jan Daly / Shutterstock

FIGURE 1

Different species exhibit different degrees of commitment to an aquatic lifestyle. The beaver **(a)** *dives briefly for food, while sea lions* **(b)** *alternate between periods on land and periods at sea. Dolphins* **(c)** *and killer whales* **(d)** *are fully aquatic.*

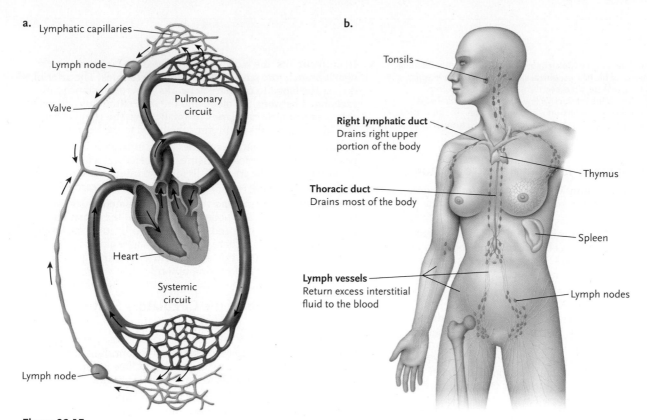

Figure 32.17

The human lymphatic system. **a)** the lymphatic system is an extensive network of vessels that collect excess interstitial fluid from the tissues and return it to the lowest pressure component of the systemic circulation, the venous system outside the heart. **b)** The tissues and organs of the lymphatic system include the lymph nodes, patches in the small intestine, the spleen, the thymus, the tonsils and the appendix.

smallest vessels of the system, are distributed throughout the body, intermixed intimately with the capillaries of the circulatory system. Although they are several times as large in diameter as the blood capillaries, the walls of lymph capillaries also consist of a single layer of endothelial cells resting on a basement membrane. Interstitial fluid becomes lymph when it enters the lymph capillaries at sites in their walls where the endothelial cells overlap, forming a flap that is forced open by the higher pressure of the interstitial fluid. The openings are wide enough to admit all components of the interstitial fluid, including bacteria, damaged cells, cellular debris, and lymphocytes.

Lymph capillaries merge into *lymph vessels,* which contain one-way valves that prevent the lymph from flowing backward. Lymph vessels lead to the thoracic duct and the right lymphatic duct (see **Figure 32.17b**), which empty the lymph into a vein beneath the clavicles (collarbones).

Breathing movements and movements of skeletal muscles adjacent to lymph vessels help move lymph through the vessels, just as they help move the blood through veins. Over a day, the human lymphatic system returns about 3 to 4 L of fluid to the bloodstream. In fishes, amphibians, and reptiles, the lymphatic vessels have lymphatic hearts, regions of the ducts equipped with striated muscle that propels the lymph through the vessels.

32.6b Lymphoid Tissues and Organs Act as Filters and Participate in the Immune Response

Tissues and organs of the lymphatic system include the *lymph nodes,* the *spleen,* the *thymus,* and the *tonsils.* They play primary roles in filtering viruses, bacteria, damaged cells, and cellular debris from the lymph and bloodstream and in defending the body against infection and cancer. Lymphoid tissue also occurs in other regions of the body, particularly the digestive tract, where patches of lymph cells can be found beneath the epithelium of the intestine, in the colon, and in the appendix.

Lymph nodes are small, bean-shaped organs spaced along the lymph vessels and clustered along the sides of the neck, in the armpits and groin, and in the centre of the abdomen and chest cavity (see Figure 32.17b). Spaces in nodes contain macrophages, a type of leukocyte that engulfs and destroys cellular debris and infecting bacteria and viruses in the lymph. The lymph nodes also contain other leukocytes, which produce antibodies that aid in the destruction of invading pathogens (see Chapter 43).

STUDY BREAK

1. Why do we need a lymphatic system? What are its three functions?
2. If this is a system, what are its main organs?

Review

CourseMate Access an interactive eBook, chapter-specific interactive learning tools, including flashcards, quizzes, videos, and more in your Biology CourseMate, accessed through NelsonBrain.com

aplia Aplia™ is an online interactive learning solution that helps you improve comprehension—and your grade—by integrating a variety of mediums and tools such as videos, tutorials, practice tests, and an interactive eBook.

32.1 Animal Circulatory Systems: An Introduction

- Those invertebrates with a simple internal structure (sponges, cnidarians, flatworms, and nematodes) have no specialized circulatory systems.

- Animals with circulatory systems have a muscular heart that pumps a specialized fluid, such as blood, from one body region to another through tubular vessels. The blood carries O_2 and nutrients to body tissues and carries away CO_2 and wastes.

- Animal circulatory systems are either open or closed. In an open system, the heart pumps hemolymph into vessels that empty into body spaces. The hemolymph is returned to the heart in various ways that may or may not involve vessels. In a closed system, the blood is confined in blood vessels throughout the body and does not mix directly with the interstitial fluid. Closed systems circulate the blood at higher pressures and allow more rapid distribution of O_2 and nutrients and clearance of CO_2 and wastes.

- In the protostome invertebrates, open circulatory systems occur in arthropods and most molluscs, whereas closed circulatory systems occur in annelids and cephalopod molluscs (squids and octopuses).

- In vertebrates, the circulatory system has evolved from a heart with a single series of chambers, pumping blood through a single circuit to the gills and then on to the brain and other organs, to a completely separated double heart in birds and mammals that pumps blood through separate pulmonary and systemic circuits.

32.2 Blood and Its Components

- Mammalian blood is a fluid connective tissue consisting of erythrocytes, leukocytes, and platelets suspended in a fluid matrix, the plasma.

- Plasma contains water, ions, dissolved gases such as O_2 and CO_2, glucose, amino acids, lipids, vitamins, hormones, and plasma proteins. The plasma proteins include albumins, which transport substances through the blood or act as enzymes; globulins, which transport lipids and include antibodies; and fibrinogen, which takes part in the clotting reaction.

- Erythrocytes contain hemoglobin, which transports O_2 between the lungs and all body regions. Erythrocytes also transport some CO_2 from interstitial fluid to the lungs and contribute to the reactions maintaining blood pH. They are formed by division of stem cells in the red bone marrow.

- Leukocytes engulf cellular debris and dead and diseased cells, and they defend the body against infecting pathogens. Leukocytes are produced by division of stem cells in the red bone marrow and by division of existing leukocytes.

- Platelets are functional cell fragments that trigger clotting reactions at sites of damage to the circulatory system.

32.3 The Heart

- The mammalian heart is a four-chambered pump. Two atria at the anterior of the heart pump the blood into two ventricles at the posterior of the heart, which pump blood into two separate pulmonary and systemic circuits of blood vessels.

- In both circuits, the blood leaves the heart in large arteries, which branch into smaller arteries, the arterioles. The arterioles deliver the blood to capillary networks, where substances are exchanged between the blood and the interstitial fluid. Blood is collected from the capillaries in small veins, the venules, which join into larger veins that return the blood to the heart.

- Contraction of the ventricles pushes blood into the arteries at a peak pressure, the systolic pressure. Between contractions, the blood pressure in the arteries falls to a minimum pressure, the diastolic pressure. The systole–diastole sequence is the cardiac cycle.

- Contraction of the atria and ventricles is initiated by signals from the sinoatrial (SA) node (pacemaker) of the heart. The signals move over the atria and then activate cells in the atrioventricular (AV) node. From there, the signals move along Purkinje fibres to trigger contraction of the ventricles, starting at the bottom of the heart and moving upward.

32.4 Blood Vessels of the Circulatory System

- The walls of arteries consist of an inner endothelial layer, a middle layer of smooth muscle, and an outer layer of elastic fibres. By expanding during systole and rebounding during diastole, the elastic arteries ensure that blood flow is continuous even though ejection of blood from the heart is not.

- Capillary walls consist of a single layer of endothelial cells and their basement membrane. Blood flow through capillaries is controlled by contraction and relaxation of the smooth muscles of arterioles and precapillary sphincters.

- In the capillary networks, the rate of blood flow is considerably slower than in arteries and veins. This maximizes the time for exchange of substances between blood and tissues. Two major mechanisms drive the exchange of substances: diffusion along concentration gradients and bulk flow.

- Venules and veins have thinner walls than arteries, allowing the vessels to expand and contract over a wide range. As a result, they act as both blood reservoirs and conduits.

- The return of blood to the heart is aided by pressure exerted on the veins when surrounding skeletal muscles contract and by respiratory movements, which force blood from the abdomen toward the chest cavity. One-way valves in the veins prevent the blood from flowing backward.

32.5 Maintaining Blood Flow and Pressure

- Local control of blood flow responds primarily to O_2 and CO_2 concentrations in tissues. Low O_2 and high CO_2 concentration cause dilation of arteriole walls, increasing the arteriole diameter and blood flow. High O_2 and low CO_2 concentrations have the opposite effects. Nitric oxide released by arterial endothelial cells acts locally to increase arteriole diameter and blood flow.

- These changes in arteriole diameter lead to changes in blood pressure. By regulating blood pressure, the total flow from the heart, the cardiac output, will match the needs of all the individual organs.

- Blood pressure and flow are regulated by controlling cardiac output, the degree of constriction of blood vessels (primarily arterioles), and the total blood volume. The autonomic nervous system and the endocrine system interact to coordinate these mechanisms.

- Regulation of cardiac output starts with baroreceptors, which detect blood pressure changes in the large arteries and veins and send signals to the medulla of the brain stem. In response, the brain stem sends signals via the autonomic nervous system that alter the rate and force of the heartbeat.

- Hormones secreted by several glands contribute to the regulation of blood pressure and flow. Epinephrine increases blood pressure by increasing the strength and rate of the heartbeat and stimulating vasoconstriction of arterioles in some areas of the body.

32.6 The Lymphatic System

- The lymphatic system is an extensive network of vessels that collect excess interstitial fluid, which becomes lymph, and return it to the venous blood. The system also collects fats absorbed from the small intestine and delivers them to the blood circulation, and it is a key component of the immune system.

- The tissues and organs of the lymphatic system include the lymph nodes, the spleen, the thymus, and the tonsils. They remove viruses, bacteria, damaged cells, and cellular debris from the lymph and bloodstream and defend the body against infection and cancer.

Questions

Self-Test Questions

Any number of answers from a to e may be correct.

1. Functions of the circulatory system include
   a. transport of oxygen
   b. nutrient transport
   c. transport of waste products
   d. hormone circulation
   e. transport of carbon dioxide

2. Which circulatory system best describes the given animal or animals?
   a. Amphibians and reptiles use a two-chambered heart to separate oxygenated and deoxygenated blood.
   b. Fishes have a single-chambered heart with an atrium that pumps blood through gills for oxygen exchange.
   c. Squids and octopuses have open circulatory systems with ventricles that pump blood away from the heart.
   d. Birds and mammals pump blood to separate pulmonary and systemic systems from two separate ventricles in a four-chambered heart.
   e. Amphibians have the most oxygenated blood in the pulmocutaneous (leading to and from the lungs and skin) circuit and the most deoxygenated blood in the systemic circuit.

3. Which of the following is a characteristic of blood circulation through or to the mammalian heart?
   a. The superior vena cava conveys blood to the head.
   b. The inferior vena cava conveys blood to the right atrium.
   c. The pulmonary veins convey blood into the left ventricle.
   d. The pulmonary arteries convey blood from the lungs to the left atrium.
   e. The aorta branches into two coronary arteries that convey blood from the heart muscle.

4. In general, the path of blood in the systemic circulation in a vertebrate occurs in the following order:
   a. veins, venules, capillaries, arterioles, arteries
   b. arterioles, capillaries, arteries, venules, veins
   c. venules, veins, capillaries, arteries, arterioles
   d. arteries, arterioles, capillaries, venules, veins

5. Pulmonary arteries carry blood that is
   a. low in O_2
   b. low in CO_2
   c. high in O_2
   d. high in CO_2
   e. on its way to the lungs

6. Which of the following is correct?
   a. Vertebrate hearts are neurogenic.
   b. Erythropoietin is secreted by red blood cells.
   c. Red blood cells in vertebrates contain no nuclei.
   d. Carotid arteries supply the brain with oxygenated blood.
   e. The mammalian aorta is derived from aortic arch VI on the left side.

7. Which of the following is a characteristic of veins and venules?
   a. thick walls
   b. large muscle mass in walls
   c. a large quantity of elastin in the walls
   d. low blood volume compared with arteries
   e. one-way valves to prevent backflow of blood

8. Functions of the blood include
   a. gas transport
   b. defence
   c. clotting
   d. buffering pH

9. Systolic pressure
   a. occurs during the relaxation phase of the heart cycle
   b. is the blood pressure at the peak of the contraction phase of the heart cycle
   c. is generated by the atrium
   d. is generated by the ventricle
   e. is measured in the pulmonary veins

10. Which of the following actions would increase cardiac output?
   a. Baroreceptors in the brain signal the sympathetic nerves.
   b. The brain stem signals the baroreceptors, causing the heart to beat faster.
   c. Chemoreceptors, stimulated by excessive blood oxygen, increase the rate of the heartbeat.
   d. The adrenal medulla and sympathetic nervous system secrete epinephrine and norepinephrine.
   e. The autonomic nervous system responds to low oxygen detected by chemoreceptors and decreases the force of the heartbeat.

Questions for Discussion

1. What is the adaptive significance of a closed circulatory system?

2. *Aplastic anemia* develops when certain drugs or radiation destroy red bone marrow, including the stem cells that give rise to erythrocytes, leukocytes, and platelets. Predict some symptoms a person with aplastic anemia would be likely to develop. Include at least one symptom related to each type of blood cell.

3. Hemoglobin occurs in the blood of many animals, but in many invertebrates, it occurs free in the plasma. What advantages can you think of that might have led to its incorporation in erythrocytes during the evolution of vertebrates? The nonvertebrate chordates do not have hemoglobin in their blood, but they do have cells in their blood that have a role in defence, suggesting that erythrocytes may have originated from such cells. What evidence could be used to examine this hypothesis?

4. Discuss possible adaptations that may occur in animals that allow them to be well suited for life at high altitude—or for life as a diver.

5. In some people, the pressure of the blood pooling in the legs leads to a condition called *varicose veins*, in which the veins stand out like swollen, purple knots. Explain why this might happen and why veins closer to the leg surface are more susceptible to the condition than those in deeper leg tissues.

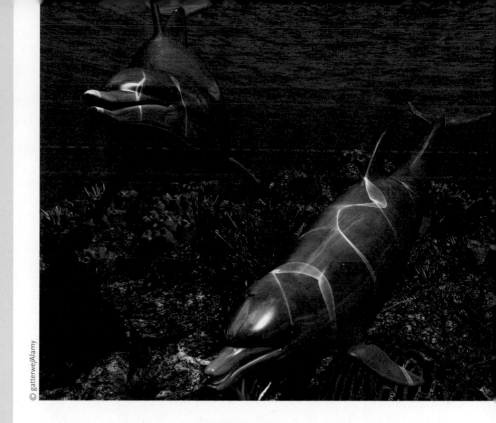

Dolphins on a coral reef.

© gatterwe/Alamy

33 Reproduction in Animals

WHY IT MATTERS

Over a few nights each year along the Great Barrier Reef off the east coast of Australia, many species of reef-building corals synchronously spawn, releasing eggs and sperm into the water. Timing is important for the corals because they rely on external fertilization. Male and female gametes must be released at the same time to maximize the chances of fertilization. The circadian clocks of the corals control the reproductive event, which is synchronized to the lunar cycle. The mass spawning occurs over several nights after the full moon. Spawning is triggered by changes in lunar irradiance intensity. Many species of corals release eggs and sperm at the same time, but chemicals in the egg coatings and in the sperm head interact to ensure fertilization of eggs only by sperm of the same species.

Bottle-nosed dolphins, on the other hand, have a breeding season during which males compete for females. Mating involves copulation that ensures that sperm and eggs from the same species meet in a protected site inside the body of the female. The fertilized egg is nourished inside the uterus of the female for 12 months on average and then the newborn is nursed by the female for a further 18 to 20 months.

MOLECULE BEHIND BIOLOGY 33.1

Cryptochromes

Acropora millepora is one coral involved in the mass reproductive event described in "Why It Matters." It is a sensitivity to blue light (see Chapter 1) that entrains the circadian clock controlling its reproduction. The light sensors are proteins called cryptochromes (CRYs) (blue, ultraviolet-A receptors).

The prefix *crypto-* was used to describe these receptors because the identity of the pigments was unknown for some time. As early as 1881, Charles Darwin had reported that the growth of plants toward the sun (heliotropism) could be eliminated by filtering blue wavelengths (380 to 500 nm) from the light reaching the plant. The proteins involved in this process, however, were first only described in higher animals (vertebrates and insects), and related but different proteins were not shown to be involved in similar processes in plants and eubacteria until 2007.

Cryptochromes are DNA photolyase-like receptor proteins **(Figure 1a).** DNA photolyases are molecules involved in DNA repair. These molecules are flavoproteins. We now know that the absorption spectrum of flavins is similar to the action spectrum of blue light and that the photoreceptors that regulate the circadian clocks in animals and plants depend on the genes for these proteins in organisms ranging from corals **(Figure 1b)** to *Arabidopsis* (a small plant related to mustard) and from *Drosophila* **(Figure 1c)** to mammals **(Figure 1d).**

FIGURE 1
(a) *DNA photolyase.*
(b) *Coral*—Acropora millepora.
(c) *Fruit* fly—Drosophila melanogaster. **(d)** *Arctic Ground Squirrel*—Spermophilus parryii.

a.

b.

c.

d.

As in plants, bacteria, fungi, and all other life, reproduction ensures the transfer of genes (as allowed by natural selection). Thus, there is a strong drive to reproduce, and considerable time and resources are devoted to reproductive processes. For animals that reproduce by eggs and sperm, the adaptations are as diverse as the number of species on Earth. This diversity allows individuals of the same species to find each other and unite eggs and sperm. Within the diversity, however, are underlying patterns that are shared by all animals. Both the underlying patterns and the diversity of animal reproduction are the subjects of this chapter. We also discuss the development of eggs and sperm and the union of egg and sperm that begins the development of a new individual. The next chapter continues with the events of development after eggs and sperm have united.

33.1 The Drive to Reproduce

The success of any species is contingent on its reproductive success. Accordingly, organisms have a strong drive to reproduce and go to considerable lengths to ensure that their genes are represented in future generations. All energy that does not go into growth, development, and maintenance goes into reproduction. This chapter outlines various strategies taken by different species to ensure that this energy is spent wisely. The strategies employed are diverse, reflecting differences in habitat and lifestyle, but all are designed to ensure that the species survives. As we go through the chapter, keep in mind that energy spent on any one activity is energy not available for other purposes, and imagine the selection pressures that have led to the diversity we see.

33.2 Asexual and Sexual Reproduction

Reproduction is the means of passing on an individual's genes to a new generation, making it the most vital function of living organisms. In **asexual reproduction**, a single individual gives rise to offspring with no genetic input from another individual. In **sexual reproduction**, male and female parents produce zygotes (fertilized eggs) through the union of egg and sperm. **CONCEPT FIX** A common misconception is that sexual reproduction is always a better reproductive strategy than asexual reproduction. As you will see in the next sections, asexual reproduction gives rise to genetic uniformity of offspring, which can be advantageous in stable, uniform environments. Sexual reproduction, on the other hand, gives rise to genetic diversity of offspring, which is advantageous in unstable, changing environments. Thus, each may be a superior strategy depending on environmental conditions. ⬢

33.2a Asexual Reproduction: Reproduction without Recombination Is Advantageous in Stable Environments

Many aquatic invertebrates and some terrestrial annelids and insects reproduce asexually. This mode of reproduction is much less common among vertebrates. In asexual reproduction, from one to many cells of a parent's body develop directly into a new individual. Cells involved in asexual reproduction in animals are usually produced by mitosis and sometimes by meiosis. When cells involved in asexual reproduction are produced by mitosis, the resulting offspring are genetically identical to one another and to the parent (clonal reproduction).

Genetic uniformity of offspring can be advantageous in stable, uniform environments. In these cases, successful individuals with the "best" combinations of genes perpetuate the most competitive genotypes through asexual reproduction. Individuals do not have to expend energy to produce gametes or find a mate. Asexual reproduction is also advantageous to individuals living in sparsely settled populations or to sessile (immobile) animals.

In animals, asexual reproduction involving mitosis occurs by three basic mechanisms: *fission, budding,* and *fragmentation*. In **fission**, the parent splits into two or more offspring of approximately equal size. Some species of planarians (Platyhelminthes) reproduce asexually by fission, dividing transversely or longitudinally **(Figure 33.1a, p. 800)**. In **budding**, a new individual grows and develops while attached to the parent. Sponges, tunicates, and some cnidarians reproduce asexually by budding, and offspring may break free from the parent or remain attached to form a *colony*. In the cnidarian *Hydra,* an offspring buds and grows from one side of the parent's body and then detaches to become a separate individual **(Figure 33.1b, p. 800)**. In corals, buds often remain attached when their growth is complete, forming colonies of thousands of interconnected individuals. In **fragmentation**, pieces separate from a parent's body and develop (regenerate) into new individuals. Many species of cnidarians, flatworms, annelids, and some echinoderms can reproduce by fragmentation **(Figure 33.1c, p. 800)**.

Some animals produce offspring by **parthenogenesis** (*parthenos* = virgin; *genesis* = birth), which is the growth and development of an unfertilized egg. Offspring produced by parthenogenesis may be haploid or diploid, depending on the species (see Chapter 9). Because the egg from which a parthenogenetic offspring is produced derives from meiosis in the female parent, the offspring are not genetically identical to the parent or to each other. (We describe below how chromosome segregation and genetic recombination during meiosis produce gametes with gene combinations different from the parent.) In some species, the offspring are all female, whereas in other species, they

a.

Dr. John D. Cunningham/Visuals Unlimited, Inc.

b.

Dr. Stanley Flegler/Visuals Unlimited, Inc.

c.

WPoelzer WPoelzer/Photolibrary

Figure 33.1
Asexual reproduction by **(a)** fission in *Planaria* species, **(b)** budding in *Hydra* species, and **(c)** fragmentation in *Echinoderm* species.

are all males. All whip-tail lizard (*Cnemidophorus* spp.; **Figure 33.2**) species consist of females produced by parthenogenesis. These females still go through the motions of mating with each other.

Parthenogenesis occurs in some invertebrates, including certain aphids, water fleas, bees, and crustaceans. In bees, haploid drones (males) are produced parthenogenetically from unfertilized eggs produced by reproductive females (queens). New queens and sterile workers develop from fertilized eggs. Parthenogenesis also occurs in some vertebrates (e.g., certain fishes, salamanders, amphibians, lizards, and turkeys).

33.2b Sexual Reproduction: Reproduction with Recombination Is Advantageous in Changing Environments

Animals reproduce sexually through the union of **sperm** (motile gamete) and **eggs** (nonmotile gametes), both produced by **meiosis**. The overriding advantage of sexual reproduction is the generation of genetic diversity among offspring. Genetic diversity of offspring is advantageous in unstable, changing environments. Genetic diversity increases the chances that at least some offspring will be better adapted to altered conditions and be more likely to survive and reproduce. Genetic recombination and independent assortment of chromosomes are two mechanisms of meiosis that give rise to genetic diversity in eggs and sperm (see Chapter 8). Genetic recombination mixes the alleles of parents into new combinations within chromosomes. Independent assortment

Dr. John D. Cunningham/Visuals Unlimited, Inc.

Figure 33.2
A whip-tail lizard (*Cnemidophorus deppei*), in which all individuals are female.

randomly combines maternal and paternal chromosomes in the gamete nuclei. Additional variability is generated at fertilization when eggs and sperm from genetically different individuals fuse together at random to initiate the development of new individuals. Adding to the effects of genetic recombination and independent assortment, random mutations in DNA are the ultimate source of variability for both sexual and asexual reproduction.

Sexual reproduction can be a disadvantage because of the costs in energy and raw materials associated with producing gametes and finding mates. Finding mates can expose animals to predation and may conflict with the need to find food and shelter and care for existing offspring.

STUDY BREAK

1. What are the advantages of sexual reproduction over asexual reproduction?
2. Which would be the better strategy (asexual versus sexual reproduction) for an organism to use if it were living in a stable versus an unstable environment? Explain your answer in detail.

33.3 Mechanisms of Sexual Reproduction

The cellular mechanisms of sexual reproduction include **gametogenesis**, the formation of male and female gametes, and **fertilization**, the union of gametes that initiates development of a new individual. Mating is the pairing of a male and a female for sexual reproduction.

33.3a Gametogenesis: Production of Gametes

Germ cells are cell lines, set aside early in embryonic development in most animals, that can undergo meiosis to produce haploid cells called gametes. They are distinct from the **somatic cells** that compose the rest of the body, which are only ever capable of undergoing mitosis. During development, germ cells collect in gonads, the specialized gamete-producing organs:

testes (singular, **testis**) in males and **ovaries** in females. Germ cells initially undergo mitotic division to produce large numbers of **spermatogonia** (singular, **spermatogonium**) in males and **oogonia** (singular, **oogonium**) in females. It is these cells that then undergo meiosis to produce gametes **(Figure 33.3)**. In some animals, germ cells also give rise to families of cells that assist gamete development.

Meiosis reduces the number of chromosomes from diploid to haploid. Thus, while somatic cells have two

a. Spermatogenesis

b. Oogenesis

Figure 33.3
The mitotic and meiotic divisions that produce eggs and sperm from germ cells. **(a)** Spermatogenesis. **(b)** Oogenesis. The first polar body may or may not divide, depending on the species, so that either two or three polar bodies may be present at the end of meiosis. Two are shown in this diagram.

copies of each chromosome, gametes have one. Fertilization, the fusion of a haploid sperm and a haploid egg, restores the diploid condition and produces a **zygote** or fertilized egg, the first cell of a new individual. The zygote will then divide by mitosis to produce a new adult within which only one cell line will retain the ability to undergo meiosis; the germ cells that produce gametes.

Spermatogenesis produces haploid cells specialized to deliver their nuclei to eggs produced by members of the same species. Two meiotic divisions produce four haploid spermatids (see Figure 33.3a, p. 801) that each develop into a mature sperm (**spermatozoa**; singular, **spermatozoon** = sperm) or eggs (**ova**; singular, **ovum**) (see **Figure 33.4**). Sperm are specialized to move toward, contact, and penetrate eggs. During sperm maturation, most of the cytoplasm is lost. Mitochondria are concentrated in the cytoplasm around the base of the flagellum. These mitochondria produce ATP, the energy source for beating of the flagellum. At the opposite end of the sperm, the acrosome is a specialized secretory vesicle forming a cap over the nucleus. The acrosome contains enzymes and other proteins that help the sperm attach to and penetrate the surface coatings of an egg of the same species.

Although sperm are usually smaller than eggs, they show considerable range in size, even in related species; for example, they are from 4.5 to 16.5 μm long among *Drosophila* species. The size of individual sperm influences the speed at which they swim (longer sperm move more quickly than shorter sperm). But producing longer sperm may reduce total sperm production and limit a male's reproductive success because sperm must be numerous to maximize the chances of fertilization. In mammals, variations in sperm size, volume of ejaculate, and sperm density often reflect mating behaviour (see Chapter 39).

Oogenesis produces ova. Only one of the cell products of meiosis develops into a functional egg, with that cell retaining almost all of the cytoplasm of the parent. The other products form polar bodies (see Figure 33.3b, p. 801). Unequal cytoplasmic divisions concentrate nutrients and other molecules required for development in the egg. In most species, polar bodies eventually disintegrate and do not contribute to fertilization or embryonic development.

The oocytes of most animals do not complete meiosis until the time of fertilization. At this time, the number of oocytes that complete meiosis may vary. In mammals, for example, oocytes stop developing at the end of the first meiotic prophase within a few weeks after a female is born. The oocytes remain in the ovary at this stage of development until the female is sexually mature. Then, one to several oocytes advance to the metaphase of the second meiotic division and are released from the ovary at intervals ranging from days to months, or at certain seasons, depending on the species. In humans, some oocytes may remain in prophase of the first meiotic division for perhaps 50 years. In other animals, such as the corals described in "Why It Matters," on the other hand, thousands of eggs are released simultaneously once a year.

The egg (**Figure 33.5**) typically has specialized features, including stored nutrients required for at least the early stages of embryonic development, as well as one or more kinds of coatings that protect the egg from mechanical injury and infection. In some species, egg

a. Human sperm

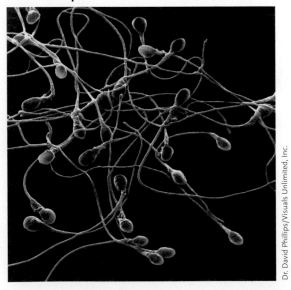

Dr. David Phillips/Visuals Unlimited, Inc.

b. Sperm structure

Acrosome Nucleus Mitochondria   Microtubules

Head   Midpiece   Tail (flagellum)

Figure 33.4
Spermatozoa. **(a)** Photomicrograph of human sperm and **(b)** the structure of a sperm.

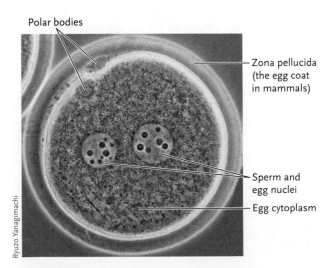

Polar bodies

Zona pellucida (the egg coat in mammals)

Sperm and egg nuclei

Egg cytoplasm

Ryuzo Yanagimachi

Figure 33.5
A mature hamster egg that has been fertilized. The sperm and egg nuclei are about to fuse together.

coats protect the embryo immediately after fertilization and prevent penetration by more than one sperm.

Egg coats are surface layers added during oocyte development or fertilization. The **vitelline coat** (the **zona pellucida** in mammals; see Figure 33.5) is a gel-like matrix of proteins, glycoproteins, and/or polysaccharides lying immediately outside the plasma membrane of the egg cell. Eggs that are laid or deposited outside the body of the female usually have extra layers to protect them and prevent desiccation. Insect eggs have additional outer protein coats forming a hard, water-impermeable layer that prevents desiccation. In amphibians and some echinoderms, egg jelly forms the outer coat protecting the egg from desiccation. In birds, reptiles, and monotremes (see Chapter 26), egg white, a thick solution of proteins, surrounds the vitelline coat. Outside the white is the *shell* of the egg, which is flexible and leathery in reptiles and mineralized and brittle in birds. Both egg white and shell are added while the egg moves along the **oviduct**, the tube connecting the ovary to the outside of the body. For the egg to be fertilized, it must encounter sperm before these layers are added to the egg.

In the mammalian ovary, the egg is surrounded by **follicle cells** during its development. Follicle cells grow from ovarian tissue and nourish the developing egg. They also make up part of the zona pellucida while the egg is in the ovary and remain as a protective layer after it is released.

Mature eggs can be the largest cells in an animal (see Figure 26.44, Chapter 26). Mammalian eggs are microscopic, with few stored nutrients, because the embryo develops inside the mother and is supplied with nutrients by her body. The eggs of birds are huge because they contain all of the nutrients required for complete embryonic development. The bird egg includes the *yolk,* which contains the nutrients for the developing egg; the ovum or egg cell; and the white. Regardless of size, cytoplasm makes up most of the volume of an animal egg, and the nucleus of the egg is usually microscopic or nearly so.

33.3b Fertilization: Union of Egg and Sperm

Eggs and sperm are delivered from the ovaries and testes to the site of fertilization by oviducts (females) and sperm ducts (males). In many species, external accessory sex organs participate in the delivery of gametes. The basic design of vertebrate and invertebrate reproductive systems **(Figure 33.6)** is similar. Nonmotile eggs move through oviducts on currents generated by the beating of cilia that line the oviducts or by contractions of the oviducts or the body wall. Sperm are ejaculated but are motile and then swim on their own.

Both eggs and sperm are small, fragile, and prone to desiccation. For fertilization to be external (outside the body of either parent), it must be in a watery medium. Otherwise it must be internal in a watery fluid inside a female's body. **External fertilization** occurs in

a. Insect (the fruit fly, *Drosophila*)

b. Amphibian (frog)

c. Mammal (cat)

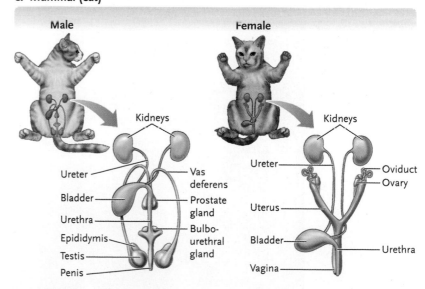

Figure 33.6

Some reproductive systems. **(a)** An insect, *Drosophila* (fruit fly). **(b)** An amphibian, a frog. **(c)** A mammal, a cat. Female systems are shown in blue and male systems in yellow.

most aquatic invertebrates, bony fishes, and amphibians. Sperm and eggs are shed into the surrounding water. Sperm swim until they collide with an egg of the same species. A disadvantage of external fertilization in an aquatic environment is the possibility of dispersion of the gametes before fertilization can occur. The process is helped by synchronization of the release of eggs and sperm and by the enormous numbers of gametes released (see "Why It Matters"). In other cases, it is helped by releasing the gametes into a protected nest. In animals such as sea urchins and amphibians, sperm are attracted to eggs by diffusible attractant molecules released by the egg.

Another means of increasing the odds of fertilization is by the juxtaposition of genital openings between the male and female during the release of gametes. Most amphibians, even terrestrial species such as toads, mate in an aquatic environment. Frogs typically mate by a reflex response called *amplexus,* in which the male clasps the female tightly around the body with his forelimbs **(Figure 33.7).** Amplexus stimulates the female to shed a mass of eggs into the water through the *cloaca.* The cloaca is the cavity into which intestinal, urinary, and genital tracts empty in reptiles, birds, amphibians, and many fishes. As the eggs are released, they are fertilized by sperm released by the male.

Internal fertilization is widespread in terrestrial animals. Internal fertilization occurs in invertebrates such as annelids, some arthropods, and some molluscs and in vertebrates from fishes and salamanders to reptiles, birds, and mammals. In internal fertilization, sperm are released by the male close to or inside the entrance to the female's reproductive tract. Sperm swim through fluids in the reproductive tract until one

reaches and fertilizes an egg. In some species, molecules released by the egg attract the sperm. Internal fertilization involves copulation, which occurs when a male's accessory sex organ (e.g., a penis) is inserted into a female's accessory sex organ (e.g., a vagina). Internal fertilization makes terrestrial life possible because the female's body provides the aquatic medium required for fertilization without the danger of gametes drying when exposed to the air. Effecting internal fertilization means close contact between individuals.

Male sharks and rays use a pair of modified pelvic fins as accessory sex organs that channel sperm directly into the female's cloaca. Male reptiles, birds, and mammals also use accessory sex organs to place sperm directly inside the reproductive tract of females, where fertilization takes place. In reptiles and birds that lay their eggs, sperm must fertilize eggs as they are released from the ovary and travel through the oviducts, before the shell is added. In mammals, the penis delivers sperm into the female's vagina, which is a specialized structure for reproduction (but see "Hormones and External Genitalia," Box 34.3, p. 808). Fertilization takes place when a sperm meets an egg in the oviducts.

Once a sperm touches the outer surface of an egg of the same species **(Figure 33.8a),** receptor proteins in the sperm plasma membrane bind the sperm to the vitelline coat or zona pellucida **(Figure 33.8b,** step 4). In most animals, only a conspecific (same species) sperm is recognized and binds to the egg surface. Species recognition between sperm and eggs is particularly important in animals using external fertilization because water surrounding the egg may contain sperm from many different species. This aspect is less important in species using internal fertilization, where structural adaptations and behavioural patterns usually limit sperm transfer from males to females of the same species (see "Variations in Internal Fertilization," Box 33.2, p. 806).

After initial attachment of sperm to egg, the events of fertilization proceed in rapid succession (see Figure 33.8b). The acrosome of the sperm releases its contents, including enzymes that dissolve a path through the egg coats. The sperm, with its tail still beating, follows the path until its plasma membrane touches and fuses with the egg's plasma membrane (step 5). Fusion introduces the sperm nucleus into the egg cytoplasm and activates the egg to complete meiosis and begin development.

33.3c Polyspermy: Keeping Sperm Out of the Fertilized Egg

Protection against polyspermy (more than one sperm fertilizing an egg) is widespread in the animal kingdom. Two mechanisms help prevent polyspermy: a **fast block** that works within seconds of fertilization and a **slow block** that works in minutes. In invertebrate species such as the sea urchin, fusion of egg and

Figure 33.7

A male leopard frog (*Rana pipiens*) clasping a female during a mating embrace known as amplexus. The tight squeeze by the male frog stimulates the female to release her eggs, which can be seen streaming from her body, embedded in a mass of egg jelly. Sperm released by the male fertilize the eggs as they pass from the female.

John Mitchell/Photo Researchers, Inc.

a. Sperm adhering to egg

David M. Phillips/Visuals Unlimited, Inc.

b. Steps in fertilization

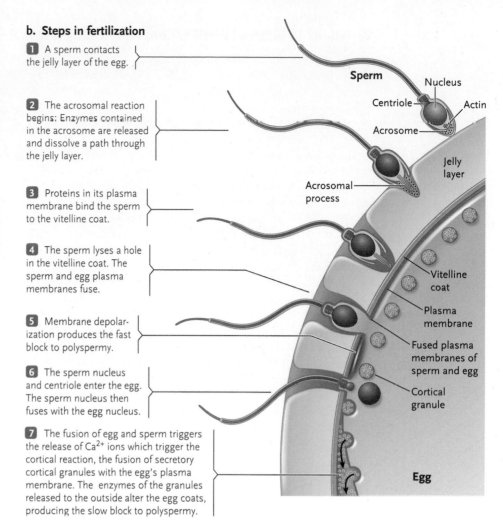

1 A sperm contacts the jelly layer of the egg.

2 The acrosomal reaction begins: Enzymes contained in the acrosome are released and dissolve a path through the jelly layer.

3 Proteins in its plasma membrane bind the sperm to the vitelline coat.

4 The sperm lyses a hole in the vitelline coat. The sperm and egg plasma membranes fuse.

5 Membrane depolarization produces the fast block to polyspermy.

6 The sperm nucleus and centriole enter the egg. The sperm nucleus then fuses with the egg nucleus.

7 The fusion of egg and sperm triggers the release of Ca^{2+} ions which trigger the cortical reaction, the fusion of secretory cortical granules with the egg's plasma membrane. The enzymes of the granules released to the outside alter the egg coats, producing the slow block to polyspermy.

Sperm · Nucleus · Centriole · Actin · Acrosome · Acrosomal process · Jelly layer · Vitelline coat · Plasma membrane · Fused plasma membranes of sperm and egg · Cortical granule · Egg

Figure 33.8

Fertilization. **(a)** Sperm adhering to the surface coat of a sea urchin egg. Of the many sperm that may initially adhere to the outer surface of the egg, usually only one accomplishes fertilization. **(b)** Steps of fertilization in a sea urchin.

---

sperm opens ion channels in the egg's plasma membrane, spreading a wave of electrical depolarization over the egg surface (much like a nerve impulse travelling along a neuron). Depolarization alters the egg plasma membrane so that it cannot fuse with any additional sperm, eliminating the possibility of more than one set of paternal chromosomes entering the egg. This fast block occurs within a few seconds of fertilization.

The fast block depends on a change in the egg's membrane potential from negative to positive. It is not established when the membrane potential of a sea urchin egg is experimentally kept at a negative value. In this case, additional sperm fuse with the plasma membrane. Fertilization was entirely blocked if the membrane was kept positive before sperm contact.

In vertebrates, the wave of membrane depolarization following sperm–egg fusion is not as pronounced as it is in sea urchins and does not prevent additional sperm from fusing with the egg. However, additional sperm nuclei that enter the egg cytoplasm usually break down and disappear, so only the first sperm nucleus to enter fuses with the egg nucleus.

In both invertebrates and vertebrates, fusion of egg and sperm also triggers the release of stored calcium (Ca^{2+}) ions from the endoplasmic reticulum (ER) into the cytosol. Ca^{2+} ions cause cortical granules to fuse with the egg's plasma membrane and release their contents to the outside (see Figure 33.8b, step 7). Enzymes released from cortical granules alter the egg coats within minutes of fertilization, so no further sperm can attach to or penetrate the egg. This process is the slow block to polyspermy.

The importance of Ca^{2+} to cortical granule release has been demonstrated experimentally. Granules are released in unfertilized eggs if Ca^{2+} is added experimentally to the cytoplasm. Conversely, if chemicals that bind Ca^{2+} are added to the cytoplasm of unfertilized eggs, the concentration of Ca^{2+} cannot rise and cortical granule release does not occur after fertilization.

After the sperm nucleus enters the egg cytoplasm, microtubules move the sperm and egg nuclei together in the egg cytoplasm until they fuse. The chromosomes of egg and sperm nuclei then assemble together and enter mitosis. The subsequent, highly programmed events of embryonic development convert

Variations in Internal Fertilization: Penetrating Sex Is Bedbug Success 33.2

Internal fertilization benefits animals in several ways. The placement of sperm in the female's reproductive system maximizes the chances of fertilization, giving both males and females more control over which sperm fertilize which eggs. Specializations of the male and female genitalia increase the precision with which sperm is delivered to the egg, and a combination of behavioural and structural (often referred to as "lock-and-key") arrangements minimizes the chances of mistaken identity (cross-species matings).

Invertebrate animals such as bedbugs, insects in the family Cimicidae, have well-developed genitalia but practise *traumatic insemination*. This involves the male bedbug (e.g., *Cimex lectularius*) piercing the female's abdominal wall with his external genitalia and delivering sperm directly into her coelom (body cavity). The male always pierces the female's body at the sperm-alege, a special site where the intromittant organ penetrates easily and the sperm are deposited **(Figure 1)**.

Females are wounded during traumatic insemination, and the sperm-alege appears to be an anatomical counter-strategy to minimize the damage associated with this form of mating. The sperm-alege also reduces the chances of infection by pathogens transferred in the mating process.

FIGURE 1

(a) The intromittant organ (penis) of Cimex lectularius (scale bar 0.1 μm) is shown with **(b)** a ventral view of the whole animal and **(c)** the ectospermalege, an incurving in one of the female's sternites that guides the male's intromittant organ (scale bar 1.5 μm).

---

the fertilized egg into an individual capable of independent existence.

The paternal chromosomes, the microtubule organizing centre, and one or two centrioles (see Chapter 8) are the only components of sperm to survive in the egg. Therefore, almost all cytoplasmic structures of the embryo and of the new individual are maternal in origin. The centrioles of the new individual are normally of paternal origin.

33.3d Patterns of Development: Moving from Zygote to Complete Organism

In animals with internal fertilization, three major types of support for embryonic development have evolved: *oviparity*, meaning egg laying; *viviparity*, meaning giving birth to live offspring; and *ovoviviparity*, meaning giving birth to live offspring that first hatch internally from eggs.

- **Oviparous** animals (*ovum* = egg, *parere* = to bring forth, to bear) lay eggs that contain the nutrients needed for development of the embryo outside the mother's body. Examples are insects, spiders, most reptiles, and birds. The only oviparous mammals are the *monotremes:* the echidnas and the duck-billed platypus (*Ornithorhynchus anatinus*), both of which are native to Australia.

- **Ovoviviparous** animals retain fertilized eggs within the body, and the embryo develops using the nutrients provided by the egg. When development is complete, the eggs hatch inside the mother and the offspring are released to the exterior. Ovoviviparity is seen in some fishes, lizards, and amphibians; many snakes; and many invertebrates.

- **Viviparous** animals (*vivus* = alive) retain the embryo within the mother's body and nourish it during at least early embryo development. All mammals except the monotremes are viviparous. Viviparity is also seen in all other vertebrate groups except for crocodilians, turtles, and birds. An exceptionally well preserved Devonian fossil placoderm (*Materpiscis attenboroughi*) reveals that viviparity is an ancient trait in vertebrates. In viviparous animals, development of the embryo takes place in a specialized portion of the female reproductive tract, the **uterus** *(womb)*. Various structural adaptations are present in different species to enhance nutrient, waste and gas exchange between the developing embryo and the mother. Perhaps the most advanced are seen among the mammals. One group, called the *placental mammals* or *eutherians,* has a specialized temporary structure, the **placenta**, which connects the embryo to the uterus. The placenta facilitates the transfer of nutrients from the blood of the mother to the embryo and the movement of wastes in the opposite direction. Humans are placental mammals. Another group of mammals, the *marsupials* or *metatherians,* were originally called nonplacental mammals because of a belief that they lacked a placenta. In fact, they do have a placenta, but it derives from a different tissue than that of eutherians and does not connect the embryo and the uterus. Instead, it provides nutrients to the embryo from an attached membranous sac containing yolk for only the early stages of its development. In many metatherians, the embryo is then born at an early stage and crawls over the mother's fur to reach the **marsupium,** an abdominal pouch within which it attaches to nipples and continue its development **(Figure 33.9).** Kangaroos, koalas, wombats, and opossums are marsupials.

33.3e Hermaphroditism: Producing Eggs and Sperm in One Individual

Hermaphroditic (from *Hermes + Aphrodite,* a Greek god and goddess) individuals can produce both eggs and sperm. **Hermaphroditism** is more common among sponges (Porifera), cnidaria, flatworms (Platyhelminthes), earthworms, land snails, and some other invertebrates than it is in vertebrates.

Simultaneous hermaphrodites are individuals that develop functional ovaries and testes at the same time. Earthworms, as shown in **Figure 33.10,** are a good example of simultaneous hermaphroditism. The only known vertebrate simultaneous hermaphrodites are hamlets (genus *Hypoplectrus*), a group of predatory sea basses **(Figure 33.11).** Most simultaneous hermaphroditic individuals do not fertilize themselves. Self-fertilization is prevented by anatomical barriers that preclude introduction of sperm into the hermaphrodite's own body or by mechanisms that cause eggs and sperm to mature at different times. The prevention of self-fertilization maintains the genetic variability of sexual reproduction.

Sequential hermaphrodites are individuals that change from one sex to the other. Sequential hermaphroditism occurs in many invertebrates (e.g., some crustaceans) and some ectothermic vertebrates. Well-known examples include the genus *Amphiprion,* in which, in some species, the initial sex is male (as in

a. Mating earthworms

© Robin Chittenden; Frank Lane Picture Agency/CORBIS

b. Sex organs

Seminal vesicles
Body segment
8
9
10
11
12
13
14
15
Seminal receptacles
Sperm funnels
Testes
Ovary
Egg funnel, sac, and oviduct
Vas deferens
Sperm is released from the ends of the vas deferens

Figure 33.10
Simultaneous hermaphroditism in the earthworm. **(a)** Copulation by a mating pair of earthworms, in which each individual releases sperm that fertilizes the eggs in its partner. **(b)** The sex organs in the earthworm.

John Cancalosi/Peter Arnold/Photolibrary

Figure 33.9
Developing offspring of a marsupial mammal, an opossum (*Didelphis virginiana*), attached to a nipple in the marsupium (pouch) of its mother.

Andrew J. Martinez/Photo Researchers, Inc.

Figure 33.11
Hypoplectrus gummigutta, a predatory sea bass that is a simultaneous hermaphrodite.

On the Road to Vivipary 33.3

Guppies, familiar aquarium fish (see "Life Histories of Guppies," Box 44.3, Chapter 44), and other related fish in the genus *Poeciliopsis* exhibit the full range of reproductive patterns described in Section 33.3d. Some species are oviparous. Females in other species retain eggs in their bodies after fertilization and give birth to live young with no further provisioning (ovoviviparous), whereas the females of still other species develop a *follicular pseudoplacenta* that functions much like the placenta of a mouse (or a human) (viviparous). The level of maternal investment (matrotrophic index) ranges from none in the oviparous species to extensive (ovoviviparous and viviparous) **(Figure 1)**. A phylogeny of *Poeciliopsis* and other species **(Figure 2)** shows repeated evolution of placenta-like structures in these fish. All species thrive and are successful; the differences in strategy employed reflect differences in habitat and life history strategies (see Section 44.4, Chapter 44).

Vivipary appears in different evolutionary lines from elasmobranchs (sharks, rays, and holocephalians; see Chapter 26) to mammals. The young of

various rays and tiger sharks (*Galeocerdo cuvier*) develop inside the mother and are nourished by her, but there is no evidence of a placenta. Species such as grey nurse sharks (*Ginglymostoma cirratum*), mako sharks

(*Isurus oxyrinchus*), porbeagle sharks (*Lamna nasus*), and thresher sharks (*Alopias* species) are oophagous. This means that while pregnant, the females of these species of sharks continue to produce large numbers of small eggs

From David N. Reznick, Mariana Mateos, Mark S. Springer, "Independent Origins and Rapid Evolution of the Placenta in the Fish Genus Poeciliopsis", *Science*, Nov 1, 2002, vol. 298, pp. 1018–1020. Reprinted with permission from AAAS.

FIGURE 1

A matrotrophy index (MI) results when values are assigned to the levels of investment that females make in their young. Matrotrophy indices range from low (ovipary) to high (some ovovivipary and vivipary), and there are intermediate conditions. This figure illustrates the range of MI indices for species in the genus Poeciliopsis. Low MI values are the most common (highest frequency values), but there are significant differences among species. In this figure, species with the same colour do not differ significantly in MI values.

clownfish), whereas in others, it is female. In still other species, individuals may waver between sexes with no discernable order, the sex of any individual being determined by the ratio of sexes in its immediate community (many species of gobies).

STUDY BREAK

1. When does meiosis occur in animal life cycles? How does this compare with the situation in plants?
2. Why do the eggs of animals differ so much in size? What are the implications for development?
3. Why do many species produce vast amounts of sperm but only a few eggs?
4. What are the costs and benefits of internal fertilization? What are the costs and benefits of external fertilization?

33.4 Sexual Reproduction in Mammals

Reproductively, humans are typical eutherian (placental) mammals. Males and females each have a pair of gonads (testes or ovaries). As in other vertebrates, gonads serve a dual function, producing gametes and secreting hormones responsible for sexual development and mating behaviour (see Chapters 34, 35, and 39).

33.4a Females Produce Eggs, Get Pregnant, and Lactate

Human females have a pair of ovaries suspended in the abdominal cavity. An oviduct leads from each ovary to the uterus, which is hollow, with walls that contain smooth muscle. The uterus is lined by the endometrium, formed by layers of connective tissue with embedded glands and richly supplied with blood vessels. If an egg is fertilized and begins development, it must that are consumed by the developing embryos. At least one species of fossil holocephalan chondrichthyian fish (*Delphyodontos dacriformes*) appears to have been oophagous.

Although mammals could be considered the archetypical viviparous animals, not all living mammals are viviparous. Furthermore, living therian mammals (marsupials and placentals) do not all have the same kind of placenta. We have no data about whether early mammals such as *Castorocauda* (see Figures 18.6 and 18.7, Chapter 18) were viviparous. At least 50 gene loci regulate the development of the placenta in placental mammals such as mice and rats. Included are gene families that produce protein hormones and hemoglobin. Some of these genes and gene families are adapted to fetal development.

By retaining developing young in their bodies, adults (usually females) better protect them from predators; provide an appropriate environment for development; and, in many cases, ensure an adequate food supply. As a recurring theme in animals, viviparity is of little value in determining phylogeny (evolutionary relationships). We explore this subject in more detail when we consider development in Chapter 34.

FIGURE 2

Matrotrophy index (MI) values are shown for species in a phylogeny (phylogram) that illustrates proposed evolutionary relationships among species in the genus Poeciliopsis and other species. This phylogeny demonstrates that different evolutionary lineages of guppy-like fish have independently achieved different levels of association between mothers and their developing young. The colour codes are as per the MI indices in Figure 1.

From David N. Reznick, Mariana Mateos, Mark S. Springer, "Independent Origins and Rapid Evolution of the Placenta in the Fish Genus Poeciliopsis", *Science*, Nov 1, 2002, vol. 298, pp. 1018–1020. Reprinted with permission from AAAS.

implant in the endometrium to continue developing. The lower end of the uterus, the cervix, opens into a muscular canal, the vagina, which leads to the exterior. Sperm enter the female reproductive tract via the vagina, and at birth, the baby passes from the uterus through the vagina to the outside.

The **vulva**, the external female sex organs (genitalia), surround the opening of the vagina **(Figure 33.12, p. 810)**. Two folds of tissue, the **labia minora**, run from front to rear on either side of the opening. Labia minora are partially covered by labia majora, a pair of fleshy, fat-padded folds that also run from front to rear on either side of the vagina. At the anterior end of the vulva, the labia minora join to partly cover the **clitoris**, a bulblike erectile organ with the same embryonic origins as the penis. Two **greater vestibular glands** open near the entrance to the vagina and secrete a mucus-rich fluid that lubricates the vulva. The urethra that conducts urine from the bladder to the outside opens between the clitoris and the vaginal opening. Most

nerve endings associated with erotic sensations are concentrated in the clitoris and the labia minora and around the opening of the vagina. When a human female is born, a thin flap of tissue, the **hymen**, partially covers the opening of the vagina. This membrane, if it has not already been ruptured by physical exercise or other disturbances, is broken during the first sexual intercourse.

In most vertebrates, **ovulation**, the release of the egg from the ovary, usually occurs during a well-defined mating season, the time of year when males and females are *fertile*—physiologically and behaviourally ready to reproduce. The timing of mating seasons is usually under the general control of day length (photoperiod), with some adjustment for local weather. This pattern ensures that the young are born at a time of year when food is plentiful. Humans, however, do not show any evidence of a mating season. Mating and fertilization can occur at any time of the year. Furthermore, ovulation appears to be cryptic in humans,

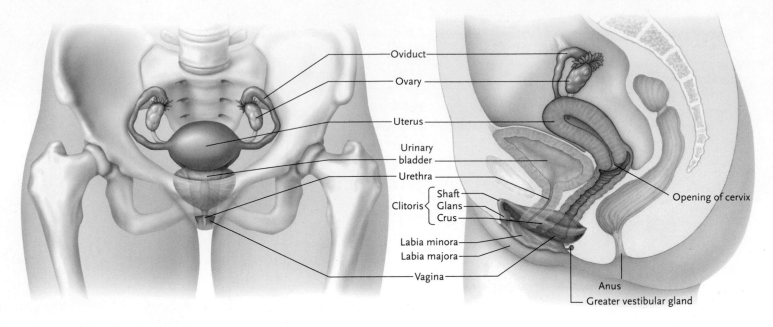

Figure 33.12
The reproductive organs of a human female.

meaning that women do not know when they are ovulating, nor do their partners.

Reproduction in human females is under neuroendocrine control, involving complex interactions between the hypothalamus, pituitary, ovaries, and uterus. The *ovarian cycle* occurs from puberty to menopause and involves the events in the ovaries leading to the release of a mature egg approximately every 28 days. In human females, at birth, each ovary contains about 1 million oocytes whose development is arrested at the end of the first meiotic prophase. Although 200 000 to 380 000 oocytes survive until a female reaches sexual maturity, only about 380 are actually ever ovulated. These are released as immature eggs, usually one per cycle, into the abdominal cavity and pulled into the nearby oviduct by the current produced by the beating of the cilia that line the oviduct. The cilia propel the egg along the oviduct and into the uterus. Fertilization usually occurs in the oviduct. The ovarian cycle is coordinated with the **uterine cycle** or **menstrual cycle** (*menses* = month), events in the uterus that prepare it for implantation of the egg if fertilization occurs.

The beginning of the ovarian cycle **(Figure 33.13, p. 812)** is stimulated by the release of gonadotropin-releasing hormone (GnRH) by the hypothalamus. GnRH stimulates the pituitary to release follicle-stimulating hormone (FSH) and luteinizing hormone (LH) into the bloodstream **(Figure 33.14a, p. 813)**. FSH stimulates 6 to 20 oocytes in the ovaries to begin meiosis. As oocytes develop, they become surrounded by cells that form a follicle (the ovum and follicle cells) (see Figure 33.13, step 1, p. 812, and Figure 33.14a, day 2, p. 813). During this phase, the follicle grows and develops and,

at its largest size, becomes filled with fluid and may be 12 to 15 mm in diameter. Usually, only one follicle develops to maturity with release of the egg (secondary oocyte) by ovulation. Multiple births can result if two or more follicles develop and their eggs ovulate in one cycle.

As the follicle enlarges, FSH and LH interact to stimulate estrogen (female sex hormone, primarily estradiol) secretion by follicular cells. Initially, estrogens are secreted in low amounts and have a negative feedback effect on the pituitary, inhibiting secretion of FSH. As a result, FSH secretion declines briefly. But estrogen secretion increases steadily, and its level peaks about 12 days after the beginning of follicle development **(Figure 33.14c,** day 12, p. 813). High estrogen level has a positive feedback effect on the hypothalamus and pituitary, increasing secretion of GnRH and stimulating the pituitary to release a burst of FSH and LH. Increased estrogen levels convert the mucus secreted by the uterus to a thin and watery consistency, making it easier for sperm to swim through the uterus.

Ovulation occurs after the burst in LH secretion stimulates the follicle cells to release enzymes that digest away the wall of the follicle, causing it to rupture and release the egg (see Figure 33.13, step 5, p. 812). LH also causes the follicle cells remaining at the surface of the ovary to grow into the corpus luteum, an enlarged, yellowish structure (*corpus* = body; *luteum* = yellow), initiating the luteal phase. The corpus luteum (see Figure 33.13, step 6, p. 812) acts as an endocrine gland that secretes estrogens, as well as large quantities of progesterone, a second female sex hormone, and inhibin, another hormone. Progesterone stimulates

Delaying Reproduction 33.4

Many animals have a distinct reproductive season. Its timing is often triggered by changes in photoperiod that herald the changing seasons of the year or by lunar events (e.g., corals). Other animals are more opportunistic. Sea turtles and seals are two examples of animals that separate the acts of mating from the timing of egg laying or birth. Both sea turtles and seals must go ashore to lay eggs or give birth to their young, but for the rest of the year, the animals lead largely pelagic lives. In sea turtles **(Figure 1),** males gather off the beaches where females come to lay their eggs, and mate with females en route to the beach. But males and females also mate during chance meetings in the open ocean. Females can store sperm for up to five years so that they can be ready to lay eggs and fertilize them (from their supply of stored sperm) at any time.

Many species of seals also disassociate the act of mating from, in their case, birth (also known as parturition). Males defend territories on beaches where females haul out to give birth. Females undergo a postpartum estrus, so they are ready to mate (fertile) immediately after giving birth. The seals mate, the egg is fertilized, and the zygote is formed, but implantation is delayed for several months, and the young are born a year later. The time between mating and birth is considerably longer than the gestation period (the time needed for growth and development of the fetus). This approach to reproduction maximizes the chances of males and females finding mates, yet still giving birth at opportune times.

Bats in the families Rhinolophidae and Vespertilionidae separate the acts

FIGURE 2
A pair of little brown bats, Myotis lucifugus, *mate in an abandoned mine in southern Ontario. The male is on the female's back.*

of copulation and ovulation. The gestation periods in these species are about 60 days. In temperate regions, species in both families mate in late summer and early autumn **(Figure 2).** Females store the sperm in their uteri and then enter hibernation. Ovulation and fertilization occur when females leave hibernation in the spring, and the young are born when spring is well advanced.

Fertilization followed by delays in development or implantation can allow males and females more control over mate choice through interactions among sperm or between sperm and the females' reproductive tract. Delays achieved by sperm storage and postponement of ovulation raise possibilities of competition between sperm or other mechanisms for selecting the sperm that fertilizes the egg.

FIGURE 1
A pair of green turtles (Chelonia mydas) *mate in the waters of Tortuguero in Costa Rica.*

growth of the uterine lining and inhibits contractions of the uterus. Progesterone and inhibin have a negative feedback effect on the hypothalamus and pituitary. Progesterone inhibits secretion of GnRH and, in turn, secretion of FSH and LH by the pituitary. Inhibin specifically inhibits FSH secretion. The fall in FSH and LH levels diminishes the signal for follicular growth, and no new follicles begin to grow in the ovary.

If fertilization does not occur, the corpus luteum gradually shrinks, perhaps because of the low levels of LH. About 10 days after ovulation, the shrinkage has inhibited secretion of estrogen, progesterone, and inhibin. In the absence of progesterone, *menstruation* begins. As progesterone and inhibin levels decrease, FSH and LH secretion is no longer inhibited, and a new monthly cycle begins.

The uterine (menstrual) cycle includes the changes in the uterus over one ovarian cycle. The hormones that control the ovarian cycle also control the menstrual cycle **(Figure 33.14d, p. 813),** physiologically connecting the two processes. Day 0 of the monthly cycle is the beginning of follicular development in the ovary **(Figure 33.14b, p. 813),** and in the uterus, menstrual flow begins.

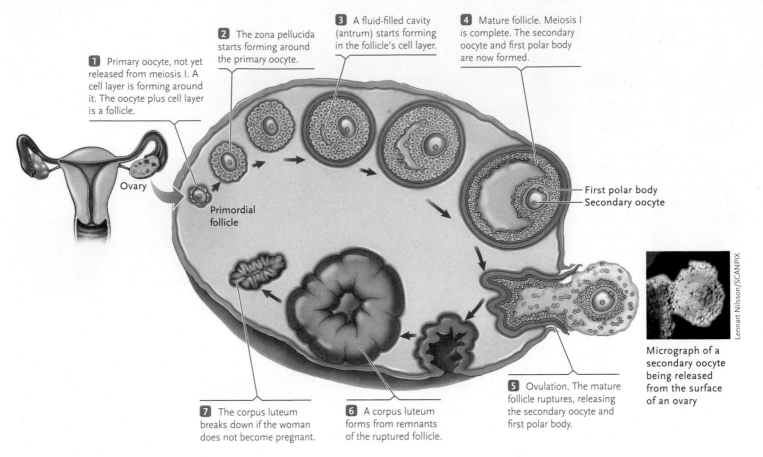

1 Primary oocyte, not yet released from meiosis I. A cell layer is forming around it. The oocyte plus cell layer is a follicle.

2 The zona pellucida starts forming around the primary oocyte.

3 A fluid-filled cavity (antrum) starts forming in the follicle's cell layer.

4 Mature follicle. Meiosis I is complete. The secondary oocyte and first polar body are now formed.

Ovary

Primordial follicle

First polar body
Secondary oocyte

Micrograph of a secondary oocyte being released from the surface of an ovary

Lennart Nilsson/SCANPIX

7 The corpus luteum breaks down if the woman does not become pregnant.

6 A corpus luteum forms from remnants of the ruptured follicle.

5 Ovulation. The mature follicle ruptures, releasing the secondary oocyte and first polar body.

Figure 33.13
The growth of a follicle, ovulation, and the formation of the corpus luteum in a human ovary.

Menstrual flow results from the breakdown of the endometrium, which releases blood and tissue breakdown products from the uterus to the outside through the vagina. When the flow ceases (at day 4 to 5 of the cycle), the proliferation phase begins as the endometrium begins to grow again. As the endometrium gradually thickens, oocytes in both ovaries begin to develop further, eventually leading to ovulation (usually a single egg from one ovary) at about 14 days into the cycle. The uterine lining continues to grow for another 14 days after ovulation. This is the secretory phase. At that time, if fertilization has not taken place, the absence of progesterone results in contraction of the arteries supplying blood to the uterine lining, shutting down the blood supply and causing the lining to disintegrate. The menstrual flow begins. Contractions of the uterus, no longer inhibited by progesterone, help expel the debris. Prostaglandins released by the degenerating endometrium add to uterine contractions, making them severe enough to be felt as the pain of cramps and sometimes producing other effects, such as nausea, vomiting, and headaches.

Menstruation occurs only in human females and our closest primate relatives, gorillas and chimpanzees. In other mammals, the uterine lining is completely reabsorbed if a fertilized egg does not implant during the period of reproductive activity. The uterine cycle in those mammals is called the *estrous* cycle, and females are said to be *in estrus* when fertile.

33.4b Males Produce and Deliver Sperm

Organs that produce and deliver sperm make up the male reproductive system **(Figure 33.15, p. 814).** Human males have a pair of testes (singular, testis), suspended in a baglike **scrotum.** Keeping the testes at cooler temperatures than the body core provides an optimal environment for sperm development. Some land mammals, such as elephants and monotremes with relatively low body temperatures, have internal (cryptic) testes carried within the body. Marine mammals such as whales and dolphins also have internal testes despite relatively high body temperatures. In these animals, countercurrent exchange between cool blood flowing from the tail flukes is delivered to the testes, cooling them enough to allow the production of fertile sperm. In many mammals (e.g., grey squirrels, *Sciurus carolinensis*), the testes descend into the scrotum only during the mating season. Otherwise, they are cryptic, kept in the body captivity, where temperatures are too warm to produce fertile sperm.

In human males, each testicle is packed with about 125 metres of seminiferous tubules, in which sperm

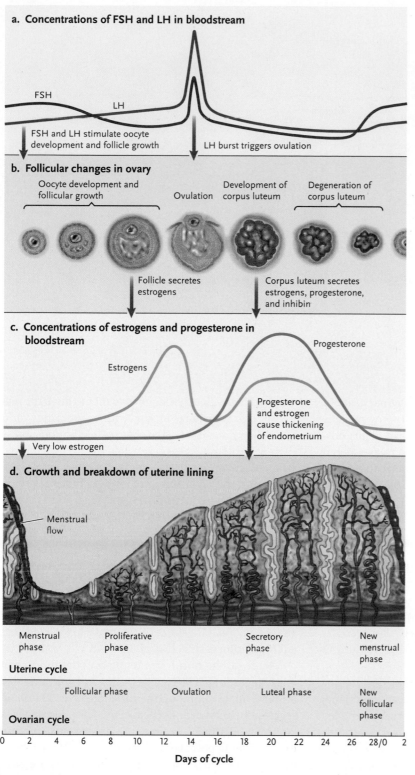

a. Concentrations of FSH and LH in bloodstream

FSH

LH

FSH and LH stimulate oocyte
development and follicle growth

LH burst triggers ovulation

b. Follicular changes in ovary

Oocyte development and
follicular growth

Ovulation

Development of
corpus luteum

Degeneration of
corpus luteum

Follicle secretes
estrogens

Corpus luteum secretes
estrogens, progesterone,
and inhibin

**c. Concentrations of estrogens and progesterone in
bloodstream**

Progesterone

Estrogens

Progesterone
and estrogen
cause thickening
of endometrium

Very low estrogen

d. Growth and breakdown of uterine lining

Menstrual
flow

| Menstrual phase | Proliferative phase | Secretory phase | New menstrual phase |

Uterine cycle

| Follicular phase | Ovulation | Luteal phase | New follicular phase |

Ovarian cycle

0 2 4 6 8 10 12 14 16 18 20 22 24 26 28/0 2

Days of cycle

Figure 33.14

The ovarian and uterine (menstrual) cycles of a human female. The days of the monthly cycle are given in the scale at the bottom of the diagram. **(a)** The changing concentrations of FSH and LH in the bloodstream, triggered by GnRH secretion by the hypothalamus. **(b)** The cycle of follicle development, ovulation, and formation of the corpus luteum in the ovary. **(c)** The concentrations of estrogens and progesterone in the bloodstream. **(d)** The growth and breakdown of the uterine lining.

proceed through all stages of spermatogenesis **(Figure 33.16, p. 815).** The entire process, from spermatogonium to sperm, takes 9 to 10 weeks, and the testes produce about 130 million fertile sperm each day.

Sertoli cells are supportive cells that completely surround the developing spermatocytes in the seminiferous tubules. Sertoli cells supply nutrients to the spermatocytes and seal them off from the body's blood supply. Leydig cells, located in the tissue surrounding the developing spermatocytes, produce the male sex hormones (**androgens**), particularly **testosterone.**

Mature sperm flow from seminiferous tubules into the **epididymis,** a coiled storage tubule attached to the surface of each testis. Rhythmic muscular contractions of the epididymis move sperm into a thick-walled, muscular tube, the **vas deferens** (plural, **vasa deferentia**), which extends through the abdominal cavity. Just below the bladder, the vasa deferentia join the urethra. During ejaculation, muscular contractions force the sperm into the urethra and out of the penis. At this time, the sperm are activated and become motile when they come into contact with alkaline secretions added to the ejaculated fluid by accessory glands.

About 150 to 350 million sperm are released in a single ejaculation. Semen, the ejaculate, is a mixture of sperm and the secretions of several accessory glands. In humans, about two-thirds of the volume is produced by a pair of **seminal vesicles** that secrete seminal fluid, a thick, viscous liquid, into the vasa deferentia near the point where they join with the urethra. Seminal fluid contains prostaglandins that, when ejaculated into the female, trigger contractions of the female reproductive tract that help move the sperm into and through the uterus.

The **prostate gland,** which surrounds the region where the vasa deferentia empty into the urethra, adds a thin, milky fluid to the semen. The alkaline prostate secretion makes up about one-third of the volume of

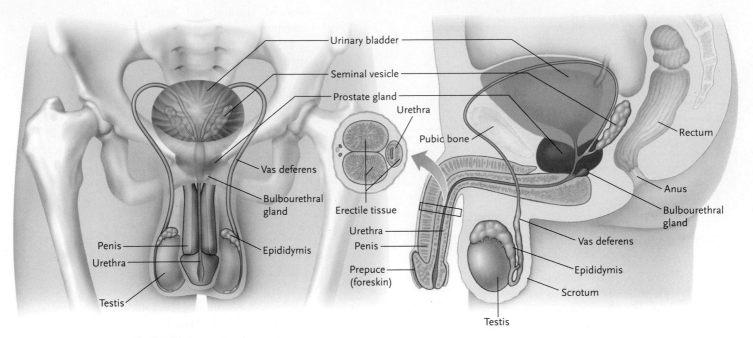

Figure 33.15
The reproductive organs of a human male.

semen, raising its pH (and that of the vagina) to about pH 6, the level of acidity best tolerated by sperm. This pH level also fosters sperm motility. As part of the prostate secretion, a fast-acting enzyme converts the semen to a thick gel at ejaculation. The thickened consistency helps keep the semen from draining from the vagina when the penis is withdrawn. A second, slower-acting enzyme in the prostate secretion gradually breaks down the semen clot and releases the sperm to swim freely in the female reproductive tract.

Finally, a pair of **bulbourethral glands** secretes a clear, mucus-rich fluid into the urethra before and during ejaculation. This fluid lubricates the tip of the penis and neutralizes the acidity of any residual urine in the urethra. In total, the secretions of the accessory glands make up more than 95% of the volume of semen; less than 5% is sperm.

Most of the interior of the penis is filled with three cylinders of spongelike tissue (corpora cavernosa) that become filled with blood and cause erection during sexual arousal. Although the human penis depends solely on engorgement of spongy tissue for erection, the males of many mammals, including bats, rodents, carnivores, and most other primates, have a baculum or penis bone **(Figure 33.17)** that helps maintain the penis in an erect state. The presence of bacula in a species usually coincides with the presence of a baubellum (clitoris bone) in females.

The penis ends in the **glans**, a soft, caplike structure. Most nerve endings producing erotic sensations are crowded into the glans and the region of the penile shaft just behind the glans. The prepuce or foreskin is a loose fold of skin that covers the glans (see Figure 33.15). In many human cultures, the foreskin is

removed for hygienic, religious, or other ritualistic reasons by **circumcision** (= around cut). In 2007, the World Health Organization stated that male circumcision is an important strategy to prevent heterosexually acquired HIV infection in males. Female circumcision, the removal of the labia minora and the clitoris, is often called female genital mutilation or FGM. FGM is practised in various countries in western, eastern, and north-eastern Africa and in parts of Asia and the Middle East. The World Health Organization estimates that 100–140 million women and girls around the world have experienced the procedure. It is now considered a human rights violation carried out to reduce libido and control women's sexuality. The United Nations holds an International Day of Zero Tolerance to Female Genital Mutilation each February 6.

Many of the hormones regulating the menstrual cycle, including GnRH, FSH, LH, and inhibin, also regulate male reproductive functions. Testosterone, secreted by the Leydig cells in the testes, also plays a key role **(Figure 33.18, p. 816)**. In sexually mature males, the hypothalamus secretes GnRH in brief pulses every 1 to 2 hours. GnRH stimulates the pituitary to secrete LH and FSH. LH stimulates the Leydig cells to secrete testosterone, which stimulates sperm production and controls the growth and function of male reproductive structures. FSH stimulates Sertoli cells to secrete a protein and other molecules required for spermatogenesis.

Concentrations of male reproductive hormones are maintained by negative feedback mechanisms. If the concentration of testosterone falls in the bloodstream, the hypothalamus responds by increasing GnRH secretion. If testosterone levels rise too high,

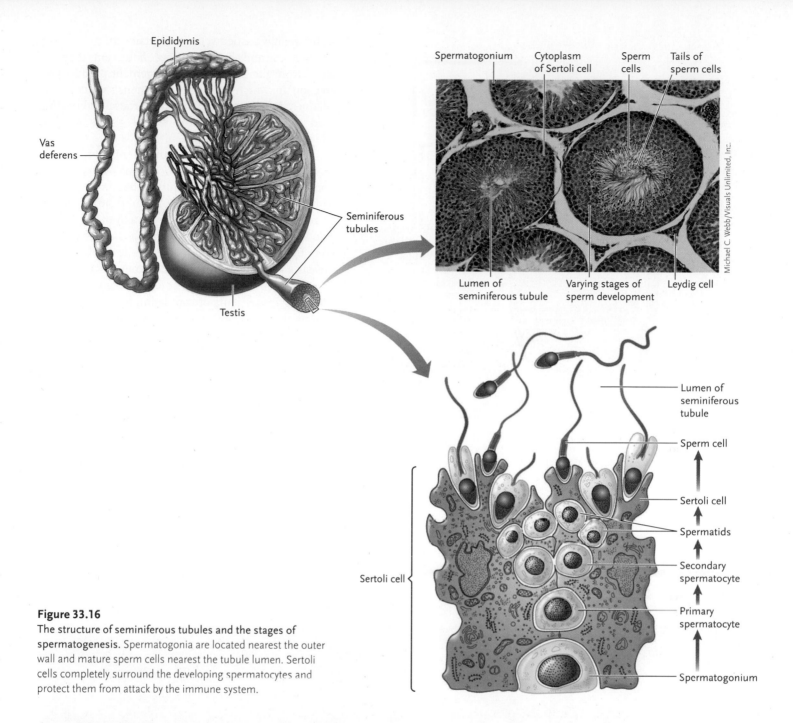

Figure 33.16
The structure of seminiferous tubules and the stages of spermatogenesis. Spermatogonia are located nearest the outer wall and mature sperm cells nearest the tubule lumen. Sertoli cells completely surround the developing spermatocytes and protect them from attack by the immune system.

Figure 33.17
The bacula of a wolverine (*Gulo luscus*), a red fox (*Vulpes fulva*), a raccoon (*Procyon lotor*), and a walrus (*Odobenus rosmarus*) (top to bottom).

the overabundance inhibits LH secretion. An overabundance of testosterone also stimulates Sertoli cells to secrete inhibin, which inhibits FSH secretion by the pituitary. As a result, testosterone secretion by the Leydig cells drops off, returning the concentration to optimal levels in the bloodstream.

When the male is sexually aroused, sphincter muscles controlling the flow of blood to the spongy erectile tissue of the penis relax, allowing the tissue to become engorged with blood (the penis is a hydrostatic skeleton structure; see Chapter 32).

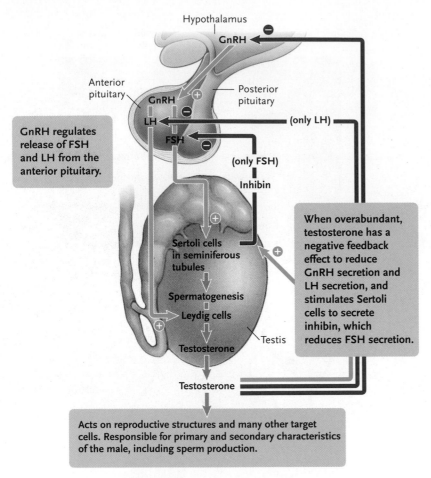

GnRH regulates release of FSH and LH from the anterior pituitary.

When overabundant, testosterone has a negative feedback effect to reduce GnRH secretion and LH secretion, and stimulates Sertoli cells to secrete inhibin, which reduces FSH secretion.

Acts on reproductive structures and many other target cells. Responsible for primary and secondary characteristics of the male, including sperm production.

Figure 33.18

Hormonal regulation of reproduction in the male and the negative feedback systems controlling hormone levels.

As the spongy tissue swells, it maintains the pressure by compressing and almost shutting off the veins draining blood from the penis. The engorgement produces an erection in which the penis lengthens, stiffens, and enlarges. During continued sexual arousal, lubricating fluid secreted by the bulbourethral glands may be released from the tip of the penis.

Female sexual arousal results in enlargement and erection of the clitoris, in a process analogous to erection of the penis. The labia minora become engorged with blood and swell in size, and lubricating fluid is secreted onto the surfaces of the vulva by the vestibular glands. In addition to these changes, the nipples become erect by contraction of smooth muscle cells, and the breasts swell in size due to engorgement with blood.

Insertion of the penis into the vagina and the thrusting movements of copulation lead to the reflex actions of ejaculation, including spasmodic contractions of muscles surrounding the vasa deferentia, accessory glands, and urethra. During ejaculation, the sphincter muscles controlling the exit from the bladder close tightly, preventing urine from mixing with the ejaculate. Ejaculation is usually accompanied by *orgasm,* a sensation of intense physical pleasure that is the peak (climax) of excitement for sexual intercourse, followed by feelings of relaxation and gratification.

The motions of copulation stretch the vagina and stimulate the clitoris, sometimes inducing orgasm in females. Vaginal stretching also stimulates the hypothalamus to secrete oxytocin, which induces contractions of the uterus. The contractions keep the sperm

PEOPLE BEHIND BIOLOGY 33.5
John P. Wiebe, University of Western Ontario

What happens to hormones after they are produced? John P. Wiebe, professor emeritus in the Department of Biology at the University of Western Ontario in London, and his graduate students study two steroid hormones derived from progesterone. Specifically, 5α-pregnane-3,20-dione (5αP) and 3α-hydroxy-4-pregen-20-one (3αP) are metabolites of progesterone. 5αP is cancer promoting, stimulating cells to proliferate

(tumour growth) and detach (metastasis). 3αP is cancer inhibiting because it suppresses cell proliferation and metastasis.

Wiebe and his colleagues have demonstrated that tumorigenic cells produce higher levels of 5αP and lower levels of 3αP. When cells become tumorigenic, there are strong increases in the mRNA expression of the enzyme that catalyzes conversion of progesterone

to 5αP, specifically 5α-reductase. This increase is paralleled by a decrease in 3α-hydroxysteroidoxidoreductase, which catalyzes conversion to 3αP.

It is clear that this work has potential in the control and treatment of breast cancer. It also alerts us to the impact of exposure to hormones, whether in the food we eat or in the water we drink (see "Molecule behind Biology," Box 44.5, Chapter 44).

in suspension and aid their movement through the reproductive tract. Uterine contractions are also induced by the prostaglandins in the semen.

Sperm reach the site of fertilization in the oviducts within 30 minutes of being ejaculated. Of the millions of sperm released in a single ejaculation, only a few hundred actually reach the oviducts. After orgasm, the penis, clitoris, and labia minora gradually return to their unstimulated size. Females can experience additional orgasms within minutes or even seconds of a first orgasm, but most males enter a *refractory period* lasting 15 minutes or longer before they can regain an erection and have another orgasm.

33.4c Fertilization of Human Eggs: Producing Zygotes

A human egg can be fertilized only during its passage through the third of the oviduct nearest the ovary. If the egg is not fertilized during the 12 to 24 hours that it is in this location, it disintegrates and dies. Sperm do not swim randomly for a chance encounter with the egg. Rather, they first swim up the cervical canal to reach the oviduct and then are propelled up the oviduct by contractions of the oviduct's smooth muscles. There is evidence that eggs release chemical attractant molecules that the sperm recognize, causing them to swim directly toward the egg.

CONCEPT FIX Although 150 to 350 million sperm are released in a single ejaculation by a human male, an ovum can only be fertilized by one sperm. It is a misconception that several sperm can enter a single ovum. ◼

Sperm must first penetrate the layer of follicle cells surrounding the egg, aided by enzymes in the sperm plasma membrane **(Figure 33.19, p. 818).** Then the sperm adhere to receptor molecules on the surface of the zona pellucida. This contact triggers the **acrosome reaction**, in which enzymes contained in the acrosome are released from the sperm onto the zona pellucida, where they digest a path to the plasma membrane of the egg. As soon as the first sperm cell reaches the egg, sperm and egg plasma membranes fuse, and the sperm cell is engulfed by the cytoplasm of the egg. Although only one sperm fertilizes the egg, the combined release of acrosomal enzymes from many sperm greatly increases the chance that a complete channel will be opened through the zona pellucida. This is in part why a low sperm count is often a source of male infertility. Low sperm counts can be caused by infection, heat, frequent ejaculation, smoking, and excess alcohol consumption.

Membrane fusion activates the egg. The sperm that enters the egg releases nitric oxide that stimulates the release of stored Ca^{2+} in the egg. Ca^{2+} triggers cortical granule release to the outside of the egg. Enzymes from the cortical granules cross-link molecules in the zona pellucida, hardening it and sealing the channels opened by acrosomal enzymes. The enzymes also destroy receptors that bind sperm to the surface of the zona pellucida. As a result, no further sperm can bind to the zona pellucida or reach the plasma membrane of the egg. The Ca^{2+} also triggers the completion of meiosis of the egg. The sperm and egg nuclei then fuse, and the cell is now considered a zygote. Mitotic divisions of the zygote soon initiate embryonic development.

The first cell divisions of embryonic development take place while the fertilized egg is still in the oviduct. About seven days after ovulation, the embryo passes from the oviduct and implants in the uterine lining. During and after implantation, cells associated with the embryo secrete **human chorionic gonadotropin (hCG)**, a hormone that keeps the corpus luteum in the ovary from breaking down. Excess hCG is excreted in the urine; its presence in urine or blood provides the basis of pregnancy tests.

Continued activity of the corpus luteum keeps estrogen and progesterone secretion at high levels, maintaining the uterine lining and preventing menstruation. The high progesterone level also thickens the mucus secreted by the uterus, forming a plug that seals the opening of the cervix from the vagina. The plug keeps bacteria, viruses, and sperm cells from further copulations from entering the uterus.

About 10 weeks after implantation, the placenta takes over the secretion of progesterone, hCG secretion drops off, and the corpus luteum regresses. However, the corpus luteum continues to secrete the hormone *relaxin*, which inhibits contraction of the uterus until near the time of birth.

STUDY BREAK

1. How does the reproductive pattern of human females differ from that of other mammals? What is the significance of this? (See also Chapters 26, 45, and 48.)
2. Given all of the changes in hormones associated with the ovarian and uterine cycles, which hormones can be used as good predictors of ovulation?
3. Compare and contrast Figures 33.8 and 33.19 (steps of fertilization in sea urchin and mammal). How would you determine whether this was a case of convergent evolution versus the retention of an ancestral trait?

33.5 Controlling Reproduction

Knowledge about the details of reproduction can allow us to control fertility. In some cases, this means increasing the chances of reproducing, whereas in other cases, it means minimizing them. In human

a. Sperm attached to zona pellucida

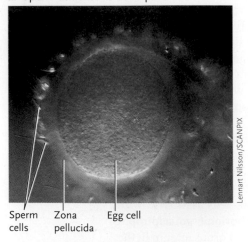

Sperm cells | Zona pellucida | Egg cell

Lennart Nilsson/SCANPIX

b. Early steps in fertilization in mammals

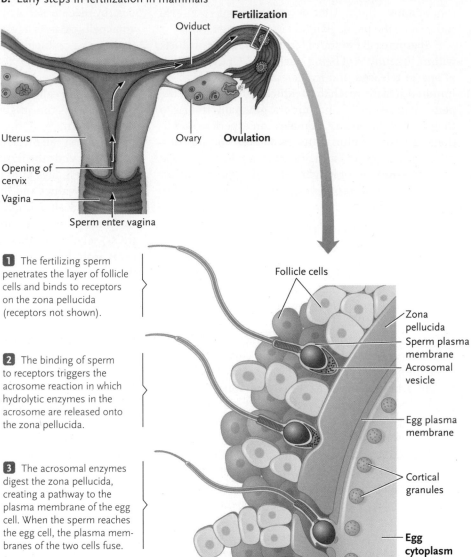

Oviduct

Fertilization

Uterus

Opening of cervix

Vagina

Ovary | **Ovulation**

Sperm enter vagina

Follicle cells

Zona pellucida
Sperm plasma membrane
Acrosomal vesicle

Egg plasma membrane

Cortical granules

Egg cytoplasm

Sperm basal body

Sperm nucleus

1 The fertilizing sperm penetrates the layer of follicle cells and binds to receptors on the zona pellucida (receptors not shown).

2 The binding of sperm to receptors triggers the acrosome reaction in which hydrolytic enzymes in the acrosome are released onto the zona pellucida.

3 The acrosomal enzymes digest the zona pellucida, creating a pathway to the plasma membrane of the egg cell. When the sperm reaches the egg cell, the plasma membranes of the two cells fuse.

4 The sperm nucleus enters the egg cytoplasm.

5 The sperm stimulates release of Ca^{2+} stored in the egg, which, in turn, triggers the cortical reaction, leading to the slow block in polyspermy.

Figure 33.19

Fertilization in mammals. **(a)** Sperm attached to the zona pellucida of a human egg cell. **(b)** Early steps in the fertilization process.

society, pregnancy can be a blessing or a disaster, depending on the situation. Statistics describing the effectiveness of different means of limiting human reproductive output **(Table 33.1)** illustrate our progress in the area of family planning. Knowledge about the timing of ovulation, for example (see Figure 33.14, p. 813), can provide the means to maximize or minimize the chances of pregnancy.

Biologists working to conserve biodiversity often attempt to control reproduction. When a species is on the brink of extinction, the goal is to maximize reproductive output. Techniques can range from the use of

foster parents to raise young to using reproductive technologies such as *in vitro* fertilization and implantation of embryos. For example, biologists working with black-footed ferrets (see "Black-Footed Ferret, *Mustela nigripes*," Box 44.2, Chapter 44), which are highly endangered, strive to maximize reproductive output to increase the population.

Similarly, when an increasing population of one species threatens to overwhelm other species or an ecosystem, the goal is to prevent reproduction. Biologists faced with growing populations of African elephants try to reduce reproductive output using

Table 33.1	Pregnancy Rates for Birth Control Methods	
Method	Lowest Expected Rate of Pregnancy[a]	Typical-Use Rate of Pregnancy[b]
Rhythm method	1–9%	25%
Withdrawal	4%	19%
Condom (male)	3%	14%
Condom (female)	5%	21%
Diaphragm and spermicidal jelly	6%	20%
Vasectomy (male sterilization)	0.1%	0.15%
Tubal ligation (female sterilization)	0.5%	0.5%
Contraceptive pill (combination estrogen–progestin)	0.1%	5%
Contraceptive pill (progestin only)	0.5%	5%
Implant (progestin)	0.09%	0.09%
Intrauterine device (IUD) (copper T)	0.6%	0.8%

[a]Rate of pregnancy when the birth control method was used correctly every time.

[b]Rate of pregnancy when the method was used typically, meaning that it may not have always been used correctly every time.

Source: U.S. Food and Drug Administration, http://www.fda.gov/fdac/features/1997/conceptbl.html. Data reported in 1997 for effectiveness of methods in a one-year period.

techniques ranging from the application of contraceptives to females (see "Molecule behind Biology," Box 44.5, Chapter 44) to culling (killing) individuals in the population. Culling usually targets females because they produce young (see Chapter 44). The same principles of controlling reproductive output have been central to humans' domestication of other organisms (see Chapter 48).

STUDY BREAK

1. How can biologists control reproduction? Why is access to control of reproduction important?
2. What are the advantages and disadvantages of different approaches to contraception for mammals?
3. What methods do zoos and botanical gardens use to control reproduction of captive organisms? Is this appropriate?
4. What steps could conservation biologists take to increase the reproductive output of rare and endangered species?

Review

Access an interactive eBook, chapter-specific interactive learning tools, including flashcards, quizzes, videos, and more in your Biology **CourseMate**, accessed through NelsonBrain.com **Aplia™** is an online interactive learning solution that helps you improve comprehension—and your grade—by integrating a variety of mediums and tools such as videos, tutorials, practice tests, and an interactive eBook.

33.1 The Drive to Reproduce

- The drive to reproduce is strong thus all energy that does not go into growth, development and maintenance goes into reproduction. The strategies employed are diverse reflecting differences in habitat and life style.

33.2 Asexual and Sexual Reproduction

- One important advantage of asexual reproduction over sexual reproduction is the exact production of successful genotypes in organisms living in stable environments. Asexual reproduction occurs by mitosis through fission, budding, or fragmentation – or by meiosis through parthenogenesis.

- One important advantage of sexual reproduction over asexual reproduction is the generation of genetic diversity in offspring. Genetic recombination and independent assortment of chromosomes during meiosis give rise to diversity and reduce vulnerability to deleterious effects carried on recessive alleles.

33.3 Mechanisms of Sexual Reproduction

- Meiosis in animals occurs only during the production of gametes. Spermatogenesis produces sperm while oogenesis produces eggs (oocytes). In plants and fungi, meiosis is not always used to produce gametes.

- The amount of yolk in eggs varies enormously reflecting the time of incubation and development; i.e. the time required until the animal can obtain nutrients from other sources. Development in eggs with large amounts of yolk often involves a small embryonic disk floating on top of the yolk (e.g., bird) as opposed to development around the yolk (e.g., frog).

- External fertilization occurs in most aquatic organisms. Various strategies exist to enhance the odds of sperm and eggs from members of the same species uniting.

- Internal fertilization can reduce the amounts of sperm necessary to achieve fertilization. Internal fertilization can also increase the certainty of mate choice where only the sperm of a male that mated come into contact with the egg(s) of a female. It requires more energy, however, leaving less for production of eggs and sperm.

- Polyspermy, more than one sperm entering an egg, is prevented in two ways. The fast block depends on a change in the egg's membrane potential from negative to positive, whereas the slow block involves Ca^{2+} ions that cause cortical granules to fuse with the egg's plasma membrane and release their enzyme contents to the outside.

- Viviparous animals give birth to live young. Before birth, the mother provides the developing embryo with food and oxygen and removes its metabolic wastes. Usually, but not always, this occurs in the body of the female. Ovoviviparous animals may also give birth to live young, but here the eggs develop and grow inside the mother using yolk as the source of energy. Oviparous animals lay eggs that develop outside the mother's body.

33.4 Sexual Reproduction in Mammals

- Most mammals show a well-defined mating season, the time when copulation, fertilization, and development take place. The onset of the mating season is often triggered by changes in photoperiod (day length). All events are timed so that the young are born at the time of year when food is most available for growth and development. Mammalian females typically display behavioural and physiological signs of fertility (estrus). Humans, on the other hand, do not have a mating season, and both sexes are receptive to mating at any time.

- Reproduction is under neuroendocrine control. In the female this consists of two cycles, the ovarian cycle and the uterine cycle, both of which are highly integrated. The ovarian cycle begins when GnRH released by the hypothalamus stimulates the pituitary to release leutinizing hormone (LH) and follicle stimulating hormone (FSH). This ultimately leads to ovulation. Subsequent steps depend upon whether fertilization occurs or not.

- Cryptic testes (e.g., elephants and whales) are housed inside the body. In many mammals, testes are housed in a scrotum outside the body because sperm develop best at temperatures below the core temperature of a mammal. A baculum is a penis bone, a feature of many mammals but not humans. The baubellum (clitoris bone) is the equivalent in females.

- Alkaline prostate secretions raise the pH of semen and the vagina to about pH 6, activating sperm motility. Prostaglandins in seminal fluid trigger contractions of the female reproductive tract that help move the sperm into and through the uterus.

- When enzymes contained within the acrosome of a sperm are released into the zona pellucida, they digest a path to the plasma membrane of the egg. This process is initiated by contact between and then adherence of the sperm to receptor molecules on the surface of the zona pellucida. When the sperm meets the egg cell the plasma membranes of the two cells fuse and the sperm nucleus enters the egg cytoplasm where it ultimately fuses with the nucleus of the egg.

33.5 Controlling Reproduction

- Controlling (promoting or reducing) reproductive output is important for our species in social and political contexts. It is also important in conservation.

Questions

Self-Test Questions

Any number of answers from a to e may be correct.

1. Which action can be involved in asexual reproduction?
   a. fission
   b. budding
   c. copulation
   d. parthenogenesis

2. A sea star is cut into two separate pieces and each develops into a complete sea star. What is this an example of?
   a. external fertilization
   b. fission
   c. budding
   d. fragmentation

3. Germ cells give rise to which of the following?
   a. eggs
   b. somatic cells
   c. sperm
   d. Only a and b are correct.

4. In which group is internal fertilization rarely seen?
   a. in platyhelminthes
   b. in bedbugs
   c. in mammals
   d. in frogs

5. In slow blocks, more than one sperm is prevented from fertilizing an egg by changes in which of the following?
   a. in Ca^{2+} ions
   b. in Cl^- ions
   c. in Na^+ ions
   d. in cortical granules

6. Ovulation in women is signalled by a rise in which of the following hormones?
   a. relaxin
   b. estrogen
   c. testosterone
   d. luteinizing hormone

7. Which mammal has cryptic testes?
   a. humans
   b. elephants
   c. dogs
   d. bulls

8. Which action is involved in the reproductive cycle of some bats and turtles?
   a. delayed fertilization
   b. delayed implantation
   c. delayed development
   d. postpartum estrus

9. What colour of light are cryptochromes sensitive to?
   a. red light
   b. white light
   c. blue light
   d. green light

10. Which animals engage in the mating behaviour termed amplexus?
    a. birds
    b. frogs and toads
    c. salmon
    d. mammals

Questions for Discussion

1. How do plants exploit animals to effect pollination and dispersal of seeds? Are there examples of animals exploiting plants to achieve reproduction?

2. How does variation in the pattern of fertilization (internal versus external) differ among the animal phyla? Do these variations indicate different ancestral conditions? How do these patterns differ between plants and animals?

3. What methods do zoos and botanical gardens use to control reproduction of captive organisms? Is this appropriate?

4. What steps could conservation biologists take to increase reproductive output of rare and endangered species?

5. Explain why species recognition is important for animals using external fertilization.

(a) A diagrammatic view of the bony birth canal of (A) a nonpregnant Brazilian free-tailed bat (*Tadarida brasiliensis*) and (B) a female in the process of giving birth. The sacrum (S), coxal bone (C), and interpubic ligament (L) are shown. (b) The ventral view of the pelvis of another nonpregnant free-tailed bat. There is no connection between the pubic bones, making it possible for the animal to achieve the expansion of the birth canal required during birth

STUDY PLAN

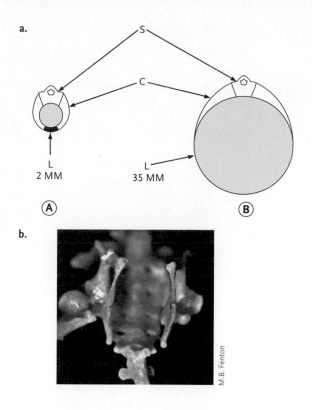

a.

b.

M.B. Fenton

34 Animal Development

WHY IT MATTERS

The size of the mother and of the young can be a challenging aspect of the process of giving birth (parturition). Bats are an extreme example when it comes to offspring size. Typically, a female bat bears a pup that is 25 to 30% of her normal body mass—the equivalent of a 60-kg woman bearing a 15- to 20-kg baby. The birth canal of placental mammals (such as bats and people) passes between the two halves of the pelvic girdle. Not surprisingly, the pelvis of adult female placental mammals differs from that of males.

The magnitude of the challenge of parturition to a female Brazilian free-tailed bat is shown above. In a nonpregnant female, the bony birth canal is 2 mm in diameter, but it expands to 35 mm in diameter during birth. In these bats, birth takes about 90 seconds.

The elasticity of the interpubic ligament is the key to the birth process in female mammals that give birth to large young. This ligament has an abundance of elastic fibres, which intermingle with collagen fibres at the ligament's core. The situation in bats appears to be the same as in other mammals: elastic fibres stretch, whereas collagen fibres slide in relation to each other. The hormone relaxin plays a fundamental role in this process, promoting the stretchability of

MOLECULE BEHIND BIOLOGY 34.1
Relaxin

The hormone relaxin **(Figure 1)** is a polypeptide produced by the ovaries during pregnancy. In humans, relaxin occurs at higher levels earlier in pregnancy than closer to parturition. Relaxin promotes angiogenesis, the growth of new blood vessels, and influences the interface between the uterus and the placenta. Relaxin inhibits muscular contractions of the uterus that could terminate pregnancy and stimulates the growth of glands that produce milk in breast tissue.

FIGURE 1
Relaxin. Near parturition, relaxin causes relaxation of the pubic ligaments and softens and enlarges the cervical opening.

interpubic ligaments at the time of parturition (see "Molecule behind Biology," Box 34.1).

The process of development takes an animal from the zygote (fertilized egg) to the complete adult stage of the life cycle. The surroundings of the developing animal (embryo or larva) can influence the process, although the mechanisms and the major patterns of development are common among multicellular animals. Genetic controls underlie the cellular and molecular processes involved in animal development and include apoptosis, programmed death of cells. Exploring the development processes in a range of animals illustrates both diversity and underlying principles.

34.1 Housing and Fuelling Developing Young

Some animal parents invest significant energy in housing and feeding their developing young. This is one aspect of the genetically selfish drive to ensure that their genes are represented in future generations.

34.1a Housing Provides a Place in Which the Embryo Can Develop

There is a recurring tendency across phyla for parents to put eggs and developing young in situations that minimize their exposure to predators and parasites while maximizing favourable conditions for growth and development. Many species of birds use nests to house their eggs and unfledged young. Parents of other species, such as some species of scorpions, frogs, and insects, carry their young with them, often on their backs. This allows the parent (parents) to avoid or actively deter would-be predators.

An escalation in parental investment is moving eggs and young inside the parent's body (vivipary and ovovivipary; see Chapter 33). This approach to parental care has several different stages (see "On the Road to Vivipary," Box 33.3). Although we associate vivipary with mammals, many species of fish are mouthbreeders, keeping eggs and, for a time, developing young in their mouths. Other fish, such as seahorses and pipefish (family Syngnathidae, order Gasterosteiformes; **Figure 34.1**), keep eggs and developing young in specialized incubation areas, called brood pouches, located on the tail or trunk of the male. "Pregnancy" in male seahorses represents an increase in parental investment. It also allows males to be confident about the paternity of the young they raise.

Figure 34.1
A male seahorse gives birth.

Some amphibians also show high levels of parental care. In Australia, female frogs, *Rheobatrachus silus,* use their stomachs as brood pouches. While the young are developing, they secrete prostaglandin E_2, which inhibits the secretion of gastric acid in the stomach and saves the developing young from being digested. On Mount Nimba in West Africa, female toads (*Nectophrynoides occidentalis*) harbour developing young in their uterus, where the young feed on uterine secretions in the absence of a placenta. The gestation period for these toads is nine months, and newborns are 7 to 8 mm long and weigh 30 to 60 mg. Retention of developing embryos in the oviducts has evolved independently in each of the three living groups of Amphibia: Anura, Urodela, and Gymnophiona (see Chapter 26).

34.1b Feeding Aids and Abets Developing Young

Almost everyone has seen pictures of parent birds feeding their young (see Figures 39.2 and 39.4 respectively). In many species, both males and females deliver food to the nestlings. Some fruit-eating adult birds feed insects to their young because a higher-protein diet promotes rapid growth of the young. Producing high-quality food is the next level of parental investment, and "milk" is a prime example.

The term *milk* is usually applied to secretions of the mammary glands of mammals, and it is the quintessentially mammalian food. However, other animals also make milk. Female cockroaches **(Figure 34.2)** house developing embryos in a brood sac and give birth to them as first-instar (first stage) larvae. The brood sac is an infolding of a ventral intersegmental membrane, and its epithelium produces the milk, a blend of water-soluble proteins encoded by a multigene family.

Both male and female discus fish **(Figure 34.3)** feed their hatchling young (known as *fry*) skin secretions, the first and only food eaten by the fry. This fish milk

Figure 34.3
Symphysodon discus, a fish that produces milk to feed its young.

appears as a slight mucus coating on the adults' bodies, particularly above the lateral lines. Skin feeding also occurs in caecilians (an amphibian). The skin in brooding females **(Figures 34.4 and 34.5, p. 824)** is transformed to provide a rich supply of nutrients, and the young have specialized teeth for peeling and eating the outer layer of their mother's skin **(Figure 34.6, p. 824).** In some other caecilians, young develop in the uterus and feed on the lining of the oviduct. Milk has also been reported in birds, where the crop milk of pigeons (*Columba livia domestica*) is fed to young (known as squabs) from hatching to about age 19 days. In some cases, pigeon lactation continues to day 28. Pigeon crop milk is composed mainly of proteins and lipids and is highly nutritious. Female mammals have not cornered the milk market, either. There are records of male mammals lactating, the most notable being *Dyacopterus spadiceus*, a fruit bat from Indonesia. Some male *D. spadiceus* produce milk, although not as much as

Figure 34.2
Diploptera punctata, a cockroach that produces live young. Starting from left, an adult female and male, egg, last stage fetus, larval instars.

Figure 34.4
A female caecilian (*Boulengerula taitanus*) feeding her young skin secretions.

Reprinted by permission from Macmillan Publishers Ltd: NATURE, Alexander Kupfer, Hendrik Müller, Marta M. Antoniazzi, Carlos Jared, Hartmut Greven et al., "Parental investment by skin feeding in a caecilian amphibian," Vol. 440, pp. 926–929, copyright (2006).

Figure 34.5

Details of the skin of **(a)** a nonbrooding and **(b)** a brooding female caecilian.

Reprinted by permission from Macmillan Publishers Ltd: NATURE, Alexander Kupfer, Hendrik Muller, Marta M. Antoniazzi, Carlos Jared, Hartmut Greven et al., "Parental investment by skin feeding in a caecilian amphibian," Vol. 440, pp. 926–929, copyright (2006).

Figure 34.6

Scanning electron micrographs of the specialized teeth of young caecilians.

Reprinted by permission from Macmillan Publishers Ltd: NATURE, Alexander Kupfer, Hendrik Muller, Marta M. Antoniazzi, Carlos Jared, Hartmut Greven et al., "Parental investment by skin feeding in a caecilian amphibian," Vol. 440, pp. 926–929, copyright (2006).

females, but the behavioural significance of male lactation in this species remains unknown.

Perhaps female tsetse flies (*Glossina* spp.) are the most astonishing in the matter of caring for developing young. Females ovulate, releasing a single egg that enters the functional equivalent of a mammalian uterus and is fertilized. A milk gland associated with the uterus provides the developing embryo with food, and eventually the female gives birth to a larva that weighs more than she does. The larva then burrows into the ground and pupates. An adult fly later emerges from the pupa.

STUDY BREAK

1. What is relaxin? What role does it play?
2. Where can embryos develop in a parent?
3. What is milk? Which animals produce it?

34.2 Mechanisms of Embryonic Development

When a sperm fertilizes an egg, a zygote is produced. At this point, embryonic development begins, ultimately producing a free-living individual. All of the instructions required for development are packed into the zygote. Mitotic divisions of the zygote are the beginning of developmental activity (see Chapter 8).

Information that directs the initiation of development is stored in two locations in the zygote. The nucleus houses the DNA derived from egg and sperm nuclei. This DNA directs development as individual genes are activated or turned off in a regulated and ordered manner. The balance of the information is stored in the zygote's cytoplasm.

Because sperm contribute essentially no cytoplasm to the zygote, the zygote's cytoplasm is maternal in origin. The mRNA and proteins stored in the egg cytoplasm are known as **cytoplasmic determinants**, which direct the first stages of animal development before genes become active. Depending on the animal group, control of early development by cytoplasmic determinants may be limited to the first few divisions of the zygote (e.g., in mammals), or it may last until the actual tissues of the embryo are formed (e.g., in most invertebrates).

The zygote's cytoplasm also contains ribosomes and other cytoplasmic components required for protein synthesis and early divisions of embryonic cells. Zygote cytoplasm contains the tubulin molecules required to form spindles for early cell divisions, as well as mitochondria and nutrients stored in granules in the yolk and in lipid droplets. In many animals, zygotes contain pigments that colour the egg or regions of it.

Yolk contains nutrients. In the eggs of typical insects, reptiles, and birds, large amounts of yolk supply all of the nutrients for development of the embryo. In contrast, the eggs of placental mammals contain very little yolk, which is used only to support the earliest stages of development.

Depending on the species, yolk may be concentrated at one end or in the centre or distributed evenly throughout the egg. Yolk distribution influences the rate and location of cell division during early embryonic development. Typically, cell division proceeds more slowly in the region of the egg containing the yolk. In the large, yolky eggs of birds and reptiles, cell division takes place only in a small, yolk-free patch at the egg's surface.

Unequal distribution of yolk and other components in the egg is termed **polarity**. In most species, the egg's nucleus is located toward one end, called the **animal pole**. The animal pole typically gives rise to surface structures and the anterior end of the embryo. The opposite end of the egg, the **vegetal pole**, typically gives rise to internal structures such as the gut, along with the posterior end of the embryo. When yolk is unequally distributed in the egg cytoplasm, it is usually concentrated in the vegetal half of the egg. Egg polarity plays a role in setting the three body axes of bilaterally symmetrical animals, namely the anterior–posterior axis, the dorsal–ventral (back-front) axis, and the left–right axis **(Figure 34.7)**.

34.2a Cleavage and Gastrulation: Zygote to Multicellular Embryo

Soon after fertilization, the zygote begins a series of mitotic cleavage divisions in which cycles of DNA replication and division occur without the production of new cytoplasm. Thus, the cytoplasm of the zygote is partitioned into successively smaller cells without increasing the size or mass of the embryo **(Figure 34.8)**. In the frog *Xenopus laevis,* 12 cleavage divisions produce an embryo of about 4000 cells that collectively occupy about the same volume and mass as the original zygote.

Cleavage is the first of three major developmental stages that, with modifications, are common to the early development of most animals. **Gastrulation**, the stage following cleavage, produces an embryo with three distinct primary tissue layers. **Organogenesis** follows gastrulation and gives rise to the development of major organ systems. At the end of organogenesis, the embryo has the body organization characteristic of its species. Cell division, cell movements, and cell rearrangements occur during gastrulation and in

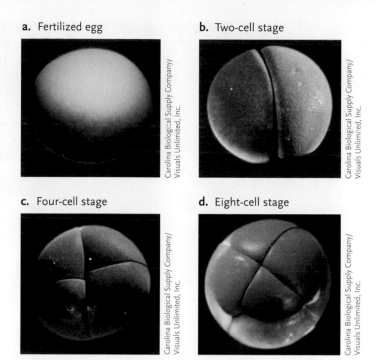

a. Fertilized egg

b. Two-cell stage

Carolina Biological Supply Company/ Visuals Unlimited, Inc.

c. Four-cell stage

d. Eight-cell stage

Carolina Biological Supply Company/ Visuals Unlimited, Inc.

Figure 34.8
The first three cleavage divisions of a frog embryo, which convert the fertilized egg into the eight-cell stage. Note that the cleavage divisions cut the volume of the fertilized egg into successively smaller cells.

organogenesis. **Figure 34.9, p. 826,** shows these stages as part of the life cycle of a frog.

In frogs, cleavage divisions form two different structures in succession. The **morula** (= mulberry) is a solid ball or layer of cells. As cleavage divisions continue, the ball or layer hollows out to form the **blastula** (*blast* = bud or offshoot; *ula* = small), the second structure in which cells, now called **blastomeres** (*mere* = part or division), enclose a fluid-filled cavity, the **blastocoel** (*coel* = hollow).

After cleavage is complete, cells of the blastula migrate and divide to produce the **gastrula** (*gaster* = gut or belly). Gastrulation, a morphogenetic process, dramatically rearranges the cells of the blastula into the three primary cell layers of the embryo: **ectoderm**, the outer layer (*ecto* = outside; *derm* = skin); **endoderm**, the inner layer (*endo* = inside); and **mesoderm** (*meso* = middle), the middle layer between ectoderm and endoderm. Gastrulation establishes the body pattern. Each tissue and organ of the adult animal originates from one of the three primary cell layers of the gastrula **(Table 34.1, p. 826).** Cell movements also contribute to the formation of the **archenteron** (*arch* = beginning; *enteron* = intestine or gut), a new cavity within the embryo that is lined with endoderm.

As the blastula develops into the gastrula, embryonic cells begin to differentiate, becoming recognizably different in biochemistry, structure, and function. The developmental potential of each cell becomes more limited than that of the zygote from which it

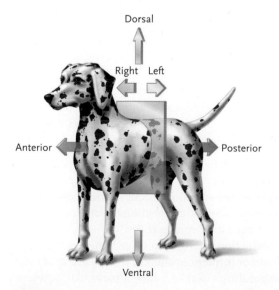

Figure 34.7
Body axes: anterior–ventral, dorsal–ventral, and left–right.

Figure 34.9
Stages of animal development shown in a frog.

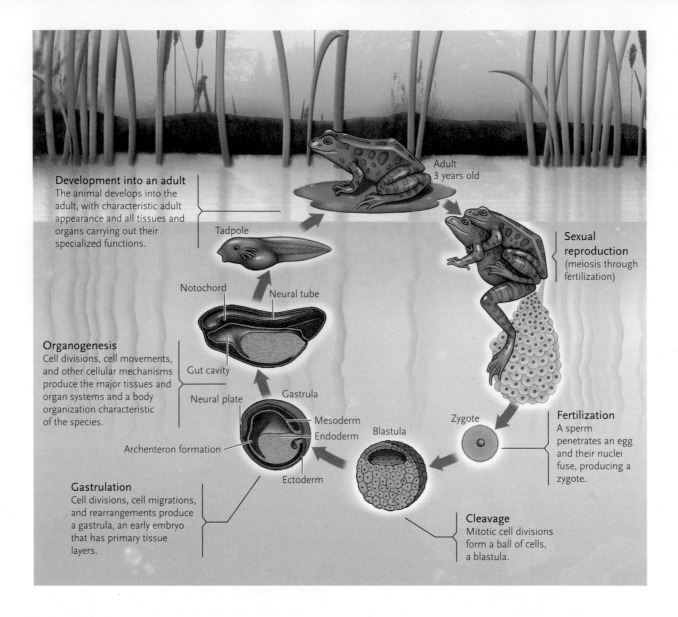

Development into an adult
The animal develops into the adult, with characteristic adult appearance and all tissues and organs carrying out their specialized functions.

Adult 3 years old

Tadpole

Sexual reproduction
(meiosis through fertilization)

Notochord

Neural tube

Organogenesis
Cell divisions, cell movements, and other cellular mechanisms produce the major tissues and organ systems and a body organization characteristic of the species.

Gut cavity

Neural plate

Gastrula

Mesoderm
Endoderm
Blastula

Zygote

Fertilization
A sperm penetrates an egg and their nuclei fuse, producing a zygote.

Archenteron formation

Ectoderm

Gastrulation
Cell divisions, cell migrations, and rearrangements produce a gastrula, an early embryo that has primary tissue layers.

Cleavage
Mitotic cell divisions form a ball of cells, a blastula.

originated. Although a fertilized egg could develop into a complete embryo, a mesoderm cell may develop into muscle or bone but does not normally develop into outside skin or brain. Scientists once thought that this restriction of developmental potential resulted because cells lost all of their genes except those required for the structure and function of the cell type they would become. However, differentiating cells each contain the complete genome of the organism, but each type of cell has a different program of gene expression.

Although development in all animals is accomplished by mechanisms under genetic control, the mechanisms are influenced to some extent by environmental factors such as temperature. The six mechanisms are as follows:

- Mitotic cells divide.
- Cells move.
- **Selective cell adhesions** occur in which cells make and break specific connections to other cells or to the extracellular matrix (ECM).
- In **induction,** one group of cells (inducing cells) causes or influences another nearby group of cells (responding cells) to follow a particular developmental pathway. The key to induction is that only certain cells can respond to the signal from the

Table 34.1	Origins of Adult Tissues and Organs in the Three Primary Tissue Layers
Primary Tissue Layer	**Adult Tissues and Organs**
Ectoderm	Skin and its elaborations, including hair, feathers, scales, and nails; nervous system, including brain, spinal cord, and peripheral nerves; lens, retina, and cornea of eye; lining of mouth and anus; sweat glands, mammary glands, adrenal medulla, and tooth enamel
Mesoderm	Muscles; most of skeletal system, including bones and cartilage; circulatory system, including heart, blood vessels, and blood cells; internal reproductive organs; kidneys and outer walls of digestive tract
Endoderm	Lining of digestive tract, liver, pancreas, lining of respiratory tract, thyroid gland, lining of urethra, and urinary bladder

inducing cells. Induction typically involves signal transduction events (see Chapter 35). Some induction events are triggered by direct cell–cell contact involving interaction between a membrane-embedded protein on the inducing cell and a receptor protein on the responding cell's surface. Others are triggered by a signal molecule released by the inducing cell that interacts with a receptor on the responding cell (e.g., paracrine regulation; see Chapter 35).

- **Determination** sets the developmental fate of a cell. Before determination, a cell has the potential to become any cell type of the adult. Afterward, the cell is committed to becoming a particular cell type. Typically, determination results from induction, although in some cases, it results from the asymmetric segregation of cellular determinants.
- **Differentiation** follows determination and involves the establishment of a cell-specific developmental program in the cells. Differentiation results in cell types with clearly defined structures and functions. These features are derived from specific patterns of gene expression in cells.

STUDY BREAK

1. What is yolk? What role does it play?
2. What mechanisms are involved in animal development from the zygote?

34.3 Major Patterns of Cleavage and Gastrulation

34.3a Sea Urchin

Cleavage divisions proceed at approximately the same rate in all regions of a sea urchin embryo **(Figure 34.10, step 1)**, reflecting uniform distribution of yolk in the egg. These divisions continue until a blastula containing about a thousand cells is formed (step 2).

Gastrulation begins at the vegetal pole of the blastula. Through induction, some cells in the middle of the vegetal pole become elongated and cylindrical, causing the region to flatten and thicken. Then some cells (primary mesenchyme; *mesen* = middle; *chyme* = juice) break loose and migrate into the blastocoel (step 3), making and breaking adhesions until eventually they attach along the ventral sides of the blastocoel. These cells form the future mesoderm (see Figure 34.10, step 7), which give rise to skeletal elements of the embryo. Next, the flattened vegetal pole of the blastula invaginates, pushing gradually into the interior (steps 4 and 5). The cells that invaginate will become endoderm cells. The inward movement, much like pushing in the side of a hollow rubber ball, generates the archenteron, a new cavity that opens through the blastopore.

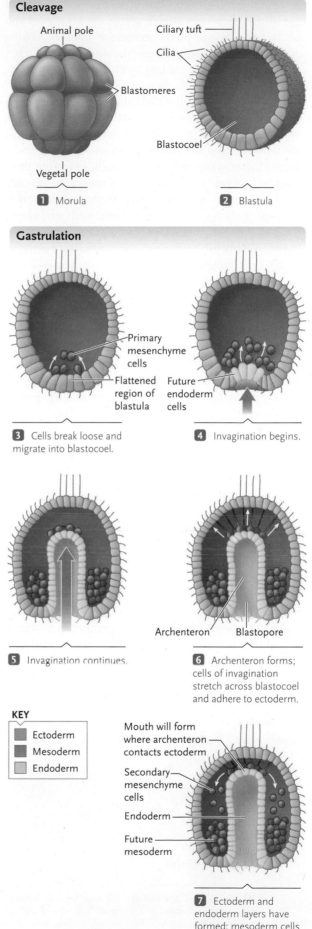

Cleavage

Animal pole

Blastomeres

Vegetal pole

1 Morula

Ciliary tuft

Cilia

Blastocoel

2 Blastula

Gastrulation

Primary mesenchyme cells

Flattened region of blastula

Future endoderm cells

3 Cells break loose and migrate into blastocoel.

4 Invagination begins.

5 Invagination continues.

Archenteron   Blastopore

6 Archenteron forms; cells of invagination stretch across blastocoel and adhere to ectoderm.

KEY

Ectoderm

Mesoderm

Endoderm

Mouth will form where archenteron contacts ectoderm

Secondary mesenchyme cells

Endoderm

Future mesoderm

7 Ectoderm and endoderm layers have formed; mesoderm cells are between them.

Figure 34.10
Cleavage and gastrulation in the sea urchin.

As the archenteron forms, extensions of cells of the invaginated layer stretch across the blastocoel and contact the inside of the ectoderm (step 6). These extensions make tight adhesions and then contract, pulling the invaginated cell layer inward with them, eliminating most of the blastocoel.

Now the embryo has two complete cell layers. The outer layer—the original blastula surface—forms embryonic ectoderm. Cells of the second, inner layer are derived from the archenteron and become endoderm. Mesodermal cells, which begin to form a third layer, are derived from the primary mesenchyme cells and from *secondary mesenchyme* cells that migrated into the space between the ectoderm and endoderm (step 7). After the formation of the three primary cell layers, cells begin to differentiate based on synthesis of different proteins in each layer.

As ectoderm, mesoderm, and endoderm layers develop, the embryo lengthens into an ellipsoidal shape, with the blastopore marking the posterior end of the embryo. From here on, further cell divisions, combined with cell movements, selective cell adhesions, induction, and differentiation, lead to differentiation of organ systems. In sea urchins and other deuterostomes, the blastopore forms the anus, and the mouth will form at the opposite, anterior end of the gut.

34.3b Amphibians

In the eggs of amphibians such as frogs, yolk is concentrated in the vegetal half, giving it a pale colour. The animal half is darkly coloured because of a layer of pigment granules just below the surface. A sperm normally fertilizes the egg in the animal half **(Figure 34.11, step 1)**. After fertilization, the pigmented layer of cytoplasm rotates toward the site of sperm entry, exposing a crescent-shaped region of underlying cytoplasm at the side opposite the point of sperm entry (step 2). This region, the **grey crescent**, establishes the dorsal–ventral axis of the embryo and marks the future dorsal side of the animal.

Normally, the first cleavage division runs perpendicular to the long axis of the grey crescent and divides the crescent equally between resulting cells (step 3). If the first two blastomeres are experimentally divided so that one does not receive grey crescent material, and the two cells are separated, the blastomere without grey crescent material divides but ends up in a disordered mass that stops developing. The blastomere receiving grey crescent produces a normal embryo. Cytoplasmic material localized in the grey crescent is essential to normal development in frog embryos.

As cleavage of the frog embryo continues, cell divisions proceed more rapidly in the animal half, producing smaller and more numerous cells there than in the yolky vegetal half. By the time cleavage has produced an embryo with 15 000 cells, the animal half has hollowed out, forming the blastula (**Figure 34.12**, step 1, and **Figure 34.13a**).

Gastrulation begins when cells from the animal pole begin to migrate across the embryo surface to reach the region derived from the grey crescent. This site is marked by a crescent-shaped depression rotated 90° clockwise and called the **dorsal lip of the blastopore** (see Figure 34.12, step 2, and **Figure 34.13b**). These cells invaginate, changing shape and pushing inward from the surface to produce the depression. The depression eventually forms a complete circle (the blastopore) after further inward movement of additional cells (see Figure 34.12, step 3, and **Figure 34.13c**).

By involution, cells migrate into the blastopore, and the pigmented cell layer of the animal half expands to cover the entire embryo surface (see Figure 34.12, step 4, and Figure 34.13c). Cells of the vegetal half are enclosed by this cell migration, becoming visible on the outside as a yolk plug in the blastopore. The blastopore gives rise to the anus.

Continuing involution moves cells into the interior and upward (see Figure 34.12, steps 3 and 4), forming two layers that line the inside top half of the embryo. Dorsal mesoderm (shown in red) is the uppermost of these induced layers. Beneath it is the endoderm (shown in yellow), containing cells originating from both the outer surface of the embryo and the yolky interior. Ectoderm (shown in blue) forms from

Figure 34.11
Rotation of the pigment layer and development of the grey crescent after fertilization in a frog egg. The grey crescent marks the site where gastrulation of the embryo will begin.

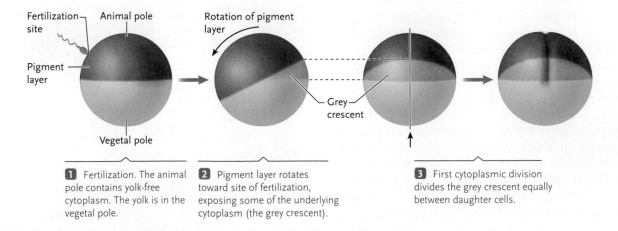

1 Fertilization. The animal pole contains yolk-free cytoplasm. The yolk is in the vegetal pole.

2 Pigment layer rotates toward site of fertilization, exposing some of the underlying cytoplasm (the grey crescent).

3 First cytoplasmic division divides the grey crescent equally between daughter cells.

Blastocoel

Cell migration

Developing archenteron

Archenteron
Endoderm — Ectoderm

Figure 34.12
Gastrulation in a frog embryo. Yolk cells are shown in paler yellow.

Dorsal lip of blastopore — Invagination

Blastocoel displaced

Developing ventral mesoderm — Yolk plug

1 Blastula

2 Gastrulation begins; cells from the animal pole reach the dorsal lip of the blastopore and invaginate.

3 Cells migrate into the blastopore (involution); pigmented cells of the animal half expand over the entire embryo surface.

4 Movement of animal half cells encloses the vegetal half cells, which are seen as a yolk plug.

KEY

- ☐ Ectoderm
- ☐ Mesoderm
- ☐ Endoderm

pigmented cells remaining at the surface of the embryo. Induction of the ventral mesoderm begins near the vegetal pole.

As mesoderm and endoderm form, the depression created by inward cell movements gradually deepens and extends inward as the archenteron (see Figure 34.12, steps 3 and 4), displacing the blastocoel. Cells of the three primary cell layers continue to increase in number by further migrations and divisions as development proceeds.

The major induction centre during frog gastrulation is the dorsal lip of the blastopore. If cells are removed from the dorsal lip and transplanted elsewhere in the egg, they form a second blastopore (and a second embryo).

34.3c Birds

Gastrulation in amniotes (see Chapter 26) such as birds and reptiles is modified by the distribution of the

yolk, which occupies almost the entire volume of the egg. A thin layer of cytoplasm at the egg's surface gives rise to primary tissues of the embryo. Although mammalian eggs have relatively little yolk, gastrulation in them follows a similar pattern.

Early cleavage divisions in birds produce the **blastodisc**, a thin layer of cells at the yolk's surface (**Figure 34.14, p. 830,** step 1). The complete blastodisc is a layer with about 20 000 cells. Cells of the blastodisc then separate into two layers, the **epiblast** (top layer) and the **hypoblast** (bottom layer). The blastocoel is the flattened cavity between them (step 2).

Gastrulation begins as cells in the epiblast stream toward the midline of the blastodisc, thickening it in this region. The thickened layer (or **primitive streak**) is first evident in the posterior end of the embryo and extends toward the anterior end as more cells of the epiblast (see Figure 34.14, p. 830) move into it (step 3). A thickening at the anterior end of the primitive streak (the **primitive knot**) is the functional equivalent of the

a. Blastula　　　　**b.** Early gastrulation　　　　**c.** Late gastrulation

Dorsal lip of blastopore

Blastopore with yolk plug in centre

Figure 34.13
Photomicrographs of a frog embryo.
(a) Blastula.
(b) Early gastrulation and the formation of the dorsal lip of the blastopore.
(c) Late gastrulation, showing the completed blastopore, closed by the yolk plug.

Peter B. Armstrong, University of California, Davis.

Figure 34.14
Gastrulation in a bird embryo.

Diagram labels and step annotations (top to bottom):

Blastodisc
Yolk

1 Cleavage divisions form blastodisc at top of yolk.

Blastocoel — Epiblast
Hypoblast

2 Blastodisc separates into two layers. Epiblast gives rise to primary tissue layers of embryo. Hypoblast cells form germ cells of the embryo and contribute to the yolk sac.

Primitive streak

3 Epiblast cells migrate from the sides toward the midline, forming a thickened layer, the primitive streak.

Primitive groove

Hypoblast — Endoderm

4 Cells migrating downward from the epiblast into the interior of the embryo form the mesoderm (red) and endoderm (yellow); cells remaining at the surface form the ectoderm.

Ectoderm
Mesoderm
Remaining hypoblast — Endoderm

Coelomic cavity

5 Ectoderm and mesoderm move downward around the sides of the endoderm to form the primitive streak. Mesoderm separates into two layers, forming the coelom.

Archenteron
Coelom

---

amphibian dorsal lip of the blastopore. The primitive streak initially marks the future posterior end of the embryo, and by the time it has elongated fully, it has established the left and right sides of the embryo. The streak forms on what will become the dorsal side of the embryo, with the ventral side below.

As the primitive streak forms, its midline sinks, forming the **primitive groove**, a conduit for migrating cells to move into the blastocoel. Epiblasts are the first cells to migrate through the primitive groove (see Figure 34.14, step 4) and produce the endoderm. Mesoderm is formed from cells migrating laterally between the epiblast and the endoderm. Epiblast cells remaining at the surface of the blastodisc form ectoderm (step 4).

In the bird embryo, all primary tissue layers arise from the epiblast. Only a few of the hypoblast cells—near the posterior end of the embryo—contribute directly to the embryo. These form **germ cells** that later migrate to developing gonads, founding cell lines leading to eggs and sperm (see Chapter 8).

Initially, ectoderm, mesoderm, and endoderm are located in three more or less horizontal layers in the chick embryo. During gastrulation, the endoderm pushes upward along its midline, and its left and right sides fold downward, forming a tube that is oriented parallel to the primitive streak (see Figure 34.14, step 5). The archenteron is the central cavity of the tube, the primitive gut. Mesoderm separates into two layers, forming the coelom, a fluid-filled body cavity lined with mesoderm. These movements complete the formation of the gastrula.

34.3d Extra-embryonic Membranes: Amnion, Chorion, Allantois

Each primary tissue layer of a bird embryo extends outside the embryo to form **extra-embryonic membranes (Figure 34.15)** that conduct nutrients from yolk to embryo, exchange gases with the environment outside the egg, or store metabolic wastes removed from the embryo. The **yolk sac** is an extension of mesoderm and endoderm enclosing the yolk. Although the yolk sac remains connected to the gut of the embryo by a stalk, yolk does not directly enter the embryo by this route. Rather, it is absorbed by blood in vessels in the membrane, which then transport the nutrients to the embryo.

The **chorion**, produced from ectoderm and mesoderm, completely surrounds the embryo and yolk sac and lines the inside of the shell. The chorion exchanges oxygen and carbon dioxide with the environment through the egg's shell. The **amnion** closes over the embryo to form the **amniotic cavity**. Cells of the amnion secrete **amniotic fluid** into the cavity, which bathes the embryo and provides an aquatic environment in which it can develop. Reptilian and mammalian embryos are also surrounded by an amnion and amniotic fluid. Providing the embryo with an

Embryo **Amnion** Amniotic cavity

Allantois

Chorion

Shell

Albumin

Yolk

Yolk sac

Allantois

Figure 34.15
The four extra-embryonic membranes in a bird embryo (in bold).

aquatic environment is presumed to have been a key factor in the evolution of fully terrestrial vertebrates, the **Amniota.**

The **allantoic membrane** forms from mesoderm and endoderm that has bulged outward from the gut. It encloses the allantois, a sac that closely lines the chorion and fills much of the space between the chorion and the yolk sac. The **allantois** stores nitrogenous wastes (primarily uric acid) removed from the embryo. The part of the allantoic membrane lining the chorion forms a rich bed of capillaries connected to the embryo by arteries and veins. This circulatory system delivers carbon dioxide to the chorion and picks up the oxygen that is absorbed through the shell and chorion. At hatching, part of the allantoic membrane becomes the lining of the bladder.

STUDY BREAK

1. What are the main developmental differences between protostomes and deuterostomes?
2. What are important differences between typical patterns of development in birds and in mammals?
3. What are the features of an amniote egg? What is its evolutionary significance?

34.4 Organogenesis: Gastrulation to Adult Body Structures

Following gastrulation, organogenesis gives rise to the body organization characteristic of the species. Organogenesis involves the same mechanisms used in gastrulation, namely cell division, cell movements,

selective cell adhesion, induction, and differentiation. Organogenesis also involves an additional mechanism, **apoptosis**, in which certain cells are programmed to die (see Chapter 8). To illustrate how cellular mechanisms of development interact in organogenesis, we follow the formation of major organ systems in the bird embryo. Then we describe the generation of one organ, the eye, which follows a pathway typical of eye development in all vertebrates.

34.4a Ectoderm and the Nervous System: Neural Tube and Neural Crest Cells

In vertebrates, organogenesis begins with **neurulation,** which is the development of nervous tissue from ectoderm. As a preliminary to neurulation, cells of the mesoderm form the notochord, a solid rod of tissue extending the length of the embryo under the dorsal ectoderm. Notochord cells carry out a major induction, causing the overlying ectoderm to form the neural plate, a thickened and flattened longitudinal band of cells (**Figure 34.16, p. 832,** steps 1 and 2). The neural plate does not form if the notochord is removed.

Once induced, the neural plate sinks downward along its midline (steps 2 and 3), creating a deep longitudinal groove and ridges (neural crests) that rise along the sides of the neural plate. The neural tube forms when the neural crests move together and close over the centre of the groove along the length of the developing embryo (steps 4 and 5). The neural tube then pinches off from the overlying ectoderm, which closes over the tube (step 6). The central nervous system, including the brain and spinal cord, develops directly from the neural tube.

During formation of the neural tube, **neural crest** cells (see Figure 34.16, p. 832) migrate into the mesoderm and follow specific routes to reach distant points in the developing embryo, where they contribute to the formation of a variety of organ systems. Some cells develop into cranial nerves in the head, whereas others contribute to the bones of the inner ear and skull, cartilage of facial structures, and teeth. Still others form ganglia of the autonomic nervous system, peripheral nerves leading from the spinal cord to body structures, and nerves of the developing gut. Neural crest cells also move to the skin, where they form pigment cells, and to the adrenal glands, where they form the medulla of the kidney. The migration of neural crest cells contributes to development in all vertebrates (see "People behind Biology," Box 34.2, p. 833).

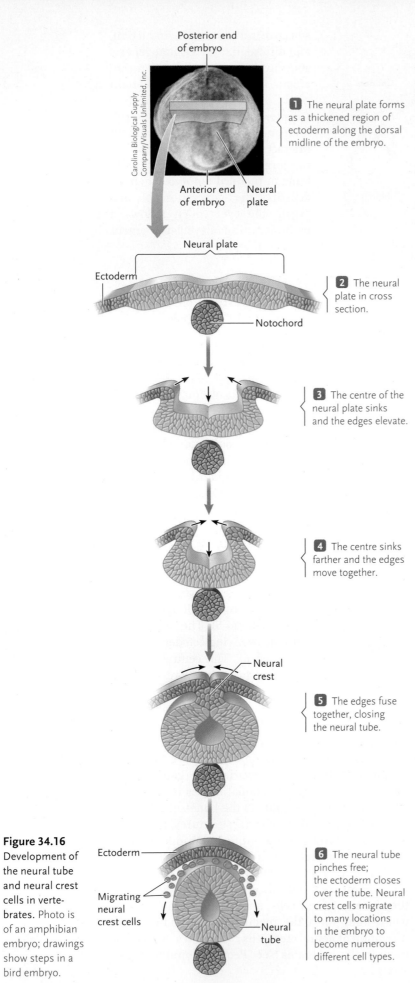

1 The neural plate forms as a thickened region of ectoderm along the dorsal midline of the embryo.

Posterior end of embryo

Anterior end of embryo

Neural plate

Neural plate

Ectoderm

Notochord

2 The neural plate in cross section.

3 The centre of the neural plate sinks and the edges elevate.

4 The centre sinks farther and the edges move together.

Neural crest

5 The edges fuse together, closing the neural tube.

Ectoderm

Migrating neural crest cells

Neural tube

6 The neural tube pinches free; the ectoderm closes over the tube. Neural crest cells migrate to many locations in the embryo to become numerous different cell types.

Figure 34.16
Development of the neural tube and neural crest cells in vertebrates. Photo is of an amphibian embryo; drawings show steps in a bird embryo.

Other structures differentiate in the embryo while the neural tube is forming. On each side of the notochord, mesoderm separates into somites, blocks of cells spaced one after the other **(Figure 34.17)**. Somites give rise to the vertebral column, ribs, repeating sets of muscles associated with the ribs and vertebral column, and limb muscles. Mesoderm outside the somites extends around the primitive gut (lateral mesoderm in Figure 34.17) and splits into two layers, one covering the surface of the gut and the other lining the body wall. The space between the layers is the adult coelom.

34.4b Development of the Eye: Interactions between Cells

Eyes develop by the same basic five-step pathway in all vertebrates **(Figure 34.18)**. The brain forms at the anterior end of the neural tube from a cluster of hollow vesicles that swell outward from the neural tube (see Figure 34.18, step 1). Each of the two optic vesicles develops into an eye. Figure 34.18 depicts the development of a frog eye; the development of the rest of the brain is not shown.

The optic vesicles grow outward until they contact the overlying ectoderm, inducing a series of developmental responses in both tissues. The optic cup, a

a. Somites, derived from mesoderm

KEY

| | Ectoderm |
| | Mesoderm |

Ectoderm

Coelom

Notochord

Lateral mesoderm

Neural tube

Somites

b. 45-hour chick embryo

Figure 34.17
Later development of the mesoderm. **(a)** Somites develop into segmented structures such as the vertebrae, the ribs, and the musculature between the ribs. The lateral mesoderm gives rise to other structures, such as the heart and blood vessels and the linings of internal body cavities. **(b)** The somites in a 45-hour chick embryo.

PEOPLE BEHIND BIOLOGY 34.2
Brian K. Hall, Dalhousie University

Brian K. Hall, a professor of biology at Dalhousie University in Halifax, Nova Scotia, and his students study developmental patterns in the embryos of fishes, frogs, and chicks, in particular the development of the skeleton. Considerable work has focused on the embryonic origins of the cells that form the cartilages of the head and shows that skeletal elements in vertebrates often originate in the developing nervous system, specifically in neural crest cells. The research provides insight into the evolution of structures by showing how they are derived and from where (see Chapter 17).

Honours thesis students working with Hall have studied a range of topics, from looking at asymmetry between the left and right limbs of

mice to the impact of thyroxine on metamorphosis in a South African frog (*Hymenochirus*). Other research on this frog has explored its capacity to regenerate hindlimbs and the patterns of migration of neural crest cells and pigment cells. This work makes Hall one of the pioneers of evolutionary developmental biology, or "evo-devo," which is really an extension of traditional developmental biology.

His work on development has led Hall to consider how biologists use words to describe what they see in the natural world. For example, how does one distinguish *rudimentary* and *vestigial* features in animals? It is well known that snakes evolved from limbed ancestors and that whales evolved from ancestors that had teeth.

Studies on the development of snakes clearly show that they have rudimentary limbs, partly formed or incomplete transformations of developing features. Vestiges, evolutionary remnants of ancestral features, also occur in animals. The tooth buds (fetal teeth) of baleen whales are examples of vestigial features, as are the rudimentary clavicles that appear in the developing embryos of toothed whales. Once again, the problem of imposing specific terms and definitions on a natural continuum can make the study of biology unnecessarily complex.

Hall's detailed studies of development make it easier to understand the patterns that emerge, which also means appreciating the shortcomings of the labels we use.

double-walled structure, forms when the outer surface of the optic vesicle thickens and flattens at the region of contact and then pushes inward. The optic cup ultimately becomes the retina. The lens forms from the lens placode, a disclike swelling that arises when the optic cup induces thickening of overlying ectoderm (step 2). The centre of the lens placode sinks inward toward the optic cup, and its edges eventually fuse together, forming the lens vesicle, a ball of cells (step 3).

The developing lens cells begin to synthesize crystallin, a fibrous protein that collects into clear, glassy

deposits. Lens cells finally lose their nuclei and form the elastic, crystal-clear lens.

As the lens develops, it contacts the overlying ectoderm that has closed over it. In response, the ectoderm cells form the cornea by losing their pigment granules and becoming clear. Eventually, the developing cornea joins with the edges of the optic cup to complete the primary structure of the eye (step 4). Other cells contribute to accessory structures of the eye. Mesoderm and neural crest cells contribute to reinforcing tissues in the wall of the eye and the

1 The expanding optic vesicle contacts the overlying ectoderm; its outer wall thickens.

2 The outer wall of the optic vesicle pushes inward, forming the optic cup; the overlying ectoderm thickens to form the lens placode.

3 As the optic cup deepens, the lens placode pushes inward and begins to pinch off, forming the lens vesicle.

4 The ectoderm closes over the lens vesicle and develops into the cornea.

5 Fully developed structures of the vertebrate eye (human eye shown).

Figure 34.18
Stages in the development of the vertebrate eye from the optic vesicle of the brain and the overlying ectoderm.

muscles that move the eye. Figure 34.18, step 5, shows a fully developed vertebrate eye.

Initial induction by optic vesicles is necessary for the development of the eye. If an optic vesicle is removed before lens formation, ectoderm fails to develop into the lens placode and vesicle. Moreover, placing a removed optic vesicle under the ectoderm in other regions of the head causes a lens to form in the new location. If ectoderm over an optic vesicle is removed and ectoderm from elsewhere in the embryo is grafted in its place, a normal lens develops in the grafted ectoderm. This occurs even though in its former location it would not differentiate into lens tissue.

Eye development also demonstrates differentiation. Ectoderm cells induced to form the lens synthesize crystallin. In other locations, ectoderm cells synthesize mainly keratin, a different protein. Keratin is a component of surface structures such as skin, hair, feathers, scales, and horns. In response to induction by the optic vesicle, genes of ectoderm cells coding for crystallin are activated, but genes coding for keratin are not.

34.4c Apoptosis: Programmed Cell Death

Induction and differentiation build complex, specialized organs from three fundamental tissue types. Apoptosis (see Chapter 8), programmed cell death, complements these processes by removing tissues needed during development but not present in the fully formed organ. Apoptosis plays an important role in the development of both invertebrates and vertebrates. The development of wings and hind feet in short-tailed fruit bats (*Carollia perspicillata*) **(Figure 34.19)** demonstrates how apoptosis in the hind limbs leads to "normal" mammalian feet, but wings on the forelimbs.

STUDY BREAK

1. What processes and embryonic layers are involved in the development of the eye?
2. How does the neural tube develop?

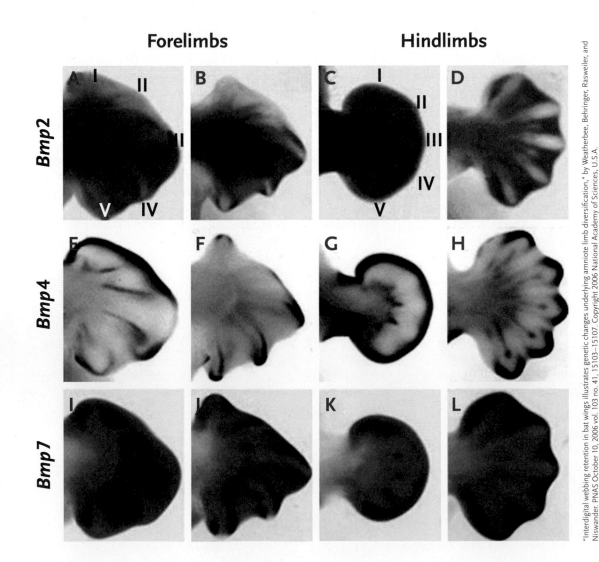

Forelimbs **Hindlimbs**

Figure 34.19
Bone morphogenetic proteins (Bmps) trigger apoptosis of interdigital mesenchyme.
In short-tailed fruit bats (*Carollia perspicillata*), apoptosis occurs in the hind feet where there are no antagonists to Bmps. Apoptosis does not occur in the forelimbs of the bats because antagonists to Bmps inhibit apoptosis. Compared here are expressions of Bmps inhibitors in the forelimbs and hind feet of the bats. Roman numerals indicate digit numbers.

"Interdigital webbing retention in bat wings illustrates genetic changes underlying amniote limb diversification," by Weatherbee, Behringer, Rasweiler, and Niswander. PNAS October 10, 2006 vol. 103 no. 41, 15103–15107. Copyright 2006 National Academy of Sciences, U.S.A.

34.5 Embryonic Development of Humans and Other Mammals

The embryonic development of humans is representative of placental mammals. In the uterus, the embryo is nourished by the placenta, which supplies oxygen and nutrients to the embryo and carries carbon dioxide and nitrogenous wastes away from it.

Pregnancy or gestation, the period of mammalian *in utero* development, varies among species. Larger mammals bearing larger young tend to have longer gestation periods. From fertilization to birth, pregnancy lasts about 600 days in elephants, about 365 days in blue whales, and 21 days in hamsters.

In humans, gestation takes an average of 266 days, about 38 weeks. Because the date of fertilization can be difficult to establish, human gestation is usually calculated from the beginning of the menstrual cycle in which fertilization took place. The nine-month period is divided into three **trimesters**, each three months long.

Major developmental events in human gestation—cleavage, gastrulation, and organogenesis—take place during the first trimester. By week 4, the embryo's heart is beating, and by the end of week 8, the major organs and organ systems have formed. From this point until birth, the developing human is called a **fetus.** Only 5 cm long by the end of the first trimester, the fetus grows during the second and third trimesters to an average length of 50 cm and an average mass of 3.5 kg.

Cleavage occurs during the passage of the developing embryo down the fallopian tube and while it is still enclosed in the zona pellucida, the original coat of the egg **(Figure 34.20).**

By day 4, the morula, a ball of 16 to 32 cells, has been produced. By the time the endometrium (uterine lining) is ready for implantation (about seven days after ovulation), the morula has reached the uterus and, through further cell divisions and differentiation, has become a blastocyst. The **blastocyst** is a hollow ball of about 120 cells in a single layer, with a fluid-filled cavity, the blastocoel, which has a dense mass of cells localized on one side. This **inner cell mass** will become the embryo itself, whereas the outer single layer of cells of the blastocyst, the **trophoblast**, will become tissues that support development of the embryo in the uterus.

When ready to implant, the blastocyst breaks out of the zona pellucida and sticks to the endometrium on its inner cell mass side **(Figure 34.21a, p. 836).** Implantation begins when the trophoblast cells that overlie the inner cell mass secrete proteases that digest pathways between endometrial cells. Dividing trophoblast cells fill in the digested spaces, appearing as fingerlike projections into the endometrium. These cells continue to digest nutrient-rich endometrial cells, producing a hole in the endometrium for the blastocyst and releasing nutrients for the

Figure 34.20
Early stages in the development of the human embryo.

developing embryo after it has consumed the small amount of yolk contained in egg cytoplasm. While the blastocyst burrows into the endometrium, the inner cell mass separates into the **embryonic disc**, which consists of two distinct cell layers (see Figure 34.21a, p. 836). The epiblast, the layer farther from the blastocoel, gives rise to the embryo proper. The hypoblast, the layer nearer the blastocoel, generates part of the extra-embryonic membranes. When implantation is complete, the blastocyst has completely burrowed into the endometrium and is covered by a layer of endometrial cells **(Figure 34.21b, p. 836).**

Gastrulation proceeds as in birds (see Figure 34.14), with the formation of a primitive streak in the epiblast. Soon after the inner cell mass separates into epiblast and hypoblast, a layer of cells separates from the epiblast along its top margin (see Figure 34.21b). The amniotic cavity is the fluid-filled space created by the separation. The layer of cells forming its roof becomes the amnion, which expands until it completely surrounds the embryo, suspending it in amniotic fluid.

Also as in birds, the hypoblast develops into the yolk sac. In mammals, the mesoderm of the yolk sac gives rise to the blood vessels in the embryonic portion of the placenta. The allantois stores nitrogenous wastes in birds, but it is a small, vestigial sac in human embryos because most nitrogenous wastes are transferred across the placenta to the mother via blood vessels in the placenta and the umbilical cord.

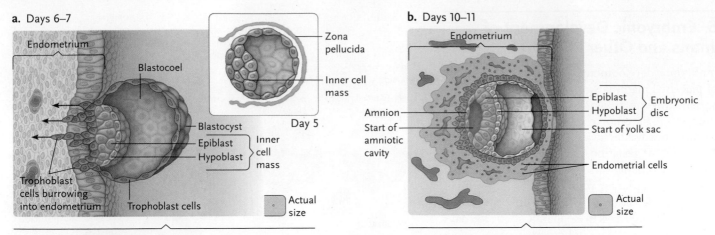

a. Days 6–7

Endometrium

Blastocoel

Blastocyst

Epiblast

Hypoblast — Inner cell mass

Trophoblast cells burrowing into endometrium

Trophoblast cells

Zona pellucida

Inner cell mass

Day 5

Actual size

Surface cells of the blastocyst attach to the endometrium and start to burrow into it. Implantation is under way.

b. Days 10–11

Endometrium

Amnion

Start of amniotic cavity

Epiblast

Hypoblast — Embryonic disc

Start of yolk sac

Endometrial cells

Actual size

A layer of epiblast cells separates, producing the amniotic cavity. The cells above the cavity become the amnion, which eventually surrounds the embryo. The hypoblast begins to form around the yolk sac.

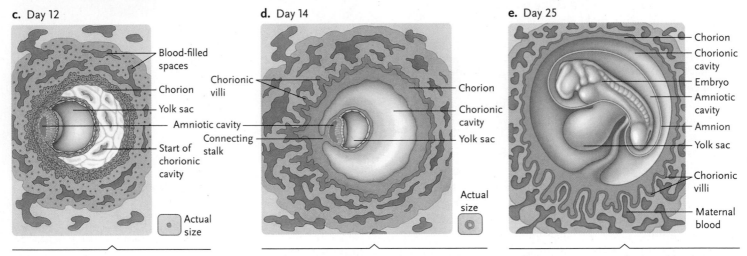

c. Day 12

Blood-filled spaces

Chorion

Yolk sac

Amniotic cavity

Start of chorionic cavity

Actual size

Blood-filled spaces form in maternal tissue. The chorion forms, derived from trophoblast cells, and encloses the chorionic cavity.

d. Day 14

Chorionic villi

Chorion

Chorionic cavity

Yolk sac

Connecting stalk

Actual size

A connecting stalk has formed between the embryonic disc and chorion. Chorionic villi, which will be features of a placenta, start to form.

e. Day 25

Chorion

Chorionic cavity

Embryo

Amniotic cavity

Amnion

Yolk sac

Chorionic villi

Maternal blood

The chorion continues to grow into the endometrium, producing the chorionic villi. The chorion growth stimulates blood vessels of the endometrium to grow into the maternal circulation of the placenta.

f. Day 45

Chorion

Amnion

Amniotic cavity

Umbilical cord

Umbilical arteries and veins

Placenta

Blood circulation has been established through the umbilical cord to the placenta.

Maternal circulation

Maternal blood vessels

Movement of solutes to and from maternal blood vessels (arrows)

Tissues of uterus

Embryonic circulation

Umbilical vein

Umbilical arteries

Umbilical cord

Blood-filled space between villi

Fused amniotic and chorionic membranes

Chorionic villus

Figure 34.21

Implantation of a human blastocyst in the endometrium of the uterus and the establishment of the placenta.

While the amnion is expanding around the embryo, blood-filled spaces form in maternal tissue, and trophoblast cells grow rapidly around both the embryo and the amnion to form the chorion **(Figure 34.21c),** the membrane that forms most of the embryonic portion of the placenta. Next, a connecting stalk forms between the embryonic disc and the chorion, which begins to grow into the endometrium as fingerlike extensions called **chorionic villi** (singular, villus) **(Figure 34.21d).** Chorionic villi increase the surface area of the chorion. The placenta forms in the area where these villi grow into the endometrium. As the chorion develops, mesodermal cells of the yolk sac grow into it and form a rich network of blood vessels, the embryonic circulation of the placenta. At the same time, the expanding chorion stimulates the blood vessels of the endometrium to grow into the maternal circulation of the placenta **(Figure 34.21e).**

Within the placenta of humans, apes, monkeys, and rodents, the maternal circulation opens into spaces where maternal blood directly bathes capillaries coming to the placenta from the embryo **(Figure 34.21f).** (Other mammals have different types of placentas.) Embryonic circulation remains closed so that the embryonic blood and the maternal blood do not mix directly. This isolation prevents the mother from developing an immune reaction against cells of the embryo, which may be recognized as foreign. Eventually, the placenta and its blood circulation grow to cover about a quarter of the inner surface of the enlarged uterus and reach the size of a dinner plate.

When the amnion forms (see Figure 34.21e), the embryo remains connected to the developing placenta through the **umbilicus,** a cord of tissue. Blood vessels in the umbilical cord conduct blood between the embryo and the placenta (see Figure 34.21f, inset). Within the placenta, nutrients and oxygen pass from the mother's circulation into the circulation of the embryo. Besides nutrients and oxygen, many other substances taken in by the mother, such as alcohol, caffeine, drugs, pesticide residues, and toxins in smog and cigarette smoke, can pass from mother to embryo. Carbon dioxide and nitrogenous wastes pass from the embryo to the mother and are disposed of by the mother's lungs and kidneys.

Cells from the embryonic portion of the placenta or from the amniotic fluid are derived from the embryo. To test for the presence of genetic diseases such as cystic fibrosis or Down syndrome, these cells can be obtained by chorionic villus sampling or by amniocentesis (*centesis* = puncture, referring to the use of a needle, which is pushed through the abdominal wall to obtain fluid from the amniotic cavity). Chorionic villus sampling can be carried out as early as the eighth week of pregnancy, compared with 14 weeks for amniocentesis.

34.5a Birth: The Fetus Leaves the Mother

By the end of its fourth week, a human embryo is 3 to 5 mm long, 250 to 500 times the size of the zygote **(Figure 34.22a).** It has a tail and gill arches,

a. Week 4   **b.** Weeks 5–6   **c.** Week 8   **d.** Week 16

Yolk sac
Connecting stalk
Embryo
Pharyngeal arches

Placenta

Week 16	
Length: 16 cm	
Mass: 200	

Week 29	
Length: 27.5 cm	
Mass: 1300	

Week 38 (full term)	
Length: 50 cm	
Mass: 3400	

Lennart Nilsson/SCANPIX

Figure 34.22
The human embryo at various stages of development, beginning at week 4. The chorion has been moved aside to reveal the embryo in the amnion at week 8 and week 16. By week 16, movements begin as nerves make functional connections with the forming muscles.

embryonic features of all vertebrates (see Chapter 26). Gill arches contribute to the formation of the face, neck, mouth, nasal cavities, larynx, and pharynx. After five to six weeks, most of the tail has disappeared, and the embryo begins to be a recognizable human form **(Figure 34.22b, p. 837)**. At eight weeks, the embryo, now a fetus, is about 2.5 cm long **(Figure 34.22c, p. 837)**. Its organ systems have formed, and its limbs, with fingers or toes at their ends, have developed.

After about 38 weeks, fetal growth comes to a close, the cervix of the uterus softens, and the fetus typically turns so that its head is downward, pressed against the cervix. At this time, a steep rise in levels of estrogen secreted by the placenta cause uterine cells to express the gene for the receptor of the hormone *oxytocin* (secreted by the pituitary). Receptors become inserted into the plasma membranes of uterine cells. Oxytocin binds to its receptors, triggering contractions of smooth muscle cells of the uterine wall, beginning the rhythmic contractions of labour. These contractions mark the beginning of the three steps culminating in birth or **parturition** (*parturire* = to be in labour).

Contractions push the fetus against the cervix and stretch its walls **(Figure 34.23,** step 1). In response, stretch receptors in the walls send nerve signals to the hypothalamus, which responds by stimulating the pituitary to secrete more oxytocin. Oxytocin stimulates more forceful contractions of the uterus, pressing the fetus more strongly against the cervix and further stretching its walls. The positive feedback cycle continues, steadily increasing the strength of the uterine contractions.

As the contractions force the head of the fetus through the cervix (step 2), the amniotic membrane bursts, releasing the amniotic fluid. Usually after 12 to 15 hours from the onset of uterine contractions, the head passes entirely through the cervix. Once the head is through, the rest of the body follows quickly and the entire fetus is forced out through the vagina, still connected to the placenta by the umbilical cord (step 3).

After the baby takes its first breath, the umbilical cord is cut and tied off by the birth attendant. Uterine contractions continue expelling the placenta and any remnants of the umbilical cord and embryonic membranes as the afterbirth, usually within 15 to 60 minutes after the infant's birth. The short length of umbilical cord still attached to the infant dries and shrivels within a few days. Eventually, it separates entirely and leaves a scar, the umbilicus or navel, to mark its former site of attachment during embryonic development. Immediately after birth, some mammals (e.g., *Gazella* species) can stand and are soon able to run. The newborns of these precocial species contrast with those of altricial species, which are immobile and helpless for some considerable time after birth. The same terms, *precocial* and *altricial*, also apply to other animals.

Many people believe that all mammals give birth to live young. In reality, mammals such as the duck-billed platypus and spiny anteater lay eggs. These mammals are the living representatives of an ancient group of mammals, the monotremes. Although they lay eggs, female platypuses and spiny anteaters feed their young milk like other mammals do.

34.5b Milk: Food for the Young

Before birth, estrogen and progesterone secreted by the placenta stimulate the growth of the mammary glands in the mother's breasts. But high levels of these hormones prevent mammary glands from

Figure 34.23
Birth of the fetus. Hormonal events of birth are at the top, and physical events are at the bottom.

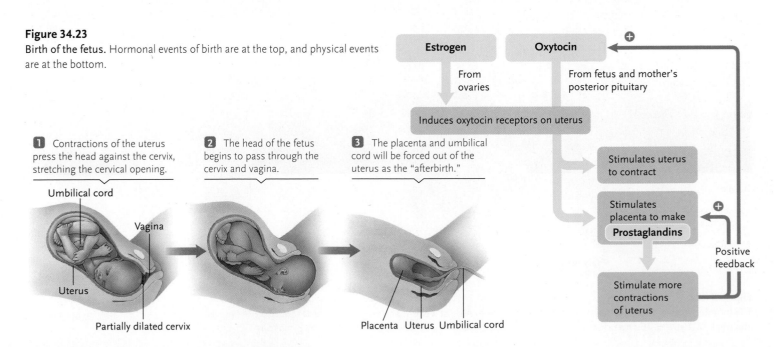

1 Contractions of the uterus press the head against the cervix, stretching the cervical opening.

2 The head of the fetus begins to pass through the cervix and vagina.

3 The placenta and umbilical cord will be forced out of the uterus as the "afterbirth."

Umbilical cord

Vagina

Uterus

Partially dilated cervix

Placenta Uterus Umbilical cord

Estrogen

Oxytocin

From ovaries

From fetus and mother's posterior pituitary

Induces oxytocin receptors on uterus

Stimulates uterus to contract

Stimulates placenta to make **Prostaglandins**

Stimulate more contractions of uterus

Positive feedback

responding to **prolactin**, the hormone secreted by the pituitary that stimulates the glands to produce milk. After birth and the release of the placenta, levels of estrogen and progesterone in the mother's bloodstream fall steeply, and the breasts begin to produce milk (stimulated by prolactin) and secrete it (stimulated by oxytocin).

Continued milk secretion depends on whether the infant suckles. Stimulation of the nipples sends nerve impulses to the hypothalamus, which responds by signalling the pituitary to release a burst of prolactin and oxytocin. Hormonal stimulation of milk production and secretion continues as long as the infant is breast-fed.

34.5c Gonadal Development: The Gender of the Fetus

Gonads and their ducts begin to develop in the fetus during week 4 of gestation. Until week 7, male and female embryos have the same set of internal structures derived from mesoderm, including a pair of gonads **(Figure 34.24a)**. Each gonad is associated with two primitive ducts, the **Wolffian duct** and the **Müllerian duct**, that lead to a cloaca. These internal structures are **bipotential** because they can develop into either male or female sexual organs.

The presence or absence of a Y chromosome determines whether the internal structures develop into male or female sexual organs. In a fetus with an XY combination of sex chromosomes, *SRY* (the sex-determining region of the Y), a single gene on the Y chromosome, becomes active in week 7. The protein encoded by *SRY* induces a molecular switch that causes primitive gonads to develop into testes. Fetal testes secrete two hormones, testosterone and the **anti-Müllerian hormone** (*AMH*). Testosterone stimulates development of Wolffian ducts into a male reproductive tract, including the epididymis, vas deferens, and seminal vesicles **(Figure 34.24b)**. *AMH* causes the Müllerian ducts to degenerate and disappear. Testosterone also stimulates development of male genitalia.

In a fetus with XX chromosomes, no *SRY* protein is produced. The primitive gonads, under the influence of estrogens and progesterone secreted by the placenta, develop into ovaries. Müllerian ducts develop into oviducts, the uterus, and part of the vagina, and the Wolffian ducts degenerate and disappear **(Figure 34.24c)**. Female sex hormones also stimulate the development of the external female genitalia (see "Hormones and External Genitalia," Box 34.3, p. 840).

34.5d Further Development

Once fetal development is over, the newborn animal follows a prescribed course of further growth and

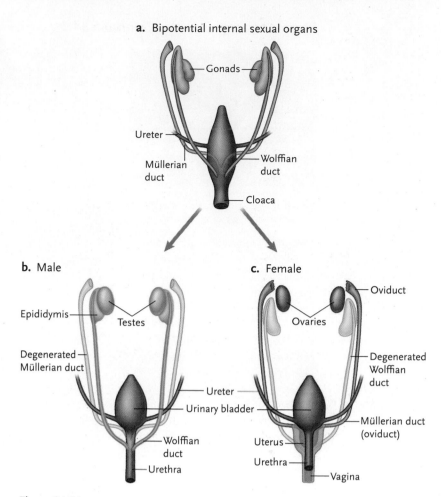

Figure 34.24

Development of the internal sexual organs of males and females from common bipotential origins.

development leading to the mature adult. In humans, internal and external sexual organs mature and secondary sexual characteristics appear at puberty (see Figure 17.22). Similar changes occur in most mammals.

There are many examples among different animal groups of developmental changes that take place after hatching or birth. In some cases, offspring hatch in forms distinctly different in structure from the adult. Examples among invertebrates include insects such as *Drosophila* and butterflies, in which eggs hatch to produce larvae that undergo metamorphosis into adults. Some frogs hatch as tadpoles, which undergo metamorphosis to produce adults.

STUDY BREAK

1. Define the terms *blastocyst, chorionic villi,* and *parturition.*
2. What is a placenta? Name some animals with placentas.
3. What is *SRY*? What role does it play?

FIGURE 1

Crocuta crocuta, *a spotted hyena.*

Many Africans believe that spotted hyenas (*Crocuta crocuta*, **Figure 1**) are hermaphroditic because the females have external genitalia resembling those of the males. Specifically, the clitoris is peniform, and there is a pseudoscrotum **(Figure 2)**. The combined effect means that anyone looking at a spotted hyena easily confuses males and females. Confusion turns to puzzlement when the apparent male is obviously lactating, nursing young. Spotted hyenas are not hermaphroditic. Males mate with females, and fertilized eggs develop into fetuses that are born as in other placental mammals.

How do females come to look like males? In mammals, the neutral condition for genitalia is the arrangement typical of females. The derived condition is what we associate with males. Genetically, female embryos exposed to testosterone during gestation develop malelike genitalia. Blood samples obtained from pregnant female spotted hyenas had relatively high levels of circulating testosterone, 5α-dihydrotestosterone, and androstenedione, albeit not as high as in males. Male and female fetuses experience the same levels of maternal androgens; therefore, females have malelike genitalia.

What selective advantage would female spotted hyenas gain from looking like males? Spotted hyenas are social animals that live in clans. As adults, females are larger and more aggressive than males. During greeting ceremonies, when members of a clan meet after a separation, individuals

Biology of reproduction by Society for the Study of Reproduction. Copyright 2002 Reproduced with permission of SOCIETY FOR THE STUDY OF REPRODUCTION in the format Textbook via Copyright Clearance Center.

FIGURE 3

*In their external genitalia, specifically their clitorises, **(c)** subadult female fossas* (Cryptoprocta ferox) *resemble **(a)** males, whereas **(b)** adult females do not.*

sniff one another's genitals. During these encounters, males erect their penises and females their peniform clitorises. Females appear to dominate spotted hyena societies even though their levels of testosterone and 5α-dihydrotestosterone are lower than in adult males. This does not support the proposal that females are more aggressive because of levels of circulating male hormones. Spotted hyena cubs are precocial and aggressive to the point of siblicide, perhaps reflecting hormone levels at birth. Masculinization of female genitalia could be a side effect of selection for aggressive neonates.

Masculinization of female genitalia occurs in some other members of the order Carnivora, for example, the fossa (*Cryptoprocta ferox*) from Madagascar **(Figure 3)**. Transient masculinization of young female (but not adult female) fossas could allow them to avoid sexual harassment by adult males and to escape from aggression by adult females.

Racey, P.A. and J.S. Skinner. 1979. Endocrine aspects of sexual mimicry in spotted hyaenas, Crocuta crocuta. *Journal of Zoology,* 187:315-326. Reprinted by permission of John Wiley and Sons.

FIGURE 2

*In spotted hyenas (**C. crocuta**), the external genitalia of a nulliparous female (left) resembles that of a male (right).* Note the peniform clitoris and pseudoscrotum on the female.

34.6 Cellular Basis of Development

Orientation and rate of mitotic cell division have special significance in the development of the shape, size, and location of organ systems of the embryo. Regulation of the orientation and rate occurs at all stages of development.

Orientation of cell division refers to the angles at which daughter cells are added to older cells as development proceeds. Orientation is determined by the location of the furrow separating the cytoplasm after mitotic division of the nucleus (see Chapter 8). The furrow forms in alignment with the spindle midpoint so that when the spindle is centrally positioned in the cell, the furrow leads to symmetrical division of the cell. When the spindle is displaced to one end of the cell, the furrow leads to asymmetrical division into a smaller cell and a larger cell. Little is known about how spindle positioning is regulated.

The rate of cell division primarily reflects the time spent in the G_1 period of interphase (see Chapter 8). Once DNA replication begins, the rest of the cell cycle takes the same time in all cells of a species. As an embryo develops and cells differentiate, the time spent in interphase increases and varies in different cell types. Therefore, different cell types proliferate at various rates as they differentiate, giving rise to tissues and organs with different cell numbers. When fully differentiated, some cells remain fixed in interphase and stop replicating DNA or dividing. Nerve cells in the mammalian brain and spinal cord stop dividing once the nervous system is fully formed. Ultimately, the rate of cell division is under genetic control.

Frog egg cleavage provides examples of how both changes in orientation and rate of mitotic division affect development. The first two cleavages start at the animal pole and extend to the vegetal pole, producing four equal blastomeres (see Figure 34.8). The third cleavage occurs equatorially, but because of yolk in the vegetal region of the embryo, this cleavage furrow forms toward the animal pole and produces an eight-cell embryo with four small blastomeres near the animal pole and four large blastomeres in the vegetal region. Blastomeres in the animal region of the embryo proceed to divide rapidly, whereas blastomeres in the vegetal region divide more slowly because division is inhibited by yolk. The resulting morula consists of an animal region with many small cells and a vegetal region with relatively few but larger blastomeres.

34.6a Microtubules and Microfilaments: Movements of Cells

Embryonic cells undergo changes in shape that generate movements, such as the infolding of surface layers to produce endoderm or mesoderm. Entire cells also move during embryonic growth, both singly and in groups. Movements are also produced by changes in rates of growth or by breakdowns of microtubules and microfilaments. Changes in both cell shape and cell movement play important roles in cleavage, gastrulation, and organogenesis.

34.6b Change in Cell Shape: Adjusting to New Roles

Changes in cell shape typically result from reorganization of the cytoskeleton. During development of the

Microtubules
Microtubules lengthen and slide farther apart to elongate cells.

Microfilaments
Microfilaments slide close together to constrict the top margin of cells.

Figure 34.25
The roles of **(a)** microtubules and **(b)** microfilaments in the changes in cell shape that produce developmental movements.

neural plate in frogs, the ectoderm flattens and thickens and cells in the ectoderm layer change from cubelike to columnar in shape **(Figure 34.25a)**.

Sinking of the neural plate downward along its midline reflects changes in cell shape from columnar to wedgelike **(Figure 34.25b)**. As one end of each cell narrows, the entire cell layer invaginates (is forced inward). How does this occur? Each wedge-shaped cell contains a group of microfilaments arranged in a circle at the top. Microfilaments slide over each other, tightening the ring like a drawstring and narrowing the top of the cell. If an experimenter adds cytochalasin, a chemical that interferes with microfilament assembly, to the cells, the microfilament circle disperses, and invagination does not occur.

34.6c Movements of Whole Cells to New Positions in the Embryo

Cell movements during gastrulation and long-distance migrations of neural crest cells are striking examples of movements of whole cells during embryonic development. These movements involve coordinated activity by microtubules and microfilaments. The typical pattern of movement is a repeating cycle of extension, anchoring, and contracting. First, a cell attaches to the substrate **(Figure 34.26, p. 842,** step 1), and then it moves forward by elongating from the point of attachment (step 2). The cell then makes a new attachment at the advancing tip (step 3) and contracts until the rearmost attachment breaks (step 4). The front attachment now serves as the base for another movement.

How do the cells know where to go? Typically, cells migrate over the surfaces of stationary cells in one of

First attachment point

Substrate (another cell, or extracellular material)

Second attachment point

1 **2** **3** **4**

Figure 34.26

The cycle of attachment, stretching, and contraction by which a cell moves over other cells or extracellular materials in embryos.

the embryo's layers. In many developmental systems, migrating cells follow tracks formed by molecules of the ECM, secreted by cells along the route over which they travel. Fibronectin, an important track molecule, is a fibrous, elongated protein of the ECM. Migrating cells recognize and adhere to fibronectin, and, in response, internal changes in cells trigger their movement in a direction based on the alignment of fibronectin molecules.

Some migrating cells follow concentration gradients rather than molecular tracks. Gradients are created by diffusion of molecules (often proteins) released by cells in one part of an embryo. Cells with receptors for the diffusing molecule follow the gradient toward or away from the source.

Selective cell adhesion—the ability of an embryonic cell to make and break specific connections to other cells—is closely related to cell movement. As development proceeds, many cells break initial adhesions, move, and form new adhesions in different locations. Final cell adhesions hold the embryo in its correct shape and form. Junctions of various kinds, including tight, anchoring, and gap junctions, reinforce final adhesions. Selective cell adhesions were first demonstrated in a classic experiment by Johannes Holtfreter and P. L. Townes (see "Making Cell Connections," Box 34.4).

Many cell surface proteins are responsible for selective cell adhesions, including **cell adhesion molecules** (CAMs) and **cadherins (calcium-dependent adhesion molecules)**. Cadherins require calcium ions to set up adhesions—hence their name. As cells develop, different types of CAMs or cadherins appear or disappear from their surfaces as they make and break cell adhesions. The changes reflect alterations in gene activity, often in response to molecular signals arriving from other cells. During early development in the chick, cells of the ectoderm are held together by E- and N-cadherins. As the neural plate appears, cells destined to form the neural tube lose their cadherins, and N-CAMs appear on their surfaces. As these surface molecules appear, the neural tube cells break loose from the ectoderm and adhere to each other to form the neural tube. If N-cadherin is added experimentally to ectoderm cells, the neural tube stays anchored and never separates.

34.6d Induction: Interactions between Cells

Induction is the process in which a group of inducing cells causes or influences a nearby group of responding cells to follow a particular developmental pathway. Induction is the major process responsible for determination, in which the developmental fate of a cell is set. Induction occurs through the combination of signal molecules with surface receptors on the responding cells. The signal molecules may be located on the surface of the inducing cells or released by inducing cells. The surface receptors are activated by binding the signal molecules. In the activated form, signal molecules trigger internal response pathways that produce the developmental changes (see Chapter 14). Responses often include changes in gene activity.

In the 1920s, Hans Spemann and Hilde Mangold conducted the first experiments identifying induction in embryos. They found that if the dorsal lip of a newt embryo was removed and grafted into a different position of another embryo, cells moving inward from the dorsal lip induced a neural plate, a neural tube, and eventually an entire embryo at the new location (see "Spemann and Mangold's Experiment Demonstrating Induction in Embryos," Box 34.5, p. 844). They proposed that the dorsal lip is an **organizer**, acting on other cells to alter the course of development. This action is now known as induction. Spemann received the Nobel Prize in 1935 for his research. (Mangold had died in a tragic accident in 1924 when her kitchen gasoline heater exploded, the year their research paper was published. She would likely have also received the Nobel Prize, but it has only once been awarded posthumously.)

Spemann and Mangold's findings touched off a search for inducing molecules that must pass from inducing cells to responding cells. In 1992, researchers constructed a DNA library from *Xenopus* gastrulas. By isolating and cloning cellular DNA in gene-sized pieces, they made mRNA transcripts of cloned genes and injected them into early *Xenopus* embryos in which the inducing ability of mesoderm had been destroyed by exposure to ultraviolet light. Some injected mRNAs, translated into proteins in the embryos, were able to induce formation of a neural plate and tube, leading to

Making Cell Connections: Selective Adhesion Properties of Cells 34.4

1. Holtfreter and Townes separated ectoderm, mesoderm, and endoderm tissue from amphibian embryos soon after the neural tube had formed. They used embryos from amphibian species that had cells of different colours and sizes, so they could follow under the microscope where each cell type ended up. (The colours shown here are for illustrative purposes only.)

Amphibian embryos of different species

2. The researchers placed the tissues individually in alkaline solutions, which caused the tissues to break down into single cells.

3. Holtfreter and Townes then combined suspensions of single cells in various ways. Shown here are ectoderm + mesoderm and ectoderm + mesoderm + endoderm. When the pH was returned to neutrality, the cells formed aggregates. Through a microscope, the researchers followed what happened to the aggregates on agar-filled Petri dishes.

KEY

Ectoderm   Mesoderm   Endoderm

RESULT: In time, the reaggregated cells sorted themselves with respect to cell type; that is, instead of the cell types remaining mixed, each cell type became separated spatially. That is, in the ectoderm + mesoderm mixture, the ectoderm moved to the periphery of the aggregate, surrounding mesoderm cells in the centre. In no case did the two cell types remain randomly mixed. The ectoderm + mesoderm + endoderm aggregate showed further that cell sorting in the aggregates generated cell positions reflecting the positions of the cell types in the embryo. That is, the endoderm cells separated from the ectoderm and mesoderm cells and became surrounded by them. In the end, the ectoderm cells were located on the periphery, the endoderm cells were internal, and the mesoderm cells were between the other two cell types.

Ectoderm + Mesoderm

Ectoderm + Mesoderm + Endoderm

CONCLUSION: Holtfreter interpreted the results to mean that cells have selective affinity for each other; that is, cells have selective adhesion properties. Specifically, he proposed that ectoderm cells have positive affinity for mesoderm cells but negative affinity for endoderm cells, whereas mesoderm cells have positive affinity for both ectoderm cells and endoderm cells. In modern terms, these properties result from cell surface molecules that give cells specific adhesion properties.

Spemann and Mangold's Experiment Demonstrating Induction in Embryos 34.5

Donor embryo

Recipient embryo

Dorsal lip

Primary notochord

Primary neural tube

Secondary neural tube

Secondary notochord

EXPERIMENT: To investigate the process of induction, Hans Spemann and Hilde Mangold performed transplantation experiments with newt embryos, the results of which demonstrated that specific induction of development occurs in the embryos. The researchers removed the dorsal lip of the blastopore from one newt embryo and grafted it onto a different position—the ventral side—of another embryo. The two embryos were from different newt species that differed in pigmentation, allowing them to follow the fate of the tissue easily. The embryo with the transplant was allowed to develop.

CONCLUSION: The grafted dorsal lip of the blastopore induced a second gastrulation and subsequent development in the ventral region of the recipient embryo. The result demonstrated the ability of particular cells to induce the development of other cells.

a normal embryo. More than 10 proteins that act as inducing molecules have been identified in the *Xenopus* system.

Differentiation produces specialized cells without the loss of genes. By this process, cells that have committed to a particular developmental fate by the determination process (see Section 34.2) develop into specialized cell types with distinct structures and functions. As part of differentiation, cells concentrate on the production of molecules characteristic of the specific types. For example, 80 to 90% of the total protein synthesized by lens cells is crystallin.

Research into differentiation confirmed that as cells specialize, they retain all of the genes of the original egg cell. Except in rare instances, differentiation does not occur through selective gene loss. Robert Briggs and Thomas King, and later John B. Gurdon, used ultraviolet light to destroy the nucleus of a fertilized frog egg. A micropipette was then used to transfer a nucleus from a fully differentiated tissue, intestinal epithelium, to the enucleated egg. Some eggs receiving transplanted nuclei subsequently developed into normal tadpoles and adult frogs. This outcome is possible only if the differentiated intestinal cells retained

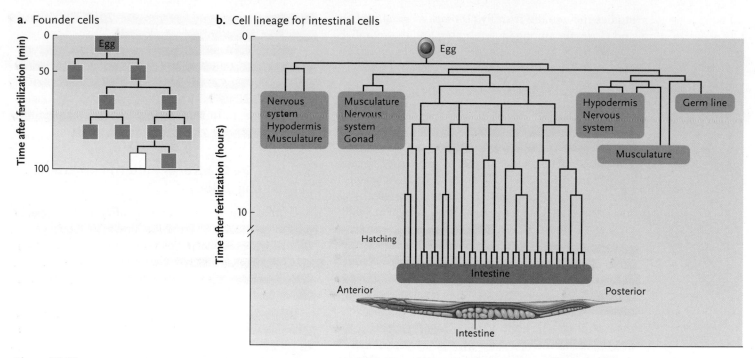

a. Founder cells

b. Cell lineage for intestinal cells

Figure 34.27

Cell lineages of *C. elegans*. **(a)** The founder cells (blue) produced in early cell divisions from which all adult somatic cells are produced. The white cell gives rise to germ-line cells. **(b)** The cell lineage for cells that form the intestine. The detailed lineages for the other parts of the adult are not shown.

the full complement of genes. This conclusion was extended to mammals in 1997 when Ian Wilmut and his colleagues successfully cloned a sheep (named Dolly) starting with an adult cell nucleus.

From the early days of studying development, embryologists focused on describing not only how embryos form and develop but also exactly how adult tissues and organs are produced from embryonic cells. An important goal of embryology was to trace cell lineages from embryo to adult. For most organisms, it is not possible to trace lineages at the individual cell level, primarily because of the complexity of the developmental process and the opacity of embryos. Experimenters developed *fate mapping*, mapping adult or larval structures onto the region of the embryo from which each structure developed. Fate mapping is done by following the development of living embryos under the microscope, either by using species in which the embryo is transparent or by marking cells so they can be followed. Cells may be marked with vital dyes (that do not kill cells), fluorescent dyes, or radioactive labels. Fate maps have been produced for *Xenopus,* the chick, and *Drosophila*.

In most cases, a fate map is not detailed enough to show how particular cells in the embryo gave rise to cells of the adult. The exception is the fate map of the nematode *Caenorhabditis elegans,* an organism with a fixed, reproducible developmental pattern. *C. elegans* has a transparent body, and scientists have mapped the fate (traced the **cell lineage**) of every cell as the zygote divides and the resulting embryo differentiates into a 959-cell adult hermaphrodite or 1031-cell adult male

(Figure 34.27). All somatic cells of the adult can be traced from five somatic **founder cells** produced during early development. Knowing the cell lineages of *C. elegans* has been a valuable tool for research into the genetic and molecular control of development because mutants affecting development can be easily visualized.

STUDY BREAK

1. What role do microtubules and microfilaments play in development?
2. What happens during induction? Where does it occur?
3. How has work with *Caenorhabditis elegans* advanced our knowledge of developmental biology? What about *Xenopus*?

34.7 Genetic and Molecular Control of Development

Developmental biologists are interested in identifying and characterizing the genes involved in development and defining how gene products regulate and bring about elaborate events. One productive research approach has been to isolate mutants that affect developmental processes and then identify the genes involved, clone these genes, and analyze them in detail to build models for molecular functions of gene products in development. Model organisms used for these studies include the fruit fly (*Drosophila melanogaster*) and *C. elegans* among invertebrates, and the zebrafish (*Danio rerio*) and the house mouse (*Mus musculus*) among vertebrates.

34.7a Genetic Control of Development

Gene expression regulates changes that occur through determination and differentiation. One well-studied example of the genetic control of these processes is the production of skeletal muscle cells from somites in mammals **(Figure 34.28)**. Somites are blocks of mesoderm cells that form along both sides of the notochord (see Figure 34.17). Under genetic control, some cells of each somite differentiate into skeletal muscle cells. First, paracrine signalling from nearby cells induces somite cells to express the master regulatory gene, *myoD*. The product of *myoD* is the transcription factor MyoD. By turning on specific muscle-determining genes, the action of MyoD brings about determination of these cells, converting them to undifferentiated muscle cells called **myoblasts**. Among genes that MyoD regulates are *myogenin* and *MEF* genes. Both are regulatory genes, expressing transcription factors in myoblasts that turn on yet another set of genes. The products of these genes, including myosin (a major protein involved in muscle contraction), promote differentiation of myoblasts

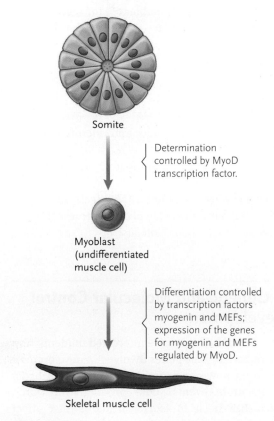

Somite

Determination controlled by MyoD transcription factor.

Myoblast (undifferentiated muscle cell)

Differentiation controlled by transcription factors myogenin and MEFs; expression of the genes for myogenin and MEFs regulated by MyoD.

Skeletal muscle cell

Figure 34.28
The genetic control of determination and differentiation involved in mammalian skeletal muscle cell formation.

into specific types of muscle cells, such as skeletal muscle cells or cardiac muscle cells.

Molecular mechanisms involved in determination and differentiation usually depend on regulatory genes that encode regulatory proteins that control the expression of other genes. Regulatory genes act as master regulators, and, in most cases, the expression of the regulatory genes is controlled by induction.

34.7b Gene Control of Pattern Formation: Developing a Body

As part of the signals guiding differentiation, cells receive positional information that tells them where they are in the embryo. Positional information is vital to **pattern formation**, the arrangement of organs and body structures in their proper three-dimensional relationships. Positional information is laid down primarily as concentration gradients of regulatory molecules produced by genetic control. In most cases, gradients of several different regulatory molecules interact to tell a cell, or a cell nucleus, where it is in the embryo. Genetic control of pattern formation is well documented in *Drosophila melanogaster*. Developmental principles discovered in *D. melanogaster* also apply to many other animal species, including humans.

34.7c Embryogenesis in *Drosophila*: Fruit Fly Model

Production of an adult fruit fly from a fertilized egg occurs in a sequence of genetically controlled development events. Following fertilization, division of the nucleus begins by mitosis. This produces a multinucleate blastoderm because the cytoplasm does not divide in the early embryo (cytokinesis does not occur) **(Figure 34.29)**. At the tenth nuclear division, the nuclei migrate to the periphery of the embryo, where, three divisions later, the 6000 or so nuclei are organized into separate cells. At this stage, the embryo is a **cellular blastoderm**, corresponding to the late blastula stage in the animals discussed above. Ten hours after fertilization, the cellular blastoderm develops into a segmented embryo (an embryo with distinct segments). About 24 hours after fertilization, the egg hatches into a larva that will undergo three moults before becoming a pupa. The adult fly emerges after metamorphosis 10 to 12 days after fertilization. The colours in Figure 34.29 illustrate how segments of the embryo can be mapped to the segments of the adult fly.

The study of developmental mutants has provided important information about *Drosophila* development. Three researchers performed key, pioneering research with developmental mutants: Edward B. Lewis, Christiane Nüsslein-Volhard, and Eric Wieschaus. The three shared a Nobel Prize in 1995 "for their discoveries about the genetic control of early embryonic development."

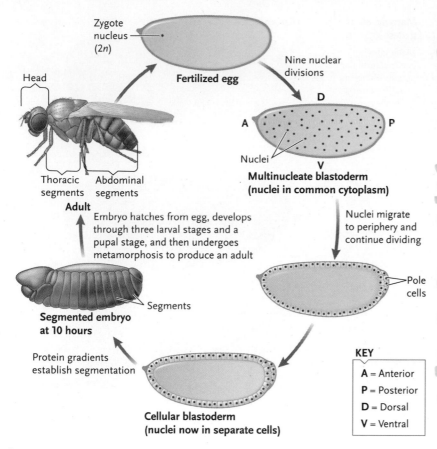

Figure 34.29

Embryogenesis in *Drosophila* and the relationship between segments of the embryo and segments of the adult.

KEY

A = Anterior
P = Posterior
D = Dorsal
V = Ventral

Nüsslein-Volhard and Wieschaus studied early embryogenesis. They searched for *every* gene required for early pattern formation in the embryo by looking for recessive, **embryonic lethal** mutations. When homozygous, these mutations result in embryo death during development. By determining the stage at which the embryo died and how development was disrupted, they gained insight into the role of the particular genes in embryogenesis.

Lewis studied mutants that changed the fates of cells in particular embryonic regions, producing structures in the adult that were normally produced by other regions. His work was the foundation of research identifying master regulatory genes that control the development of body regions in a wide range of organisms.

34.7d Maternal-Effect Genes and Segmentation Genes: Segmenting the Body

A number of genes control the establishment of the embryo's body plan. These genes regulate the expression of other genes. Two classes, maternal-effect genes and segmentation genes, work sequentially **(Figure 34.30, p. 848)**. Many **maternal-effect genes** are expressed by the mother during oogenesis. These genes control egg polarity and thus embryo polarity.

Some of these genes control formation of embryonic anterior structures, whereas others control formation of posterior structures. Still others control formation of the terminal end.

The *bicoid* gene is the key maternal-effect gene responsible for development of the head and thorax. This gene is transcribed in the mother during oogenesis, and the resulting mRNAs are deposited in the egg, localizing near the anterior pole **(Figure 34.31, p. 848)**. After fertilization, translation of mRNAs produces BICOID protein, which diffuses through the zygote to form a gradient with concentration highest at the anterior end, fading to none at the posterior end. BICOID is a transcription factor that activates some genes and represses others along the anterior–posterior axis of the embryo. Embryos with mutations in the *bicoid* gene lack thoracic structures but have posterior structures at each end. In normal embryos, the *bicoid* gene is a master regulator gene controlling the expression of genes for the development of anterior structures (head and thorax).

The activities of products of other maternal-effect genes in gradients in the embryo are also involved in axis formation. The *nanos* gene is the key maternal-effect gene for the posterior structures. When the *nanos* gene is mutated, embryos lack abdominal segments.

Once the axis of the embryo is set, expression of at least 24 **segmentation genes** progressively subdivides the embryo into regions, determining the segments of the embryo and the adult (see Figure 34.30, p. 848). Gradients of BICOID and other proteins encoded by maternal-effect genes regulate expression of the embryo's segmentation genes differentially. So each segmentation gene is expressed at a particular time and in a particular location during embryogenesis.

Three sets of segmentation genes are regulated in a cascade of gene activations. Gap genes such as *hunchback* and *tailless* are the first to be expressed. These genes are activated based on their positions in the maternally directed anterior–posterior axis of the zygote by reacting to the concentrations of BICOID and other proteins. Products of gap genes control subdivision of the embryo into several broad regions along the anterior–posterior axis. Mutations in gap genes result in the loss of one or more body segments in the embryo **(Figure 34.32a, p. 848)**.

Figure 34.30

Maternal-effect genes and segment-ation genes and their role in *Drosophila* embryogenesis.

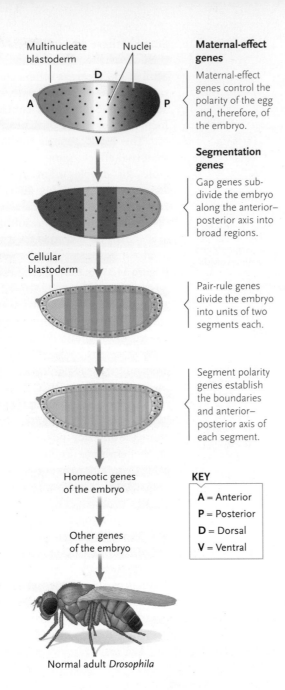

Maternal-effect genes

Maternal-effect genes control the polarity of the egg and, therefore, of the embryo.

Segmentation genes

Gap genes sub-divide the embryo along the anterior–posterior axis into broad regions.

Pair-rule genes divide the embryo into units of two segments each.

Segment polarity genes establish the boundaries and anterior–posterior axis of each segment.

Homeotic genes of the embryo

Other genes of the embryo

Normal adult *Drosophila*

KEY

A = Anterior
P = Posterior
D = Dorsal
V = Ventral

Maternal *bicoid* mRNA

mRNA

BICOID protein

Protein

Maternal *bicoid* mRNA

BICOID protein

KEY

A = Anterior
P = Posterior

Figure 34.31

Gradients of *bicoid* mRNA and BICOID protein in the *Drosophila* egg.

Products of gap genes are transcription factors that activate **pair-rule genes**, such as *even-skipped* and *fushi tarazu*. The products of pair-rule genes divide the embryo into units of two segments each. Mutations in pair-rule genes lead to the deletion of every other segment of the embryo **(Figure 34.32b).**

Expression of segment polarity genes, *engrailed* and *gooseberry*, is regulated by products of pair-rule

Figure 34.32

Examples of mutations in the different types of segmentation genes of *Drosophila*. Orange highlights indicate wild-type segments that are mutated. **(a)** Gap gene mutants lack one or more segments. **(b)** Pair-rule gene mutants are missing every other segment. **(c)** Segment polarity genes have segments with one part missing and the other part duplicated as a mirror image.

a. Gap genes **b.** Pair-rule genes **c.** Segment polarity genes

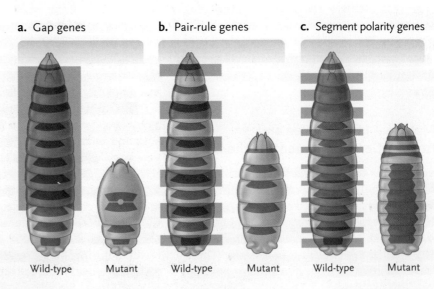

Wild-type   Mutant   Wild-type   Mutant   Wild-type   Mutant

genes. The actions of the products of segment polarity genes set boundaries and the anterior–posterior axis of each segment in the embryo. Mutations in segment polarity genes produce segments in which one part is missing and the other part is duplicated as a mirror image **(Figure 34.32c).** The products of segment polarity genes are transcription factors and other molecules that regulate other genes involved in laying down the pattern of the embryo.

34.7e Homeotic Genes: Structure and Determining Outcomes

Once the segmentation pattern has been set, **homeotic** (structure-determining) **genes** of the embryo specify what each segment will become after metamorphosis. In normal flies, homeotic genes are master regulatory genes controlling development of structures such as eyes, antennae, legs, and wings on particular segments **(Figure 34.33).** Mutations of these genes allowed researchers to discover the role of homeotic genes. In the *Antennapedia* mutant fly, legs develop instead of antennae (see Figure 34.33, bottom).

How do homeotic genes regulate development? Homeotic genes encode transcription factors that regulate expression of genes responsible for the development of adult structures. Each homeotic gene has a common region called a homeobox that is key to its function. A homeobox corresponds to an amino acid section of the encoded transcription factor called the **homeodomain.** The homeodomain of each protein binds to a region in the promoters of the genes whose transcription it regulates.

Eight homeobox (*Hox*) genes in *Drosophila* are organized along a chromosome in the same order as they are expressed along the anterior–posterior body axis **(Figure 34.34).** The discovery of *Hox* genes in *Drosophila* led to a search for equivalent genes in other organisms. *Hox* genes are present in all major animal phyla, where they control the development of segments or regions of the body and are arranged in order in the genome. Homeobox sequences in *Hox* genes are highly conserved, indicating common function in the wide range of animals in which they occur. Homeobox sequences of mammals are the same as or similar to those of the fruit fly (see Figure 34.34). Homeotic genes are also found in plants, where they affect flower development. Homeobox genes have been identified and analyzed in *Arabidopsis* (see Chapter 30).

Normal

Antennapedia mutant

Oliver Meckes/Nicole Ottawa/Photo Researchers, Inc.

Eye of Science/Photo Researchers, Inc.

Figure 34.33

Antennapedia, a homeotic mutant of *Drosophila,* in which legs develop in place of antennae.

Figure 34.34

The *Hox* genes of the fruit fly and the corresponding regions of the embryo they affect. The mouse has four sets of *Hox* genes on four different chromosomes. Their relationship to the fruit fly genes is shown by the colours.

34.7f Cell-Death Genes: Apoptosis

Apoptosis plays a role in the breakdown of a tadpole's tail and in many other patterns of development in vertebrates and invertebrates. In humans, developing fingers and toes are initially connected by tissue, forming paddle-shaped structures. Later in development, cells of this tissue die by apoptosis, resulting in separated fingers and toes. Like many other mammals, kittens and puppies are born with their eyes sealed shut by an unbroken layer of skin. Just after birth, cells die in a thin line across the middle of each eyelid, freeing the eyelids and allowing them to open. During pupation from caterpillar to butterfly, many tissues of the larva break down by apoptosis to be replaced by newly formed adult tissues.

Apoptosis results from gene activation in response to molecular signals from receptors on the surfaces of marked cells. In effect, the signals are death notices, delivered at a specific time during embryonic development. In the nematode *C. elegans*, division of the zygote produces 1090 cells. Of these, exactly 131 die at prescribed times to produce a total of 959 cells in the adult hermaphrodite.

In *C. elegans*, a death signal molecule that binds to a receptor in the plasma membrane of the target cell results in apoptosis. When the receptor is activated, it leads to activation of proteins that kill the cell. The killing proteins remain inactive in the absence of the death signal.

In the absence of a death signal, the membrane receptor is inactive (Figure 34.35a). This allows CED-9, a protein associated with the outer mitochondrial membrane (encoded by the *ced-9* cell-death gene), to inhibit CED-4 (encoded by the *ced-4* gene) and CED-3 (encoded by the *ced-3* gene). These two proteins are needed to turn on the cell-death program. Cells with the *ced-9* gene expressed and its product CED-9 active normally survive in the adult nematode. When a death signal binds to and activates a receptor, the resulting events are typical of signal transduction pathways (see Figure 34.35b). Now the activated receptor leads to inactivation of CED-9. In the absence of CED-9, CED-4 is activated, which, in turn, activates CED-3. Activated CED-3 triggers a cascade of reactions, including activation of proteases and nucleases that degrade cell structures and chromosomes.

Studies of mutants have helped us understand the role of cell-death genes in *C. elegans*. In mutants lacking normal *ced-3* or *ced-4* genes, the 131 marked cells fail to die, producing a disorganized embryo. In

a. No death signal **b.** Death signal

Apoptosis is inhibited as long as CED-9 protein is active; cell remains alive.

When a death signal binds to the death signal receptor, it activates the receptor, which leads to inactivation of CED-9 protein. As a result, CED-4 protein is no longer inhibited and becomes active, activating CED-3 protein. Active CED-3 triggers a cascade of activations producing active proteases and nucleases, which cause the changes seen in apoptotic cells and eventually lead to cell death.

Figure 34.35

The molecular basis of apoptosis in *C. elegans*. **(a)** In the absence of a death signal, no apoptosis occurs. **(b)** In the presence of a death signal, activation of CED-4 and CED-3 proteins triggers a pathway that leads to the cell's death.

the nervous system, the 103 cells that normally die by apoptosis live to form extra neurons in mutants. These extra neurons are inserted at random in the embryo, leading to a disorganized, nonfunctional nervous system.

Genes related to *ced-3* and *ced-4* occur in all animals tested for their presence. In humans and other mammals, the *caspase-9* gene is equivalent to *ced-3*. The *caspase-9* gene, which encodes a protease that degrades cell structures, is activated in cells that form the webbing between the fingers and toes in a human embryo, causing it to break down. The equivalent of *ced-4* is the *Apaf* gene (for *apoptotic protease-activating factor*). Mammalian cells are saved from death by the *Bcl* family of genes, which are the equivalent of *ced-9* in *C. elegans*. The genes are so closely related that they retain their effects if they are exchanged between *C. elegans* and human cells.

34.7g Epigenetics

Each cell in a multicellular organism has identical DNA, so how does the animal end up with so many different cell phenotypes—why does your hair look different from your fingernails? Epigenetics (*epi* = above) refers to nongenetic cellular memory that reflects developmental and environmental conditions. Note that epigenetic modifications alter the expression of DNA but not its sequence. Epigenetic changes are not mutations. Epigenetic features should be self-perpetuating and reversible, because they literally cause genes to be switched on and off. These changes may involve modifications to histones, proteins around which DNA wraps and that can be involved in down-regulating or transcription of genes. Methylation tightens packing of genes around histones, affecting down-regulating and inhibiting transcription, so demethylation can play an important role in epigenesis. Acetylation loosens packing and encourages transcription and translation. Without these epigenetic modifications, all genes would be functional in every cell, severely inhibiting or preventing cell differentiation.

During gametogenesis and embryogenesis, many metazoan animals show genome-wide epigenetic reprogramming involving DNA methylation and histone modification. In mammals, epigenetic processes occur at two stages during development, first in primordial germ cells and second in the zygote from just after fertilization to just before implantation. These changes can involve erasure of DNA methylation throughout the genome in the zygote and in primordial germ cells.

Epigenetic changes account for different patterns of activation of the X chromosome in mammals. Each female embryo receives two X chromosomes (one maternal, the other paternal), but often only one is activated. The details of activation vary among mammals, differing considerably among mice, rabbits, and humans. The situation also varies among cell lines within a developing embryo, sometimes differing between the inner cell mass of the blastocyst and the epiblast. In mice, the paternal X is inhibited early in embryogenesis by imprinted (parental influence on the genome is genetic imprinting) expression of regulatory RNA. In embryonic humans and rabbits, both X chromosomes are activated in many cells. It is clear that epigenetic effects can account for striking differences among cells and in whole organism phenotypes. An epigenetic effect associated with the X chromosome causes tortoiseshell colouring in female cats, so only female cats can be true tortoiseshell in colour.

The impact of such changes is also very obvious in some insects. In a hive of honeybees (*Apis mellifera*), the queen (diploid) and workers (haploid) have the same genome even though they differ behaviourally and reproductively. These postmitotic differences result from the relative amounts of royal jelly consumed during the larval stage acting in concert with different patterns of DNA methylation. A comparison of the brains of worker and queen bees revealed that over 550 genes showed significant differences in methylation, apparently partly caused by modifications to sites for gene splicing. Once again, epigenetic factors influence phenotype.

Epigenetic factors may also play a role in hybrid sterility (see Chapter 19), providing another example of postzygotic isolation. Specifically, in mice, the gene *Prdm9* (responsible for protein coding) activates proteins essential for meiosis by methylation of histone H3 at lysine 4.

{ restricts? meiosis.

Now biologists better appreciate the many implications of epigenetics across the spectrum, from developmental and medical settings to the processes of speciation.

STUDY BREAK

1. Give two examples of genetic control of development.
2. What are maternal-effect genes?
3. What are homeotic genes, and what do they do?

Review

CourseMate Access an interactive eBook, chapter-specific interactive learning tools, including flashcards, quizzes, videos, and more in your Biology **CourseMate**, accessed through NelsonBrain.com **Aplia™** is an online interactive learning solution that helps you improve comprehension—and your grade—by integrating a variety of mediums and tools such as videos, tutorials, practice tests, and an interactive eBook.

34.1 Housing and Fuelling Developing Young

- In mammals, relaxin is a polypeptide hormone produced by the ovaries during pregnancy. Relaxin inhibits muscular contractions of the uterus and promotes the growth of glands that produce milk. As the time for parturition approaches, relaxin causes relaxation of the pubic ligaments and softens and enlarges the opening to the cervix.

- Viviparous animal embryos often develop in the uterus (or a uterus-like structure in the reproductive tract). Ovoviviparous animal embryos may develop in the oviduct, the stomach (at least one species of frog), the mouth (several species of fish), or a brood pouch (other fish, such as seahorses). Oviparous animals lay eggs, and the embryos develop outside the body.

- Strictly defined, milk is produced by female mammals to feed their young. Milklike substances (milk analogues) are produced by many other animals: the crop milk of pigeons, secretions of the skin in some fish and caecilians, or the uterine milk of a variety of animals, from some cockroaches to elasmobranchs.

- Yolk is food housed within the egg and used to support the growth and development of the embryo. The eggs of birds, insects, reptiles, and many other animals have large deposits of yolk that support the complete development of the young. Other animals have varying amounts of yolk corresponding to shorter periods of in-egg development.

34.2 Mechanisms of Embryonic Development

- The process of progressing from a zygote to a complete organism involves mitotic cell divisions, movements of cells, selective cell adhesions, induction, determination, and differentiation.

- The zygote divides by cleavage, without increasing the overall size or mass of the embryo. It forms a morula, or sphere of blastomeres (cells), which forms the blastula, a hollow ball of cells in a single layer enclosing the blastocoel, a fluid-filled cavity. The blastula invaginates to form the gastrula, a hollow ball of cells with an opening, the blastopore.

34.3 Major Patterns of Cleavage and Gastrulation

- Protostomes show determinant development in the progression from egg to animal. From the first divisions, blastomeres develop into specific tissues and organs. Deuterostomes show indeterminant development. Blastomeres produced by the first several divisions remain totipotent, capable of developing into a complete organism.

- Differences in the patterns of development of birds and typical mammals are functions of ovipary (egg-laying) versus vivipary (bearing live young). Mammalian eggs have little yolk, and the developing embryo depends on its mother for food and oxygen, as well as the collection and removal of wastes. The eggs of birds have large amounts of yolk, and the complete development of the embryo takes place independent of the mother's body. Bird embryo development begins with the formation of the blastodisc, a layer of cells on the surface of the yolk.

34.4 Organogenesis: Gastrulation to Adult Body Structures

- In the amniote egg, the amnion (an extra-embryonic membrane) encloses the developing embryo in a pool of amniotic fluid. The chorion, another extra-embryonic membrane, is produced from ectoderm and mesoderm and lines the inside of the egg shell. It is the site of oxygen exchange for the developing embryo. The allantois is enclosed by the allantoic membrane, which forms from mesoderm and endoderm. The allantois is the storage site for metabolic end products such as uric acid. The amniote egg allows development outside of water and was a fundamental breakthrough in the evolution of fully terrestrial vertebrates.

- In vertebrates, the eye forms when two sides of the anterior end of the neural tube (optic vesicles) swell outward until they contact the ectoderm. The optic cup, a double-walled structure, forms when the outer surface of the optic vesicle thickens and flattens at the region of contact and then pushes inward. The optic cup becomes the retina. The lens forms from the lens placode, a swelling arising when the optic cup induces thickening of the overlying ectoderm. Developing lens cells synthesize crystallin, a fibrous protein that collects into glassy deposits. Lens cells lose their nuclei and form the lens.

34.5 Embryonic Development of Humans and Other Mammals

- The chorion of the mammalian embryo forms chorionic villi, fingerlike extensions into the endometrium that increase the surface area of the chorion where the placenta will form.

- The placenta is the interface between the developing embryo and its mother. There are a variety of placental structures in mammals, and placenta-like structures (analogues) occur in fishes and insects. There is a rich diversity of placentas in guppylike fishes, demonstrating repeated evolution of this type of structure.

- *SRY* is the sex-determining region of the Y chromosome. *SRY* encodes a protein that induces a molecular switch causing the primitive gonads to develop into testes. Fetuses with XX chromosomes do not produce *SRY*, and under the influence of estrogens and progesterone, the primitive gonads develop into ovaries. High levels of circulating testosterone in a pregnant female cause masculinization of the genitalia in some mammals.

- In many animals, a larval stage is intermediate between embryo and adult. Larval stages occur in some species that produce eggs with small amounts of yolk. Larvae are often strikingly different from the adults and may be the feeding and/or dispersal stage of the species.

34.6 Cellular Basis of Development

- Microtubules and microfilaments produce movements of whole cells and changes in cell shape.

- Induction is a process by which a group of cells causes or influences changes in a nearby group of cells, leading them to follow a particular pathway. Induction works through interactions between signal molecules from inducing cells and surface receptors on responding cells. When signal molecules bind to surface receptors, the responding cells are activated or inactivated.

34.7 Genetic and Molecular Control of Development

- Work with the nematode worm *Caenorhabditis elegans* has allowed biologists to follow development patterns and trace the fate of every cell produced from the zygote. *C. elegans* is transparent, making it even more appropriate for this kind of work.

- Skeletal muscles in mammals develop from somites, blocks of mesoderm along either side of the notochord. Paracrine signalling by nearby cells induces somite cells to express *myoD*, which turns on specific muscle-determining genes, converting them to myoblasts, undifferentiated muscle cells.

- Maternal-effect genes expressed by the mother during oogenesis control egg polarity and thus embryo polarity. The *bicoid* gene is a key maternal-effect gene responsible for the develop-ment of the head and thorax. Segmentation genes subdivide the embryo into regions, determining the segmentation in the body plan.

- Homeotic genes determine structure. In *Drosophila*, they are master regulatory genes controlling the development of body parts such as eyes, antennae, legs, and wings. In each homeotic gene is a common region called a homeobox. Homeobox-containing genes are called *Hox* genes.

- Apoptosis is programmed cell death, a process central to the development of some parts of the body. The process results from gene activation in response to molecular signals from receptors on the surfaces of marked cells.

- Epigenetics refers to nongenetic, cellular memory reflecting developmental and environmental conditions.

Questions

Self-Test Questions

1. Vivipary occurs in
   a. class Osteichthyes
   b. class Amphibia
   c. class Chondrichthyes
   d. All of the above are correct.

2. Gastrulation occurs
   a. only in amniotes
   b. only in echinoderms
   c. only in amphibians
   d. in all metazoa

3. Large amounts of yolk occur in the eggs of all
   a. bony fish
   b. birds
   c. mammals
   d. None of the above.

4. In vertebrates, the blastopore becomes
   a. the mouth
   b. the nostrils
   c. the anus
   d. the auditory meatus

5. Apoptosis occurs in the development of
   a. mammals
   b. reptiles
   c. bony fish
   d. all of the above

6. In which of the following does *Pax-6* genes control the development of eyes?
   a. in chordates
   b. in arthropods
   c. in cnidarians
   d. all of the above

7. Milk produced by mammary glands is a characteristic of
   a. discus fish
   b. pigeons
   c. caecilians
   d. mammals

8. Induction results from interactions between cells and occurs in the development of
   a. tissues
   b. embryos
   c. nervous systems
   d. all of the above

9. Segmentation of developing embryos is controlled by
   a. *Pax-6* genes
   b. gap genes
   c. homeotic genes
   d. b and c

10. Relaxin is important in the process of birth in
    a. sharks
    b. mammals
    c. birds
    d. cockroaches

Questions for Discussion

1. How could apoptosis be used in the treatment of cancer?

2. How does the process of development differ between fraternal and identical twins? In humans, what is the incidence of fraternal twins with two fathers? How does this compare with other species of mammals?

3. How does the pattern of development of compound eyes differ from that of the eyes of vertebrates and molluscs?

4. What is the role of ectoderm in the development of the nervous system?

5. What is the main advantage of vivipary?

The larva, pupa, and adult moth of the tobacco hornworm, *Manduca sexta*, a model insect that has been used in exploring the hormonal control of metamorphosis.

Dr. Richard G. Vogt

STUDY PLAN

35 Control of Animal Processes: Endocrine Control

WHY IT MATTERS

The larva, or caterpillar, of the tobacco hornworm, *Manduca sexta*, having reached its critical weight, stops feeding, drops to the ground, and burrows into the soil, where it moults into the pupal stage. Within the pupa, nearly all of the old larval tissues are destroyed and replaced by the tissues of the adult moth, which have been waiting in embryonic form for the signal to develop. When the moth is formed, it wriggles, still enclosed in the pupal cuticle, to the surface of the soil. It begins the behaviour leading to rupture of the pupal cuticle and its emergence as the adult moth, a soft animal with still rumpled wings. Once emergence is complete, it inflates its body and expands its wings. Only then does the cuticle harden. Moths are nocturnal, and the female, feeding on the nectar of several species of flowers, completes the development of her eggs, begun in the pupal stage, and releases a pheromone that will attract males. After mating, the female takes flight and searches for a suitable host plant in the family Solanaceae, where she lays the 100 or so eggs that she carries. The eggs hatch into larvae and the cycle begins again.

This carefully timed sequence of developmental and behavioural events is orchestrated by several hormones released in response to internal and external environmental cues. This marvel of communication between the environment and the cells, tissues, and organs of animals involving interactions between the nervous system and endocrine structures is a feature of everyday life in even the simplest of organisms.

As discussed in Chapter 31, multicellular organisms have specialized tissues and organs that allow them to function in a highly efficient manner. This requires communication between the highly differentiated cells in different organ systems leading to the effective coordination of their functions. Along with the central nervous system (CNS), hormones of the endocrine system provide the communication that coordinates the activities of multicellular life. These two systems are structurally, chemically, and functionally related, but they control different types of activities. It is impossible to understand the functioning of any animal in the absence of knowledge of the endocrine and nervous systems.

Hormones (*horme* = to excite) are secreted by cells of the **endocrine system** (*endo* = within; *krinein* = separate). In general, the endocrine system controls activities that involve slower, longer-acting responses of multiple tissues or organs. Some of these responses may be relatively quick (less than a minute) and directed, as in the stimulation of milk secretion by the suckling of an infant (see discussion of oxytocin, Section 35.3b), but many also involve transcription and translation of DNA, leading to sustained long-lasting responses (hours, weeks, months, or even years), incorporating the activities of many tissues and organs. For more complex animals such as insects and mammals, a galaxy of hormones regulates a host of functions, from the concentration of salt and glucose in body fluids to body growth and sexual maturation.

The nervous system (Chapter 36), on the other hand, acts through high-speed electrical signals to enable an organism to react rapidly to changes in its internal or external environment. The nervous system also activates or inhibits highly specific localized targets. Ultimately, the nervous system also controls many aspects of the endocrine system.

The mechanisms and functions of the endocrine system are the subjects of this chapter, while those of the nervous system are the subjects of Chapters 36 and 37.

35.1 Hormones and Their Secretion

Cells signal other cells in several ways. Local regulators are used to communicate between neighbouring cells, while hormones and neurotransmitters (see Chapter 36) are used to communicate with distant organs. Our focus in this chapter is on hormones and local

regulators, while the following chapter examines the role of neurotransmitters.

35.1a The Endocrine System Includes Four Major Types of Cell Signalling

Four types of cell signalling occur in the endocrine system. In *autocrine regulation,* a local regulator acts on the same cells that release it **(Figure 35.1a, p. 856)**. This is a common mechanism used by cells to either reduce or increase their sensitivity to other stimuli. In *paracrine regulation,* a cell releases a signalling molecule that diffuses through the extracellular fluid and acts on nearby cells **(Figure 35.1b, p. 856).** In both of these instances, regulation is *local* rather than at a distance. Many of the growth factors that regulate cell division and differentiation act in both an autocrine and a paracrine fashion. In *classical endocrine regulation,* hormones are secreted into the blood or extracellular fluid by the cells of ductless secretory organs called **endocrine glands (Figure 35.1c, p. 856).** Hormones are circulated throughout the body in the blood or other body fluids, and, as a result, most body cells are constantly exposed to a wide variety of hormones. Only the *target cells* of a hormone, those with *receptor proteins* (Chapter 5) recognizing and binding that hormone, respond to it. Hormones are cleared from the body at a steady rate by enzymatic breakdown in their target cells or blood or organs such as the liver or kidneys, and the breakdown products are excreted.

CONCEPT FIX *Exocrine glands,* such as the sweat and salivary glands, release their secretions into ducts that lead outside the body or into the cavities of the digestive tract (see Chapter 31) **(Figure 35.2a, p. 856)**. Secretions from the stomach, liver, pancreas, gall bladder, intestine, and so on, that are released into the digestive tract are not endocrine secretions **(Figure 35.2b, p. 856)** but, rather, are exocrine, since the lumen of the digestive tract is technically outside the body. The digestive tract extends from the mouth to the anus, and unless substances are absorbed across cell membranes along the digestive tract, they never really enter the body. As a result, secretions that enter the digestive tract via ducts from glands along its length are exocrine in nature. ⬡

In *neuroendocrine regulation,* specialized **neurosecretory neurons** respond to and conduct electrical signals, but rather than synapsing with target cells, they release a neurohormone into the circulation when appropriately stimulated **(Figure 35.1d, p. 856).** The hormone is produced in the cell body and packaged in membrane-bound vesicles that are transported along the axon to the release sites. The neurohormone is usually distributed in blood or other body fluids and elicits a response in target cells some distance away that have receptors for the neurohormone. For instance, the peptide vasopressin secreted by the pituitary gland in the brain circulates in the blood and acts on the kidney, reducing the water excreted in the urine,

a. Autocrine regulation

Diffuses through
extracellular fluid

Modulates response

Local regulator

Receptor protein

b. Paracrine regulation

Diffuses through
extracellular fluid

Receptor protein

Response

Local regulator

Target cell

Receptor protein

c. Classical endocrine regulation

Transported in blood

Endocrine cell

Receptor protein

Response

Hormone

Target cell

d. Neuroendocrine regulation

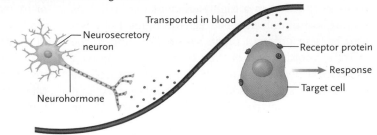

Transported in blood

Neurosecretory
neuron

Receptor protein

Response

Neurohormone

Target cell

e. Classical neural regulation

Neurotransmitter

Sensory
neuron

Inter
neuron

Diffuses across
synapse

Figure 35.1

The major types of
cell signalling in
the endocrine and
nervous systems.

and on muscles of blood vessels, increasing blood pressure. It is also released directly into the brain to cause a myriad of social effects, such as pair bonding in some mammals. In contrast, in *neural regulation,* **neurons** synapse directly with target cells, releasing neurotransmitters into a synapse **(Figure 35.1e)** or neuromuscular junction (see Chapters 36 and 38, respectively, for details). Note that both neurohormones and neurotransmitters are secreted by neurons. Neurohormones are distinguished from neurotransmitters in that neurohormones affect distant target cells, whereas neurotransmitters affect adjacent cells.

However, both neurohormones and neurotransmitters function in the same way—they cause cellular responses by interacting with specific receptors on target cells.

35.1b Hormones and Local Regulators Can Be Grouped into Four Classes Based on Their Chemical Structures

More than 60 hormones and local regulators have been identified in humans. Many human hormones are either identical or very similar in structure and function to those in other animals, but other vertebrates, as well as invertebrates, may have hormones not found in humans. Most of these chemicals can be grouped into four molecular classes: amine, peptide, steroid, and fatty acid-derived molecules.

Amine hormones are involved in classical endocrine signalling and neuroendocrine signalling. Most amine hormones are based on tyrosine. With one major exception, they are hydrophilic molecules, which diffuse readily into the blood and extracellular fluids. On reaching a target cell, they bind to receptors at the cell surface. The amine hormones include dopamine; epinephrine; norepinephrine; and, in protostomes, octopamine, which are all neurotransmitters released by some neurons (see Chapter 36). The exception is the thyroid hormones secreted by the thyroid gland. These hormones, based on a pair of tyrosines,

a. Exocrine gland

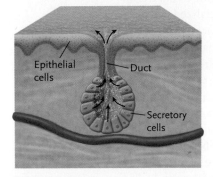

Epithelial
cells

Duct

Secretory
cells

b. Endocrine gland

Secretory
cells

Circulatory system

Figure 35.2

The structure of exocrine and endocrine glands. Exocrine glands **(a)** secrete chemicals into ducts that lead to the surface of the body or the digestive tract, while endocrine glands **(b)** secrete hormones directly into body fluids, especially the circulatory system.

enter the cell by receptor-mediated endocytosis. Inside the cell, one form of the hormone binds to nuclear receptors in the same way as described for steroids below. Thyroid hormones also act via membrane receptors not only on the surface of the cells but also on mitochondrial membranes.

Peptide hormones consist of amino acid chains, ranging in length from as few as 3 amino acids to more than 200. Some have carbohydrate groups attached. They are involved in classical endocrine signalling and neuroendocrine signalling. Mostly hydrophilic hormones, peptide hormones are released into the blood or extracellular fluid by exocytosis when cytoplasmic vesicles containing the hormones fuse with the plasma membrane. One large group of peptide hormones, the **growth factors**, regulates the division and differentiation of many cell types in the body. Many growth factors act in both a paracrine and an autocrine manner, as well as in classical endocrine signalling. Because they can switch cell division on or off, growth factors are an important focus of cancer research.

Steroid hormones are involved in classical endocrine signalling. All are hydrophobic molecules derived from cholesterol and are sparingly soluble in water. They combine with hydrophilic carrier proteins to form water-soluble complexes that diffuse easily in blood or other fluids. On contacting a cell, the hormone is released from its carrier protein, passes through the plasma membrane of the target cell (a process that is sometimes mediated by receptors), and binds to internal receptors in the nucleus or cytoplasm. Steroid hormones include aldosterone; cortisol; the vertebrate sex hormones; and ecdysone, the hormone that governs the formation of new cuticles in ecdyzoan protostomes. Steroid hormones may vary little in structure but produce very different effects. Testosterone and estradiol, two major sex hormones responsible for the development of mammalian male and female characteristics, respectively, differ only in the presence or absence of a methyl group. Steroids can also act via membrane receptors, controlling cellular events such as apoptosis and cell proliferation and more complex events such as behaviour.

Fatty acids represent a very specialized category of hormones. In arthropods and possibly annelids, hormones derived from farnesoic acid include the juvenile hormones that govern metamorphosis and reproduction (see "Molecule behind Biology," Box 25.4, Chapter 25). Prostaglandins and their relatives are important local regulators derived from arachidonic acid. They are involved in paracrine and autocrine regulation in all animals. First discovered in semen, they enhance the transport of sperm through the female reproductive tract by increasing the contractions of muscle cells in both vertebrates and insects. In at least some insects, prostaglandins act as endocrines: they are synthesized in the sperm storage organs of mated females and initiate egg laying by acting on the oviducts and possibly the nervous system.

35.1c Many Hormones Are Regulated by Feedback Pathways

The secretion of many hormones is regulated by feedback pathways, some of which operate partially or completely independently of neuronal controls. Most pathways are controlled by negative feedback, in which a product of the pathway inhibits an earlier step in the pathway. In vertebrates, secretion by the thyroid gland is regulated by a negative feedback loop **(Figure 35.3)**. Neurosecretory neurons in the hypothalamus secrete thyroid-releasing hormone (TRH) into a vein connecting the hypothalamus to the pituitary (neuroendocrine regulation). In response, the pituitary releases thyroid-stimulating hormone (TSH) into the blood, which stimulates the thyroid gland to release thyroid hormones (classical endocrine regulation). As the thyroid hormone concentration in the blood increases, it begins to inhibit TRH secretion by the hypothalamus. In turn, TSH and secretion of the thyroid hormones are reduced.

35.1d Body Processes Are Regulated by Coordinated Hormone Secretion

Although we mostly discuss individual hormones in the remainder of the chapter, body processes are affected by more than one hormone. The blood concentrations of glucose; fatty acids; and ions such as Ca^{2+}, K^+, and Na^+ are regulated by the coordinated activities of several hormones secreted by different glands. Similarly, body processes such as oxidative metabolism, digestion, growth, sexual development, and reactions to stress are all controlled by multiple hormones.

In many of these systems, negative feedback loops adjust the levels of secretion of hormones that act in antagonistic (opposing) ways, creating a balance in

Figure 35.3
A negative feedback loop regulating secretion of the thyroid hormones. As the concentration of thyroid hormones in the blood increases, the hormones inhibit an earlier step in the pathway (indicated by the negative sign).

their effects that maintains body homeostasis (see Chapter 42). Consider the regulation of fuel molecules such as glucose, fatty acids, and amino acids in the blood. We usually eat three meals a day and fast to some extent between meals. During these periods of eating and fasting, five hormone systems act in a coordinated fashion to keep the fuel levels in balance: (1) gastrin and ghrelin secreted by the stomach and secretin from the intestine; (2) insulin and glucagon, secreted by the pancreas; (3) growth hormone, secreted by the anterior pituitary; (4) epinephrine–norepinephrine, released by the sympathetic nervous system and the adrenal medulla; and (5) glucocorticoid hormones, released by the adrenal cortex.

The entire system of hormones regulating fuel metabolism resembles the fail-safe mechanisms designed by engineers in which redundancy, overlapping controls, feedback loops, and multiple safety valves ensure that vital functions are maintained at appropriate levels in the face of changing and even extreme circumstances.

STUDY BREAK

1. What are the functions of the endocrine and nervous systems? How are they the same, and how do they differ? What is the significance of this?
2. What are the major types of cell signalling that occur in the endocrine system? How do they work?

35.2 Mechanisms of Hormone Action

Hormones control cell functions by binding to receptor molecules on or in their target cells. Small quantities of hormones can typically produce profound effects in cells and body functions due to **amplification**. In amplification, an activated receptor activates many proteins, which then activate an even larger number of proteins for the next step in the cellular pathway and so on in each subsequent step (see Chapter 5). It has been estimated that, by amplification, a single molecule of epinephrine acting on a liver cell will liberate 106 molecules of glucose from stored glycogen.

35.2a The Secreted Hormone May Not Be in an Active Form

Many hormones are secreted in an inactive or less active form (a *prohormone*) and converted by target cells or enzymes in the blood or other tissues to the active form. The best-known example is thyroxine, discussed below. Many other hormones are subject to similar processes. **Ecdysone**, a steroid governing the formation of new cuticle in insects, is converted to the much more active functional hormone 20-OH ecdysone by the addition in the target cells of a single hydroxyl group. Peptide hormones are commonly synthesized as prohormones that

undergo post-translational conversion to the active forms in the source cell. In some cases, however, further conversion occurs once the hormone has been secreted. Angiotensin is a hormone that governs blood pressure in humans. It is secreted by the liver as angiotensinogen. An inactive form of angiotensin is cleaved from angiotensinogen by an enzyme. This inactive form is converted to the active hormone by angiotensin-converting enzyme (ACE). ACE inhibitors are often prescribed for control of high blood pressure.

35.2b Hydrophilic Hormones Bind to Surface Receptors, Activating Protein Kinases Inside Cells

Hormones that bind to receptor molecules in the plasma membrane produce their responses through signal transduction pathways. In brief, when a surface receptor binds a hormone, it transmits a signal through the plasma membrane. Within the cell, the signal is transduced, changing into a form that causes the cellular response **(Figure 35.4a)**. Typically, the reactions of signal transduction pathways involve protein kinases, which are enzymes that add phosphate groups to proteins. Adding a phosphate group to a protein may activate or inhibit it, depending on the protein and the reaction. The particular response produced by a hormone depends on the kinds of protein kinases activated in the cell and the types of target proteins they phosphorylate (Chapter 8). The receptor molecule may be a tyrosine kinase molecule, a receptor with a built-in protein kinase on the cytoplasmic side of the receptor itself, or it may be a G-protein-coupled receptor that secondarily activates protein kinases within the cell. These hormones generally act on functional proteins already present in the cell, such as enzymes, ion channels, transport proteins, and so on, although the signal transduction pathway may not stop at the cytoplasm: many growth factors and some peptide hormones ultimately affect events in the nucleus. Although action via membrane receptors is characteristic of and most extensively studied in peptide and amine hormones, many steroid and fatty acid hormones also exert some of their actions in this way.

The peptide hormone glucagon illustrates the mechanisms triggered by surface receptors. When glucagon binds to surface receptors on liver cells, it triggers a series of steps leading to the phosphorylation and activation of the enzyme governing the breakdown of glycogen stored in those cells into glucose.

35.2c Hydrophobic Hormones Bind to Receptors Inside Cells, Activating or Inhibiting Genetic Regulatory Proteins

After passing through the plasma membrane, the hydrophobic steroid and thyroid hormones bind to internal receptors in the nucleus or cytoplasm **(Figure 35.4b)**. Binding of the hormone activates the receptor, which

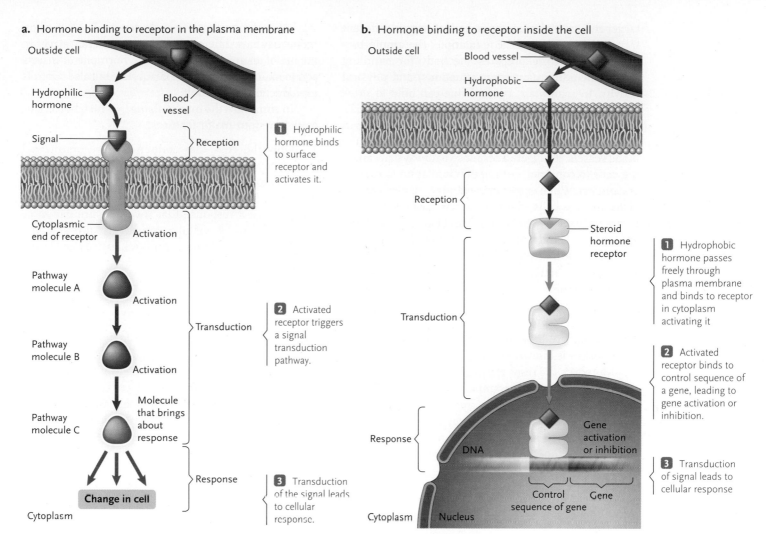

a. Hormone binding to receptor in the plasma membrane

Outside cell

Hydrophilic hormone

Blood vessel

Signal

Reception

Cytoplasmic end of receptor

Activation

Pathway molecule A

Activation

Pathway molecule B

Activation

Transduction

Pathway molecule C

Molecule that brings about response

Response

Change in cell

Cytoplasm

1 Hydrophilic hormone binds to surface receptor and activates it.

2 Activated receptor triggers a signal transduction pathway.

3 Transduction of the signal leads to cellular response.

b. Hormone binding to receptor inside the cell

Outside cell

Blood vessel

Hydrophobic hormone

Reception

Steroid hormone receptor

Transduction

Response

DNA

Gene activation or inhibition

Control sequence of gene

Gene

Cytoplasm

Nucleus

1 Hydrophobic hormone passes freely through plasma membrane and binds to receptor in cytoplasm activating it

2 Activated receptor binds to control sequence of a gene, leading to gene activation or inhibition.

3 Transduction of signal leads to cellular response

Figure 35.4

The reaction pathways activated by hormones that bind to receptor proteins in plasma membrane (a) or inside cells (b). In both mechanisms, the signal—the binding of the hormone to its receptor—is transduced to produce the cellular response. **a.** Hormone binding to a receptor in the plasma membrane **b.** Hormone binding to a receptor inside the cell.

then binds to a control sequence of specific genes. Depending on the gene, binding the control sequence either activates or inhibits its transcription, leading to changes in protein synthesis that accomplish the cellular response. The characteristics of the response depend on the specific genes controlled by the activated receptors and on the presence of other proteins that modify the activity of the receptor.

One of the actions of the steroid hormone aldosterone illustrates the mechanisms triggered by internal receptors. If blood pressure falls below optimal levels, aldosterone is secreted by the adrenal glands. The hormone circulates throughout the body in the blood but affects only cells (mostly in the kidney but also in sweat glands and the colon) that contain the aldosterone receptor in their cytoplasm (step 1 in Figure 35.4b). When activated by aldosterone, the receptor binds to the control sequence of a gene (step 2 in Figure 35.4b), leading to the synthesis of proteins that increase reabsorption of Na^+ by the kidney cells (step 3 in Figure 35.4b). The resulting increase in Na^+

concentration in body fluids increases water retention and, with it, blood volume. The increase in blood volume returns (increases) blood pressure back to normal, removing the stimulus for aldosterone secretion from the adrenal glands.

35.2d Target Cells May Respond to More Than One Hormone, and Different Target Cells May Respond Differently to the Same Hormone

A single target cell may have receptors for several hormones and respond differently to each hormone. Vertebrate liver cells have receptors for the pancreatic hormones insulin and glucagon. Insulin increases glucose uptake and conversion to glycogen, which decreases blood glucose levels, whereas glucagon stimulates the breakdown of glycogen into glucose, which increases blood glucose levels.

Conversely, particular hormones interact with different types of receptors in or on a range of target cells. Different responses are then triggered in each target cell type because the receptors trigger different transduction pathways. For example, the amine hormone epinephrine prepares the body for handling stress (including dangerous situations) and physical activity. In mammals, epinephrine can bind to three different plasma membrane-embedded receptors: α, β_1, and β_2 receptors. When epinephrine binds to α receptors on smooth muscle cells, such as those of the blood vessels, it triggers a response pathway that causes the cells to constrict, cutting off circulation to peripheral organs. When epinephrine binds to β_1 receptors on heart muscle cells, the contraction rate of the cells increases, which, in turn, enhances blood supply. When epinephrine binds to β_2 receptors on liver cells, it stimulates the breakdown of glycogen to glucose, which is released from the cell. The overall effect of these and a number of other responses to epinephrine secretion is to supply energy to the major muscles responsible for locomotion, preparing the animal for stress or for physical activity. Similar tissue-specific diversification of responses is known for many hormones.

Moreover, the response to a hormone may differ in different animals. For example, melatonin, an amine derived from tryptophan, is important in regulating daily and annual cycles in most animals. However, it also plays a role in regulating the salt gland of marine birds. Thyroxine promotes metamorphosis in amphibians but inhibits metamorphosis in cyclostomes. The same hormone may have different functions at different stages in the life of an animal. The juvenile hormone of insects acts to maintain insects in a larval state but also controls reproduction in the adult.

In summary, the mechanisms by which hormones work have four major features:

1. Only the cells that contain surface or internal receptors for a particular hormone respond to that hormone.
2. Once bound by their receptors, hormones may produce a response that involves stimulation or inhibition of cellular processes through the specific types of internal molecules activated by the hormone action.
3. Because of the amplification that occurs through both the surface and internal receptor mechanisms, hormones are effective in very small concentrations.
4. The response to a hormone differs among target organs.

In the next two sections, we discuss the major endocrine cells and glands of vertebrates. The locations of these cells and glands in mammals (including humans) and their functions are summarized in **Figure 35.5** and **Table 35.1**.

Figure 35.5
This diagram shows the major endocrine glands in a mammal's body, using a human and a bear as models.

Hypothalamus
Produces and secretes releasing and inhibiting hormones that regulate secretions by the anterior pituitary

Produces ADH and oxytocin, which are stored and released by the posterior pituitary

Pineal gland
Secretes melatonin

Anterior pituitary
Secretes ACTH, TSH, FSH, and LH, which stimulate other glands, as well as prolactin, GH, MSH, and endorphins

Posterior pituitary
Stores and releases ADH and oxytocin

Parathyroid glands
Secrete parathyroid hormone

Thyroid gland
Secretes thyroxine triiodothyronine, and calcitonin

Adrenal cortex
Secretes cortisol and aldosterone and small amounts of androgens

Adrenal medulla
Secretes epinephrine and norepinephrine

Islets of Langerhans (in pancreas)
Secrete insulin and glucagon

Ovaries
Secrete estrogens and progestins

Testes
Secrete androgens

Table 35.1 | **The Major Human Endocrine Glands and Hormones**

Secretory Tissue or Gland	Hormones	Molecular Class	Target Tissue	Principal Actions
Hypothalamus	Releasing and inhibiting hormones	Peptide	Anterior pituitary	Regulate secretion of anterior pituitary hormones
Anterior pituitary	Thyroid-stimulating hormone (TSH)	Peptide	Thyroid gland	Stimulates secretion of thyroid hormones and growth of thyroid gland
	Adrenocorticotropic hormone (ACTH)	Peptide	Adrenal cortex	Stimulates secretion of glucocorticoids by adrenal cortex
	Follicle-stimulating hormone (FSH)	Peptide	Ovaries in females, testes in males	Stimulates egg growth and development and secretion of sex hormones in females; stimulates sperm production in males
	Luteinizing hormone (LH)	Peptide	Ovaries in females, testes in males	Regulates ovulation in females and secretion of sex hormones in males
	Prolactin (PRL)	Peptide	Mammary glands	Stimulates breast development and milk secretion
	Growth hormone (GH)	Peptide	Bone, soft tissue	Stimulates growth of bones and soft tissues; helps control metabolism of glucose and other fuel molecules
	Melanocyte-stimulating hormone (MSH)	Peptide	Melanocytes in skin of some vertebrates	Promotes darkening of the skin
	Endorphins	Peptide	Pain pathways of PNS	Inhibit perception of pain
Posterior pituitary	Antidiuretic hormone (ADH)	Peptide	Kidneys	Raises blood volume and pressure by increasing water reabsorption in kidneys
	Oxytocin	Peptide	Uterus, mammary glands	Promotes uterine contractions; stimulates milk ejection from breasts
Thyroid gland	Calcitonin	Peptide	Bone	Lowers calcium concentration in blood
	Thyroxine and triiodothyronine	Amine	Most cells	Increase metabolic rate; essential for normal body growth
Parathyroid glands	Parathyroid hormone (PTH)	Peptide	Bone, kidneys, intestine	Raises calcium concentration in blood; stimulates vitamin D activation
Adrenal medulla	Epinephrine and norepinephrine	Amine	Sympathetic receptor sites throughout body	Reinforce sympathetic nervous system; contribute to responses to stress
Adrenal cortex	Aldosterone (mineralocorticoid)	Steroid	Kidney tubules	Helps control body's salt–water balance by increasing Na^+ reabsorption and K^+ excretion in kidneys
	Cortisol (glucocorticoid)	Steroid	Most body cells, particularly muscle, liver, and adipose cells	Increases blood glucose by promoting breakdown of proteins and fats
Testes	Androgens, such as testosterone*	Steroid	Various tissues	Control male reproductive system development and maintenance; most androgens are made by the testes
	Oxytocin	Peptide	Uterus	Promotes uterine contractions when seminal fluid is ejaculated into vagina during sexual intercourse
Ovaries	Estrogens, such as estradiol**	Steroid	Breasts, uterus, other tissues	Stimulate maturation of sex organs at puberty and development of secondary sexual characteristics
	Progestins, such as progesterone**	Steroid	Uterus	Prepare and maintain uterus for implantation of fertilized eggs and the growth and development of embryos

*Small amounts secreted by ovaries and adrenal cortex.
**Small amounts secreted by testes.

(continued)

Table 35.1 | The Major Human Endocrine Glands and Hormones (*continued*)

Secretory Tissue or Gland	Hormones	Molecular Class	Target Tissue	Principal Actions
Pancreas (islets of Langerhans)	Glucagon (alpha cells)	Peptide	Liver cells	Raises glucose concentration in blood; promotes release of glucose from glycogen stores and production from noncarbohydrates
	Insulin (beta cells)	Peptide	Most cells	Lowers glucose concentration in blood; promotes storage of glucose, fatty acids, and amino acids
Pineal gland	Melatonin	Amine	Brain, anterior pituitary, reproductive organs, immune system, possibly others	Helps synchronize body's biological clock with day length; may inhibit gonadotropins and initiation of puberty
Many cell types	Growth factors	Peptide	Most cells	Regulate cell division and differentiation
	Prostaglandins	Fatty acid	Various tissues	Have many diverse roles

In addition to these major endocrine organs, important hormones are also secreted by organs that have other primary functions, including the kidney, heart, liver, and intestine. In particular, the digestive system is the source of several peptide hormones, many of which are also produced elsewhere. It is the only known source for peptides such as gastrin, secretin, and ghrelin, which coordinate the digestive secretions of the gut and its associated glands and send signals associated with hunger to the brain. The gut is increasingly recognized as an important endocrine organ in many animals. Among vertebrates, it is a more important source for circulating levels of melatonin than the pineal body with which that hormone is traditionally associated. In insects, several peptide hormones, such as proctolin, produced by neuroendocrine cells in the CNS are also produced by cells in the intestine.

STUDY BREAK

1. What are the four major features of the mechanism by which hormones work?
2. Explain how one type of target cell could respond to different hormones, and how the same hormone could produce different effects in different cells.
3. Explain how a small amount of hormone can produce very large responses.

35.3 The Hypothalamus and Pituitary

Hormones of vertebrates work in coordination with the nervous system. The action of several hormones is closely coordinated by the hypothalamus–pituitary complex.

The hypothalamus is a region of the brain located in the floor of the cerebrum (see Chapter 36). The **pituitary**, consisting mostly of two fused lobes, is suspended just below the hypothalamus by a slender stalk of tissue that contains both neurons and blood vessels **(Figure 35.6)**. The **posterior pituitary** contains axons and endings of neurosecretory neurons that originate in the hypothalamus. The **anterior pituitary** contains non-neuronal endocrine cells that form a distinct gland. The two lobes are separate in structure and embryonic origins.

35.3a Under Regulatory Control by the Hypothalamus, the Anterior Pituitary Secretes Eight Hormones

The secretions of the anterior pituitary are under the control of peptide neurohormones, called **releasing hormones (RHs)** and **inhibiting hormones (IHs)**, produced by the hypothalamus. These neurohormones are carried in the blood to the anterior pituitary in a *portal vein,* a special vein that connects the capillaries of the two glands. The portal vein provides a critical link between the brain and the endocrine system, ensuring that most of the blood reaching the anterior pituitary first passes through the hypothalamus.

Hypothalamus
Pituitary gland

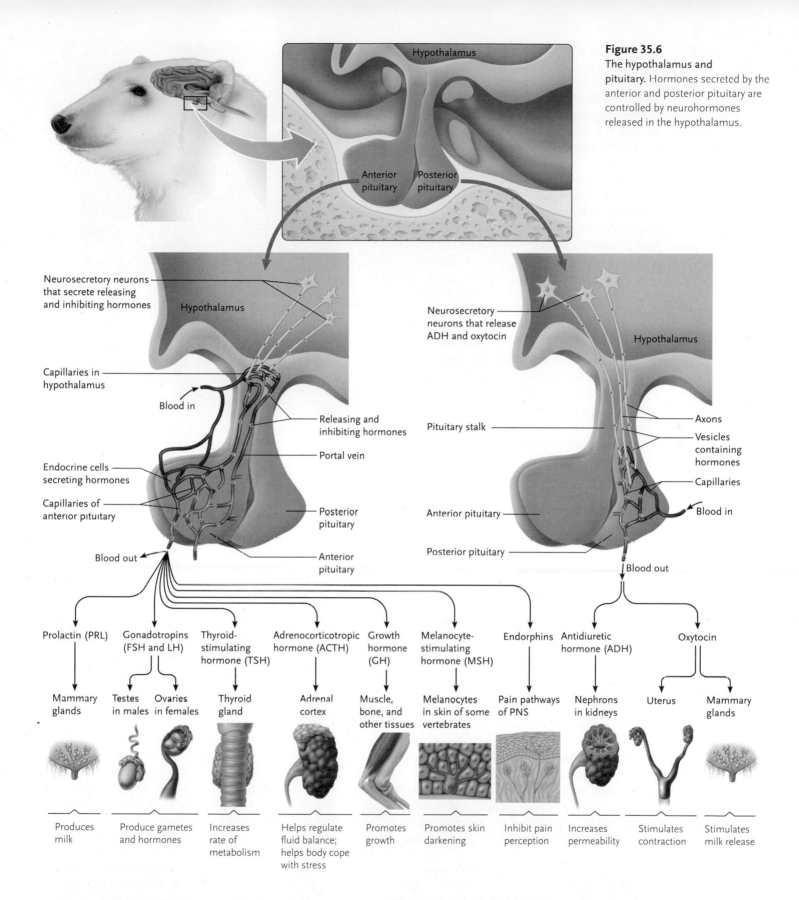

Figure 35.6
The hypothalamus and pituitary. Hormones secreted by the anterior and posterior pituitary are controlled by neurohormones released in the hypothalamus.

RHs and IHs are **tropic hormones** (*tropic* means "stimulating," not to be confused with *trophic,* which means "nourishing") that regulate hormone secretion by another endocrine gland, in this case, the anterior pituitary. The hormones of the anterior pituitary, in turn, control many other endocrine glands of the body and some body processes directly.

Secretion of hypothalamic RHs is controlled by neurons containing receptors that monitor the blood to detect changes in body chemistry and temperature. For example, when body temperature drops, TRH is secreted. Input to the hypothalamus also comes through numerous connections from control centres elsewhere in the brain, including the brain stem and the limbic system. Negative feedback pathways regulate secretion of the releasing hormones, such as the pathway-regulating TRH secretion.

Under the control of the hypothalamus, the anterior pituitary secretes six major hormones into the bloodstream (see Figure 35.6): prolactin, growth hormone, thyroid-stimulating hormone, adreno-corticotropic hormone, follicle-stimulating hormone, and luteinizing hormone. **Prolactin (PRL)**, a *nontropic hormone* (a hormone that does not regulate hormone secretion by another endocrine gland), influences reproductive activities and parental care in verte-brates. In mammals, PRL stimulates development of the secretory cells of mammary glands during late pregnancy and milk synthesis after birth. Stimulation of the mammary glands and the nipples, as occurs during suckling, leads to PRL release. PRL occurs in nonmammalian vertebrates, where it has a variety of functions. In fish, for example, it is among the hor-mones controlling water balance. In all vertebrates, it has a role in promoting both maternal and paternal behaviour.

Growth hormone (GH) stimulates cell division, protein synthesis, and bone growth in children and adolescents, thereby causing body growth. GH also stimulates protein synthesis and cell division in adults. For these actions, GH acts as a tropic hormone by binding to target tissues, mostly liver cells, causing them to release **insulin-like growth factor (IGF)**, a pep-tide that directly stimulates growth processes. GH also acts as a nontropic hormone to control a number of major metabolic processes in mammals of all ages, including the conversion of glycogen to glucose and fats to fatty acids as a means of regulating their levels in the blood. GH also stimulates body cells to take up fatty acids and amino acids and limits the rate at which muscle cells take up glucose. These actions help main-tain the availability of glucose and fatty acids to tissues and organs between feedings; this is particularly important for the brain. In humans, deficiencies in GH secretion during childhood produce *pituitary dwarfs,* who remain small in stature **(Figure 35.7).** Over-production of GH during childhood or adolescence, often due to a tumour of the anterior pituitary, pro-duces *pituitary giants,* who may grow to above 2 m in height.

Many of the other hormones secreted by the anterior pituitary are tropic hormones that control endocrine glands elsewhere in the body. **Thyroid-stimulating hormone (TSH)** stimulates the thyroid gland to grow in size and secrete thyroid hormones. **Adrenocorticotropic hormone (ACTH)** triggers hor-mone secretion by cells in the adrenal cortex. **Follicle-stimulating hormone (FSH)** affects egg development

Figure 35.7
The results of overproduction and underproduction of growth hormone by the anterior pituitary. The man on the left is of normal height. The man in the centre is a pituitary giant, whose pituitary produced excess GH during childhood and adolescence. The man on the right is a pituitary dwarf, whose pituitary produced too little GH.

in females and sperm production in males. It also has a tropic effect by stimulating the secretion of sex hormones in female mammals. **Luteinizing hormone (LH)** regulates part of the menstrual cycle in human females and the secretion of sex hormones in males. FSH and LH are grouped together as **gonadotropins** because they regulate the activity of the gonads (ovaries and testes). The roles of the gonadotropins and sex hormones in the reproductive cycle are described in Chapter 33.

Melanocyte-stimulating hormone (MSH) and **endorphins** are nontropic hormones secreted by the anterior pituitary. MSH is named because of its effect in some vertebrates on melanocytes, skin cells that con-tain the black pigment melanin. An increase in secre-tion of MSH produces a marked darkening of the skin of fishes, amphibians, and reptiles. The darkening is produced by a dispersal of melanin in melanocytes so that it covers a greater area. In humans, an increase in MSH secretion also causes skin darkening, although the effect is by no means as obvious as in the other vertebrates mentioned. MSH secretion increases in pregnant women. Combined with the effects of increased estrogens, MSH results in increased skin pigmentation. The effects are reversed after the birth of the child.

Endorphins, nontropic peptide hormones produced by the hypothalamus and pituitary, are also released by the intermediate lobe of the pituitary. In the peripheral nervous system (PNS), endorphins act as neurotransmitters in pathways that control pain, thereby inhibiting the perception of pain. Hence, endorphins are often called natural painkillers.

35.3b The Posterior Pituitary Secretes Two Hormones into the Body Circulation

The neurosecretory neurons in the posterior pituitary secrete two nontropic peptide hormones, antidiuretic hormone and oxytocin, directly into the body circulation (see Figure 35.6).

Antidiuretic hormone (ADH, also known as vasopressin) stimulates kidney cells to absorb more water from urine, thereby increasing the volume of the blood. The hormone is released when sensory receptor cells of the hypothalamus detect an increase in the blood's Na^+ concentration during periods of dehydration or after a salty meal. Ethyl alcohol and caffeine inhibit ADH secretion, explaining in part why alcoholic drinks and coffee increase the volume of urine excreted. Nicotine and emotional stress, in contrast, stimulate ADH secretion and water retention. After severe stress is relieved, the return to normal ADH secretion often makes a trip to the bathroom among our most pressing needs. The hypothalamus also releases a flood of ADH when an injury results in heavy blood loss or some other event triggers a severe drop in blood pressure. ADH helps maintain blood pressure by reducing water loss and by causing small blood vessels in some tissues to constrict.

Hormones with structure and action similar to those of ADH are also secreted in fishes, amphibians, reptiles, and birds. In amphibians, these ADH-like hormones increase the amount of water entering the body through the skin and from the urinary bladder.

Oxytocin stimulates the ejection of milk from the mammary glands of a nursing mother. Stimulation of the nipples in suckling sends neuronal signals to the hypothalamus and leads to the release of oxytocin from the posterior pituitary. The released oxytocin stimulates more oxytocin secretion by a positive feedback mechanism. Oxytocin causes the smooth muscle cells surrounding the mammary glands to contract, forcibly expelling the milk through the nipples. The entire cycle, from the onset of suckling to milk ejection, takes less than a minute in mammals. Oxytocin also plays a key role in childbirth (see Chapter 33).

In males, oxytocin is secreted into the seminal fluid by the testes. When the seminal fluid is ejaculated into the vagina during sexual intercourse, the hormone stimulates contractions of the uterus that aid movement of sperm through the female reproductive tract.

STUDY BREAK

1. Distinguish between tropic and nontropic hormones. What is the significance of having different types?
2. Distinguish between the anterior and the posterior pituitary. How is the release of hormones from each of these controlled?
3. If oxytocin stimulates more oxytocin release, what terminates milk ejection.

35.4 Other Major Endocrine Glands of Vertebrates

In addition to the hypothalamus and pituitary, the body has seven major endocrine glands or tissues, many of them regulated by the hypothalamus–pituitary connection. Included are the thyroid gland, parathyroid glands, adrenal medulla, adrenal cortex, gonads, pancreas, and pineal gland (shown in Figure 35.5 and summarized in Table 35.1).

35.4a The Thyroid Hormones Stimulate Metabolism, Development, and Maturation

The **thyroid gland** is located in the front of the throat in all terrestrial vertebrates, including humans, and is shaped like a bowtie. It also secretes the same hormones in all vertebrates. The thyroid hormones have an extraordinarily wide range of effects. The primary thyroid hormone, **thyroxine,** is known as T_4 because it contains four iodine atoms. The thyroid also secretes smaller amounts of a closely related hormone, **triiodothyronine** or T_3, which contains three iodine atoms. A supply of iodine in the diet is necessary for production of these hormones. Normally, their concentrations are kept at finely balanced levels in the blood by negative feedback loops such as the loop described in Figure 35.3. Most of the circulating hormone is bound to a transport protein, thyroglobulin, and only the free hormone is available to enter cells.

Once inside a cell, the T_4 is deiodinated, forming T_3. T_3 is the form that combines with internal receptors in the nucleus. Binding of T_3 to receptors alters gene expression, which brings about many of the hormone's effects.

Thyroid hormones are vital to growth, development, maturation, and metabolism in all vertebrates. They interact with GH for their effects on growth and development. Thyroid hormones also increase the sensitivity of many body

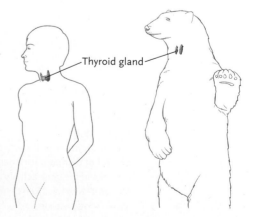

Thyroid gland

cells to the effects of epinephrine and norepinephrine, hormones released by the adrenal medulla as part of the *fight-or-flight response* (discussed further below).

Insufficient iodine in the diet can cause *goitre*, enlargement of the thyroid. Without iodine, the thyroid cannot make T_3 and T_4 in response to stimulation by TSH. Because the thyroid hormone concentration remains low in the blood, TSH continues to be secreted, and the thyroid grows in size. Dietary iodine deficiency has been eliminated in developed regions of the world by the addition of iodine to table salt.

In amphibians, rising concentrations of thyroid hormones trigger **metamorphosis**, or a change in body form from tadpole to adult **(Figure 35.8)**. Teleost fish undergo a form of metamorphosis during their early development, and the transformation from a hatchling *larval* form to a juvenile form is also triggered by rising concentrations of thyroid hormones. Curiously, however, the opposite is true in the agnathan lamprey. Their metamorphosis is triggered by decreasing concentrations of T_4. Thyroid hormones also contribute to seasonal moulting, leading to changes in the plumage of birds and coat colour in mammals.

The thyroid also has specialized cells that secrete **calcitonin**, a peptide originally discovered in fish by Harold Copp, working at the University of British Columbia. The hormone lowers the level of Ca^{2+} in the blood by inhibiting the ongoing dissolution of calcium from bone. Calcitonin secretion is stimulated when Ca^{2+} levels in blood rise above the normal range and inhibited when Ca^{2+} levels fall below the normal range.

Although the specialized cells of the thyroid are the principal source, calcitonin is also synthesized in the lung and intestine. In nonmammalian vertebrates, a separate gland, the ultimobrachial gland, produces calcitonin.

35.4b The Parathyroid Glands Regulate Ca²⁺ Levels in the Blood

The **parathyroid glands** occur only in tetrapod vertebrates (amphibians, reptiles, birds, and mammals). Each is a spherical structure about the size of a pea. Mammals have four parathyroids located on the posterior surface of the thyroid gland, two on each side. The single hormone they produce, a nontropic hormone called **parathyroid hormone (PTH)**, is secreted in response to a fall in blood Ca^{2+} levels. PTH stimulates bone cells to dissolve the mineral matter of bone tissues, releasing both calcium and phosphate ions into the blood. The released Ca^{2+} is available for enzyme activation, conduction of nerve signals across synapses, muscle contraction, blood clotting, and other uses. How blood Ca^{2+} levels control PTH and calcitonin secretion is shown in **Figure 35.9.**

PTH also stimulates enzymes in the kidneys that convert **vitamin D**, a steroidlike molecule, into its fully active form in the body. The activated vitamin D increases the absorption of Ca^{2+} and phosphates from ingested food by promoting the synthesis of a calcium-binding protein in the intestine. It also increases the release of Ca^{2+} from bone in response to PTH.

PTH underproduction causes Ca^{2+} concentration to fall steadily in the blood, disturbing nerve and muscle function—the muscles twitch and contract uncontrollably, and convulsions and cramps occur. Without treatment, the condition is usually fatal because the severe muscular contractions, particularly of the muscles of the abdomen and thorax, interfere with breathing. Overproduction of PTH results in the loss of so much calcium from the bones that they become thin and fragile. At the same time, the elevated Ca^{2+} concentration in the blood causes calcium deposits to form in soft tissues, especially in the lungs, arteries, and kidneys (where the deposits form kidney stones).

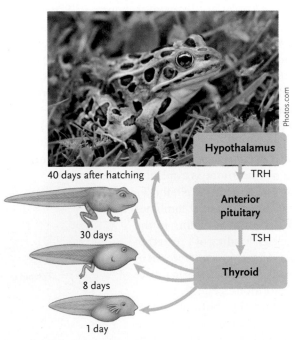

Figure 35.8
Metamorphosis of a tadpole into an adult frog, under the control of thyroid hormones. As part of the metamorphosis, changes in the gene activity lead to a change from an aquatic to a terrestrial habitat. TRH: thyroid-releasing hormone; TSH: thyroid-stimulating hormone.

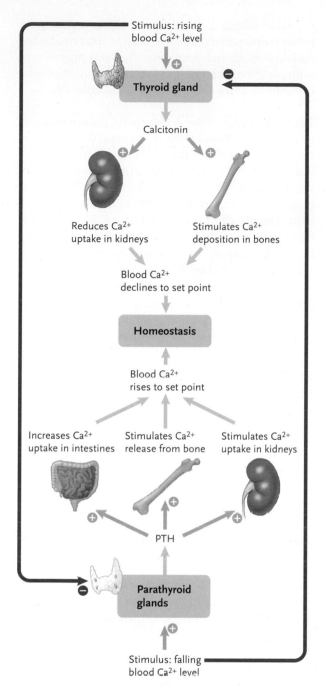

Figure 35.9
Negative feedback control of PTH and calcitonin secretion by blood Ca²⁺ levels.

Although fish do not have a parathyroid gland, they produce PTH, and PTH receptors are known to be present in fish, but the origin of the hormone and its precise function remain uncertain.

35.4c The Adrenal Medulla Releases Two Fight-or-Flight Hormones

The adrenal glands (*ad* = next to; *renes* = kidneys) of mammals have two distinct regions. The central region, the **adrenal medulla**, contains highly modified neurosecretory neurons that have lost their axons and dendrites. The tissue surrounding it, the **adrenal cortex**,

contains non-neural endocrine cells. The two regions secrete hormones with entirely different functions. Nonmammalian vertebrates have glands equivalent to the adrenal medulla and adrenal cortex of mammals, but the two parts are separate entities. Most of the hormones produced by these glands have essentially the same functions in all vertebrates. The only major exception is aldosterone, which is secreted by the adrenal cortex or its equivalent only in tetrapod vertebrates.

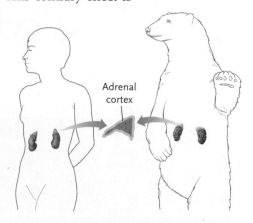

In most species, the adrenal medulla secretes two nontropic amine hormones, **epinephrine** and **norepinephrine**, which are **catecholamines**, chemicals derived from tyrosine that can act as hormones or neurotransmitters. They bind to receptors in the plasma membranes of their target cells. Norepinephrine is also released as a neurotransmitter by neurons of the sympathetic nervous system.

Epinephrine and norepinephrine reinforce the action of the sympathetic nervous system and are secreted when the body encounters stresses such as emotional excitement, danger (fight-or-flight situations), anger, fear, infections, injury, and even midterm and final exams. Epinephrine in particular prepares the body for handling stress or physical activity. The heart rate increases. Glycogen and fats break down, releasing glucose and fatty acids into the blood as fuel molecules. In the heart, skeletal muscles, and lungs, the blood vessels dilate to increase blood flow. Elsewhere in the body, the blood vessels constrict, raising blood pressure, reducing blood flow to the intestine and kidneys, and inhibiting smooth muscle contractions, which reduces water loss and slows down the digestive system. Airways in the lungs also dilate, helping to increase the flow of air.

The effects of norepinephrine on heart rate, blood pressure, and blood flow to the heart muscle are similar to those of epinephrine. However, in contrast to epinephrine, norepinephrine causes blood vessels in skeletal muscles to constrict. This contrary effect is largely cancelled out because epinephrine is secreted in much greater quantities.

35.4d The Adrenal Cortex Secretes Two Groups of Steroid Hormones

The adrenal cortex of mammals secretes two major classes of steroid hormones: **glucocorticoids** help maintain the blood concentration of glucose and other fuel molecules, and **mineralocorticoids** regulate the levels of Na$^+$ and K$^+$ ions in the blood and extracellular fluid.

The Glucocorticoids. The glucocorticoids help maintain glucose levels in the blood by three major mechanisms: (1) stimulating the synthesis of glucose from noncarbohydrate sources such as fats and proteins; (2) reducing glucose uptake by body cells except those in the CNS; and (3) promoting the breakdown of fats and proteins, which releases fatty acids and amino acids into the blood as alternative fuels when glucose supplies are low. The favouring of glucose uptake in the CNS keeps the brain well supplied with glucose between meals and during periods of extended fasting. **Cortisol** is the major glucocorticoid secreted by the adrenal cortex.

Secretion of glucocorticoids is ultimately under the control of the hypothalamus **(Figure 35.10)**. Low glucose concentrations in the blood, or elevated levels of epinephrine secreted by the adrenal medulla in response to stress, are detected in the hypothalamus, leading to secretion of the tropic hormone ACTH by the anterior pituitary. ACTH promotes the secretion of glucocorticoids by the adrenal cortex.

Glucocorticoids also have anti-inflammatory properties; consequently, they are used to treat conditions such as arthritis and dermatitis. They also suppress the immune system and are used in the treatment of autoimmune diseases such as rheumatoid arthritis.

The Mineralocorticoids. In tetrapods, the mineralocorticoids, primarily **aldosterone**, increase the amount of Na$^+$ reabsorbed from the urine in the kidneys and absorbed from foods in the intestine. They also reduce the amount of Na$^+$ secreted by salivary and sweat glands and increase the rate of K$^+$ excretion by the kidneys. The net effect is to keep Na$^+$ and K$^+$ balanced at the levels required for normal cellular functions, including those of the nervous system. Secretion of aldosterone is linked tightly to blood volume and indirectly to blood pressure. The adrenal cortex also secretes small amounts of androgens, steroid sex hormones responsible for maintenance of male characteristics, which are synthesized primarily by the gonads.

35.4e The Gonadal Sex Hormones Regulate the Development of Reproductive Systems, Sexual Characteristics, and Mating Behaviour

The **gonads**, the testes and ovaries, are the primary source of sex hormones in vertebrates. The steroid hormones they produce, the **androgens**, **estrogens**, and **progestins**, have similar functions in regulating the development of male and female reproductive systems, sexual characteristics, and mating behaviour. Both males and females produce all three types of hormones, but in different proportions. Androgen production is predominant in males, whereas estrogen and progestin production is predominant in females. An outline of the actions of these hormones is presented here; a more complete picture was given in Chapter 33.

The **testes** (singular, **testis**) of male vertebrates secrete androgens, steroid hormones that stimulate and control the development and maintenance of male reproductive systems. The principal androgen is testosterone, the male sex hormone. In young

Figure 35.10

Pathways linking secretion of glucocorticoids to low blood sugar and epinephrine secretion in response to stress.

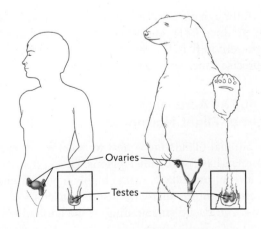

adult males, a jump in **testosterone** levels stimulates puberty and the development of secondary sexual characteristics, including the growth of facial and body hair, muscle development, changes in vocal cord morphology, and development of normal sex drive. The synthesis and secretion of testosterone by cells in the testes are controlled by the release of LH from the anterior pituitary, which, in turn, is controlled by **gonadotropin-releasing hormone (GnRH)**, a tropic hormone secreted by the hypothalamus.

Androgens are natural types of **anabolic steroids**, hormones that stimulate muscle development. Natural and synthetic anabolic steroids have been in the news over the years because of their use by bodybuilders and other athletes from sports in which muscular strength is important.

The **ovaries** of females produce estrogens, steroid hormones that stimulate and control the development and maintenance of female reproductive systems. The principal estrogen is **estradiol**, which stimulates maturation of sex organs at puberty and the development of secondary sexual characteristics. Ovaries also produce progestins, principally **progesterone**, the steroid hormone that prepares and maintains the uterus for implantation of a fertilized egg and the subsequent growth and development of an embryo. The synthesis and secretion of progesterone by cells in the ovaries are controlled by the release of FSH from the anterior pituitary, which, in turn, is controlled by the same GnRH as in males.

35.4f The Pancreatic Islets of Langerhans Hormones Regulate Glucose Metabolism

Most of the **pancreas**, a relatively large gland located just behind the stomach, forms an exocrine gland that secretes digestive enzymes into the small intestine (see Chapter 40). About 2% of the cells in the pancreas are endocrine cells that form the **islets of Langerhans**. Found in all vertebrates, the islets secrete the peptide hormones insulin and glucagon into the bloodstream.

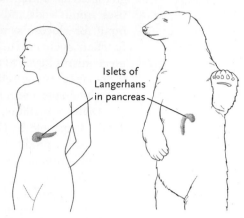

Islets of Langerhans in pancreas

Insulin and glucagon regulate the metabolism of fuel substances in the body. **Insulin** (see "Molecule behind Biology," Box 35.1) is secreted by *beta cells* in the islets. It acts mainly on nonworking skeletal muscles, liver cells, and adipose tissue (fat). Brain cells do not require insulin for glucose uptake. Insulin lowers blood glucose, fatty acid, and amino acid levels and promotes their storage. The actions of insulin include stimulation of glucose transport into cells, glycogen synthesis from glucose, uptake of fatty acids by adipose tissue cells, fat synthesis from fatty acids, and protein synthesis from amino acids. Insulin inhibits glycogen degradation to glucose, fat degradation to fatty acids, and protein degradation to amino acids.

MOLECULE BEHIND BIOLOGY 35.1

Insulin: More than Diabetes

Insulin was discovered in 1922 by J. R. Banting and his colleagues, J. J. R. McLeod, Charles Best, and James Collip, working at the University of Toronto. Banting and McLeod were awarded the Nobel Prize in 1923. (They were disturbed that their colleagues had not been recognized and shared the prize with them, Banting with Best, and McLeod with Collip.) In 1955, Frederick Sanger of Cambridge University worked out insulin's complete amino acid sequence (the first protein to be fully sequenced) and was awarded a Nobel Prize in 1958 for this work.

Insulin is a very large peptide of 51 amino acids. Molecular studies show that the insulin gene is present in all vertebrates but is absent from invertebrates. Insulin is a member of a family of genes. Two other members of that family encode two structurally related peptides, insulin-like growth factor (IGF) I and II. Although they are similar in structure to insulin, they have different but structurally related receptors, and their cellular action is different. They act as growth factors, regulating cell and tissue growth. IGFs are widely distributed in animals, protists, bacteria, and fungi. In molluscs, insects, and nematodes, these insulin-like peptides (ILPs) are neurohormones, expressed in neurosecretory cells in the brain. Surgical removal of these cells and their reimplantation demonstrate that they control growth, like the IGFs in vertebrates. The impact of these studies on the origin and evolution of the insulin gene is not yet clear.

Glucagon, secreted by *alpha cells* in the islets, has effects opposite to those of insulin: it stimulates glycogen, fat, and protein degradation. Glucagon also uses amino acids and other noncarbohydrates as the input for glucose synthesis; this aspect of glucagon function operates during fasting. Negative feedback mechanisms keyed to the concentration of glucose in the blood control secretion of both insulin and glucagon to maintain glucose homeostasis **(Figure 35.11)**.

Diabetes mellitus, a disease that afflicts more than 2 million people in Canada, results from problems with insulin production or action. The three classic diabetes symptoms are frequent urination, increased thirst (and consequently increased fluid intake), and increased appetite. Frequent urination occurs because the ability of body cells to take up glucose is impaired in diabetics, leading to abnormally high glucose concentration in the blood. Excretion of the excess glucose in the urine requires water to carry it, which causes increased fluid loss and frequent trips to the bathroom.

The need to replace the excreted water causes increased thirst. Increased appetite comes about because cells have low glucose levels as a result of the insulin defect; therefore, proteins and fats are broken down as energy sources. Food intake is necessary to offset the negative energy balance, or weight loss will occur. Two of these classic symptoms gave the disease its name: diabetes is derived from a Greek word meaning "siphon," referring to the frequent urination, and mellitus, a Latin word meaning "sweetened with honey," refers to the sweet taste of a diabetic's urine. (Before modern blood or urine tests were developed, physicians tasted a patient's urine to detect the disease.)

The disease occurs in two major forms, called *type 1* and *type 2*. Type 1 diabetes, which occurs in about 10% of diabetics, results from insufficient insulin secretion by the pancreas. This type of diabetes is usually caused by an autoimmune reaction that destroys pancreatic beta cells. To survive, type 1 diabetics must receive regular insulin injections (typically, a genetically engineered human insulin called Humulin); careful dieting and exercise also have beneficial effects, because active skeletal muscles do not require insulin to take up and utilize glucose.

In type 2 diabetes, insulin is usually secreted at or above normal levels, but the target cells of affected people have significantly reduced responsiveness to the hormone compared with the cells of normal people. About 90% of patients in the developed world with type 2 diabetes are obese. A genetic predisposition can also be a factor. Most affected people can lead a normal life by controlling their diet and weight, exercising, and taking drugs that enhance insulin action or secretion.

Diabetes has long-term effects on the body. Its cells, unable to utilize glucose as an energy source, start breaking down proteins and fats to generate energy. The protein breakdown weakens blood vessels throughout the body, particularly in the arms and legs and in critical regions such as the kidneys and retina of the eye. The circulation becomes so poor that tissues degenerate in the arms, legs, and feet. At advanced stages of the disease, bleeding in the retina causes blindness. The breakdown of circulation in the kidneys can lead to kidney failure. In addition, in type 1 diabetes, acidic products of fat breakdown (ketones) are produced in abnormally high quantities and accumulate in the blood. The resulting lowering of blood pH can disrupt heart and brain function, leading to coma and death if the disease is untreated.

35.4g The Pineal Gland Regulates Some Biological Rhythms

The **pineal gland** is found at different locations in the brains of vertebrates. In most vertebrates, it is on the surface of the brain just under the skull and is directly sensitive to light. For the most part in birds and mammals the gland is exclusively endocrine and no longer involved in photoreception. The pineal gland regulates some biological rhythms.

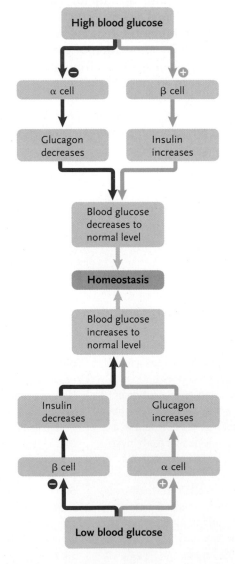

Figure 35.11

The action of insulin and glucagon in maintaining the concentration of blood glucose at an optimal level.

PEOPLE BEHIND BIOLOGY 35.2

William Rowan, University of Alberta

In the 1920s, it was generally accepted that birds migrated south from Canada in response to falling temperatures. William Rowan of the University of Alberta had a different view. Recognizing that temperature is an unreliable indicator of seasons, he hypothesized that day length was important. In addition, he recognized that migration was simply part of the annual breeding cycle: birds migrating south were known to have inactive reproductive organs, which became active when they returned in the spring. Rowan conducted two very simple but crucial experiments. In the first, he exposed Juncos (*Junco hyemalis*) to artificially lengthened daily light in the autumn; their gonads became active. In the second, he used 500 crows. These were caged in the autumn, and half were exposed to increasing day length, and the others to natural day length. He dyed their tails yellow and released them, alerting surrounding homesteaders to be on the lookout for crows with yellow tails. Those exposed to increased day length headed north, whereas those experiencing normal day length headed south. The association of day length with migration and gonadal development implicated the endocrine system, and these simple experiments set in motion the entire field of photobiology. Rowan is recognized as among the most influential biologists in the field.

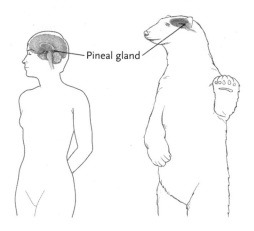

Pineal gland

The earliest vertebrates had a third, light-sensitive eye at the top of the head, and *Sphenodon* and some lizards have an eyelike structure in this location. In most vertebrates, the third eye became modified into a pineal gland, which in many groups retains some degree of photosensitivity. In mammals, it is too deeply buried in the brain to be affected directly by light; nonetheless, specialized photoreceptors in the eyes make connections to the pineal gland.

The pineal gland secretes the amine hormone **melatonin**, derived from tryptophan, which helps maintain daily biorhythms. Secretion of melatonin is regulated by an inhibitory pathway. Light hitting the eyes generates signals that inhibit melatonin secretion; consequently, the hormone is secreted most actively during periods of darkness. Melatonin targets a part of the hypothalamus called the *suprachiasmatic nucleus,* which is the primary structure coordinating body activity to a daily cycle. The nightly release of melatonin may help synchronize the biological clock with daily cycles of light and darkness. The physical and mental discomfort associated with jet lag may reflect the time required for melatonin secretion to reset a traveller's daily biological clock to match the period of daylight in a new time zone.

Melatonin occurs throughout the animal kingdom, as well as in many plants and fungi. In some fishes, amphibians, and reptiles, melatonin and other hormones produce changes in skin colour through their effects on *melanophores,* the pigment-containing cells of the skin. Skin colour may vary with the season, the animal's breeding status, or the colour of the background. In invertebrates, it is known to be important in the control of diurnal (daily) rhythms.

STUDY BREAK

1. What are the hormones controlling Ca^{2+} levels in the blood of vertebrates and how do they control Ca^{2+} levels? Why is it important to control Ca^{2+} levels?
2. Distinguish between the adrenal medulla and the adrenal cortex. What hormones do they secrete and what are their functions?
3. How are levels of glucose in the blood maintained?
4. How do you explain the fact that both epinephrine and norepinephrine produce the same effect in some cells but different effects in other cells?

35.5 Endocrine Systems in Invertebrates

Some invertebrates have fewer hormones, regulating a narrower range of body processes and responses, than vertebrates. However, in even the simplest animals, such as the cnidarian *Hydra,* hormones produced by neurosecretory neurons control the reproduction,

The notion of *stress* may be familiar to all as a vague concept. It was originated by Hans Selye, working with rats at the University of Montreal, as the "General Adaptation Syndrome," in which what he called "nocuous agents" ranging from physical damage to psychological events led to the activation of the fight-or-flight response. This was characterized at the time as the activation of the hypothalamus–pituitary pathway leading to the release of a number of hormones, particularly those from the adrenal glands, which led to increased heart rate and blood pressure. They also lead to release of glucose and fatty acids into the blood and increased blood flow to heart, lungs and skeletal muscle. This prepares the body for handling stress or physical activity. They reduce blood flow to organs not involved in the fight-or-flight response. If stress persists, however, continued release of these hormones causes cessation of growth; and, in severe cases, tissue damage and, ultimately, death.

Although we are accustomed to thinking of stress as a human or mammalian phenomenon, it has emerged as a response in a wide range of animals. Any unaccustomed sensory input (whether from external or internal events) leads to release of many hormones, and if the input continues, this can result in pathology or death. Stress, with the release of the corticosteroid hormones, is well studied in most vertebrates. Even in cockroaches, forced activity or forced inactivity will cause the release of many neurohormones, and the insect will die.

growth, and development of some body features. In annelids, arthropods, and molluscs, endocrine cells and glands produce hormones that regulate development, reproduction, water balance, heart rate, sugar levels, and behaviour.

The known vertebrate hormones, particularly the peptides, also occur in a wide range of organisms. Thus, insulin-like hormones can be found in most invertebrates, and receptors are known from insects and nematodes. The protist *Tetrahymena* binds and exhibits responses to insulin and T_4. Whereas some hormones, such as the peptide proctolin and the insect juvenile hormones, do not occur in vertebrates, many of the growing number of peptide hormones identified in invertebrates have structural homologues in the vertebrates, although their functions may be different. Some peptides controlling diuresis in insects are structural homologues of vertebrate corticotropin-releasing factor. Other diuretic peptides in insects are related to calcitonin. The larva of the tapeworm *Spirometra mansonoides* has developed the capacity to secrete vertebrate growth hormone so that its host rat grows larger.

The endocrinology of the more complex invertebrates, formerly thought to be relatively simple, is emerging as very complex: about 200 bioactive peptides have thus far been described in insects, which are probably more closely governed by hormones than any other animals. The development of the eggs and the egg-laying behaviour of insects are controlled by more than a dozen hormones.

35.5a Hormones Regulate Development in Insects

Among the best known invertebrate hormonal systems is the one governing growth and development in insects **(Figure 35.12)**. As insects grow, they undergo a series of moults during which a new cuticle is laid down beneath the old cuticle and the old cuticle is shed (see Chapter 25). The signal to the epidermal cells to begin the process is provided by a steroid hormone, ecdysone, from the prothoracic glands. The prothoracic glands are stimulated to secrete ecdysone by a tropic peptide, prothoracicotropic hormone (PTTH), produced in neuroendocrine cells in the brain and released from the corpus cardiacum. The corpus cardiacum secretes several other hormones and contains both the nerve endings of neurons in the brain and neuroendocrine cells that lack axons and dendrites.

The corpus allatum is an endocrine gland that secretes **juvenile hormone**, a fatty acid derivative (see "Molecule behind Biology," Box 25.4, Chapter 25). Juvenile hormone controls metamorphosis: when it is present, the insect remains larval. In its absence, the next moult is metamorphic, producing a pupa and then an adult in those insects with a pupal stage or proceeding directly to the adult in those lacking a pupal stage. In the adult of most insects, the corpus allatum becomes active once more, secreting juvenile hormone and stimulating a number of reproductive processes, especially egg development. The secretion of juvenile hormone by the corpus allatum is controlled by both inhibitory and stimulatory tropic peptides from the brain.

The intricate process of shedding the old cuticle involves complex behaviours that are controlled by the interaction of up to five neurohormones, and the hardening of the new cuticle requires a sixth.

Hormones that control moulting have also been detected in crustaceans, including lobsters, crabs, and crayfish. During the period between moults, **moult-inhibiting hormone (MIH)**, a peptide neurohormone secreted by cells in the eyestalks (extensions of the brain leading to the eyes), inhibits

Figure 35.12
The roles of brain hormone, ecdysone, and juvenile hormone in the development of a silkworm moth.

Neurosecretory neurons in brain

Corpora cardiaca

Corpora allata

1 Prothoracicotropic hormone (PTTH) stimulates the prothoracic glands to release ecdysone.

Brain hormone

Juvenile hormone

(present)   (absent)

Prothoracic glands

2 Ecdysone promotes growth of a new cuticle under the old one, and declining levels of ecdysone lead to the release of a cascade of peptide hormones that control the intricate process of ecdysis, the shedding of the old cuticle.

Ecdysone (moulting hormone)

3 If the concentration of juvenile hormone (JH) is high, the moulting produces a larger larva.

Larva

Larval moulting

4 If the JH is absent, the moulting leads to pupation.

Larva

Pupation

5 After the adult emerges from the pupa, JH levels rise again and help trigger full mature sexual behaviour.

Pupa

Metamorphosis

Adult

ecdysone secretion. The first step in the moulting process is the inhibition of MIH secretion. Ecdysone secretion increases, and the processes leading to the replacement of the exoskeleton are initiated. As in insects, metamorphosis and reproduction are governed by a hormone different from but structurally related to JH.

STUDY BREAK

1. How can an invertebrate surrounded by a rigid exoskeleton grow? Describe the process of moulting and growth in insects and describe how it is regulated.
2. How are the pituitary of vertebrates and the corpus cardiacum of invertebrates similar? How do they differ?
3. The occurrence in many invertebrates of peptide hormones that closely resemble those in vertebrates is striking. What are the possible explanations for this in evolutionary terms? What research would you do to help you choose among the possibilities?

Review

CourseMate Access an interactive eBook, chapter-specific interactive learning tools, including flashcards, quizzes, videos, and more in your Biology **CourseMate**, accessed through NelsonBrain.com **Aplia™** is an online interactive learning solution that helps you improve comprehension—and your grade—by integrating a variety of mediums and tools such as videos, tutorials, practice tests, and an interactive eBook.

35.1 Hormones and Their Secretion

- Hormones are molecules secreted by cells of the endocrine system that control the activities of cells elsewhere in the body. The cells that respond to a hormone are its target cells. This contrasts with the nervous system, which controls specific target cells in close proximity to its endings.

- The endocrine system includes four major types of cell signalling: classical endocrine signalling, in which endocrine glands secrete hormones; neuroendocrine signalling, in which neurosecretory neurons release neurohormones into the circulation; paracrine regulation, in which cells release local regulators that diffuse through the extracellular fluid to regulate nearby cells; and autocrine regulation, in which cells release local regulators that regulate the same cells that produced them.

- Most hormones and local regulators fall into one of four molecular classes: amines, peptides, steroids, and fatty acids.

- Neurosecretory neurons secrete hormones under direct control of the CNS.

- Many hormones are controlled by negative feedback mechanisms in which a hormone inhibits the reactions that synthesize or release it when its concentration rises in the body.

35.2 Mechanisms of Hormone Action

- Many hormones undergo modification after release that renders them more active.

- Only cells that have receptors for the hormone can respond to the hormone. Cells may respond by stimulation or inhibition of a process. Because of amplification involved in receptor mechanisms, hormones are present in body fluids at low concentrations. The response to a hormone may differ among cells and tissues.

- Hormones may bind to receptor proteins in the plasma membrane. When a receptor binds a hormone, its cytoplasmic end is activated, triggering a series of cytoplasmic reactions that may include the activation of protein kinases.

- Hydrophobic hormones bind to receptors in the cytoplasm or nucleus, activating them so that they can bind to the control sequences of specific genes in the cell nucleus. Binding to the control sequence either stimulates or inhibits transcription of the target gene, leading to changes in protein synthesis. They may also bind to membrane receptors.

- The major endocrine cells and glands of vertebrates are the hypothalamus, pituitary, thyroid gland, parathyroid gland, adrenal medulla, adrenal cortex, testes, ovaries, islets of Langerhans of the pancreas, and pineal gland.

35.3 The Hypothalamus and Pituitary

- The hypothalamus and pituitary together regulate many other endocrine cells and glands in the body. The posterior pituitary contains the terminals of neurosecretory cells in the hypothalamus.

- The anterior pituitary contains endocrine cells derived from non-nervous tissue.

- The hypothalamus produces tropic hormones (releasing hormones and inhibiting hormones) that control the secretion of

eight hormones by the anterior pituitary. Prolactin (PRL), a nontropic hormone, regulates mammary gland development and milk secretion in mammals. As a nontropic hormone, growth hormone (GH) stimulates body growth in children and adolescents, and as a tropic hormone, it stimulates liver cells to make insulin-like growth factor (IGF), which stimulates growth processes. Melanocyte-stimulating hormone (MSH) controls reversible skin darkening. Endorphins can reduce pain. The four other hormones are tropic hormones: thyroid-stimulating hormone (TSH) stimulates secretion by the thyroid gland, adrenocorticotropic hormone (ACTH) regulates hormone secretion by the adrenal cortex, follicle-stimulating hormone (FSH) controls egg development and the secretion of sex hormones by the ovaries in female mammals and the production of sperm cells in males, and luteinizing hormone (LH) regulates part of the menstrual cycle in human females and the secretion of sex hormones in males.

- Antidiuretic hormone (ADH) and oxytocin are secreted by the posterior pituitary. ADH regulates body water balance. In female mammals, oxytocin stimulates the contraction of smooth muscle in the uterus as part of childbirth and triggers milk release from the mammary glands during suckling of the young.

- The intermediate lobe of the pituitary produces the nontropic hormones MSH and endorphins. MSH secretion in some vertebrates produces a darkening of the skin. Endorphins are neurotransmitters that affect pain pathways in the peripheral nervous system, inhibiting the perception of pain.

35.4 Other Major Endocrine Glands of Vertebrates

- The thyroid gland secretes the thyroid hormones and, in mammals, calcitonin. In mammals, the thyroid hormones stimulate the oxidation of carbohydrates and lipids and coordinate with growth hormone to stimulate body growth and development. Calcitonin lowers the Ca^{2+} level in the blood by inhibiting the release of Ca^{2+} from bone. In many vertebrates, thyroid hormones control metamorphosis.

- The parathyroid gland secretes parathyroid hormone (PTH), which stimulates bone cells to release Ca^{2+} into the blood. PTH also stimulates the activation of vitamin D, which promotes Ca^{2+} absorption into the blood from the small intestine.

- The adrenal medulla secretes epinephrine and norepinephrine, which reinforce the sympathetic nervous system in responding to stress. The adrenal cortex secretes glucocorticoids and mineralocorticoids. Glucocorticoids help maintain glucose at normal levels in the blood; mineralocorticoids regulate Na^+ balance and extracellular fluid volume. The adrenal cortex also secretes small amounts of androgens.

- The gonadal sex hormones—androgens, estrogen, and progestins—regulate the development of reproductive systems, sexual characteristics, and mating behaviour. Both sexes secrete all three, but males primarily produce androgens (secreted by the testes), and females primarily produce estrogens and progestins (secreted by the ovaries).

- The islets of Langerhans of the pancreas secrete insulin and glucagon. Insulin lowers the concentration of glucose in the blood by stimulating glucose uptake by cells, glycogen synthesis from glucose, uptake of fatty acids by adipose tissue cells, fat synthesis from fatty acids, and protein synthesis from amino acids; it inhibits the conversion of noncarbohydrate molecules into glucose. Glucagon raises blood glucose by stimulating glycogen, fat, and protein degradation. The balance of insulin and glucagon regulates the concentration of fuel substances in the blood.

- The pineal gland secretes melatonin, which interacts with the hypothalamus to set the body's daily rhythms.

35.5 Endocrine Systems in Invertebrates

- Even the simplest protostomes use hormones to coordinate growth and reproduction.
- Many of the hormones that occur in vertebrates also occur in invertebrates, although their function may be different.
- Three major hormones—prothoracicotropic hormone (PTTH) from the brain, ecdysone from prothoracic glands, and juvenile hormone (JH) from the corpus allatum—control moulting and metamorphosis in insects. PTTH is a tropic hormone that stimulates the secretion of ecdysone, which initiates and

maintains the secretion of the new cuticle. If JH is present, metamorphosis is suppressed, and in its absence, metamorphosis proceeds. The activity of the corpus allatum is governed by stimulatory and inhibitory tropic hormones from the brain. The shedding of the old cuticle and the hardening of the new cuticle are governed by a cascade of neuropeptides.

- JH controls reproduction in the adult insect.
- Similar hormones that control moulting and reproduction are also present in crustaceans, but the secretion of ecdysone is under the control of an inhibitory neurohormone.

Questions

Self-Test Questions

1. Which of the following is a chemical released from an epithelial cell in a gland that enters the blood to affect the activity of another cell some distance away?
   a. hormone
   b. neurohormone
   c. pheromone
   d. bile

2. Control of hormone secretion by a negative feedback mechanism generally includes
   a. no change in hormone secretion
   b. decrease in hormone secretion
   c. change that maintains homeostasis
   d. increase in hormone secretion

3. When the concentration of thyroid hormone in the blood increases, which of the following does it do?
   a. It activates a positive feedback loop.
   b. It stimulates the pituitary to secrete TSH.
   c. It stimulates the pituitary to secrete TRH.
   d. It stimulates a secretion by the hypothalamus.
   e. It inhibits TRH secretion by the hypothalamus.

4. Which molecules directly regulate blood levels of calcium?
   a. PTH made by the pituitary
   b. vitamin D activated in the liver
   c. calcitonin secreted by specialized thyroid cells
   d. insulin synthesized by the alpha cells of the pancreas
   e. prolactin synthesized by the intermediate lobe of the pituitary

5. Proctolin
   a. is a peptide secreted by insects
   b. is a steroid acting on nematodes
   c. is secreted by the intestine of mammals
   d. acts on smooth muscle in invertebrates
   e. governs egg development in invertebrates

6. Which function in mammals is NOT controlled by a hormone from the anterior pituitary?
   a. metabolic rate
   b. egg production
   c. milk production
   d. growth of muscle
   e. contraction of uterine muscles

7. During an acute stress response, what do catecholamines cause?
   a. an increase in heart rate
   b. an increase in blood pressure
   c. the breakdown of glycogen and fatty acids
   d. dilation of airways

8. Increased skeletal growth results directly and/or indirectly from the activity of
   a. aldosterone
   b. growth hormone
   c. hormones produced by the hypothalamus
   d. progestins
   e. epinephrine

9. Diabetes mellitus is a condition that can be described by which of the following?
   a. lack of insulin
   b. lack of glucagon
   c. lack of antidiuretic hormone (ADH)
   d. lack of cortisol
   e. none of the above

10. Which event occurs when blood glucose rises in healthy humans?
    a. Target cells decrease their insulin receptors.
    b. Glucagon uses amino acids as an energy source.
    c. The beta cells of the pancreas increase insulin production.
    d. The alpha cells of the pancreas increase glucagon secretion.
    e. The pituitary secretes a tropic hormone controlling the pancreas.

Questions for Discussion

1. The occurrence in many invertebrates of peptide hormones that closely resemble those in vertebrates is striking. What are the possible explanations for this in evolutionary terms? What research would you do to help you choose among the possibilities?

2. Stress is commonly regarded as a diseaselike condition that can lead to death. Stresslike phenomena are widely spread in other taxa. If it is pathological, why has evolution not eliminated it? What are the advantages that have led to its retention?

3. Juvenile hormone in insects controls very different functions in the larva than in the adult. Propose different ways that this can occur and design experiments to test these hypothesis.

4. An increasing number of sports figures have been charged and even found guilty of using performance-enhancing drugs such as steroids, growth hormone, insulin like growth factors, erythropoietin, and other drugs. What are the benefits of each of these hormones for performance enhancement, and what are the potential side effects of each on the athlete?

5. Although this is less common, hormones are also involved in some positive feedback cycles. Identify one such case and explain it in detail. Include a statement illustrating why this is beneficial.

Primary rat hippocampal neurons (630×) (confocal light micrograph). Neurons, the cells that send and receive signals, are green; glial cells, which provide structural and functional support for neurons, are red; and nuclei are blue.

© Paul Cuddon, The Babraham Institute, Sawston, Cambridgeshire, U.K.

STUDY PLAN

36 Control of Animal Processes: Neural Control

WHY IT MATTERS

On a warm evening in early summer, the twilight in a garden in Montréal is punctuated by brief bursts of light from the abdomen of a flying male of the beetle *Photuris versicolor,* the lightning bug. The flashes of light have a specific duration and come at specific intervals, constituting a code unique to that species. These visible mating calls are answered by a female perched on the vegetation below **(Figure 36.1)**, which emits flashes with the same code. The male flies toward her. This photonic conversation continues until the male lands on the vegetation and mates with the female, which then ceases flashing. A day or two later, the mated female has begun to make eggs and again responds to flashes from males flying overhead. But now she responds to and mimics codes of flashing from males of other species of firefly. A male, lured to her by her mimicry of the flashing code for his species, lands and expects to mate but becomes prey and provides nutrition, enabling her to enhance egg production.

This behaviour requires the complex interaction of cells within the nervous systems of the flies. The brain or central nervous system (CNS) of the male sends the appropriate rhythmic signals (the code)

Darwin Dale/Photo Researchers, Inc.

Figure 36.1
Photinus species female with abdomen flashing.

nervous system (PNS), the long slender projections of neurons (*axons*) are bundled into cablelike projections called *nerves* that provide a common pathway between different structures and the CNS. In the CNS, networks are organized into *ganglia* and *brains*.

36.1 Neurons and Their Organization in Nervous Systems: An Overview

Communication between cells in an animal by **neural signalling** involves the flow of information at two levels: within a single neuronal cell or **neuron** and between neurons within networks or circuits. In most animals, the four components of neural signalling are *reception, transmission, integration,* and *response*.

- **Reception** is the detection of a stimulus.
- **Integration** is the sorting and interpretation of sensory inputs or neural messages and determination of the appropriate response(s).
- **Transmission** is the sending of a message along a neuron to another neuron or to a muscle or gland.
- **Response** is the output or action resulting from the integration of neural messages. For a *P. versicolor* male flying at dusk, for example, sensors in the eye (see Chapter 37) detect flashes of light, and this information is transmitted to the brain, where it is integrated with internal information to determine whether or not to send outputs along nerves controlling the flight muscles commanding them to fly toward the female.

36.1a Neurons and Neural Circuits Are Specialized for the Reception, Integration, and Transmission of Informational Signals

Neurons vary widely in shape and size. All have an enlarged cell body and two types of extensions or processes: dendrites and axons **(Figure 36.2, p. 878)**.

- **Reception:** The **dendrites**, and often the **cell body**, receive signals that they integrate and transmit toward a specialized part of the neuron called the **spike initiation zone.** The dendrites are generally highly branched, forming a treelike outgrowth at one end of the neuron (*dendros* = tree). Dendrites and cell bodies conduct graded electrical signals produced by ions flowing down electrochemical gradients through channels in the plasma membrane.
- **Integration:** The spike initiation zone is the first site along the neuron capable of generating an action potential. If the magnitude of the signal arriving from the dendrites and cell body is large enough, an action potential is initiated (see Section 36.2c).
- **Transmission:** Axons (*axon* = axis) conduct signals away from the spike initiation zone to another

to the light-producing organ in his abdomen. It also sends signals to the muscles controlling the wings so that he can fly toward the female. The female's eyes detect the light flashes, and her nervous system processes the information, causing her brain to send the appropriate signals to her own light-producing organ so that she responds with the appropriate code. All of this can happen in under a second. Mating is a complex behaviour involving coordinated movements not only of the genital apparatus but also of the other appendages. This act of mating turns off the flashing response of the female and signals the endocrine system of the female to release the hormones involved in egg production. A chemical transferred by the male in his semen acts on the brain of the female so that it no longer responds to the code for her species and causes her to mimic the codes of other species. Sensing of the environment leading to rapid, specific communication between cells in multicellular organisms is the domain of the nervous system and the topic of this chapter.

One of the consequences of multicellularity and tissue differentiation, discussed in Chapter 31, is that cells must communicate over long distances. There are several ways this can occur, but the fastest is via transmission by neurons. Most multicellular animals have a nervous system. Hundreds to billions of neurons (depending on the animal) compose the nervous system and work together carrying electrical messages that control every aspect of the body. Messages are carried in the form of action potentials, and the rate of conduction and strength of each message are affected by various physical and chemical factors. Neurons are connected to one another and other body tissues via chemical or electrical synapses. The detection and flow of information from the environment and between the individuals, and the instantaneous analysis and processing of that information to produce specific behaviour, are astounding, even in relatively simple animals. In this chapter, we first examine the properties of the cells that make up the nervous system that are responsible for receiving, transmitting, and analyzing the information. These functions result from the activities of only two major cell types: *neurons* and *glial cells*. In most animals, these cells are organized into complex networks called *nervous systems*. In the peripheral

Figure 36.2

Neural signals: steps in processing of information in single neurons. There is considerable variation in the size and shape of neurons, but most of them are divided into distinct regions that serve in receiving signals, integrating them, conducting them, and transmitting them to other cells.

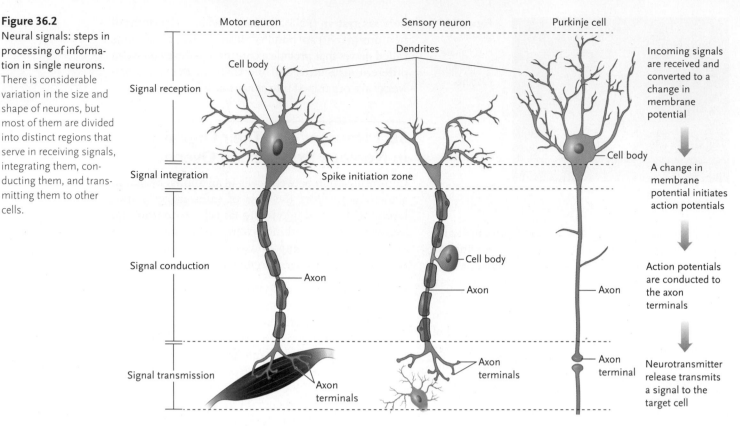

neuron or an effector. Neurons typically have a single axon that arises from a junction with the cell body called an **axon hillock.** The axon has branches at its tip that end as small, buttonlike swellings called **axon terminals.** The more terminals contacting a neuron, the greater its capacity to integrate incoming information.

- **Response:** This is the output or action resulting from the generation of the action potential. It could be the stimulation of another neuron, the release of a hormone from a gland, or the contraction of a muscle.

The cell body, which contains the nucleus and the majority of cell organelles, synthesizes most of the proteins, carbohydrates, and lipids of the neuron.

Connections between the axon terminals of one neuron and the dendrites or cell body of a second neuron link neurons into **neuronal circuits.** These circuits involve the same four components of neural signalling but at a higher level.

- **Reception: Afferent neurons** (also called **sensory neurons**) transmit stimuli collected by sensory receptors on those neurons to interneurons.
- **Integration: Interneurons** integrate the information to formulate an appropriate response. In humans and some other primates, 99% of all neurons are interneurons. Interneurons may receive input from several axons and may, in turn, connect to other interneurons and several efferent neurons. In this

way, circuits combine into networks that interconnect the parts of the nervous system.

- **Transmission: Efferent neurons** carry the signals initiating a response away from the interneuron networks to the **effectors.**
- **Response:** This is carried out by muscles and glands. Efferent neurons that carry signals to skeletal muscle are called **motor neurons.**

In vertebrates, the afferent (sensory) neurons and efferent neurons collectively form the PNS. The interneurons form the brain and spinal cord, which make up the CNS. As depicted in **Figure 36.3,** afferent (carrying toward) information is ultimately transmitted to the CNS, where efferent (carrying away) information is initiated. The nervous systems of most invertebrates are also composed of central and peripheral divisions.

36.1b Neurons Are Supported Structurally and Functionally by Glial Cells

Glial cells are nonneuronal cells that provide nutrition and support to neurons. One type, called **astrocytes** because they are star-shaped **(Figure 36.4),** were formerly thought to play only a supporting role in the CNS by maintaining ion concentrations in the interstitial fluid surrounding the neurons. More recently, however, scientists have realized that in vertebrates and some invertebrates, astrocytes communicate with neurons and may influence their activity (see next Concept Fix).

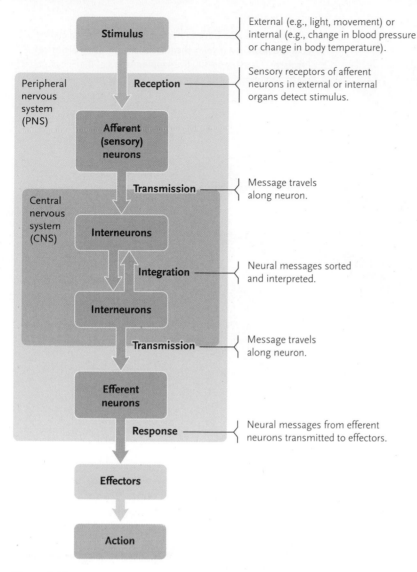

External (e.g., light, movement) or internal (e.g., change in blood pressure or change in body temperature).

Stimulus

Reception — Sensory receptors of afferent neurons in external or internal organs detect stimulus.

Peripheral nervous system (PNS)

Afferent (sensory) neurons

Transmission — Message travels along neuron.

Central nervous system (CNS)

Interneurons

Integration — Neural messages sorted and interpreted.

Interneurons

Transmission — Message travels along neuron.

Efferent neurons

Response — Neural messages from efferent neurons transmitted to effectors.

Effectors

Action

Figure 36.3

Neural signalling: the information-processing steps in neural circuits.

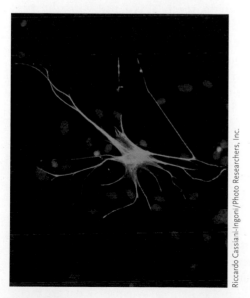

Riccardo Cassiani-Ingoni/Photo Researchers, Inc.

Figure 36.4

An astrocyte.

Two other types of glial cells, **oligodendrocytes** in the CNS and **Schwann cells** in the PNS, form tightly wrapped layers of plasma membrane, called myelin sheaths, around axons **(Figure 36.5, p. 880)**. These myelin sheaths act as electrical insulators due to the membrane's high lipid content. The gaps between Schwann cells, called **nodes of Ranvier**, expose the axon membrane directly to extracellular fluids. This arrangement of insulated stretches of the axon punctuated by gaps speeds the rate at which electrical impulses move along the axons they protect.

Unlike most neurons, glial cells retain the capacity to divide throughout the life of the animal. This capacity allows glial tissues to replace damaged or dead cells but also makes them the source of almost all brain tumours, which are produced when regulation of glial cell division is lost.

CONCEPT FIX That glial cells only support and provide nutrition to neurons no longer appears to be an accurate assessment of their roles! Some glial cells regulate the clearance of neurotransmitters from the synaptic cleft and release factors such as ATP, which modulate presynaptic function. During early embryogenesis, other glial cells also direct the migration of neurons and produce molecules that modify the growth of axons and dendrites. In the past, glial cells were not believed to have chemical synapses or to release neurotransmitters. They were regarded as a "glue" in the nervous system, as their name implies. More recently it has been shown that the only notable differences between neurons and glial cells are that the latter lack axons and dendrites and they lack the ability to generate action potentials. Attention is now being paid to their roles in the formation and modulation of synapses and in the repair of neurons after injury. ●

CONCEPT FIX Neurons are sometimes called nerve cells, but this is technically incorrect. Many neurons, such as those within the CNS, do not form nerves, and nerves usually contain nonneuronal cells, such as Schwann cells, that coat the axons in myelin. ●

36.1c Neurons Function as Circuits and Communicate via Synapses

A **synapse** (*synapsis* = juncture) is a site where a neuron makes a communicating connection with either another neuron or an effector such as a muscle

C. Raines/Visuals Unlimited, Inc.

Figure 36.5
Myelinated neuron have axons wrapped in Schwann cells that coat the axon in a myelin sheath, which acts as an electrical insulator. As many as 300 overlapping layers of the Schwann cell plasma membrane wind around an axon like a jelly roll.

Node of Ranvier

Myelin sheath of Schwann cell

Myelin sheath of Schwann cell

Cytoplasm of axon

Plasma membrane of axon

Axon of neuron

fibre or gland. On one side of the synapse is the axon terminal of a **presynaptic cell**, the neuron that transmits the signal. On the other side is the dendrite or cell body of a **postsynaptic cell**, the neuron or the surface of an effector that receives the signal. Communication across a synapse may occur by the direct flow of an electrical signal or by means of a **neurotransmitter**, a chemical released by an axon terminal at a synapse.

In **electrical synapses**, the plasma membranes of the presynaptic and postsynaptic cells are in direct contact **(Figure 36.6a)**. When an electrical impulse arrives at the axon terminal, gap junctions (see Chapter 31) allow ions to flow directly between the two cells, leading to unbroken transmission of the electrical signal. Electrical synapses are useful for two types of functions:

- They allow for very rapid transmission. They were first discovered in the nervous system of crayfish, where they are involved in the rapid movements for escape from predators.
- They allow for synchronous activity in a group of neurons. For example, the neurons controlling the secretion of hormones from the hypothalamus of mammals are connected by electrical synapses, thus ensuring a coordinated burst of secretion of some hormones.

The vast majority of vertebrate neurons, however, communicate by means of neurotransmitters **(Figure 36.6b)**. In these **chemical synapses**, the plasma membranes of the presynaptic and postsynaptic cells are separated by a narrow gap, about 25 nm wide, called the **synaptic cleft.** When an electrical impulse arrives at an axon terminal, it causes the release of a neurotransmitter into the synaptic cleft. The neurotransmitter diffuses across the synaptic cleft and binds to a receptor in the plasma membrane of the postsynaptic cell. If enough neurotransmitter molecules bind to these receptors, an action potential will be generated at the spike initiation zone of the postsynaptic cell that will then travel along its axon to reach a synapse with the next neuron or effector in the circuit. Many factors determine whether a new electrical impulse will be generated in the postsynaptic cell, including the levels of neurotransmitters that excite the cell and neurotransmitters that inhibit that cell rather than stimulate it. The balance of stimulatory and inhibitory effects in chemical synapses contributes to the integration of incoming information in a receiving neuron.

STUDY BREAK

1. Describe *reception, integration, transmission,* and *response* at the level of a single neuron as well as in a complex neural circuit.
2. What are the differences between an electrical synapse and a chemical synapse? What are the advantages of each?

a. Electrical synapse

Axon terminal of presynaptic cell

Plasma membrane of axon terminal

Ions

Gap junctions

Plasma membrane of postsynaptic cell

In an electrical synapse, the plasma membranes of the presynaptic and post-synaptic cells make direct contact. Ions flow through gap junctions that connect the two membranes, allowing impulses to pass directly to the postsynaptic cell.

b. Chemical synapse

Axon terminal of presynaptic cell

Vesicle releasing neurotransmitter molecules

Synaptic cleft

Receptors that bind neurotransmitter molecules

Ion channels associated with neurotransmitter receptors

Plasma membrane of postsynaptic cell

In a chemical synapse, the plasma membranes of the presynaptic and post-synaptic cells are separated by a narrow synaptic cleft. Neurotransmitter molecules diffuse across the cleft and bind to receptors in the plasma membrane of the postsynaptic cell. The binding opens channels to ion flow that may generate an impulse in the postsynaptic cell.

Figure 36.6
The two types of synapses by which neurons communicate with other neurons or effectors.

36.2 Signal Initiation by Neurons

36.2a All Cells Have a Resting Membrane Potential

As you learned in Chapter 5, plasma membranes are *selectively* permeable in that they allow some molecules but not others to move across the membrane through protein channels embedded in the phospholipid bilayer. Many of these molecules are charged (remember that anions are ions that carry a positive charge and cations are ions that carry a negative charge; see *The Purple Pages*). All animal cells have more nega-tively charged molecules (anions, amino acids, nucleic acids, etc.) inside the cell than outside the cell. The separation of positive and negative charges across the plasma membrane produces an electrical gradient or potential difference across the plasma membrane called a **membrane potential.** All cells exhibit a resting potential and are said to be *polarized.*

In all cells at rest, there are more K⁺ ions inside the cell, with a net tendency to diffuse out due to their concentration gradient, but a net tendency to remain inside the cell due to their electrical charge (like charges repel and unlike charges attract). These don't quite balance out, and thus there is a small net ten-dency (i.e., a small net **electrochemical gradient**) for K⁺ to diffuse out of the cell through various channels.

There are more Na⁺ ions outside the cell than inside, and both electrical and concentration gradients (i.e., electrochemical gradient) favour movement into the cell. The plasma membrane, however, is not normally very permeable to Na⁺, and so only a small amount leaks in. Plasma membrane-embedded Na⁺/K⁺ active transport pumps use energy from ATP hydrolysis to simultaneously pump three Na⁺ out of the cell for every two K⁺ pumped in, maintaining a steady state and a steady resting membrane potential. For most cells, this membrane potential is very stable. The distribution of ions inside and outside an axon that produces the membrane potential is shown in **Figure 36.7, p. 882.**

Like all cells, neurons also have a voltage differ-ence between the inside and the outside of the cell. However, neurons and muscle cells are *excitable.* In response to electrical, chemical, mechanical, and cer-tain other types of stimuli, their membrane potential changes rapidly and transiently. Excitability, produced by a sudden flow of ions across the plasma membrane, is the basis for nerve impulse generation. It also gives neurons the ability to store, recall, and distribute information.

The membrane of a neuron that is not conducting an impulse exhibits a steady negative membrane potential called the **resting potential** because the neuron is at rest. The resting potential has been meas-ured at about −70 mV in isolated neurons. The change

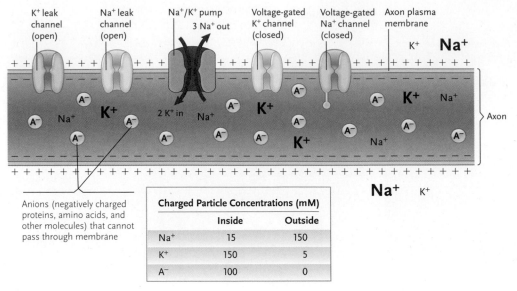

Figure 36.7

The distribution of ions inside and outside an axon that produces the resting potential, –70 mV. A⁻ incorporates the distribution of Cl⁻ and other negatively charged anions, amino acids, and nucleic acids. Na⁺ and K⁺ diffuse along their electrochemical gradients through *leak* channels, and the Na⁺/K⁺ pump returns them back again. The voltage-gated ion channels only open when the membrane potential changes.

Charged Particle Concentrations (mM)		
	Inside	Outside
Na⁺	15	150
K⁺	150	5
A⁻	100	0

Anions (negatively charged proteins, amino acids, and other molecules) that cannot pass through membrane

---

cell or negatively charged ions (such as Cl⁻) enter, the membrane will become more polarized, or **hyperpolarized**. The more ions that cross the membrane, the greater the depolarization or hyperpolarization; that is, these events are graded. As the ions are restored to their initial levels, the membrane is **repolarized** and the cell membrane returns to its resting membrane potential. These changes in membrane potential due to changes in membrane permeability to ions are called graded potentials. Because the ions that enter through any channel will disperse within the cell, graded potentials will radiate over the cell membrane, decreasing in magnitude as they move farther away from the open ion channel. They can occur in any cell and are not confined to nerve cells. In neurons, graded potentials are part of the integration that takes place in dendrites and cell bodies.

in membrane potential that occurs when a neuron is excited is the action potential, which will be discussed shortly. As we will see in the following discussion, the action potential results from the opening and closing of *voltage-gated ion channels* for Na⁺ and K⁺.

CONCEPT FIX The statement that the diffusion of ions is due to differences in concentration between two sites is not always true! While ions diffuse along concentration gradients, this is not the only factor that determines the direction of the net diffusion of ions. Ions really diffuse along energy gradients, and the energy gradient for any specific ion is also determined by electrical charge (for charged molecules), temperature, and pressure. Diffusion is only due to concentration gradients alone if all other factors are equal, something that is not common in living cells. ⬡

36.2b Graded Potentials Can Occur in All Cells Due to Changes in Membrane Permeability to Ions and Can Vary in Magnitude

The permeability of most membranes to ions is not constant but changes as various channels in the membrane open and close. If, as a result of such events, positively charged ions (such as Na⁺) enter the cell or negatively charged ions leave the cell, the charge across the membrane will become less negative and the membrane will be less polarized, or **depolarized (Figure 36.8).** If, on the other hand, positively charged ions (such as K⁺) leave the

36.2c An Action Potential Is Not Graded but Is a Rapid, Reversible Event

Although graded potentials cannot be transmitted over long distances, action potentials can. Only certain parts of a neuron can generate action potentials (as a rule, dendrites and cell bodies cannot), and the site where action potentials are initiated in the neuron is referred to as the spike initiation zone (or trigger zone; see Figure 36.2, p. 878). If graded potentials spreading over the dendrites and cell body are sufficient to depolarize the membrane at the site of the spike initiation zone to a level known as the **threshold potential**, about –50 to –55 mV in isolated neurons, an action potential occurs at this site. In less than 1 ms (= millisecond), the inside of the

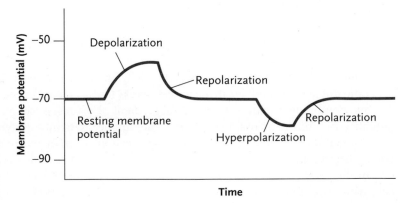

Figure 36.8

Changes in membrane potential in a cell due to changes in ion permeability. The resting membrane potential in this cell is –70 mV. During depolarization, the membrane potential becomes less negative. During hyperpolarization, the membrane potential becomes more negative. During repolarization, the membrane potential returns to its resting level.

Figure 36.9

Changes in membrane potential during an action potential.

plasma membrane at this site becomes positive because of an influx of positive ions across the cell membrane, momentarily reaching a value of +30 mV or more **(Figure 36.9)**. The membrane potential at this site then falls, in many cases becoming hyperpolarized and dropping to about –80 mV before rising again to the resting potential. The entire change, from initiation of the action potential to the return to the resting potential, takes less than 5 ms in the fastest neurons. Action potentials take the same basic form in neurons of all types, although there may be differences in the values of the resting potential and the peak of the action potential and in the time required to return to the resting potential.

An action potential is produced only if the depolarization arriving at the spike initiation zone is strong enough to cause the membrane potential to reach threshold. Furthermore, once triggered, the changes in membrane potential take place independently of the strength of the stimulus. No matter how strong the stimulus, once threshold is reached, the action potential will always be the same size. This is referred to as the **all-or-nothing principle.**

Beginning at the peak of an action potential, the membrane enters a **refractory period** of a few milliseconds, during which the threshold required for generation of an action potential is much higher than normal. The refractory period lasts until the membrane has stabilized at the resting potential. As we will see, the refractory period keeps impulses travelling in a one-way direction in neurons.

36.2d The Action Potential Is Produced by Ion Movements through the Plasma Membrane

The action potential is produced by movements of Na^+ and K^+ through the plasma membrane that are controlled by specific **voltage-gated ion channels,** membrane-embedded proteins that open and close as the membrane potential changes (see **Figure 36.10, p. 884**). Voltage-gated Na^+ channels have two gates, an *activation gate* and an *inactivation gate,* whereas voltage-gated K^+ channels have one gate, an *activation gate.*

Figure 36.10, p. 884 shows how the two voltage-gated ion channels operate when generating an action potential. When the membrane is at its resting potential, the activation gates of both the Na^+ and the K^+ channel are closed. A depolarizing stimulus, such as a neurotransmitter substance, produces a graded depolarization that spreads to the spike initiation zone and raises the membrane potential to the threshold. This change in membrane charge pulls the activation gate of the voltage-gated Na^+ channels open, allowing Na^+ ions to flow into the axon along their electrochemical gradient. Once above the threshold, the more the membrane depolarizes, the more Na^+ channels open, causing a rapid inward flow of positive charges that raises the membrane potential to the peak of the action potential. As the action potential peaks, the change in charge at the plasma membrane causes the inactivation gates of the Na^+ channels to close (resembling putting a stopper in a sink), which stops the inward flow of Na^+. The refractory period now begins.

At the same time, the activation gates of the K^+ channels begin to open, allowing K^+ ions to flow rapidly outward in response to their electrochemical gradient (the cell is now positive on the inside and negative on the outside so that both concentration and electrical gradients favour the movement of K^+ out of the cell). The movement of K^+ ions contributes to the refractory period and compensates for the inward movement of Na^+ ions, returning the membrane to the resting potential. As the resting potential is re-established, the activation gates of the K^+ channels close, as do those of the Na^+ channels, and the inactivation gates of the Na^+ channels open. These events end the refractory period and ready the membrane for another action potential. The opening and closing of the gates are the result of interactions between charge on the plasma membrane and charge on the gates themselves, either pulling the gates toward the membrane and opening them or pushing the gates away and closing them; this is the basis of the operation of all voltage-gated channels.

In some neurons, closure of the voltage-gated K^+ channels lags, and K^+ continues to flow outward for a brief time after the membrane returns to the resting potential. This excess outward flow causes the hyperpolarization shown in Figure 36.9 and Figure 36.10, p. 884 (step 6), in which the membrane potential dips briefly below the resting potential.

At the end of an action potential, the membrane potential has returned to its resting state, but the ion distribution has been changed slightly. That is, some Na^+ has entered the cell and some K^+ has left the cell. Actually, relatively few of the total number of Na^+ and

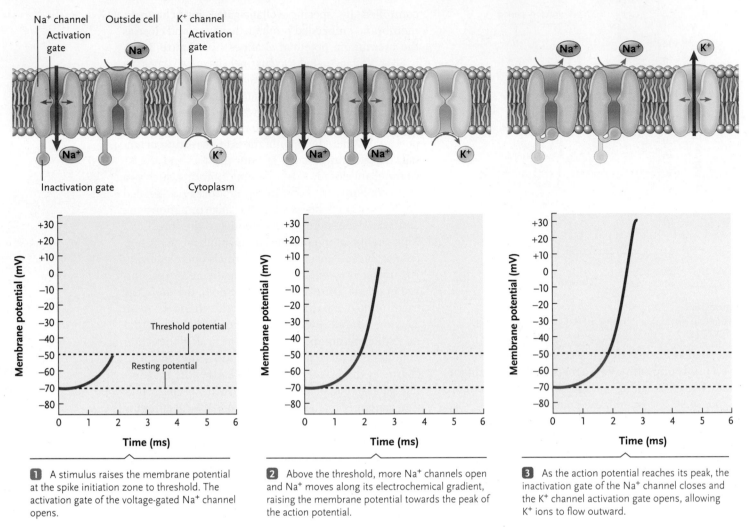

Figure 36.10
Changes in voltage-gated Na⁺ and K⁺ channels that produce the action potential.

1 A stimulus raises the membrane potential at the spike initiation zone to threshold. The activation gate of the voltage-gated Na⁺ channel opens.

2 Above the threshold, more Na⁺ channels open and Na⁺ moves along its electrochemical gradient, raising the membrane potential towards the peak of the action potential.

3 As the action potential reaches its peak, the inactivation gate of the Na⁺ channel closes and the K⁺ channel activation gate opens, allowing K⁺ ions to flow outward.

K⁺ ions change locations during an action potential (ions only flow for 5 ms). Hence, additional action potentials can occur without the need to completely correct the altered ion distribution. In the long term, the Na⁺/K⁺ active transport pumps restore the Na⁺ and K⁺ to their original locations.

36.2e Sensory Receptors Are the First Step in Transmitting Information to the Nervous System

Sensory systems begin with **sensory receptors (transducers)** that detect sensory information, convert it to neural activity, and pass the information along neurons to the CNS. Sensory receptors are formed by the dendrites of afferent neurons or by specialized receptor cells **(Figure 36.11, p. 886)**. Receptors collect information about the internal and external environments of organisms. In organisms with a developed head region (cephalized), many receptors for external stimuli are located there so that the organism can collect information about where it is going. Receptors associated with eyes, ears, skin, and other surface organs detect stimuli from the external environment. Sensory receptors associated with internal organs detect stimuli arising in the body interior.

Sensory transduction occurs when stimuli cause changes in membrane potentials in the sensory receptors. This is usually achieved by changes in rates at which channels conduct positive ions (Na⁺, K⁺, or Ca²⁺) across the plasma membrane. Stimuli may be in the form of light, heat, sound waves, mechanical stress, or chemicals **(Figure 36.12, p. 886)**. The change in membrane potential may generate one or more action potentials that travel along the axon of an afferent neuron to reach interneuron networks of the CNS. These interneurons integrate the action potentials, and the brain formulates a compensating response, that is, a response appropriate for the stimulus. In animals with complex nervous systems, interneuron networks may produce an awareness of a stimulus in the form of a conscious sensation or perception.

4 The outward flow of K⁺ along its electrochemical gradient causes the membrane potential to begin to fall.

5 As the membrane potential reaches the resting value, the activation gate of the Na⁺ channel closes and the inactivation gate opens. The K⁺ activation gate also closes.

6 Closure of the K⁺ activation gate stabilizes the membrane potential at the resting value.

36.2f Basic Types of Receptors: What Can Animals Sense?

Many sensory receptors are positioned individually in body tissues. Others are part of complex sensory organs, such as the eyes or ears, specialized for reception of physical or chemical stimuli (see Chapter 37). Receptors, particularly for external information, usually occur in pairs, providing the opportunity for the animal to localize the stimulus. Eyes, ears, and antennae are examples of paired sensory organs. There are exceptions. *Opabinia* species from the Burgess Shale (see Chapter 25) had five eyes, and some species of praying mantis have only one ear. Some spiders have rows of simple eyes.

Sensory receptors are classified into five major types, based on the type of stimulus that each detects:

- **Mechanoreceptors** detect mechanical energy when it deforms membranes (Figure 36.12, p. 886). Changes in pressure, body position, or acceleration are detected by mechanoreceptors, for instance. The auditory receptors in the ears are examples of mechanoreceptors.
- **Photoreceptors** detect the energy of light. In vertebrates, photoreceptors are mostly located in the retina of the eye.

- **Chemoreceptors** detect specific molecules or chemical conditions such as acidity. Taste buds on the tongue are examples of chemoreceptors.
- **Thermoreceptors** detect the flow of heat energy. Receptors of this type are located in the skin, where they detect changes in the temperature of the body surface.
- **Nociceptors** detect tissue damage or noxious chemicals; their activity registers as pain. Pain receptors are located in the skin and in some internal organs.

Some animals also have receptors that detect electrical or magnetic fields. Traditionally, humans are said to have five senses: vision, hearing, taste, smell, and touch. In reality, we can detect many more types of environmental stimuli. The traditional list should also include external heat, internal temperature, gravity, acceleration, the positions of muscles and joints, body balance, internal pH, and the internal concentrations of substances such as oxygen, carbon dioxide, salts, and glucose. Note, however, that these are all detected by one of the five classes of receptors listed above.

CONCEPT FIX Not all parts of neurons can generate action potentials! In most, the dendrites and cell bodies can only generate graded potentials. As a result, some integration takes place at every synapse in a neural

a. Sensory receptor consisting of free nerve endings—dendrites of an afferent neuron

In sensory receptors consisting of the dendrites of afferent neurons, a stimulus causes a change in membrane potential that generates action potentials in the axon of the neuron. Examples are pain receptors and some mechanoreceptors.

b. Sense organ—sensory receptor involving nerve endings of an afferent neuron enclosed in a specialized structure

In sensory receptors involving nerve endings enclosed in a specialized structure, a stimulus affecting the structure triggers an action potential in the afferent neuron. Some mechanoreceptors are of this type.

c. Sensory receptor formed by a cell that synapses with an afferent neuron

In sensory receptors consisting of separate cells, a stimulus causes a change in membrane potential that releases a neurotransmitter from the cell. The neurotransmitter triggers an action potential in the axon of an afferent neuron to which the sensory receptor cell is synapsed. Examples are photoreceptors, chemoreceptors, and some mechanoreceptors.

Figure 36.11
Sensory receptors, formed **(a)** by the dendrites of an afferent neuron, **(b)** by nerve endings enclosed in specialized structures, or **(c)** by a separate cell or structure that communicates with an afferent neuron via a neurotransmitter.

Figure 36.12
Sensory cell membrane proteins respond to stimuli. Sensory stimuli modify receptor proteins in the membranes of sensors, which in turn modify ion channels. The receptors in mechanoreceptors, thermosensors, and electrosensors are themselves ion channels. In chemosensors and photosensors, activated receptor proteins initiate biochemical cascades that eventually open or close ion channels.

circuit. Higher-level integration takes place in the CNS, where interneurons are recruited specifically to integrate information coming in from many different sites in the body. ⬡

STUDY BREAK

1. What is the difference between an excitable cell, such as a neuron, and other cells, such as liver or blood cells?
2. Can all parts of a neuron generate an action potential? Why or why not?
3. What mechanism ensures that an electrical impulse in a neuron is conducted in only one direction down the axon? Why is this important?
4. How do sensory neurons differ from other neurons? How do different stimuli produce changes in ion conductance in sensory cells?

36.3 Conduction of Action Potentials along Neurons and across Chemical Synapses

36.3a Nerve Impulses Move by Propagation of Action Potentials

Once an action potential is initiated at the spike initiation zone, it passes along the surface of a neuron as an automatic wave of depolarization. It travels away from the stimulation point without requiring further triggering events (**Figure 36.13**). This is called **propagation** or **conduction** of the action potential.

Figure 36.13

Propagation of an action potential along an unmyelinated axon by ion flow between a firing segment and an adjacent unfired region of the axon. Each firing segment induces the next to fire, causing the action potential to move along the axon.

In a segment of an axon generating an action potential, the outside of the membrane becomes temporarily negative and the inside positive. Because opposites attract, as the membrane potential reverses in the region of the spike initiation zone, local current flow occurs between the area undergoing an action potential and the adjacent downstream inactive area, both inside and outside the membrane (see arrows, Figure 36.13). This current flow (flow of charge, like the flow of electrical current in a wire) makes nearby regions of the axon membrane less positive on the outside and more positive on the inside; in other words, the membrane of these adjacent regions depolarizes.

In regions of the neuron capable of propagating action potentials, voltage-gated channels occur throughout the membrane. The local depolarization spreading from the spike initiation zone is large enough to push the membrane potential of the neighbouring voltage-gated Na^+ and K^+ channels past the threshold, starting an action potential in the downstream adjacent region. In this way, each segment of the axon stimulates the next segment to fire, and the action potential moves rapidly along the axon as a nerve impulse.

The refractory period keeps an action potential from reversing direction at any point along an axon; only the region in front of the action potential can fire. The refractory period begins when the inactivation gate closes on the voltage-gated Na^+ channel; this site on the membrane is not capable of generating another action potential until this gate reopens and the activation gates on the Na^+ and K^+ channels are reset. That is, once they are opened to their activated state, the upstream voltage-gated ion channels need time to reset to their original positions before they can open again. Therefore, only downstream voltage-gated ion channels are able to open, ensuring the one-way movement of the action potential along the axon toward the axon terminals. By the time the refractory period ends in a membrane segment that has just fired an action potential, the action potential has moved too far away to cause a second action potential to develop in the same segment.

The magnitude of an action potential stays the same as it travels along an axon, even where the axon branches at its tips. This is because the action potential is being regenerated at each voltage-gated channel along the membrane. Thus, the propagation of an action potential resembles a burning fuse, which burns with the same intensity along its length and along any branches, once it is lit at one end. Unlike a fuse, however, an axon can fire another action potential of the same intensity within a few milliseconds after an action potential passes through and the refractory period is complete.

The all-or-nothing principle of action potential generation means that the intensity of a stimulus is reflected in the *frequency* of action potentials rather than the size of the action potential. The greater the stimulus, the more action potentials per second, up to a limit depending on the axon type. For most neuron types, the limit lies between 10 and 100 action potentials per second.

36.3b Saltatory Conduction Increases Propagation Rate in Small-Diameter Axons

In the propagation pattern shown in Figure 36.13, an action potential is regenerated at every voltage-gated channel along the length of the axon. The rate of conduction increases with the rate of local current flow, which increases with the diameter of the axon. Some specialized axons with very large diameters occur in invertebrates such as lobsters, earthworms, and squids, as well as a few marine fishes. Giant axons typically carry signals that produce an escape or withdrawal response, such as the sudden flexing of the tail (abdomen) in lobsters that propels the animal backward. The largest known axons, 1.7 mm in diameter, occur in fanworms (Phylum Annelida, Class Polychaeta; see Figure 25.30, Chapter 25). The signals they carry contract a muscle that retracts the fanworm's body into a protective tube when the animal is threatened. The giant axons of the squid were used in the early experiments that led to the current conceptual model of how axons work.

Although large-diameter axons can conduct impulses as rapidly as 25 m/s, they take up a great deal of space. In the jawed vertebrates, insulating axons with myelin sheaths (Figure 36.5, p. 880) produces **saltatory conduction** (*saltere* = to leap), allowing action potentials to "hop" rapidly along axons instead of burning slowly like a fuse.

Saltatory conduction depends on the gaps in the insulating myelin sheath that surrounds many axons. These gaps, known as nodes of Ranvier, expose the axon membrane to extracellular fluids. Voltage-gated Na^+ and K^+ channels crowded into the nodes allow action potentials to develop at these positions **(Figure 36.14)**. The inward movement of Na^+ ions produces depolarization, but the excess positive ions are unable to leave the axon through the neighbouring membrane regions covered by the myelin sheath. Because the ions cannot leave, the insulation provided by the myelin sheath prevents the potential change from decaying as rapidly as it spreads along the neuron. Instead, the local current spreads much farther. As long as the next node is close enough that the local current does not decay below threshold, it will cause depolarization, inducing an action potential at that node. As this mechanism repeats, the action potential jumps rapidly along the axon from node to node. Saltatory conduction proceeds at rates up to 130 m/s, whereas an unmyelinated axon of the same diameter conducts action potentials at about 1 m/s.

Saltatory conduction allows thousands to millions of fast-transmitting axons to be packed into a relatively small diameter. For example, in humans, the 3-mm-diameter

Saltatory conduction

Myelin sheath

Voltage-gated Na⁺ and K⁺ channels

Axon

Node of Ranvier

optic nerve leading from the eye to the brain is packed with more than a million axons. If those axons were unmyelinated, each would have to be about 100 times as thick to conduct impulses at the same velocity, producing an optic nerve about 300 mm in diameter.

Among invertebrates, Schwann cells also form concentric coatings around many nerves, but the layers are not so compact, leaving some cytoplasm in the Schwann cells and some intercellular space between the layers. Nevertheless, fully myelinated fibres occur in oligochaete annelids and some crustaceans, complete with gaps to permit saltatory transmission. The occurrence of myelin in some protostome invertebrates and its absence from the lower vertebrates suggests that this important mechanism has evolved more than once, presenting another example of convergent evolution. The embryonic origin of Schwann cells is different in vertebrates and invertebrates, confirming the independent evolution of myelination in vertebrates and invertebrates.

The disease *multiple sclerosis* (*sclero* = hard) underscores the importance of myelin sheaths to the operation of the vertebrate nervous system. In this disease, myelin is attacked by the immune system and is progressively lost from axons and replaced by hardened scar tissue. The changes block or slow the transmission of action potentials, producing numbness, muscular weakness, faulty coordination of movements, and paralysis that worsens as the disease progresses. Although clear genetic factors are involved, the environment also plays a role: the incidence of the disease increases with the distance from the equator. The incidence in Canada, 2.4 people per 1000 population, is one of the highest in the world.

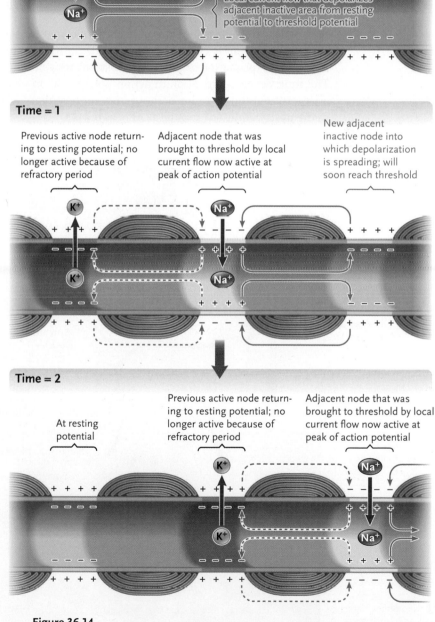

Direction of propagation of action potential

Time = 0

Active node at peak of action potential

Adjacent inactive node into which depolarization is spreading; will soon reach threshold

Remainder of nodes still at resting potential

Local current flow that depolarizes adjacent inactive area from resting potential to threshold potential

Time = 1

Previous active node returning to resting potential; no longer active because of refractory period

Adjacent node that was brought to threshold by local current flow now active at peak of action potential

New adjacent inactive node into which depolarization is spreading; will soon reach threshold

Time = 2

At resting potential

Previous active node returning to resting potential; no longer active because of refractory period

Adjacent node that was brought to threshold by local current flow now active at peak of action potential

Figure 36.14

Saltatory conduction of the action potential by a myelinated axon. The action potential jumps from node to node, greatly increasing the speed at which it travels along the axon.

36.3c Nerve Impulses Are Conducted across Chemical Synapses by Neurotransmitters

Action potentials are transmitted directly across electrical synapses (Figure 36.6, p. 881), but they cannot jump across the synaptic cleft in a chemical synapse. Instead, the arrival of an action potential causes neurotransmitter molecules synthesized in the cell body of the neuron to be released across the plasma membrane of the axon terminal, called the **presynaptic membrane (Figure 36.15).** The neurotransmitter diffuses across the cleft and alters ion conduction by activating *ligand-gated ion channels* in the **postsynaptic membrane**, the plasma membrane of the postsynaptic cell. **Ligand-gated ion channels** are channels that open or close when a specific chemical, the ligand, binds to the channel.

Neurotransmitters work in one of two ways. **Direct neurotransmitters** (Figure 36.15) bind directly to a ligand-gated ion channel in the postsynaptic membrane, which opens or closes the channel gate and alters the flow of a specific ion or ions in the postsynaptic cell. The time between arrival of an action potential at an axon terminal and alteration of the membrane potential in the postsynaptic cell may be as little as 0.2 ms.

Indirect neurotransmitters work more slowly (on the order of hundreds of milliseconds). They act as *first messengers,* binding to G-protein-coupled receptors in the postsynaptic membrane, which activates the receptors and triggers the generation of a *second messenger* such as cyclic AMP or other processes. The cascade of second-messenger reactions opens or closes ion-conducting channels in the postsynaptic membrane. Indirect neurotransmitters typically have effects that may last for minutes or hours. Some substances can act as either direct or indirect neurotransmitters, depending on the types of receptors they bind to in the receiving cell.

Not all of the chemicals released at nerve terminals directly stimulate the postsynaptic neuron to fire. Some may inhibit the neuron from firing, whereas others may enhance the action of other transmitters. Actions that modify the effects of other transmitters may not be confined to the single synaptic cleft but may act to coordinate groups of neurons. These transmitters are sometimes called neuromodulators.

The time required for the release, diffusion, and binding of neurotransmitters across chemical synapses delays transmission compared with the almost

Figure 36.15
Structure and function of chemical synapses.

Axon terminal of presynaptic neuron

Cell body of postsynaptic neuron

Synaptic vesicles

Synaptic cleft

Dennis Kunkel/Visuals Unlimited, Inc.

Presynaptic neuron

Postsynaptic neuron

1 Action potential reaches axon terminal of presynaptic neuron.

2 Ca^{2+} enters axon terminal.

3 Neurotransmitter released by exocytosis.

4 Neurotransmitter binds to postsynaptic receptor.

Presynaptic neuron

Dendrite of postsynaptic neuron

Presynaptic membrane

Synaptic vesicle

Axon terminal

Synaptic cleft

Voltage-gated Ca^{2+} channel

Ca^{2+}

Ca^{2+}

Postsynaptic membrane

Receptor for neurotransmitter

Neurotransmitter molecule

Ion channel for Na$^+$, K$^+$, or Cl$^-$

5 Ion channel associated with receptor in postsynaptic membrane opens or closes.

(Micrograph: © Dennis Kunkel/Visuals Unlimited.)

instantaneous transmission of impulses across electrical synapses. However, communication through chemical synapses allows postsynaptic neurons to integrate inputs from many presynaptic axons at the same time. Some neurotransmitters have stimulatory effects, whereas others have inhibitory effects. All of the information received at a postsynaptic membrane is integrated to produce a response that consists of the receptor neuron firing with a particular frequency.

36.3d Neurotransmitters Are Released by Exocytosis

Neurotransmitters are stored in secretory vesicles, called synaptic vesicles, in the cytoplasm of an axon terminal. The arrival of an action potential at the terminal releases the neurotransmitters by *exocytosis:* the vesicles fuse with the presynaptic membrane and release the neurotransmitter molecules into the synaptic cleft (Figure 36.15).

The release of synaptic vesicles depends on voltage-gated Ca^{2+} channels in the plasma membrane of an axon terminal (see Figure 36.15). Ca^{2+} ions are constantly pumped out of all animal cells by an active transport protein in the plasma membrane, keeping their concentration higher outside than inside. As an action potential arrives, the change in membrane potential opens the Ca^{2+} channel gates in the axon terminal, allowing Ca^{2+} to flow back into the cytoplasm. The rise in Ca^{2+} concentration triggers a protein in the membrane of the synaptic vesicle that allows the vesicle to fuse with the plasma membrane, releasing neurotransmitter molecules into the synaptic cleft.

Each action potential arriving at a synapse typically causes approximately the same number of synaptic vesicles to release their neurotransmitter molecules. For example, arrival of an action potential at one type of synapse causes about 300 synaptic vesicles to release a neurotransmitter called acetylcholine. Each vesicle contains about 10 000 molecules of the neurotransmitter, giving a total of some 3 million acetylcholine molecules released into the synaptic cleft by each arriving action potential.

When a stimulus is no longer present, action potentials are no longer generated. When action potentials stop arriving at the axon terminal, the voltage-gated Ca^{2+} channels in the axon terminal close, and the Ca^{2+} in the axon cytoplasm is quickly pumped to the outside. The drop in cytoplasmic Ca^{2+} stops vesicles from fusing with the presynaptic membrane, and no further neurotransmitter molecules are released. Any free neurotransmitter molecules remaining in the cleft are broken down by enzymes in the cleft or else reuptake occurs, meaning that the neurotransmitter molecules are pumped back into the axon terminals or into glial cells by active transport. Transmission of impulses across the synaptic cleft ceases within milliseconds after action potentials stop arriving at the axon terminal.

36.3e Most Neurotransmitters Alter Flow through Na+ or K+ Channels

Most neurotransmitters work by opening or closing membrane-embedded ligand-gated ion channels that conduct Na^+ or K^+ across the postsynaptic membrane, although some regulate chloride ions (Cl^-). The resulting ion flow may stimulate or inhibit the generation of action potentials by the postsynaptic cell. If Na^+ channels are opened, the inward Na^+ flow brings the membrane potential of the postsynaptic cell toward the threshold (the membrane becomes depolarized). If K^+ channels are opened, the outward flow of K^+ has the opposite effect (the membrane becomes hyperpolarized). The combined effects of the various stimulatory and inhibitory neurotransmitters at all of the chemical synapses of a postsynaptic neuron or muscle cell determine whether the postsynaptic cell triggers an action potential (see Section 36.4).

36.3f Many Different Molecules Act as Neurotransmitters

Nearly 100 different substances are known or suspected to be neurotransmitters. Most of them are relatively small molecules that diffuse rapidly across the synaptic cleft. Some axon terminals release only one type of neurotransmitter, whereas others release several types. Depending on the type of receptor to which it binds, the same neurotransmitter may stimulate or inhibit the generation of action potentials in the postsynaptic cell. **Table 36.1, p. 892** lists some examples of neurotransmitters, the types of molecules they represent, their sites and type of action, and some drugs and other molecules that affect neurotransmission.

STUDY BREAK

1. How does the presence of a myelin sheath affect the conduction of impulses in neurons? What type of cell forms the myelin sheath?
2. Describe the steps from the arrival of an action potential at an axon terminal to the release of a neurotransmitter.
3. Describe how a direct neurotransmitter in a presynaptic neuron controls ion flow in a postsynaptic neuron.
4. Why aren't synaptic vessicles being released all the time? Why are they only released when an action potential arrives? How is this controlled?

Table 36.1   **Examples of Neurotransmitters and Drugs That Affect Neurotransmission**

Neurotransmitter	Site(s) of Action	Type of Action	Drugs and Other Molecules That Affect Neurotransmission
Acetylcholine	Between some neurons of CNS and at neuromuscular junctions in PNS; acetylcholine-releasing neurons in the brain degenerate in people with Alzheimer disease, in which memory, speech, and perceptual abilities decline	Mostly excitatory; inhibitory at some sites	• Curare—blocks release; blocks muscle contraction and produces paralysis, potentially leading to death • Atropine—blocks receptors; used to relax iris muscles to dilate pupils for eye exam • Nicotine—activates receptors, causing increased attention and decreased stress and irritability
Monoamines (biogenic amines)			
Norepinephrine	CNS interneurons involved in diverse brain and body functions, such as memory, mood, sensory perception, muscle movements, maintenance of blood pressure and sleep; also released into body circulation as a hormone	Excitatory or inhibitory	• Amphetamines—stimulate release of norepinephrine and dopamine and block their reuptake; cause increased attention and focus and decreased fatigue • Methylphenidate (Ritalin)—increases release; used to treat attention deficit hyperactivity disorder (ADHD) • Certain antidepressants—prevent reuptake; used to treat depression and obsessive-compulsive disorder
Dopamine	CNS interneurons involved in many pathways similar to norepinephrine, but especially involved in reinforcements and addiction; not released into circulation	Mostly excitatory	• Amphetamines—stimulate release of norepinephrine and dopamine and block their reuptake; cause increased attention and focus and decreased fatigue • Cocaine—stimulates release of norepinephrine and dopamine and blocks dopamine reuptake; produces intense euphoria followed by depression
Serotonin	CNS interneurons in a number of pathways, including those regulating appetite, reproductive behaviour, muscular movement, sleep, and emotional states such as anxiety	Inhibitory or modulatory	• Fluoxetine (Prozac), sertraline (Zoloft), paroxetine (Paxil)—block serotonin reuptake; used to treat depression and obsessive-compulsive disorder
Amino Acids			
Glutamate	Many CNS pathways, including those involved in vital brain functions such as memory and learning	Excitatory	• Phencyclidine (PCP or angel dust)—blocks receptor; causes feelings of power and confusion; can cause violent behaviour
Gamma-aminobutryic acid (GABA)	Many CNS pathways; often acts in same circuits as glutamate	Inhibitory (main inhibitory neurotransmitter in mammalian CNS)	• Alcohol (ethanol)—stimulates GABA neurotransmission, increases dopamine neurotransmission, and inhibits glutamate neurotransmission; causes relaxation, a sense of euphoria, and sleepiness • Some antianxiety/sedative drugs such as diazepam (Valium), alprazolam (Xanax), and flunitrazepam (Rohypnol, the "date rape" drug)—bind to GABA receptors and increase GABA neurotransmission; result in sedation, sleepiness, and possibly amnesia • Tetanus toxin—released by bacterium *Clostridium tetani*; blocks GABA release in synapses that control muscle contraction, causing muscles to contract forcibly (once respiratory muscles are affected, victim dies quickly)
Purines			
ATP	Released simultaneously with many neurotransmitters; may have independent actions, an area under active investigation	Modulates action of other neurotransmitters	

(continued)

Table 36.1   Examples of Neurotransmitters and Drugs That Affect Neurotransmission (*continued*)

Neurotransmitter	Site(s) of Action	Type of Action	Drugs and Other Molecules That Affect Neurotransmission
Neuropeptides			
Endorphins ("endogenous morphines")	Most act on CNS and PNS as well as on effectors such as muscle, reducing pain and, in some cases, also inducing euphoria; released during periods of pleasurable experience (such as eating or sexual intercourse), or physical stress (such as childbirth or extended physical exercise)	Inhibitory— modulate pain response	
Enkephalins (subclass of endorphins)	Active only in CNS	Inhibitory— modulate pain response	
Substance P	Released by special, unmyelinated sensory neurons in spinal cord, which produce rapid conduction for resulting signals; increases neural signals associated with intense, persistent, or severe pain. Endorphins are antagonistic to substance P, reducing the perception of pain.	Excitatory	
Gaseous neurotransmitters			
Nitrous oxide (NO)	Diffuses across cell membranes in PNS rather than being released at synapses; relaxes smooth muscles in walls of blood vessels, causing vessels to dilate, which increases blood flow; contributes to many nervous system functions such as learning, sensory responses, and muscle movements	Modulatory	• Sildenafil citrate (Viagra, an impotency drug)—aids erection by inhibiting enzyme that normally reduces effects of NO in vascular beds of penis

MOLECULE BEHIND BIOLOGY 36.1

Botulinum Toxin: Potent Toxin, Valuable Therapy and "Good-Looking" Poison

Botulinum toxin is the product of the bacterium *Clostridium botulinum*, a common organism that thrives in anaerobic environments, such as preserved foods. The toxin is a protein that is destroyed by heat, but if it is ingested, it is extraordinarily toxic—1 000 000 times as toxic as strychnine. The protein is produced as a large molecule that is cleaved into a toxin and a protease. The toxin acts at acetylcholine-mediated synapses (nerve–muscle junctions in vertebrates) by promoting the entry of the protease into the neuron at the synapse, where the enzyme attacks one of the molecules essential for the release of acetylcholine. As a result this prevents muscles from contracting. The effect is long lasting: up to several months. Recovery from the effect has been hypothesized to involve the sprouting of new axon terminals.

These properties have been used since 1989 to treat a number of disorders that involve muscle spasms, such as strabismus (crossed eyes), by injecting minute quantities of the A serotype directly into the muscles. Ophthalmologists using the toxin in this way noted that frown lines around the eyes disappeared as a side effect, and the Botox cosmetic industry was born.

36.4 Integration of Incoming Signals by Neurons

Most neurons receive a multitude of stimulatory and inhibitory signals carried by both direct and indirect neurotransmitters. These signals are integrated by the postsynaptic neuron into a response that reflects their combined effects. The integration depends primarily on the patterns, number, types, and activity of the synapses that the postsynaptic neuron receives from presynaptic neurons. Inputs from other sources, such as indirect neurotransmitters and other signal molecules, can modify the integration. The response of the postsynaptic neuron is elucidated by the frequency of action potentials it generates.

36.4a Integration at Chemical Synapses Occurs by Summation

As mentioned earlier, depending on the type of receptor to which it binds, a neurotransmitter may stimulate or inhibit the generation of action potentials in the postsynaptic neuron. If a neurotransmitter opens a ligand-gated Na^+ channel, Na^+ enters the cell, causing a depolarization. This change in membrane potential pushes the neuron closer to threshold; that is, it is excitatory and is called an **excitatory postsynaptic potential**, or **EPSP.** On the other hand, if a neurotransmitter opens a ligand-gated ion channel that allows Cl^- to flow into the cell and K^+ to flow out, hyperpolarization occurs. This change in membrane potential pushes the neuron farther from threshold; that is, it is inhibitory and is called an **inhibitory postsynaptic potential**, or **IPSP.** EPSPs and IPSPs are **graded potentials**, in which the membrane moves up or down in potential without necessarily triggering an action potential. There are no refractory periods for EPSPs and IPSPs.

A neuron typically has hundreds to thousands of chemical synapses formed by axon terminals of presynaptic neurons contacting its dendrites and cell body **(Figure 36.16).** The events that occur at each synapse produce either an EPSP or an IPSP in that postsynaptic neuron. But how is an action potential produced if a single EPSP is not sufficient to push the postsynaptic neuron to threshold? The answer involves the summation of all the inputs received through all the chemical synapses formed by presynaptic neurons. At any given time, some or many of the presynaptic neurons may be firing, producing EPSPs and/or IPSPs in the postsynaptic neuron. The sum of all the EPSPs and IPSPs at a given time determines the total potential in the postsynaptic neuron and, therefore, how that neuron responds. **Figure 36.17** shows, in a greatly simplified way, the effects of EPSPs and IPSPs on membrane potential and how the summation of inputs brings a postsynaptic neuron to threshold.

The postsynaptic neuron in Figure 36.17 has three neurons, N1 to N3, forming synapses with it. Suppose that the axon of N1 releases a neurotransmitter that produces an EPSP in the postsynaptic cell (see Figure 36.17a). The membrane depolarizes, but not enough to reach threshold. If N1 input causes a new EPSP after the first EPSP has died down, it will be of the same magnitude as the first EPSP, so no progression toward threshold happens because no summation has occurred. If, instead, N1 input causes a new EPSP before the first EPSP has died down, the second EPSP will sum with the first, leading to a greater depolarization (see Figure 36.17b). This summation of several EPSPs at a common site produced by successive firing of a single presynaptic neuron over a short period of time is called **temporal summation.** If the total depolarization achieved in this way spreads to the axon hillock or spike initiation zone and brings it to threshold, an action potential will be produced in the postsynaptic neuron.

The postsynaptic cell may also be brought to threshold by **spatial summation,** the summation of EPSPs produced by the firing of different presynaptic neurons at different sites on the postsynaptic cell, such as N1 and N2 (see Figure 36.17c). Lastly, EPSPs and IPSPs can cancel each other out. In the example shown in Figure 36.17d, firing of N1 alone produces an EPSP, and firing of N3 alone produces an IPSP, whereas the simultaneous firing of N1 and N3 produces no change in the membrane potential.

The key summation point for EPSPs and IPSPs is the axon hillock or spike initiation zone of the postsynaptic neuron. EPSPs and IPSPs spread over the membrane of the dendrites and cell body as graded potentials summing or cancelling each other as they meet. If the net change in membrane potential is sufficient to bring the spike initiation zone (the first site along the neuron where voltage-gated Na^+ and K^+ channels occur) to threshold, an action potential will result. This action potential will then be conducted or propagated along the neuron.

36.4b The Patterns of Synaptic Connections Contribute to Integration

The total number of connections made by a neuron may be very large. Some single interneurons in the human brain, for example, form as many as 100 000 synapses with other neurons. The synapses are not absolutely fixed; they can change through modification, addition, or removal of synaptic connections, or even entire neurons, as animals mature and experience changes in their environments. The combined activities of all the neurons in an animal provide the

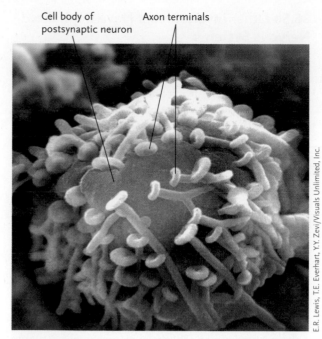

Cell body of postsynaptic neuron   Axon terminals

Figure 36.16

The multiple chemical synapses relaying signals to a neuron. The drying process used to prepare the neuron for electron microscopy has toppled the axon terminals and pulled them away from the neuron's surface.

E.R. Lewis, T.E. Everhart, Y.Y. Zevi/Visuals Unlimited, Inc.

flow of information on which the integrated functioning of increasingly complex organisms depends. In the remainder of this chapter, we explore the ways that neurons are organized into nervous systems in the various major groups of animals.

STUDY BREAK

1. Differentiate between spatial and temporal summation.
2. Describe the steps from the repeated release of an excitatory neurotransmitter at a synapse to the initiation of an action potential at an axon hillock.

36.5 Evolutionary Trends in Neural Integration: Networks, Nerves, Ganglia, and Brains

The nervous systems of all animals are designed to effectively sense environmental changes (internal and external), integrate this information, and produce appropriate responses. The organization of the nervous systems of the different groups of invertebrate and vertebrate animals reflects differences in lifestyle and habitat. Most nervous systems contain sensory (afferent) pathways that collect information, integrating

Presynaptic neurons

A. No summation: The axon of Ex1 releases a neurotransmitter, which produces an EPSP in the postsynaptic cell. The membrane depolarizes, but not enough to reach threshold. If Ex1 input causes a new EPSP after the first EPSP has died down, it will be of the same magnitude as the first EPSP and no progression toward threshold has taken place—no summation has occurred.

B. Temporal summation: If instead, Ex1 input causes a new EPSP before the first EPSP has died down, the second EPSP will sum with the first and a greater depolarization will have taken place. This summation of two (or more) EPSPs produced by successive firing of a single presynaptic neuron over a short period of time is temporal summation. If the total depolarization achieved in this way reaches threshold, an action potential is produced in the postsynaptic neuron.

C. Spatial summation: The postsynaptic neuron may be brought to threshold by spatial summation, the summation of EPSPs produced by the simultaneous firing of two different excitatory presynaptic neurons, such as Ex1 and Ex2.

D. Summation resulting in cancellation: EPSPs and IPSPs can sum to cancel each other out. In the example, firing of the excitatory presynaptic neuron Ex1 alone produces an EPSP, firing of presynaptic inhibitory neuron In3 alone produces an IPSP, while firing of Ex1 and In3 simultaneously produces no change in the membrane potential.

Figure 36.17

Summation of EPSPs and IPSPs by a postsynaptic neuron.

centres (where decisions are made), and motor (afferent) pathways that produce responses.

36.5a Cnidarians Have Nerve Nets

Cnidarians (including jellyfish and sea anemones) are radially symmetrical protostomes with body parts arranged around a central axis. Their nervous systems are composed of **nerve nets**, loose meshes of neurons that extend over the entire organism just beneath the epithelium **(Figure 36.18a).** The processes of their neurons do not fit the normal description of dendrites and axons. Instead, all processes can conduct action potentials, and instead of having synapses at their terminals, there are synapses wherever the processes of neurons cross processes of other neurons. Moreover, both processes involved in a synapse may produce transmitters and have receptors for transmitters. When part of the animal is stimulated, impulses are conducted through the nerve net in all directions from the point of stimulation. Although there is no cluster of neurons that plays the coordinating role of a brain, nerve cells may be more concentrated in some regions. In the cnidarian hydra, they are more concentrated around the oral opening, allowing better coordination of tentacles for feeding. In the cnidarian jellyfish, which swim by rhythmic contraction of their bells, neurons are denser in a ring around the bell, in the same area as the contractile cells that produce the swimming movements.

36.5b Other Invertebrates Have Cephalized Nervous Systems

More complex invertebrates have neurons with clearly defined axons and dendrites and more specialized functions. Some neurons are concentrated into functional clusters called ganglia (singular, ganglion) **(Figure 36.19).** This anatomical localization of interconnections allows rapid integration of sensory information and more complex reactions to that information. We saw in Chapter 25, that segmental development has occurred twice in the evolution of the protostomes, which had profound effects on the development of the nervous system. In these organisms, each segment has a separate pair of ganglia, joined by interconnections, both between members of a pair within a segment and between the pairs of ganglia in the segments in front and behind.

Another key evolutionary development in invertebrates is a trend toward *cephalization,* the formation of a distinct head region. This head region usually contains major sensory structures, reflecting the tendency for the head of the animal, as it moves through its environment, to encounter new stimuli first. The formation of a distinct head is the result of the fusion of anterior segments and the paired ganglia associated with these segments to form a **brain.** This concentration of neurons at a site close to the sensory structures reduces the transmission times for processing incoming signals and for integrating signals to produce appropriate responses. One

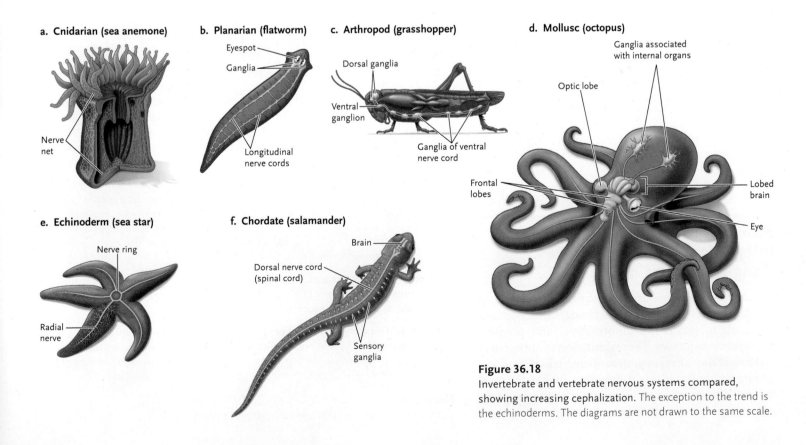

a. Cnidarian (sea anemone)

Nerve net

b. Planarian (flatworm)

Eyespot
Ganglia
Longitudinal nerve cords

c. Arthropod (grasshopper)

Dorsal ganglia
Ventral ganglion
Ganglia of ventral nerve cord

d. Mollusc (octopus)

Ganglia associated with internal organs
Optic lobe
Frontal lobes
Lobed brain
Eye

e. Echinoderm (sea star)

Nerve ring
Radial nerve

f. Chordate (salamander)

Brain
Dorsal nerve cord (spinal cord)
Sensory ganglia

Figure 36.18
Invertebrate and vertebrate nervous systems compared, showing increasing cephalization. The exception to the trend is the echinoderms. The diagrams are not drawn to the same scale.

Anterior sensory organs

n

n

n

n

Figure 36.19

A section of a typical invertebrate cerebral ganglion. The cell bodies (blue) are located on the periphery, with a mass of axons and dendrites forming the neuropile in the centre. Nerves (n) bring sensory information into the ganglion and carry motor information outward.

or more solid **nerve cords**—bundles of nerves—extend from the central ganglia to the rest of the body; they are connected to smaller nerves. Another evolutionary trend is toward bilateral symmetry of the body and the nervous system, in which body parts are mirror images on left and right sides. These trends toward cephalization and bilateral symmetry are well illustrated in flatworms, arthropods, and molluscs.

In flatworms, a small brain consisting of a pair of ganglia at the anterior end is connected by two or more longitudinal nerve cords to nerve nets in the rest of the body **(Figure 36.18b).** The brain integrates inputs from sensory receptors, including a pair of anterior eyespots with receptors that respond to light. The brain and longitudinal nerve cords constitute the flatworm's CNS, the simplest one known, while the nerves from the CNS to the rest of the body constitute the PNS (see Section 36.5d).

Arthropods such as insects have a head region that contains a brain, consisting of dorsal and ventral pairs of ganglia, and major sensory structures, usually eyes and antennae **(Figure 36.18c).** The brain exerts centralized control over the remainder of the animal. A ventral nerve enlarges into a pair of ganglia in each body segment. In arthropods with fused body segments, as in the thorax of insects, the ganglia are also fused into masses forming secondary control centres.

Although different in basic plan from the arthropod system, the nervous systems of molluscs (such as clams, snails, and octopi) also rely on neurons clustered into paired ganglia connected by major nerves. Different molluscs have varying degrees of cephalization, with cephalopods having the most pronounced cephalization of any invertebrate group. In the head of an octopus, for example, a cluster of ganglia fuses into a complex, lobed brain with clearly defined sensory and motor regions. Paired nerves link different lobes with muscles and sensory receptors, including prominent optic lobes linked by nerves to large, complex eyes **(Figure 36.18d).** Octopuses are capable of rapid movement to hunt prey and to escape from predators, behaviours that rely on rapid, sophisticated processing of sensory information.

The echinoderms, including sea stars, are an exception to this trend. Like cnidarians, this group is also radially symmetrical. These animals lack a *cephalized brain* and instead have a series of ganglia connected by a nerve ring that surrounds the centrally located mouth. Neurons are organized into radial nerves **(Figure 36.18e).** If the nerve serving an arm is cut, the arm can still move in response to stimuli, but not in coordination with the other arms. Echinoderms are descended from bilaterally symmetrical ancestors, and in many species the larvae are bilaterally symmetrical and develop radial symmetry during metamorphosis into adults.

36.5c Vertebrates Have Complex Nervous Systems

In vertebrates, the CNS consists of the brain and spinal cord, and the PNS consists of all the nerves and ganglia that connect the brain and spinal cord to the rest of the body **(Figure 36.18f).** All vertebrate nervous systems are highly cephalized, with major concentrations of neurons in a brain located in the head. In contrast to invertebrate nervous systems, which have solid nerve cords located ventrally, the brain and nerve cord of vertebrates are hollow, fluid-filled structures located dorsally. The head contains specialized sensory organs, which are connected directly to the brain by nerves. Compared with those in invertebrates, the ganglia are greatly reduced in mass and functional activity (except in the gut, which contains extensive interneuron networks), while the brains are greatly enlarged.

The structure of the vertebrate nervous system reflects its pattern of development. The nervous system of a vertebrate embryo begins as a hollow **neural tube** (discussed more in Chapter 34), the anterior end of which develops into the brain and the rest into the **spinal cord.** The cavity of the neural tube becomes the fluid-filled **ventricles** of the brain and the **central canal** through the spinal cord. Adjacent tissues give rise to nerves that connect the brain and spinal cord with all the body regions. Just as in the invertebrates, the brain and longitudinal nerve cord (now the spinal cord) constitute the CNS, while the nerves connecting the CNS to the rest of the body constitute the PNS.

36.5d The Vertebrate Central Nervous System and Its Functions

Early in development, the anterior part of the neural tube enlarges into three distinct regions: the **forebrain**, **midbrain**, and **hindbrain (Figure 36.20).** A little later, the embryonic hindbrain subdivides into the *metencephalon* and *myelencephalon,* the midbrain develops into the *mesencephalon,* and the forebrain subdivides into the *telencephalon* and *diencephalon.*

The myelencephalon gives rise to the *medulla oblongata* (commonly shortened to medulla), which controls many vital involuntary tasks, such as respiration and blood circulation. The metencephalon, associated with the developing ear (when present)

and balance organs gives rise to the *cerebellum,* which integrates sensory signals from the eyes, ears, and muscle spindles, and the *pons,* a major traffic centre for information passing between the cerebellum and the higher integrating centres of the adult telencephalon. The midbrain, or mesencephalon, receives nerves from the optic nerves and from the ear and coordinates reflex responses (involuntary reactions) to visual and auditory (hearing) input and also relays this information to the telencephalon for further processing. The diencephalon gives rise to the *thalamus,* a centre that receives sensory input and relays it to the regions of the cerebral cortex concerned with motor responses to such input, and the *hypothalamus,* the primary centre for homeostatic control over the internal environment. The embryonic telencephalon develops into the adult *cerebrum.* The cerebrum controls higher functions such as thought, memory, language, and emotions as well as voluntary movements.

Regions in 4-week embryo	Regions in 5-week embryo	Regions in adult	Functions in adult
Forebrain	Telencephalon	Telencephalon (cerebrum)	Higher functions, such as thought, action, and communication
	Diencephalon	Thalamus Hypothalamus	Receives sensory input and relays it to regions of the cerebral cortex Center for homeostatic control of internal environment
Midbrain	Mesencephalon	Midbrain	Coordinates involuntary reactions and relays signals to telencephalon
Hindbrain	Metencephalon	Cerebellum Pons	Integrates signals for muscle movement Center for information flow between cerebellum and telencephalon
	Myelencephalon	Medulla oblongata	Controls many involuntary tasks

Figure 36.20

Development of the human brain from the anterior end of an embryo's neural tube.

4-week embryo   **5-week embryo**   **Adult brain regions**

The general pattern of brain development underwent major modification in the evolution of various groups of animals **(Figure 36.21)**. In sharks, the cerebrum is relatively small, but the olfactory bulbs are prominent, testifying to the importance of olfaction in these very successful predators. Frogs are hunters that rely on vision, so the optic lobes of the mesencephalon are prominent, whereas the olfactory bulbs are less so. Birds also rely on vision for feeding and navigation, and their optic lobes reflect that.

One of the major trends in the evolution of the brain, however, is the increasing prominence of the cerebrum. Beginning with reptiles, it increased in size relative to the rest of the brain. In mammals, convolutions or folds appeared, increasing the amount of brain material in a particular volume. As well, the total mass of the brain relative to the size of the animal increased, permitting animals to undertake more complex tasks. The mass of bird and mammal brains is about 15 times that of other taxa when corrected for the size of the animal. With their advanced locomotor and navigational skills, birds and mammals also exhibit an increase in the cerebellum, a major coordinating centre for automatic activities.

36.5e The Vertebrate Peripheral Nervous System and Its Functional Parts

The PNS can be divided into two main systems. The afferent system of the PNS includes all the neurons that transmit sensory information from receptors to the CNS. The efferent system consists of the axons of neurons that carry signals to the muscles and glands acting as effectors. The efferent system is further divided into somatic and autonomic systems **(Figure 36.22, p. 900)**.

The Somatic System Controls the Contraction of Skeletal Muscles. The **somatic nervous system** controls body movements that are primarily conscious and voluntary. Its efferent neurons, called motor neurons, carry signals from the CNS to the skeletal muscles. The dendrites and cell bodies of motor neurons are located in the spinal cord. Their axons extend from the spinal cord, emanating from between the vertebrae, to the skeletal muscles they control. The cell bodies for the sensory nerves (the afferent neurons) are located outside the spinal cord within the dorsal root, forming the dorsal root ganglion.

Although the somatic system is primarily under conscious, voluntary control, some contractions of skeletal muscles are unconscious and involuntary. These include reflexes, shivering, and the constant muscle contractions that maintain body posture and balance.

The Autonomic System Is Divided into Sympathetic and Parasympathetic Pathways. The **autonomic nervous system** controls largely involuntary processes such as digestion, secretion by sweat glands, circulation of the blood, many functions of the reproductive and excretory systems, and contraction of smooth muscles in all parts of the body. It is organized into *sympathetic* and *parasympathetic* divisions, which are always active and have opposing effects on the organs that they affect, thereby enabling precise control **(Figure 36.23, p. 900)**. For example, in the circulatory system, sympathetic neurons stimulate the force and rate of the heartbeat, and parasympathetic neurons inhibit these activities.

Figure 36.21

A comparison of brain structures in five different groups of vertebrates, illustrating the evolutionary trends described in the text.

Figure 36.22

The CNS and PNS and their subsystems.

KEY

■ Central nervous system
■ Peripheral nervous system
■ Afferent and somatic systems
■ Autonomic system

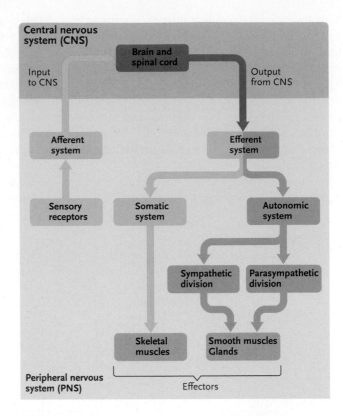

Central nervous system (CNS)

Brain and spinal cord

Input to CNS

Output from CNS

Afferent system

Efferent system

Sensory receptors

Somatic system

Autonomic system

Sympathetic division

Parasympathetic division

Skeletal muscles

Smooth muscles Glands

Peripheral nervous system (PNS)

Effectors

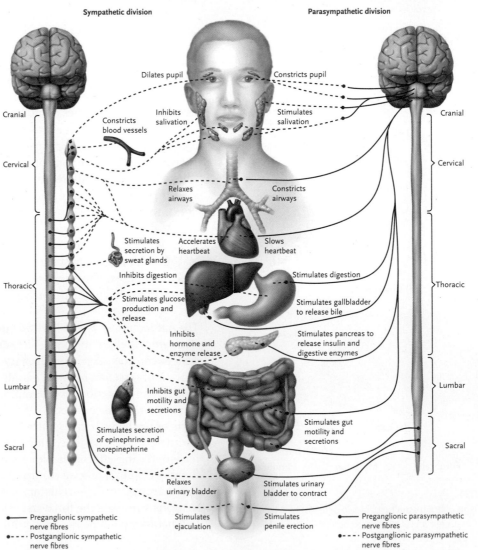

Sympathetic division

Parasympathetic division

Cranial

Cervical

Thoracic

Lumbar

Sacral

Cranial

Cervical

Thoracic

Lumbar

Sacral

Dilates pupil — Constricts pupil

Inhibits salivation — Stimulates salivation

Constricts blood vessels

Relaxes airways — Constricts airways

Stimulates secretion by sweat glands

Accelerates heartbeat — Slows heartbeat

Inhibits digestion — Stimulates digestion

Stimulates glucose production and release — Stimulates gallbladder to release bile

Inhibits hormone and enzyme release — Stimulates pancreas to release insulin and digestive enzymes

Inhibits gut motility and secretions — Stimulates gut motility and secretions

Stimulates secretion of epinephrine and norepinephrine

Relaxes urinary bladder — Stimulates urinary bladder to contract

Stimulates ejaculation — Stimulates penile erection

•— Preganglionic sympathetic nerve fibres
•--- Postganglionic sympathetic nerve fibres

•— Preganglionic parasympathetic nerve fibres
•--- Postganglionic parasympathetic nerve fibres

Figure 36.23

Effects of sympathetic and parasympathetic divisions on organ and gland function. Only one side of each division is shown; both are duplicated on the left and right sides of the body.

| Preganglionic neuron | Preganglionic neurotransmitter | Postganglionic neuron | Postganglionic neurotransmitter |

Figure 36.24
An autonomic nervous system pathway.

Neuron of CNS   Autonomic ganglion of PNS   Effector organ that carries out the response

In the digestive system, sympathetic neurons inhibit the smooth muscle contractions that move materials through the small intestine, whereas parasympathetic neurons stimulate the same activities. These opposing effects control involuntary body functions precisely.

The pathways of the autonomic nervous system include two neurons **(Figure 36.24).** The first neuron has its dendrites and cell body in the CNS, and its axon extends to a ganglion outside the CNS. There it synapses with the dendrites and cell body of the second neuron in the pathway. The axon of the second neuron extends from the ganglion to the effector carrying out the response.

The **sympathetic division** predominates in situations involving stress, danger, excitement, or strenuous physical activity. Signals from the sympathetic division increase the force and rate of the heartbeat, raise the blood pressure by constricting selected blood vessels, dilate air passages in the lungs, induce sweating, and open the pupils wide. Activities that are less important in an emergency, such as digestion, are suppressed by the sympathetic system. The ganglia between the first and second neurons in each sympathetic pathway occur as a chain of segmental ganglia just outside (ventral to) the vertebral column in the thoracic and abdominal regions (see Figure 36.23).

The **parasympathetic division,** in contrast, predominates during quiet, low-stress situations, such as relaxation. Under its influence, the effects of the sympathetic division, such as rapid heartbeat and elevated blood pressure, are reduced, and maintenance activities such as digestion predominate. The parasympathetic pathways originate either directly from the brain or from the sacral region of the spinal cord. The ganglia between the first and second neurons in the parasympathetic pathways are associated with the target organs (see Figure 36.23).

STUDY BREAK

1. Distinguish between a neuron, a nerve net, nerves, and nerve cords.
2. What is cephalization and why does it occur?
3. What is the significance of ganglia, brains, and nerve cords?
4. How do differences in brain structure reflect differences in lifestyle?
5. What two systems make up the PNS, and what do they generally control?
6. When an elk attempts to evade an attacking pack of wolves, what division of its autonomic nervous system dominates? What effects might result?

Review

Access an interactive eBook, chapter-specific interactive learning tools, including flashcards, quizzes, videos, and more in your Biology **CourseMate**, accessed through NelsonBrain.com **Aplia™** is an online interactive learning solution that helps you improve comprehension—and your grade—by integrating a variety of mediums and tools such as videos, tutorials, practice tests, and an interactive eBook.

36.1 Neurons and Their Organization in Nervous Systems: An Overview

- Neurons are excitable cells specialized for the rapid transmission of signals. They have dendrites and cell bodies, which receive and integrate information, and axons, which generate and conduct signals away from the cell body to another neuron or an effector.

- The nervous system of an animal (1) receives information about conditions in the internal and external environment, (2) integrates the information to formulate an appropriate response, (3) conducts the message along neurons and (4) transmits the signal to effector organs to produce a response.

- Afferent neurons conduct information from sensory receptors to interneurons, which integrate the information into a response. The response signals are passed to efferent neurons, which activate the effectors carrying out the response.

- Glial cells provide structural and functional support to neurons. They help maintain the balance of ions surrounding neurons and form insulating layers around the axons.

- Neurons make connections by two types of synapses, electrical and chemical. In an electrical synapse, impulses pass directly from the sending to the receiving cell. In a chemical synapse, neurotransmitter molecules released by the presynaptic neuron diffuse across a narrow synaptic cleft and bind to receptors in the plasma membrane of the postsynaptic cell. Binding of the neurotransmitters may generate an electrical impulse in the postsynaptic cell.

36.2 Signal Initiation by Neurons

- The membrane potential of a cell results from the unequal distribution of positive and negative charges on either side of the membrane. This establishes a potential difference, the resting potential, across the membrane.

- The resting potential is maintained by an active transport pump that maintains the concentration gradients of Na^+ ions (higher outside) and K^+ ions (higher inside).

- Not all parts of a neuron can generate an action potential; only those parts that possess voltage-gated Na^+ and K^+ channels can.

- An action potential is generated when a stimulus pushes the resting potential at the spike initiation zone to the threshold value at which voltage-gated Na^+ channels open in the plasma membrane. The inward flow of Na^+ changes the membrane potential abruptly from a negative to a positive peak, which opens the voltage-gated K^+ channels. The potential falls to the resting value again as the gated K^+ channels allow this ion to flow out.

- Action potentials move along an axon as the ion flows generated in one location on the axon depolarize the potential in the adjacent location.

- Action potentials are prevented from reversing direction by a brief refractory period (a few milliseconds), during which a sector of membrane that has just generated an action potential cannot be stimulated to produce another. During this period, the action potential has moved too far away for its electrical disturbances to cause the preceding sector to depolarize again.

- In myelinated axons, ions can flow across the plasma membrane only at the nodes of Ranvier, where the insulating myelin sheath is interrupted.

- The intensity of a stimulus is reflected in the frequency of action potentials.

- Receptors in the sensory system collect information (i.e., stimuli) from internal and external sensors (transducers) and convert (transduce) the information into neural activity. Dendrites of an afferent neuron pick up the stimuli. The axon of the afferent neuron conveys the stimulus to the CNS, providing the organisms with sensory data used to influence behaviour and homeostasis.

- Mechanoreceptors detect mechanical energy (pressure), photoreceptors detect the energy of light, chemoreceptors detect specific molecules or chemical conditions, thermoreceptors detect the flow of heat energy, and nociceptors detect tissue damage or noxious chemicals.

36.3 Conduction of Action Potentials along Neurons and across Chemical Synapses

- Neurotransmitters released into the synaptic cleft bind to receptors in the plasma membrane of the postsynaptic cell, altering the flow of ions across the plasma membrane of the postsynaptic cell and pushing its membrane potential toward or away from the threshold potential.

- A direct neurotransmitter binds to a receptor associated with a ligand-gated ion channel in the postsynaptic membrane; the binding opens or closes the channel.

- An indirect neurotransmitter works as a first messenger, binding to a receptor in the postsynaptic membrane and triggering generation of a second messenger, which leads to the opening or closing of a gated channel.

- Neurotransmitters are released from synaptic vesicles into the synaptic cleft by exocytosis, which is triggered by entry of Ca^{2+} ions into the cytoplasm of the axon terminal through voltage-gated Ca^{2+} channels opened by the arrival of an action potential.

- Neurotransmitter release stops when action potentials cease arriving at the axon terminal. Neurotransmitters remaining in the synaptic cleft are broken down by enzymes or taken up by the axon terminal or glial cells.

- Types of neurotransmitters include acetylcholine, amino acids, biogenic amines, neuropeptides, and gases such as NO and CO.

36.4 Integration of Incoming Signals by Neurons

- Integration of incoming information by a neuron determines the frequency at which the receiving neuron sends out action potentials.

- Neurons carry out integration by summing excitatory postsynaptic potentials (EPSPs) and inhibitory postsynaptic potentials (IPSPs). The summation may occur over time (temporal) or from different neurons at the same time (spatial). This summation pushes the membrane potential of the receiving cell toward or away from the threshold for an action potential.

36.5 Evolutionary Trends in Neural Integration: Networks, Ganglia, and Brains

- Identifiable nerves first appear in radially symmetrical animals as nerve nets composed of single neurons that are more concentrated around the mouth and that may have localized groupings of cell bodies that control particular functions.

- The development of bilateral symmetry resulted in the concentration of parts of the nerve net into several longitudinal nerve cords composed of several axons, with paired ventral cords becoming increasingly dominant.

- Ganglia, local concentrations of nerve cell bodies permitting enhanced coordination of sensory and motor functions, first appeared in the flatworms, with the anterior ganglia prominent and acting as a brain. Protostome ganglia have the cell bodies at the periphery and the neuropile of axons and dendrites in the interior.

- Molluscs have well-developed nervous systems with paired ventral nerve cords and a brain consisting of several fused ganglia that permits advanced behaviour in the cephalopods.

- The protovertebrate nervous system, represented by the lancelet, is a hollow dorsal tube with nerves leading to each segmental block of muscle. The anterior end of the tube is larger, and three regions equivalent to the forebrain, midbrain, and hindbrain of the vertebrate embryonic brain can be recognized.

- In the development of the vertebrate brain, the hindbrain subdivides into the myelencephalon, which becomes the medulla oblongata, or brain stem, responsible for many involuntary functions, and the metencephalon, associated with hearing and balance. The cerebellum, a major processing centre for balance and navigation, is an outgrowth of the metencephalon. The midbrain, or mesencephalon, coordinates hearing and vision. The forebrain subdivides into the diencephalon, which gives rise to the optic nerves, and the telencephalon, which is responsible for olfaction and gives rise to the cerebrum, the major processing centre of the brain.

- During evolution, some parts of the brain become more prominent depending on the lifestyle of the animal. Sharks have large olfactory centres, whereas frogs have larger optic centres.

- The evolution of the brain also involves an increase in its mass relative to the body mass of the animal and, in particular, an increase in the mass of the cerebrum relative to the rest of the brain. Birds and mammals also exhibit an increased prominence of the cerebellum.

- Afferent neurons in the PNS conduct signals to the CNS, and signals from the CNS go via efferent neurons to the muscles and glands that carry out responses.

- The somatic system of the PNS controls the skeletal muscles that produce voluntary body movements, as well as involuntary muscle contractions that maintain balance, posture, and muscle tone.
- The autonomic system of the PNS controls involuntary functions such as heart rate and blood pressure, glandular secretion, and smooth muscle contraction.
- The autonomic system is organized into sympathetic and para-sympathetic divisions that balance and fine-tune involuntary body functions. The sympathetic system predominates in situations involving stress, danger, or strenuous activities, whereas the parasympathetic system predominates during quiet, low-stress situations.

Questions

Self-Test Questions

1. What does neural signalling involve?
   a. differentiation
   b. integration
   c. response
   d. transmission
   e. reception

2. The nodes of Ranvier
   a. speed up conduction of electrical impulses
   b. make up a myelin sheath
   c. expose the axon
   d. are gaps between adjacent Schwann cells

3. Electrical synapses
   a. occur where the cytoplasm of pre- and postsynaptic cells are in direct contact
   b. have narrow gaps called clefts between cells
   c. are electrical impulses that flow between cells through gap junctions
   d. involve the release of neurotransmitters

4. What does the resting potential result from
   a. differential permeability of membranes that results in accumulation of more proteins and other anions carrying negative charge inside the cell
   b. an opening of voltage-gated sodium channels
   c. higher concentrations of Na^+ and K^+ inside and outside the cells created by the Na^+/K^+ pump
   d. an opening of ligand-gated sodium channels

5. Which statement best describes how nerve signals travel?
   a. The axons of oligodendrocytes transmit nerve impulses to the dendrites of astrocytes.
   b. An axon of a motor neuron receives the signal, its cell body transmits the signal to a sensory neuron's dendrite, and the signal is sent to the target.
   c. A dendrite of a sensory neuron receives the signal, its cell body transmits the signal to a motor neuron's axon, and the signal is sent to the target.
   d. Efferent neurons conduct nerve impulses toward the cell body of sensory neurons, which send them on to interneurons and, ultimately, to afferent motor neurons.
   e. A dendrite of a sensory neuron receives a signal, the cell's axon transmits the signal to an interneuron, and then the signal is transmitted to dendrites of a motor neuron and sent via its axon to the target.

6. A synapse could be the site where which of the following takes place?
   a. Postsynaptic neurons transmit a signal across a cleft to a presynaptic neuron.
   b. The axons of a presynaptic neuron directly contact the dendrites of a postsynaptic neuron.
   c. The neurotransmitters released by an axon travel across a gap and are picked up by receptors on a muscle cell.
   d. An electrical impulse arrives at the end of a dendrite, causing ions to flow onto axons of presynaptic neurons.
   e. An on–off switch stimulates an electrical impulse in a presynaptic cell to stimulate, not inhibit, other presynaptic cells.

7. Nerve impulses
   a. always travel in both directions along an axon
   b. sometimes travel in both directions along an axon
   c. travel in only one direction along an axon
   d. always travel with the same intensity along the length of an axon
   e. diminish in intensity as they travel along an axon

8. Spatial summation
   a. is the change in membrane potential of a postsynaptic cell brought on by the firing of different presynaptic neurons
   b. is the change in membrane potential of a postsynaptic cell brought on by successive firing of a single presynaptic neuron over a short period of time
   c. is the total of the membrane potentials that occur along an axon as the electrical impulse is transmitted

9. Ganglia first became enlarged and fused into a lobed brain in the evolution of which of the following?
   a. vertebrates
   b. annelids
   c. flatworms
   d. cephalopods
   e. mammals

10. The metencephalon is the origin of which of the following?
    a. the spinal cord
    b. the cerebellum
    c. the mesencephalon
    d. the medulla oblongata
    e. the cerebrum

Questions for Discussion

1. The mechanism for the propagation of the action potential along an axon was worked out using the giant axons of squids. How confident should we be that this model applies to vertebrates? Is there an evolutionary link between the nerves of vertebrates and those of molluscs, or did the mechanism arise twice?

2. How did evolution of chemical synapses make higher brain function possible?

3. Describe the fundamental ways in which different sensory modalities (chemical, thermal, mechanical, electrical, light) lead to changes in the membrane potential of sensory cells. How are they similar? How are they different?

4. Discuss the selective pressure for cephalization in animals. Would there be a difference between those with sessile or motile life histories?

5. Many types of local anesthetic compounds are used to reduce pain sensations during medical procedures. Identify different types of local anesthetics and explain how they work to reduce pain sensations.

Close-up view of a blue-eyed scallop (*Argopecten irradians*) showing some of the many blue eyes that detect light and movement, allowing it to escape from predators such as sea stars and crabs.

Ken Read/Photo Researchers, Inc.

37 Control of Animal Processes: Neural Integration

WHY IT MATTERS

An insectivorous bat leaves its cave to look for food. As it flies the bat emits a steady stream of ultrasonic clicking noises. Receptors in the bat's ears detect echoes of the clicks bouncing off objects in the environment and send signals to the brain, where they are integrated into a sound map that the animal uses to navigate through the complex environment. This ability, called **echolocation**, is so keenly developed that a bat can detect and avoid a thin wire in the dark.

Besides recognizing obstacles, the bat's auditory system is sharply tuned to the distinctive pattern of echoes from the fluttering wings of its favourite food, a moth. Although the slow-flying moth seems doomed to become a meal for the foraging bat, natural selection has provided some species of moths with an astoundingly sensitive auditory sense as well. On each side of its abdomen is an "ear," a thin membrane that resonates at the frequencies of the clicks emitted by the bat. The moth's ears register the clicks while the bat is still about 30 m away and initiate a response that turns its flight path directly away from the source of the clicks.

In spite of the moth's evasive turns, if the bat approaches within about 6 m of it, echoes from the moth begin to register in the bat's auditory system, and the bat increases the frequency of its clicks, enabling it to pinpoint the moth's position **(Figure 37.1)**.

The moth has not exhausted its evasive tactics, however. As the bat closes in, the increased frequency of the clicks sets off another programmed response that alters the moth's flight into sudden loops and turns, ending with a closed-wing, vertical fall toward the ground. After dropping a few feet, the moth resumes its fluttering flight and may or may not be detected again by the bat.

Echolocation is not confined to bats. Porpoises and dolphins use echolocation to locate food fishes in murky waters, and whales use echolocation to keep track of the sea bottom and rocky obstacles. Bird species, such as the oilbird and the cave swiftlet, use echolocation to avoid obstacles and find their nests in dark caves.

Natural selection has produced highly adaptive sensory receptors and neural circuits to integrate and process their input in all animals. These systems, the subject of this chapter, provide animals with a steady stream of information about their internal and external environments, leading to appropriate responses. By integrating sensory information in the central nervous system (CNS), animals respond in ways that enable them to survive and reproduce.

The focus of this chapter is on neural integration. While integration occurs at every synapse in the nervous system through the processes of spatial and temporal summation, as described in the previous chapter (see Section 36.4), integration occurs on a larger scale in two areas: at sensory structures, where information is first transduced into electrical signals (see Sections 36.2e and 36.2f), and in the CNS (central ganglia and brains), where information from multiple sources is collected and interpreted (see Section 36.5). We begin this chapter with a survey of animal sensory systems. Sensory receptors are involved in neural signalling via the same four basic components as described in the previous chapter: reception, transduction, integration, and response. At the level of the single receptor cell, this ultimately involves the opening or closing of ion channels that alter the membrane potential of the cell. Depending on the nature of the stimulus, the manner in which it leads to changes in channel configuration varies. In highly specialized sensory organs, different anatomical features have evolved to amplify, filter, or modulate the stimulus. These are secondary sensory structures such as the ear or the eye; the primary structures are the sensory neurons themselves. The characteristics of several of these are examined for individual receptor types in the first part of the chapter. This sensory information is conducted by peripheral nerves to the CNS, where complex neural processing occurs, integrating information from many sources to produce memory and appropriate responses. This is described for the vertebrate CNS (and, in particular, for the human nervous system, for which the most is known) in the second part of this chapter.

Figure 37.1
A greater horseshoe bat (*Rhinolophus ferrumequinum*) hunting a moth. The bat uses its sensory systems to pursue prey, and the moth uses its sensory systems to avoid capture.

© Stephen Dalton/Animals, Animals - Earth Scenes

37.1 Overview of Sensory Integration

37.1a The Strength of a Stimulus Is Encoded in Several Ways

Sensory pathways begin at a sensory receptor and proceed by afferent neurons to the CNS. Each type of receptor conveys information to a specific part of the CNS. Action potentials arising in the retina of the eye, for instance, travel along the optic nerves to the visual cortex, where they are interpreted by the brain as differences in pattern, colour, and intensity of light.

The frequency of action potentials that the stimulus generates in the afferent neuron (number per unit time) can indicate the intensity and extent of the stimulus. Stronger stimuli cause more action potentials than weaker ones (see Chapter 36). A light touch to the hand, for example, causes action potentials to flow at low frequencies along the axons leading to the primary somatosensory area of the cerebral cortex. As the pressure increases, the number of action potentials per second rises in proportion. In the brain, the increase is interpreted as greater pressure on the hand.

The number of afferent neurons sending action potentials in response to a stimulus can also convey information about the intensity and extent of a stimulus. The more sensory receptors that are activated, the more axons carry information to the brain. A light touch activates a relatively small number of receptors in a small area near the surface of the finger. But as the pressure increases, the resulting indentation of the finger's surface increases in area and depth, activating more receptors. In the appropriate somatosensory area of the brain, the larger number of axons carrying action potentials is interpreted as an increase in pressure spread over a greater area of the finger.

37.1b Many Receptors Adapt When Stimuli Remain Constant

In many sensory systems, the effect of a stimulus is reduced if it continues at a constant level. This reduction is called **sensory adaptation** (do not confuse this with adaptation used in the context of evolution). Some receptors adapt quickly and broadly; other receptors adapt only slightly. For example, when you walk outside on a pleasantly sunny day, it may seem exceptionally bright for a minute or two but the sensation passes and normal vision returns. In contrast, receptors detecting painful stimuli show little or no adaptation. Pain signals a danger to some part of the body, and the signal is maintained until a response by the animal compensates for the stimulus causing the pain. Being able to adapt to light intensity, on the other hand, allows the visual system to retain its sensitivity whether on a moonlit night or in the middle of a sunny afternoon.

Sensory adaptation also increases the sensitivity of receptor systems to *changes* in environmental stimuli. For some stimuli, these can be more important to survival than keeping track of constant environmental factors. For example, when something touches your skin you are initially aware of the touch and pressure. Within a few minutes, however, the sensation lessens or is lost, even though the pressure remains the same. The loss reflects adaptation of mechanoreceptors in your skin. If the intensity of the stimulus changes, the mechanoreceptors again become active. There are some sensations that organisms must always be aware of and others where receiving constant reminders are of less value than being able to perceive changes in the level of a stimulus.

37.1c Perception of a Stimulus Results from Interpretation of Sensory Input

Perception is the conscious awareness of our external and internal environments derived from the processing of sensory input. That is, the action potentials from sensory receptors are the signals the brain uses to generate an interpretation—the perception—of the external and internal environments. There are multiple aspects of this. In the first instance, an organism's perception of the world depends on the types of receptors it possesses. Our human perception of the world is significantly different from the perceptions of other organisms. For instance, many animals can detect much higher sound frequencies and many insects can "see" ultraviolet light, making their perception of the same environment different than ours (see Figure 1.28, Chapter 1). Then, during processing, different forms of sensory input are given unique characteristics. Action potentials arriving in the sensory cortex from different receptors on the tongue may create a sweet or a tart sensation. These are a result of the processing. All taste receptors generate action potentials, but the action potentials arriving from different receptors give rise to different sensations. Finally, input is further processed by the cerebral cortex, including comparison of the particular input with other incoming sensory input and with memories of similar situations. Each individual (perhaps with the exception of identical twins) has slightly different perceptions of the world.

Next, we will examine several individual receptor types (mechanoreceptors, photoreceptors, chemoreceptors, thermoreceptors, electroreceptors, and magnetoreceptors; see Chapter 36) and their characteristics. The focus will be on receptors that sense the external environment, but keep in mind that there is also a rich variety of receptors that sense the internal environment; many of these will be discussed briefly in subsequent chapters dealing with the regulation of the internal environment.

1. What are the different roles of primary and secondary sensory structures? What do the secondary structures contribute?
2. How is the strength of a sensory stimulus conveyed to the brain?
3. Why is it important that some receptors allow the effect of a stimulus to be reduced, whereas other receptors do not?

37.2 Mechanoreceptors and the Tactile and Spatial Senses

Mechanoreceptors detect mechanical stimuli such as touch and pressure. The mechanical force of a stimulus creates tension in the plasma membrane of a receptor cell, which causes ion channels to open. Ion flow changes the membrane potential of the receptors and generates action potentials in afferent neurons leading from the receptors to the CNS. Sensory information from these receptors informs the brain of the body's contact with objects in the environment, providing information on the movement, position, and balance of body parts, and underlies the sense of hearing. Mechanoreceptors are involved in sensing the external environment (touch and pressure), the internal environment (position and movement of the limbs, blood pressure, lung inflation), and the relationship between the two environments (balance and equilibrium related to position in space). As we will see, while the mechanism of transduction remains constant at the level of the receptor cell, there is a variety of ways in which the mechanical event leads to the deformation of the receptor cell.

37.2a Receptors for Touch and Pressure Occur throughout the Body

In vertebrates, mechanoreceptors that detect touch and pressure are embedded in the skin and other surface tissues, in skeletal muscles, in the walls of blood vessels, and in internal organs. In humans, touch receptors in the skin are concentrated in greatest numbers in the fingertips, lips, and tip of the tongue, giving these regions the greatest sensitivity to mechanical stimuli. In other areas, such as the skin of the back, arms, and legs, the receptors are more widely spaced.

You can compare the spacing of receptors by pressing two toothpicks lightly against a fingertip and then against the skin of your arm or leg. On your fingertip, two toothpicks separated by ~1 mm can be discerned as two separate points. On your arm or leg, the two toothpicks must be nearly 5 cm apart to be distinguished as two separate points.

Skin contains several types of touch and pressure receptors **(Figure 37.2)**. Some are free nerve endings:

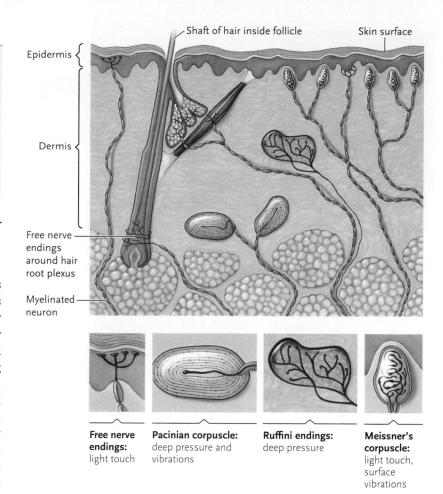

Figure 37.2
In human skin, four types of mechanoreceptors detect tactile stimulation.

dendrites of afferent neurons with no specialized structures surrounding them. Free nerve endings wrapped around hair follicles respond when the hair is bent, making you instantly aware of a spider exploring your arm or leg as it brushes against the hairs. Other mechanoreceptors, such as Pacinian corpuscles, have structures surrounding the nerve endings that contribute to reception of stimuli.

37.2b Proprioceptors Provide Information about Movements and the Position of the Body

Proprioceptors are mechanoreceptors (*proprius* = one's own) that detect stimuli that are used by the CNS to maintain body balance and equilibrium and to monitor changes in the position of the head and limbs. The activity of proprioceptors allows you to touch the tip of your nose with your eyes closed or to precisely reach and scratch an itch on your back.

Statocysts (*statos* = standing; *kystis* = bag) are proprioceptors in aquatic invertebrates such as jellyfishes, some gastropods, and some arthropods. Most statocysts are fluid-filled chambers enclosing one or more movable stonelike bodies called **statoliths**. The chamber walls contain **sensory hair cells (Figure 37.3, p. 908)**.

Figure 37.3
A statocyst, an organ of equilibrium in invertebrates, is located at the base of the antenna of a lobster. The statoliths inside are usually formed from fused grains of sand (calcium carbonate) in lobsters.

In lobsters (*Homarus americanus*), statoliths are sand grains stuck together by mucus. When the animal moves, the statoliths lag behind the movement, bending the sensory hairs and triggering action potentials in afferent neurons. Thus, statocysts signal the brain about the body's position and orientation with respect to gravity. If you replace the sand grain statoliths with iron filings, you can use a magnet and emulate the lobster's response to the pull of gravity. In plants, statoliths control the direction of growth (see Chapter 30).

Information about self-motion is particularly important for flying animals and must be quickly (almost instantaneously) available. Typical insects have two pairs of wings, but species in the order Diptera (flies) have one. The second pair are reduced and persist as *halteres* **(Figure 37.4)**. Halteres are club-shaped and oscillate at the wing-beat frequency. They transduce information about pitch (oscillation around a horizontal axis perpendicular to the direction of movement), roll (sway on the axis parallel to the direction of movement), and yaw (oscillation about a vertical axis) movements to the CNS. Coriolis (gyroscopic) forces cause the halteres to deviate in their plane of motion. Hawk moths, with two pairs of wings, use mechanosensors on their antennae to mediate flight control.

Mechanical input is essential for flight stability in moths. In bats, small hairs on the ventral surfaces of the wings are important for complex flight manoeuvres. Birds must also have mechanoreceptors associated with wings and flight, and, presumably, pterosaurs did as well.

The **lateral line system** in fishes and some aquatic amphibians uses mechanoreceptors to detect vibrations and currents in the water **(Figure 37.5)**. Fishes have *neuromasts,* mechanoreceptors that provide information about the fish's orientation with respect to gravity, as well as its swimming velocity. In some fishes, neuromasts are exposed on the body surface; in others, they are recessed in water-filled canals with porelike openings to the outside (see Figure 37.5). Sensory hairs are clustered at the base of each dome-shaped neuromast hair cell. One surface of the hair cell is covered with **stereocilia**, microvilli or cell processes reinforced by bundles of microfilaments. Stereocilia extend into a gelatinous structure, the **cupula** (*cupule* = little cup), which moves with pressure changes in the surrounding water. Movement of the cupula bends the stereocilia, causing depolarization of the hair cell's plasma membrane and release of neurotransmitter molecules that generate action potentials in associated afferent neurons.

Vibrations detected by the lateral line enable fishes to avoid obstacles, orient in a current, and monitor the presence of other moving objects in the water. The system is also responsible for the ability of schools of fish to move in unison, turning and diving in what appears to be a perfectly synchronized aquatic ballet. In actuality, the movement of each fish creates a pressure wave in the water that is detected by the lateral line systems of other fishes in the school. Schooling fishes can still swim in unison even if blinded, but if the nerves leading from the lateral line system to the brain are severed, the ability to school is lost.

37.2c The Vestibular Apparatus of Vertebrates Provides a Sense of Balance and Orientation

The inner ear of most terrestrial vertebrates has two specialized sensory structures, the *vestibular apparatus* and the *cochlea*. The **vestibular apparatus** is responsible for perceiving the position and motion of the head and is essential for maintaining equilibrium and for coordinating head and body movements. The cochlea is used in hearing (see Section 37.3).

The vestibular apparatus **(Figure 37.6)** consists of three **semicircular canals** and two chambers, the **utricle** and the **saccule**, filled with a fluid called *endolymph*. The semicircular canals are positioned at angles corresponding to the three planes of space. They detect rotational (spinning) motions. Each canal has an *ampulla*, a swelling at its base that is topped with sensory hair cells embedded in a cupula similar to that found in lateral line systems. Cupulas protrude into

Figure 37.4
Halteres, vestigial hind wings of flies (enlarged image on the right at the end of the arrow), transduce information about pitch, roll, and yaw during flight. The fly shown here is a *Drosophila*.

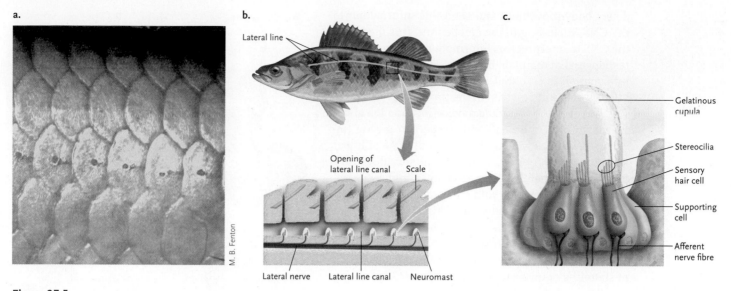

Figure 37.5

The lateral line system of fishes. **(a)** Pores along the lateral line of an arrowhana (*Scleropages* species). **(b)** Neuromasts are the sensory receptors in the lateral line system. **(c)** Neuromasts have a gelatinous cupula that is pushed and pulled by vibrations and currents transmitted through the lateral line canal. As the cupula moves, the stereocilia of the sensory hair cells are bent, generating action potentials in afferent neurons that lead to the brain.

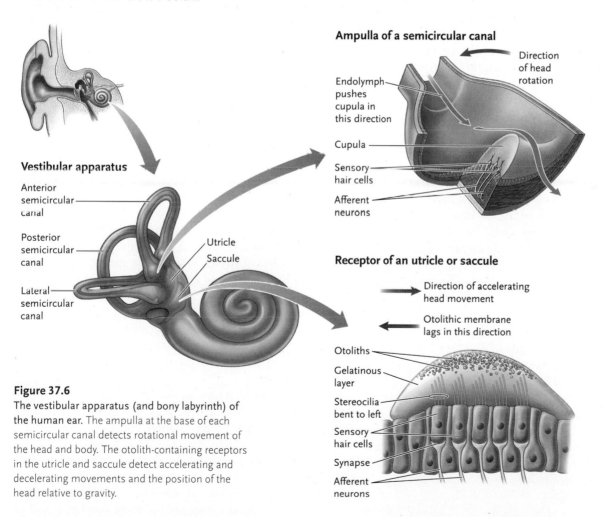

Figure 37.6

The vestibular apparatus (and bony labyrinth) of the human ear. The ampulla at the base of each semicircular canal detects rotational movement of the head and body. The otolith-containing receptors in the utricle and saccule detect accelerating and decelerating movements and the position of the head relative to gravity.

the endolymph of the canals. When the body or head rotates horizontally, vertically, or diagonally, endolymph in the semicircular canal corresponding to that direction lags behind, pulling the cupula with it. Displacement of the cupula bends the sensory hair cells and generates action potentials in afferent neurons that make synapses with the hair cells.

CONCEPT FIX It is commonly thought that the semicircular canals are responsible for maintaining body balance. In fact, the semicircular canals only detect body movement and send this information to the CNS, including to the cerebellum. It is the job of the CNS to interpret this information and produce the responses that maintain balance. Clearly, receiving this information is essential for maintenance of balance, but it is only the first step in the process. ⬡

The utricle and saccule provide information about the position of the head with respect to gravity (up versus down), as well as changes in the rate of linear movement of the body. The utricle and saccule are oriented approximately 30° to each other, and each contains sensory hair cells with stereocilia. The hair cells are covered with a gelatinous *otolithic membrane* (which is similar to a cupula) in which **otoliths**, small crystals of calcium carbonate (*oto* = ear; *lithos* = stone), are embedded; the function of otoliths is analogous to that of statoliths of invertebrates (see Figure 37.3).

When a tetrapod is standing in its normal posture, the sensory hairs in the utricle are oriented vertically and those in the saccule are oriented horizontally. When the head is tilted in any other direction or when there is a change in the linear motion of the body, the otolithic membrane of the utricle moves and bends the sensory hairs. Depending on the direction of movement, the hair cells release more or less neurotransmitter, and the brain integrates the signals it receives and generates a perception of the movement. In humans, the saccule responds to the tilting of the head away from the horizontal (such as in diving) and to a change in movement up and down (such as in jumping). The utricle and saccule adapt quickly to the body's motion, decreasing their response when there is no change in the rate and direction of movement.

Senses of up and down vary among animals, suggesting differences in how data from the utricle and saccule are interpreted. The "normal" posture of upside-down catfish (*Synodontis nigriventris*), many bats (Chiroptera), and sloths (genera *Choloepus* and *Bradypus*) differs from what is "normal" in other animals, so interpretation of information from the labyrinth must differ as well. As bipeds, the normal posture of humans is also aberrant, so interpretation of postural information must differ here too.

The bony labyrinths of mammals vary considerably **(Figure 37.7)**, reflecting lifestyle. Agile, arboreal mammals have semicircular canals with large radii. The large radii make the vestibular system extremely sensitive to changes in body position. Such sensitivity is not compatible with the lifestyles of cetaceans because they frequently make fast body rotations. Cetaceans typically have semicircular canals with small radii (see Figure 37.7).

37.2d Stretch Receptors in Vertebrates Keep Track of Tension on Muscles

Stretch receptors are proprioceptors in the muscles and tendons of vertebrates that detect the position and

Reprinted by permission from Macmillan Publishers Ltd: NATURE, F. Spoor, S. Bajpai, S. T. Hussain, K. Kumar and J. G. M. Thewissen, "Vestibular evidence for the evolution of aquatic behaviour in early cetaceans", Vol. 417, pp. 163–166, copyright (2002).

Figure 37.7

Bony labyrinths of four species of mammals. Lateral left view of the labyrinth organs of *Galago moholi* **(a)**, *Ichthyolestes pinfoldi* **(b)**, *Indocetus ramani* **(c)**, and *Tursiops truncatus* **(d)**. *I. pinfoldi* and *I. ramani* are fossil cetaceans (whales), *T. truncatus* is an extant species of dolphin, and *G. moholi* is an arboreal primate.

movement, for example, of the limbs. Stretch receptors in muscles are **muscle spindles**, bundles of small, specialized muscle cells wrapped with the dendrites of afferent neurons and enclosed in connective tissue **(Figure 37.8)**. When the muscle stretches, the spindle stretches too, stimulating the dendrites and triggering the production of action potentials. The strength of the response of stretch receptors to stimulation depends on how much and how fast the muscle is stretched. Proprioceptors of tendons, called **Golgi tendon organs**, are dendrites that branch within the fibrous connective tissue of the tendon (shown in Figure 37.8). These nerve endings measure stretch and compression of the tendon as muscles contract and move limbs.

Proprioceptors allow the CNS to monitor the body's position and help keep the body in balance. They allow muscles to apply constant force under a constant load and to adjust almost instantly as the load changes. When you hold a cup while someone fills it with coffee, the muscle spindles in your biceps muscle detect the additional stretch as the cup becomes heavier. Signals from the spindles allow you to compensate for the additional weight by increasing the contraction of the muscle, keeping your arm level with no conscious effort on your part. Proprioceptors are typically slow to adapt, so the body's position and balance are constantly monitored.

Figure 37.8
Muscle spindles, which detect the stretch and tension of muscles, and Golgi tendon organs, which detect the stretch of tendons.

Labels: Tendon / Golgi tendon organ / Sensory nerve fibre / Biceps muscle / Muscle fibres of biceps surrounding muscle spindle / Specialized fibres of muscle spindle / Dendrites of afferent neurons

STUDY BREAK

1. If two fruit flies landed on you, one on your face and the other on your leg, which one would you be most likely to detect by touch receptors? Why?
2. What is the purpose of the vestibular apparatus in the inner ear of most vertebrates?
3. On what does the strength of the response of stretch receptors depend?

37.3 Mechanoreceptors and Hearing

37.3a Sound

Sounds are vibrations that travel as waves produced by the alternating compression and decompression of air or water. The loudness, or *intensity,* of a sound depends on the amplitude (height) of the wave. It is measured in decibels (dB). The *pitch* of a sound—a musical tone, for example, is a high note or a low note—depends on the frequency of the waves, measured in hertz (Hz; cycles per second). The more cycles per second, the higher the pitch. Some animals, such as the bat in the introduction to this chapter, can hear sounds well above 100 000 Hz. Humans can hear sounds between about 20 and 20 000 Hz, which is why we cannot hear the bat's sonar clicks. Although sound waves travel through air at about 340 m · s⁻¹ at sea level, individual air molecules transmitting the waves move back and forth over only a short distance as the wave passes. Water is denser than air, so sounds move approximately three times as

fast under water. Infrasounds, frequencies below the range of human hearing (20 Hz), are used by African elephants to communicate.

37.3b Hearing in Invertebrates Involves Mechanoreceptors and Ears

Most invertebrates detect sound and other vibrations through mechanoreceptors in their skin or on other surface structures. An earthworm, for example, quickly retracts into its burrow at the smallest vibration of the surrounding earth, even though it has no specialized structures serving as ears. Cephalopods (squids and octopuses) have a system of mechanoreceptors on their head and tentacles, similar to the lateral line of fishes. These mechanoreceptors detect vibrations in the surrounding water. In many insects and other arthropods, hairs or bristles act as sensory receptors, vibrating in response to sound waves, often at particular frequencies.

Insects such as grasshoppers and crickets have ears, complex auditory organs on each side of the abdomen or on the first pair of walking legs **(Figure 37.9)**, whereas in moths, these "ears" have been found on the head (mouthpart), thorax, and abdomen. These "ears" consist of a thinned region of the insect's exoskeleton forming a **tympanum** (= drum) over a hollow chamber.

Figure 37.9
The tympanum or eardrum of a cricket, located on the front walking legs.

Labels: Tympanum / Tympanum

Andrew Syred/Photo Researchers, Inc.

Sounds reaching the tympanum cause it to vibrate. Mechanoreceptors connected to the tympanum translate vibrations into nerve impulses. Some insect ears respond to sounds only at certain frequencies, such as the pitch of a cricket's song.

37.3c Hearing in Vertebrates Involves Auditory Systems

The auditory structures of terrestrial vertebrates transduce vibrations in air (sound) to sensory hair cells that respond by triggering action potentials. The auditory system of humans is typical for mammals **(Figure 37.10)**.

The *pinna* (**outer ear**; *pinna* = wing or leaf) concentrates and focuses sound waves. Some animals have pinnae; others lack them **(Figure 37.11)**. Sound waves enter the auditory canal and strike a thin sheet of tissue (tympanic membrane or eardrum) and start it vibrating.

Vibrations in the tympanic membrane generate vibrations in the auditory ossicles located in the middle ear, which is an air-filled cavity. Mammals have three auditory ossicles, the **malleus** (hammer), **incus** (anvil), and **stapes** (stirrup). The manubrium of the malleus sits immediately behind the eardrum, and the eardrum's vibrations are conducted from the malleus to the incus and the stapes. The stapes abuts the inner ear

Figure 37.10
Structures of the human ear.

Vibrations transmitted from the eardrum through the fluid in the inner ear make the basilar membrane vibrate, bending the hair cells against the tectorial membrane and generating action potentials in afferent neurons that lead to auditory regions of the brain.

a.

b.

c.

M. B. Fenton

d.

M. B. Fenton

Figure 37.11

Pinnae (external ears) are lacking in mammals such as **(a)** the beluga (*Delphinapterus leucas*), **(b)** birds (*Struthio camelus*), and **(c)** reptiles (*Varanus komodoensis*), but large and conspicuous in **(d)** a bat (*Otonycteris hemprichii*).

at the **oval window**, a thin, elastic membrane where vibrations in bone are converted to vibrations in the fluid in the vestibular canal. Between the eardrum and the oval window, sounds are amplified at least 20 times.

The **inner ear** contains several fluid-filled compartments, the vestibular apparatus (see Section 37.2), and the **cochlea**, a spiral tube (*kochlias* = snail). In humans, the cochlea twists through about 2.5 turns (if flattened, it would be about 3.5 cm long in an adult). The spiralling of the cochlea appears to make it more sensitive to lower-frequency sounds. Thin membranes divide the cochlea into three longitudinal chambers, the *vestibular canal* at the top, the *cochlear duct* in the middle, and the *tympanic canal* at the bottom (see Figure 37.10). The vestibular canal and the tympanic canal join at the outer tip of the cochlea, so the fluid they contain is continuous. The **organ of Corti** lies within the cochlear duct. It contains sensory hair cells that detect vibrations transmitted to the inner ear (see Figure 37.10). Vibrations of the oval window pass through the fluid in the vestibular canal, make the turn at the end, and travel back through the fluid in the tympanic canal. At the end of the tympanic canal, they are transmitted to the **round window**, a thin membrane that faces the middle ear.

Vibrations in the fluid of the inner ear cause vibrations in the **basilar membrane**. The basilar membrane forms part of the floor of the cochlear duct and anchors the sensory hair cells in the organ of Corti. The stereocilia of these cells are embedded in the *tectorial membrane* extending the length of the cochlear canal. Vibrations of the basilar membrane cause the hair cells to bend, stimulating them to release a neurotransmitter that triggers action potentials in afferent neurons leading from the inner ear.

The basilar membrane is narrowest near the oval window and gradually widens toward the outer end of the cochlear duct. High-frequency vibrations produced by high-pitched sounds vibrate the basilar membrane most strongly near its narrow end, whereas vibrations of lower frequency vibrate the membrane nearer the outer end. Thus, each frequency of sound waves causes hair cells in a different segment of the basilar membrane to initiate action potentials. More than 15 000 hair cells are distributed in small groups along the basilar membrane. Each group of hairs is connected by synapses to afferent neurons, the axons of which are bundled together in the *auditory nerve*, a cranial nerve leading to the thalamus. From there, the signals are routed to specific regions in the auditory centre of the temporal lobe.

The **eustachian tube**, a duct leading from the air-filled middle ear to the throat (see Figure 37.10), protects the eardrum from damage caused by changes in environmental atmospheric pressure. As we swallow or yawn, the tube opens, allowing air to flow into or out of the middle ear, equalizing pressure on both sides of the eardrum. When swelling or congestion prevents the tube from admitting air, we complain of having stopped-up ears because we sense a pressure difference between the outer and middle ear caused by the eardrum bulging inward or outward; this interferes with the transmission of sounds.

STUDY BREAK

1. How do most invertebrates detect sound? Give an example.
2. Explain in detail how a human detects sound. Is this fundamentally different from the way an invertebrate hears?
3. Why are the echolocation calls of many bats inaudible to humans despite their high intensity? If humans can't hear bats, how did they discover that bats could emit calls and hear in this frequency range?

PEOPLE BEHIND BIOLOGY 37.1

John Ford, Department of Fisheries and Oceans and the University of British Columbia

In 1973, Mike Biggs, working at the Pacific Biological Station in Nanaimo, British Columbia, revolutionized field studies of killer whales when he realized that the natural markings on the bodies of the whales could be used to identify individuals. By photographing the dorsal fin and grey "saddle" patch at the base of the fin, along with the unique pattern of nicks and scars, he developed a technique of photo-identification that allowed his group to begin to examine the natural history and population ecology of this charismatic species in detail **(Figure 1)**.

In 1977, John Ford began to study the underwater vocalizations of the whales with respect to their behaviour and social structure. Killer whales, like other toothed whales, produce a wide variety of sounds that serve different purposes. Rapid series of clicks are used for echolocation and navigation (like

the bats mentioned at the start of this chapter), while other sounds resembling whistles, squeals, squawks, and screams are used for social communication. A large percentage of these sounds are distinctively different in different groups of whales. These vocal variations, known as dialects, have allowed researchers to distinguish family groups. A group's dialect appears to be learned by each calf by mimicking its mother, and thus each pod of killer whales can be readily identified using sound analyzers. Dialects appear to be used by the whales as acoustic indicators of group identity and membership. As a result, they have been used to gain insight into the social history of populations. Pods with similar dialects belong to a clan, a continuous lineage descended from a common ancestral pod. As pods grew in size over time, they gradually split into new pods and their common dialect drifted apart. Pods with similar dialects probably split in the recent past, while others with fewer similarities are likely more

distantly related. Different clans have no dialect features in common and probably have very ancient links. Thus, vocal dialects of resident killer whale pods provide information on how communities have evolved in the past **(Figure 2)**.

FIGURE 2

This diagram shows all 19 resident pods of killer whales organized according to the degree of similarity in their call repertoire. Pods with almost identical dialects are linked with a high index of acoustic similarity. Pods that have related dialects belong to the same clan. The four resident clans have no acoustic similarity and are not linked together. The family tree shown for each clan reflects its historical genealogy.

Reprinted with permission from *Killer Whales*, 2nd edition by John Ford, Kenneth Balcomb and Graeme Ellis © University of British Columbia Press, 2000. All rights reserved by the Publisher.

FIGURE 1

A pod of killer whales foraging off the coast of British Columbia.

37.4 Photoreceptors and Vision

The great majority of animals have receptors that can detect and respond to light. As animals evolved and became more complex, the complexity of their visual sensory receptors increased, leading to the highly developed eyes of cephalopods and vertebrates.

37.4a Vision Involves Detection and Perception of Radiant Energy

Photoreceptors detect light at particular wavelengths, and centres in a brain or central ganglion integrate signals arriving from the receptors into a perception of light. All animals use forms of a single lipidlike pigment, *retinal* (synthesized from vitamin A), in photoreceptors to absorb light energy. The simplest eyes are capable only of distinguishing light from dark; the most complex eyes distinguish shapes and colours and

focus an accurate image of objects being viewed onto a layer of photoreceptors.

37.4b Invertebrate Eyes Take Many Forms

Some invertebrates, such as earthworms, do not have visual organs; instead, photoreceptors in their skin allow them to sense and respond to light. Earthworms respond negatively to light, as you can easily discover by shining a flashlight on an earthworm outside its burrow at night.

The eyes of other invertebrates are diverse, ranging from collections of photoreceptors with no lens and no image-forming capability to eyes remarkably like those of vertebrates. The photoreceptors of invertebrates are depolarized when they absorb light, and they generate action potentials or increase their release of neurotransmitter molecules when they are stimulated. Vertebrate photoreceptors function differently, as we will see.

The simplest eye is the **ocellus** (plural, **ocelli**; also called an *eyespot* or *eyecup*). An ocellus, which detects light but does not form an image, consists of fewer than 100 photoreceptor cells lining a cup or pit. In planarians, for example, photoreceptor cells in a cuplike depression below the epidermis are connected to the dendrites of afferent neurons, which are bundled into nerves that travel from the ocelli to the cerebral ganglion **(Figure 37.12)**. Each ocellus is covered on one side by a layer of pigment cells that blocks most of the light rays arriving from the opposite side of the animal. As a result, most of the light received by the pigment cells enters the ocellus from the side that it faces. Through integration of information transmitted to the cerebral ganglion from the eyecups, planarians orient themselves so that the amount of light falling on the two ocelli is equal and diminishes as they swim. This reaction carries them directly away from the source of the light. Similar ocelli are found in a variety of animals, including insects, arthropods, and molluscs.

Two main types of image-forming eyes have evolved in invertebrates: compound eyes and single-lens eyes. The **compound eye** of insects, crustaceans, and a few annelids and molluscs contains hundreds to thousands of faceted visual units called **ommatidia** (*omma* = eye) fitted closely together **(Figure 37.13)**. Each ommatidium samples a small part of the visual field. In insects, light entering an ommatidium is focused by a transparent **cornea** and a *crystalline cone* (just below the cornea) onto a bundle of photoreceptor cells. Microvilli of these cells interdigitate like the fingers of clasped hands, forming a central axis rich in rhodopsin, a retinal-containing **photopigment** (light-absorbing pigment). Absorption of light by rhodopsin causes action potentials to be generated in afferent

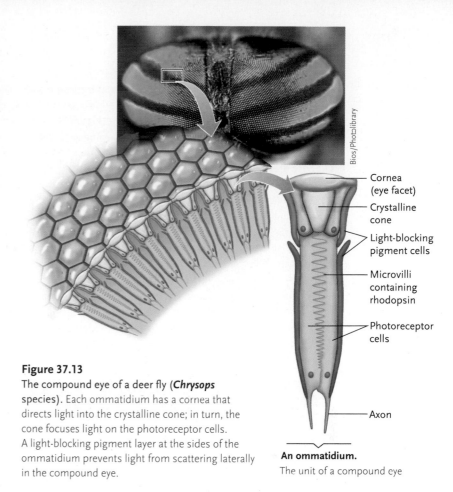

Figure 37.13
The compound eye of a deer fly (***Chrysops*** species). Each ommatidium has a cornea that directs light into the crystalline cone; in turn, the cone focuses light on the photoreceptor cells. A light-blocking pigment layer at the sides of the ommatidium prevents light from scattering laterally in the compound eye.

An ommatidium.
The unit of a compound eye

neurons connected to the base of the ommatidium. From these signals, the brain receives a mosaic image of the world. Because even the slightest motion is detected simultaneously by many ommatidia, compound eyes are extraordinarily adept at detecting movement—a lesson soon learned by fly-swatting humans.

The **single-lens eye** of cephalopods **(Figure 37.14)** resembles a vertebrate eye in that both types operate like a camera. In the cephalopod eye, light enters through the transparent cornea, a **lens** concentrates the light, and a layer of photoreceptors at the back of the eye, the **retina**, records the image. Behind the cornea is the **iris**, which surrounds the **pupil**, the opening through which light enters the eye. Muscles in the iris adjust the size of the pupil to vary the amount of light entering the eye. When the light is bright, circular muscles in the iris contract, shrinking the size of the pupil and reducing the amount

Figure 37.14
The eye of an octopus, a cephalopod mollusc.

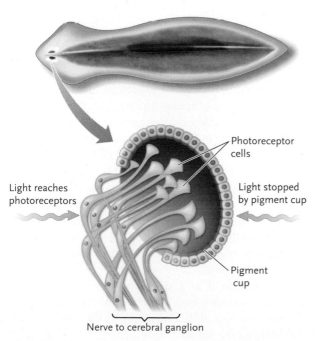

Figure 37.12
The ocellus of a planarian flatworm, and the arrangement of pigment cells on which its orientation response is based.

USING THE GENOME AS AN INVESTIGATIVE TOOL 37.2
Seeing with Your Feet

It is one thing to demonstrate that an animal responds behaviourally to external stimuli, but it may be more challenging to determine how the stimuli were detected. For example, there is evidence of animals such as garden toads (*Bufo bufo*) changing their behaviour in advance of an earthquake, but we do not know what cues trigger the response.

For some time, it has been clear that echinoderms such as sea urchins respond to changing light conditions, but nobody had found photoreceptors in these animals (see Chapter 1 for a discussion of the significance of light and light sensing). The publication of the genome of purple urchins (*Strongylocentrotus purpuratus*) **(Figure 1)** provided biologists with a means of investigating photoreception in these animals.

Specifically, data in the genome showed that sea urchins possess several genes that code for a widely occurring eye protein, opsin. Discovering this, the researchers designed antibodies against different opsin proteins and performed *in situ* hybridization (see Chapter 15 for a discussion of DNA technologies and genomics). They found that the urchins possess *Sp-opsin4* and *Sp-pax6*, two proteins that regulate phototaxis. This approach also allowed them to visualize where the photoreceptor cells were located—in the urchin's tube feet. The sea urchin photoreceptive cells are microvillar r-opsin, previously known only from protostomes. Since tube feet are found all over the body of the sea urchin, it appears that the entire adult sea urchin acts as a huge compound eye!

There are many other mysteries about the sensory world of animals. We know that many animals show a magnetic sense, but in most cases we do not know the details of the receptor.

FIGURE 1

(a) The purple sea urchin Strongylocentrotus purpuratus. *(b) Close-up showing the tube feet between the spines. The photoreceptors are located at the tips of the tube feet.*

---

of light that enters. In dim light, radial muscles contract and enlarge the pupil, increasing the amount of light that enters the eye. Muscles move the lens forward and back with respect to the retina to focus the image. This is an example of **accommodation**, a process by which the lens changes to enable the eye to focus on objects at different distances. A neural network lies under the retina, meaning that light rays do not have to pass through the neurons to reach the photoreceptors. The vertebrate eye has the opposite arrangement. This and other differences in structure and function indicate that cephalopod and vertebrate eyes evolved independently.

37.4c Vertebrate Eyes Have a Complex Structure

The human eye **(Figure 37.15)** has similar structures—cornea, iris, pupil, lens, and retina—to those of the cephalopod eye just described. Light entering the eye through the cornea passes through the iris and then the lens. The lens focuses an image on the retina, and the axons of afferent neurons originating in the retina converge to form the optic nerve leading from the eye to the brain. A clear fluid called the **aqueous humour** fills the space between the cornea and the lens. This fluid carries nutrients to the lens and cornea, which do not contain any blood vessels. The main chamber of the eye, located between the lens and the retina, is filled with the jellylike **vitreous humour** (*vitrum* = glass). The outer wall of the eye contains a tough layer of connective tissue (the *sclera*). Inside it is a darkly pigmented layer (the *choroid*) that prevents light from entering except through the pupil. It also contains the blood vessels nourishing the retina.

Two types of photoreceptors, rods and cones, occur in the retina along with layers of neurons that carry out an initial integration of visual information before it is

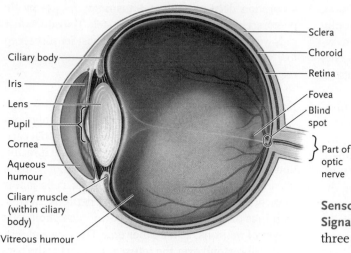

Figure 37.15
Structures of the human eye.

*Labels (clockwise from left): Ciliary body, Iris, Lens, Pupil, Cornea, Aqueous humour, Ciliary muscle (within ciliary body), Vitreous humour, Sclera, Choroid, Retina, Fovea, Blind spot, Part of optic nerve*

sent to the brain. The **rods** are specialized for detection of light at low intensities; the **cones** are specialized for detection of different wavelengths (colours). Accommodation does not occur by forward and backward movement of the lens, as described for cephalopods. Rather, the lens of most terrestrial vertebrates is focused by changing its shape. The lens is held in place by fine ligaments that anchor it to a surrounding layer of connective tissue and muscle, the **ciliary body.** These ligaments keep the lens under tension when the ciliary muscle is relaxed. The tension flattens the lens, which is soft and flexible, and focuses light from distant objects on the retina **(Figure 37.16a).** When the ciliary muscles contract, they relieve the tension of the ligaments, allowing the lens to assume a more spherical shape and focusing light from nearby objects on the retina **(Figure 37.16b).**

37.4d The Retina of Mammals and Birds Contains Rods and Cones and a Complex Network of Neurons

The retina of a human eye contains about 120 million rods and 6 million cones organized into a densely packed, single layer. Neural networks of the retina are layered on top of the photoreceptor cells, so that light rays focused by the lens on the retina must pass through the neurons before reaching the photoreceptors. The light must also pass through a layer of fine blood vessels that covers the surface of the retina.

In mammals and birds with eyes specialized for daytime vision, cones are concentrated in and around a small region of the retina, the **fovea** (see Figure 37.15). The image focused by the lens is centred on the fovea, which is circular and less than a millimetre in diameter in humans. The rods are spread over the remainder of the retina. We can see distinctly only the image focused on the fovea; the surrounding image is what we term *peripheral vision.* Mammals and birds with eyes specialized for night vision have retinas containing mostly rods and

lacking a defined fovea. Some fishes and many reptiles have cones generally distributed throughout their retina and very few rods.

The rods of mammals are much more sensitive than the cones to low-intensity light; in fact, they can respond to a single photon of light. This is why, in dim light, we can detect objects better by looking slightly to the side of the object. This action directs the image away from the cones in the fovea to the highly light-sensitive rods in surrounding regions of the retina.

Sensory Transduction by Rods and Cones: Converting Signals to Electrical Impulses. A photoreceptor cell has three parts:

- an outer segment, consisting of stacked, flattened, membranous discs;
- an inner segment, where the cell's metabolic activities occur; and
- the synaptic terminal, where neurotransmitter molecules are stored and released **(Figure 37.17a, p. 918).**

a. Focusing on distant object

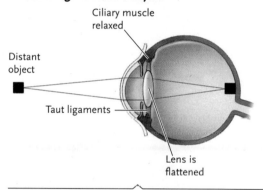

Labels: Ciliary muscle relaxed, Distant object, Taut ligaments, Lens is flattened

When the eye focuses on a distant object, the ciliary muscles relax, allowing the ligaments that support the lens to tighten. The tightened ligaments flatten the lens, bringing the distant object into focus on the retina.

b. Focusing on near object

Labels: Ciliary muscle contracted, Near object, Slack ligaments, Lens is rounded

When the eye focuses on a near object, the ciliary muscles contract, loosening the ligaments and allowing the lens to become rounder. The rounded lens focuses a near object on the retina.

Figure 37.16
Accommodation in terrestrial vertebrates occurs when the lens changes shape to focus on distant **(a)** and near **(b)** objects.

The light-absorbing pigment of rods and cones, retinal, is bonded covalently to **opsins** to produce **photopigments**. The photopigments are embedded in the membranous discs of the photoreceptors' outer segments **(Figure 37.17b)**. The retinal-opsin photopigment in rods is **rhodopsin.**

In the dark, the retinal segment of unstimulated rhodopsin is *cis*-retinal, an inactive form (see Figure 37.17b), and rods steadily release the neurotransmitter glutamate. When rhodopsin absorbs a photon of light, retinal converts to *trans*-retinal, the active form, and the rods *decrease* the amount of glutamate they release.

Rhodopsin is a membrane-embedded G protein–coupled receptor. An extracellular signal received by a G protein–coupled receptor activates the receptor, triggering a signal transduction pathway within the cell and generating a cellular response. Here, activated rhodopsin triggers a signal transduction pathway that leads to the closure of Na$^+$ channels in the plasma membrane **(Figure 37.18)**. Closure of the channels hyperpolarizes the photoreceptor's membrane, decreasing neurotransmitter release. The response is graded because as light absorption by photopigment molecules increases, the amount of neurotransmitter released is reduced proportionately. If light absorption decreases, neurotransmitter release by the photoreceptor increases proportionately. Transduction in rods works in the opposite way from most sensory receptors in which a stimulus increases neurotransmitter release.

Visual Processing in the Retina: Events at the Back of the Eye. In the vertebrate retina, the two types of photoreceptors are linked to a network of neurons that carry out initial integration and processing of visual information. The retina of mammals has four types of neurons **(Figure 37.19)**. There is a layer of bipolar cells just in front of the rods and cones. These neurons synapse with rods or cones at one end and with ganglion cells, a layer of neurons, at the other end. The axons of ganglion cells extend over the retina and collect at the back of the eyeball to form the optic nerve, which transmits action potentials to the brain. The point where the optic nerve exits the eye lacks photoreceptors. This *blind spot* can be several millimetres in diameter in humans. Horizontal cells connect photoreceptor cells, whereas amacrine cells connect bipolar and ganglion cells.

In the dark, the steady release of glutamate from rods and cones depolarizes some postsynaptic bipolar cells and hyperpolarizes others. In the light, the

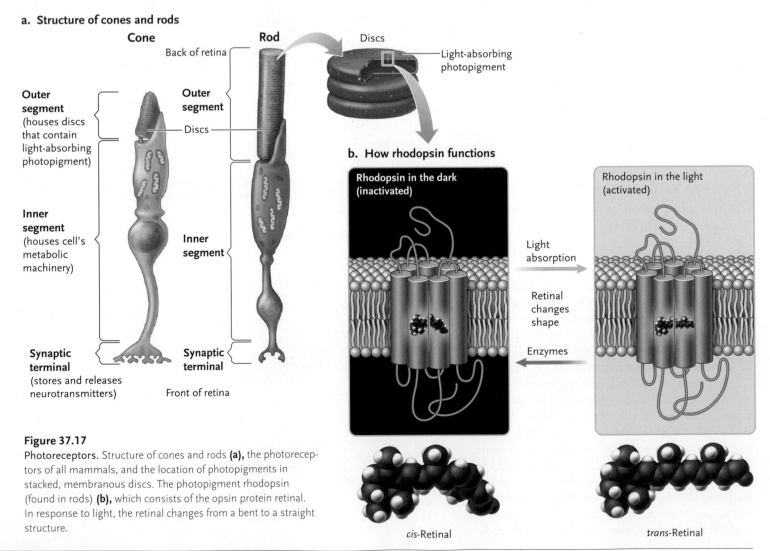

a. Structure of cones and rods

b. How rhodopsin functions

Figure 37.17

Photoreceptors. Structure of cones and rods **(a),** the photoreceptors of all mammals, and the location of photopigments in stacked, membranous discs. The photopigment rhodopsin (found in rods) **(b),** which consists of the opsin protein retinal. In response to light, the retinal changes from a bent to a straight structure.

Figure 37.18

The signal transduction pathway that closes Na⁺ channels in photoreceptor plasma membranes when rhodopsin absorbs light.

1 cis-Retinal absorbs light; is converted to trans-retinal.

2 The protein segment (opsin) of rhodopsin is activated, triggering activation of the G protein transducin.

3 The activated G protein activates phosphodiesterase.

4 Activated phosphodiesterase breaks down cGMP to 5'-GMP, which then detaches from the Na⁺ channel.

5 Loss of cGMP closes the Na⁺ channel.

6 Membrane hyperpolarizes and reduces neurotransmitter release.

decrease in neurotransmitter release from rods and cones results in the depolarized bipolar cells becoming hyperpolarized and the hyperpolarized bipolar cells becoming depolarized.

Signals from the rods and cones may move vertically or laterally in the retina. Signals move vertically from the photoreceptors to bipolar cells and then to ganglion cells. Whereas the human retina has over 120 million photoreceptors, it has only about 1 million ganglion cells. This disparity is explained by the fact that each ganglion cell receives signals from a clearly defined set of photoreceptors constituting the *receptive field* for that cell. Therefore, stimulating numerous photoreceptors in a ganglion cell's receptive field results in only a single message to the brain from that cell. Receptive fields are typically circular and are of different sizes. Smaller receptive fields result in sharper images because they send more precise information to the brain about the location in the retina where the light was received.

Lateral movement of signals from a rod or cone proceeds to a horizontal cell and continues to bipolar cells with which the horizontal cell makes inhibitory connections. To understand this, consider a spot of light falling on the retina. Photoreceptors detect the light and send a signal to bipolar cells and horizontal cells. Horizontal cells inhibit more distant bipolar cells that are outside the spot of light, causing the light spot to appear lighter and its surrounding dark area to appear darker. This type of visual processing is called **lateral inhibition** and serves both to sharpen the edges of objects and to enhance contrast in an image.

Figure 37.19

Microscopic structure of the retina showing the network of neurons (bipolar cells, horizontal cells, amacrine cells, and ganglion cells) that carry out the initial integration of visual information.

37.4e Three Kinds of Opsin Pigments Underlie Colour Vision

Many invertebrates and some species in each class of vertebrates have colour vision, which depends on cones in the retina. Most mammals have two types of cones, whereas humans and other primates have three types. Each human or primate cone cell contains one of three photopsins in which retinal is combined with different opsins. The three photopsins absorb light over different, but overlapping, wavelength ranges, with peak absorptions at 445 nm (blue light), 534 nm (green light), and 570 nm (red light). The farther a wavelength is from the peak colour absorbed, the less strongly the cone responds. Having more types of cones translates into better colour vision. Birds have four photopsins and are able to distinguish shades of colour that humans cannot.

Overlapping wavelength ranges for the three photoreceptors mean that light at any visible wavelength stimulates at least two of three types of cones. Maximal absorption by each type of cone at a different wavelength leads to differential stimulation of different types of cones. These differences are relayed to the visual centres of the brain, where they are integrated into the perception of a colour corresponding to the particular wavelength absorbed. Light stimulating all three receptor types equally is seen as white.

Colour-blindness results from inherited defects in opsin proteins of one or more of the three types of cones.

For example, people with a mutation preventing cones from making a functional form of red-absorbing opsin see orange, yellow, and red as the same grey or greenish colour.

37.4f The Visual Cortex Generates Images in the Brain

Just behind the eyes, the optic nerves converge before entering the base of the brain. A portion of each optic nerve crosses over to the opposite side, forming the **optic chiasm** (*chiasma* = crossing place). Most axons enter the **lateral geniculate nuclei** in the thalamus, where they synapse with interneurons leading to the visual cortex **(Figure 37.20)**.

Because of the optic chiasm, the left half of the image seen by both eyes is transmitted to the visual cortex in the right cerebral hemisphere, and the right half of the image is transmitted to the left cerebral hemisphere. The right hemisphere thus sees objects to the left of the centre of vision, and the left hemisphere sees objects to the right of the centre of vision. Communication between the right and left hemispheres integrates this information into a perception of the entire visual field seen by the two eyes.

If you look at a nearby object with one eye and then the other, you will notice that the point of view is slightly different. Integration of the visual field by the brain creates a single picture with a sense of distance and depth. The greater the difference between the images seen by the two eyes, the closer the object appears to the viewer.

Archerfish **(Figure 37.21)** live in fresh water and knock flying or resting insects onto the water's surface with spit droplets. The fish then catch and eat the insects. During the spitting attacks, the fishes' eyes are below the surface of the water, posing a potentially serious problem because of refraction, the deflection of rays of light at the air–water interface. Some evidence suggests that archerfish spit from directly under the prey, but further observations show that this is not always true. Archerfish correctly set their spitting angle to compensate for the refraction they experience at different positions. They also correct for curvature of the water droplet's trajectory. Other fish also spit at aerial

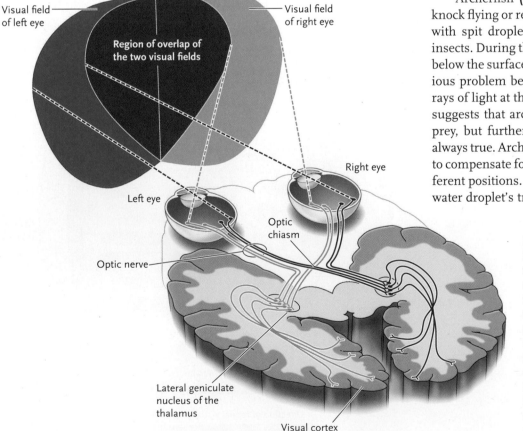

Figure 37.20

Neural pathways for vision. Because half of the axons carried by the optic nerves cross over in the optic chiasm, the left half of the field seen by both eyes (green segment) is transmitted to the visual cortex in the right cerebral hemisphere. The right half of the field seen by both eyes (red segment) is transmitted to the visual cortex in the left cerebral hemisphere. As a result, the right hemisphere of the brain sees objects to the left of the centre of vision, and the left hemisphere sees objects to the right of the centre of vision.

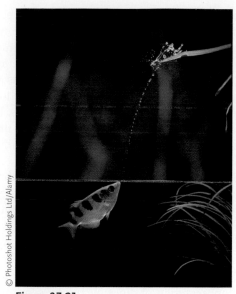

Figure 37.21

An archerfish, *Toxotes chatareus*, projecting spit at an insect prey.

prey, and some birds hunt fish from above the water's surface; both deal with the problems of refraction from a different standpoint.

In humans, the two optic nerves together contain more than a million axons, more than all other afferent neurons of the body put together. Almost one-third of the grey matter of the cerebral cortex is devoted to visual information. These numbers give some idea of the complexity of the information integrated into the visual image formed by the brain and the importance of visual information for everyday activity.

STUDY BREAK

1. What is the "simplest" eye? Why is it an eye, and how does it differ from image-forming eyes?
2. What causes colour-blindness?
3. Why are compound eyes so adept at detecting motion?
4. What is accommodation?

37.5 Chemoreceptors

Chemoreceptors provide information about taste (gustation) and smell (olfaction), as well as measures of intrinsic levels of molecules such as oxygen, carbon dioxide, and hydrogen ions. All chemoreceptors probably work through membrane receptor proteins that are stimulated when they bind with specific molecules in their environment (internal or external) and generate action potentials in afferent nerves leading to the CNS. In this section, we only discuss sensing of external stimuli through taste and smell.

37.5a Invertebrate Animals Experience a Rich World of Odours

In many invertebrates, the same receptors serve for sensing smell and taste. These receptors may be concentrated around the mouth or distributed over the body surface. The cnidarian *Hydra* has chemoreceptors around its mouth that respond to glutathione, a chemical released from prey organisms ensnared in the cnidarian's tentacles. Stimulation of chemoreceptors by glutathione causes the tentacles to retract, resulting in ingestion of the prey. In contrast, earthworms have taste and smell receptors distributed over the entire body surface.

Some terrestrial invertebrates have clearly differentiated receptors for taste and smell. In insects, taste receptors occur inside hollow sensory bristles called *sensilla* (singular, *sensillum*), usually located on the antennae, mouthparts, or feet **(Figure 37.22)**. Pores in the sensilla admit molecules from potential food to the chemoreceptors, which are specialized to detect sugars, salts, amino acids, or other chemicals. Many female insects have chemoreceptors on their ovipositors, allowing them to lay their eggs on food appropriate for the larvae when they hatch.

Olfactory receptors detect airborne molecules such as pheromones, the chemicals used in communication by both animals and plants (see Chapter 39). Insects are excellent examples of animals that make extensive use of pheromones. Female insects use pheromones to attract males, and vice versa. Olfactory

Figure 37.22

Taste receptors on the foot of a fruit fly, *Drosophila*.

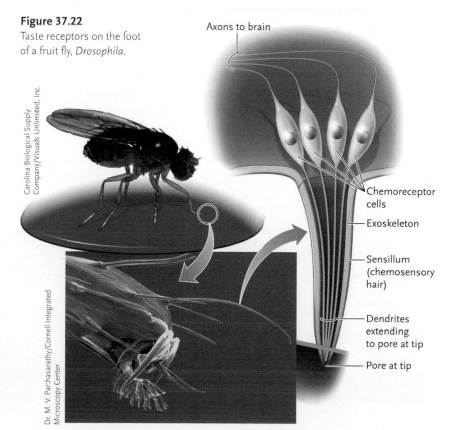

Axons to brain

Chemoreceptor cells

Exoskeleton

Sensillum (chemosensory hair)

Dendrites extending to pore at tip

Pore at tip

receptors in the bristles on the antennae of male silkworm moths (*Bombyx mori*) **(Figure 37.23)** bind a pheromone released by female conspecifics. If an antenna from a silkworm moth is connected to electrodes at its base and tip, action potentials from olfactory receptors can be detected at pheromone concentrations as low as one attractant molecule per 10^{17} air molecules! The male moth responds by flying rapidly when as few as 40 of the 20 000 receptor cells on an antenna have been stimulated by pheromone molecules. Ants, bees, and wasps may use odour to recognize conspecifics, to identify members of the same hive or nest, or to alert nestmates to danger.

37.5b Vertebrate Animals: More Variations on the Sense of Taste and Smell

Taste involves the detection of potential food molecules in objects touched by a receptor. Smell involves the detection of airborne molecules. Taste and smell receptors have hairlike extensions that contain proteins that bind environmental molecules. Hairs of taste receptors are derived from microvilli and contain microfilaments. Hairs of smell receptors are derived from cilia and contain microtubules. Information from taste receptors is typically processed in the parietal lobes of the brain, whereas information from smell receptors is processed in olfactory bulbs and the temporal lobes of the brain.

Taste. Taste receptors of most vertebrates form part of a structure called a taste bud, a small, pear-shaped capsule with a pore at the top opening to the exterior **(Figure 37.24)**. Sensory hairs of taste receptors pass through the pore of a taste bud and project to the exterior. The opposite end of the receptor cells synapses with dendrites of an afferent neuron.

Taste receptors of aquatic vertebrates (e.g., fishes and amphibian tadpoles) are generally found throughout the oral cavity but in some species may be found distributed all over the body surface. In terrestrial vertebrates, they are concentrated in the mouth.

Humans have about 10 000 taste buds, each 30 to 40 μm in diameter, scattered over the tongue, roof of the mouth, and throat. Those on the tongue are embedded in outgrowths called *papillae* (*papula* = pimple), which give the surface of the tongue its rough or furry texture. Taste receptors on the human tongue respond to five basic tastes: sweet, sour, salty, bitter, and umami (savoury). Some receptors for umami respond to the amino acid glutamate (familiar as monosodium glutamate or MSG).

Signals from taste receptors are relayed to the thalamus. From there, some signals lead to gustatory centres in the cerebral cortex, which integrate them into the perception of taste. Others lead to the brain stem and limbic system, which link tastes to involuntary visceral and emotional responses. Through brain stem and limbic connections, a pleasant taste may lead to salivation, secretion of digestive juices, sensations of pleasure, and sexual arousal, whereas an unpleasant taste may produce revulsion, nausea, and vomiting.

Smell. For water-dwelling vertebrates (e.g., fishes and amphibian tadpoles), the olfactory system detects chemicals present in the surrounding water. These receptors are found inside nasal sacs that open to the water through nares but that are blind ending and not used for breathing. For air-breathing vertebrates, the olfactory system primarily detects volatile (airborne) chemicals by receptors located in the nasal cavities. Bloodhounds have more than 200 million olfactory receptors in patches of olfactory epithelium in the upper nasal passages; humans have about 5 million olfactory receptors. On one end, each olfactory receptor cell has 10 to 20 sensory hairs projecting into a layer of mucus covering the olfactory area in the nose. To be detected, airborne molecules must dissolve in the watery mucus solution. At the other end, the olfactory receptor cells synapse with interneurons in the olfactory bulbs. Olfactory receptors are the only receptor cells that make direct connections with brain interneurons rather than via afferent neurons. It has commonly been believed that, at least in mammals, the

25 μm

A. Shay/Oxford Scientific/Getty Images

Louisa Howard, Dartmouth College EM Facility

Figure 37.23
The brushlike antennae of a male silkworm moth. Fine sensory bristles containing olfactory receptor cells cover the filaments of the antennae.

Figure 37.24

Taste receptors in the human tongue. The receptors occur in microscopic taste buds that line the sides of the furry papillae.

Papilla (cutaway)

Taste bud

Sensory hair of taste receptor

Tongue

Papillae

Taste buds

Papilla

Afferent nerve

olfactory epithelium does not detect odorants in water. However, star-nosed moles (*Condylura cristata*) and water shrews (*Sorex palustris*) exhale bubbles while diving. They re-inhale the bubbles that equilibrate with the water around them and, in this way, gain access to airborne olfactory cues **(Figure 37.25)**.

From the olfactory bulbs, nerves conduct signals directly to the olfactory centres of the cerebral cortex. This is the only sense that is not relayed through the thalamus in the brain (see Section 37.9f). Here they are integrated into the perception of tantalizing or unpleasant odours from a rose to a rotten egg. Most odour perceptions arise from combinations of different olfactory receptors. About 1000 different human genes give rise to an equivalent number of olfactory receptor types, each specific for a different class of chemicals. Recent experiments demonstrate that rats smell in stereo, accurately localizing odours in one or two sniffs. They could do so only with bilateral sampling. Some neurons in the olfactory bulb respond differently to stimuli from the left than from the right. Furthermore, some receptors in the olfactory cortex of mammals fire only upon stimulation by combinations of odorants, perhaps explaining why mixes of odours are perceived as novel by humans.

As in taste, other connections from the olfactory bulbs lead to the limbic system and brain stem, where the signals elicit emotional and visceral responses similar to those caused by pleasant and unpleasant tastes. Olfaction contributes to the sense of taste because vaporized molecules from foods are conducted from the throat to the olfactory receptors in the nasal cavities. This is the reason why anything that dulls your sense of smell, such as a head cold or holding your nose, diminishes the apparent flavour of food.

Many mammals use odours as a means of communication. Individuals of the same family or colony are identified by their odour; odours are also used to attract mates and to mark territories and trails. Dogs, for example, use their urine to mark home territories with identifying odours. Humans use the fragrances of perfumes and colognes as artificial sexual attractants.

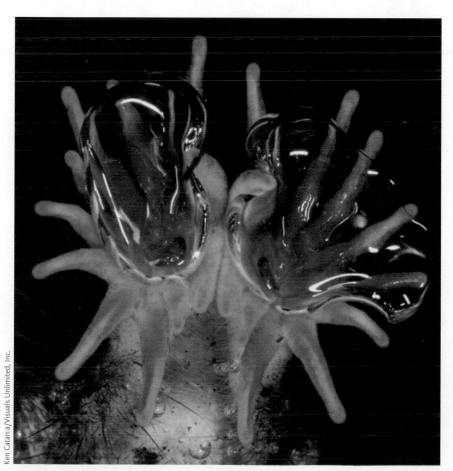

Ken Catania/Visuals Unlimited, Inc.

Figure 37.25

Star-nosed moles (*Condylura cristata*) have papillae around their noses. Shown here, the papillae capture bubbles of air, allowing the submerged mole to smell airborne odours.

Forked Tongues 37.3

The forked tongues of serpents (see Figure 37.26) are deeply embedded in the world's religious iconography, often as a representation of deceit and malevolence. Aristotle thought that the forked tongue could double taste sensations. Hodierna proposed that the forked tongue allowed snakes to pick dirt out of both nostrils simultaneously.

Snake tongues are involved in chemoreception and serve as the delivery mechanism for paired sensors in Jacobson's organs (vomeronasal organs) on the roofs of snakes' mouths. Jacobson's organs connect with the oral cavity through two small openings in the palate (vomeronasal fenestrae).

However, forked tongues are not restricted to snakes. Lepidosaurian reptiles (see Chapter 26) show considerable variation in tongue structure **(Figure 1).** Forked tongues allow snakes and lizards to follow the pheromone trails of prey and conspecifics. The forked tongue specifically allows animals to use tropotaxis, which means simultaneously sampling chemical stimuli at two points. In some snakes, varanid lizards, and teiid lizards, the distance between the tongue tips exceeds the width of the head. Forked tongues have evolved at least twice and perhaps as many as four times in lepidosaurian reptiles **(Figure 2).**

From Kurt Schwenk, "Why Snakes Have Forked Tongues," *Science,* Mar 18, 1994, vol. 263, pp. 1573–1577. Reprinted with permission from AAAS.

FIGURE 1

Tongue tips vary in squamate reptiles, from simple notches to deep forks. *Shown here, from left to right, are the tongues of Sceloporus (Iguania), Coleonyx (Gekkonidae), Cnemidophorus (Teiidae), Lacerta (Lacertidae), Bipes (Amphisbaenia), Scincella (Scincidae), Abronia (Anguidae), and Varanus (Varanidae). Most snake tongues look like that of the Varanus.*

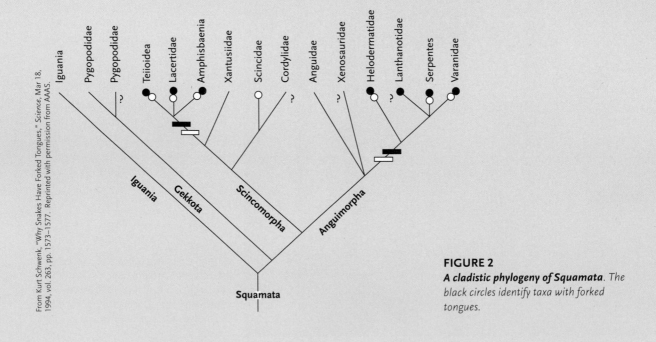

From Kurt Schwenk, "Why Snakes Have Forked Tongues," *Science,* Mar 18, 1994, vol. 263, pp. 1573–1577. Reprinted with permission from AAAS.

FIGURE 2

A cladistic phylogeny of Squamata. *The black circles identify taxa with forked tongues.*

STUDY BREAK

1. What is the difference between taste and smell? What are the similarities?
2. Distinguish among receptor proteins, receptor cells, and receptor organs.
3. For terrestrial vertebrates, describe the pathway by which a signal generated by taste receptors leads to a response.

37.6 Thermoreceptors and Nociceptors

Thermoreceptors detect changes in the surrounding temperature. Nociceptors respond to stimuli that may potentially damage the surrounding tissues. Both types of receptors consist of free nerve endings formed by the dendrites of afferent neurons, with no specialized receptor structures surrounding them.

37.6a Thermoreception Is Heat Detection

Most animals have thermoreceptors. Invertebrates such as mosquitoes and ticks use thermoreceptors to locate warm-blooded prey. Some vertebrates, notably snakes such as rattlesnakes and pythons, also use thermoreceptors to detect the body heat of warm-blooded prey animals. These receptors are located in the pits of some pit vipers **(Figure 37.26)**, whereas those of pythons and boas may not have an opening to the surface. Vampire bats have infrared receptors on their noseleafs **(Figure 37.27)**, allowing them to detect places where blood (their food) flows close to the skin.

In vertebrates, distinct thermoreceptors respond to heat and cold. Researchers have shown that three members of the *transient receptor potential* (TRP)-gated

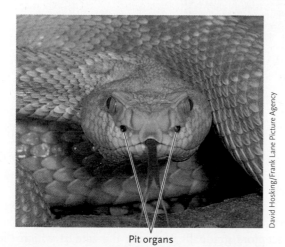

Figure 37.26

The pit organs of an albino western diamondback rattlesnake (*Crotalus atrox*) are located in depressions on both sides of the head below the eyes. These thermoreceptors detect infrared radiation emitted by warm-blooded prey such as mice and kangaroo rats.

Pit organs

Figure 37.27

The noseleaf on the face of a vampire bat (*Desmodus rotundus*) houses an infrared detector, allowing the bat to find places where blood flows close to the skin. The bat then uses razor-sharp teeth to remove a divot of skin and anticlotting chemicals in its saliva to allow it to get a blood meal.

Ca^{2+} channel family act as heat receptors. One responds when the temperature reaches 33°C and another responds above 43°C, at which point, heat starts to be painful. Both receptors are believed to be involved in thermoregulation. The third receptor responds at 52°C and above, in this case producing a pain response rather than being involved in thermoregulation.

Two cold receptors are known in mammals. One responds between 8 and 28°C and is thought to be involved in thermoregulation. The second responds to temperatures below 8°C and appears to be associated with pain rather than thermoregulation. The molecular mechanisms controlling the opening and closing of heat and cold receptor chemical channels are not currently known.

Some neurons in the hypothalamus of mammals function as thermoreceptors, sensing changes in brain temperature and receiving afferent thermal information. They are highly sensitive to shifts from the normal body temperature and trigger involuntary responses such as sweating, panting, or shivering, which restore normal body temperature.

37.6b Nociceptors Detect Pain

Signals from nociceptors in mammals and possibly other vertebrates detect damaging stimuli that are interpreted by the brain as pain. Pain is a protective mechanism. In humans, pain prompts us to do something immediately to remove or decrease the damaging stimulus. Pain often elicits a reflex response, such as withdrawing the hand from a hot stove, that proceeds before we are consciously aware of the sensation.

Mechanical damage, such as a cut, pin prick, or blow to the body, and temperature extremes can cause pain. Some nociceptors are specific for a particular type of damaging stimulus, whereas others respond to

MOLECULE BEHIND BIOLOGY 37.4

Capsaicin

Biting into a jalapeño pepper (a variety of *Capsicum annuum*) can produce a burning pain in your mouth strong enough to bring tears to your eyes. This painfully hot sensation is due primarily to capsaicin, a chemical that probably evolved in pepper plants as a defence against foraging animals. The defence is obviously ineffective for the humans who relish peppers and other foods containing capsaicin (such as hot sauce).

David Julius and his coworkers revealed the molecular basis for detection of capsaicin by nociceptors. They designed their experiments to test the hypothesis that the responding nociceptors have a cell surface receptor that binds capsaicin. Binding the chemical opens a membrane channel in the receptor that admits cations and initiates action potentials interpreted by the brain as pain **(Figure 1)**.

The Julius team isolated the total complement of messenger RNAs from nociceptors that respond to capsaicin and made complementary DNA (cDNA) clones of the mRNAs (see Section 15.1). The cDNAs contained thousands of different sequences that encode proteins made in the nociceptors. The team transferred the cDNAs individually into embryonic kidney cells (which do not normally respond to capsaicin), and the transformed cells were screened with capsaicin to identify which took in calcium ions. These would be the cells that had received a cDNA encoding a capsaicin receptor. Messenger RNA transcribed from the identified cDNA clone was injected into both frog oocytes and cultured mammalian cells. Both oocytes and cultured cells responded to capsaicin by admitting calcium ions, confirming that the researchers had found the capsaicin receptor cDNA.

Among the effects noted when the receptor was introduced into oocytes was a response to heat. Increasing the temperature of the solution surrounding the oocytes from 22°C to about 48°C produced a strong calcium inflow. In short, by binding to the nociceptor, the capsaicin molecule produces the same sensation that excessive heat would, explaining the feeling that your mouth is on fire when you eat a hot pepper. As far as your nociceptors and CNS are concerned, it *is* on fire.

The ion channel involved in producing the flow of cations has subsequently been shown to be a member of the superfamily of TRP ion channels, and as such is now referred to as TRPV1. A number of different TRP ion channels have been shown to be sensitive to different ranges of temperature and probably are responsible for our range of temperature sensation.

Chilli peppers were domesticated in different parts of the New World (from Chile to the Caribbean) by 6000 years B.P., and their use in cooking has spread throughout the world (see Chapter 48).

a.

b.

FIGURE 1

(a) A capsaicin molecule. (b) A TRPV1 channel allows cations to flow across the membrane of a heat-sensitive neuron in response to capsaicin, depolarizing the cell and generating action potentials.

more than one kind. Axons that transmit pain are part of the somatic system of the PNS (see Section 37.9). They synapse with interneurons in the grey matter of the spinal cord and activate neural pathways to the CNS by releasing the neurotransmitter glutamate or substance P (see Chapter 36). Glutamate-releasing axons produce sharp, prickling sensations that can be localized to a specific body part, such as the pain of stepping on a tack. Substance P–releasing axons produce dull, burning, or aching sensations that are not easily localized, such as the pain of tissue damage when you stub your toe.

As part of their protective function, pain receptors adapt very little, if at all (see Section 37.1b). Some pain receptors gradually intensify the rate at which they send out action potentials if the stimulus continues at a constant level. The CNS also has a pain-suppressing system. In response to stimuli, such as exercise, hypnosis, and stress, the brain releases *endorphins* (See Table 36.1, page 893), natural painkillers that bind to membrane receptors on substance P neurons, reducing the amount of neurotransmitter released.

Nociceptors contribute to the taste of some spicy foods, particularly those containing capsaicin, the active ingredient in hot peppers (see "Molecule behind Biology," Box 37.4, p. 926). Researchers who study pain use capsaicin to identify nociceptors. To some, the burning sensation from capsaicin is addictive because in its presence, nociceptors in the mouth, nose, and throat immediately transmit pain messages to the brain. The brain responds by releasing endorphins that act as a painkiller and create temporary euphoria.

Study Break

1. What do thermoceptors and nociceptors have in common?
2. Why is it important that pain receptors not adapt?

37.7 Electroreceptors and Magnetoreceptors

Some animals gain information about their environment by sensing electrical or magnetic fields. In so doing, they directly sense stimuli that humans can detect only with scientific instruments.

37.7a Electroreception

Electroreception is an ancient trait in vertebrates. Although it was lost in ancestral bony fishes, it persists today in many sharks and has reappeared in some bony fishes and some amphibians. Mammals such as the star-nosed mole and duck-billed platypus detect electric fields with specialized **electroreceptors.**

Electroreceptors depolarize in an electric field, and the plasma membrane of an electroreceptor cell generates action potentials. The electrical stimuli detected by the receptors are used in different ways. Electrical information can be used to locate prey; to negotiate a way around obstacles in muddy water; or, by some fishes, to communicate. Some electroreception systems are passive, detecting electric fields in the environment, not the animal's own electric currents. Passive systems are used mainly to find prey. Sharks and rays use electroreceptors to locate prey buried under sand by detecting electrical currents generated by the prey's heartbeat or by the muscle contractions moving water over the gills.

37.7b Electric Fishes

Fishes in the orders Mormyriformes (elephant fish from Africa) and Gymnotiformes (knifefish from South America; **Figure 37.28a**) emit and receive low-voltage electrical signals, using them in prey location (electrolocation)

and intraspecific communication. Some electric fishes can produce discharges of several hundred volts (e.g., *Electrophorus electricus,* the electric eel, **Figure 37.28b,** and *Malapterurus electricus,* the electric catfish) that stun or kill prey. The voltage discharged by an electric eel is high enough to stun, but not kill, a human.

37.7c Magnetoreception and Navigation

Just as the development of a magnetic compass was a pivotal point in humans' ability to navigate, some animals use magnetic compasses in long-distance navigation. Magnetoreceptors allow animals to detect and use Earth's magnetic field as a source of directional information. The list includes butterflies, beluga whales, sea turtles (see "Magnetic Sense in Sea Turtles," Box 37.5, p. 928), homing pigeons, and foraging honeybees (*Apis mellifera*).

The pattern of Earth's magnetic field differs from region to region yet remains almost constant over time, largely unaffected by changing weather or day and night. Animals with magnetic receptors can reliably monitor their location. Although little is known about the receptors that detect magnetic fields, they may depend on the fact that moving a conductor, such as an electroreceptor cell, through a magnetic field generates an electric current. Some magnetoreceptors may

a.

b.

Figure 37.28

Two electric fishes from South America. *Eigenmannia eigenmannia* **(a)** is a weakly electric fish that uses electrolocation, whereas *Electrophorus electricus* **(b),** the electric eel, stuns prey with an electric discharge.

Magnetic Sense in Sea Turtles 37.5

To determine if loggerhead sea turtles (*Caretta caretta*) use a magneto-receptor system for orientation, Kenneth Lohmann and colleagues tested the responses of hatchling turtles to magnetic fields. They placed each turtle hatchling they tested in a harness and tethered it to a swivelling, electronic system in the centre of a circular pool of water **(Figure 1a)**. The pool was surrounded by a large coil system, allowing the researchers to reverse the direction of the magnetic field **(Figure 1b)**. The direction the turtle swam was recorded by the tracking system and relayed to a computer.

The turtles swam under two experimental conditions: half of them in Earth's magnetic field and the other half in a reversed magnetic field. Turtle hatchlings tested in Earth's magnetic field swam, on average, in an east-to-northeast direction, mimicking the direction they follow normally when migrating at sea. The hatchlings tested in the reversed magnetic field swam, on average, in a direction 180° opposite that of the hatchlings swimming in Earth's magnetic field.

The results indicate that loggerhead sea turtle hatchlings can detect Earth's magnetic field and use it to help them orient their migration. Their direction of migration, east to northeast, matches the inclination of Earth's magnetic field in the Atlantic Ocean where they migrate (see **Figure 1c**).

a.

Kenneth Lohmann/University of North Carolina

FIGURE 1

Harnessed hatchling loggerhead sea turtles (a) were tested in a circular pool in which the magnetic field could be altered (b). (c) Hatchlings swimming in the normal magnetic field of Earth swam in the directions they would travel at sea on migration.

b.

Coil system to control magnetic field

Tether   Lever arm   Digital encoder

Turtle

Coil system control computer

Output to data analysis computer

c.

75°
75°   60°
60°   45°
45°   Sargasso sea   30°
15°
30°   0°
15°
0°

KEY
← Ocean current
--- Inclination of Earth's magnetic field

depend on the effect of Earth's magnetic field on the mineral *magnetite,* which is found in the bones or teeth of many vertebrates, including humans, and in insects, such as the abdomen of the honeybee and the heads and abdomens of certain ants.

Animals such as Homing Pigeons (*Columbia livia*), famous for their ability to find their way back to their nests even when released far from home, navigate by detecting their position with reference to both Earth's magnetic field and the Sun. Magnetite is located in the beaks of these birds, which is where magneto-reception likely occurs. Big brown bats (*Eptesicus fuscus*) also have a magnetic sense that influences their navigational abilities.

STUDY BREAK

1. How do animals use electrical information?
2. What are the advantages of a magnetic navigational system?

37.8 Overview of Central Neural Integration

The sensory pathways just described conduct information by afferent neurons to the CNS. Each type of receptor conveys information to a specific part of the CNS. Action potentials arising in the retina of the eye, for instance, travel along the optic nerves to the visual cortex, where they are interpreted by the brain as differences in pattern, colour, and intensity of light. In the next part of the chapter, we describe the roles of the major areas of the CNS where complex neural processing occurs. This is described for the vertebrate CNS (and, in particular, for the human nervous system, about which the most is known).

CONCEPT FIX It is commonly thought that our perception of the environment arises from the sensory cells themselves. Perception, however, is the consequence of the processing of sensory information by the CNS. Action potentials arriving in the sensory cortex from different receptors on the tongue may create a sweet or a tart sensation. These are a result of the processing. All taste receptors generate action potentials, but the action potentials arriving from different receptors give rise to different sensations. ⬡

37.9 The Central Nervous System and Its Functions

The CNS consists of the brain and spinal cord. It manages body activities by integrating incoming sensory information from the PNS into compensating responses.

37.9a The Central Nervous System is Protected by the Meninges and by Cerebrospinal Fluid

The brain and spinal cord are surrounded and protected by three layers of connective tissue, the **meninges** (*meninga* = membrane), and by the **cerebrospinal fluid**, which circulates through the central canal of the spinal cord, through the ventricles of the brain, and between two of the meninges. The fluid cushions the brain and spinal cord from jarring movements and impacts, nourishes the CNS, and protects the CNS from toxic substances.

37.9b The Spinal Cord Relays Signals between the Peripheral Nervous System and the Brain and Controls Reflexes

The spinal cord, which extends dorsally from the base of the brain, carries impulses between the brain and the PNS and also contains interneuron circuits that control motor reflexes. In cross section, the spinal cord has a butterfly-shaped core of **grey matter**, consisting of nerve cell bodies and dendrites. This is surrounded by **white matter**, consisting of axons, many of them surrounded by myelin sheaths (**Figure 37.29,** step 3). Pairs of spinal nerves connect with the spinal cord at spaces between the vertebrae.

Figure 37.29

Organization of the spinal cord and the withdrawal reflex. The withdrawal reflex is an example of a relatively simple neuron circuit that integrates incoming information to produce an appropriate response. The reflex movement produced by this circuit is so rapid that the hand is withdrawn before the brain recognizes the sensation of pain.

The afferent (incoming) axons entering the spinal cord synapse with interneurons in the grey matter, which send axons upward through the white matter of the spinal cord to the brain. Conversely, axons from interneurons of the brain pass downward through the white matter of the cord and synapse with the dendrites and cell bodies of efferent neurons in the grey matter of the cord. The axons of these efferent (outgoing) neurons exit the spinal cord through the spinal nerves.

The grey matter of the spinal cord also contains interneurons of the pathways involved in reflexes, programmed movements that take place without conscious effort, such as the sudden withdrawal of a hand from a hot surface (shown in Figure 37.29). When your hand touches a hot surface, the heat stimulates an afferent neuron, which makes connections with at least two interneurons in the spinal cord. One of these interneurons stimulates an efferent neuron, causing the *flexor* muscle of the arm to contract. This bends the arm and withdraws the hand almost instantly from the hot surface. The other interneuron synapses with an efferent neuron connected to an *extensor* muscle, relaxing it so that the flexor can move more quickly. Interneurons connected to the reflex circuits also send signals to the brain, making you aware of the stimulus causing the reflex. You know from experience that when a reflex movement withdraws your hand from a hot surface or other damaging stimulus, you feel the pain shortly *after* the hand is withdrawn. This is the extra time required for impulses to travel from the neurons of the reflex to the brain.

37.9c The Brain Integrates Sensory Information and Formulates Compensating Responses

The brain is the major centre that receives, integrates, stores, and retrieves information. Its interneuron networks generate responses that provide the basis for our voluntary movements, consciousness, behaviour, emotions, learning, reasoning, language, and memory, among many other complex activities.

Major Brain Structures. You learned earlier that the three major divisions of the embryonic brain—the forebrain, the midbrain, and the hindbrain—give rise to the structures of the adult brain. Like the spinal cord, each brain structure contains both grey matter and white matter (the myelination of the axons gives white matter its colour) and is surrounded by meninges and circulating cerebrospinal fluid **(Figure 37.30)**.

The hindbrain of vertebrates develops into the *medulla oblongata* (the *medulla*) (see Figure 36.20, Chapter 36). In many vertebrates, a mass of fibres connecting the cerebellum to higher centres in the brain is so prominent that it is identified as the *pons* (bridge). The medulla and pons, along with the midbrain, form a stalklike structure known as the **brain stem**, which

Figure 37.30

The mammalian brain, illustrating the distribution of grey matter, and the locations of the ventricles (in blue) with their connection to the central canal of the spinal cord.

connects the forebrain with the spinal cord. All but 2 of the 12 pairs of cranial nerves also originate from the brain stem. The *cerebellum,* with its deeply folded surface, is an outgrowth of the pons.

The forebrain, which makes up most of the mass of the brain in mammals, forms the *telencephalon (cerebrum)*. Its surface layer, the **cerebral cortex**, is a thin layer of grey matter in which numerous unmyelinated neurons are found. The cerebrum, which is divided into right and left *cerebral hemispheres*, is corrugated by fissures and folds that increase the surface area of the cerebral cortex (see Figure 37.30). This structure reflects two of the evolutionary tendencies in the brain of mammals: the corrugation of the hemispheres and the development of a layer of grey matter on the periphery. The *basal nuclei*, consisting of several regions of grey matter (cell bodies), are located deep within the white matter.

The Blood–Brain Barrier. Unlike the epithelial cells that form capillary walls elsewhere in the body, which allow small molecules and ions to pass freely from the blood to surrounding fluids, those forming capillaries in the brain are sealed together by tight junctions (Chapter 31). The tight junctions set up a **blood–brain**

barrier that prevents most substances dissolved in the blood from entering the cerebrospinal fluid, protecting the brain and spinal cord from viruses, bacteria, and toxic substances that may circulate in the blood. A few types of nonpolar molecules and ions, such as oxygen, carbon dioxide, alcohol, and anesthetics, can move directly across the lipid bilayer of the epithelial cell membranes by diffusion. A few other substances are moved across the plasma membrane by highly selective transport proteins. The most significant of these transported molecules is glucose, an important source of metabolic energy for the cells of the brain.

37.9d The Brain Stem Regulates Many Vital Housekeeping Functions of the Body

Physicians and scientists have learned much about the functions of various brain regions by studying animals as well as patients with brain damage from stroke, infection, tumours, and mechanical disturbances. Techniques such as *functional magnetic resonance imaging* (*fMRI*) and *positron emission tomography* (*PET*) allow researchers to identify the normal functions of specific brain regions in noninvasive ways. The instruments record a subject's brain activity during various mental and physical tasks by detecting increases in blood flow or metabolic activity in specific regions (Figure 37.31).

From such analyses, we know that grey-matter centres in the brain stem control many vital body functions without conscious involvement or control by the cerebrum. Among these functions are the heart and respiration rates, blood pressure, constriction and dilation of blood vessels, coughing, and reflex activities of the digestive system such as vomiting. These functions are so vital to life that damage to the brain stem has serious and often lethal consequences.

37.9e The Cerebellum Integrates Sensory Inputs to Coordinate Body Movements

 The cerebellum is separate in structure and function from the brain stem. Through its extensive connections with other parts of the brain, the **cerebellum** receives sensory input originating from receptors in muscles and joints; from balance receptors in the inner ear; and from the receptors of touch, vision, and hearing. These signals convey information about how the body trunk and limbs are positioned, the degree to which different muscles are contracted or relaxed, and the direction in which the body or limbs are moving. The cerebellum integrates these sensory signals and compares them with signals from the cerebrum that control voluntary body movements. Outputs from the cerebellum to the cerebrum, brain stem, and spinal cord modify and fine-tune the movements to keep the body in balance

Figure 37.31
Activity in the human brain while reading aloud. The image combines an fMRI of a male brain with a PET scan, which shows the blood circulation increases in the language, hearing, and vision areas of the brain, especially in the left hemisphere.

© Sovereign/ISM/SPL/Phototake, Inc.

and directed toward targeted positions in space. The cerebellum is particularly important in flying birds, which make greater use of three-dimensional space, and, like the mammalian cerebellum, it has a folded structure, increasing its relative size.

37.9f The Basal Nuclei, the Thalamus, and the Hypothalamus Control a Variety of Functions

Grey-matter centres derived from the embryonic telencephalon include the thalamus, hypothalamus, basal nuclei, and limbic system (see Figure 37.30). They contribute to the control and integration of voluntary movements, body temperature, glandular secretions, osmotic balance of the blood and extracellular fluids, wakefulness, and the emotions, among other functions. Some of the grey-matter centres route information to and from the cerebral cortex and between the forebrain, brain stem, and cerebellum.

The **thalamus** (see Figure 37.30, p. 930) forms a major switchboard that receives sensory information and relays it to the appropriate regions of the cerebral cortex. It also plays a role in alerting the cerebral cortex to full wakefulness or in inducing drowsiness or sleep.

The **hypothalamus** is a relatively small conical area found in all vertebrates. It contains centres that regulate basic homeostatic functions of the body. Some centres set and maintain body temperature by triggering reactions such as shivering and sweating. Others constantly monitor the osmotic balance of the blood by testing its composition of ions and other substances. If departures from normal levels are detected, the hypothalamus triggers responses such as thirst or changes in urine output that restore the osmotic and fluid balance. The hypothalamus is an important part of the endocrine system (see Chapter 35). It produces some of the hormones released by the pituitary and governs the release of other pituitary hormones.

The centres of the hypothalamus that detect blood composition and temperature are directly exposed to the bloodstream: they are the only parts of the brain *not* protected by the blood–brain barrier. Parts of the hypothalamus also coordinate responses triggered by the autonomic system (see Section 36.10), making it an important link in such activities as control of the heartbeat, contraction of smooth muscle cells in the digestive system, and glandular secretion. Some regions of the hypothalamus establish a biological clock that sets up daily metabolic rhythms, such as the regular changes in body temperature, metabolic rate, and sleep state that occur on a daily cycle.

The **basal nuclei** are grey-matter centres that surround the thalamus on both sides of the brain (see Figure 37.30, p. 930). They moderate voluntary movements directed by motor centres in the cerebrum and can be recognized in all amniotes. Damage to the basal nuclei can affect the planning and fine-tuning of movements, leading to stiff, rigid motions of the limbs and unwanted or misdirected motor activity, such as tremors of the hands and inability to start or stop intended movements at the intended place and time. Parkinson's disease, in which affected individuals exhibit all of these symptoms, results from degeneration of centres in and near the basal nuclei.

Parts of the thalamus, hypothalamus, and basal nuclei, along with other nearby grey-matter centres—the amygdala, hippocampus, and olfactory bulbs—form a functional network called the **limbic system** (*limbus* = belt), sometimes called our emotional brain. The **amygdala** works as a switchboard, routing information about experiences that have an emotional component through the limbic system. The **olfactory bulbs** relay inputs from odour receptors to both the cerebral cortex and the limbic system. The olfactory connection to the limbic system may explain why certain odours can evoke particular, sometimes startlingly powerful, emotional responses.

The limbic system controls emotional behaviour and influences the basic body functions regulated by the hypothalamus and brain stem. Stimulation of different parts of the limbic system produces anger, anxiety, fear, satisfaction, pleasure, or sexual arousal. Connections between the limbic system and other brain regions bring about emotional responses such as smiling, blushing, or laughing.

37.9g The Cerebral Cortex Carries Out All Higher Brain Functions

Over the course of evolution, the surface area of the cerebral cortex increased by continuously folding in on itself, thereby expanding the structure into sophisticated information-encoding and processing centres. Primates have cerebral cortices with the largest number of convolutions. In humans, each cerebral hemisphere is divided by surface folds into *frontal, parietal, temporal,* and *occipital* lobes **(Figure 37.32).** Uniquely in mammals, the top layer of the cerebral hemispheres is organized into six layers of neurons called the *neocortex* (*neo* = new; these layers are the newest part of the cerebral cortex in an evolutionary sense).

The two cerebral hemispheres can function separately, and each has its own communication lines internally and with the rest of the CNS and the body. The left cerebral hemisphere responds primarily to sensory signals from, and controls movements in, the right

Frontal association area (planning, personality)

General motor association area

Primary motor area

Primary somatosensory area

General sensory association area

Frontal lobe

Parietal lobe

Taste

Wernicke's area (understanding language)

Visual association area

Smell

Temporal lobe

Occipital lobe

Broca's area (expressing language)

Auditory area (hearing input)

Auditory association area

Facial recognition area (on inner side of cortex)

Primary visual cortex (visual input)

Cerebellum

Brain stem

Figure 37.32
The lobes of the cerebrum of the human brain, showing major regions and association areas of the cerebral cortex.

side of the body. The right hemisphere has the same relationships to the left side of the body. The opposite connection and control reflect the fact that the nerves carrying afferent and efferent signals cross from left to right within the spinal cord or brain stem. Thick axon bundles, forming a structure called the **corpus callosum**, connect the two cerebral hemispheres and coordinate their functions.

Sensory Regions of the Cerebral Cortex. Areas that receive and integrate sensory information are distributed over the cerebral cortex. In each hemisphere, the **primary somatosensory area,** which registers information on touch, pain, temperature, and pressure, runs in a band across the parietal lobes of the brain (see Figure 37.32). Experimental stimulation of this band in one hemisphere causes prickling or tingling sensations in specific parts on the opposite side of the body, beginning with the toes at the top of each hemisphere and running through the legs, trunk, arms, and hands, to the head (**Figure 37.33, p. 934** and "People behind Biology," Box 37.6, p. 934).

Other sensory regions of the cerebral cortex have been identified with hearing, vision, smell, and taste (see Figure 37.33). Regions of the temporal lobes on both sides of the brain receive auditory inputs from the ears, whereas inputs from the eyes are processed in the primary visual cortex in both occipital lobes. Olfactory input from the nose is processed in the olfactory lobes, located on the ventral side of the temporal lobes. Regions in the parietal lobes receive inputs from taste receptors on the tongue and other locations in the mouth.

Motor Regions of the Cerebral Cortex. The **primary motor area** of the cerebral cortex runs in a band just in front of the primary somatosensory area (see

Figure 37.33). Experimental stimulation of points along this band in one hemisphere causes movement of specific body parts on the opposite side of the body, corresponding generally to the parts registering in the primary somatosensory area at the same level (see Figure 37.33, p. 934). Other areas that integrate and refine motor control are located nearby.

In both the primary somatosensory and motor areas, some body parts, such as the lips and fingers, are represented by large regions, and others, such as the arms and legs, are represented by relatively small regions. As shown in Figure 37.33, p. 934, the relative sizes produce a distorted image of the human body that is quite different from the actual body proportions. The differences are reflected in the precision of touch and movement in structures such as the lips, tongue, and fingers.

Association Areas. The sensory and motor areas of the cerebral cortex are surrounded by **association areas** (see Figure 37.32) that integrate information from the sensory areas, formulate responses, and pass them on to the primary motor area. Two of the most important association areas are *Wernicke's area* and *Broca's area,* which function in spoken and written language. They are usually present on only one side of the brain, in the left hemisphere in 97% of the human population. Comprehension of spoken and written language depends on Wernicke's area, which coordinates inputs from the visual, auditory, and general sensory association areas. Interneuron connections lead from Wernicke's area to Broca's area, which puts together the motor program for coordination of the lips, tongue, jaws, and other structures producing the sounds of speech and passes the program to the primary motor area. The brain-scan

PEOPLE BEHIND BIOLOGY 37.6

Wilder Penfield, McGill University

Born in the United States at the end of the nineteenth century, Wilder Penfield graduated in literature from Princeton and won a Rhodes Scholarship to Oxford. He graduated as an M.D. from Johns Hopkins and worked in neurosurgery at Columbia. Attracted to McGill University in Montreal in 1928, he realized his dream by establishing the Montreal Neurological Institute, where scientists and clinicians could work together. It was here that he established the "Montreal Procedure" for the treatment of epilepsy. With patients under local anesthesia and fully conscious, he exposed the entire cerebrum and stimulated various parts of the brain while the patients described their sensations. In this way, he could identify the area of the brain responsible for the epileptic seizures and, if feasible, remove or destroy it. In the course of this work, he was able to identify those areas of the cerebral cortex that related to particular parts of the body and developed the well-known map shown in Figure 37.33. This was a remarkably courageous procedure at the time and required his patients to trust him absolutely.

images in Figure 37.31, p. 931 dramatically illustrate how these brain regions participate as a person performs different linguistic tasks.

37.9h Some Higher Functions Are Distributed in Both Cerebral Hemispheres, While Others Are Concentrated in One Hemisphere

Most of the other higher functions of the human brain, such as abstract thought and reasoning; spatial recognition; mathematical, musical, and artistic ability; and the associations forming the basis of personality, involve the coordinated participation of many regions of the cerebral cortex. Some of these regions are equally distributed in both cerebral hemispheres, and some are more concentrated in one hemisphere.

Among the functions more or less equally distributed between the two hemispheres is the ability to recognize faces. Consciousness, the sense of time, and

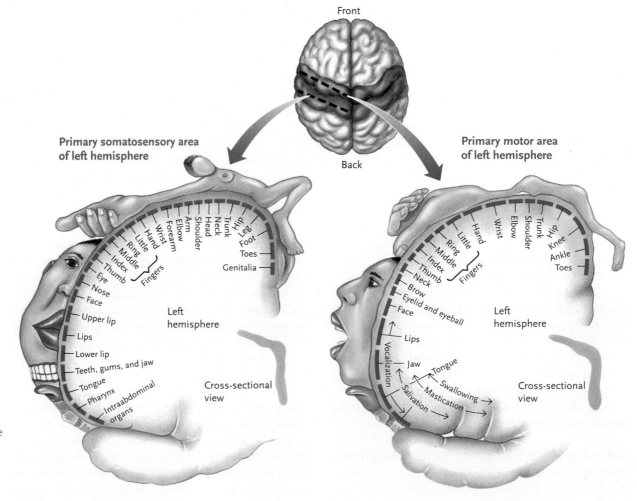

Figure 37.33
The primary somatosensory and motor areas of the cerebrum. The distorted images of the human body show the relative areas of the sensory and motor cortex devoted to different body regions.

recognizing emotions also seem to be distributed in both hemispheres.

Typically, some brain functions are more localized in one of the two hemispheres, a phenomenon called lateralization. Studies of people with split hemispheres and surveys of brain activity by PET and fMRI have confirmed that, for the vast majority of people, the left hemisphere specializes in spoken and written language, abstract reasoning, and precise mathematical calculations. The right hemisphere specializes in nonverbal conceptualizing; intuitive thinking; musical and artistic abilities; and spatial recognition functions, such as fitting pieces into a puzzle. The right hemisphere also handles mathematical estimates and approximations that can be made by visual or spatial representations of numbers. Thus, the left hemisphere in most people is verbal and mathematical, and the right hemisphere is intuitive, spatial, artistic, and musical.

STUDY BREAK

1. What is the blood–brain barrier and what is its function?
2. What is the difference between white matter and grey matter?
3. What is the function of the brain stem?
4. Distinguish the functions of the cerebellum from those of the cerebral cortex.

37.10 Memory, Learning, and Consciousness

We set memory, learning, and consciousness apart from the other CNS functions because they appear to involve coordination of structures from the brain stem to the cerebral cortex. **Memory** is the storage and retrieval of a thought or a sensory or motor experience. **Learning** involves a change in the response to a stimulus, based on information or experiences stored in memory. **Consciousness** is not easily defined. In a narrow sense, it involves awareness, a state of alertness to our surroundings. But there is a broader and deeper meaning that involves awareness of ourselves, our identity, and an understanding of the significance and likely consequences of events that we experience. In this section, we deal with sleep as a decrease in awareness.

37.10a Memory Takes Two Forms: Short Term and Long Term

Psychology research and our everyday experience indicate that humans have at least two types of memory. **Short-term memory** stores information for seconds, minutes, or at most an hour or so. **Long-term memory** stores information from days to years or even for life. Short-term memory, but not long-term memory, is usually erased if a person experiences a disruption such as a sudden fright, a blow, a surprise, or an electrical shock. For example, a person knocked unconscious by an accident typically cannot recall the accident itself or the events just before it, but long-standing memories are not usually disturbed.

To explain these differences, investigators propose that short-term memories depend on transient changes in neurons that can be erased relatively easily, such as changes in the membrane potential of interneurons caused by excitatory and inhibitory postsynaptic potentials (EPSPs and IPSPs) and the action of indirect neurotransmitters that lead to reversible changes in ion transport. By contrast, storage of long-term memory is considered to involve more or less permanent molecular, biochemical, or structural changes in interneurons, which establish signal pathways that cannot be switched off easily.

All memories probably register initially in short-term form. They are then either erased and lost or committed to long-term form. The intensity or vividness of an experience, the attention focused on an event, emotional involvement, and the degree of repetition may all contribute to the conversion from short-term to long-term memory.

The storage pathway typically starts with an input at the somatosensory cortex that then flows to the amygdala, which relays information to the limbic system, and to the hippocampus, which sends information to the frontal lobes, a major site of long-term memory storage. People with injuries to the hippocampus cannot remember information for more than a few minutes; long-term memory is limited to information stored before the injury occurred. Squirrels hoard food for the winter in a number of caches and can locate these by remembering the location from landmarks rather than by tracking a smell. Each autumn, the hippocampus of a squirrel increases in size by about 15%.

How are neurons and neuron pathways permanently altered to create long-term memory? One change that has been much studied is **long-term potentiation**: a long-lasting increase in the strength of synaptic connections in activated neural pathways following brief periods of repeated stimulation. The synapses become increasingly sensitive over time, so that a constant level of presynaptic stimulation is converted into a larger postsynaptic output that can last hours, weeks, months, or years. Other changes consistently noted as part of long-term memory include more or less permanent alterations in the number and the area of synaptic connections between neurons, in the number and branches of dendrites, and in gene transcription and protein synthesis in interneurons. Experiments on both vertebrates and invertebrates demonstrate that long-term memory depends on protein synthesis. For example, goldfish were trained to avoid an electrical shock by swimming to one end of an aquarium when a light was turned on. The fish could remember the training for about a month under normal conditions, but if they were exposed to a protein synthesis inhibitor while being trained, they forgot the training within a day.

37.10b Learning Involves Combining Past and Present Experiences to Modify Responses

As with memory, most animals appear to be capable of learning to some degree. Learning involves three sequential mechanisms: (1) storing memories, (2) scanning memories when a stimulus is encountered, and (3) modifying the response to the stimulus in accordance with the information stored as memory.

One of the simplest forms of learning is an increased responsiveness to mild stimuli after experiencing a strong stimulus, often called sensitization. The process was nicely illustrated by Eric Kandel of Columbia University and his associates in experiments with a shell-less marine snail, the Pacific sea hare, *Aplysia californica*. The first time the researchers administered a single sharp tap to the siphon (which admits water to the gills), the slug retracted its gills by a reflex movement. However, at the next touch, whether hard or gentle, the siphon retracted much more quickly and vigorously. Sensitization in *Aplysia* has been shown to involve changes in synapses, which become more reactive when more serotonin is released by action potentials. The cephalopod molluscs, such as the octopus, are capable of much more complex learning: they can distinguish and remember shapes and textures using only their tentacles.

37.10c Consciousness Involves Different States of Awareness

Most animals that have been investigated, including some invertebrates, experience a daily rhythm of activity and inactivity. The inactive period, sleep, is essential to normal functioning. Sleep deprivation leads to disruption of a number of functions, including memory and learning, and, if prolonged, can be fatal. During sleep, there is some degree of awareness since external stimuli such as sound or internal stimuli such as a full bladder can interrupt sleep.

In humans and other mammals, sleep is accompanied by changes in the electrical activity of the cerebrum as detected by electrodes applied to the scalp during an *electroencephalogram*. The waking state is characterized by rapid, irregular *beta waves* (**Figure 37.34**). As the eyes close and you become fully relaxed, these give way to slower, more regular *alpha waves*. As you become more drowsy, these are replaced by slower *theta waves*. Full sleep is characterized by

Figure 37.34
Brain waves characteristic of various states of consciousness.

even slower *delta waves*. The heart rate falls, and the muscles are relaxed.

During full sleep, the brain returns at intervals to periods of beta waves, during which the heart rate increases, the muscles may twitch, and the eyes move rapidly behind the closed lids, giving these periods the name **rapid eye movement**, or **REM, sleep.** This brief period of about 10 to 15 minutes occurs every 90 minutes or so in healthy adults. Sleepers do most of their dreaming during REM sleep, and most individuals awakened from REM sleep report they were experiencing vivid dreams.

This pattern of alternating periods of greater or lesser cerebral activity is also characteristic of bird sleep, although birds may sleep on one side of the brain while the other remains fully alert as protection against predators. This is also true of some marine mammals. Reptiles, with their less-developed cerebrum, experience alternating patterns of activity in the amygdala.

Although we know that sleep is essential, we do not understand the physiological basis for these effects. What do these patterns of neural activity in the brain reflect and why are they necessary? The fruit fly *Drosophila melanogaster* exhibits cycles of sleep. At night, it feeds and then seeks out an isolated place and becomes inactive for about eight hours. Interrupting the sleep interferes with memory and learning in the flies. Many labs are now using the flies as models to identify genes involved in the sleep process.

STUDY BREAK

Using long-term potentiation as an example, describe how neurons and neuron pathways can be altered to create memory.

Review

CourseMate Access an interactive eBook, chapter-specific interactive learning tools, including flashcards, quizzes, videos, and more in your Biology **CourseMate**, accessed through NelsonBrain.com **Aplia™** is an online interactive learning solution that helps you improve comprehension—and your grade—by integrating a variety of mediums and tools such as videos, tutorials, practice tests, and an interactive eBook.

37.1 Overview of Sensory Integration

- Receptors in the sensory system collect information (i.e., stimuli) from internal and external sensors (transducers) and convert (transduce) the information into neural activity. Dendrites of an afferent neuron pick up the stimuli. The axon of the afferent neuron conveys the stimulus to the CNS, providing the organisms with sensory data used to influence behaviour and homeostasis.

- Mechanoreceptors detect mechanical energy (pressure), photoreceptors detect the energy of light, chemoreceptors detect specific molecules or chemical conditions, thermoreceptors detect the flow of heat energy, and nociceptors detect tissue damage or noxious chemicals.

- Some receptors allow the effect of a stimulus to be reduced over time. This adaptation also allows receptors to retain their sensitivity over a broad range of stimulus intensities.

37.2 Mechanoreceptors and the Tactile and Spatial Senses

- You would more likely detect a fruit fly walking on your face than on your leg because touch receptors are closer together on a human's face than on a human's leg.

- The vestibular apparatus and cochlea are specialized sensory structures. The vestibular apparatus is responsible for maintaining equilibrium and coordinating head and body movements. The cochlea is used in hearing.

- The strength of the responses of stretch receptors depends on how much and how fast the muscle is stretched.

37.3 Mechanoreceptors and Hearing

- Most invertebrates detect sound through mechanoreceptors in their skin or other surface structures. An example are ears in the common cricket. Crickets detect sound using tympana (ears) on each side of the abdomen or on the first pair of walking legs. The ears are areas of thin exoskeleton.

- Sound waves cause vibrations of the tympanum, which are converted into nerve impulses that travel along the auditory nerve to the CNS.

- Vertebrates use ears to hear sounds. Some vertebrates have pinnae (outer ears) that collect sounds (vibrations) and channel them down the auditory canal to the tympanum (eardrum). There, vibrations in air are converted (transduced) into vibrations of the membrane making up the tympanum. These vibrations are amplified by vibrations of the malleus, incus, and stapes (auditory ossicles) and conveyed to the oval window, where they are converted to vibrations in the fluid of the coiled cochlea. Vibrations in the fluid inside the cochlea cause vibrations of the basilar membrane, which are detected by cilia and converted to nerve impulses. The nerve impulses move down the auditory nerve to the brain, where they are processed and interpreted.

- The echolocation calls of bats range from about 8 kHz to over 200 kHz. Many are inaudible to humans because they are ultrasonic, above the range of human hearing. Infrasounds (<20 Hz), used by elephants and whales, are below the range of human hearing.

37.4 Photoreceptors and Vision

- The ocellus, the simplest "eye," lacks a lens and is therefore not image forming. Ocelli are light receptors that often allow animals to detect differences in the brightness of light. Image-forming eyes (compound eyes and single-lens eyes) are photoreceptors too, but they have lenses that allow light to be focused on the retina, the layer with photosensitive cells.

- Colour-blindness is a result of inherited defects in opsin proteins of one or more of the three types of cones. Genes controlling colour vision are located on the X chromosome. Therefore, human males have only one set of genes controlling colour vision, whereas females have two sets. Colour-blindness is relatively common in men and relatively rare in women.

- Compound eyes are composed of ommatidia, many individual visual units. Each ommatidium samples a small part of the visual field, and many ommatidia provide the animal with an image that is a mosaic of many individual views. Motion is detected by many ommatidia at once, giving compound eyes special sensitivity to motion.

- Accommodation is the movement of the lens to focus the image on the retina. In cephalopods, muscles move the lens forward and back. In terrestrial vertebrates, muscles change the shape of the lens.

- Rods and cones, the photoreceptor cells in the retina, consist of an outer segment of stacked, flattened membranous discs with photopigments; an inner segment for cellular metabolic activities; and the synaptic terminal for storage and release of neurotransmitter.

37.5 Chemoreceptors

- Taste is the detection of potential food molecules *touched* by a receptor, whereas smell is the detection of *airborne* particles and molecules. Information from taste receptors is processed in the parietal lobes. Information from smell is processed in the olfactory bulb and temporal lobes. Both taste and smell receptors have hairlike extensions that bind molecules.

- The five basic tastes are sweet, sour, bitter, salty, and umami (savoury). Some lead to the gustatory centres of the cerebral cortex, whereas others are linked to the brain stem and limbic system, producing visceral and emotional responses, including physiological responses such as salivation and secretion of gastric juices. The same responses may occur in response to smells.

37.6 Thermoreceptors and Nociception

- Thermoreceptors and nociceptors consist of free nerve endings formed by the dendrites of afferent neurons. No specialized receptor structures surround them. All are members of the *transient receptor potential* (TRP)-gated Ca^{2+} channel family. There are three types of heat receptors; one responds to temperatures above 33°C, one to temperatures above 43°C, and the third to temperatures of 52°C and above. The first two are involved in thermoregulation, whereas the last elicits a strong pain response. There are two types of cold receptors; one responds to temperatures between 8 and 28°C and one to temperatures below 8°C. The first is involved in thermoregulation and the last elicits a strong pain response.

- The pain response (nociception) is a protective mechanism. These receptors do not adapt; otherwise, organisms would not withdraw from a prolonged painful stimulus, increasing the level of damage associated with the pain.

37.7 Electroreceptors and Magnetoreceptors

- Electric field information can be used to detect prey, for example, a shark's passive system. Some fishes generate electric signals to detect obstacles and prey and to communicate.

- The pattern of the magnetic field of Earth varies from region to region. Animals with a magnetic compass can detect the magnetic field and use the information in navigation (as people use compasses). Earth's magnetic field remains constant over time and so is reliable from year to year. Many animals have magnetic receptors. Other animals use Sun compasses.

37.8 Overview of Central Neural Integration

- In vertebrates, the CNS consists of a large brain located in the head and a hollow spinal cord, and the PNS consists of all the nerves and ganglia connecting the CNS to the rest of the body.

37.9 The Central Nervous System and Its Functions

- The CNS consists of the brain and spinal cord. The spinal cord carries signals between the brain and the PNS. Its neuron circuits also control reflex muscular movements and some autonomic reflexes.

- The adult derivatives of the hindbrain—the pons, medulla oblongata, and cerebellum—together with the relatively reduced midbrain, form the brain stem, which connects the telencephalon with the spinal cord.

- The telencephalon (cerebrum) is divided into right and left cerebral hemispheres, which are connected by a thick band of nerve fibres, the corpus callosum. The cerebral cortex, the surface of the cerebrum, is formed by grey matter. Other collections of grey matter, such as the thalamus, hypothalamus, and basal nuclei, lie at deeper layers of the telencephalon.

- Cerebrospinal fluid provides nutrients to and cushions the CNS. A blood–brain barrier set up by tight junctions between the cells of the capillary walls in the CNS allows only selected substances to enter the cerebrospinal fluid.

- Grey-matter centres in the pons and medulla control involuntary functions such as heart rate, blood pressure, respiration rate, and digestion. Centres in the midbrain coordinate responses to visual and auditory sensory inputs.

- The cerebellum integrates sensory inputs on the positions of muscles and joints, along with visual and auditory information, to coordinate body movements.

- Certain grey-matter centres of the telencephalon control a number of functions. The thalamus receives, filters, and relays sensory and motor information to and from regions of the cerebral cortex. The hypothalamus, the only part of the brain not protected by the blood–brain barrier, regulates basic homeostatic functions of the body and contributes to the endocrine control of body functions. The basal nuclei affect the planning and fine-tuning of body movements.

- The limbic system includes parts of the thalamus, hypothalamus, and basal nuclei, as well as the amygdala and hippocampus. It controls emotional behaviour and influences the basic body functions controlled by the hypothalamus and brain stem.

- The primary somatosensory areas of the cerebral cortex register incoming information on touch, pain, temperature, and pressure from all parts of the body. The temporal lobes receive input from the ears, the primary visual cortex from the eyes, the olfactory lobes from the nose, and the parietal lobes from taste receptors in the mouth. In general, the right cerebral hemisphere receives sensory information from the left side of the body, and vice versa.

- The primary motor areas of the cerebrum control voluntary movements of skeletal muscles in the body.

- The association areas integrate sensory information and formulate responses that are passed on to the primary motor areas. Importantly, Wernicke's area integrates visual, auditory, and other sensory information into the comprehension of language, whereas Broca's area coordinates movements of the lips, tongue, jaws, and other structures to produce the sounds of speech.

- Some functions, such as long-term memory and consciousness, are equally distributed between the two cerebral hemispheres. In contrast, the left hemisphere in most people specializes in spoken and written language, abstract reasoning, and precise mathematical calculations. The right hemisphere specializes in nonverbal conceptualizing, mathematical estimation, intuitive thinking, spatial recognition, and artistic and musical abilities.

37.10 Memory, Learning, and Consciousness

- Memory is the storage and retrieval of a sensory or motor experience, or a thought. Short-term memory involves temporary storage of information, probably resulting from changes in the membrane potential of interneurons, whereas long-term memory is essentially permanent, involving molecular, biochemical, or structural changes in interneurons.

- Learning involves modification of a response through comparisons made with information or experiences that are stored in memory.

- Consciousness is the awareness of ourselves, our identity, and our surroundings. It varies through states from full alertness to sleep.

- Sleep is characterized by alternations in patterns of electrical activity in the cerebrum between slow, relatively regular delta waves, characteristic of deep sleep, and brief periods of rapid, irregular beta waves signalling REM sleep.

Questions

Self-Test Questions

1. Which change would be involved in sensory adaptation?
   a. a reduction in the effect of stimuli
   b. the loss of eyes in cave-dwelling fish
   c. the development of an acute sense of smell
   d. the development of ears in insects preyed upon by bats

2. Which of the following is an example of proprioceptors?
   a. eyes
   b. statocysts
   c. ears
   d. halteres
   e. b and d

3. Which structure is involved in the vestibular system of vertebrates?
   a. retina
   b. utricle
   c. Golgi apparatus
   d. semicircular canals
   e. c and d

4. Which of the following is vital to the development of vision?
   a. vitamin E
   b. rhodopsin
   c. vitamin A
   d. fatty acids
   e. chlorophyll

5. When does accommodation occur in the eyes of cephalopods?
   a. when light is focused on the fovea
   b. when the shape of the lens is changed
   c. when the retina moves toward the lens
   d. when the retina moves away from the lens
   e. when the lens moves toward or away from the retina

6. Thermoreceptors are widespread in
   a. birds
   b. mammals
   c. pit vipers
   d. earthworms
   e. vampire bats

7. Which is the principle integration centre of homeostatic regulation and leads to the release of hormones?
   a. the cerebellum
   b. the thalamus
   c. the cerebrum
   d. the hypothalamus
   e. the association area

8. The regulation of blood pressure is primarily under the control of the
   a. somatic nervous system
   b. autonomic nervous system
   c. parasympathetic nervous system
   d. sympathetic nervous system

9. What part of the brain coordinates muscular activity?
   a. the cerebrum
   b. the cerebellum
   c. the myencephalon
   d. the medulla oblongata

10. Which of the following are nociceptors sensitive to?
   a. pheromones
   b. pain
   c. touch
   d. light
   e. vibration

Questions for Discussion

1. What is an eye? What are the key elements in the definition? Can robots have eyes?

2. Which are better at evoking memories in humans: visual or olfactory stimuli? What is the evidence supporting either point of view? Why would one kind of stimulus be more effective than the other?

3. Find examples of redundancy in the sensory systems of animals. What are the advantages of redundant systems? What are the disadvantages?

4. In some individuals, a genetic mutation causes them to perceive colours when listening to music. This condition is called synesthesia. In terms of the sensory systems, explain how this can occur.

5. The cerebellum is relatively large in fishes. It is much larger in free-swimming fishes than in bottom-dwelling species. Why might this be so?

Zacarias Pereira da Mata/Shutterstock

A successful strike by a great blue heron (*Ardea herodias*). All voluntary movements of animals occur as a result of contractions and relaxations of skeletal muscles. When stimulated by the nervous system, actin filaments in the muscles slide over myosin filaments to cause muscle contractions.

STUDY PLAN

38 Muscles, Skeletons, and Body Movements

WHY IT MATTERS

On an early summer morning throughout the lakes of much of Canada one can hear the haunting calls of loons **(Figure 38.1)**. These charismatic birds are excellent divers specialized for catching fish. They may dive as deep as 60 m while foraging. They are also excellent fliers, capable of long-distance migrations. During diving, they "fly" underwater using their feet for propulsion. To aid in this, their legs are positioned near the rear of their bodies. While ideal for diving, this is not ideal for walking. As a result, these birds are clumsy on land. All of these activities, vocalization, diving, and flying, require the coordinated activity of skeletal muscles. In the case of vocalization, the muscles act on the lungs to force air over the vocal cords at the entrance to the respiratory system, while for locomotion they act on bones of the limbs to produce movement of feet and wings. Not visible but also involved in all of these activities are the actions of the heart and blood vessels, which deliver oxygen to the skeletal muscles to support their work. These too depend on muscles—cardiac muscle in the case of the heart and smooth muscle in the case of the blood vessels. These muscles act to produce the forces needed to propel the nutrient-containing blood throughout the body.

Figure 38.1
A loon (*Gavia sp.*).

Muscle is the other excitable tissue described in Chapter 31. Like the cells of the nervous system, cells of the muscular system, called **muscle fibres**, can generate and propagate action potentials. These cells, however, also contain a special group of proteins, contractile proteins, that are capable of shortening when excited. Thus, action potentials generated by muscle fibres lead to muscle contraction. The speed and strength of contraction vary as a result of the manner in which individual cells are constructed and excited. The action produced by the contraction, from the churning of the stomach to the flapping of wings, will be a function of the structures to which the muscles are attached. In this chapter, we describe the structure and function of skeletal muscles, the skeletal systems found in invertebrates and vertebrates, and the methods by which skeletal muscles bring about movement.

38.1 Vertebrate Skeletal Muscle: Structure and Function

Most skeletal muscles in vertebrates are attached at both ends, across a joint, to bones of the skeleton. Some, such as those that move the lips, are attached to other muscles or connective tissues under the skin. Skeletal muscles are attached to bones by cords of connective tissue called *tendons* (see Chapter 31 and **Figure 38.2a**). Tendons vary in length from a few millimetres to over a metre long (such as those in the forelimbs of a giraffe). Depending on its points of attachment, contraction of a single skeletal muscle may extend or bend body parts or may rotate one body part with respect to another. Most vertebrates (humans included) have more than 600 skeletal muscles, ranging in size from the small muscles that move the eyelids to the large muscles that move the legs. Skeletal muscles are controlled by the somatic nervous system (see Chapter 36).

38.1a The Striated Appearance of Skeletal Muscle Fibres Results from a Highly Organized Internal Structure

A skeletal muscle consists of bundles of elongated, cylindrical cells called muscle fibres, which are 10 to 100 μm

Figure 38.2
Skeletal muscle structure. Skeletal muscles are only attached at their ends to bones by tendons. Muscles are composed of bundles of cells called muscle fibres; within each muscle fibre are longitudinal bundles of contractile proteins called myofibrils.

in diameter and run the entire length of the muscle **(Figure 38.2b)**. These fibres are formed by the fusion of cells, called myoblasts, generated during embryonic development in response to the appropriate signalling mechanisms. Reflecting this multicellular developmental origin, a single muscle fibre contains multiple nuclei. Some very small muscles, such as some of the muscles of the face, contain only a few hundred muscle fibres; others, such as the larger leg muscles, contain hundreds of thousands. In both cases, the muscle fibres are held in parallel bundles by sheaths of connective tissue that surround them in the muscle **(Figure 38.2c)** and merge with the tendons that connect muscles to bones or other structures. Muscle fibres are richly supplied with nutrients and oxygen by an extensive network of blood vessels that penetrates the muscle tissue.

Muscle fibres are packed with **myofibrils**, cylindrical bundles of contractile proteins about 1 μm in diameter that run lengthwise inside the cells **(Figure 38.2d)**. Each myofibril **(Figure 38.3a, p. 942)** consists of a regular arrangement of **thick filaments** (13–18 nm in diameter) and **thin filaments** (5–8 nm in diameter) **(Figure 38.3 b and c, p. 942)**. The thick and thin filaments alternate with one another in a stacked set.

The arrangement of thick and thin filaments forms a pattern of alternating dark bands and light bands, giving skeletal muscle a striated appearance under the

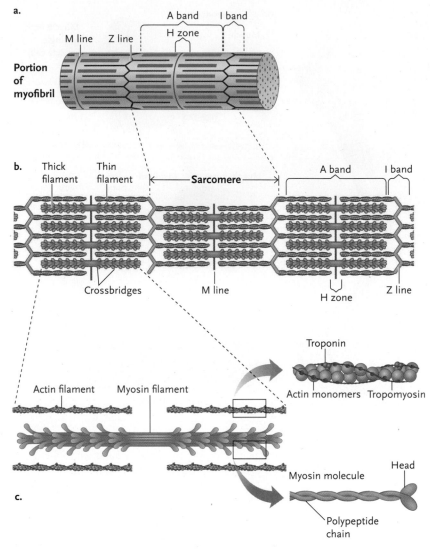

a.

Portion of myofibril

M line Z line

A band I band
H zone

b.

Thick filament Thin filament ← **Sarcomere** → A band I band

Crossbridges M line H zone Z line

c.

Actin filament Myosin filament

Troponin

Actin monomers Tropomyosin

Head

Myosin molecule

Polypeptide chain

Figure 38.3

The unit of contraction within a myofibril, the sarcomere, consists of overlapping myosin thick filaments and actin thin filaments. The myosin molecules in the thick filaments each consist of two subunits organized into a head and a double-helical tail. The actin subunits in the thin filaments form twisted, double helices, with tropomyosin molecules arranged head to tail in the groove of the helix and troponin bound to the tropomyosin at intervals along the thin filaments.

The thick filaments are parallel bundles of myosin molecules; each myosin molecule consists of two protein subunits that together form a *head* connected to a long double helix forming a *tail* (Figure 38.3). The head is bent toward the adjacent thin filament to form a *crossbridge*. In vertebrates, each thick filament contains some 200 to 300 myosin molecules and forms as many crossbridges. The thin filaments consist mostly of two linear chains of actin molecules twisted into a double helix, which creates a groove running the length of the molecule. Bound to the actin are *tropomyosin* and *troponin* proteins. Tropomyosin molecules are elongated fibrous proteins that are organized end to end next to the groove of the actin double helix. Troponin is a three-subunit globular protein that binds to tropomyosin at intervals along the thin filaments. While these proteins are not involved directly in muscle shortening, they play key roles in regulating muscle shortening (as described below).

At each junction of an A band and an I band, the plasma membrane folds in to form a **T (transverse) tubule (Figure 38.4),** which extends deep within the muscle fibre and contains extracellular fluid vital for conducting electrical signals. The tubules come into close proximity with the intracellular endoplasmic reticulum, which in muscle cells takes a specialized form that wraps around the myofibrils and is referred to as the sarcoplasmic reticulum. The association between the T tubules and the sarcoplasmic reticulum is critical for coordinating the contraction of all of the individual myofibrils in a muscle fibre.

An axon of an efferent neuron leads to each muscle fibre. The axon terminal makes a single, broad synapse with a muscle fibre called a **neuromuscular junction** (see Figure 38.4). The neuromuscular junction, T tubules, and sarcoplasmic reticulum are key components in the pathway for stimulating skeletal muscle contraction by neural signals—which starts with action potentials travelling down the efferent neuron—as described next.

38.1b During Muscle Contraction, Thin Filaments on Sarcomeres Slide over Thick Filaments

The precise control of body motions depends on an equally precise control of muscle contraction by a signalling pathway that carries information from nerves to muscle fibres. An action potential arriving at the neuromuscular junction leads to an increase in the concentration of Ca^{2+} in the cytosol of the muscle fibre. The increase in Ca^{2+} triggers a process in which the thin filaments on each side of a sarcomere slide over the thick filaments toward the centre of the A band, which brings the Z lines closer together, shortening the sarcomeres and contracting the muscle (see Figure 38.5). This *sliding filament mechanism* of muscle contraction depends on dynamic interactions between

---

microscope (see Figure 38.2c, p. 941). As a result, skeletal muscle is often called **striated muscle.** The dark bands, called *A bands,* consist of stacked thick filaments along with the parts of thin filaments that overlap both ends (see Figure 38.3). The lighter-appearing middle region of an A band, which contains only thick filaments, is the *H zone.* In the centre of the H zone is a disk of proteins called the *M line,* which holds the stack of thick filaments together. The light bands, called *I bands,* consist of the parts of the thin filaments not in the A band. In the centre of each I band is a thin *Z line,* a disk to which the thin filaments are anchored. The region between two adjacent Z lines is a **sarcomere** (*sarco* = flesh; *meros* = segment). Sarcomeres are the basic units of contraction in a myofibril and are repeated along the entire length of each myofibril.

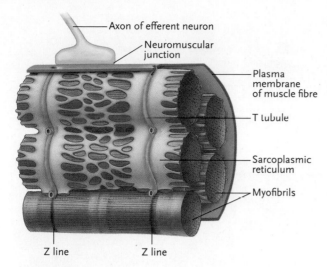

Figure 38.4

Components in the pathway for the stimulation of skeletal muscle contraction by neural signals. T (transverse) tubules are infoldings of the plasma membrane into the muscle fibre originating at each Z line in a sarcomere. The sarcoplasmic reticulum encircles the sarcomeres, and segments of it end in close proximity to the T tubules.

actin and myosin proteins in the two filament types. That is, the myosin crossbridges make and break contact with actin and pull the thin filaments over the thick filaments—the action is similar to the rowing, or ratcheting, process described for kinesin in Chapter 2 (Figure 2.20). A model for muscle contraction is shown in **Figure 38.5**. The precise details of this process are described below.

Conduction of an Action Potential into a Muscle Fibre. Like neurons, skeletal muscle fibres are *excitable,* meaning that the electrical potential of their plasma membrane can change in response to a stimulus. When an action potential arrives at the neuromuscular junction, the axon terminal releases a neurotransmitter, *acetylcholine,* which triggers an action potential in the muscle fibre (see **Figure 38.6, p. 944**, step 1). The action potential travels in all directions over the muscle fibre's surface membrane and penetrates into the interior of the fibre along the walls of the T tubules, which are extensions of the plasma membrane.

Release of Calcium into the Cytosol of the Muscle Fibre. In the absence of a stimulus, the Ca^{2+} concentration is kept low in the cytosol by active transport proteins that continuously pump Ca^{2+} out of the cytosol and into the sarcoplasmic reticulum. When an action potential reaches the end of a T tubule, it opens ion channels in the sarcoplasmic reticulum that allow Ca^{2+} to flow out into the cytosol (see Figure 38.6, p. 945, step 2).

When Ca^{2+} flows into the cytosol, the troponin molecules of the thin filament bind the calcium and

QUESTION: What is the mechanism of muscle contraction?

EXPERIMENT: By 1954, researchers had established the locations and arrangements of actin and myosin in striated muscle. In that year, two independent teams—Andrew Huxley and Ralph Niedergerke of the University of Cambridge, UK, and Hugh Huxley and Jean Hanson of Massachusetts Institute of Technology—used high-resolution light microscopy techniques to study how the actin and myosin arrangements changed during muscle contraction.

RESULTS: Their micrographs provided important evidence for the sliding of filaments. The stages of muscle contraction they outlined are shown in the figure.

a. Relaxed sarcomere

b. Contracted sarcomere

The figure illustrates a muscle fibre in a completely relaxed state (a); and (b) as completely contracted. Note how the H zone, I band, and A band relate to one another at each stage. As the muscle fibre contracted, the key observations the researchers made were that: (1) the I band and the H zone each decrease in length in proportion to the shortening of the sarcomere; and (2) the A band remains constant in length.

CONCLUSION: The light microscopy evidence supported a model—the sliding filament model—in which muscle shortening (sarcomere shortening) results from increased overlap of thick and thin filaments not from any change in length of those filaments. This model was revolutionary in the field of muscle physiology, as models for muscle contraction at the time all proposed folding or coiling of the protein molecules in the filaments.

Sources: A. F. Huxley and R. Niedergerke. 1954. Structural changes in muscle during contraction. *Nature* 173:971–973; H. Huxley and J. Hanson. 1954. Changes in the cross-striations of muscle during contraction and stretch and their structural interpretation. *Nature* 173:973–976.

Figure 38.5

Shortening of sarcomeres by the sliding filament mechanism, in which the thin filaments are pulled over the thick filaments toward the M line in the middle of the A band.

undergo a conformational change that causes the tropomyosin fibres to slip into the grooves of the actin double helix. The slippage uncovers the actin's binding sites for the myosin crossbridges (see Figure 38.6, p. 945, step 3), and the myosin heads bind to the actin (step 4).

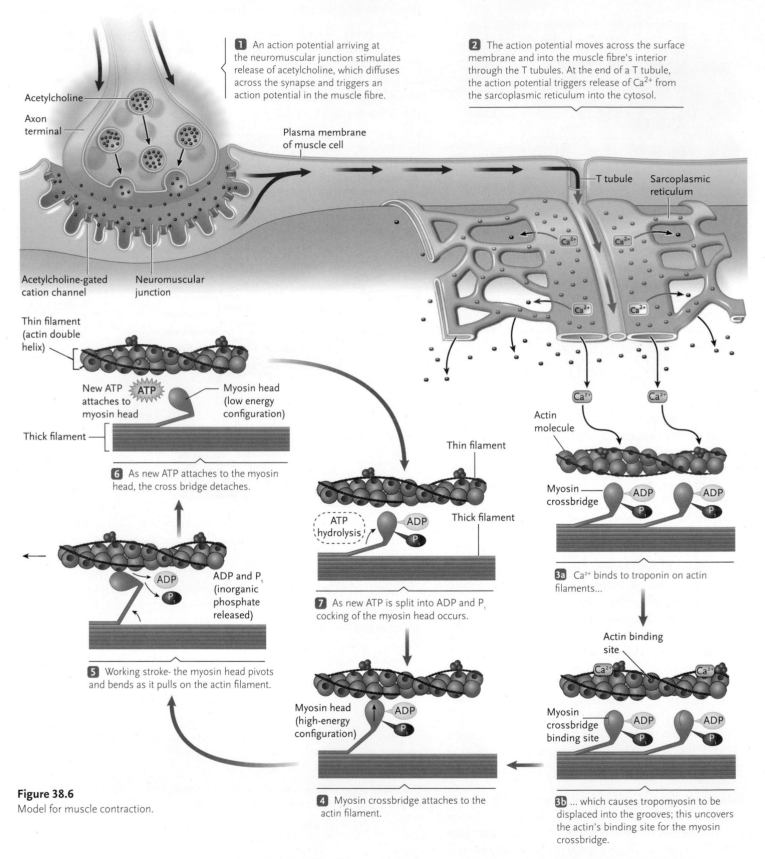

1 An action potential arriving at the neuromuscular junction stimulates release of acetylcholine, which diffuses across the synapse and triggers an action potential in the muscle fibre.

2 The action potential moves across the surface membrane and into the muscle fibre's interior through the T tubules. At the end of a T tubule, the action potential triggers release of Ca^{2+} from the sarcoplasmic reticulum into the cytosol.

Acetylcholine

Axon terminal

Plasma membrane of muscle cell

T tubule

Sarcoplasmic reticulum

Acetylcholine-gated cation channel

Neuromuscular junction

Thin filament (actin double helix)

New ATP attaches to myosin head

ATP

Myosin head (low energy configuration)

Thick filament

6 As new ATP attaches to the myosin head, the cross bridge detaches.

Thin filament

ATP hydrolysis

ADP

P_i

Thick filament

Actin molecule

Ca^{2+} Ca^{2+}

Myosin crossbridge

ADP   ADP

P_i P_i

3a Ca^{2+} binds to troponin on actin filaments...

ADP and P_i (inorganic phosphate released)

ADP

P_i

5 Working stroke- the myosin head pivots and bends as it pulls on the actin filament.

7 As new ATP is split into ADP and P_i cocking of the myosin head occurs.

Actin binding site

Ca^{2+} Ca^{2+}

Myosin crossbridge binding site

ADP   ADP

P_i P_i

Myosin head (high-energy configuration)

ADP

P_i

4 Myosin crossbridge attaches to the actin filament.

3b ... which causes tropomyosin to be displaced into the grooves; this uncovers the actin's binding site for the myosin crossbridge.

Figure 38.6
Model for muscle contraction.

The Crossbridge Cycle. The crossbridge cycle that causes sarcomere shortening is driven by chemical and structural changes occurring solely within the myosin head. It is essential to remember that every time a bond is made or broken, there are conformational

or structural changes in the shapes of the proteins involved and in their energy states.

During the period of muscle relaxation, ATP bound to the myosin head is hydrolyzed, and the ADP, phosphate, and energy released are all stored in the myosin head. The binding of myosin to actin creates a crossbridge between the two molecules and results in a change in the conformation of the myosin head that triggers the release of the ADP and phosphate. It also releases the stored energy, which snaps the head of the myosin back toward the tail, producing the power stroke (motor) that pulls the thin filament over the thick filament (step 5). If no ATP is available, the myosin remains tightly bound to actin in this position. If ATP is available, it binds to an ATP-binding site on the myosin head. When the ATP binds, the myosin changes conformation and loses its affinity for actin and the crossbridge is released (step 6). Myosin is an ATPase, and when the crossbridge is released, the ATPase is activated and ATP is hydrolyzed. This causes the myosin crossbridge to bend away from the tail (step 7) and bind to a newly exposed myosin crossbridge binding site farther along the actin molecule, and the cycle repeats (starting at step 4). Crossbridge cycles based on actin and myosin power movements in all living organisms, from cytoplasmic streaming in plant cells and amoebas to muscle contractions in animals. (Go to www .biologyedl2e.nelson.com to access animations illustrating crossbridge cycling.)

CONCEPT FIX For a long time, it was believed that ATP remains bound to the myosin head in relaxed muscle. It is now believed that while the binding of ATP to the myosin head causes the bond between myosin and actin to break, the ATP is quickly hydrolyzed to ADP and phosphate. This causes a change in the shape of the myosin, returning the head to its initial position (the position found in a relaxed muscle). The ADP, phosphate, and energy, however, are all stored in the myosin head. At the start of the next contraction, the binding of the myosin head to an actin molecule causes a conformational change in the myosin head, releasing the ADP, phosphate, and energy. The energy is then used to create the working stroke of the crossbridge cycle. ⬡

Although we have focused on the events taking place between a single myosin head and an actin filament in this discussion, within a sarcomere, each thick filament is surrounded by six thin filaments, and each thin filament is surrounded by three thick filaments **(Figure 38.7, p. 946)**. While the force produced by a single myosin crossbridge is comparatively small, it is multiplied by the hundreds of crossbridges formed between a single thick filament and the thin filaments that surround it, and by the billions of thin filaments sliding in a contracting sarcomere. The force, multiplied further by the many sarcomeres and myofibrils in a muscle fibre, is transmitted to the plasma membrane of a muscle fibre by the attachment of myofibrils to elements of the cytoskeleton. From the plasma membrane, it is transmitted to bones and other body parts by the connective tissue sheaths surrounding the muscle fibres and by the tendons.

From Contraction to Relaxation. As long as action potentials continue to arrive at the neuromuscular junction, Ca^{2+} is released and remains in high concentration in the cytosol. As long as ATP is available, the crossbridge cycle continues to run, shortening the sarcomeres and contracting the muscle fibres. When action potentials stop, excitation of the T tubules ceases, and the Ca^{2+} release channels in the sarcoplasmic reticulum close. The active transport pumps quickly remove the remaining Ca^{2+} from the cytosol. In response, troponin releases its Ca^{2+} and the tropomyosin fibres are pulled back to cover the myosin-binding sites in the thin filaments. The crossbridge cycle stops, and contraction of the muscle fibre ceases.

When an animal dies, ATP levels decline. As a result, Ca^{2+} is no longer actively sequestered in the sarcoplasmic reticulum but enters the cytosol. This allows the myosin to bind actin, but with no ATP available, these bonds remain firmly attached and muscles become locked in *rigor mortis*.

38.1c The Response of a Muscle Fibre to Action Potentials Ranges from Twitches to Tetanus

A single action potential arriving at a neuromuscular junction usually causes a single, weak contraction of a muscle fibre called a **muscle twitch (Figure 38.8a, p. 946)**. After a muscle twitch begins, the tension of the muscle fibre increases in magnitude for about 30 to 40 ms and then peaks as the action potential runs its course through the T tubules and the Ca^{2+} channels begin to close. Tension then decreases as the Ca^{2+} ions are pumped back into the sarcoplasmic reticulum, falling to zero about 50 ms after the peak.

If a muscle fibre is restimulated after it has relaxed completely, a new twitch identical to the first is generated (see Figure 38.8a, p. 946). However, if a muscle fibre is restimulated before it has relaxed completely, the second twitch is added to the first, producing what is called *twitch summation,* or *temporal summation,* which is basically a summed, stronger contraction **(Figure 38.8b, p. 946)**. And if action potentials arrive so rapidly (about 25 ms apart) that the fibre cannot relax between stimuli, the Ca^{2+} channels remain open continuously and twitch summation produces a peak level of continuous contraction called **tetanus (Figure 38.8c, p. 946)**. Contractile activity will then decrease if either the stimuli cease or the muscle fatigues.

Don Fawcett/Visuals Unlimited, Inc.

Figure 38.7

Three-dimensional arrangement of thick and thin filaments within a sarcomere.

We can adjust a handshake from a gentle squeeze to a strong grasp or exactly balance a feather or dumbbell in the hand. How are entire muscles controlled in this way? The answer lies in activation of the muscle fibres in blocks called **motor units.**

The muscle fibres in each motor unit are controlled by branches of the axon of a single efferent neuron **(Figure 38.9).** As a result, all of those fibres contract each time the neuron fires an action potential. When a motor unit contracts, its force is distributed throughout the entire muscle because the fibres are dispersed throughout the muscle rather than being concentrated in one segment, as shown in the figure.

For a delicate movement, only a few efferent neurons carry action potentials to a muscle, and only a few motor units contract. For more powerful movements, more efferent neurons carry action potentials, and more motor units contract. This is called *spatial summation,* the summing together of the activities of many motor units.

Muscles that can be precisely and delicately controlled, such as those moving the fingers in monkeys and humans, have many motor units in a small area, with only a few muscle fibres—about 10 or so—in each unit. Muscles that produce grosser body movements, such as those moving the legs, have fewer motor units in the same volume of muscle but thousands of muscle fibres in each unit. In the calf muscle that raises the

Tetanus is an essential part of muscle fibre function. Even body movements that require relatively little effort, such as standing still but in balance, involve tetanic contractions of some muscle fibres.

38.1d Skeletal Muscle Control Is Divided among Motor Units

The control of muscle contraction extends beyond the simple ability to turn the crossbridge cycle on and off.

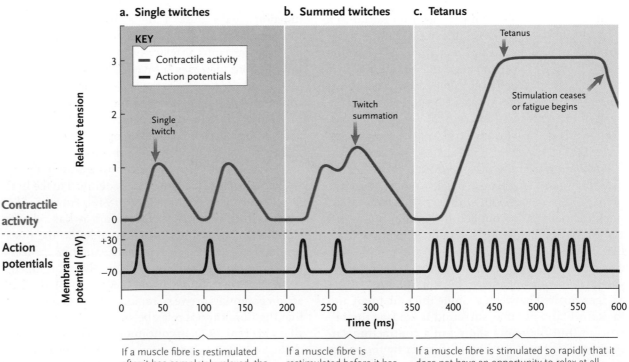

Figure 38.8

The relationship of the tension produced in a muscle fibre to the frequency of action potentials.

If a muscle fibre is restimulated after it has completely relaxed, the second twitch is the same magnitude as the first twitch.

If a muscle fibre is restimulated before it has completely relaxed, the second twitch is added on to the first twitch, resulting in summation.

If a muscle fibre is stimulated so rapidly that it does not have an opportunity to relax at all between stimuli, a peak level of continuous contraction known as *tetanus* occurs.

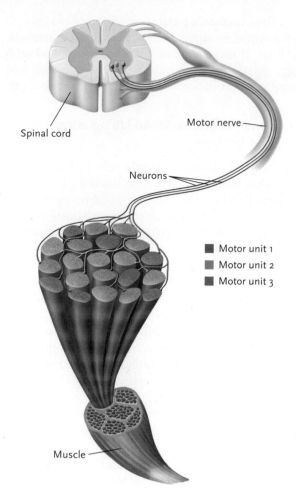

Spinal cord

Motor nerve

Neurons

■ Motor unit 1
■ Motor unit 2
■ Motor unit 3

Muscle

Figure 38.9

Motor units in vertebrate skeletal muscles. Each motor unit consists of groups of muscle fibres activated by branches of a single efferent (motor) neuron.

	Table 38.1	**Characteristics of Slow and Fast Muscle Fibres in Skeletal Muscle**	

	Fibre Type		
Property	Slow	Fast Aerobic	Fast Anaerobic
Contraction speed	Slow	Fast	Fast
Contraction intensity	Low	Intermediate	High
Fatigue resistance	High	Intermediate	Low
Myosin–ATPase activity	Low	High	High
Oxidative phosphorylation capacity	High	High	Low
Enzymes for anaerobic glycolysis	Low	Intermediate	High
Mitochondria	Many	Many	Few
Myoglobin content	High	High	Low
Fibre colour	Red	Red	White
Glycogen content	Low	Intermediate	High

heel, for example, most motor units contain nearly 2000 muscle fibres. Other skeletal muscles fall between these extremes, with an average of about 200 muscle fibres per motor unit.

The maximum force any muscle can produce comes when there is maximal temporal and spatial summation; all motor units are tetanically stimulated.

38.1e Muscle Fibres Differ in Their Rate of Contraction and Susceptibility to Fatigue

Muscle fibres differ in their rate of contraction and resistance to fatigue and thus can be classified as slow, fast aerobic, and fast anaerobic muscle fibres. Their properties are summarized in **Table 38.1**. The proportions of the three types of muscle fibres tailor the contractile characteristics of each muscle to suit its function within the body.

Slow muscle fibres contract relatively slowly, and the intensity of contraction is low because their myosin crossbridges hydrolyze ATP relatively slowly. They can remain contracted for relatively long periods

without fatiguing. Slow muscle fibres typically contain many mitochondria and make most of their ATP by oxidative phosphorylation (aerobic respiration). They have a low capacity to make ATP by anaerobic glycolysis. They also contain high concentrations of the oxygen-storing protein **myoglobin**, which greatly enhances their oxygen supplies. Myoglobin is closely related to hemoglobin, the oxygen-carrying protein of red blood cells. Myoglobin gives slow muscle fibres, such as those in the legs of ground birds such as quail, chickens, and ostriches, a deep red colour. In sharks and bony fishes, strips of slow muscles concentrated in a band on either side of the body are used for slow, continuous swimming and maintaining body position.

Fast muscle fibres contract relatively quickly and powerfully because their myosin crossbridges hydrolyze ATP faster than those of slow muscle fibres. *Fast aerobic fibres* have abundant mitochondria, a rich blood supply, and a high concentration of myoglobin, which makes them red in colour. They have a high capacity for making ATP by oxidative phosphorylation, and an intermediate capacity for making ATP by anaerobic glycolysis. They fatigue more quickly than slow fibres, but not as quickly as fast anaerobic fibres. Fast aerobic muscle fibres are abundant in the flight muscles of migrating birds such as ducks and geese.

Fast anaerobic fibres typically contain high concentrations of glycogen, relatively few mitochondria, and a more limited blood supply than fast aerobic fibres. They generate ATP mostly by anaerobic respiration (glycolysis) and have a low capacity to produce ATP by oxidative respiration. Fast anaerobic fibres produce especially rapid and powerful contractions but are more susceptible to fatigue. Because their myoglobin supply is limited and they contain few mitochondria,

CHAPTER 38 MUSCLES, SKELETONS, AND BODY MOVEMENTS

they are pale in colour. Some ground birds have flight muscles consisting almost entirely of fast anaerobic muscle fibres. These muscles can produce a short burst of intensive contractions, allowing the bird to escape a predator, but they cannot produce sustained flight. Most muscles of lampreys, sharks, fishes, amphibians, and reptiles also contain fast anaerobic muscle fibres, allowing the animals to move quickly to capture prey and avoid danger.

The muscles of most animals are mixed and contain different proportions of slow and fast muscle fibres, depending on their functions. Muscles specialized for prolonged, slow contractions, such as the postural muscles of the back, have a high proportion of slow fibres and are a deep red colour. The muscles of the forearm that move the fingers have a higher proportion of fast fibres and are a paler red than the back muscles. These muscles can contract rapidly and powerfully, but they fatigue much more rapidly than the back muscles. It is worth noting that all muscle fibres in a single motor unit are of the same fibre type.

CONCEPT FIX It is commonly believed that lactic acid is only produced by muscles under anaerobic conditions and is the source of muscle fatigue. There are several myths associated with this.

To begin with, muscles do not produce lactic acid but rather they produce lactate. As a result, lactate production does not cause the acidosis associated with strenuous exercise. The hydrogen ions that cause the acidosis are produced from the breakdown of ATP to ADP + phosphate. Under aerobic conditions, when there is no acidosis, the protons produced by the breakdown of ATP are consumed by the mitochondria during ATP production. Under anaerobic conditions, however, the mitochondria are incapable of consuming all of the hydrogen ions produced from ATP breakdown, so hydrogen ions accumulate and acidosis ensues.

Secondly, some muscle cells produce lactate even under resting conditions when there is ample oxygen available. The lactate can remain in the cell for energy or leave the cell and travel to the heart and to active and inactive muscles to be used as a fuel (many cells prefer lactate as a fuel source over glucose). It will also travel to the liver, where it is converted back into glucose.

Finally, it has recently been shown that the accumulation of hydrogen ions (acidosis) may actually counteract the effects of muscle fatigue. Strenuous muscle contraction also precipitates a variety of other disturbances to cell homeostasis, including perturbations to energy charge and ion balances (particularly K^+) that lead to loss of tetanic force. Whether K^+ imbalance always, sometimes, or hardly ever leads to fatigue during exercise is uncertain. In muscles studied *in isolation*, however, hydrogen ion accumulation offered a degree of protection against fatigue produced by extracellular K^+ accumulation.

Thus, increased lactate production coincides with cellular acidosis but is not the cause of the metabolic acidosis. If muscle did not produce lactate and acidosis, muscle fatigue would occur more quickly and exercise performance would be severely impaired. ⬡

38.1f Invertebrates Move Using a Variety of Striated Muscles

Invertebrates also have muscle cells in which actin-based thin filaments and myosin-based thick filaments produce movements by the same sliding mechanism as in vertebrates. In most invertebrates (annelids, molluscs, echinoderms, nematodes, and arthropods), the actin and myosin fibrils are arranged in sarcomeres, forming striated muscle. In general, this is the dominant muscle type for these invertebrates and functions not only in locomotion but also in movements of the viscera, such as the gut and heart. In some invertebrates, such as Cnidaria and flatworms, muscle cells lacking striations may occur. In the muscles that close the shells of clams and other bivalves (see Chapter 25), smooth muscle cells are present among the striated muscle cells.

In invertebrates, an entire muscle is typically controlled by one or a few motor neurons. Nevertheless, invertebrate muscles are capable of finely graded contractions because individual neurons make large numbers of synapses with the muscle cells. In arthropods, the muscles may receive up to three types of innervation: fast, slow, and inhibitory. All muscles receive fast innervation, in which release of a neuromuscular transmitter produces a twitch. Some also receive slow innervation, in which a graded response results from increased action potentials. As action potentials arrive more frequently, more Ca^{2+} is released into the cells, and they contract more strongly. In addition, there may be inhibitory nerves that prevent the release of Ca^{2+}. The excitatory transmitter for both fast and slow nerves is glutamate, and the inhibitory transmitter is GABA (see Chapter 36).

The muscles responsible for the movement of the wings in insects are highly specialized striated muscles called fibrillar muscles. They possess a large number of gigantic mitochondria, in some cases about the size of a vertebrate red blood cell, so that the energetic demands of flight can be met. The frequency of wing beat of many flies, bees, and wasps is very high, up to 600 beats per second in mosquitoes. How is this achieved without tetanus being induced? The answer is that each contraction does not require new activation by another action potential. Flight muscles are stretch activated and occur in antagonistic pairs **(Figure 38.10).** When one muscle of the pair contracts, the other is stretched back to its relaxed length. The stretching of one activates the other and vice versa. Nerve impulses arrive only about three times per second, and this keeps the

Dave Massey/Shutterstock

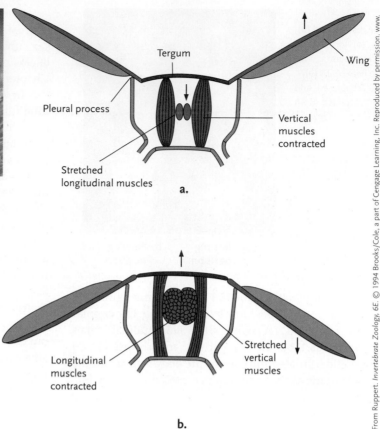

Figure 38.10

The muscles in a flying insect. When the vertical flight muscles contract, they pull on the cuticle forming the top of the segment, elevating the wings. The segment is constructed so that this action also elongates the cuticle of the thorax from front to rear (at right angles to the plane of the page), extending the longitudinal muscles. This stimulates the activated longitudinal muscles to contract, pushing up the tergum, elevating the wings, and elongating the vertical muscles. Because the cuticle is elastic, the whole system vibrates, producing very rapid wing beats.

From Ruppert. *Invertebrate Zoology*, 6E. © 1994 Brooks/Cole, a part of Cengage Learning, Inc. Reproduced by permission. www.cengage.com/permissions

muscles activated. The frequency with which they contract is determined by the elastic properties of the whole system.

STUDY BREAK

1. Compare thick and thin muscle filaments. How does their structure determine their function?
2. What is the role of the sarcoplasmic reticulum in muscle contraction?
3. What are the three types of muscle fibres, and how do they differ?
4. Greyhounds have muscles specialized for extreme speed over short distances. Sled dogs have muscles specialized for endurance over long distances. What kinds of muscle characteristics would each have?

38.2 Skeletal Systems

Animal skeletal systems provide physical support for the body and protection for the soft tissues. They also act as a framework against which muscles work to move parts of the body or the entire organism. Three main types of skeletons are found in both invertebrates and vertebrates: hydrostatic skeletons, exoskeletons, and endoskeletons.

38.2a A Hydrostatic Skeleton Consists of Muscles and Fluid

A **hydrostatic skeleton** (*hydro* = water; *statikos* = causing to stand) is a structure consisting of muscles and fluid that, by themselves, provide support for the animal or part of the animal; no rigid support, such as bone, is involved. A hydrostatic skeleton consists of a body compartment or compartments filled with water or body fluids, which are incompressible liquids. When the muscular walls of the compartment contract, they pressurize the contained fluid. If muscles in one part of the compartment are contracted while muscles in another part are relaxed, the pressurized fluid will move to the relaxed part of the compartment, distending it. In short, the contractions and relaxations of the muscles surrounding the compartments change the shape of the animal.

Hydrostatic skeletons are the primary support systems of cnidarians, flatworms, roundworms, and annelids. In all of these animals, compartments containing fluids under pressure make the body semirigid and provide a mechanical support on which muscles act. For example, sea anemones have a hydrostatic skeleton consisting of several fluid-filled body cavities. The body wall contains longitudinal and circular muscles that work against that skeleton. Between meals, longitudinal muscles are contracted (shortened), whereas the circular ones are relaxed, and the animal looks

Figure 38.11

Sea anemones in (a) the resting and (b) the feeding positions. In **(a)**, longitudinal muscles in the body wall are contracted, and circular muscles are relaxed. In **(b)**, the longitudinal muscles are relaxed, and the circular muscles are contracted. Both sets of muscles work against a hydrostatic skeleton.

a. Resting position   b. Feeding position

short and squat **(Figure 38.11a)**. It lengthens into its upright feeding position by contracting the circular muscles and relaxing the longitudinal ones **(Figure 38.11b)**. In flatworms, roundworms, and annelids, striated muscles in the body wall act on the hydrostatic skeleton to produce creeping, burrowing, or swimming movements. Among these animals, annelids have the most highly developed musculoskeletal systems, with an outer layer of circular muscles surrounding the body, and an inner layer of longitudinal muscles **(Figure 38.12)**. Contractions of the circular muscles reduce the diameter of the body and increase the length; contractions of the longitudinal muscles shorten the body and increase its diameter. Because the coelom and musculature are divided into segments, expansion and contraction can be localized to individual segments. Annelids move along a surface or burrow by means of alternating waves of contraction of the two muscle layers that pass along the body, working against the fluid-filled body compartments of the hydrostatic skeleton.

Some structures of echinoderms are supported by hydrostatic skeletons. The tube feet of sea stars and sea urchins, for example, have muscular walls enclosing the fluid of the water vascular system (see Chapter 26).

In vertebrates, the erectile tissue of the penis is a fluid-filled hydrostatic skeletal structure, although many mammals other than humans also possess a penis bone, the *os penis* or baculum (see Figure 38.14d, p. 953 and Figure 33.17, page 815).

Hydrostatic movement may not involve a fluid but may simply depend on the incompressibility of muscles themselves. Although the muscles in the structure may contract, the total body of muscles remains at a constant volume. Our tongues and lips are capable of a range of movements, but no skeletal element supports the movement. The elephant's trunk can lift a large log but can also pick up objects of a few millimetres. How is this achieved? The trunk is basically an extension of the nose and upper lip. It has no skeleton but consists of an enormous number of muscle units attached to the skin or to one another. The muscle mass remains at a constant volume, and contractions of local muscle groups result in movement.

38.2b An Exoskeleton Is a Rigid External Body Covering

An **exoskeleton** (*exo* = outside) is a rigid external body covering, such as a shell that provides support. In an exoskeleton, the force of muscle contraction is applied against that covering. An exoskeleton also protects delicate internal tissues.

Many molluscs, such as clams and oysters, have an exoskeleton consisting of a hard calcium carbonate shell secreted by glands in the mantle. Arthropods, such as insects, spiders, and crustaceans, have an external skeleton in the form of a chitinous

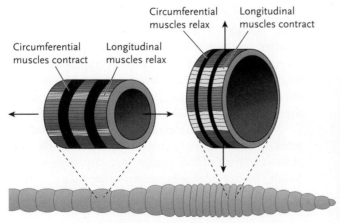

Circumferential muscles contract   Longitudinal muscles relax

Circumferential muscles relax   Longitudinal muscles contract

Figure 38.12

Movement of an earthworm, showing how muscles in the body wall act on its hydrostatic skeleton. Contraction of the circular muscles reduces body diameter and increases body length, whereas contraction of the longitudinal muscles decreases body length and increases body diameter.

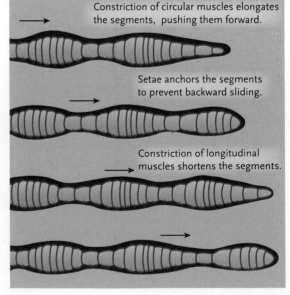

Constriction of circular muscles elongates the segments, pushing them forward.

Setae anchors the segments to prevent backward sliding.

Constriction of longitudinal muscles shortens the segments.

Chitin

Chitin is a polymer composed of many repeating units of *N*-acetyl-D-glucosamine (**Figure 1**). It is a strong, insoluble material that is the principal component of the cuticle of arthropods, where it is crosslinked to proteins. When arthropods moult, the proteins are resorbed, and the cast cuticle is made up almost entirely of chitin. Given the dominance of arthropods in the Earth's biomass, it is not surprising that, after cellulose, chitin is the most abundant polymer on Earth, with an annual production of about 10 billion tonnes. Chitin also occurs in molluscs, the eggshells of nematodes, and the cell walls of fungi and algae.

Chitin is degraded by bacteria, particularly members of the genus *Vibrio*. Because chitin does not occur in vertebrates, chitin synthesis is a target of some successful insecticides.

Chitin and its closely related compound chitosan, produced by heating chitin in a strongly alkaline solution, are widely used in a variety of fields. Chitosan was found to have healing properties and has been used for medical sutures and as a support for growing skin over severe wounds. The compounds are also said to confer protection against disease in plants, and seeds treated with chitosan have gained some acceptance. Chitin

stimulates the growth of soil bacteria that secrete material toxic to nematodes that attack plants; compounds for this purpose are under development. Because the compounds have a strong positive charge, they have the potential to bind negatively charged compounds. Chitosans have been used in water purification plants for many years. More recently, chitosans, because of their ability to bind fats, have been promoted by the natural health products industry as a means to prevent fat absorption, leading to weight loss, but these claims are not supported by good scientific evidence.

FIGURE 1

Chitin is a polymer made up of many repeating units of N-acetyl-D-glucosamine and is the principal component of the exoskeletons of arthropods.

---

cuticle (see "Molecule behind Biology," Box 38.1), secreted by the underlying epidermis, that covers the outside surfaces of the animals. Like a suit of armour, the arthropod exoskeleton has movable joints, flexed and extended by muscles. Most muscles attach directly to the cuticle by extensions of the myofibrils and extend from the inside surface of one section of the cuticle to the inside surface of another section. Since the sections are separated by flexible cuticle, contraction results in movement about the joint **(Figure 38.13, p. 952).** The exoskeleton protects against dehydration, serves as armour against predators, and provides the levers against which muscles work.

In many flying insects, elastic flexing of the exoskeleton contributes to the movements of the wings (see Figure 38.10).

In vertebrates, the shell of a turtle or tortoise is an exoskeletal structure.

38.2c An Endoskeleton Consists of Supportive Internal Body Structures Such as Bones

An **endoskeleton** (*endon* = within) consists of internal body structures, such as bones, that provide support. In an endoskeleton, the force of contraction is applied against those structures. The endoskeleton

Figure 38.13

Muscles are attached to the inside surfaces of the exoskeleton in a typical insect leg, such as those of the grasshopper shown here.

*(left circle label)* Flexor muscle contracts

*(right circle label)* Extensor muscle contracts

Stephen Dalton/Minden Pictures/Getty Images

is the primary skeletal system of vertebrates. Most vertebrates have an endoskeleton arranged in two structural groups **(Figure 38.14)**. The **axial skeleton**, which includes the skull, vertebral column, sternum, and ribcage, forms the central part of the structure (shaded in red in Figure 38.14a), defines the long axis of the vertebrate body, provides sites for muscle attachment, and supports most of the weight. The **appendicular skeleton** (shaded in green) includes the shoulder, hip, leg, and arm bones and provides the levers that are used to produce locomotion. Four mammalian skeletons are included in Figure 38.14, illustrating how skeletons are adapted for particular lifestyles. The human skeleton reflects our upright movement, using only our hindfeet, while those of the monkey, lemur, and raccoon reflect arboreal (tree-living), gliding, and terrestrial lifestyles. Like exoskeletons, endoskeletons also protect delicate internal tissues such as the brain and respiratory organs.

38.2d Bones of the Vertebrate Endoskeleton Are Organs with Several Functions

The vertebrate endoskeleton supports and maintains the overall shape of the body and protects internal organs. Bones are complex organs built up from multiple tissues, including bone tissue with cells of several kinds; blood vessels; nerves; and, in some, stores of adipose tissue. Bone tissue is distributed between dense, compact bone regions, which have essentially no spaces other than the microscopic canals of the

osteons (see Chapter 31), and spongy bone regions, which may open into larger spaces (see Figure 38.14). Compact bone tissue generally forms the outer surfaces of bones and spongy bone tissue the interior. The interior of some flat bones, such as the hip bones and the ribs, are filled with *red marrow,* a tissue that is the primary source of new red blood cells in mammals and birds. The shaft of long bones such as the femur is opened by a large central canal filled with adipose tissue called *yellow marrow,* which is a source of some white blood cells.

Throughout the life of a vertebrate, calcium and phosphate ions are constantly deposited and withdrawn from bones. Hormonal controls maintain the concentration of Ca^{2+} ions at optimal levels in the blood and extracellular fluids (see Chapter 35), ensuring that calcium is available for proper functioning of the nervous system, muscular system, and other physiological processes.

STUDY BREAK

1. Describe the similarities and differences between hydrostatic skeletons, exoskeletons, and endoskeletons. Give examples of each and describe which animal groups each can be found in.
2. Explain how the endoskeleton differs in humans compared with monkeys, lemurs, and raccoons (Figure 38.14), and, as best as you can, explain why these differences occur.
3. Astronauts in zero gravity tend to lose bone mass, particularly in the hips, the long bones of the legs, and the vertebrae. Instruments that measure bone loss cannot be taken on space missions. Can you think of experimental procedures that might be used on Earth to explore the phenomenon?

38.3 Vertebrate Movement: The Interactions between Muscles and Bones

The skeletal system acts as a framework against which muscles work to move parts of the body or the entire organism. In this section, the muscle–bone interactions that are responsible for the movement of vertebrates are described.

38.3a Joints of the Vertebrate Endoskeleton Allow Bones to Move and Rotate

The bones of the vertebrate skeleton are connected by joints, many of them movable. The most movable joints, including those of the shoulders, elbows,

a. Skull

Cranial bones —
Enclose, protect brain
and sensory organs

Facial bones —
Provide framework
for facial area,
support for teeth

Ribcage

Encloses and protects
internal organs and
assists breathing

Sternum (breastbone) —

Ribs (12 pairs) —

Vertebral column (backbone)

Vertebrae (24 bones) —
Enclose, protect spinal cord;
support skull and upper
extremities; provide
attachment sites for
muscles; separated by
cartilaginous disks that
absorb movement-related
stress and impart flexibility

Cartilage layer —

Yellow marrow —

Compact bone tissue —

Spongy bone —
(spaces containing
red marrow)

**Shoulder (pectoral) girdle and
upper extremities**
Provide extensive muscle
attachments and freedom
of movement

Clavicle (collarbone) —

Scapula (shoulder blade) —

Humerus (upper arm bone) —

Ulna (forearm bone) —

Radius (forearm bone) —

Carpals (wrist bones) —
Metacarpals (palm bones) —

Phalanges (thumb, finger bones) —

**Hip (pelvic) girdle and
lower extremities**

Pelvic girdle (six fused bones) —
Supports weight of vertebral
column, helps protect organs

Femur (thighbone) —
Plays key role in locomotion and in
maintaining upright posture

Patella (kneebone) —
Protects knee joint, aids leverage

Tibia (lower leg bone) —
Plays major load-bearing role

Fibula (lower leg bone) —
Provides muscle attachment sites
but is not loadbearing

Tarsals (ankle bones) —
Metatarsals (sole bones) —

Phalanges (toe bones) —

KEY

■	Axial skeleton
■	Appendicular skeleton

Figure 38.14

Mammalian skeletons. **(a)** Major
bones in the human. Inset shows
the structure of the femur (thigh
bone), with the location of red
and yellow marrow. Internal
spaces lighten the bone's
density. At the joints a cartilage
layer forms a smooth slippery
cushion between bones. Compare the general features of this
skeleton with those shown in **(b)**,
(c), and **(d)**. Note general and
specific resemblances among
the skeletons of the four mammals. **(b)** The new world monkey
(family Cebidae) lives in trees.
(c) The gliding lemur (family
Cynocephalidae) is also arboreal,
but a glider. **(d)** The raccoon
(family Procyonidae) is terrestrial. Note the differences in skull
shape, limb lengths, and feet.
The raccoon is a male, reflected
in the conspicuous baculum or
penis bone (see also Figure
33.17, Chapter 33).

b.

M. B. Fenton

c.

M. B. Fenton

d.

M. B. Fenton

CHAPTER 38 MUSCLES, SKELETONS, AND BODY MOVEMENTS

a. Synovial joint cross section

- Bone (femur)
- Cartilage layer
- Synovial fluid
- Cartilage layer

Connective tissue capsule

- Bone (tibia)

b. Knee joint ligaments

- Bone (femur)
- Ligaments (in blue)
- Bone (tibia)

Bone (fibula)

Figure 38.15

A synovial joint. **(a)** Cross section of a typical synovial joint. **(b)** Ligaments reinforcing the knee joint.

wrists, fingers, knees, ankles, and toes, are *synovial joints,* consisting of the ends of two bones enclosed by a fluid-filled capsule of connective tissue **(Figure 38.15a).** Within the joint, the ends of the bones are covered by a smooth layer of cartilage and lubricated by synovial fluid, which makes the bones slide easily as the joint moves. Synovial joints are held together by straps of connective tissue called *ligaments,* which extend across the joints outside the capsule **(Figure 38.15b).** The ligaments restrict the motion of the joint and help prevent it from buckling or twisting under heavy loads.

In other, less movable joints, called *cartilaginous joints,* the ends of bones are covered with layers of cartilage but have no fluid-filled capsule surrounding them. Fibrous connective tissue covers and connects the bones of these joints, which occur between the vertebrae and some rib bones.

In still other joints, called *fibrous joints,* stiff fibres of connective tissue join the bones and allow little or no movement. Fibrous joints occur between the bones of the skull and hold the teeth in their sockets.

The bones connected by movable joints work like levers. A lever is a rigid structure that can move around a pivot point known as a *fulcrum* **(Figure 38.16a).** The most common type of lever system in the body—exemplified by the elbow joint—has the fulcrum at one end, the load at the opposite end, and the force applied at a point between the ends. Levers differ with respect to where the muscle is attached along the lever and, hence, where the force is applied **(Figure 38.16b).** If the muscle is inserted (attached) near the fulcrum, the muscle favours speed, as a short contraction will move the lever a large distance in a short period of time **(Figure 38.16c,** left). If the muscle is inserted more distally to the fulcrum, it favours strength. The same amount of contraction will move the forearm a shorter distance in the same period of time (i.e., it moves more slowly), but it will lift more weight (Figure 38.16c, right). Levers also differ with respect to where the fulcrum is located along the lever. In this case, if the fulcrum is located more distally, it favours speed, while if it is located more proximally, it favours strength **(Figure 38.16d).** A good example of the difference in design for speed versus strength is seen by comparing the forelimbs of burrowing and running species. Burrowing mammals have short, very stout forelimbs with muscles arranged so that contraction provides relatively little movement but great force **(Figure 38.17a).** Running species, on the other hand, have long, slender forelimbs with muscles arranged so that contraction provides rapid motion but less force **(Figure 38.17b).**

Most of the bones of vertebrate skeletons are moved by muscles arranged in **antagonistic pairs:** *extensor muscles* extend the joint, meaning increasing the angle between the two bones, whereas *flexor muscles* do the opposite. (Antagonistic muscles are also used in invertebrates for movement of body parts—e.g., the limbs of insects and arthropods.) In humans, one such pair is formed by the biceps brachii muscle at the front of the upper arm and the triceps brachii muscle at the back of the upper arm **(Figure 38.18).** When the biceps muscle contracts, the bone of the lower arm is bent (flexed) around the elbow joint, and the triceps muscle is passively stretched (see Figure 38.18a); when the triceps muscle contracts, the lower arm is straightened (extended), and the biceps muscle is passively stretched (see Figure 38.18b).

38.3b Vertebrates Have Muscle–Bone Interactions Optimized for Specific Movements

Vertebrates differ widely in the relative size and shapes of individual bones, the patterns by which muscles connect to the bones, the sites of the joints along the bones, and the length and mechanical advantage of the levers produced by these connections. All of these

Force

Load

Fulcrum

5 cm

35 cm

Proximal insertion

Distal insertion

Proximal insertion of muscle—speed

Distal insertion of muscle—strength

Distal site of fulcrum in runner—speed

Proximal site of fulcrum in digger—strength

Figure 38.16

A body lever. **(a)** The lever formed by the bones of the forearm. The fulcrum (the hinge or joint) is at one end of the lever, the load is placed on the opposite end, and the force is exerted at a point on the lever between the fulcrum and the load. **(b)** Muscles can be attached proximal or distal to the fulcrum. **(c)** Proximal insertion favours speed, while distal insertion favours strength. **(d)** The fulcrum can also vary in position, favouring either speed or strength.

differences reflect the lifestyles of the animals as reflected in the need for strength and speed of movement. Through evolutionary pressures to produce optimal interactions for specific movements, we see many examples of both conserved traits and convergent evolution.

An example of an optimal strategy that has been conserved is seen in the undulatory movements of many vertebrate species. The segmental muscles of fish are attached to the vertebrae, ribs, and skin. They are efficient in propelling fish through the water with side-to-side movements. With the appearance of

Figure 38.17

Design for strength versus speed in forelimbs can be seen by comparing (a) an armadillo with (b) a cat. Both forelimbs are drawn to be the same overall length. Note the differences in the size and mass of the bones, the points of insertion of the muscles, and the position of the joints along the bones.

a. When the biceps muscle contracts and raises the forearm, its antagonistic partner, the triceps muscle relaxes.

b. When the triceps muscle contracts and extends the forearm, the biceps muscle relaxes.

Triceps relaxes.

Biceps contracts at the same time and pulls forearm up.

Triceps contracts and pulls the forearm down.

At the same time, biceps relaxes.

Figure 38.18

The arrangement of skeletal muscles in antagonistic pairs. **(a)** When the biceps muscle contracts and raises the forearm, its antagonistic partner, the triceps muscle, relaxes. **(b)** When the triceps muscle contracts and extends the forearm, the biceps muscle relaxes.

PEOPLE BEHIND BIOLOGY 38.2
Keir Pearson, University of Alberta

The act of walking is both unconscious and deceptively simple when viewed from a human perspective, involving two legs. But in insects, in which walking on six legs usually involves two legs on one side and one leg on the other being lifted, while the remaining legs form a triangular support, and in nonhuman mammals, in which the order of movement of the legs may differ for various speeds of locomotion, the real complexity of walking becomes more obvious.

Keir G. Pearson of the University of Alberta became interested in this challenging problem while he was a Rhodes Scholar at Oxford University, where he demonstrated the complexity of the patterns of nervous activity controlling a single muscle. He has continued that interest for more than 40 years, progressing to an analysis of walking in insects and vertebrates (usually cats). The techniques he has used are challenging, involving the recording of electrical activity in the leg muscles and the ganglia controlling those muscles. They have revealed that walking in insects is driven by a pattern of rhythmic activity, the central pattern generator (CPG) in the neurons of the ganglia associated with the limbs, influenced by information flowing from proprioceptors (see Chapter 37) in the limbs and by environmental information processed through the brain. These results have influenced the construction of walking robots and physiotherapy for humans with spinal cord damage.

Pearson recently turned his attention to the way in which visual information influences walking. A simple and revealing experiment involved cats **(Figure 1)**. A cat approaching a small barrier steps over the barrier, first with the forelegs and then with the hindlegs. To a less inquiring mind, that might seem simple enough. But a scientist such as Pearson notes that when the hindlegs step over the barrier, the barrier is no longer in the visual field. The CPG in some sense remembers the position of the barrier. Pearson then asked the question: What if there is a delay after the forefeet step over? By offering food, he was able to interrupt the cat before its hindlegs had stepped over the barrier. It turns out that the hindlegs remember the position of the barrier for at least 10 minutes, even if the barrier is removed after the front feet have stepped over it. This is far longer than the memory of the image in the eye. These clear and simple results demonstrate the way in which information processed unconsciously through the brain influences "automatic" events.

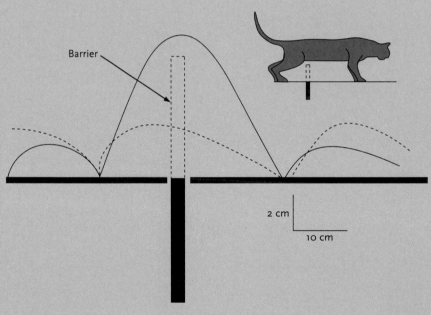

Barrier

2 cm

10 cm

FIGURE 1
Experiment demonstrating the memory of CPG in the cat. *The cat stepped over the barrier with the front feet but was then delayed by offering it food. The barrier, which it could no longer see, was removed. The solid line indicates the path taken by the hindfoot when walking resumed up to 10 minutes later. The dotted line indicates the path taken by the hindfoot when the cat does not encounter a barrier.*

limbs and the movement onto land, this form of locomotion was combined with leg movement in most amphibians and reptiles but reappears as the dominant form of locomotion in snakes **(Figure 38.19)**.

There are many examples of convergent evolution. Sea turtles, for instance, have paddlelike forelimbs that they use in swimming, very much like those of penguins and sea lions **(Figure 38.20)**.

The development of flight, represented by birds and, among the mammals, bats, is accompanied by some common modifications **(Figure 38.21)**. In both groups, but particularly in birds, the sternum is greatly enlarged to provide attachment for the powerful pectoral muscles. The bones of the forelimbs are greatly modified to produce wings. While this is another example of convergent evolution, note that the way in which each wing has formed is different. In bats, the bones of the hand are extended to provide a framework for the sheets of skin that form the wing. In birds, the bones of the hand are fused

Figure 38.19
Almost all fish, amphibians, and reptiles depend on lateral undulations of the body wall for locomotion, but this is best seen in long, limbless species such as eels **(a)** and snakes **(b)**.

Figure 38.20
(a) A sea turtle. Note that the forelegs are winglike paddles that enhance swimming. **(b)** A penguin swimming, using modified forelimbs (wings).
(c) A sea lion swimming using modified forelimbs for manoeuvring. Note the resemblance in shape of the forelimbs in all three species.

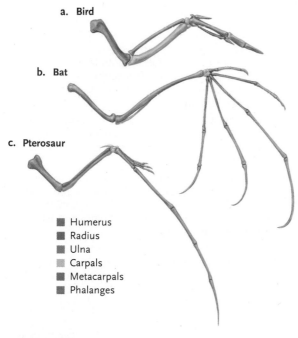

a. Bird

b. Bat

c. Pterosaur

■ Humerus
■ Radius
■ Ulna
■ Carpals
■ Metacarpals
■ Phalanges

Figure 38.21
The bones of the wing of (a) a bird, (b) a bat, and (c) a pterosaur. Note the convergent evolution presented here in the structures.

and support the feathers that make up the wing. The bones generally contain many cavities or spaces, making the body lighter.

Also note that in both examples of convergent evolution presented here, the structures (wings in bats and birds; forelimb paddles in turtles, penguins, and sea lions) are examples where the structure of the forelimb has diverged from that of other members of their classes. The bodies of animals are full of many similar examples, and these are the topic of comparative, functional anatomy.

STUDY BREAK

1. Distinguish synovial joints, cartilaginous joints, and fibrous joints.
2. Distinguish between ligaments and tendons.
3. What differences are there in the design of musculoskeletal systems for speed versus strength?
4. What are antagonistic muscle pairs? Give an example describing how they differ in the bone movements they produce.

Review

CourseMate Access an interactive eBook, chapter-specific interactive learning tools, including flashcards, quizzes, videos, and more in your Biology **CourseMate**, accessed through NelsonBrain.com

aplia **Aplia™** is an online interactive learning solution that helps you improve comprehension—and your grade—by integrating a variety of mediums and tools such as videos, tutorials, practice tests, and an interactive eBook.

38.1 Vertebrate Skeletal Muscle: Structure and Function

- Skeletal muscles move the joints of the body. They are formed from long, cylindrical cells called muscle fibres, which are packed with myofibrils, which are contractile elements consisting of myosin thick filaments and actin thin filaments. The two types of filaments are arranged in an overlapping pattern of contractile units called sarcomeres.

- Infoldings of the plasma membrane of the muscle fibre form T tubules. The sarcomeres are encircled by the sarcoplasmic reticulum, a system of vesicles with segments separated from T tubules by small gaps.

- In the sliding filament mechanism of muscle contraction, the simultaneous sliding of thin filaments on each side of sarcomeres over the thick filaments shortens the sarcomeres and the muscle fibres, producing the force that contracts the muscle.

- The sliding motion of thin and thick filaments is produced in response to an action potential arriving at the neuromuscular junction. The action potential causes the release of acetylcholine, which triggers an action potential in the muscle fibre that spreads over its plasma membrane and stimulates the sarcoplasmic reticulum to release Ca^{2+} into the cytosol. The Ca^{2+} combines with troponin, inducing a conformational change that moves tropomyosin away from the myosin-binding sites on thin filaments. Exposure of the sites allows myosin crossbridges to bind and initiate the crossbridge cycle in which the myosin heads of thick filaments attach to a thin filament, pull, and release in cyclic reactions powered by ATP hydrolysis.

- When action potentials stop, Ca^{2+} is pumped back into the sarcoplasmic reticulum, leading to Ca^{2+} release from troponin, which allows tropomyosin to cover the myosin-binding sites in the thin filaments, thereby stopping the crossbridge cycle.

- A single action potential arriving at a neuromuscular junction causes a muscle twitch. Restimulation of a muscle fibre before it has relaxed completely causes a second twitch, which is added to the first, causing a summed, stronger contraction. Rapid arrival of action potentials causes the twitches to sum to a peak level of contraction called tetanus (temporal summation). Normally, muscles contract in a tetanic mode.

- Vertebrate muscle fibres occur in three types. Slow muscle fibres contract relatively slowly but do not fatigue rapidly. Fast aerobic fibres contract relatively quickly and powerfully and fatigue more quickly than slow fibres. Fast anaerobic fibres can contract more rapidly and powerfully than fast aerobic fibres, but fatigue more rapidly. The fibres differ in their number of mitochondria and capacity to produce ATP.

- Skeletal muscles are divided into motor units, consisting of a group of muscle fibres activated by branches of a single motor neuron. The total force produced by a skeletal muscle is determined by the number of motor units that are activated (spatial summation).

- Most invertebrate muscles contain thin and thick filaments arranged in sarcomeres, and contract by the same sliding filament mechanism that operates in vertebrates. In arthropods, fast twitches and slower, graded contractions result from differences in innervation. Insect flight muscle is specialized to contract at high frequency.

38.2 Skeletal Systems

- A hydrostatic skeleton is a structure consisting of a muscle-surrounded compartment or compartments filled with fluid under pressure. Contraction and relaxation of the muscles changes the shape of the animal.

- In an exoskeleton, a rigid external covering provides support for the body. The force of muscle contraction is applied against the covering. An exoskeleton can also protect delicate internal tissues.

- In an endoskeleton, the body is supported by rigid structures within the body, such as bones. The force of muscle contraction is applied against these structures. Endoskeletons also protect delicate internal tissues. In vertebrates, the endoskeleton is the primary skeletal system. The vertebrate axial skeleton consists of the skull, vertebral column, sternum, and ribcage, whereas the appendicular skeleton includes the shoulder bones, the forelimbs, the hip bones, and the hindlimbs.

- Bone tissue is distributed between compact bone, with no spaces except the microscopic canals of the osteons, and spongy bone tissue, which has spaces filled by red or yellow marrow.

- Calcium and phosphate ions are constantly exchanged between the blood and bone tissues. The turnover keeps the Ca^{2+} concentration balanced at optimal levels in body fluids.

38.3 Vertebrate Movement: The Interactions between Muscles and Bones

- The bones of a skeleton are connected by joints. A synovial joint, the most movable type, consists of a fluid-filled capsule surrounding the ends of the bones forming the joint. A cartilaginous joint, which is less movable, has smooth layers of cartilage between the bones, with no surrounding capsule. The bones of a fibrous joint are joined by connective tissue fibres that allow little or no movement.

- The bones moved by skeletal muscles act as levers, with a joint at one end forming the fulcrum of the lever, the load at the opposite end, and the force applied by attachment of a muscle at a point between the ends.

- At a joint, an agonist muscle, perhaps assisted by other muscles, causes movement. Most skeletal muscles are arranged in antagonistic pairs, in which the members of a pair pull a bone in opposite directions. When one member of the pair contracts, the other member relaxes and is stretched.

- Vertebrates have a variety of patterns in which muscles connect to bones, giving different properties to the levers produced. These properties are specialized for the activities of the animal.

Questions

Self-Test Questions

Any number of answers from a to e may be correct.

1. Vertebrate skeletal muscle
   a. may bend but not extend body parts
   b. is attached to bone by means of ligaments
   c. is usually attached at each end to the same bone
   d. may rotate one body part with respect to another
   e. is found in the walls of blood vessels and intestines

2. Which term refers to the connective tissue that joins bones together on either side of a joint?
   a. periosteum
   b. stratum corneum
   c. tendons
   d. ligaments
   e. meninges

3. Which of the following occurs in a resting muscle fibre?
   a. Sarcomeres are regions between two H zones.
   b. Z lines are adjacent to H zones, which attach thick filaments.
   c. I bands are composed of the same thick filaments seen in the A bands.
   d. Disks of M line proteins called the A band separate the thick filaments.
   e. Dark A bands contain overlapping thick and thin filaments with a central thin H zone composed only of thick filaments.

4. Which statement describes the sliding filament contractile mechanism?
   a. It lengthens the sarcomere to separate the I regions.
   b. It is inhibited by the influx of Ca^{2+} into the muscle fibre cytosol.
   c. It uses myosin crossbridges to stimulate delivery of Ca^{2+} to the muscle fibre.
   d. It depends on the isolation of actin and myosin until a contraction is completed.
   e. It causes thick and thin filaments to slide toward the centre of the A band, bringing the Z lines closer together.

5. During the crossbridge cycle, ATP
   a. causes the detachment of myosin from actin
   b. causes the bending of myosin crossbridges
   c. causes rigor mortis
   d. binds to troponin

6. Where is Ca^{2+} that is directly involved in muscle contraction stored?
   a. in the T tubules
   b. in the cytosol
   c. in the sarcoplasmic reticulum
   d. in the extracellular fluid

7. Fast anaerobic muscle fibres
   a. contain a high concentration of glycogen
   b. have few mitochondria
   c. have extensive vascularization
   d. are red in colour

8. In skeletal muscles, how is the force of contraction adjusted?
   a. by controlling the recruitment of motor units
   b. by controlling the speed of contraction
   c. by contracting antagonistic muscle pairs
   d. by tetanic contractions

9. Which of the following is NOT an example of a hydrostatic skeletal structure?
   a. the penis of mammals
   b. the body wall of annelids
   c. the tube feet of sea urchins
   d. the body wall of cnidarians
   e. the body wall of a grasshopper

10. Endoskeletons
    a. cannot be found in molluscs and echinoderms
    b. are composed of appendicular structures that form the skull
    c. are composed of the arms and legs, which are part of the axial skeleton
    d. differ from exoskeletons in that endoskeletons do not support the external body
    e. protect internal organs and provide structures against which the force of muscle contraction can work

Questions for Discussion

1. Not all snakes move by undulatory movement. Some use concertina movement for locomotion. What is this and how does it differ from undulatory movement? Why is it necessary?

2. If you were a leading researcher in a pharmaceutical company interested in controlling bone loss, what cells and processes would you target?

3. What are muscle cramps and what is their most likely cause?

4. Based on your knowledge of muscle contraction, explain what causes rigor mortis (stiffening of the body following death).

5. Phosphocreatine is a high-energy store for muscles. Why is energy stored in this fashion rather than as ATP? In your answer consider speed of availability and also refer back to Chapter 4 and the discussion of end-product feedback.

6. For a gram of tissue, muscle can be fast or strong but not both. Why? In your answer, consider what the need for mitochondria and sarcoplasmic reticulum do to the numbers of myofibrils contained in that gram of tissue and what the consequences of this would be.

M.B. Fenton

A little brown bat (*Myotis lucifugus*) flies through an abandoned mine. Mouth open, the animal produces echolocation calls that, in this setting, allow it to orient through the underground space.

39 Animal Behaviour

WHY IT MATTERS

When it comes to food, many animals quickly learn to take advantage of new opportunities and show great versatility in behaviour from hunting to planning. Here are five examples.

During the Vietnam War (1959–1975), tigers (*Panthera tigris*) learned to associate the sound of gunfire with an opportunity to eat. The tigers' behaviour meant that some wounded soldiers waiting for treatment received a different kind of attention than what they expected. During World War II, wolves (*Canis lupus*) showed the same behaviour in some areas of Poland. A food reward is a strong reinforcer of behaviour.

In the 1970s, Kim McCleneghan and Jack Ames were studying sea otters (*Enhydra lutris*) in California waters. These otters dive and collect food (sea urchins, *Pisaster brevispinus,* and clams, *Saxidomus nuttalli*) from the bottom and bring their catch to the surface to eat it. The observers were surprised to see some otters resurfacing with empty beverage cans. These otters would lie on their backs in the ocean swells, take a can, bite it open, and, in some cases, remove and eat something before discarding the can. Some cans appeared to be empty and were discarded after opening. The biologists collected their own beverage cans and discovered that many harboured young octopods

(*Octopus* species). Populations of these cephalopods are limited by the number of shelters available. Young octopods were exploiting new opportunities for shelter, and the sea otters, in turn, were taking advantage of the molluscs' behaviour.

Meanwhile, in savannah woodlands in Senegal (West Africa), Jill Pruetz and Paco Bertolani observed chimpanzees (*Pan troglodytes*) hunting bushbabies (*Galago senegalensis*). The fact that the chimps were not vegetarians was no surprise because they had been reported using grass stalks to fish for termites and working in gangs to hunt young baboons (*Papio ursinus*). The discovery that savannah chimps in Senegal used "spears" to impale bushbabies hidden in tree hollows extended the repertoire of chimps. Pruetz and Bertolani watched chimps modifying branches they had broken off by biting to sharpen them before using them against bushbabies. The chimps that Pruetz and Bertolani studied appeared to plan their hunts in advance.

Other experiments have revealed how Western Scrub Jays (*Aphelocoma californica*) cache food in preparation for the next day's breakfast. Proving that animals plan ahead means that the experiments have to demonstrate that the animal executes a novel action or combination of actions and anticipates an emotional state different from the one at the time of planning. These two conditions rule out behaviours associated with migration and hibernation or those associated with meeting an immediate need for food.

In foraging behaviour, animals exhibit an array of opportunism and adaptation that we often believe is the exclusive domain of *Homo sapiens*. The purpose of this chapter is to introduce you to the topic of animal behaviour.

The behaviour of animals is an excellent overall indication of their diversity. Behaviour reflects a rich blend of genetic and environmental control, as well as a combination of instinct and learning. Hormones exert a strong influence over an animal's behaviour, and the structure of the nervous system and, by extension, the sensory system, often stimulates and mediates behaviour. Some animals are territorial, defending all or part of their home range, usually in association with reproduction. Migration involves movements to and from different areas, usually between seasons, and implies the use of navigational cues. Animals show rich repertoires of behaviour around mating and reproduction. A few species live in large groups, and others exhibit complex social behaviour.

39.1 Genes, Environment, and Behaviour

Learning, as demonstrated by the foraging animals introduced above, illustrates how some behaviour patterns are acquired rather than inherited. But animal behaviourists had long debated whether animals are born with the ability to perform most behaviours completely or whether experience is necessary to shape their actions. Today, the emerging picture is that no behaviour is determined entirely by genetics or entirely by environmental factors. Rather, behaviours develop through complex gene–environment interactions.

Why do adult male White-crowned Sparrows sing a song that no other species sings **(Figure 39.1)**? They could have an innate (inborn) ability to produce their particular song, an ability so reliable that young males sing the "right" song the first time they try. According

White-crowned Sparrow   Song Sparrow   Swamp Sparrow

Figure 39.1

Songbirds and their songs. Sound spectrograms (visual representations of sound graphed as frequency versus time) illustrate differences in the songs of the White-crowned Sparrow (*Zonotrichia leucophrys*), Song Sparrow (*Melospiza melodia*), and Swamp Sparrow (*Melospiza georgiana*).

to this hypothesis, their distinctive song would be an **instinctive behaviour,** one genetically or developmentally "programmed" that appears in complete and functional form the first time it is used. An alternative hypothesis is that they acquire the song as a result of certain experiences, such as hearing the songs of adult male White-crowned Sparrows that live nearby. If so, this species' distinctive song might be an example of a **learned behaviour,** one that depends on having a particular kind of experience during development.

How can we determine which of these two hypotheses is correct? If the White-crowned Sparrow's song is instinctive, isolated male nestlings that have never heard other members of their species should be able to sing their species' song when they mature. If the learning hypothesis is correct, young birds deprived of certain essential experiences should not sing "properly" when they become adults.

Peter Marler tested these two hypotheses. He took newly hatched White-crowned Sparrows from nests in the wild and reared them individually in soundproof cages in his laboratory. Some of the chicks heard recordings of a male White-crowned Sparrow's song when they were 10 to 50 days of age, whereas others did not. Juvenile males in both groups first started to vocalize at about 150 days of age. For many days, the birds produced whistles and twitters that only vaguely resembled the songs of adults. Gradually, the young males that had listened to tapes of their species' song began to sing better and better approximations of that song. At about 200 days of age, these males were right on target, producing a song that was nearly indistinguishable from the one they had heard months before. Captive-raised males that had not heard recordings of White-crowned Sparrow songs never sang anything close to the songs typical of wild males.

These results show that learning is essential for a young male White-crowned Sparrow to acquire the full song of its species. Although birds isolated as nestlings sang instinctively, they needed the acoustical experience of listening to their species' song early in life if they were to reproduce it months later. These data allow us to reject the hypothesis that White-crowned Sparrows hatch from their eggs with the ability to produce the "right" song. Their species-specific song, and perhaps the songs of many other songbirds, include both instinctive and learned components.

Early researchers generally classified behaviours as either instinctive or learned, but we now know that most behaviours include both instinctive and learned components. Nevertheless, some behaviours have a stronger instinctive component than others.

STUDY BREAK

1. How can the study of bird song lend itself to understanding the influence of genes on behaviour?
2. How is behaviour learned?

39.2 Instinct

Instinctive behaviours can presumably be performed without the benefit of previous experience. They can be grouped into functional categories, such as feeding, defence, mating, and parental care. We assume that they have a strong genetic basis and that natural selection has preserved them as adaptive behaviours.

Many instinctive behaviours are highly stereotyped. When an animal is triggered by a specific cue, it performs the same response over and over in almost exactly the same way. These **fixed action patterns** are triggered by **sign stimuli.** Very young Herring Gull chicks use a begging response **(Figure 39.2a),** a fixed action pattern, to secure food from their parents. Begging chicks peck at the red spot on the parent's bill, and the tactile stimulus serves as a sign stimulus inducing the adult to regurgitate food from its crop. Baby gulls eat the chunks of fish, clams, or other food that have been regurgitated for them. We know that the spot on the parent's bill releases the begging response of the young gull because the same response is triggered by an artificial bill that looks only vaguely like an adult bill, provided that it has

a.

Marie Read Natural History Photography

b.

Relative pecking response

100

92

35

Model presented

Figure 39.2
(a) A Herring Gull (*Larus argentatus*) chick begs its parent for food. **(b)** Nestling Herring Gulls also begged when presented with various models of an adult gull. In the experiment, nestlings pecked at a model with a red spot on the lower jaw almost as often as they did to a real gull. A model lacking the jaw spot elicited much fewer begging pecks from the nestling.

a dark contrasting spot near the tip **(Figure 39.2b).** Simple cues can activate fixed action patterns.

Human infants often respond innately to the facial expressions of adults **(Figure 39.3).** Researchers can trigger smiling in even very young babies simply by moving a mask toward the infant, as long as the mask has two simple, diagrammatic eyes. Clearly, the infant, like a nestling Herring Gull, is not reacting to every feature of a face but rather to simple cues that function as sign stimuli releasing a fixed behavioural response.

Natural selection has moulded the behaviour of some parasitic species to exploit the relationship between sign stimuli and fixed action patterns for their own benefit. In effect, they have broken another species' code. Birds that are brood parasites lay their eggs in the nests of other species. When the brood parasite's egg hatches, the alien nestling mimics sign stimuli ordinarily exhibited by their hosts' own chicks. The parasitic chick begs for food by opening its mouth, bobbing its head, and calling more vigorously than the host's chicks. These exaggerated behaviours elicit feeding by the foster parents, and the young brood parasite often receives more food than the hosts' own young **(Figure 39.4).**

Although instinctive behaviours are often performed completely the first time an animal responds to a stimulus, they can be modified by an individual's experiences. The fixed action patterns of a young Herring Gull change over time. Although the youngster initially begs by pecking at almost anything remotely similar to an adult gull's bill, it eventually learns to recognize the distinctive visual and vocal features associated with its parents. The chick uses this information to become increasingly selective about which stimuli elicit its begging behaviour. During their early performances, instinctive behaviours can be modified in response to particular experiences.

Behavioural differences between individuals may reflect genetic differences because performance of instinctive behaviours does not depend on previous experience. Stevan Arnold studied innate responses of

Figure 39.4
This European Cuckoo (*Cuculus canorus*) is a brood parasite that stimulates food delivery by its foster parent, a Hedge Sparrow (*Prunella modularis*). The cuckoo elicits food delivery by displaying exaggerated versions of the sign stimuli used by the host offspring. The exaggerated stimuli are *releasers*, initiating the appropriate behaviour from a parent with food.

captive newborn garter snakes to olfactory stimuli provided by potential food items they had never before encountered. Arnold measured the snakes' responses to cotton swabs that had been dipped in a smelly extract of banana slug, a shell-less mollusc. Young snakes born to a mother captured in coastal California, where adult garter snakes regularly eat banana slugs, almost always began tongue-flicking at slug-scented cotton swabs **(Figure 39.5).** Newborn snakes whose parents came from central California, where banana slugs do not occur, rarely tongue-flicked at the swabs. Although

a. Banana slug

b. Adult coastal garter snake eating a banana slug

c. Newborn garter snake "smelling" slug extract

Figure 39.5
Genetic control of food preference. **(a)** Banana slugs (*Ariolimax columbianus*) are a preferred food of **(b)** an adult garter snake (*Thamnophis elegans*) from coastal California. **(c)** A newborn snake from a coastal population of garter snakes flicks its tongue at a cotton swab drenched with tissue fluids from a banana slug.

Figure 39.3
Instinctive responses in humans. The smiling face of an adult is a sign stimulus that triggers smiling in very young infants.

the coastal and inland snakes belong to the same species, their instinctive responses to banana slug chemicals differed markedly.

Arnold then tested whether newborn snakes would eat bite-sized chunks of slug. After a brief flick of the tongue, 85% of newborn snakes from a coastal population routinely struck at the piece of slug and swallowed it even though they had no previous experience with this food. Even when no other food was available, only 17% of newborn snakes from the inland population consistently tongue-flicked at or ate pieces of slug. Arnold hypothesized that coastal and inland garter snakes have different alleles at one or more gene loci controlling their odour-detection mechanisms and leading to differences in their behaviour. Arnold crossbred coastal and inland snakes. If genetic differences contribute to the food preferences of snakes from the two populations, hybrid offspring receiving genetic information from each parent should behave in an intermediate fashion. The results of the experiment confirmed the prediction. When presented with bite-sized chunks of slug, 29% of the newborn snakes of mixed parentage ate them every time.

Many other experiments have confirmed that genetic differences between individuals can translate into behavioural differences between them (see "Knockouts: Genes and Behaviour," Box 39.1). Bear in mind, however, that single genes do not control complex behaviour patterns directly. Rather, the alleles determine the kinds of enzymes that cells can produce, influencing biochemical pathways involved in the

Knockouts: Genes and Behaviour 39.1

Almost all eukaryotic organisms share a series of developmental interactions called the *wingless/Wnt* pathway. The name comes from the original discovery of the pathway in the fruit fly *Drosophila melanogaster,* in which mutant genes of the pathway cause alterations in the wings and other segmental structures. Recently, three genes closely related to *dishevelled,* one of the genes of the **Drosophila** *wingless/Wnt* pathway, were isolated from and identified in mice. No functions have yet been identified for the proteins encoded in the three mouse *dishevelled* genes, but they are highly active in both embryos and adults. Their function must be important, but what could it be?

Nardos Lijam and his coworkers sought an answer to this question by developing a line of mice that totally lacked one of the *dishevelled* genes, *Dvl1* in genetic shorthand. First, they constructed an artificial copy of the *Dvl1* gene with the central section scrambled so that no functional proteins could be made from its encoded directions. Next, they introduced the artificial gene into embryonic mouse cells. Cells that successfully incorporated the gene were injected into very early mouse embryos. Some mice grown from these embryos were heterozygotes, with one normal copy of the *Dvl1* gene and one nonfunctional copy. Interbreeding of the heterozygotes produced some individuals that carried two copies of the altered *Dvl1* gene and no normal copies. Individuals lacking the normal gene are called *knockout* mice for the missing gene.

Surprisingly, knockout mice grew to maturity with no apparent morphological defects in any tissue examined, including the brain. Their motor skills, sensitivity to pain, cognition, and memory all appeared to be normal. However, their social behaviour was different. In cages with normal mice, the knockouts failed to take part in the common activities of mouse social groups: social grooming, tail pulling, mounting, and sniffing. Although normal mice build nests and sleep in huddled groups, knockouts tended to sleep alone, without constructing full nests from cage materials. Mice heterozygous for the *Dvl1* gene (those with one normal and one altered copy of the gene) behaved normally in all of these social activities.

The knockout mice also jumped around wildly in response to an abrupt, startling sound, whereas the response of normal mice was less extreme. A neural circuit of the brain inhibits the startle response of normal mice, so the reaction of knockout mice suggested that this inhibitory circuit was probably altered. Humans with schizophrenia, obsessive-compulsive disorders, Huntington disease, and some other brain dysfunctions also show an intensified startle reflex similar to that of the *Dvl1* knockout mice.

The researchers' analysis revealed that the *Dvl1* gene modifies developmental pathways affecting complex social behaviour in mice and probably in other mammals. It is one of the first genes identified that affects mammalian behaviour. The similarity in startle reflex intensity between the knockout mice and humans with neurological or psychiatric disorders suggests that mutations in the *Dvl* genes and the *wingless* developmental pathway may underlie some human mental illnesses. If so, further studies of the *Dvl* genes may give us clues to the molecular basis of these diseases and a possible means to their cure.

development of an animal's nervous system. The resulting neurological differences can translate into a behavioural difference between individuals that have certain alleles and those that do not.

STUDY BREAK

1. What are the differences between instinctive and learned behaviours?
2. What are fixed action patterns and sign stimuli?
3. How did experiments with garter snakes demonstrate the influence of genetics on behaviour?

39.3 Learning

Unlike instinctive behaviours, learned behaviours are not performed accurately or completely the first time an animal responds to a specific stimulus. They change in response to environmental stimuli that an individual experiences as it develops. Behavioural scientists generally define learning as a process in which experiences change an animal's behavioural responses. Different types of learning occur under different environmental circumstances.

Imprinting occurs when animals learn the identity of a caretaker or the key features of a suitable mate during a **critical period**, a stage of development early in life. Newly hatched geese imprint on their mother's appearance and identity, staying near her for months. When they reach sexual maturity, young geese try to mate with other geese exhibiting the visual and behavioural stimuli on which they had imprinted as youngsters. When Konrad Lorenz, a founder of ethology (the study of animal behaviour), tended a group of newly hatched Greylag Geese, they imprinted on him rather than on an adult of their own species **(Figure 39.6)**. Male geese not only followed Lorenz, but at sexual maturity, they also courted humans.

Other forms of learning can occur throughout an animal's lifetime. Ivan Pavlov, a Russian physiologist, demonstrated classical conditioning in experiments with dogs. Like many other animals, dogs developed a mental association between two phenomena that are usually unrelated. Dogs typically salivate when they eat. Food is an *unconditioned stimulus* because the dogs instinctively respond to it and do not need to learn to salivate when presented with food. Pavlov rang a bell just before offering food to dogs. After about 30 trials in which dogs received food immediately after the bell rang, the dogs associated the bell with feeding time and drooled profusely whenever it rang, even when no food was forthcoming. The bell had become a *conditioned stimulus*, one that elicited a particular learned response. In classical conditioning, an animal learns to respond to a conditioned stimulus (e.g., the bell) when it precedes an unconditioned stimulus (e.g., food) that normally triggers the response (e.g., salivation). If your pet cat becomes exceptionally friendly whenever it hears the sound of a can opener, its behaviour is the result of classical conditioning.

Operant conditioning, trial-and-error learning, is another form of associative learning. Here animals learn to link a voluntary activity, an **operant**, with its favourable consequences, a **reinforcement**. A laboratory rat will explore a new cage randomly. If the cage is equipped with a bar that releases food when it is pressed, the rat eventually leans on the bar by accident (the operant) and immediately receives a morsel of food (the reinforcement). After a few such experiences, a hungry rat learns to press the bar in its cage more frequently, provided that the bar-pressing behaviour is followed by access to food. Laboratory rats have also learned to press bars to turn off disturbing stimuli, such as bright lights.

Insight learning occurs when an animal can abruptly learn to solve problems without apparent trial-and-error attempts at the solution. Captive chimpanzees solved a novel problem: how to get bananas hung far out of reach. The chimps studied the situation and then stacked several boxes, stood on them, and used a stick to knock the fruit to the floor.

Habituation occurs when animals lose their responsiveness to frequent stimuli not quickly followed by the usual reinforcement. Habituation can save the animal the time and energy of responding to stimuli that are no longer important. Sea hares (*Aplysia* species) are shell-less molluscs that typically retract their gills when touched on the side. Gill retraction helps protect sea hares from approaching predators. But a sea hare stops retracting its gills when it is touched repeatedly over a short period of time with no harmful consequences.

Learning occurs across different time frames, from habituation (above) to lifelong changes in behaviour. Cross-fostering experiments with two songbirds, Blue Tits (*Cyanistes caeruleus*) and Great Tits (*Parus major*), revealed that early learning is essential to the realization of ecological niches. In this work, Tore Slagsvold and Karen Wiebe transferred fertilized eggs from the nests of Great Tits to those of Blue Tits and vice versa. Compared with their genetic parents, the

Figure 39.6

Imprinting. Having imprinted on him shortly after hatching, young Greylag Geese (*Anser anser*) frequently joined Karl Lorenz for a swim.

© Nina Leen/Time and Life Pictures/Getty Images

fostered young shifted their feeding niches, and the shift was lifelong. The changes in foraging behaviour were greater for fostered Great Tits, the species with more specialized foraging behaviour.

STUDY BREAK

1. How do the examples of feeding behaviour (see also "Why It Matters") inform us about learning?
2. Distinguish between instinctive and learned behaviours. Give examples of each.

39.4 Neurophysiology and Behaviour

Research in neuroscience has shown that all behavioural responses, whether mostly instinctive or mostly learned, depend on an elaborate physiological foundation provided by the biochemistry and structure of the nerve cells. Nerve cells that regulate an innate response and make it possible for an animal to learn something are products of a complex developmental process. Here genetic information and environmental contributions are intertwined. Although the anatomical and physiological basis for some behaviours is present at birth, an individual's experiences alter the cells of its nervous system in ways that produce particular patterns of behaviour.

Marler's experiments helped explain the physiological underpinnings of singing behaviour in male White-crowned Sparrows. If acoustical experience shapes singing, a sparrow chick's brain must be able to acquire and store information present in the songs of other males. Then, months later, when the young male starts to sing, its nervous system must have special features enabling the bird to match its vocal output to the stored memory of the song that it heard earlier. Eventually, when it achieves a good match, the sparrow's brain must "lock" on the now complete song and continue to produce it when the bird sings.

Additional experiments demonstrated that when young birds did not hear a taped song during their critical period (10–50 days of age), they never produced the full song of their species, even if they heard it later in life. In addition, young birds that heard recordings of *other* bird species' songs during the critical period never generated replicas of those songs as they matured. These and other findings suggested that certain nerve cells in the young male's brain are influenced only by appropriate stimuli, in this case, acoustical signals from individuals of its own species, and only during the critical period. Neuroscientists have identified nuclei, clusters of nerve cells that make song learning and song production possible.

Every behavioural trait appears to have its own neural basis. Another songbird, a male Zebra Finch **(Figure 39.7)**, can discriminate between the songs of

Figure 39.7

Zebra Finches (*Taeniopygia guttata*) are native to Indonesia. They have played an important role in studies of the physiological basis of song learning. The male has the striped throat.

strangers and those of established neighbours. These finches live in territories (see Section 39.8), plots of land defended by individual males or breeding pairs. Defence of the territory ensures that the residents have exclusive access to food and other necessary resources.

Zebra Finches' ability to discriminate between the songs of neighbours and those of strangers involves a nucleus in the forebrain. Cells in this nucleus fire frequently the first time the Zebra Finch hears the song of a new conspecific. As the song is played again and again, the cells of this nucleus cease to respond, indicating that the bird has become habituated to a now familiar song. The same bird still reacts to the songs of strangers. Neurophysiological networks that make this selective learning possible enable male Zebra Finches to behave differently toward familiar neighbours, which they largely ignore, than they do to unfamiliar singers, which they attack and drive away.

Molecular and cellular techniques have been used to identify the role of genes in learning. When a bird is exposed to relevant acoustical stimuli, such as songs of potential rivals, certain genes are quickly "turned on" within neurons in the song-controlling nuclei of the bird's brain. When a Zebra Finch hears the elements of its species' song, a gene called *zenk* rapidly becomes active in the brain, producing an enzyme that changes the structure and function of neurons. The ZENK enzyme programs nerve cells of the bird's brain to anticipate key acoustical events of potential biological importance. When they occur, these events trigger additional changes in the bird's brain, affecting its actions. In this way, a territory owner learns to ignore (= habituate to) a singing neighbour with which it shares an established territorial boundary. The same bird retains the ability to detect and respond to new intruding conspecifics because they are a real threat to its continued control of its territory.

STUDY BREAK

1. What role does the ZENK enzyme play?
2. How do nerve connections influence behaviour?

39.5 Hormones and Behaviour

Hormones are chemical signals that can trigger the performance of specific behaviours. Hormones often work by regulating the development of neurons and neural networks or by stimulating cells within endocrine organs to release chemical signals.

How did the neurons in an adult Zebra Finch acquire the remarkable capacity to change in response to specific stimuli? In Zebra Finches, only males produce courtship songs. Very early in its life, certain cells in the brain of a male songbird produce estrogen, which affects target neurons in the higher vocal centre, an area of the developing brain. Estrogen leads to a complex series of biochemical changes resulting in the production of more nerve cells in the parts of the brain that regulate singing. Brains of developing females do not produce estrogen. In the absence of estrogen, the number of neurons in the higher vocal centre of females *declines* over time **(Figure 39.8)**. If young female Zebra Finches are given estrogen, they produce more nerve cells in the higher vocal centre and are capable of singing. Specific stimuli, such as the songs of familiar or unfamiliar males, can alter the genetic activity of the nerve cells that control the behaviour of adult birds.

Just as estrogen influences the development of singing ability in Zebra Finches, other hormones mediate the development of the nervous system in other species. A change in the concentration of a certain hormone can be the physiological trigger that induces important changes in an animal's behaviour as it matures.

As they age, worker honeybees perform different tasks. Nurse bees, typically less than 15-day-old adults, tend to care for larvae and maintain the hive. Forager bees, typically more than 15-day-old adults, often make foraging excursions from the hive to collect food, nectar, and pollen **(Figure 39.9)**. These behavioural changes are induced by rising concentrations of juvenile hormone (see Chapter 35) released by a gland near the bee's brain. Despite its name, circulating levels of juvenile hormone actually increase as a honeybee ages.

Juvenile hormone may exert its effect on bee behaviour by stimulating genes in certain brain cells to produce proteins that affect nervous system function. Octopamine, for example, stimulates neural transmissions and reinforces memories. Octopamine is concentrated in the antennal lobes, parts of the bee's brain that contribute to the analysis of chemical scents in the external environment. Octopamine is found at

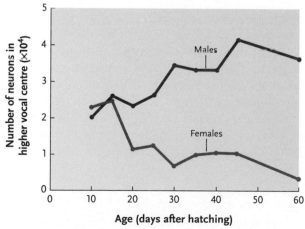

Figure 39.8
Hormonally induced changes in brain structure. The brains of young male Zebra Finches secrete estrogen, which stimulates production of additional neurons in the higher vocal centre. Lacking estrogen, young female Zebra Finches have fewer neurons in this region of the brain.

Figure 39.9
Age and task specialization in honeybee (*Apis mellifera*) workers. Newly emerged adult bees (nurses) typically clean cells and feed the brood, whereas older workers (foragers) leave the hive to forage for food.

higher concentrations in older, foraging bees that have higher levels of juvenile hormone. When extra juvenile hormone is experimentally administered to bees, their production of octopamine increases. Increased octopamine levels in the antennal lobes may help a foraging bee home in on the odours of flowers from which it can collect nectar and pollen.

The honeybee example illustrates how genes and hormones interact in the development of behaviour. Genes code for the production of hormones that become part of the intracellular environment of assorted target cells. Hormones then directly or indirectly change genetic activity and enzymatic biochemistry in their targets. When the target cells are neurons, changes in biochemistry translate into changes in the animal's behaviour.

The African cichlid fish illustrates how hormones regulate reproductive behaviour. Some adult males maintain nesting territories on the bottom of Lake Tanganyika in East Africa (Figure 39.10). Territory holders are relatively brightly coloured and exhibit elaborate behavioural displays to attract egg-laden females. These males defend their real estate aggressively against neighbouring territory holders and against incursions by males without territories of their own. Nonterritorial males (called *drifters*) are much less colourful and aggressive and do not control a patch of suitable nesting habitat. They make no effort to court females.

Differences in levels of GnRH (gonadotropin-releasing hormone; see Chapter 35) cause behavioural differences between the two types of males. In the hypothalamus of the brain of territorial males, large, biochemically active cells produce GnRH. The same cells in the brains of drifters are small and inactive.

GnRH stimulates the testes to produce testosterone and sperm. When circulating sex hormones are carried to the brain of the fish, they modulate the activity of nerve cells that regulate sexual and aggressive behaviour. In the absence of GnRH, male fish do not court females or attack other males.

What causes the differences in the neuronal and hormonal physiology of the two types of male fish? Russell Fernald and his students manipulated the territorial status of males. Some territorial males were changed into nonterritorial males and vice versa, whereas the territorial status of other males was left unchanged as a control. Four weeks after the changes, Fernald and his students compared experimental and control fishes. They considered colouration and behaviour, as well as the size of the GnRH-producing cells in the brains. Territorial males that had been changed to nonterritorial males quickly lost their bright colours and stopped being combative. Moreover, their GnRH-producing cells were smaller than those of the territory-holding controls. Conversely, males that gained a territory in the experiment quickly developed bright colours and displayed aggressive behaviours toward other males. GnRH-producing cells in their brains were larger than those of fish that had maintained their status as non-territory-holding controls.

This example shows that what is happening inside a fish affects its environmental situation—its success or failure at gaining and holding a territory. Fish can detect and store information about their aggressive interactions. Neurons that process this information transmit their input to the hypothalamus, where it affects the size of cells producing GnRH, in turn dictating the hormonal state of the male. A decrease in GnRH production can turn a feisty territorial male into a subdued drifter. Drifters bide their time and build energy reserves for a future attempt at defeating a weaker male and taking over his territory. If successful in regaining territorial status, the male's GnRH levels will increase again. The once peaceful male reverts to vigorous sexual and aggressive behaviour.

Note the general similarity of these processes to those described for the White-crowned Sparrow's song learning. The fish's brain has cells that can change its biochemistry, structure, and function in response to well-defined social stimuli. These physiological changes make it possible for the fish to modify its behaviour depending on its social circumstances.

African cichlid fish (*Haplochromis burtoni*)

Nonterritorial male

Territorial male

Figure 39.10
Photograph compares a nonterritorial male *Haplochromis burtoni* (top) with a territorial one. Photomicrographs at right compare gonadotropin-releasing (GnRH) cells in the corresponding nonterritorial and territorial males.

Russell Fernald, Stanford University

STUDY BREAK

1. How has research on White-crowned Sparrows and Zebra Finches advanced our knowledge of the impact of neurobiology on behaviour?
2. How does juvenile hormone affect the behaviour of adult bees?
3. How does GnRH affect the behaviour of fish?

39.6 Neural Anatomy and Behaviour

Some specific behaviours are produced by anatomical structures in an animal's nervous system. The nervous systems of many animal species allow them to respond rapidly to key stimuli. Sensory systems are often structured to acquire a disproportionately large amount of information about the stimuli that are most important to survival and reproductive success.

Important information acquired by the senses can be relayed directly to motor neurons, for example, providing prey animals with behaviour that can save them from a predator's attack. Insects such as crickets that fly mainly at night avoid predatory birds that typically fly by day; however, flying at night exposes them to attacks by insectivorous bats.

Insectivorous bats hunting at night use echolocation to detect and track flying prey (see Chapter 37). The echolocation calls of bats hunting flying insects are usually intense, with a sound pressure level of about 130 dB at 10 cm, making the calls stronger than the sound of a smoke detector alarm. The bats' calls can cover frequencies from ~10 kHz to >200 kHz, well beyond the 20 kHz upper limit of human hearing. By comparing its calls with the echoes from its calls, the bat uses echolocation to detect, assess, and track its flying prey. However, a bat's echolocation calls give crickets (and other prey; see Chapter 37) warning of their approach (see "Echolocation: Communication," Box 39.2, p. 970).

With ears on their front legs, black field crickets hear bat echolocation calls (see Figure 37.9, p. 967), and the anatomical structure of the cricket's nervous system produces a behavioural response that takes the cricket out of harm's way. Sensory neurons connected to the ears fire in response to the bat's calls, and the information is immediately translated into evasive action. When a bat attacks from the cricket's right side, the right ear receives a stronger stimulation than the left ear. The cricket's nervous system relays incoming messages from the *right* ear to the motor neurons controlling the *left* hindleg. Sufficient stimulation on the right side induces firing by motor neurons for the left hindleg, causing the leg to jerk up. This, in turn, blocks the movement of the left hindwing and reduces the flight power generated on the left side of the cricket's body. These changes cause the flying cricket to swerve sharply to the left and lose altitude, effectively diving down and away from the approaching bat (**Figure 39.11**).

The structure and neural connections of sensory systems allow some animals to distinguish potentially life-threatening situations from more mundane stimuli. Fiddler crabs live and feed on mud flats, where they dig burrows that provide safe refuge from predators such as crab-hunting shorebirds. By distinguishing between predatory gulls and other fiddler crabs, a crab

Figure 39.11

A neural mechanism for escape behaviour in the black field cricket (*Teleogryllus oceanicus*).

May, M. 1991. Aerial defense tactics of flying insects. American Scientist, Volume 79, Issue 4, p. 316–328.

A flying cricket usually holds its hind legs close to the body so that they don't get in the way of its wings.

Sound waves from a predatory bat

When a cricket hears the ultrasonic call of a bat coming from its left side, it automatically lifts its right hind leg.

The raised leg interrupts the right wing's movement, causing the insect to swerve down to the right and away from the approaching predator.

can use its burrow to best advantage and does not dash for cover whenever anything moves in its field of vision.

Fiddler crabs have long-stalked eyes held above their carapaces and perpendicular to the ground (**Figure 39.12**). John Layne wondered whether a crab might use a divided field of view to distinguish dangerous predators from fellow crabs. An approaching large gull would stimulate receptors on the upper part of the eye, whereas another crab's movements would be slightly below the midpoint of the eyes. A split field of view would allow the crab to distinguish between the two kinds of stimuli. To achieve this, receptors above and below the retinal equator must relay signals to different groups of neurons, effectively wiring the crab's nervous system to distinguish for a split field of view. If this were the case, stimulation of receptors above the midline of the eye would activate neurons controlling an escape response, triggering a dash for the burrow. A moving stimulus at or below eye level would stimulate a different response. Responses to other crabs are likely to be gender dependent.

Figure 39.12

A fiddler crab, *Uca pugilator*.

Echolocation: Communication 39.2

In echolocation, the echolocator stores the outgoing signal in its brain for comparison with returning echoes. The difference between what the animal says and what it hears is the data used in echolocation. However, when an echolocating bat (see the photo at the beginning of the chapter) or dolphin produces echolocation signals, the signals can also be heard by other animals.

When the bat or dolphin is foraging, potential prey (certain insects for the bat; certain fish for the dolphin) hear the signals and flee from the sound source (= negative phonotaxis) in an effort to evade the approaching predator. When the bat is close (strong echolocation signals), moths with ears dive to the ground or go into erratic flight to evade the bats. Moths with ears sensitive to bat echolocation calls avoid bat attacks 40% of the time. Insects lacking bat detectors are caught at much higher rates, sometimes >90% of the time. Acoustic warfare between bats and insects entertains biologists, involving measures and countermeasures by both predator and prey.

The same echolocation calls that alert potential prey are also available to any other animals within earshot, provided that their ears are sensitive to the frequencies in the signals. Little brown bats may use feeding buzzes (signals associated with attacks on prey) to locate concentrations of prey.

Spotted bats (*Euderma maculatum*) either approach a calling conspecific, apparently to chase it away, or turn and leave the area. Resident killer whales (*Orcinus orca*) in the Pacific Ocean off the west coast of Canada typically use echolocation to detect, track, and locate the salmon they eat. Transient killer whales in the same area feed mainly on marine mammals. These killer whales rarely echolocate. Local marine mammals, such as seals, quickly leave the water when they hear killer whales approaching.

The study of echolocation is a rich source of information about signals, signal design, hearing systems, and behaviour.

To explore this, Layne placed crabs one at a time in a glass jar on an elevated platform. He presented a black square to each crab from two different heights. Sometimes the stimulus circled the jar above the crab's eyes; sometimes it circled below them. Stimuli activating the upper part of the retina induced escape behaviour, whereas those below the retinal equator were usually ignored **(Figure 39.13)**. Specific nervous system connections between a fiddler crab's eyes and brain provide appropriate responses to different specific stimuli.

The match between the structure of an animal's nervous system and the real-world challenges it faces extends beyond the ability to avoid predators. Star-nosed moles live in wet tunnels in North American marshlands and spend almost all of their lives in complete darkness. Like nocturnal insect-eating bats, star-nosed moles must find food without the benefit of visual cues. Like the bats, its receptor–perceptual system enables it to feed effectively. A star-nosed mole eats mainly earthworms it locates with its nose, but not by smell. As the mole proceeds down its tunnel, 22 fingerlike tentacles on its nose sweep the area directly ahead of it. Each tentacle is covered with thousands of Eimer's organs (touch receptors; **Figure 39.14**). Sensory nerve terminals in Eimer's organs generate complex and detailed patterns of signals about the objects they contact. These messages are relayed by neurons to the cortex of the mole's brain, much of which is devoted to the analysis of information received from the nose's touch receptors.

The structural basis of the mole's sensory analysis is reflected by the amount of brain tissue responding to signals from its nose. The mole's brain contains many more cells decoding input from Eimer's glands than the combined input received from all other parts of the animal's body (see Figure 39.14b). Moreover, the brain does not treat inputs from all 22 of the mole's "nose fingers" equally. Instead, the brain devotes more cells to input from tentacles closest to the mouth. Fewer cells analyze messages from those farther away. Processing tactile information by star-nosed moles is related to the importance of finding food in dark, underground tunnels. Moreover, the extra attention given to signals from certain tentacles helps the star-nosed mole locate prey that are close to its mouth, in turn allowing it to feed more efficiently (see Figure 37.25, Chapter 37).

Animals' nervous systems do not offer neutral and complete pictures of the environment. Instead, the pictures are distorted, but the unbalanced perceptions

Figure 39.13
Stimuli that activated the upper part of the retinas of *Uca pugilator* elicited escape behaviour much more often than those activating the lower retinas.

a. Sensory organs on the tentacle of a star-nosed mole

A star-nosed mole

Mouth with tentacles

Rod Plarck/Photo Researchers, Inc.

Ken Catania/Visuals Unlimited, Inc.

Eimer's organs on a tentacle

An Eimer's organ in longitudinal section

Sensory nerve terminals

Epidermis

Dermis

Ken Catania/Visuals Unlimited, Inc.

A star-nosed mole collects sensory information via tactile receptors (Eimer's organs) on its tentacles.

b. Comparison of anatomical proportions and cortical proportions

Anatomical proportions

Cortical proportions

Most of the mole's cereberal cortex is devoted to the tentacles and front, digging feet.

Figure 39.14
The collection and analysis of sensory information by the star-nosed mole (*Condylura cristata*). **(a)** The mole's nose has 22 fleshy tentacles covered with cylindrical tactile receptors called Eimer's organs. Each Eimer's organ contains sensory nerve terminals. **(b)** The mole's cerebral cortex devotes far more space and neurons to analysis of input from the tentacles than from elsewhere on the body. These drawings compare the relative amounts of sensory information coming from different parts of a mole's body.

of the world are advantageous because certain types of information are far more important than others for the animals' survival and reproductive success.

Study Break

1. How do crickets hear the echolocation calls of bats?
2. How does what they see influence the behaviour of fiddler crabs?

39.7 Communication

In animal communication, one individual produces a signal that is received by another, changing the behaviour of one or both individuals in a way that benefits the signaller and/or the signal receiver. The signaller is the individual transmitting information (the signal), and the signal receiver **(Figure 39.15, p. 972)** is the one receiving the signal. Some animals have broken the signal codes of others and exploited them to their advantage. Some people who study animal communication

Figure 39.15
Song birds, such as this Grey Vireo (*Vireo vincinior*), use songs to advertise their presence to unmated females and to other males.

M.B. Fenton

a.

Courtesy of Jürgen Otto

b.

Courtesy of Jürgen Otto

Figure 39.16
Visual display. A male peacock spider (*Maratus volans*; Salticidae) approaches a female **(a)** and then displays to her **(b)**.

consider that only signals intended to communicate should be called communication (think back to problems with the definition of species or genes).

Animals use a variety of sensory modalities when producing signals, including acoustical, chemical, electrical, vibrational, and visual. Some signals combine modalities. Sometimes the animal itself is a signal; in other situations, the animal's excretory or eliminated products are signals.

Bird songs are acoustical signals heard by the signal receivers. The song of a male Whippoorwill (*Caprimulgus vociferus*) advertises his presence to females and may help him secure a mate. The same song is heard by other males, who recognize it as a territorial display. After the eggs have been laid, the same song is heard by the young developing in the eggs. Other birds, such as male Club-winged Manakins (e.g., *Machaeropterus deliciosus*), use sounds produced by feather stridulations as their acoustic courting signal. Sounds are used as signals by many other animals, such as insects and rattlesnakes. Pacific herring (*Clupea pallasii*) communicate with conspecifics through the noise generated with little bursts of gas (known colloquially as "farts") passed from the anus.

A striped skunk's (*Mephitis mephitis*) black and white stripes constitute a visual signal. Other examples are humans' facial expressions and body language. These visual signals are available to anyone viewing them. Visual signals can be enhanced by morphological features, such as the erectile crest of a Royal Kingbird (*Tyrannus melancholicus*), or semaphore flags used by people. In darkness, some animals use bioluminescent signals (e.g., Figure 40.29, Chapter 40). In many animals, visual signals are *ritualized*—they have become exaggerated and stereotyped, enhancing their function as signals **(Figure 39.16).**

Many species produce chemical signals, well known to anyone who has walked a dog. Pheromones

are distinctive volatile chemicals released in minute amounts to influence the behaviour of conspecifics. The body of a worker ant contains a battery of glands, each releasing a different pheromone **(Figure 39.17).** One set of pheromones recruits fellow workers to battle colony invaders, whereas another stimulates workers to collect food that has been discovered outside the colony. Pheromones are used by some animals to attract mates. Female silkworm moths (*Bombyx mori*) produce the pheromone bombykol (see "Molecule behind Biology," Box 39.3). A single molecule of bombykol can generate a message in specialized receptors on the antennae of any male silkworm moth that is downwind (see more about the influence of genes on behaviour in

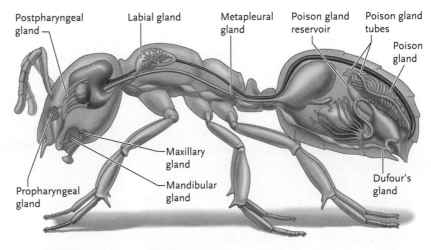

Postpharyngeal gland

Labial gland

Metapleural gland

Poison gland reservoir

Poison gland tubes

Poison gland

Maxillary gland

Mandibular gland

Propharyngeal gland

Dufour's gland

Figure 39.17
Chemical signals. An ant's body contains a host of pheromone-producing glands, each of which manufactures and releases its own volatile chemical or chemicals.

MOLECULE BEHIND BIOLOGY 39.3

Bombykol

Male silkworm moths (*Bombyx mori*) respond to the pheromone bombykol **(Figure 1)** produced and released by females. Bombykol is a pheromone designed to function in communication. Animals use pheromones to bring males and females together. Male *B. mori* detect bombykol using specialized receptors on their antennae (see Chapter 37).

Not surprisingly, predators exploit the powerful attractiveness of pheromones to lure prey. Female bolas spiders (*Mastophora cornigera* and other species in the genus) use a sticky ball of web impregnated with a chemical that mimics the odour of sex pheromones secreted by female moths. Male moths respond to the lure of these odours, approach the pheromone-soaked web, and are captured by the spiders.

Bolas spiders do not prey on just one species of moth. Adult female *M. cornigera* produce three sex pheromone

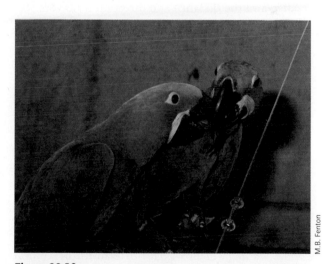

FIGURE 1
Bombykol.

compounds, (Z)-9-tetradecenyl acetate, (Z)-9-tetradecenal, and (Z)-11-hexadecenal. These pheromones attract several different species of

moths. Moth attractants produced by *Mastophora hutchinsoni* are effective on several moths that use quite different pheromones. *M. hutchinsoni* adjust the production of pheromone mimic to match the times of maximum activity by *Tetanolita mynesalis* (smoky tetanolita) and *Lacinipolia renigera* (bristly cutworm). The pheromone blend for the early flying *L. renigera* interferes with attraction of the late flying *T. mynesalis,* so the spider adjusts the blend of pheromone it uses in its lure. This spider lures the early flying moth with one blend and the late flying one with another.

"Knockouts: Genes and Behaviour," Box 39.1, p. 964). Chemicals used as signals are often exploited by predators.

In many species, touch conveys important messages from a signaller to a receiver. **Tactile signals** can operate only over very short distances, but for social animals living in close company, they play a significant role in the development of friendly bonds between individuals **(Figure 39.18)**.

Some freshwater fish species, especially those that occupy murky tropical rivers where visual signals cannot be seen, use weak **electrical signalling** to communicate (see Figure 37.28, p. Chapter 37). These fish have electric organs that can release charges of variable intensity, duration, and frequency, allowing substantial modulation of the message that a signaller sends. Among the New World knifefish (order Gymnotiformes), including the electric eel (Figure 37.28b, Chapter 37), electrical discharges can signal threats, submission, or a readiness to breed.

Animals often use several channels of communication simultaneously. Karl von Frisch demonstrated that the famous dance of the honeybee involves tactile, acoustical, and chemical modes **(Figure 39.19 , p. 974).** When a foraging honeybee discovers a source of pollen

Figure 39.18
Tactile signals. Grooming by Hyacinth Macaws (*Anodorhynchus hyacinthinus*) removes ectoparasites and dirt from feathers. The close physical contact promotes friendly relationships between groomer and groomee.

or nectar, it returns to its colony. There, in the darkness of the hive, it performs a dance on the vertical surface of the honeycomb. The dancer moves in a circle, attracting a crowd of workers. Some workers follow

a. Round dance

b. Waggle dance

c. Coding direction in the waggle dance

When the bee moves straight down the comb, other bees fly to the source directly away from the Sun.

When the bee moves 45° to the right of vertical, other bees fly at a 45° angle to the right of the Sun.

When the bee moves straight up the comb, other bees fly straight toward the Sun.

Figure 39.19

Dance communication by honeybees (*Apis mellifera*). Foraging honeybees transmit information about the location and quality of a food source by dancing on a vertical honeycomb. **(a)** If the food source is close to the hive, the forager performs a *round dance*. **(b)** When food is farther from the hive, the honeybee performs a *waggle dance*. **(c)** The dancing bee indicates the direction to the distant food source by the angle of the waggle run.

and maintain physical contact with the dancer. The dance delivers information about the food source, its quality, and the distance and direction observers will need to fly to locate it.

When the food source is less than 75 m from the hive, the bee performs a *round dance* (see Figure 39.19a). Here the bee moves in tight circles, swinging its abdomen back and forth. Bees surrounding the dancer produce a brief acoustical signal that stimulates the dancer to regurgitate a sample of the food it discovered. The regurgitated sample serves as a chemical cue for other workers that search for the food.

When the food source is farther away, the forager performs the *waggle dance*: a half-circle in one direction, then a straight line while waggling its abdomen, and then a half-circle in the other direction (see Figure 39.19b). With each waggle, the dancer produces a brief buzzing sound. The angle of the waggle run relative to the vertical honeycomb indicates the direction of the food source relative to the position of the Sun (see Figure 39.19c). The duration of the waggles and buzzes carries information about distance to the food. The more time spent waggling and buzzing, the farther the food is from the hive.

Signal receivers often respond to communication from signallers in predictable ways. A male White-crowned Sparrow generally avoids entering a neighbouring territory simply because it hears the song of the resident male. Similarly, young male baboons and

mandrills often retreat without a fight when they see an older male's visual threat display (**Figure 39.20**), even with the loss of a chance to mate with a female. Why do these receivers behave in ways that appear to be beneficial to their rivals but not to themselves?

Explaining behavioural interactions often means considering how an animal's actions affect its reproductive output. The retreating White-crowned Sparrow avoids wasting time and energy on a battle it is likely to lose. By retreating, the would-be intruder minimizes the chances of being injured or killed by a resident male. Moreover, ousting the current resident might be more tiring and risky than finding a suitable unoccupied breeding site. Resident males usually win physical contests, and intruders typically succeed in gaining a territory from a resident only after a prolonged series of exhausting clashes. Observations of territorial species, such as birds, lizards, frogs, fish, and insects, generally support these predictions.

Applying a similar argument to competition among male mandrills, we can predict that smaller or younger males will concede females to threatening older rivals without fighting. The signal receiver retreats after receiving the threat because he judges that he would not win—a male mandrill's canine teeth are not just for show. Evolutionary analyses suggest that the signaller and signal receiver benefit from the exchange of signals, for example, by allowing two animals to avoid a physical altercation that might result in injury.

In winter, Common Ravens (*Corvus corax*) may emit a strange "yell" call when they find the carcass of a deer. The loud yell attracts a crowd of hungry ravens. The calling behaviour puzzled Bernd Heinrich, who noted that when paired, territory-holding adult ravens found a carcass, they fed quietly and did not yell. Yells are produced by young, wandering ravens that happen on a carcass in another bird's territory. The yells attracted

Tom and Pat Leeson/Ardea

Figure 39.20

Threat display. Exposed canines epitomize the threat display of a dominant male mandrill (*Mandrillus sphinx*), which is used to drive away rival males.

other ravens, which collectively overwhelmed the residents' efforts to defend the carcass and their territory. Wanderers used yells to exploit the food supply, whereas residents just ate. Heinrich concluded that the reproductive benefit of resident ravens was enhanced by uninterrupted feeding. Wandering ravens succeeded in their trespassing only when they attracted others.

39.7a Language Consists of Syntax and Symbols

Although language is communication, not all communication is language. Many people believe that language is the exclusive domain of humans, but the distinction is not clear. The round and waggle dances of honeybees contain both syntax (the order in which information is presented) and symbols (a display that represents something else) and are considered by many to meet the criteria for language. Furthermore, by blackening the dancer's ocelli (see Chapter 37), James L. Gould was able to get a dancing bee to lie to other bees. When there is a light in the hive, the dancer orients the waggle dance to the light as if it were the Sun. Dancers with blackened ocelli do not see the light as do other bees—thus, the "lie."

Vervet monkeys (see Figure 19.2, Chapter 19) have a repertoire of signals to alert conspecifics to different predators. Vervet monkeys use one signal for snakes, another for leopards, and still another for raptors, and they show different predator-specific defensive behaviours. Chickadees (*Parus atricapillus*) also use different alarm calls to alert others to approaching danger. Captive, trained chimpanzees and gorillas (*Gorilla gorilla*) have been reported to use American Sign Language (ASL).

In the area of communication, humans are not as distinct from other animals as some people would like to believe. To appreciate redundancy in animal communication, observe the body language and facial expressions of someone talking on a telephone. The eloquence of these signals is not conveyed to the signal receiver at the other end of the phone!

STUDY BREAK

1. What sensory modalities do animals use in communication?
2. How do "yells" influence the behaviour of ravens? Explain.
3. What is the meaning and importance of syntax and symbols in signalling?

39.8 Space

The geographic range of many animal species includes a mosaic of habitat types. The breeding ranges of White-crowned Sparrows can encompass forests, meadows, housing developments, and city dumps. Other animals have a limited range; for example, a Kirtland's Warbler (*Dendroica kirtlandii*) is found only in young jackpine forests. An animal's choice of habitat is critically important because the habitat provides food, shelter, nesting sites, and the other organisms with which it interacts. If an animal chooses a habitat that does not provide appropriate resources, it will not survive and reproduce.

On a large spatial scale, animals almost certainly use multiple criteria to select the habitats they occupy, but no research has yet established any general principles about how animals make these choices. When a migrating bird arrives at its breeding range, it probably cues on large-scale geographic features, such as a pond or a patch of large trees. If the bird does not find the food or nesting resources it needs, or if other individuals have already occupied the space and perhaps depleted those resources, it may move to another habitat patch.

On a very fine spatial scale, basic responses to physical factors enable some animals to find suitable habitats. Kinesis (*kine* = movement; *es* = inward) is a change in the rate of movement or the frequency of turning movements in response to environmental stimuli. Wood lice (terrestrial crustaceans in the order Isopoda) typically live under rocks and logs or in other damp places. Although these arthropods are not attracted to moisture *per se*, when a wood louse encounters dry soil, it scrambles around, turning frequently. When it reaches a patch of moist soil, it moves much less. This kinesis results in wood lice accumulating in moist habitats. Wood lice exposed to dry soil quickly dehydrate and die, so those that move to moister habitats are more likely to survive.

A **taxis** (= ordered movement) is a response directed either toward or away from a specific stimulus. Cockroaches (order Blattodea) exhibit negative phototaxis, meaning that they actively avoid light and seek darkness. Negative phototaxis makes cockroaches less vulnerable to predators that use vision to find their food.

Biologists generally assume that habitat selection is adaptive and has been shaped by natural selection. Some animals instinctively select habitats where they are well camouflaged and less detectable by predators. Predators would discover and eliminate individuals that did not select a matching background, along with any alleles responsible for the mismatch. Many insects have inherited preferences for the plants they eat as larvae (e.g., caterpillars). Adults often lay their eggs only on appropriate food plants, effectively selecting the habitats where their offspring will live and feed.

Vertebrates sometimes exhibit innate preferences, as demonstrated by two closely related species of European birds, Blue Tits (*Cyanistes caeruleus*) and Coal Tits (*Parus ater*). Adult Blue Tits forage mainly in oak trees and Coal Tits in pines. When researchers reared the young of both species in cages without any vegetation and then offered them a choice between oak branches

Figure 39.21

Habitat selection by birds. Wild Blue Tits (*Cyanistes caeruleus*) show a strong preference for oak trees; Coal Tits (*Parus ater*) show a strong preference for pines. Hand-reared birds raised in a vegetation-free environment showed identical but slightly weaker responses.

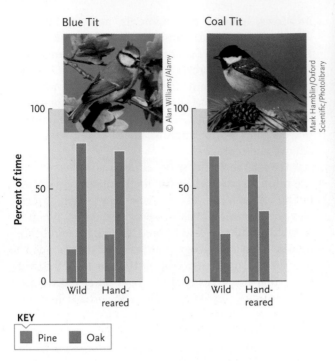

KEY

Pine	Oak

Figure 39.22
Pronghorn antelopes, *Antilocapra americana*.

and pine branches, Coal Tits immediately gravitated toward pines and Blue Tits toward oaks, suggesting an innate preference **(Figure 39.21).** Each species feeds most efficiently in the tree species it prefers.

Habitat preferences can also be moulded by experiences early in life. Tadpoles of red-legged frogs (*Rana aurora*) usually live in aquatic habitats cluttered with sticks, strands of algae, and plant stems. In the laboratory, these tadpoles prefer striped backgrounds to plain ones. In contrast, tadpoles of the closely related cascade frog (*Rana cascadae*) live over gravel bottoms and prefer plain substrates over striped ones. These habitat preferences do not appear when red-legged frogs are reared over plain substrates and cascade frogs over striped substrates and are later given a choice of substrate.

39.8a Home Range and Territory Are Occupied and Defended Areas, Respectively

Space is an important resource for animals. Although many animals are motile, moving about in space, others are sessile. Sessile species such as barnacles (see Chapter 25) anchor themselves to the substrate but are motile as larvae. Barnacles that live on whales or the hulls of ships are sessile but mobile because of the substrate they selected. Motile animals have a home range, the space they regularly traverse during their lives. Home ranges or parts of home ranges become territories when they are defended. In species such as pronghorn antelopes **(Figure 39.22),** some males hold territories, but others do not. Females are not usually territorial. There is a direct connection between territory quality and male reproductive success. Male pronghorn antelopes defending the "best" territories (those with the best food resources) attract

the most females, offering the male the most opportunities to mate with the most females.

Male Jarrow's spiny lizards **(Figure 39.23)** are normally territorial during the autumnal mating season, when they have elevated levels of testosterone in their blood. Catherine Marler and Michael Moore implanted small doses of testosterone or a placebo under the skins of experimental animals during the nonmating season (June and July). Testosterone-enhanced males were more active and displayed more often than control males. Experimental males spent less time feeding, even though they used about 30% more energy per day than control males. In one seven-week period, testosterone-enhanced males suffered significantly higher mortality than placebo males. It can be expensive to be territorial.

Territorial defence is always a costly activity. Patrolling territory borders, performing displays hundreds of times per day, and chasing intruders take time and energy. Moreover, territorial displays increase an animal's likelihood of being injured or detected and captured by a predator.

But territorial behaviour has its benefits, such as access to females. Territorial surgeonfish (*Acanthurus lineatus*) living in coral reefs around American Samoa may engage in as many as 1900 chases per day, defending their small territories from incursions by other algae-eating fish. Territorial surgeonfish eat five

Figure 39.23
Jarrow's spiny lizard, *Sceloporus jarrovi.*

times as much food as nonterritory holders because they have more exclusive access to the food in their territories. It also costs the territory holders more to patrol and defend their realm.

STUDY BREAK

1. Define kinesis and taxis.
2. What is the difference between a home range and a territory?
3. How are home ranges and territories different from a species' range?

39.9 Migration

CONCEPT FIX Our knowledge of bird migration makes it easy to believe that migrating animals travel in groups. It is now clear that many animals migrate alone, and we have evidence of this from a variety of animals, including birds, bats, fur seals, and sea turtles. The reality, however, is that we know very little about the migrations and migratory behaviour of most animals. ⬡

Many animal species make a seasonal **migration**, travelling from the area where they were born or hatched to a distant and initially unfamiliar destination. The migration is complete when they later return to their natal site. The Arctic Tern, a seabird, makes an annual round-trip migration of 40 000 km **(Figure 39.24)**. Other vertebrate species, such as grey whales (*Eschrichtius robustus*) and salmon (*Salmo* species), undertake long and predictable journeys. The same is true of arthropods such as spiny lobsters that form long conga lines and move seasonally between coral reefs and the open ocean floor **(Figure 39.25, p. 978)**.

Moving animals use various mechanisms to find their way during migration. There are three categories of way-finding mechanisms: **piloting**, **compass orientation**, and **navigation**. Many species probably use some combination of these mechanisms to guide their movements.

39.9a Piloting Is Finding the Way

Piloting is the simplest way-finding mechanism, involving the use of familiar landmarks to guide a journey. Grey whales migrate from Alaska to Baja California and back using visual cues provided by the Pacific coastline of North America. When it is time to breed and lay eggs, Pacific salmon use olfactory cues to pilot their way from the ocean back to the stream in which they hatched.

"Tracking of Arctic terns *Sterna zaradisaea* reveals longest animal migration." Carsten Egevang, Iain J. Stenhouse, Richard A. Phillips, Aevar Petersen, Jarres W. Fox, and Janet R. D. Silk. PNAS February 2, 2010 vol. 107 no. 5 2078-2081.

Wildlife Preservation of Canada

Photos.com

Figure 39.24
Geolocators provided details of the movements of 11 Arctic Terns tagged at breeding colonies in Greenland (10) and Iceland (1). Two migration routes emerged, one along the coast of Africa **(a),** the other along the coast of South America **(b).** Left inset, a small geolocator; right an Arctic Tern.

Howard Hall/Oxford Scientific/Photolibrary

Figure 39.25

Migrating arthropods. Spiny lobsters (*Panulirus argus*) make seasonal migrations between coral reefs and the open ocean floor. As many as 50 individuals march in single file for several days.

Animals that do not migrate also use specific landmarks to identify their nest site or places where they have stored food. Female digger wasps (*Philanthus triangulum*) nest in soil. In 1938, Niko Tinbergen showed that after foraging flights, these wasps used visual landmarks to find their nests **(Figure 39.26)**. While the female wasp was in the nest, Tinbergen arranged pinecones in a circle around it. As she left, the wasp flew around the area, apparently noting nearby landmarks. Tinbergen then moved the circle of pinecones a short distance away. Each time the female returned, she searched for her nest within the pinecone circle. She never once found her nest unless the pinecones were returned to their original position. Later, Tinbergen rearranged the pinecones into a triangle after females left their nests and added a ring of stones

nearby. The returning females looked for their nest in the stone circle. Tinbergen concluded that digger wasps respond to the general outline or geometry of landmarks around their nests and not to the specific objects making up the landmarks.

39.9b Compass: Which Way Is North?

Animals using compass orientation move in a particular direction, often over a specific distance or for a prescribed length of time. Some day-flying migratory birds orient themselves using the Sun's position in the sky in conjunction with an internal biological clock (see Chapter 1). The internal clock allows the bird to use the Sun as a compass, compensating for changes in its position through the day. The clock may also allow some birds to estimate how far they have travelled since beginning their journey. Other animals, including birds, mammals, reptiles, amphibians, fish, crustaceans, and insects, use Earth's magnetic field as a compass. This requires detection of weak magnetic fields (~50 µT—microteslas). In 2008, some biologists suggested that magnetically sensitive free radical reactions could be the basis of a magnetic sense, but the search for the transducer(s) (see Chapter 37) continues.

39.9c Stars Are Used for Celestial Navigation

Some birds that migrate at night determine their direction by using the positions of stars. The Indigo Bunting flies about 3500 km from the northeastern United States to the Caribbean or Central America each fall and makes the return journey each spring. Stephen Emlen demonstrated that Indigo Buntings direct their migration using celestial cues **(Figure 39.27)**. Emlen

Wasp's flight pattern on leaving nest

Wasp's return, looking for nest

Nest

Figure 39.26

Female digger wasps find their nets. A ring of pinecones serves as a landmark for a female digger wasp (*Philanthus triangulum*). By manipulating the location of landmarks, Nikko Tinbergen demonstrated the role they serve in the wasp's orientation behaviour.

Indigo Bunting

Mark Tegges/Shutterstock

Blotting paper

Indigo Bunting

Inkpad

Figure 39.27
Orientation by Indigo Buntings. The footprints of inked Indigo Buntings (*Passerina cyanea*) demonstrated migrating birds' responses to celestial cues.
Based on S. T. Emlen. 1967. "Migratory orientation of the indigo bunting, Passerina cyanea. Part I: Evidence for use of celestial cues." *The Auk* 84: 309–342.

Side (left) and overhead (right) views of the test cage with blotting paper on the sides and an inkpad on the bottom.

In autumn, the bunting footprints indicated that they were trying to fly south.

In spring, the bunting footprints indicated that they were trying to fly north.

On cloudy nights, when buntings could not see the stars, their footprints indicated a random pattern of movement.

confined individual buntings in cone-shaped test cages whose sides were lined with blotting paper. He placed inkpads on the cage bottoms and kept the cages in an outdoor enclosure so that the birds had a full view of the night sky. Whenever a bird made a directed movement, its inky footprints indicated the direction in which it was trying to move. On clear nights in fall, the footprints pointed to the south, but in spring, they pointed north. On cloudy nights, when the buntings could not see the stars, Emlen recorded that their footprints were evenly distributed in all directions. The data indicated that the compass of Indigo Buntings required a view of the stars.

39.9d Navigation Is a Complex Challenge

Navigation is the most complex way-finding mechanism. It occurs when an animal moves toward a specific destination, using both a compass and a *mental map* of where it is in relation to the destination. Hikers in unfamiliar surroundings routinely use navigation to find their way home. They use a map to determine their current position and the necessary direction of movement and a compass to orient themselves in that direction. Scientists have documented true navigation in a few animal species, notably the Homing Pigeon (*Columba livia*). These birds can navigate to their home

coops from any direction, probably using the Sun's position as their compass and olfactory cues as their map.

39.9e Animals Migrate for Several Reasons

Migrations by White-crowned Sparrows and many other species are triggered by changes in day length. Shortening day length indicates approaching fall and winter; lengthening day length indicates spring. Day length changes the anterior pituitary of the bird's brain to generate a series of hormonal changes. In response, birds feed heavily and accumulate the fat reserves necessary to fuel their long journey. Sparrows also become increasingly restless at night until, one evening, they begin their nocturnal migration. Their ability to adopt and maintain a southerly orientation in autumn (and a northerly one in spring) rests in part on their capacity to use the positions of stars to provide directional information.

Migratory behaviour entails obvious costs, such as the time and energy devoted to the journey and the risk of death from exhaustion or predator attack. Migratory behaviour is not universal—many animals never migrate, spending their lives in one location. Why do some species migrate? What ecological pressures give migrating individuals higher fitness than individuals that do not migrate? Remember that many species of terrestrial animals migrate, such as wildebeest and caribou.

For migratory birds, seasonal changes in food supply are the most widely accepted hypothesis to explain migratory behaviour. Insects can be abundant in higher-latitude (greater than 50° N or S) habitats during the warm spring and summer, providing excellent resources for birds to raise offspring. As summer wanes and fall and winter approach, insects all but disappear. Bird species that remain in temperate habitats over winter eat mainly seeds and dormant insects. When it is winter at higher latitudes, energy supplies are more predictably available in the tropical grounds used by overwintering migratory birds.

Two-way migratory journeys may provide other benefits. Avoiding the northern winter is probably adaptive because endotherms must increase their metabolic rates just to stay warm in cold climates (see Chapter 42). Moreover, summer days are longer at high latitudes than they are in the tropics (see *The Purple Pages*), giving adult birds more time to feed and rear a brood.

Seasonal changes in food supply also underlie the migration of monarch butterflies that eat milkweed leaves as caterpillars and milkweed nectar as adults **(Figure 39.28a).** In eastern North America, milkweed plants grow only during spring and summer. Many adult monarchs head south in late summer, when the plants begin to die. Some migrate as much as 4000 km from eastern and central North America to central Mexico, where they cluster in spectacular numbers **(Figure 39.28b and c),** apparently using olfactory cues to find preferred resting places. Unlike migrant birds, these insects do not feed while at their overwintering grounds. Instead, their metabolic rate decreases in the cool mountain air, and the butterflies become inactive for months, conserving precious energy reserves. When spring arrives, the butterflies become active again and begin the return migration to northern breeding habitats. The northward migration is slow, however, and many individuals stop along the way to feed and lay eggs. These offspring, and their offspring, continue the northward migration through the summer. Some descendants of these migrants eventually reach Canada for a final round of breeding. The summer's last generation then returns south to the spot where their ancestors,

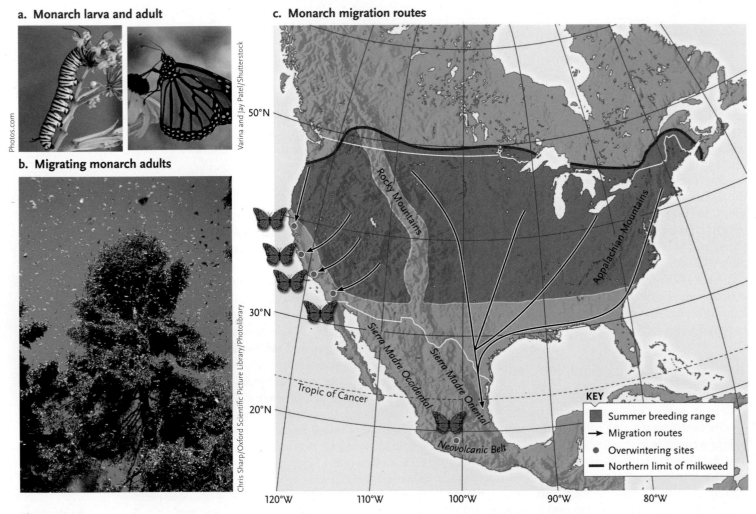

Figure 39.28

Migrating monarch butterflies. (a) Monarch butterflies (*Danaus plexippus*) eat milkweed plants as caterpillars. **(b)** When milkweed plants in their breeding range die back at the end of summer, monarchs migrate south. The following spring, after passing the winter in a semidormant state, they migrate north. **(c)** Monarchs that live and breed east of the Rocky Mountains migrate to Mexico. Those living west of the Rocky Mountains overwinter in coastal California.

two to five generations removed, spent the previous winter.

For other animals, migration to breeding grounds may provide the special conditions necessary for reproduction. Grey whales migrate south, where females give birth to their young in quiet, shallow lagoons where predators are rare and warm water temperatures are more conducive to the growth of their calves.

STUDY BREAK

1. Define migration. Give examples of migratory animals, including some not mentioned in the text. Do any humans migrate?
2. How do migrating animals find their way? Distinguish between navigation and compass orientation.

39.10 Mates as Resources

Mating systems have evolved to maximize reproductive success, partly in response to the amount of parental care that offspring require and partly in response to other aspects of a species' ecology. **Monogamy** describes the situation in which a male and a female form a pair bond for a mating season or, in some cases, for the individuals' reproductive lives. **Polygamy** occurs when one male has active pair bonds with more than one female (**polygyny**) or one female has active pair bonds with more than one male (**polyandry**). **Promiscuity** occurs when males and females have no pair bonds beyond the time it takes to mate. In polygyny, males often contribute nothing to reproduction but sperm; in polyandry, females nothing but eggs. The details will vary according to the physiology of reproduction. In viviparous animals, the animals that get pregnant (usually females) may bear the costs of housing and feeding developing young.

When young require a great deal of care that both parents can provide, monogamy often prevails. Songbirds, such as the White-crowned Sparrow **(Figure 39.29)**, are altricial (naked and helpless) when they hatch. They beg for food, and both parents can bring it to them. Males and females achieve higher rates of reproduction when both parents are actively involved with raising young. In mammals, the situation is different because females provide the food (milk). Monogamy occurs in species in which males indirectly feed the young by bringing food to the mother.

If males have high-quality territories, the females living there may be able to raise young on their own. These males may be polygynous (mate with several females). The male's role is that of sperm donor and protector of the space rather than that of an active parent to all of his young. In birds such as Red-winged Blackbirds (*Agelaius phoenecius*), some males hold

Figure 39.29

Reproductive success. Parental care is just one of the many behaviours required for successful reproduction in White-crowned Sparrows and in many other animal species. The number of surviving nestlings will determine the reproductive success of their parents and the representation of their genes in the next generation.

large, resource-filled territories that support several females. These males will be attractive to females even if a female (or females) already lives on the territory. Polygyny is prevalent among mammals because, compared with males, females make a much larger investment in raising young (through egg development and care of the young).

Promiscuous mating systems occur when females are only with males long enough to receive sperm and there is no pair bond. These males make no contribution to raising young. Sage Grouse **(Figure 39.30)** and hammerheaded bats (*Hypsignathus monstrosus*) are examples of this approach. Both species form **leks**, congregations of

Figure 39.30

Lekking behaviour. Male Sage Grouse (*Centrocercus urophasianus*) use their ornamental feathers in visual courtship displays performed at a lek. There each male has his own small territory. The smaller brown females observe the performing males before picking a mate.

displaying males, where females come only to mate. There are more details about Sage Grouse below.

STUDY BREAK

What do the terms *monogamy, polygamy,* and *promiscuity* mean?

39.11 Sexual Selection

Given the drive to reproduce (see Chapter 33), competition for access to mates coupled with mate choice sets the stage for sexual selection. Sexual dimorphism, in which one gender is larger or more colourful than the other, can be an outcome of sexual selection. When males compete for females, males are often larger than females and may have ornaments and weapons, such as horns and antlers, useful for attracting females and for butting, stabbing, or intimidating rival males. Displays of adornments or weapons can simultaneously warn off other males and attract the attention of females. Peacocks strut in front of female peahens while spreading a gigantic fan of tail feathers, which they shake, rattle, and roll.

Why should females choose males with exaggerated structures conspicuously displayed? A male's large size, bright feathers, or large horns might indicate that he is particularly healthy. His appearance could indicate that he can harvest resources efficiently or simply that he has managed to survive to an advanced age. The features are, in effect, signals of male quality, and if they reflect a male's genetic makeup, he is likely to fertilize a female's eggs with sperm containing successful alleles. Large showy males may hold large, rich territories. Females that choose these males can gain access to the resources their territories contain.

The degree to which females *actively* choose genetically superior mates varies among species. In northern elephant seals, female choice is more or less passive. Large numbers of females gather on beaches to give birth to their pups before becoming sexually receptive again (see "Delaying Reproduction," Box 33.4, Chapter 33). Males locate clusters of females and fight to keep other males away (see Figure 16.8, Chapter 16). Males that win have exceptional reproductive success because they mate with many females, but only after engaging in violent and relentless combat with rival males. In this mating system, the females struggle during a male's attempts to mate with them. A female's struggles attract other males, who try to interrupt the attempted mating. Only the largest and most powerful males are not interrupted in their copulations, and they inseminate the most females. These attributes may be associated with alleles that will increase their offspring's chances of living long enough to reproduce.

In other species, females exercise more active mate choice, mating only after inspecting several potential partners. Among birds, active female mate choice is most apparent at leks, display grounds where each male holds a small territory from which it courts attentive females. The male is the only resource on the territory. Male Sage Grouse in western North America gather in open areas among stands of sagebrush. Each male defends a few square metres, where it struts in circles while emitting booming calls and showing off its elegant tail feathers and big neck pouches (see Figure 39.30, p. 981). Females wander among displaying males, presumably observing the males' visual and acoustical displays. Eventually, each female selects one mate from among the dozens of males that are present. Females repeatedly favour males that come to the lek daily, defend their small area vigorously, and display more frequently than the average lek participant. Males preferred by females sustain their territorial defence and high display rate over long periods, abilities that may correlate with other useful genetic traits. Ultimately, the male holding the "best" position in the lek mates with the most females.

The results of experiments with peafowl suggest that the top Peacocks (*Pavo cristatus*) supply advantageous alleles to their offspring. In nature, peahens prefer males whose tails have many ornamental eyespots **(Figure 39.31).** In an experiment on captive birds, some peahens were mated to peacocks with highly attractive tails, but others were paired with males whose tails were less impressive. The offspring of both groups were reared under uniform conditions for several months and then released into an English

© Ashley Cooper/Corbis

Figure 39.31

Sexual selection for ornamentation. The attractiveness of a peacock to peahens depends in part on the number of eyespots in his extraordinary tail. The offspring of males with elaborate tails are more successful than the offspring of males with plainer tails.

woodland. After three months on their own, the offspring of fathers with impressive tails survived better and weighed significantly more than did those whose fathers had less attractive tails. The evidence demonstrates that a peahen's mate choice influences her offspring's chances of survival.

According to the handicap hypothesis, females select males that are successful—the ones with ornate structures. These structures may impede their locomotion, and their elaborate displays may attract the attention of predators. Females select ornate males because they have survived *despite* carrying such a handicap. Successful alleles responsible for the ornamental handicap are passed to the female's offspring.

STUDY BREAK

What are the distinguishing features of a lek?

39.12 Social Behaviour

Social behaviour, the interactions that animals have with other members of their species, has profound effects on an individual's reproductive success. Some animals are solitary, getting together only briefly to mate (e.g., house flies and leopards). Others spend most of their lives in small family groups (e.g., gorillas). Still others live in groups with thousands of relatives (e.g., termites and honeybees). Some species, such as caribou and humans, live in large social units composed primarily of nonrelatives. In many species, the level of social interactions varies seasonally, usually reflecting the timing of reproduction, which, in turn, is influenced by changes in day length.

39.12a African Lions May Commit Infanticide

African lions (*Panthera leo*) usually live in prides, one adult male with several females and their young. Males typically sire the young born to the females in their pride, achieving a high reproductive output. Females benefit from the support of the others in the group, which includes caring for young and cooperating in foraging. Female lions living in prides wean more young per litter than those living alone. The females in a pride are often genetically related, and their estrus cycles are usually synchronized. Male lions are bigger (~200 kg) than females (~150 kg), and males fight vigorously for the position of pride male. Males protect their females from incursions by other males.

When a new male takes over a pride, he kills all nursing young, bringing the females into estrus. At first, this infanticide seems counterproductive. However, it benefits the male because it increases the chances of his succeeding at reproducing. Were he to wait until the females had raised their dependent young, his reproductive contributions could be delayed for some time, perhaps as much as a year or more. Furthermore, in the intervening period he could lose the opportunity to sire any young at all.

Females are not large enough to protect their young from the male. If a female takes her nursing young and leaves the pride, her efficiency as a hunter declines, and she is less able to protect her young. Her reproductive success plummets. Females can be more productive (measured by output of young) when they are part of a pride.

But why live in a group in the first place? By hunting together, lions are more efficient foragers than when they hunt alone; therefore, they raise more young. Perhaps more important is the threat posed by spotted hyenas, which live in large groups (clans). Although individually smaller (~60 kg), when spotted hyenas outnumber lions, they can chase lions from their kills. Furthermore, many of the lion's main prey also live in groups, and group defences affect lions' hunting success.

The situation in lions exemplifies some biological realities. Males and females do not have the same strategies when it comes to reproduction. Understanding behaviour means considering genetic relatedness and production of offspring, as well as the setting in which the animals live.

39.12b Group Living Has Its Costs and Benefits

Social Behaviours. Ecological factors have a large impact on the reproductive benefits and costs of social living. Groups of cooperating predators frequently capture prey more effectively than they would on their own. White Pelicans (*Pelecanus erythrorhynchos*) often encircle a school of fish before attacking, so being part of a group provides a better yield to individuals than working alone. On the other hand, prey subject to intense predation may benefit from group defence. This can mean more pairs of watchful eyes or ears to detect an approaching danger. It may also translate into multiple lures so that when a predator attacks, it is more difficult to focus on an individual. When you are part of a group that is attacked, it may be someone other than you that is captured, diluting the risk to any one group member.

When attacked by wolves, adult muskoxen form a circle around the young, so attackers are always confronted by horns and hooves **(Figure 39.32, p. 984)**. Insects such as Australian sawfly caterpillars also show cooperative defensive behaviour **(Figure 39.33, p. 984)**. When predators disturb the caterpillars, all group members rear up, writhe about, and regurgitate sticky, pungent oils. The caterpillars collect the oils from the eucalyptus leaves they eat. The oils do not harm the caterpillars but are toxic and repellent to birds.

Living in groups can also be expensive. One cost can be increased competition for food. When thousands

40.2a Soil Components and Particle Sizes Determine Properties of Soil

Most soils initially develop from the physical or chemical weathering of rock, which also liberates mineral ions. Different kinds of soil particles range in size from sand (2.0–0.02 mm in diameter) to silt (0.02–0.002 mm) and clay (<0.002 mm). The relative proportions of different sizes of mineral particles help determine the number and volume of pores—air spaces—soil contains. A soil that is sticky when wet with few air spaces is mostly clay, whereas one that dries quickly and may wash or blow away is mostly sand. The mineral particles alone do not make a soil; it also depends on the presence of living organisms and the accumulation of their products and decomposing bodies. In most soils, mineral particles are intermixed with various organic components, including **humus**, the decomposing parts of plants and animals, animal droppings, and other organic matter. Humus can absorb a great deal of water, contributing to the soil's capacity to hold water. Humus is a reservoir of nutrients vital to living plants, including N, P, and S. Organic material in humus feeds decomposers, whose metabolic activities, in turn, release minerals that plant roots can take up.

As soils develop naturally, they tend to take on a characteristic vertical profile, with a series of layers or **horizons (Figure 40.5)**. Each horizon has a distinct texture and composition that varies with soil type. The *A horizon,* or topsoil, is the region with the most biological activity and is usually the most fertile layer. Most plant roots are concentrated in this layer, although some roots can extend much deeper in the soil (see Figure 45.13, Chapter 45). Below the topsoil is the *B horizon,* or subsoil, characterized by the accumulation of mineral ions, including those needed by plants, washed down from above. Mature tree roots generally extend into this layer. The *C horizon,* the lowest layer, is the parent material. Regions where the topsoil is deep and rich in humus are ideal for agriculture, such as the vast grasslands of the Canadian prairies and Ukraine. Without soil management and intensive irrigation, crops usually cannot be grown in deserts because of the lack of rainfall and low humus in the soil—nor can agriculture flourish for long on cleared tropical rainforest land because rainforest soil is surprisingly poor and has very little humus.

40.2b Soil Characteristics Affect Nutrient Uptake by Plants

Some nutrients that plants require are present as mineral ions dissolved in the soil water. Soil composition influences the ability of plant roots to obtain nutrients, as outlined below.

Water Availability. As water flows through soil, gravity pulls much of it down through the spaces between soil particles into deeper soil layers. This available water is part of the **soil solution (Figure 40.6)**, a combination of water and dissolved substances that coats soil particles and partially fills pore spaces. The solution develops through ionic interactions between water molecules and soil particles. The surfaces of clay particles and humus particles are often negatively charged and so attract polar water molecules, which form hydrogen bonds with the soil particles.

The proportion of the water entering a soil that is actually available to plants depends on the soil's composition—the size of the air spaces that allow water to flow and the proportions of water-attracting particles of clay and organic matter. By volume, soil is about one-half solid particles and one-half air space.

The size of the particles in a soil has a major effect on how well plants will grow there. Sandy soil has relatively large air spaces, so water drains rapidly down from the top two soil horizons, where most plant roots are located. Soils rich in clay or humus are often high in water content, but in the case of clay, ample water is not necessarily an advantage for plants. Whereas a humus-rich soil contains lots of air spaces, the closely spaced particles in

Fallen leaves and other organic material littering the surface of mineral soil.

A horizon
Topsoil, which contains some percentage of decomposed organic material and is of variable depth; here it extends about 30 cm below the soil surface.

B horizon
Subsoil; larger soil particles than the A horizon, not much organic material, but greater accumulation of minerals; here it extends about 60 cm below the A horizon.

C horizon
No organic material, but partially weathered fragments and grains of rock from which soil forms; extends to underlying bedrock.

Bedrock

William Ferguson

Figure 40.5
A representative profile of soil horizons.

Figure 40.6
Location of the soil solution. Negatively charged ions on the surfaces of soil particles attract water molecules, which coat the particles and fill spaces between them (blue). Hydrogen bonds between water and soil components counteract the pull of gravity and help hold some water in the soil spaces.

Figure 40.7
Cation exchange on the surface of a clay particle. When cations come into contact with the negatively charged surface of a clay particle, they become adsorbed. As one type of cation (e.g., H^+) is adsorbed, other ions are liberated and can be taken up by the roots of plants.

clay allow few air spaces, and existing spaces tend to hold on to the water that enters them. "Air" spaces in clay soils filled with water also severely limit the supplies of oxygen to roots for cellular respiration, and the plant's metabolic activity suffers. Thus, few plants can grow well in clay soils, even when water content is high. Overwatered houseplants die because their roots are similarly "smothered" by water.

Mineral Availability. Most mineral ions enter plant roots passively along with the water in which they are dissolved. Plant cell membranes have ion-specific transport proteins by which they selectively absorb ions from soil (see Chapter 28). Some mineral nutrients enter plant roots as cations and others as anions. Although both cations and anions may be present in soil solutions, they are not equally available to plants.

Cations such as Mg^{2+}, Ca^{2+}, and K^+ cannot easily enter roots because they are attracted by the net negative charges on the surfaces of soil particles. To varying degrees, they become reversibly bound to negative ions on the surfaces. Attraction in this form is called *adsorption*. Cations are made available to plant roots through **cation exchange**, a mechanism in which one cation, usually H^+, replaces a soil cation **(Figure 40.7).** There are two main sources of H^+ ions. Respiring root cells release carbon dioxide, which dissolves in the soil solution, yielding carbonic acid (H_2CO_3). Subsequent reactions ionize H_2CO_3 to produce bicarbonate (HCO_3^-) and hydrogen ions (H^+). Reactions involving organic acids inside roots also produce H^+, which is excreted. As H^+ enters the soil solution, it displaces adsorbed mineral cations attached to clay and humus, freeing them to move into roots. Other types of cations may also participate in this type of exchange (see Figure 40.7).

Meanwhile, anions in the soil solution, such as nitrate (NO_3^-), sulfate (SO_4^{2-}), and phosphate (PO_4^-), are only weakly bound to soil particles, so they generally move fairly freely into root hairs. However, because they are so weakly bound compared with cations, anions are more subject to loss from soil by leaching (draining from the soil, carried by excess water).

Soil pH also affects the availability of some mineral ions. Soil pH is a function of the balance between cation exchange and other processes that raise or lower the concentration of H^+ in soil. Areas receiving heavy rainfall tend to have acidic soils because moisture promotes the rapid decay of organic material in humus. As the material decomposes, the organic acids it contains are released. Acid precipitation, which results from the release of S and N oxides into the air, also contributes to soil acidification. Soils in arid regions are often alkaline.

Although most plants are not directly sensitive to soil pH, chemical reactions in very acid (pH <5.5) or very alkaline (pH >9.5) soils can have a major impact on whether plant roots can take up certain mineral cations. In the presence of OH^- ions in alkaline soil, Ca^{2+} and P^{3+} ions react to form insoluble calcium phosphates. Phosphate captured in these compounds is as unavailable to roots as if it were completely absent from the soil.

For a soil to sustain plant life over long periods, mineral ions that the plants take up must be replenished naturally or artificially. In the long run, some mineral nutrients enter the soil from ongoing weathering of rocks and smaller bits of minerals. Over the shorter term, nutrients are returned to the soil by the decomposition of organisms and their parts or wastes. Other inputs occur when airborne compounds, such as S in volcanic and industrial emissions, become dissolved in rain and fall to Earth. Still others, including compounds of N and P, enter soil in fertilizers.

Although using commercial fertilizers maintains high crop yields (see Chapter 48), it does not add humus to the soil. Fertilizers can also cause serious problems, as when N-rich runoff from agricultural fields promotes the overgrowth of algae in lakes and ocean shorelines.

STUDY BREAK

1. Why is humus an important component of fertile soil?
2. How does the composition of a soil affect a plant's ability to take up water?
3. What factors affect a plant's ability to absorb minerals from the soil?

40.3 Obtaining and Absorbing Nutrients

Natural habitats show a wide range of soil conditions (minerals, humus, pH, biota, and other factors) that influence the growth and health of plants. Soil managed for agriculture can be plowed, precisely irrigated, and chemically adjusted to provide air, water, and nutrients in optimal quantities for a particular crop. Natural habitats, on the other hand, show wide variations in soil minerals, humus, pH, the presence of other organisms, and other factors that influence the availability of essential elements. Some nutrients, particularly N, P, and K, are often relatively scarce in soil. The evolutionary solutions to these challenges include an array of adaptations in the structure and functioning of plant roots.

40.3a Acquisition of Nutrients by Plants

Immobile organisms such as plants must locate nutrients in their immediate environment. For plants, root systems are the adaptive solution to this problem. Roots make up 20 to 50% of the dry weight of many plants and even more in species that grow where water or nutrients are especially scarce, such as the Arctic tundra. As long as a plant lives, its root system continues to grow, branching out through the surrounding soil. Roots do not necessarily grow *deeper* as a root system branches out, however. In arid regions, a shallow but broad root system may be better positioned than a deep one to take up water from occasional rains that may never penetrate below the first few centimetres of soil.

A root system grows most extensively in soil where water and mineral ions are abundant (see Chapter 28). Roots take up ions in regions just above the root tips. Over successive growing seasons, long-lived plants such as trees can develop millions, even billions, of root tips, each one a potential absorption site. Root hairs are diminutive absorptive structures (see Figure 27.20a,

Chapter 27) that are also associated with the uptake of mineral ions and water. In a plant such as a mature red oak (*Quercus rubra*) with a vast root system, the total number of root hairs is astonishing. Even in young plants, root hairs greatly increase the root surface area available for absorbing water and ions.

Plant cell membranes (see Chapter 28) have ion-specific transport proteins by which they selectively absorb ions from soil. Studies of *Arabidopsis thaliana*, a plant that has become a model organism for plant research, show that transport channels for K^+ are embedded in the cell membranes of root cortical cells. These ion transporters absorb more or less of a particular ion depending on chemical conditions in the surrounding soil.

Plants can only take up inorganic or mineral forms of nutrients. A plant growing in a soil rich in organic forms of N such as proteins cannot access the N until decomposers have converted the protein into mineral forms such as ammonium (NH_4^+) or nitrate (NO_3^-). Associations with fungi and bacteria allow many plants to shortcut the decomposition process and gain access to organic and other forms of nutrients. **Mycorrhizas**, symbiotic associations between a fungus and the roots of a plant (see Chapter 23), increase the uptake of nutrients, especially P and N, by most species of vascular plants. The fungal partner in the association grows inside the plant's roots and in the soil beyond the roots, forming an extensive network of hyphal filaments. This network provides a very large surface area for absorbing ions from a large volume of soil. Furthermore, many mycorrhizal fungi can access forms of nutrients not available to plants. For instance, many fungi obtain nutrients from organic forms of nutrients (e.g., proteins) and even obtain other nutrients directly from rocks!

40.3b Movements of Nutrients in Plants

Most mineral ions enter plant roots passively along with the water in which they are dissolved. Some mineral ions enter root cells immediately, whereas others travel in solution *between* cells until they meet the endodermis sheathing the root's stele (see Figure 28.6, Chapter 28). Here the ions are actively transported into the endodermal cells and then into the xylem for transport throughout the plant.

Inside cells, most mineral ions enter vacuoles or cell cytoplasm, where they become available for metabolic reactions. Nutrients, such as N-containing ions, move in phloem from site to site in the plant, as dictated by growth and seasonal needs. In plants that shed their leaves in autumn (= deciduous), significant amounts of N, P, K, and Mn move out of them and into twigs and branches before the leaves age and fall. This adaptation conserves the nutrients, which will be used in new growth the next season. Likewise, in late summer, mineral ions move to the roots and lower stem tissues of perennial range grasses that typically die back during the winter. These activities are regulated by hormonal signals (see Chapter 30).

40.3c Plants Can Be Limited by the Availability of Nitrogen

A lack of N is the single most common limit to plant growth. Although air contains plenty of gaseous N (~80% by volume), plants lack the enzyme necessary to break the three covalent bonds in each N_2 molecule ($N{\equiv}N$). Some N from the atmosphere reaches the soil in the form of nitrate, NO_3^-, and ammonium ions, NH_4^+. Plants can absorb both of these inorganic nitrogen compounds, but there is usually not nearly enough of them to meet plants' ongoing needs for N.

Organic N also enters the soil through decomposition of dead organisms and animal wastes. Dried blood is about 12% N by weight and chicken manure about 5%. But this N is bound up in complex organic molecules such as proteins that are not available to plants. The actions of bacteria are the main natural processes that replenish soil N and convert it to the absorbable form (see Figure 46.11, Chapter 46). They are part of the *nitrogen cycle* (see Figure 46.14, Chapter 46), the global movement of N in its various chemical forms from the environment to organisms and back to the environment.

N fixation is the incorporation of atmospheric N into compounds accessible to plants. Metabolic pathways of *nitrogen-fixing bacteria,* which live in the soil or in mutualistic association with plant roots, add H to atmospheric N_2, producing two molecules of NH_3 and one H_2 for each N_2 molecule (**Figure 40.8**). The process requires a substantial input of ATP and is catalyzed by the enzyme nitrogenase. In a final step, H_2O and NH_3 react, forming NH_4^+ and OH^-. Ammonification is another bacterial process producing NH_4^+ when ammonifying soil bacteria break down decaying organic matter. This process recycles nitrogen previously incorporated in plants and other organisms. N fixation and ammonification form NH_4^+, which plant cells can use to synthesize organic compounds.

Most plants absorb N as nitrate, NO_3^-, which is produced in the soil by **nitrification** when NH_4^+ is oxidized to NO_3^-. Soils generally teem with *nitrifying bacteria* that carry out this process. Because of ongoing nitrification, nitrate is far more abundant than ammonium in most soils. Plants usually take up ammonium directly only in highly acidic soils, such as in bogs, where the low pH is toxic to nitrifying bacteria.

Within root cells, absorbed NO_3^- is converted by a multistep process back to NH_4^+, which is rapidly used to synthesize organic molecules, mainly amino acids. Amino acids pass into the xylem, which transports them throughout the plant. In some plants, nitrogen-rich precursors travel in xylem to leaves, where different organic molecules are synthesized and, in turn, travel to other plant cells in the phloem.

Although some N-fixing bacteria live free in the soil (see Figure 40.8), by far the largest percentage of nitrogen is fixed by species of *Rhizobium* and *Bradyrhizobium* that form mutualistic associations with the roots

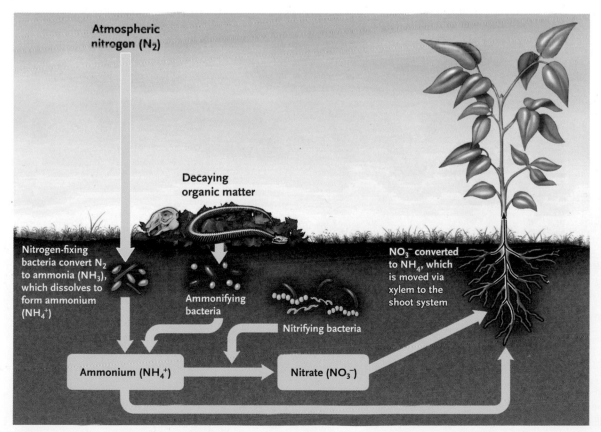

Nitrogen-fixing bacteria convert N_2 to ammonia (NH_3), which dissolves to form ammonium (NH_4^+)

Ammonifying bacteria

Nitrifying bacteria

NO_3^- converted to NH_4, which is moved via xylem to the shoot system

Ammonium (NH_4^+)

Nitrate (NO_3^-)

Figure 40.8
How plants obtain nitrogen from soil. Many commercial N fertilizers are nitrates that plant roots readily take up. Others are ammonium (NH_4), which nitrifying bacteria convert to nitrate.

of plants in the legume family (e.g., peas, beans, clover, alfalfa). The host plant supplies organic molecules used by the bacteria for cellular respiration, and the bacteria supply NH_4^+, which the plant uses to produce proteins and other nitrogenous molecules. The N-fixing bacteria reside in **root nodules**, localized swellings on legume roots **(Figure 40.9)**. Rotating legumes with other crops (e.g., corn) allows farmers to increase soil N. When the legume crop is harvested, root nodules and other tissues remaining in the soil enrich its N content.

Decades of research have revealed the details of how the remarkable relationship between plants and bacteria unfolds. Usually, a single species of N-fixing bacteria colonizes a single legume species, drawn to the plant's roots by flavonoids, chemical attractants secreted by the roots. Through a sequence of exchanged molecular signals, bacteria penetrate a root hair and form a colony inside the root cortex **(Figure 40.10)**.

The soybean (*Glycine max*) and its bacterial partner (*Bradyrhizobium japonicum*) illustrate the process. In response to a specific flavonoid released by the soybean's roots, *nod* (for nodule) genes in the bacteria begin to be expressed (see Figure 40.10a). Products of the *nod* gene cause the tip of the root hair to curl toward the bacteria and trigger the bacteria to release enzymes that break down the cell wall of the root hair (see Figure 40.10b). As bacteria enter the cell and multiply, the plasma membrane forms an *infection thread,* a tube that extends into the root cortex, allowing the bacteria to invade cells of the cortex (see Figure 40.10c). The enclosed bacteria, now called **bacteroids**, enlarge and become immobile. Stimulated by still other *nod* gene products, cells of the root cortex begin to divide, and this region of proliferating cortex cells forms the root nodule (see Figure 40.10d). Each cell in a root nodule

typically contains several thousand bacteroids. The plant takes up some of the N fixed by the bacteroids, whereas the bacteroids use some compounds produced by the plant.

Inside bacteroids, nitrogenase catalyzes the reduction of N_2 to NH_4^+ using ATP produced by cellular respiration. NH_4^+ can be highly toxic to cells if it accumulates, so it is immediately moved out of the bacteroids and into the surrounding nodule cells and converted, for example, to the amino acids glutamine and asparagine.

The protein *leghemoglobin* ("legume hemoglobin") also results from stimulation of plant nodule cells by a product of the bacterial *nod* genes. Like the hemoglobin of animal red blood cells, leghemoglobin contains a reddish, iron-containing heme group that binds oxygen. Its colour gives root nodules a pinkish cast (see Figure 40.10). Leghemoglobin picks up oxygen at the cell surface and shuttles it inward to bacteroids. This method of oxygen delivery is vital because nitrogenase, the enzyme responsible for nitrogen fixation, is irreversibly inhibited by excess O_2. Leghemoglobin delivers just enough oxygen to maintain bacteroid respiration without shutting down the action of nitrogenase.

40.3d Animals Eat to Acquire Nutrients

Animals are adapted to obtain the food they need (see Chapter 39. There are four basic groups of overall feeding methods and the physical states of the organic molecules they eat: fluid feeders, suspension feeders, deposit feeders, and bulk feeders **(Figure 40.11)**.

Fluid feeders ingest liquids containing organic molecules in solution. Among invertebrates, aphids, mosquitoes, leeches, butterflies, and spiders are fluid feeders. Among vertebrates, lamprey eels, hummingbirds,

a. Root nodules

Root nodule

Adrian P. Davies/Bruce Coleman

b. Field experiment with soybeans (*Glycine max*) and *Rhizobium*

NifTAL Project, University of Hawaii, Maui

c. Bacteroids

© Dr. Jeremy Burgess/SPL/Photo Researchers, Inc.

Figure 40.9

(a) Root nodules. **(b)** When soybeans (*Glycine max*) are grown in nitrogen-poor soil (left), they do not thrive compared with their growth in soils innoculated with *Rhizobium* cells (right). Also, the plants on the right developed root nodules. **(c)** A false colour transmission electron micrograph shows membrane-bound bacteroids as red in a root nodule cell. Membranes that enclose the bacteroids appear blue. The large yellow-green structure is the nucleus.

a. Root signal and bacterial response

Soil particles
Root hair
Bacteria

Root

Root cortex

Bacterial *nod* genes expressed

Flavonoid secreted from root hair

Soybean root releases a flavonoid; *Rhizobium nod* genes are expressed in response.

b. Bacterial signal and root response

Effects of the *nod* gene

Products of the *nod* gene cause the root hair tip to curl; bacterial enzymes break down the cell wall.

c. Integration of bacteria

Infection thread

Swelling bacteroid in cortex cell

An infection thread develops and bacteroids form as *Rhizobium* bacteria become enclosed in root cortex cells.

d. Micrograph of a developing root nodule

Mark E. Dudley and Sharon R. Long

Infection thread

Figure 40.10
Root nodule formation in legumes, which interact mutualistically with the nitrogen-fixing bacteria *Rhizobium* and *Bradyrhizobium*.

nectar-feeding bats, and vampire bats are examples of fluid feeders (see Figure 40.11). Many fluid feeders have mouthparts specialized for reaching the source of their nourishment. Mosquitoes, bedbugs, and aphids have needlelike mouthparts that pierce body surfaces. Nectar-feeding butterflies, birds, and bats have long tongues that can extend deep within flowers. Some fluid feeders use enzymes or other chemicals to liquefy their food or to keep it liquid during feeding. Spiders inject digestive enzymes that liquefy tissues inside their victim, providing a nutrient soup they can ingest. The saliva of mosquitoes, leeches, and vampire bats includes chemicals that keep blood from clotting.

Suspension feeders ingest small organisms suspended in water, such as bacteria, protozoa, algae, and small crustaceans, or fragments of these organisms.

a. Fluid feeder

Sanford/Anglioic/Corbis

b. Suspension feeder

Baleen

© James Watt/maXximages.com

c. Deposit feeder

Joe McDonald/Corbis

d. Bulk feeder

Gunter Ziesler/Bruce Coleman, Inc.

Figure 40.11
General feeding methods in animals. **(a)** Fluid feeders, for example, the hummingbird, which eats nectar. **(b)** Suspension feeders, for example, the northern right whale (*Balaena glacialis*), which gulps tonnes of water and filters out plankton. **(c)** Deposit feeders, for example, the fiddler crab (*Uca* species), which sifts edible material from detritus. **(d)** Bulk feeders, for example, this python, which can open its mouth very wide and take in large objects such as a gazelle.

Suspension feeders include aquatic invertebrates, such as clams, mussels, and barnacles, and vertebrates, such as many species of fishes, as well as some birds, pterosaurs, and whales (see Figure 40.11b, p. 1009). Suspension feeders strain (filter) food particles suspended in water through a body structure covered with sticky mucus or through a filtering network of bristles, hairs, or other body parts. Trapped particles are funnelled into the animal's mouth, and the water is pushed out. Bits of organic matter are trapped by the gills of bivalves such as clams and oysters, and plankton is filtered from water by the sievelike fringes of horny fibre, called baleen, hanging in the mouths of baleen whales (see Figure 40.11b).

Deposit feeders pick up or scrape particles of organic matter from solid material they live in or on. Earthworms are deposit feeders that eat their way through soil, taking the soil into their mouth and digesting and absorbing any organic material it contains. Some burrowing molluscs and tube-dwelling polychaete worms use body appendages to gather organic deposits from the sand or mud around them. Mucus on the appendages traps the organic material, and cilia move it to the mouth. The fiddler crab (*Uca* species) is a deposit feeder (see Figure 40.11c, p. 1009) with front claws differing dramatically in size. The small claw picks up sediment and moves it to the mouth, where the contents are sifted (the large claw is used in signalling). The edible parts of the sediment are ingested, and the rest is put back on the sediment as a small ball. The feeding-related movement of the small claw over the larger claw looks as if the crab is playing the large claw like a fiddle, giving the crab its name.

Bulk feeders consume sizeable food items whole or in large chunks. Most mammals eat this way, as do reptiles, most birds and fishes, and adult amphibians. Depending on the animal, adaptations for bulk feeding include teeth for tearing or chewing, as well as claws and beaks for holding large food items. Some bulk feeders have flexible jaws, allowing them to ingest objects that are larger in diameter than their head (see Figure 40.11d, p. 1009).

STUDY BREAK

1. What role do roots and root hairs play in the lives of plants?
2. What do mycorrhizas do for plants?
3. Describe the four basic feeding types in animals.

40.4 Digestive Processes in Animals

Most invertebrates and all vertebrates have a tubelike digestive system with two openings, a mouth for ingesting food and an anus for eliminating unused material. In these animals, contents move in one direction along the tube. The lumen of a digestive tube (also known as a gut, alimentary canal, digestive tract, or gastrointestinal tract) is external to all body tissues.

Mechanical and chemical digestive processes break food into its component parts, eventually breaking molecules into molecular subunits that can be absorbed into body fluids and transported to and moved into cells. Mechanical breakdown often involves grinding, sometimes with teeth or sometimes in a muscular gizzard. Chemical breakdown occurs by enzymatic hydrolysis, in which chemical bonds are broken by the addition of H^+ and OH^-, the components of water (see *The Purple Pages*). Specific enzymes speed these reactions: *amylases* catalyze the hydrolysis of starches, *lipases* break down fats and other lipids, *proteases* hydrolyze proteins, and *nucleases* digest nucleic acids. Enzymatic hydrolysis of food molecules may take place inside or outside the body cells, depending on the animal.

40.4a Intracellular Digestion

In intracellular digestion, primarily in sponges and some cnidarians, cells take in food particles by endocytosis. Inside the cell, endocytic vesicles containing food particles fuse with a lysosome, a vesicle containing hydrolytic enzymes. The molecular subunits produced by the hydrolysis pass from the vesicle to the cytosol. Any undigested material remaining in the vesicle is released to the outside of the cell by exocytosis.

In sponges, water-containing particles of organic matter and microorganisms enter the body through pores in the body wall (see Figure 25.8, Chapter 25). In the body cavity, individual *choanocytes* (collar cells) lining the body wall trap food particles, take them in by endocytosis, and transport them to amoeboid cells, where intracellular digestion takes place.

40.4b Extracellular Digestion

Extracellular digestion takes place in a pouch or tube enclosed within the body but outside the body cells—the digestive tract. Epithelial cells lining the pouch or tube secrete enzymes that digest the food. Processing food in this specialized compartment prevents self-digestion of the body tissues of the animal itself. Extracellular digestion, which occurs in most invertebrates and all vertebrates, greatly expands the range of available food sources by allowing animals to deal with much larger food items than those that can be engulfed by single cells. Extracellular digestion also allows animals to eat large batches of food that can be stored and digested while the animal continues other activities.

Some animals, including flatworms and cnidarians such as hydras, corals, and sea anemones, have a saclike digestive system with a single opening that serves as both the entrance for food and the exit for undigested material. In some of these animals, such as the flatworm *Dugesia* **(Figure 40.12)**, the digestive

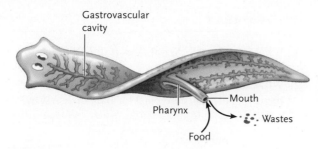

Figure 40.12

The digestive system of a flatworm (*Dugesia* species). The gastro-vascular cavity (in blue) is a blind sac with one opening to the exterior through which food is ingested and wastes are expelled.

cavity is called a gastrovascular cavity because it circulates and digests food. Food is brought to the mouth by a protrusible pharynx (a throat that can be everted) and then enters the gastrovascular cavity (see Figure 40.11, p. 1009), where glands in the cavity wall secrete enzymes that begin the digestive process. Cells lining the cavity then take up the partially digested material by endocytosis and complete digestion intracellularly. Undigested matter is released to the outside through the pharynx and mouth.

40.4c Gastrointestinal Tracts

In most animals with a digestive tube, digestion occurs in five successive steps, each taking place in a specialized region of the tube. The tube is a biological disassembly line, with food entering at one end and leftovers leaving from the other. Five main processes occur from ingestion of food to expulsion of wastes:

1. *Mechanical processing.* Chewing, grinding, and tearing food chunks into smaller pieces makes them easier to move through the tract and increases the surface area exposed to digestive enzymes.
2. *Secretion of enzymes and other digestive aids.* Enzymes and other substances that aid the process of digestion, such as acids, emulsifiers, and lubricating mucus, are released into the tube.
3. *Enzymatic hydrolysis.* Food molecules are broken down through enzyme-catalyzed reactions into absorbable molecular subunits.
4. *Absorption.* The molecular subunits are absorbed from the digestive contents into body fluids and cells.
5. *Elimination.* Undigested materials are expelled through the anus.

Material being digested is pushed through the digestive tube by peristalsis, muscular contractions of its walls. During its progress through the tube, the digestive contents may be stored temporarily at one or more locations. Storage allows animals to take in larger quantities of food than they can process immediately, so feedings can be spaced in time rather than continuous.

Digestion in an Annelid. The earthworm (*Lumbricus* species, **Figure 40.13a**) is a deposit feeder that ingests a great deal of material, only some of which is edible. As it burrows, it pushes soil particles into its mouth. The particles pass from the mouth, through the esophagus, and into the crop (an enlargement of the digestive tube), where contents are stored and mixed with

a. Earthworm

Anus

Mouth   Esophagus   Crop   Gizzard   Intestine   Typhlosoles (increase digestive area of intestine)

Cross section of intestine

Digestive cavity

b. Grasshopper

Gastric ceca extending from stomach

Esophagus

Pharynx
Mouth

Anus

Crop   Gizzard   Intestine

c. Pigeon

Esophagus
Crop
Proventriculus (glandular portion of stomach)
Liver
Small intestine
Gizzard
Pancreas
Duodenum
Cecum
Cloaca

Figure 40.13
The digestive systems of **(a)** an annelid (earthworm), **(b)** an insect (grasshopper), and **(c)** a bird (pigeon).

lubricating mucus. This mixture enters the muscular gizzard, where muscular contractions and abrasion by sand grains grind the food mixture into fine particles. The pulverized mixture then enters a long intestine, where organic matter is hydrolyzed by enzymes secreted into the digestive tube. As muscular contractions of the intestinal wall move the mixture along, cells lining the intestine absorb the molecular subunits produced by digestion. The absorptive surface of the intestine is increased by folds of the wall called *typhlosoles*. At the end of the intestine, the undigested residue is expelled through the anus.

Digestion in an Insect. Herbivorous insects such as grasshoppers **(Figure 40.13b)** are more selective in what they ingest. When eating, grasshoppers tear leaves and other plant parts into small particles with their mandibles, the hard external mouthparts. From the mouth, food particles pass through the pharynx, where salivary secretions moisten the mixture before it enters the esophagus and passes into the crop and begins the process of chemical digestion. From the crop, the food mass enters the muscular gizzard, where it is ground into smaller pieces. Food particles then enter the stomach, where food is stored and digestion continues. In gastric ceca (saclike outgrowths of the stomach; *cecum* = blind), enzymes hydrolyze food, and the products of digestion are absorbed through the walls of the ceca. Undigested food moves into the intestine for further digestion and absorption. At the end of the intestine, water is absorbed from undigested matter and the remnants (frass) are expelled through the anus. The digestive systems of other arthropods are similar to the insect system.

Digestion in a Bird. A pigeon **(Figure 40.13c)** is also selective in what it ingests. A pigeon picks up seeds with its bill and uses its tongue to move them into its mouth, where they are moistened by mucus-filled saliva and swallowed whole. Seeds pass through the pharynx and into the esophagus. Birds such as parrots or cardinals use their bills to crack open seeds, but ingestion occurs as it does in pigeons. The anterior end of the esophagus is tubelike, but it opens into a crop, where food can be stored. The food moves to the proventriculus, the anterior glandular portion of the stomach that secretes digestive enzymes and acids. The food then passes to the gizzard, where muscular action grinds the seeds into fine particles, aided by ingested bits of sand and rock. Food particles then enter the intestine, where secretions from the liver (bile) and pancreas (digestive enzymes) are added. Molecular subunits produced by enzymatic digestion are absorbed as the mixture passes along the intestine, and the undigested residues are expelled through the anus, which opens to the cloaca. Structures such as the mouth, pharynx, esophagus, stomach, intestine, liver, and pancreas occur in almost all vertebrates.

STUDY BREAK

1. What is a gizzard? What does it do? Which animals have one?
2. What are choanocytes? What do they do?
3. Is the diet of *Dugesia* typical for flatworms? Why?

40.5 Digestion in Mammals

The mammalian digestive system is a series of specialized regions, including the mouth, pharynx, esophagus, stomach, small and large intestines, rectum, and anus, that perform the five steps listed above **(Figure 40.14)**. These regions are under the control of the nervous and endocrine systems, allowing mammals to meet basic needs for fuel molecules and for a wide range of nutrients, including the molecular building blocks of carbohydrates, lipids, proteins, and nucleic acids. If the diet is adequate, the digestive system also absorbs the essential nutrients (the amino acids, fatty acids, vitamins, and minerals that cannot be synthesized within our bodies). In other mammals, differences in diet are reflected by the structure of the digestive tract **(Figure 40.15, p. 1014)**. A carnivore's diet is relatively easy to digest; therefore, it does not require as long an intestine as a herbivore does. Plant matter, especially the cell walls, is particularly difficult to digest—hence the longer intestine. The rabbit cecum houses symbiotic, plant-digesting microorganisms that help extract nutrients from plants (see "Digesting Cellulose: Fermentation," Box 40.2, p. 1015).

40.5a Gut Layers

The wall of the gut in mammals and other vertebrates contains four major layers, each with specialized functions **(Figure 40.16, p. 1014),** from the inner surface outward:

1. The **mucosa** contains epithelial and glandular cells and lines the inside of the gut. Epithelial cells absorb digested nutrients and seal off the digestive contents from body fluids. The glandular cells secrete enzymes, aids to digestion such as lubricating mucus, and substances that adjust the pH of the digestive contents.

2. The **submucosa** is a thick layer of elastic connective tissue containing neuron networks and blood and lymph vessels. Neuron networks provide local control of digestive activity and carry signals between the gut and the central nervous system. Lymph vessels carry absorbed lipids to other parts of the body.

3. In most regions of the gut, the **muscularis** is formed by two smooth muscle layers, a *circular layer* that constricts the diameter of the gut when it contracts and a *longitudinal layer* that shortens and widens the gut. The stomach also has an

FIGURE 40.14
The human digestive system.

Mouth (oral cavity)
Entrance to system; food is moistened and chewed; polysaccharide digestion starts.

Pharynx
Muscular contractions move food to esophagus by swallowing reflex.

Esophagus
Muscular, mucus-moistened tube moves food from pharynx to stomach.

Stomach
Muscular sac; stretches to store food; secretes mucus and gastric juice that contains pepsinogen, the precursor to the protein-digesting enzyme pepsin, and hydrochloric acid (HCl).

Small intestine
Duodenum receives secretions from liver, gallbladder, and pancreas. Produces enzymes that complete digestion of proteins, carbohydrates, and nucleic acids; absorbs products of digestion.

Large intestine
Absorbs water and mineral ions; secretes mucus and bicarbonate ions; concentrates undigested matter into feces.

Rectum
Stores feces; distension stimulates expulsion of feces.

Anus
End of system; opening through which feces are expelled.

Salivary glands
Secrete saliva, which contains lubricating mucus, amylase (a starch-digesting enzyme), lysozyme (an enzyme that kills bacteria), and bicarbonate ions.

Liver
Secretes bile, which emulsifies fats, and bicarbonate ions.

Gallbladder
Stores and concentrates bile secreted by liver.

Pancreas
Secretes enzymes (proteases, amylases, lipases, nucleases) that break down all major food molecules and bicarbonate ions that neutralize digestive contents.

oblique layer running diagonally around its wall. Peristalsis occurs when circular and longitudinal muscle layers of the muscularis coordinate their activities to push the digestive contents through the gut **(Figure 40.17, p. 1016)**. In **peristalsis**, the circular muscle layer contracts in a wave that passes along the gut, constricting the gut and pushing the digestive contents onward. Just in front of the advancing constriction, the longitudinal layer contracts, shortening and expanding the tube and making space for the contents to advance.

4. The **serosa** is the outermost gut layer. It consists of connective tissue that secretes an aqueous, slippery fluid that lubricates areas between the digestive organs and other organs, reducing friction between them as they move together as a result of muscle movement. The serosa is continuous with the mesentery along much of the length of the digestive system.

Mesenteries, thin tissues attached to the stomach and intestines, suspend the digestive system from the inner wall of the abdominal cavity.

Sphincters are powerful rings of smooth muscle that form valves between major regions of the digestive tract. By contracting and relaxing, the sphincters control the passage of the digestive contents from one region to another and through the anus. The adult human digestive tract in its normal living contracted state is about 4.5 m long. It is about twice as long when fully extended, as in a cadaver (all muscles relaxed).

Carnivore (a dog)

Herbivore (a rabbit)

Fred Bruemmer

Jane Burton/Bruce Coleman

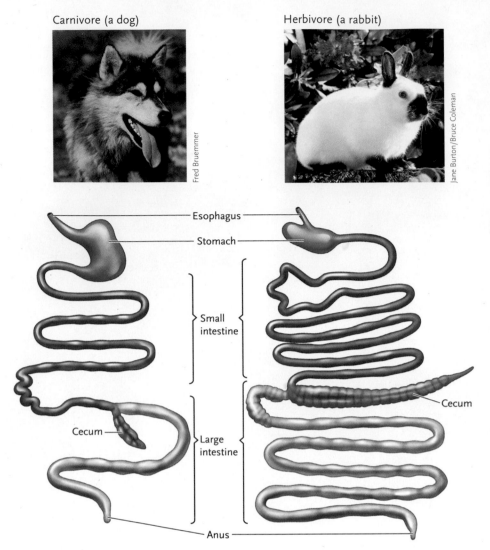

Esophagus

Stomach

Small
intestine

Cecum

Cecum

Large
intestine

Anus

Figure 40.15
Comparison of the lengths of the digestive systems of a carnivore (*Canis familiaris*) and a herbivore (*Oryctolagus cuniculus*). Note differences in length and the development of the ceca.

40.5b Down the Tube

Figure 40.16
Layers of the gut wall in vertebrates as seen in the stomach wall.

Food begins its travel through the gastrointestinal tract in the mouth, where the teeth cut, tear, and crush food items. During chewing, three pairs of **salivary glands** secrete saliva through ducts that open on the inside of

the cheeks and under the tongue. Saliva, which is more than 99% water, moistens the food and, as we have seen, begins digestion (salivary amylase; see "Why It Matters"). Saliva also contains mucus to lubricate the food mass, and bicarbonate ions (HCO_3^-) to neutralize acids in the food and keep the pH of the mouth between 6.5 and 7.5, the optimal range for salivary amylase to function. Saliva also contains a *lysozyme*, an enzyme that kills bacteria by breaking open their cell walls.

After a suitable period of chewing, the food mass, called a bolus, is pushed by the tongue to the back of the mouth, where touch receptors detect the pressure and trigger the *swallowing reflex* **(Figure 40.18, p. 1016).** This reflex is an involuntary action produced by contractions of muscles in the walls of the pharynx that direct food into the esophagus. Peristaltic contractions of the esophagus, aided by mucus secreted by the esophagus, propel the bolus toward the stomach. The passage down the esophagus stimulates the gastroesophageal sphincter at the junction between the esophagus and the stomach to open and admit the bolus to the stomach. After the bolus enters the stomach, the sphincter closes tightly. If the closure is imperfect, the acidic stomach contents can enter the esophagus, in humans causing *acid reflux* or heartburn.

Mammals consciously initiate the swallowing reflex, but once it has begun, they cannot stop it because whereas the muscles of the pharynx and upper esophagus are skeletal muscles under voluntary control, the muscles below are smooth muscles under involuntary control.

Involuntary movements of the tongue and soft palate at the back of the mouth prevent food from backing into the mouth or nasal cavities. The glottis (space between vocal cords) and the epiglottis, a flap-like valve, prevent entry of food into the trachea.

Stomach

Esophagus

Gastroesophageal sphincter

Serosa

Longitudinal muscle

Circular muscle

Oblique muscle

Muscularis

Duodenum Pyloric sphincter

Submucosa

Mucosa

Dr. Richard Kessel & Dr. Randy Kardon/Tissues & Organs/ Visuals Unlimited

Digesting Cellulose: Fermentation 40.2

The digestive tracts of mammals vary in length (see Figure 40.14). Most animals cannot digest cellulose because they lack cellulase, which hydrolyzes cellulose into glucose subunits. Many herbivorous animals (primary consumers) use the hydrolytic capabilities of microorganisms that do produce cellulase. In this way, bacteria, protists, and fungi help other animals to digest plant material.

Herbivores using microorganisms house these symbionts in specialized structures along the alimentary canal. These structures occur in the esophagus, stomach, or ceca, depending on the species. Ruminant mammals (Bovidae, Cervidae) and termites are well-known examples of animals that use symbionts to digest cellulose.

Ruminants use their teeth to crop and chew plant material. They swallow the masticated material, moving it to a complex, four-chambered rumen **(Figure 1)**. The first three chambers of the rumen are derived from the esophagus, whereas the fourth, the abomasum, is the stomach. Swallowed food material arrives in the reticulum and then moves to the rumen. Then ruminants chew their cuds, regurgitating material from the reticulum and rumen, rechewing it, and macerating it into smaller fragments before swallowing it again. This exposes more surface area to microbial enzymes, giving them more time to act.

Fermentation by the microorganisms occurs in the reticulum and in the rumen. Oxygen levels in the chambers are too low to support mitochondrial reactions (see Chapter 7). Matter digested and liquefied by microorganisms moves to the *omasum*, where water is absorbed from the mass. In the *abomasum* (the ruminant's true stomach), acids and pepsin are added to the food mass, killing the microorganisms and starting the process of "typical" vertebrate digestion. As the food mass moves to the small intestine, dead microorganisms, themselves a rich source of proteins, vitamins, and other nutrients, are digested and absorbed along with other hydrolyzable molecules.

Fermentation generates products such as alcohols and amino acids that are used as nutrients. It also produces volatile fatty acids that move from the rumen to the blood and are used as sources of carbon and energy. Microorganisms use 40 to 60% of the food protein produced by fermentation, and, in turn, their bodies are protein for the host. Methane, another product, collects in the fermentation chambers, so ruminants belch the gas in huge quantities. One cow can release more than 400 L of methane per day. Cattle are estimated to contribute 20% of the methane polluting our atmosphere. A 500 kg cow with a 70 L rumen produces about 60 L of saliva a day and ingests 40 L of water. Fermentation takes time: the leaves eaten by a cow take about 55 hours to move through its digestive system.

Many other mammals have esophageal or gastric chambers that house plant-digesting symbiotic microorganisms. Biologists had long thought that the weight of the fermentation chamber made digestion by fermentation inaccessible to birds. But at least one species of bird, the South American Hoatzin, uses fermentation **(Figure 2)**. Freshly caught Hoatzins smell like cattle dung, perhaps giving a clue to their use of fermentation. Hoatzins eat young leaves that are fermented in the enlarged forestomach. This fermentation centre takes up some space occupied by flight muscles in "normal" birds. Hoatzins are weak fliers, probably because of reduction in the mass of their flight muscles to accommodate the enlarged forestomach.

From ALEJANDRO GRAJAL, STUART D. STRAHL, RODRIGO PARRA, MARIA GLORIA DOMINGUEZ, ALFREDO NEHER, "Foregut Fermentation in the Hoatzin, a Neotropical Leaf-Eating Bird", *Science*, vol. 245, Sep 15, 1989, pp. 1236–1238. Reprinted with permission from AAAS.

Upper esophagus

Lower esophagus

Proventriculus

Crop

Gizzard

Small intestine

Ceca

10 cm

FIGURE 2
The Hoatzin (Opisthocomus hoazin) *uses foregut fermentation to digest cellulose to meet a high percentage of its energy requirements. The contents of the crop and lower esophagus account for over 15% of adult mass. Deep ridges in the lining of the crop increase its surface area.*

D. Robert Franz

FIGURE 1
Ruminants, such as the pronghorn (Antilocapra americana), *have a four–chambered stomach system for digesting plant material (cellulose) by fermentation. Some other mammalian herbivores use the same approach, but others, such as the rabbit O. cuniculus, achieve fermentation in other parts of the digestive tract (see Figure 40.14).*

Chewing, swallowing, regurgitation, rechewing, and reswallowing of food through esophagus

II. Rumen

I. Reticulum

III. Omasum

IV. Abomasum (true stomach)

To small intestine

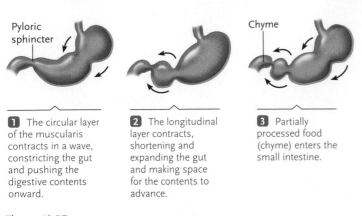

1 The circular layer of the muscularis contracts in a wave, constricting the gut and pushing the digestive contents onward.

2 The longitudinal layer contracts, shortening and expanding the gut and making space for the contents to advance.

3 Partially processed food (chyme) enters the small intestine.

Figure 40.17
The waves of peristaltic contractions moving food through the stomach.

40.5c Stomach

The stomach is a muscular, elastic sac that stores food and adds secretions, furthering digestion. The stomach lining, the mucosa, is covered with tiny *gastric pits,* entrances to millions of *gastric glands.* These glands extend deep into the stomach wall and contain cells that secrete some of the products needed to digest food. Entry of food into the stomach activates stretch receptors in its wall. Signals from stretch receptors stimulate the secretion of gastric juice **(Figure 40.19)**, which contains the digestive enzyme pepsin, hydrochloric acid (HCl), and lubricating mucus. The stomach secretes about 2 L of gastric juice each day.

Pepsin begins the digestion of proteins by introducing breaks in polypeptide chains. Pepsin is secreted in the form of an inactive precursor molecule, pepsinogen, by cells called *chief cells.* Pepsinogen is converted to pepsin by the highly acidic conditions of the stomach. Once produced, pepsin itself can catalyze the reaction, converting more pepsinogen to pepsin. The activation of pepsin illustrates a common theme in digestion. Powerful hydrolytic enzymes such as pepsin would be dangerous to the cells that secrete them. However, enzymes are synthesized as inactive precursors and not converted into active form until exposed to digestive contents.

Parietal cells secrete H⁺ and Cl⁻, which combine to form HCl in the lumen of the stomach. The HCl lowers the pH of the digestive contents to pH ≤2, the level at which pepsin reaches optimal activity. To put this pH in perspective, lemon juice is pH 2.4, and sulfuric acid or battery acid is about pH 1. The acidity of the stomach helps break up food particles and causes proteins in the stomach contents to unfold, exposing their peptide linkages to hydrolysis by pepsin. The acid also kills most bacteria that reach the stomach and stops the action of salivary amylase. Some

Figure 40.18
The swallowing reflex.

Individual not swallowing

Nasal passages
Food bolus
Tongue
Epiglottis (up)
Glottis (open)
Larynx
Esophagus
Trachea
Soft palate
Pharynx

1 The pharyngoesophageal sphincter muscle is contracted, closing the esophagus, the epiglottis is up, and the glottis is open to let air enter the lungs.

Pharyngoesophageal sphincter muscle

Swallowing reflex

2 Swallowing reflex begins when bolus reaches the pharynx.

3 Elevation of soft palate prevents food bolus from entering nasal passages.

4 Pressure of tongue seals back of mouth and prevents bolus from backing up.

5 Larynx moves upward, pushing glottis against epiglottis to prevent bolus from entering airway.

6 Pharyngoesophageal sphincter muscle relaxes, permitting bolus to enter the esophagus.

Glottis (closed)

Peristalsis in esophagus

7 Once food is in the esophagus, the structures of the mouth and pharynx reset to the nonswallowing state.

8 Circular muscles of the esophagus contract behind the food, constricting the esophagus and blocking upward movement.

9 Longitudinal muscles of the esophagus contract, opening up the esophagus. In concert with the constricting circular muscles, this pushes the bolus down the esophagus. A series of alternating contractions and relaxations of the circular and longitudinal muscles produces peristaltic waves that move the bolus to the stomach.

Stomach

KEY
→ Circular muscles
→ Longitudinal muscles

Gastric lumen

Gastric pits

Mucosa

Gastric pit

Submucosa

Gastric gland

3 Pepsin catalyzes conversion of more pepsinogen to pepsin, leading to high amounts of pepsin.

Gastric lumen

Pepsinogen (precursor)

Pepsin (active enzyme)

Digestion of proteins

1 Pepsinogen and HCl are secreted into gastric lumen.

HCl

2 HCl cleaves pepsinogen to produce pepsin.

Surface epithelial cell

Mucous cell: secretes mucus

Parietal cell: secretes H⁺ and Cl⁻

Chief cell: secretes pepsinogen

Figure 40.19
Cells that secrete mucus, pepsin, and HCl in the stomach lining.

nectar-feeding bats that digest pollen drink their own urine to make their stomach more acid.

A thick coating of alkaline mucus is secreted by *mucus cells* and protects the stomach lining from attack by pepsin and HCl. Behind the mucus barrier, tight junctions between cells prevent gastric juice from seeping into the stomach wall. Even so, there is some breakdown of the stomach lining. The damage is normally repaired by rapid division of mucosal cells, which replaces the entire stomach lining about every three days. Most bacteria cannot survive the highly acid environment of the stomach, but one, *Helicobacter pylori*, thrives there. Ulcers result when *H. pylori* breaks down the mucus barrier and exposes the stomach wall to attack by HCl and pepsin (see "People behind Biology," Box 20.2).

Contractions of the stomach walls continually mix and churn the contents. Peristaltic contractions move the digestive contents toward the *pyloric sphincter* (*pylorus* = gatekeeper) at the junction between the stomach and the small intestine. The arrival of a strong stomach contraction relaxes and opens the valve briefly, releasing a pulse of the stomach contents, **chyme**, into the small intestine.

Feedback controls regulate the rate of gastric emptying, matching it to the rate of digestion, so that food is not moved along more quickly than it can be chemically processed. In particular, chyme with high fat content and high acidity stimulates the secretion of hormones by cells in the mucosal layer of the duodenum. These hormones slow the process of stomach emptying. Fat is digested in the lumen of the small intestine and more slowly than other nutrients, so further emptying of the stomach is prevented until fat processing has been completed in the small intestine. This is why a fatty meal, such as a greasy pizza, feels so heavy in the stomach. Highly acidic chyme must be neutralized by bicarbonate in the small intestine. Unneutralized stomach acid inactivates digestive enzymes secreted in the small intestine and inhibits further emptying of the stomach until it is neutralized.

40.5d Small Intestine

The small intestine completes digestion and begins the absorption of nutrients. Nutrients are not absorbed in the mouth, pharynx, or esophagus. Substances such as alcohol, aspirin, caffeine, and water are absorbed in the stomach, but most absorption occurs in the small intestine, where digestion is completed. The small intestine is smaller in diameter than the large intestine. The lining of the small intestine is folded into ridges densely covered by microscopic, fingerlike extensions, the intestinal villi (singular, *villus*). In

Section of small intestine

Mark Nielsen, University of Utah

Folds of small intestine

Villus

Figure 40.20

The structure of villi in the small intestine. The plasma membrane of individual epithelial cells of the villi extends into finger-like projections, the microvilli, which greatly expand the absorptive surface of the small intestine. Collectively, the microvilli form the brush border of an epithelial cell of the intestinal mucosa.

Capillaries

Lymphatic vessel

Villus

Brush border

Microvilli

D.W. Fawcett/Photo Researchers, Inc.

Intestinal epithelial cell

addition, the epithelial cells covering the villi have microvilli, a *brush border* consisting of fingerlike projections of the plasma membrane **(Figure 40.20).** The intestinal villi and microvilli in humans increase the absorptive surface area of the small intestine to 300 m², about the size of a doubles tennis court.

Figure 40.21

The ducts delivering bile and pancreatic juice to the duodenum of the small intestine.

Liver

Bile duct from liver

Stomach

Gallbladder

Pancreas

Duodenum

Duct from pancreas

Exocrine cells secreting pancreatic enzymes

Endocrine cells secreting insulin and glucagon into bloodstream

Digestion in the small intestine depends on enzymes and other substances secreted by the intestine itself and by the pancreas and liver. Secretions from the pancreas and liver enter a common duct that empties into the lumen of the dudodenum, a 20-cm-long segment of the small intestine **(Figure 40.21).**

About 95% of the volume of material leaving the stomach is absorbed as water and nutrients as digestive contents travel along the small intestine. Movement of the contents from the duodenum to the end of the small intestine takes three to five hours. By the time the digestive contents reach the large intestine, almost all nutrients have been hydrolyzed and absorbed.

In humans, the pancreas is an elongated, flattened gland located between the stomach and the duodenum (Figure 40.21; see also Figure 40.14, p. 1013). Exocrine cells in the pancreas secrete bicarbonate ions ($H_2CO_3^-$) and pancreatic enzymes into ducts that empty into the lumen of the duodenum. The bicarbonate ions neutralize the acid in chyme, bringing the digestive contents to a slightly alkaline pH. Alkaline pH allows optimal activity of the enzymes secreted by the pancreas, including proteases, an amylase, nucleases, and lipases. All of these enzymes act in the lumen of the small intestine. Like pepsin, the proteases released by the pancreas are secreted in an inactive precursor form and are activated by contact with the digestive contents. The enzyme mixture includes trypsin, which hydrolyzes bonds within polypeptide chains, and carboxypeptidase, which cuts amino acids from polypeptide chains one at a time.

The liver secretes bicarbonate ions and bile, a mixture of substances including bile salts, cholesterol, and bilirubin. Bile salts are derivatives of cholesterol and amino acids that aid fat digestion through their detergent action. They form a hydrophilic coating around fats and other lipids, allowing the churning motions of the small intestine to emulsify fats. During emulsification, fats are broken down into tiny droplets called micelles, much the same effect as mixing oil and vinegar in a salad dressing. Lipase, a pancreatic enzyme, can then hydrolyze fats in the micelles to produce monoglycerides and free fatty acids. Bilirubin, a waste product derived from worn-out red blood cells, is yellow and gives the bile its colour. Bacterial enzymes in the intestines modify the pigment, resulting in the characteristic brown colour of feces.

The liver secretes bile continuously. Between meals, when no digestion is occurring, bile is stored in the gallbladder, where it is concentrated by the removal of water. After a meal, entry of chyme into the small intestine stimulates the gallbladder to release the stored bile into the small intestine.

Microvilli on the villi of the small intestine secrete water and mucus into the intestinal contents. They also carry out intracellular digestion by transporting products of earlier digestion, including disaccharides, peptides, and nucleotides, across their plasma membranes and producing enzymes to complete hydrolysis of these nutrients. Different disaccharidases break maltose, lactose, and sucrose into individual monosaccharides. Two proteases complete protein digestion: an aminopeptidase cuts amino acids from the end of a polypeptide, and a dipeptidase splits dipeptides into individual amino acids. Nucleases and other enzymes complete digestion of nucleic acids into five-carbon sugars and nitrogenous bases **(Figure 40.22)**.

Water-soluble products of digestion enter the intestinal mucosal cells by active transport or facilitated diffusion **(Figure 40.23a, p. 1020)**, and water follows by osmosis. The nutrients are then transported from the mucosal cells into the extracellular fluids, from where they enter the bloodstream in the capillary networks of the submucosa. The absorption of fatty acids, monoglycerides, fat-soluble vitamins, and cholesterol and other products of lipid breakdown by lipase occurs with the assistance of the micelles formed by bile salts **(Figure 40.23b, p. 1020)**. When a micelle contacts the plasma membrane of a mucosal cell, the hydrophobic molecules within the droplet penetrate the membrane and enter the cytoplasm.

In mucosal cells, fatty acids and monoglycerides are combined into fats (triglycerides) and packaged into chylomicrons, small droplets covered by a protein coat. Cholesterol absorbed in the small intestine is also packed into the chylomicrons. The protein coat of the chylomicrons provides a hydrophilic surface that keeps

	Carbohydrates	Proteins	Fats	Nucleic acids
Mouth	Polysaccharides ↓ **Salivary amylase** Smaller polysaccharides, disaccharides			
Stomach		Proteins ↓ **Pepsin** Peptides		
Lumen of small intestine	Polysaccharides ↓ **Pancreatic amylase** Disaccharides	Proteins ↓ **Trypsin, chymotrypsin** Peptides Large peptides ↓ **Carboxypeptidase** Amino acids	Triglycerides and other lipids ↓ **Lipase** Fatty acids, monoglycerides	DNA, RNA ↓ **Pancreatic nucleases** Nucleotides
Epithelial cells (brush border) of small intestine	Disaccharides (maltose, sucrose, lactose) ↓ **Disaccharidases** Monosaccharides (e.g., glucose)	Large peptides Dipeptides ↓ **Amino peptidase** ↓ **Dipeptidase** Amino acids Amino acids		Nucleotides ↓ **Nucleotidases, nucleosidases, phosphatases** Nitrogenous bases, five-carbon sugars, and phosphates

Figure 40.22
Enzymatic digestion of carbohydrates, proteins, fats, and nucleic acids in the human digestive system.

a. Absorption of water-soluble products of digestion by intestinal mucosal cells

b. Absorption of fat-soluble products of digestion by intestinal mucosal cells

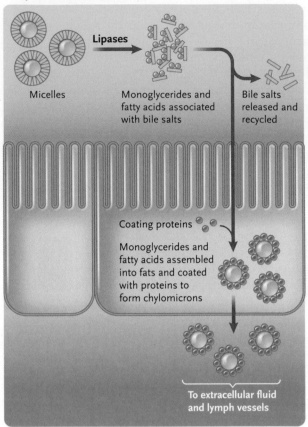

Water-soluble molecules are broken into absorbable subunits at brush borders of mucosal cells and transported inside; the subunits are transported on the other side to extracellular fluid and blood.

Micelles (fats coated with bile salts) are digested to monoglycerides and fatty acids, which penetrate into cells and are assembled into fats. The fats are coated with proteins to form chylomicrons, which are released by exocytosis to extracellular fluids, where they are picked up by lymph vessels.

Figure 40.23
Absorption of digestive products by the epithelial cells of the intestinal mucosa.

the droplets suspended in the cytosol. After travelling across the mucosal cells, the chylomicrons are secreted into the interstitial fluid of the submucosa, where they are taken up by lymph vessels. Eventually, they are transferred by lymph into the blood circulation.

Many nutrients absorbed by the small intestine are processed by the liver. Capillaries absorbing nutrient molecules in the small intestine collect into veins that join to form the hepatic portal vein, a larger blood vessel that leads to capillary networks in the liver. In the liver, some nutrients leave the bloodstream and enter liver cells for chemical processing. Among the reactions taking place in the liver is the combination of excess glucose units into glycogen that is stored in liver cells. This reaction reduces the glucose concentration in the blood exiting the liver to about 0.1%. If the glucose concentration in the blood entering the liver falls below 0.1% between meals, the reaction reverses. The reversal adds glucose to return the blood concentration to the 0.1% level before it exits the liver.

The liver also synthesizes lipoproteins that transport cholesterol and fats in the bloodstream, detoxifies

ethyl alcohol and other toxic molecules, and inactivates steroid hormones and many types of drugs. As a result of the liver's activities, the blood leaving it has a markedly different concentration of nutrients than the blood carried into the liver by the hepatic portal vein. From the liver, blood goes to the heart and is then pumped to deliver nutrients to all parts of the body.

40.5e Large Intestine

From the small intestine, the contents move on to the large intestine, or colon. A sphincter at the junction between the small and large intestines controls the passage of material and prevents backward movement of contents. The inner surface of the large intestine is relatively smooth and contains no villi.

The large intestine has several distinct regions. At the junction with the small intestine, a part of the large intestine forms the **cecum**, a blind pouch. A fingerlike sac, the **appendix**, extends from the cecum. The cecum merges with the colon, which forms an inverted U, finally connecting with the **rectum**, the terminal part of the large intestine.

1. Where and why is methane produced along the gastrointestinal tract?
2. What is peristalsis? What does it do? Is it unique to mammals?
3. How many species of bacteria can occur in a mammalian gastrointestinal tract?

The large intestine secretes mucus and bicarbonate ions and absorbs water and other ions, primarily Na^+ and Cl^-. The absorption of water condenses and compacts the digestive contents into solid masses, the feces. Normally, fecal matter reaching the rectum contains less than 200 mL of the fluid that enters the digestive tract each day. Animals suffering from diarrhea produce liquid fecal matter. Diarrhea is a higher-than-normal rate of movement of materials through the small intestine, which does not leave adequate time for absorption of water. Diarrhea can be caused by infection, emotional stress, or irritation of the small intestine wall.

As many as 500 species of bacteria make up 30 to 50% of the dry matter of feces in humans and other vertebrates. Most of these bacteria live as essentially permanent residents in the large intestine. *Escherichia coli* is the most common in humans and other mammals. Intestinal bacteria metabolize sugars and other nutrients remaining in the digestive residue. They produce useful fatty acids and vitamins (such as vitamin K, the B vitamins, folic acid, and biotin), some of which are absorbed in the large intestine. Bacterial activity in the large intestines produces large quantities of gas (*flatus*), primarily CO_2, methane, and hydrogen sulfide. Most of the gas is absorbed through the intestinal mucosa, and the rest is expelled through the anus in the process of *flatulence*. The amount and composition of flatus depend on the type of food ingested and the particular population of bacteria present in the large intestine. Foods such as beans contain carbohydrates that humans cannot digest. These carbohydrates can be metabolized by gas-producing intestinal bacteria, explaining the folkloric connection between beans and flatulence.

Feces entering the rectum stretch its walls, at some point triggering a *defecation reflex* that opens the *anal sphincter* and expels the feces through the anus. Because the anal sphincter contains rings of voluntary skeletal muscle as well as involuntary smooth muscle, animals can resist the defecation reflex by voluntarily tightening the striated muscle ring—to a point.

40.6 Regulation of the Digestive Processes

Most of the digestive process is regulated and coordinated by largely automated controls, most of which originate in the neuron networks of the submucosa. Other controls, particularly those regulating appetite and oxidative metabolism, originate in the brain, in control centres that form part of the hypothalamus (see "People behind Biology," Box 40.3, p. 1022).

Movement of food through the digestive system is controlled by receptors in and hormones secreted by various parts of the system (**Figure 40.24**). Control starts with the mouth, where the presence of food activates receptors that increase the rate of salivary secretion by as much as tenfold over the resting state.

Swallowed food expands the stomach and sets off signals from stretch receptors in the stomach walls. Chemoreceptors in the stomach respond to the presence of food molecules, particularly proteins. Signals from these receptors are integrated in neuron networks in the stomach and the autonomic nervous system to produce several reflex responses. One response is an increase in the rate and strength of stomach contractions. Another is secretion of a hormone, *gastrin*, into the blood leaving the stomach. After travelling through the circulatory system, gastrin returns to the stomach, where it stimulates the secretion of HCl and pepsinogen. These molecules are

Figure 40.24
Control of digestion by receptors and hormones in the digestive system.

Hormonal controls

Acidic chyme stimulates release into the bloodstream of the hormone **secretin** from glandular cells in the small intestine. Secretin inhibits gastric emptying and gastric secretion and stimulates HCO_3^- secretion into the duodenum.

Fat (mostly) in chyme stimulates release of the hormone **cholecystokinin (CCK)**. CCK inhibits gastric activity and stimulates secretion of pancreatic enzymes.

A meal entering the digestive tract stimulates **GIP** (glucose-dependent insulinotropic peptide) secretion, which triggers **insulin** release. Insulin stimulates the uptake and storage of glucose from the digested food.

Receptor controls

Receptors in the mouth respond to food by increasing salivary secretion.

Stretch receptors in the stomach respond to food, signalling neuron networks to increase stomach contractions.

Chemoreceptors in the stomach respond to food, signalling neuron networks to stimulate the stomach to secrete the hormone **gastrin**, which in turn stimulates the stomach to secrete HCl and pepsinogen.

Richard E. Peter, University of Alberta

Our knowledge about the neuroendocrine regulation of reproduction and growth in fish was strongly influenced by the work of Dick Peter (1943–2007). Peter studied the physiological role of nuclei in the hypothalamus.

He and his colleagues were among the first to measure the secretion of fish pituitary hormones, contributing to both our knowledge of fish and the broader field of comparative endocrinology.

In vertebrates, a complex set of interactions governs regulation of appetite and body mass. By combining techniques from animal behaviour, molecular biology, and immunohisto-chemistry, Peter explored neuroendocrine regulation of feeding behaviour

and food intake in fish. Key factors from the hypothalamus stimulate food intake (orexigenic factors), whereas other factors inhibit it (anorexigenic factors). Pathways of interactions of various factors are shown in **Figure 1.**

Peter also contributed to the advancement of comparative endocrinology by initiating regional, national, and international meetings and organizations. At these meetings, colleagues and their students could interact and share ideas and data. His leadership extended into other areas, serving as chair of the Department of Zoology at the University of Alberta and later as the dean of science there.

Peter is particularly remembered for the excellence of his mentorship. During his career, he supervised the work of 17 Ph.D. students.

FIGURE 1

General schematic diagram showing how central and peripheral peptides regulate food intake in fish. AgRP—agouti-related protein; BBS/GRP—bombesin/gastrin releasing protein; CART—cocaine and amphetamine regulated transcript; CCK—cholecystokinin; CRF—corticotropin-releasing factor; GH—growth hormone; GLP—glucagon-like peptide; MSH—melanocyte-stimulating hormone; NPY—neuropeptide Y; POMCD—proopiomelanocortin.

used in the digestion of the protein in the food that was responsible for their secretion. Gastrin also stimulates stomach and intestinal contractions, activities serving to keep the digestive contents moving through the digestive system when a new meal arrives.

Three hormones secreted into the lumen of the duodenum participate in regulating digestive processes. When chyme is emptied into the duodenum, its acidic nature stimulates the release of the hormone *secretin*. Secretin inhibits further gastric emptying to prevent more acid from entering the duodenum until the newly arrived chyme is neutralized. Secretin also inhibits gastric secretion to reduce acid production in the stomach and stimulates HCO_3^- secretion into the lumen of the duodenum to neutralize the acid. If the acid is not neutralized, the duodenal wall can be damaged.

Fat and, to a lesser extent, protein in the chyme entering the duodenum stimulate the release of the hormone *cholecystokinin (CCK)*. CCK inhibits gastric activity, allowing time for nutrients in the duodenum to be digested and absorbed. CCK also stimulates the

secretion of pancreatic enzymes to digest macromolecules in chyme.

The hormone glucose-dependent insulinotrophic peptide (GIP) acts primarily to stimulate insulin release into the blood by the pancreas. Insulin changes the metabolic state of the body after a meal is ingested so that new nutrients, particularly glucose, are used and stored. Glucose in the duodenum increases GIP secretion, triggering the release of insulin.

Two interneuron centres in the hypothalamus work in opposition to control appetite and oxidative metabolism. One centre stimulates appetite and reduces oxidative metabolism; the other stimulates the release of α-melanocyte-stimulating hormone (α-MSH), a peptide hormone inihibiting appetite. Leptin (*leptos* = thin), a peptide hormone, is a major link between these two pathways. Leptin was discovered in mice by Jeffrey Friedman and his coworkers. Fat-storing cells secrete leptin when deposition of fat increases in the body. Leptin travels in the bloodstream and binds to receptors in both centres in the hypothalamus. Binding stimulates the centre that

Hovering flight is extremely expensive in terms of fuel consumption, whether the hoverer is a Harrier Jump Jet, a helicopter, or a hummingbird. In a hovering hummingbird, more than 90% of the animal's metabolic rate (overall energy consumption) is accounted for by the flight muscles. Hovering allows hummingbirds and some nectar-feeding bats to feed at flowers and tank up with nectar, which is essentially sugar-water. How do these animals pay the costs of hovering?

Some humans eat a lot of sugar before exercising, but only 25 to 30% of the energy they burn comes from the sugar ingested just before or during exercise. It is a mistake to think that eating a bar of chocolate as you run will immediately increase the energy available to you.

In contrast, hummingbirds fuel around 95% of the cost of hovering from the sugar they are ingesting as they hover. High levels of sucrase activity in the birds' intestines translate into rapid hydrolysis of sucrose, explaining the rapid mobilization of this fuel. Nectar produced by the flowers visited by hummingbirds is high in sucrose.

What happens with flower-visiting bats? The Pallas' long-tongued bat (*Glossophaga soricina*, family Phyllostomidae) appears to be a nocturnal version of a hummingbird. These bats hover in front of flowers and use long, extensible tongues to extract nectar. Kenneth Welch and two colleagues used measures of oxygen consumption to indicate metabolism and the ratios of $^{13}\Delta/^{12}\Delta$ carbon to identify sources of energy for hovering Pallas' long-tongued bats. Their measurements indicated that these bats mobilized about 78% of the energy needed for hovering from sucrose ingested during hovering. Sucrase levels in the intestines of the bats are about half of those recorded for hummingbirds, probably accounting for the difference in immediate access to fuel. These results suggest convergent evolution between flower-visiting bats and birds. It remains to be determined if the flower-visiting bats of the Old World tropics (family Pteropodidae) have evolved the same adaptations.

The nectar content of flowers pollinated by hummingbirds is about 60% sucrose, whereas that of flowers pollinated by bats is 20% sucrose. These differences may make the bats less efficient at immediately covering the costs of hovering than the hummingbirds. Hovering to extract high-energy food (nectar) amounts to living on the edge, and animals that do so are highly adapted to pay the costs of this specialized flight behaviour (see "The Puzzling Biology of Weight Control," Box 40.5, p. 1025).

---

reduces appetite and inhibits the centre that stimulates appetite. Leptin also binds to receptors on body cells, triggering reactions that oxidize fatty acids rather than converting them to fats. When fat storage is reduced, leptin secretion drops off, and signals from other pathways activate the appetite-stimulating centre in the hypothalamus and turn off the appetite-inhibiting centre. These controls closely match the activity of the digestive system to the amount and types of foods ingested and coordinate appetite and oxidative metabolism with the body's needs for stored fats (see "The Puzzling Biology of Weight Control," Box 40.5, p. 1025, and "Molecule behind Biology," Box 40.6, p. 1027).

STUDY BREAK

What is leptin? What role does it play in digestion?

40.7 Variations in Obtaining Nutrients

The leaves of plants may be specialized to catch insect prey (see "Pitcher Plant Ecosystems," Box 46.5, Chapter 46), whereas the teeth of vertebrates, particularly those of mammals and fish, indicate the range of diets these animals can exploit (see Chapter 26). This is also reflected in the general lengths of the gastrointestinal tracts and the size and shape of ceca (see Figure 40.15, p. 1014). Some species of fungi lasso nematodes (see Chapter 23), whereas some sponges (see Chapter 25) use specialized spicules to impale prey. Many interesting adaptations and specializations are involved with feeding and digestion.

40.7a Bladderworts: Vacuum Feeding

Worldwide, about 200 species of aquatic bladderworts (*Utricularia* species) use underwater bladders to capture aquatic animals (**Figure 40.25a, p. 1024**). Bladderworts lack roots and get their name from their small bladderlike organs (utricles), thin-walled suction traps that draw in small animals. Bladderworts use active water transport to generate negative pressure inside the bladder, achieved by a two-step ATP-driven pump. Bladderworts have modified cytochrome *c* oxidase, a rate-limiting enzyme in cellular respiration (see Chapter 6), to set their traps. Opening the portal to the bladder is triggered by release of elastic instability.

40.7b Dodders: Parasitic Plants

Dodders (**Figure 40.25b, p. 1024**) and several thousand other species of flowering plants are parasites that obtain some or all of their nutrients from the tissues

a. Bladderwort (*Ultricularia sp.*)

Perennou Nuridsany / Photo Researchers, Inc.

b. Dodder (*Cuscuta*)

© Grant Heilman Photography

c. Snow plant (*Sarcodes sanguinea*)

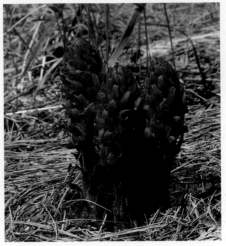

Beverly McMillan

d. Lady-of-the-night orchid (*Brassavola nodosa*)

© Prem Subrahmanyam/www.premdesign.com

Figure 40.25

(a) A bladderwort (*Utricularia sp.*) has bladders that serve as insect traps. **(b)** About 150 species of dodder (*Cuscuta* species) have slender yellow to orange stems that twine around host plants before producing specialized invasive roots that absorb nutrients and water from the host's xylem and phloem. **(c)** A snow plant (*Sarcodes sanguinea*) pops up in the deep humus of shady coniferous forests after snow melt in spring. Snow plants lack chlorophyll and do not photosynthesize, but their roots intertwine with the hyphae of soil fungi that are also associated with the roots of conifers. **(d)** The lady-of-the-night orchid (*Brassavola nodosa*) is a tropical epiphyte.

of other plants. Parasitic species develop specialized invasive roots (similar to the specialized hyphae produced by plant pathogenic fungi) that penetrate deep into the host plant and tap into its vascular tissues. Although some parasitic plants, such as mistletoe, contain chlorophyll and thus can photosynthesize, dodders and other nonphotosynthesizers rob the host of sugars as well as water and minerals.

40.7c Mycoheterotrophic Plants

A snow plant (*Sarcodes sanguinea*) is another variation on this theme. As its deep red colour suggests **(Figure 40.25c)**, a snow plant lacks chlorophyll and does not have invasive roots. Rather, these plants are mycoheterotrophs, which obtain carbon from other plants via shared mycorrhizal fungi (see Chapter 23).

40.7d Epiphytes: Plant Hangers-On

Epiphytes, such as some tropical orchids **(Figure 40.25d)** and Spanish moss **(Figure 40.26, p. 1026)**, are not parasitic even though they grow on other plants. Spanish moss is not a moss but a vascular plant, despite its common name. Some epiphytes trap falling debris and rainwater among their leaves, whereas their roots (including mycorrhizas, in the case of the orchid) invade the moist leaf litter and absorb nutrients from it as the litter decomposes. In temperate forests, many mosses and lichens are epiphytes.

40.7e Gutless Animals

Most molluscs have a prominent alimentary tract, from mouth to stomach to intestine to anus, whether the animal is a bivalve, a gastropod, or a cephalopod. But several species in the bivalve genus *Solemya* have smaller guts. At least one benthic species (*Solemya borealis*) from the northeastern Pacific is gutless, lacking any evidence of a digestive tract. This burrow-dwelling species lives in areas rich in nutrients and appears to use secretions from the pedal gland to effect extraorganism digestion. Ctenidial lamellae on the gills are probably used to absorb dissolved organic molecules. The lamellae are well serviced by circulating blood, and cilia clean the sediment from them. Gutlessness is also known from species in the phylum Pogonophora (beardworms), as well as in tapeworms (Platyhelminthes, Cestoda).

The Puzzling Biology of Weight Control 40.5

Obesity can lead to elevated blood pressure, heart disease, stroke, diabetes, and other ailments. Obese humans are 20% or more heavier than an optimal body weight. The body mass index (BMI), a measure of an individual's body fat, is a standard way to estimate obesity: BMI = weight in kilograms ÷ (height in metres)^2.

People with a BMI between 18.5 and 24.9 have a normal weight, whereas those with a BMI of 25 to 29.9 are considered overweight. People with a BMI of 30.0 or more are considered obese. People with a BMI greater than 27 have a moderately increased risk for developing type 2 diabetes, high blood pressure, and heart disease. Those with a BMI greater than 30 have a greatly increased risk for these conditions.

Conventional wisdom asserts that eating less is the way to lose weight. The relationship between eating and excessive body weight, however, is much more complex. One complicating factor is the probable existence of a genetically determined, homeostatic set point for body weight. If our body weight varies from the set point, compensating mechanisms adjust metabolism and eating behaviour to return body weight to the set point. Thus, if we diet and eat fewer calories, compensating mechanisms reduce the number of calories we use and make the diet less effective. Research shows that the metabolic activity of most body cells in a person on a crash diet decreases by about 15. Each person has a different set point: people of the same height who eat the same number of daily calories vary widely in body weight. Some remain thin, whereas others grow fatter every day on the same amount of food.

If a genetically determined set point governs human body weight, then why is the incidence of obesity increasing in the population? Some researchers speculate that our set points are changing toward greater deposition of fat because, on average, we are less active physically and have greater access to food, especially fatty foods and sugars. The average male Mennonite farmer takes more then 20 000 steps a day. Wear a pedometer and see how your activity compares. Our evolutionary history may also be a factor. Humans evolved under conditions in which food was occasionally scarce, so our built-in physiological mechanisms may actually favour raising the set point and thus storing extra nutrients when food is available. This would provide some protection against starvation if food became unavailable.

The search for factors governing the set point and general concern over growing obesity have sparked intensive research into the genetic mechanisms that might control fat deposition and maintain body weight. In this area, Jeffrey Friedman discovered leptin, and Louis Tartaglia and coworkers found leptin receptors. Leptin is a circulating hormone derived from adipocytes (fat cells). It informs the brain about energy stores. Mice with mutant forms of the genes encoding leptin or leptin receptors become morbidly fat.

The discovery of leptin seemed to offer a "magic bullet" to control human obesity: administer leptin to people and they will lose weight. Further studies revealed, however, that the genetics of weight control are considerably more complex in humans than they are in mice. In addition to genes controlling the production of leptin and the formation of receptors for it, in humans, at least four other genes are involved in appetite control and weight gain, complicating the effects of leptin compared with the situation in mice. In trials with humans, obese patients with mutant leptin genes benefited from leptin injections, but some with normal leptin genes unexpectedly gained weight. Furthermore, none of the obese patients with normal leptin genes had any deficiency in leptin production. Obese individuals produced more leptin than people of normal weight.

Inconclusive results of leptin trials have turned attention to the development of other drugs to control obesity. PYY (pancreatic polypeptide YY), a recently discovered hormone, stimulates the appetite-suppressive centre in the hypothalamus and inhibits the appetite-stimulating centre. Trial injections of PYY in mice, rats, and humans have led to a significant decrease in appetite and eating.

Perhaps one of the best examples of weight control in nature is that of some of the species of hibernating mammals. These animals spend the summer months eating and putting on weight in the form of fat as energy stores for the long winter when food is not available. In winter they go into hibernation, greatly reducing their metabolic demands for energy and living off the stored fat. It has been shown in some studies that animals maintained under summer conditions all year are pre-programmed to loose this stored weight. Thus, during the winter months when they should have been hibernating, they ate less and slowly lost weight at the same rate as the animals that were hibernating without access to food. Thus both hibernating and non-hibernating animals emerged in the spring weighing roughly the same.

40.7f A Termite-Eating Flatworm: Unusual Lifestyles

At night in a garden in Harare, Zimbabwe, flatworms, *Microplana termitophaga*, gather around the vents of termite mounds where they harvest termites, *Odontotermes transvaalensis* (**Figure 40.27, p. 1026**). *M. termitophaga* are most numerous at termite mounds one to two hours after dawn, with peaks of activity after a rain. When hunting termites, *M. termitophaga* attach the posterior third of their bodies to the ground at the entrance to the termite mound, leaving the anterior end of the body mobile. The planarians appear to visually detect termites at ranges of 5 mm. Their eyes consist of groups of photoreceptors (see Figure 1.12, Chapter 1), and

a.

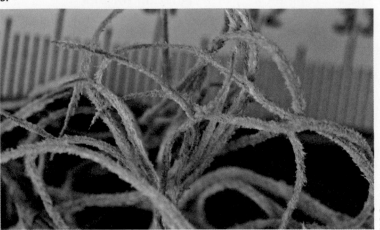

b.

Figure 40.26

(a) A forest in the southeastern United States has lush azaleas (*Rhododendron species*) as well as a southern oak (*Quercus virginiana*) draped with Spanish moss (*Tillandsia usneoides*), an unusual flowering plant. The roots of trees and shrubs and most other plants take up water and minerals from the soil. **(b)** Spanish moss is an epiphyte because it lives independently on other plants and obtains nutrients via absorptive hairs on its leaves and stems (background scale is in millimetres).

although not image forming, their eyes allow them to detect movement.

The flatworm uses its head, apparently with mucus and perhaps suction, to capture a termite, which is subdued and held against the pharyngeal region. In this position, *M. termitophaga* digests its prey, ingests the juices produced by digestion, and then expels the undigestable remains. In 135 captures, *M. termitophaga* took mainly worker termites rather than soldiers. On average, a flatworm ate a termite in 5 minutes 58 seconds. In 3 hours 14 minutes, one *M. termitophaga* ate 13 termites.

This pattern of feeding appears to be typical of predatory planarians. They may release poisonous secretions (to immobilize prey), adhesive mucus (to hold it), and copious amounts of digestive fluid from their extensible pharynges. Other species of flatworms eat earthworms (see Chapter 48), and some make group attacks on giant African land snails (*Achatina* species).

40.7g Fish Predation: More than You Imagined

Invisible in the inky darkness, a deep-sea anglerfish (*Chaenophryne longiceps;* order Lophiiformes) lies in wait for prey, its gaping mouth lined with sharp teeth. Just above the mouth dangles a glowing lure suspended from a fishing rodlike structure that is a spine of the fish's dorsal fin **(Figure 40.28).** The lure resembles a tiny fish, wiggling back and forth. The glow is produced by bioluminescent bacteria that live symbiotically in the fish's lure.

Attracted to the lure, a hapless fish comes within range. The oral cavity of the anglerfish expands suddenly, and powerful suction draws the prey into the gaping mouth. The angler's backward-angling teeth keep the prey from escaping, and it is swallowed. The strike takes 6 ms, among the fastest of any known fish. Contractions of throat muscles send the prey to the anglerfish's stomach, which can expand to accommodate

Figure 40.27

Microplana termitophaga hunting termites at a termite mound in Harare, Zimbabwe. One planarian (centre) has caught a termite. The termites include both soldiers (large head and jaws) and workers.

Figure 40.28

An anglerfish with a bioluminescent lure.

MOLECULE BEHIND BIOLOGY 40.6

Salivary Amylase—What Makes Food Taste Sweet

Salivary amylase **(Figure 1),** an enzyme produced by the saliva glands in mammals, initiates digestion of starch during chewing and can break down significant amounts of starch even before the food is swallowed. Although most digestion in mammals occurs beyond the esophagus, salivary amylase presents an interesting exception. There are several benefits to this. Taste buds sense the levels of sugar and starch and give the animal an indication of the quality of the food it is eating. By hydrolyzing starch into the disaccharide maltose, salivary amylase can have an immediate impact on levels of blood sugar. The same impact on blood sugar is not achieved when people eat (and carefully chew) low-starch foods such as apples. Immediate oral access to energy can be important. Furthermore, in the stomach and intestines, salivary amylase augments the activity of pancreatic amylase and may further buffer the body against the impact of digestive disorders.

In humans, the salivary amylase gene (*AMY1*) varies in the numbers of copies according to the amount of starch in the diet of different populations. More copies of *AMY1* coincides with higher levels of salivary amylase in saliva **(Figure 2)** among seven populations of people, three with high-starch diets and four with low-starch diets. Humans living in agricultural societies and those in hunter–gatherer societies in arid environments have high-starch diets. Hunter–gatherers in rainforest and circumarctic habitats, as well as some pastoralists, have low-starch diets.

Nicholas Curtis and Raymond Martinez

FIGURE 1
Salivary amylase molecule

FIGURE 2
Salivary amylase. **(a)** In humans, more copies of the gene *AMY1* correlates with higher levels of salivary amylase **(b)** and more starch in the diet.
Reprinted by permission from Macmillan Publishers Ltd: NATURE GENETICS, Vol. 39: pp. 1256–1260, "Diet and the evolution of human amylase gene copy number variation" by Paul George H Perry, Nathaniel J Dominy, Katrina G Claw, Arthur S Lee, Heike Fiegler et al., copyright (2007).

---

a meal as large as the fish itself. The anglerfish now digests, sits, and waits. Some cephalopods, some other fish, and the siphonophore *Erenna* species are examples of other animals using bioluminescent lures.

Other predatory fish hunt from ambush. Moray eels, such as *Muraena retifera,* lie in wait in holes. Their eel-like shape makes it easy for them to fit into small openings. Like the anglerfish, moray eels can swallow items (fish and cephalopods) larger than their heads. But although moray eels lack the effective suction mechanisms of anglerfish, they have two sets of jaws **(Figure 40.29, p. 1028).** Like other gnathostomes, the moray eel's mouth is bordered by upper (maxilla and premaxilla) and lower (mandibular) jaws bearing teeth. Unlike other gnathostomes, moray eels also have pharyngeal jaws. In the two upper pharyngeal jaws, pharyngobranchial bones bear teeth and connect to the lower pharyngeal jaws, which also bear teeth. Upper and lower pharyngeal jaws are connected by the epibranchial bones. The jaw arrangement of moray eels allows them to grab and transport (swallow) prey in a system similar to the mechanisms in snakes. The combination of hunting from ambush and quick swallowing of prey makes moray eels efficient predators.

Vandellia cirrhosa, the dreaded candiru **(Figure 40.30, p.1028),** is a specialized catfish that takes a completely different approach to feeding. Normally living as a gill parasite on larger fish, this small and slender predator lodges itself in the gills of a fish. There, like a leech, mosquito, tick, or lamprey eel, candirus drink the host's blood. To understand why the candiru is "dreaded," consider other aspects of its behaviour. Candirus locate hosts by swimming into currents, especially those bearing metabolic end products. Freshwater fish often pass metabolic end products out across their gills. The behaviour can also lead

Figure 40.29
(a) A moray eel with its mouth open does not reveal its pharyngeal jaws, the second part of its bite. **(b)** The skeleton and teeth of the pharyngeal jaws. **(c)** A scanning electron micrograph view of the upper pharyngeal recurved teeth. Scale bars 1 cm (b) and 500 μm (c).

a.

M.B. Fenton

b.

Upper jaw
(pharyngobranchial)

Epibranchial

Lower jaw

Ceratobranchial

c.

Reprinted by permission from Macmillan Publishers Ltd: NATURE, Vol. 449: pp. 79–82, "Raptorial jaws in the throat help moray eels swallow large prey" by Rita S. Mehta and Peter C. Wainwright, copyright (2007).

it into the urethra of an animal urinating while submerged in the water. In South American waters inhabited by candirus, local humans avoid urinating when swimming or bathing and may wear protective covers cut from coconuts to foil invasive candirus.

40.7h Egg-Eating Snakes: Caviar of a Different Sort

Eggs well provisioned with yolk may be the ultimate food, rich in proteins and carbohydrates—everything a predator could want. Mammals such as mongooses break ostrich eggs by throwing rocks against them. Egyptian vultures (*Neophron percnopterus*) break these large eggs by dropping sticks or stones on them. But egg-eating snakes cannot throw stones or sticks.

Dasypeltis scabra is one of the best studied species of egg-eating snakes. Widespread in Africa, these snakes find birds' nests and help themselves to eggs. Like many other snakes, the jaws of *D. scabra* are loosely connected with elastic tendons and ligaments, allowing them to open their mouths extremely wide **(Figure 40.31)**. In a bird's nest, the snake can push an egg against the rim of the nest and swallow it whole. A wide gape is important, but so are an extensible epiglottis and a ribbed trachea, which together allow the snake to breathe while it swallows an egg.

After the egg has passed out of the mouth and into the esophagus, the snake makes a coil in front of the swallowed egg. By moving the coil backward along its body, the snake moves the egg down its digestive tract. You can watch the egg move down the snake, but then,

Figure 40.30
The candiru, *Vandellia cirrhosa*, is a catfish specialized as a gill parasite. The upper view shows the spines that help hold the fish in place.
SOURCE: Based on illustration from Norman, J.R. 1963. A history of fishes; Fig. 96.

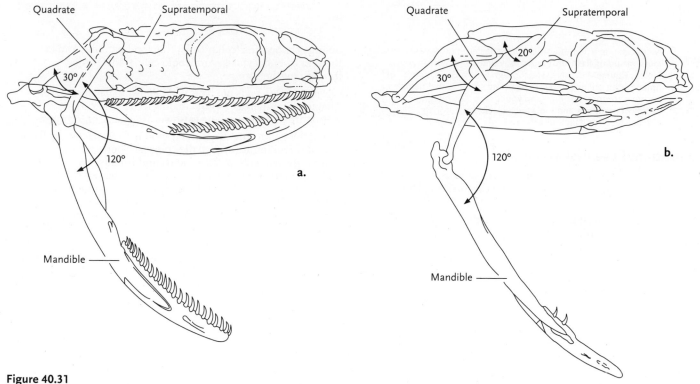

Figure 40.31

The articulation between the supratemporal bone and the braincase (more than between the quadrate and the supratemporal bones) is responsible for a great increase in the gape of a snake. Combined with the position of the quadrate, these features allow one snake **(b)** a 20% larger gape than the other **(a)**.

SOURCE: Based on illustration from Gans 1974 Biomechanics Fig. 2-22.

with a cracking noise, the outline of the egg disappears. The snake has pushed the egg against ventral hypophyses, anteriorly pointed extensions of specialized vertebrae **(Figure 40.32)** that protrude into the lumen of the gastrointestinal tract, *D. scabra* has a built-in egg-cracker.

STUDY BREAK

1. What do anglerfish and bladderworts have in common?
2. Define *carnivorous* in your own words.

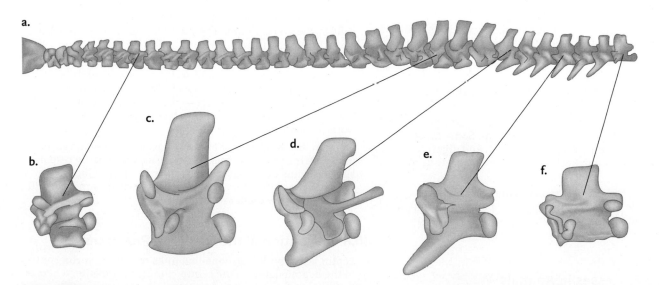

Figure 40.32

Dasypeltis scabra has **(a)** a specialized vertebral column. **(b)** The anterior vertebrae are not especially modified, **(c)** whereas high neural arches make more posterior vertebrae highly modified. **(d)** Other vertebrae are transitional to **(e)** the highly modified, egg-breaking vertebrae. **(f)** Posterior, the vertebrae are more typical of snakes. The spines on the egg-breaking vertebrae are ventral hypophyses.

SOURCE: Based on illustration from Gans 1974 Biomechanics Fig. 2-16.

Review

Access an interactive eBook, chapter-specific interactive learning tools, including flashcards, quizzes, videos, and more in your Biology **CourseMate**, accessed through NelsonBrain.com **Aplia™** is an online interactive learning solution that helps you improve comprehension—and your grade—by integrating a variety of mediums and tools such as videos, tutorials, practice tests, and an interactive eBook.

40.1 Nutrition: Essential Materials

- Living organisms require a variety of materials to survive. Use Table 40.1 to review and compare nutrients essential to plants and animals.

- Malnutrition can manifest itself as undernutrition or overnutrition, involving inadequate intake of organic fuels or abnormal ingestion of fuels, respectively. Undernutrition is commonly referred to as malnutrition and may involve ingestion of too little energy to fuel daily activities or failure to ingest essential nutrients. Malnutrition kills thousands of people annually (see Chapter 48). Overnutrition can result in excessive gain in body mass and other health problems.

- Hydroponics allowed biologists to explore the details of nutrients essential to plants and recognize symptoms of deficiencies of different nutrients in plants.

- Animals such as birds on long migratory flights may mobilize energy from their own bodies during prolonged periods of not feeding.

- In animals, vitamins are essential for different metabolic operations.

40.2 Soil

- Soil is the living skin of much terrestrial habitat on Earth. It provides essential materials for plants and a habitat for animals. Soil consists of particles of different sizes (<0.00222 mm in diameter). Three main horizons (A, B, and C) develop in many soils.

- Soil composition influences plants' access to water and nutrients in soil. Roots anchor plants and also serve as connections between plants and soil.

40.3 Obtaining and Absorbing Nutrients

- Nutrients such as N, P, and K are often scarce in soil, so they are supplied in fertilizers used in agricultural operations.

- Mycorrhizas are symbiotic associations between fungi and the roots of plants.

- Specialized structures in plant roots, stems, and leaves conduct materials up and down the plant.

- Nitrogen can be an important limiting factor for many plants because atmospheric N is not available to them. Some carnivorous plants obtain N from animals they catch and digest. Other plants use associations with nitrogen-fixing bacteria to obtain N.

- Deposit feeders such as some burrowing molluscs and tube-dwelling polychaete worms (see Chapter 25) pick up or scrape particles of organic matter from their surroundings. Arthropods such as fiddler crabs sift food (organic matter) from sediments.

40.4 Digestive Processes in Animals

- The gizzard is a muscular structure that grinds food into small particles. In annelids such as earthworms, the gizzard uses sand to increase abrasive action. Birds and reptiles often pick up stones for the gizzard to achieve the same effect. Insects often have gizzards.

- Sponge chanocytes (collar cells) trap food particles and take them in by endocytosis. Amoeboid cells transfer food throughout the sponge.

- The diet of *Dugesia* is not typical of free-living flatworms (see Chapter 25). Whereas *Dugesia* mainly feed on detritis, other flatworms are predatory, taking earthworms, snails, or termites.

- Along the gastrointestinal tract, food is first mechanically processed, breaking it into smaller pieces. Then enzymes and other digestive aids, such as acids and mucus, are secreted and commence chemical breakdown of food. Enzymatic hydrolysis breaks food molecules into absorbable molecular subunits. This involves reactions catalyzed by enzymes. Then the food molecules are absorbed from the gastrointestinal tract. Finally, undigested materials are expelled through the anus.

- The hoatzin is a flying bird known to use fermentation to digest cellulose. Just-caught hoatzins often smell like cow dung. Their digestive systems include a fermentation centre that uses space normally occupied by flight muscles. Hoatzins are not strong fliers. Other animals, from termites to some mammals, use fermentation to digest cellulose.

40.5 Digestion in Mammals

- Living birds lack teeth and use the gizzard to break food into finer particles. Many (but not all) mammals use teeth to mechanically break up food.

- Mammals such as humans require eight essential amino acids: lysine, tryptophan, phenylalanine, threonine, valine, methionine, leucine, and isoleucine.

- The layers in the gut of a mammal are the mucosa, submucosa, muscularis, and serosa. Each plays a different role in the operation of the gastrointestinal tract. Sphincter muscles control the movement of material through the gastrointestinal tract.

- Peristalsis is rhythmic contractions of circular bands of smooth muscle. Peristalsis constricts the gut and moves food along the gastrointestinal tract. Peristalsis usually occurs in waves.

- Gastric juices are produced in gastric glands that line the stomach. Production and release of gastric juices are stimulated by output of stretch receptors. The 2 L of gastic juices secreted daily by the average human includes pepsin, hydrochloric acid, and lubricating mucus.

- The liver secretes bile salts, cholesterol, and bilirubin. Bile salts are derivates of cholesterol and amino acids and aid the digestion of fat. They operate by forming a hydrophilic coating around fats and other lipids, allowing the churning of the intestine to emulsify fats. Bilirubin is a waste product derived from worn-out erythrocytes.

- As many as 500 species of bacteria may be living in the gastrointestinal tract of mammals. Bacterial activity is partly responsible for flatus in the gastrointestinal tract: the production of CO_2, methane, and hydrogen sulfide. Bacteria may make up 20 to 50% of the dry matter in feces.

40.6 Regulation of the Digestive Processes

- Leptin is a peptide hormone that links two interneuron centres in the hypothalamus. One centre stimulates appetite, whereas the other reduces oxidative metabolism. Fat-storing cells secrete leptin when deposition of fat increases in the body. Leptin moves through the bloodstream and binds to receptors in both centres in the hypothalamus. Binding stimulates the centre that reduces appetite and inhibits the centre that increases appetite.

40.7 Variations in Obtaining Nutrients

- Bladderworts are vacuum-feeding carnivorous plants.
- Dodders are parasitic plants.
- Some plants are mycoheterotrophs.
- Epiphytes grow on other plants.
- Tapeworms and some species of molluscs lack digestive tracts.

- Some moray eels have two functional sets of jaws, each armed with teeth. In addition to their "normal" jaws, moray eels have pharyngeal jaws that make it easier for them to seize and then swallow prey. The mechanism works like a ratchet and is reminiscent of similar systems in some snakes.
- Some egg-eating snakes swallow birds' eggs whole. They use hypophyses—ventral, anterior-pointing processes from some vertebrae—as egg-crackers.

Questions

Self-Test Questions

1. Vitamins are
   a. coenzymes
   b. fatty acids
   c. organic molecules
   d. amino acids
   e. carbohydrates

2. Which of the following is NOT a means by which plants can gain access to nitrogen (N)?
   a. direct absorption of atmospheric N
   b. carnivory
   c. Symbiosis with nitrogen-fixing bacteria
   d. fertilizers

3. Mycorrhizas are associations between which combination of organisms?
   a. fungi and mammals
   b. roots of terrestrial plants and fungi
   c. solar slugs and fungi
   d. fungi and algae

4. In which type of animal is the crop part of the digestive tract?
   a. birds
   b. reptiles
   c. earthworms
   d. a and c

5. How many essential amino acids do humans require?
   a. 2
   b. 5
   c. 8
   d. 10

6. In humans, at what pH does pepsin reach optimal levels of activity?
   a. pH 2
   b. pH 4
   c. pH 6
   d. pH 8

7. Epiphytes grow on other plants, usually trees. Which of the following is NOT an example of an epiphyte?
   a. lichens
   b. Spanish moss
   c. some orchids
   d. dodders

8. Cellulose is digested by fermentation in which of the following animals?
   a. humans
   b. ruminants
   c. the hoatzin
   d. b and c.

9. Which set of animals are among those that eat blood and body fluids?
   a. leeches, vampire bats, and candirus
   b. tapeworms, flukes, and mosquitoes
   c. blackflies, lamprey eels, and bedbugs
   d. wolves, cats, and vampire bats
   e. a and c

10. Why is sorbitol an effective substitute for glucose?
    a. Sorbitol contains less energy.
    b. Digesting sorbitol burns more energy than it produces.
    c. Sorbitol is much sweeter than glucose.
    d. Sorbitol is not toxic.

Questions for Discussion

1. How does secondment of chloroplasts benefit animals (see Chapter 22)? In what animals does it occur? Do these animals have genetic control over the chloroplasts? If so, how do they acquire this control?

2. Although humans evolved as omnivores, some eat only meat, others are vegetarian, and many (perhaps most) eat a combination of plant and animal material. What should a balanced diet include?

3. If you are planting a vegetable garden, what fertilizers would you plan to apply? For the vegetables to qualify as "organic" produce, what kinds of fertilizers would you be allowed to use? What constitutes "organic" meat?

4. Do animals that are usually vegetarian readily eat animal protein? Find an example of a disease associated with this behaviour.

5. Gardeners often plant legumes such as clover between growing seasons. Explain why this practice would be beneficial.

Lining of the trachea (windpipe) shown in a colourized scanning electron micrograph, with mucus-secreting cells (white) and epithelial cells with cilia (pink). The trachea is positioned between the larynx and the lungs, providing a conduit for air entering and leaving the body.

© Steve Gschmeissner/Science Photo Library/Photo Researchers, Inc.

41 Gas Exchange: The Respiratory System

WHY IT MATTERS

In Africa, a huge swarm of the desert locust, *Schistocerca gregaria* **(Figure 41.1)**, composed of millions of individuals, takes off, looking to replace the food source they just voraciously devoured (a swarm may consume the equivalent of food for 2500 people in a single day). Driven by the wind, the swarm normally descends in the evening to take off again in the morning but may remain airborne for more than 24 hours. A swarm may continue to fly during the day for several days until the wind delivers it to food. The wings of each locust, which weighs about 2.5 g, beat about 20 times per second. Their relatively large flight muscles require very large amounts of oxygen to provide the energy derived from fat stores. Insects in flight have the highest O_2 consumption per gram ever recorded for animals.

Like these locusts, all organisms with active metabolism need to exchange gases with their surroundings. The chloroplasts of plant cells need CO_2 for the Calvin cycle, and in the light, these chloroplasts release O_2 by the action of photosystem II (see Chapter 7). Likewise, the mitochondria of eukaryotic cells need a constant supply of O_2, which is required as the terminal electron acceptor of respiratory electron transport (see Chapter 6). In addition, respiration also produces CO_2, which

Figure 41.1

(a) Migratory locust. **(b)** A small portion of a locust swarm in Mauritania in 2004.

needs to be rapidly removed from animal cells because high cellular CO_2 is a narcotic poison that damages nerve function. High cellular CO_2 also produces changes in cellular pH, which in turn alter the activity levels of all functional proteins (enzymes, receptors, transport proteins, etc.).

In this chapter, we introduce the physical basis for gas exchange and describe how evolution has produced a range of adaptations that maximizes the rate of gas exchange both into and out of the tissues of animals living in different environments. For single-celled organisms, exchange is simply across the plasma membrane. For large, multicellular organisms, however, exchange generally entails a series of steps known as the gas transport cascade. These steps (shown for an air-breathing vertebrate in **Figure 41.2**) transport oxygen and carbon dioxide between the environment and chloroplasts or mitochondria.

41.1 General Principles of Gas Exchange

Air normally contains about 78% diatomic nitrogen (N_2), 21% diatomic oxygen (O_2), and less than 1% carbon dioxide (CO_2) and other gases.

This percentage composition of air remains constant from sea level up into the atmosphere. As you climb a mountain, however, the air gets thinner; there are fewer molecules of O_2 (and any other gas) in the environment. The density (thickness or thinness) of the air in the atmosphere is measured as the atmospheric pressure, which is greater the closer you are to sea level and falls with increasing altitude. The unit of measurement is often millimetres of mercury (mm Hg). At sea level, the atmospheric pressure is 760 mm Hg: the pressure generated by a column of air descending from the atmosphere to the surface of Earth is sufficient to support a vertical column of mercury 760 mm high. This

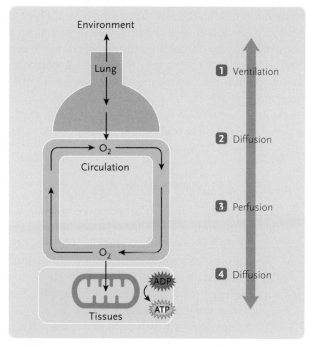

Figure 41.2

The steps in the cascade for the transport of oxygen between the environment and the mitochondria in an air-breathing vertebrate are shown here. There are four steps: (1) ventilation to move gas into and out of the lungs, (2) diffusion of oxygen into the blood, (3) perfusion or transport of blood by the heart to the tissues, and (4) diffusion of oxygen from the blood in the capillaries in the tissues into the mitochondria in the cells. The steps for the transport of CO_2 from the cells to the environment are the reverse of this.

pressure is the sum of the pressures of all of the gases in a mixture. This is Dalton's law of partial pressures. The individual pressure exerted by each gas within a mixture of gases such as air is defined as its **partial pressure.** For any one gas, the partial pressure is calculated by multiplying the fractional composition of that gas by the atmospheric pressure. Given that O_2 is 0.21 of air, the partial pressure of O_2, abbreviated P_{O_2}, at sea level is 0.21×760 mm Hg or 160 mm Hg.

CONCEPT FIX It is a myth that dissolved gases in aqueous solutions always diffuse from areas of high to areas of low concentration. Gases are not equally soluble in different fluids or in the same fluid at different temperatures. For instance, oxygen is far more soluble in lipid than it is in water, and it is more soluble in cold fluids than in warm ones. Thus, when oxygen is in equilibrium between two different solutions, the concentrations in each may be very different if the solubility of the gas in each solution is different, but their partial pressures will be the same. Just as a solute will move by simple diffusion from an area of high concentration to an area of low concentration, a gas will move down a partial pressure gradient from a region of high partial pressure to an area of low partial pressure. ⬡

41.1a Fick's Equation of Diffusion

While gases diffuse between two sites due to differences in partial pressure, the rate (amount per unit time) at which a gas will diffuse depends on a set of factors, only one of which is the difference in partial pressure between two regions. Fick's equation, which is important to understanding the diffusion of gases, recognizes the importance of these other factors. Fick's equation can be stated in a number of ways, but for the diffusion of gas across a membrane or other surface, it can be stated as

$$Q = \frac{DA \times \Delta P}{L}$$

where the variables are defined as follows:

- Q is the rate of diffusion between the two sides of the membrane.
- D is the diffusion coefficient for the gas involved. This is simply a factor specific to the gas molecule that recognizes its size and vibrational activity, the medium (gas, solid, liquid) in which the diffusion occurs, and the temperature.
- A is the area across which diffusion takes place.
- ΔP is the difference in partial pressures of the gases at the two locations.
- L is the path length or distance between the two locations (the thickness of the membrane).

It can be seen from this equation that anything that increases the diffusion coefficient, increases the surface area of the exchange surface, enhances the partial pressure gradient, or reduces the diffusion path will speed the rate of diffusion. We will briefly discuss some of these factors next.

41.1b Diffusion Coefficients Vary with the Medium; Water and Air Have Advantages and Disadvantages

An important variable in Fick's equation is the diffusion coefficient, D. This factor varies with the gas, the medium, and the temperature. The difference between

D in gas and D in water is large: for O_2 at 20°C, the value in water is 1.97×10^{-5}, whereas in air, it is 0.219—approximately 10 000 times as great. The rate of diffusion in air is thus 10 000 times as fast as in water. In addition, for the same volume, there is approximately $\frac{1}{30}$ the amount of O_2 in water as in air at 15°C for the same partial pressure. These two factors require animals that rely on water for their gas exchange to pass a vastly greater volume of water over the respiratory surface in order to be exposed to the same volume of O_2 as an animal relying on air. Moreover, the density of water is about 1000 times that of air, and its viscosity is about 50 times that of air. Therefore, it takes significantly more energy to move water than air over a respiratory surface.

In addition, temperature and solutes affect the O_2 content of water. That is, as either the temperature or the amount of solute increases, the amount of gas that can dissolve in water decreases. Therefore, with respect to obtaining O_2, aquatic animals that live in warm water are at a disadvantage compared with those that live in cold water. And because solutes (such as sodium chloride) are higher in sea water compared with fresh water, animals living in a marine environment are at a disadvantage compared to those living in an aquatic environment.

There are advantages to breathing water, however. Since CO_2 is roughly 20 times as soluble in water as is O_2, CO_2 excretion is easily achieved as a result of the ventilation required to obtain oxygen in aquatic organisms. Another advantage is that the exchange surface is always moist. Thus, aquatic animals face challenges in obtaining O_2 from water compared with terrestrial animals but have a much easier time eliminating CO_2.

For air-breathing organisms, the relatively high O_2 content, low density, and low viscosity of air greatly reduce the energy required to ventilate the respiratory surface to obtain O_2. There are disadvantages to breathing air, however. CO_2 is not eliminated as easily in air-breathing organisms, so the excretion of CO_2 becomes the major drive to breathe. A second major disadvantage of air is that it constantly evaporates water from the respiratory surface unless it is saturated with water vapour. Therefore, except in an environment with 100% humidity, animals lose water by evaporation during breathing and must replace the water to keep the respiratory surface from drying.

41.1c Some Adaptations Increase the Surface Available for Gas Exchange in Organisms

In all plants and animals, gas exchange occurs across a **respiratory surface,** which may consist of each individual cell of the organism, the general external surface of the organism, or highly specialized exchange surfaces restricted to specialized areas of the body **(Figure 41.3).** The first two strategies are only effective if all cells of the body are close to the body surface (Figure 41.3a). It is the evolution of larger specialized respiratory surfaces and/or some means of transporting

a. Extended body surface: flatworm

b. External gills: mudpuppy

c. Lungs: human

Figure 41.3

Adaptations increasing the area of the respiratory surface. **(a)** The flattened and elongated body surface of a flatworm. **(b)** The highly branched, feathery structure of the external gills in an amphibian, the mudpuppy (*Necturus*). **(c)** The many branches and pockets expanding the respiratory surface in the human lung.

gases to and from the surfaces of cells within the organism that has permitted the development of larger and more complex organisms. In aquatic organisms, these specialized surfaces usually take the form of gills as outward extensions of the body surface (Figure 41.3b). In terrestrial organisms, they take the form of inward, moist, protected surfaces such as lungs (Figure 41.3c). The specialized respiratory surfaces are often very large, increasing *A* in Fick's equation. The total area of the lungs in humans is about 100 m². In addition, the cells that make up the specialized respiratory layer are squamous epithelium, decreasing *L*.

41.1d Ventilation and Perfusion Are Adaptations That Increase Gas Exchange Across a Surface

Although all gas exchange occurs by diffusion, two adaptations help most animals maintain the difference in concentration between gases outside and inside the respiratory surface. In Fick's equation, they maximize the value of ΔP, maintaining a steep gradient of the partial pressure of the gas across the respiratory surface and enhancing the rate of diffusion. One is **ventilation**, the flow of the respiratory medium (air or water, depending on the animal) over the respiratory surface. The second is **perfusion**, the flow of blood or other body fluids on the internal side of the respiratory surface (Figure 41.2).

Ventilation. As they respire, animals remove O_2 from the respiratory medium and replace it with CO_2. Without ventilation, the concentration of O_2 would fall in the respiratory medium close to the respiratory surface, and the concentration of CO_2 would rise, gradually reducing the value of ΔP in Fick's equation for both gases and reducing the rate of diffusion to below that necessary to sustain life. Examples of ventilation include the one-way flow of water over the gills in fishes and many other aquatic animals and the in-and-out flow of air in the lungs of most vertebrates and in the tracheal system of insects at rest.

Perfusion. The rate at which blood or other fluids are replaced on the internal side of the respiratory surface similarly helps keep ΔP at an acceptable level. The circulatory system in animals that have one brings blood to the internal side of the respiratory surface, transporting CO_2 (often in the form of bicarbonate) from all cells of the body. At the surface, CO_2 is released into the medium, and a fresh supply of O_2 is picked up. Insects, as we will see, do not use blood to transport these gases.

The evolution of muscular pumps to ventilate specialized gas exchange surfaces and hearts to transport gases between the environment and the tissues throughout the bodies of animals were essential for the evolution of large multicellular organisms.

STUDY BREAK

1. What are the variables in Fick's equation that affect the rate of diffusion across a membrane?
2. What are the advantages and disadvantages of air versus water as a respiratory medium?

41.2 Adaptations for Gas Exchange

For the gases to pass across an epithelium and enter the cells of plants and animals, they must be dissolved and in solution. For aquatic organisms, for which the **respiratory medium** is water, that is already the case. For terrestrial organisms, the respiratory medium is air, and, thus, the respiratory epithelium must be covered by a thin film of fluid. In animals, the most highly evolved respiratory exchange surfaces are correspondingly large, thin, moist, and delicate and are usually highly protected to prevent damage and desiccation (see Figure 41.3c).

41.2a Gas Can Be Exchanged by Simple Diffusion

Relying on diffusion alone for gas exchange limits both the size and to some degree the shape of the organism. The importance of these factors is made obvious by a consideration of the surface to volume ratio. Bacteria, with a volume of about 10^{-18} m³ and a surface area of about 6×10^{-12} m², have a surface area to volume ratio of 6 000 000:1. They can clearly rely on diffusion alone for gas exchange because the surface area is large with respect to the volume, and the distance that the gases must diffuse is relatively small. The same is true of protists, with a surface area to volume ratio of about 60 000:1. Among multicellular organisms, however, an increase in size can be accommodated only if the distance over which diffusion must occur is minimized. Gas exchange by diffusion can only occur if the organisms are thin and flat.

Flatworms (see Figure 41.3a) represent an example of a multicellular organism that relies on simple diffusion for gas exchange. Most free-living flatworms are small, but they may range up to 10 cm or more in length, and parasitic forms such as tapeworms may be as long as 3 m or more (see Chapter 25). But all are thin, so L in Fick's equation is minimized and A is maximized.

41.2b The Plant Leaf Is a Special Case

Like flatworms, a plant leaf has a large surface area over which gas exchange can take place. However, unlike the flatworm, the external surface of a leaf is not available for gas exchange: leaves are covered by a waxy cuticle that is impermeable to gases. We learned in Chapter 27, that gases gain access to the interior of the leaf through pores called stomata. Inside the leaf, there is gas-filled space where gases can move such that the diffusion distance (L in Fick's equation) between the external environment (the air *within* the leaf) and the individual cells is very short **(Figure 41.4)**. Moreover, the total area (A in Fick's equation) of the cell walls inside the leaf is large. These two factors maximize the rate of diffusion of gases between the cells and the environment.

41.2c Insects Use a Tracheal System for Gas Exchange

Insects breathe air by a unique respiratory system consisting of air-conducting tubes called tracheae (*trachea* = windpipe) **(Figure 41.5)**. The tracheae are invaginations of the outer epidermis of the animal and as such consist of the epithelial cells and the cuticle secreted by those cells. They are lined with a thin layer of the same cuticle as the exoskeleton and are

Photographer: Michael Clayton. University of Wisconsin Plant Teaching Collection, http://botit.botany.wisc.edu

Figure 41.4

A cross section of a leaf of a lilac bush. The network of interconnecting spaces, marked by asterisks, brings most cells in direct contact with gases. S marks a stoma through which gases gain access to the spaces inside the leaf.

reinforced by rings of cuticle. They lead from the body surface and branch repeatedly. With each branching, the diameter of the tracheae is reduced, and the tracheae ultimately end as tracheoles less than 1 μm in diameter. Every cell except the hemocytes in an insect's body makes contact with at least one tracheole. In the case of large, metabolically active cells, such as the flight muscles (see "Why It Matters"), tracheoles may penetrate the cell via invaginations of the cell membrane. Tracheoles are dead-end tubes with very small tips filled with fluid that are in contact with cells of the body. Air is transported by the tracheal system to those tips, and gas exchange occurs directly across the very thin cuticle and epithelium of the tracheoles and the plasma membranes of the body cells. At places within the body, the tracheae may expand into internal air sacs that act as reservoirs to increase the volume of air in the system.

Air enters and leaves the tracheal system at openings in the insect's chitinous exoskeleton called **spiracles** (*spiraculum* = airhole). The spiracles are located in a row on either side of the thorax and abdomen, typically one pair per body segment. Each spiracle incorporates a muscle that allows the spiracles to open and close. For many insects at rest, the spiracles are minimally open, allowing a very small current of air to enter. O_2 is consumed by the tissues, and CO_2 is taken up by the bicarbonate buffering system, resulting in a small negative pressure inside the tracheal system. The small inward current of air flowing through the reduced opening of the spiracle prevents water vapour from escaping. As the bicarbonate buffering system becomes saturated, free CO_2 builds up inside the insect, causing the spiracles to open briefly, allowing CO_2 (and water

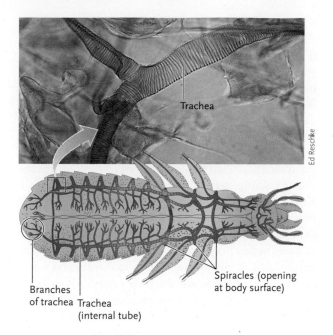

Trachea

Ed Reschke

Branches
of trachea Trachea
(internal tube)

Spiracles (opening
at body surface)

Ed Reschke

Figure 41.5

The tracheal system of insects. The photograph shows the chitinous rings that reinforce the tracheae, keeping them from collapsing. The tracheal system terminates in many tracheolar end cells that have branches with a diameter of less than 1 μm.

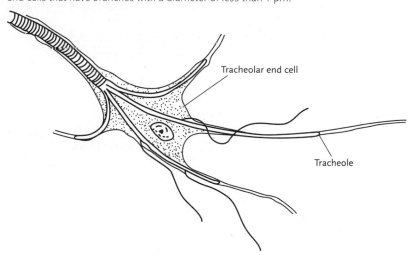

Tracheolar end cell

Tracheole

vapour) to escape. In periods of greater activity, as in flight, this mechanism is replaced by one in which alternating compression and expansion of the thorax by the flight muscles also pumps air through the tracheal system. The spiracles open and close in synchrony with this rhythm.

41.2d Some Animals Have External and Others Have Internal Gills

Gills are respiratory surfaces that are branched and folded evaginations (outward extensions) of the body. They increase the area over which diffusion can take place. **External gills (Figure 41.6a)** extend out from the body and do not have protective coverings. They occur in some molluscs, some annelids, the larvae of some aquatic insects, the larvae of some fishes, and the larvae of amphibians. **Internal gills (Figure 41.6b, c, d)** are located within chambers of the body. This not only provides protection for delicate structures but also allows currents of water to be directed over the gills.

Most crustaceans, molluscs, sharks, and bony fishes have internal gills. Some invertebrates, such as clams and oysters, use beating cilia to circulate water over their internal gills (Figure 41.6b). Others, such as the cuttlefish, use contractions of the muscular mantle to pump water

a. External gills: nudibranch

Kerry L. Werry/Shutterstock

b. Internal gills: clam

Gills

Water flows out through exhalant siphon.

Water flows in through inhalant siphon.

c. Internal gills: cuttlefish

Water flows in around edges of mantle.

Water flows out through siphon. Gills

d. Internal gills: fish

Water in Gills Water out

Operculum

Figure 41.6

External and internal gills. (a) The external gills of a nudibranch (*Flabellina iodinea*). **(b)** The internal gills in a clam. **(c)** The internal gills of a cuttlefish. **(d)** The internal gills of a bony fish. Water enters through the mouth and passes over the filaments of the gills before exiting through an opening at the edges of the flaplike protective covering, the operculum.

over their gills (see Figure 41.6c, p. 1037). In adult bony fishes, the gills extend into a chamber covered by gill flaps or *opercula* (singular, *operculum* = little lid) on either side of the head. The operculum serves as part of a one-way pumping system that ventilates the gills (Figure 41.6d).

41.2e Many Animals with Internal Gills Use Countercurrent Flow to Maximize Gas Exchange

Sharks, fishes, and some Crustacea take advantage of one-way flow of water over the gills to maximize the amounts of O_2 and CO_2 exchanged with water. In this mechanism, called **countercurrent exchange**, the water flowing over the gills moves in a direction opposite to the flow of blood under the respiratory surface.

Figure 41.7 illustrates countercurrent exchange in the uptake of O_2. At the point where fully oxygenated

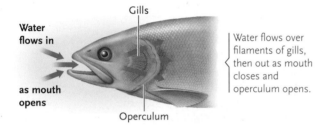

a. The flow of water around the gill filaments

b. Countercurrent flow in fish gills, in which the blood and water move in opposite directions

c. In countercurrent exchange, blood leaving the capillaries has the same O_2 content as fully oxygenated water entering the gills.

Figure 41.7

Ventilation and countercurrent exchange in bony fishes. **(a)** Water flows around the gill filaments. **(b)** Water and blood flow in opposite directions through the gill filaments. **(c)** Countercurrent exchange: oxygen from the water diffuses into the blood, raising its oxygen content. The percentages indicate the degree of oxygenation of water (blue) and blood (red).

water first passes over a gill filament in countercurrent flow, the blood flowing beneath it in the opposite direction is also almost fully oxygenated. However, the water still contains O_2 at a higher concentration than the blood, and the gas diffuses from the water into the blood, raising the concentration of O_2 in the blood almost to the level of the fully oxygenated water. At the opposite end of the filament, much of the O_2 has been removed from the water, but the blood flowing under the filament, which has just arrived from body tissues and is fully deoxygenated, contains even less O_2. As a result, O_2 also diffuses from the water to the blood at this end of the filament. All along the gill filament, the same relationship exists, so that at any point, the water is more highly oxygenated than the blood. ΔP is maximized, and O_2 diffuses at a high rate from the water and into the blood across the respiratory surface.

The overall effect of countercurrent exchange is the removal of 80 to 90% of the O_2 content of water as it flows over the gills. In comparison, by breathing in and out and constantly reversing the direction of air flow, mammals manage to remove only about 25% of the O_2 content of air. Efficient removal of O_2 from water is important because of the much lower O_2 content of water compared with air.

Countercurrent exchange is a remarkably efficient method of exchange and has been exploited frequently in biological systems. Other examples include heat exchange in birds and mammals (see Section 42.7) as well as exchange of ions and water in vertebrate kidneys (see Section 42.3).

41.2f Lungs Allow Animals to Live in Completely Terrestrial Environments

Lungs are one of the primary adaptations that allowed vertebrates to fully invade terrestrial environments. Many researchers believe that the bony fish evolved from a freshwater ancestor that had both fins and lungs, which arose as invaginations of the upper digestive tract. Two lines evolved from this ancestor. In one line, the lung lost its connection to the digestive system and became the swim bladder, which controls buoyancy in the modern teleosts. The other line (Sarcopterygii), represented by only a few living species, retained the lung, enabling them to survive in O_2-poor water or in periods when pools dried up. This line gave rise to the tetrapod vertebrates. In these fish, air is obtained by **positive pressure breathing**, a gulping or swallowing motion that forces air into the lungs (see Chapter 26).

The lungs of mature amphibians such as frogs and salamanders are also thin-walled sacs with relatively little folding or pocketing. Amphibians also fill their lungs by positive pressure breathing **(Figure 41.8)**. In most adult amphibians, a breathing cycle begins with expansion of the buccal (mouth) cavity with the nostrils open and the entrance into the lungs constricted by the

Figure 41.8
Positive pressure breathing in an amphibian (frog).

1 The frog lowers the floor of the mouth and inhales through its nostrils.

2 Air in the lungs is exhaled when the glottis opens due to elastic recoil of the lungs and body wall.

3 The frog closes its nostrils and elevates the floor of the mouth, forcing air into the lungs.

4 Rhythmic movements flush the mouth cavity with fresh air for the next cycle.

glottis. This draws fresh air into the mouth. Next, the glottis opens, and gas from the lungs enters the buccal cavity, where it mixes with the fresh air to varying degrees as it exits via the mouth and nares, which remain open. The nares and mouth then close, and buccal compression forces buccal gas into the lungs. The glottis then closes, and any excess gas left in the buccal cavity is expelled through the nares or mouth at the end of the buccal compression phase. Rhythmic motions of the floor of the mouth with the nostrils open ensure that the buccal cavity contains fresh air for the beginning of the next cycle. The efficiency of the system is increased because much of the CO_2 is lost through the skin. (Remember from Chapter 32 that frogs have a pulmonary-cutaneous circulation.)

In reptiles, birds, and mammals, the lungs become more folded, with many pockets, increasing the surface for gas exchange. Mammalian lungs consist of millions of tiny air pockets, the **alveoli** (singular, **alveolus**), each surrounded by dense capillary networks. Reptiles, birds, and mammals fill their lungs by **negative pressure breathing**, in which muscular contractions expand the chest and lungs, lowering the pressure of the air in the lungs and causing air to be pulled inward. The muscles involved in doing this are largely those of the ribcage but can be assisted by other muscles. In crocodilians, for example, the contraction of a muscle connecting the liver to the pelvis pulls the liver back, causing the lungs to expand, while compression of the abdomen pushes the liver forward, forcing gases out of the lungs. The mechanism in mammals is described in detail in the next section.

In birds, a crosscurrent exchange system makes their lungs the most efficient vertebrate lungs **(Figure 41.9)**. In addition to paired lungs, birds have up to nine pairs of air sacs that branch off the respiratory tract.

a. Lungs and air sacs of a bird

b. Crosscurrent exchange

Cycle 1

1 During the first inhalation, most of the oxygen flows directly to the posterior air sacs. The anterior air sacs also expand but do not receive any of the newly inhaled oxygen.

2 During the following exhalation, both anterior and posterior air sacs contract. Oxygen from the posterior sacs flows into the gas-exchanging tubes (bronchi) of the lungs.

Cycle 2

1 During the next inhalation, air from the lung (now deoxygenated) moves into the anterior air sacs.

2 In the second exhalation, air from anterior sacs is expelled to the outside through the trachea.

Figure 41.9
Crosscurrent exchange in bird lungs. **(a)** Unlike mammalian lungs, bird lungs do not expand and contract. Changes in pressure in the expandable air sacs move air in and out. **(b)** Air flows in one direction through the tubes of the lungs; blood flows across this direction in the surrounding capillary network. Two cycles of inhalation and exhalation are needed to move a specific volume of air through the bird respiratory system.

Figure 41.10

The three patterns of gas transfer encountered in vertebrate gas exchange organs are countercurrent, crosscurrent, and uniform (mixed) pool.

The air sacs, which collectively contain several times as much air as the lungs, are not respiratory surfaces. Unlike other vertebrate lungs, bird lungs are rigid and do not expand or contract. The air sacs do, however, and they set up a pathway that allows air to flow in one direction through the lungs rather than in and out, as in other vertebrates. As illustrated in Figure 41.9, two cycles of inhalation and exhalation are needed to move a specific volume of air through the bird respiratory system. Within the lungs, air always flows from back to front through an array of fine, parallel tubes that are surrounded by a capillary network. The blood flows in a direction across that of the air flow, setting up a crosscurrent exchange. The crosscurrent exchange allows bird lungs to extract more of the O_2 from the air than the lungs of mammals do, but less than with the countercurrent exchange system seen in fish **(Figure 41.10)**.

STUDY BREAK

1. What variable in Fick's equation is most affected by the countercurrent mechanism in gas exchange in teleost fish?
2. What is the difference between positive pressure breathing and negative pressure breathing?

41.3 The Mammalian Respiratory System

All mammals have a pair of lungs and a diaphragm in the chest cavity that plays an important role in negative pressure breathing. Rapid ventilation of the respiratory surface and perfusion by blood flow through dense capillary networks maximizes gas exchange.

41.3a The Airways Leading from the Exterior to the Lungs Filter, Moisten, and Warm the Entering Air

The human respiratory system is typical for a terrestrial mammal **(Figure 41.11)**. Air enters and leaves the respiratory system through the nostrils and mouth. Hairs in the nostrils and mucus covering the surface of the airways filter out and trap dust and other large particles. Inhaled air is moistened and warmed as it moves through the mouth and nasal passages.

Next, air moves into the throat or **pharynx**, which forms a common pathway for air entering the **larynx** or voice box and food entering the esophagus, which leads to the stomach. The airway through the larynx is open except during swallowing.

From the larynx, air moves into the **trachea**, which branches into two airways, the **bronchi** (singular, **bronchus**). The bronchi lead to the two elastic, cone-shaped lungs, one on each side of the chest cavity. Inside the lungs, the bronchi narrow and branch repeatedly, becoming progressively narrower and more numerous. The terminal airways, the **bronchioles**, lead into cup-shaped pockets, the alveoli (shown in Figure 41.11 insets).

Each of the 150 million alveoli in each lung is surrounded by a dense network of capillaries. By the time inhaled air reaches the alveoli, it has been moistened to the saturation point and brought to body temperature. The many alveoli provide an enormous area for gas exchange. If the alveoli of an adult human were flattened out in a single layer, they would cover an area approaching 100 m², about the size of a tennis court! The epithelium of the alveoli is composed of very thin squamous cells. In terms of Fick's law, A is very large and D is minimized.

The trachea and larger bronchi are nonmuscular tubes encircled by rings of cartilage that prevent the tubes from compressing (recall the analogous but not homologous arrangement in the tracheae of insects). The largest of the rings, which reinforces the larynx, stands out at the front of the throat as the Adam's apple, which is more prominent in males. The walls of the smaller bronchi and the bronchioles contain smooth muscle cells that contract or relax to control the diameter of these passages and with it the amount of air flowing to and from the alveoli.

The epithelium lining each bronchus contains cilia and mucus-secreting cells. Bacteria and airborne particles such as dust and pollen are trapped in the mucus (see "Molecule behind Biology," Box 41.1, p. 1042) and then moved upward and into the throat by the beating of the cilia lining the airways. Infection-fighting macrophages (see Chapter 43) also patrol the respiratory epithelium.

41.3b Contractions of the Diaphragm and Muscles between the Ribs Ventilate the Lungs

The lungs are located in the ribcage above the *diaphragm,* a dome-shaped sheet of skeletal muscle separating the chest cavity from the abdominal cavity.

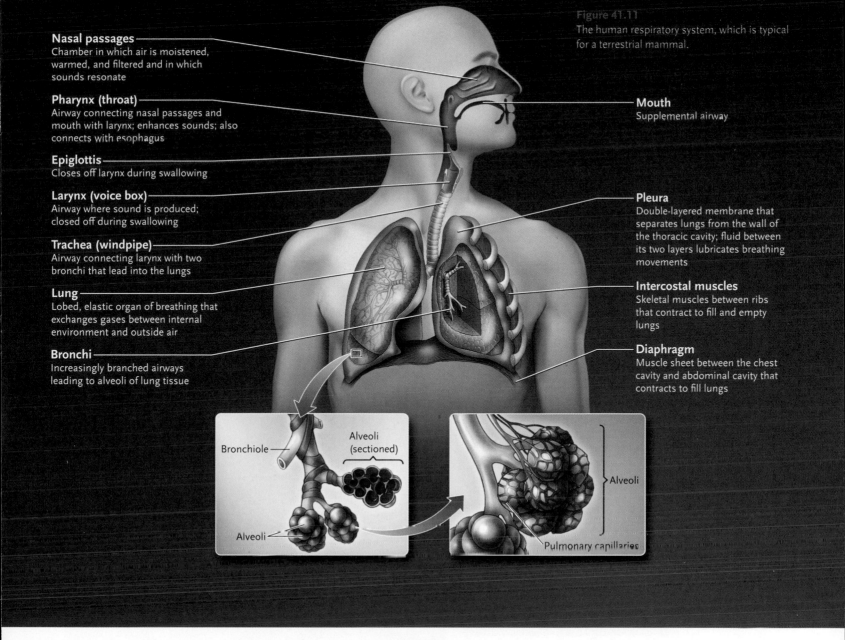

Nasal passages
Chamber in which air is moistened, warmed, and filtered and in which sounds resonate

Pharynx (throat)
Airway connecting nasal passages and mouth with larynx; enhances sounds; also connects with esophagus

Epiglottis
Closes off larynx during swallowing

Larynx (voice box)
Airway where sound is produced; closed off during swallowing

Trachea (windpipe)
Airway connecting larynx with two bronchi that lead into the lungs

Lung
Lobed, elastic organ of breathing that exchanges gases between internal environment and outside air

Bronchi
Increasingly branched airways leading to alveoli of lung tissue

Mouth
Supplemental airway

Pleura
Double-layered membrane that separates lungs from the wall of the thoracic cavity; fluid between its two layers lubricates breathing movements

Intercostal muscles
Skeletal muscles between ribs that contract to fill and empty lungs

Diaphragm
Muscle sheet between the chest cavity and abdominal cavity that contracts to fill lungs

Bronchiole

Alveoli (sectioned)

Alveoli

Alveoli

Pulmonary capillaries

The lungs are covered by a double layer of epithelial tissue called the **pleura**. The inner pleural layer is attached to the surface of the lungs, and the outer layer is attached to the surface of the chest cavity. A narrow space between the inner and outer layers is filled with slippery fluid, which allows the lungs to move within the chest cavity without rubbing or abrasion as they expand and contract. This fluid also creates a surface tension between the chest wall and the outer covering of the lung. As a result, the lungs cling to the chest wall (like any two wet surfaces) and expand and contract passively as the volume of the chest cavity changes. If air is introduced into this space, due to either rupture of the lung or a penetrating injury to the chest wall (pneumothorax), the lung on that side will collapse.

Contraction of the diaphragm and the intercostal muscles between the ribs brings air into the lungs by a negative pressure mechanism. As an inhalation begins, the diaphragm contracts and flattens, and one set of muscles between the ribs, the external intercostal muscles, contracts, pulling the ribs upward and outward **(Figure 41.12, p. 1043).** These movements expand the chest cavity and lungs, lowering the air pressure in the lungs below that of the atmosphere. As a result, air is drawn into the lungs, expanding and filling them.

The expansion of the lungs is much like filling two rubber balloons. Like balloons, the lungs are elastic and resist stretching as they are filled. And also like balloons, the stretching stores energy that can be released to expel air from the lungs. During an exhalation by a person at rest, the diaphragm and muscles

MOLECULE BEHIND BIOLOGY 41.1

Mucin: Sticky Lubricant

The airways leading to the lungs have a surface coating of mucus secreted by specialized epithelial cells. The sticky mucus traps dust particles, bacteria, and other foreign bodies and is swept upward by the action of cilia to be swallowed into the digestive tract or expelled by the act of blowing your nose or spitting. Mucus is composed of a rodlike protein, mucin, that is very heavily glycosylated (the addition of sugars) after translation (see Section 15.3) and that forms giant polymers up to 10 million Da (daltons, a *unit* used for mass on a molecular scale). The very dense coating of sugar provides a lot of water-holding capacity. This gives mucin its slippery character, which makes it useful as a lubricant. Mucins constitute a family of proteins,

and at least 19 genes are known for humans. Three of these are expressed in airway epithelium. Mucins are also important in the mucus that coats the intestinal epithelium, where it serves as a lubricant and protects the epithelium from gastric acids and enzymes. Mucus also lines the reproductive tract. Mucins are important constituents of saliva, keeping the membranes of the oral cavity moist and lubricating the food as it is chewed. Tears contain mucins, continuously washing the eye free of dust. All of these mucins are produced continuously, often in large quantities.

Other mucins, the *tethered* or membrane-associated mucins, are attached to cell membranes, where they serve a variety of functions. In

addition to the mucins in tears, mucins are also attached to the membranes of the surface of the eye, a slippery surface over which tears can move more easily. The function of the several membrane-associated mucins is far from clear. They may have a role in preventing infection or in cell-to-cell attachment, or, in some cases, they may be part of a cell-signalling mechanism.

Mucins are ancient molecules and occur in most metazoan phyla as well as in protists. In insects, a mucin gene is expressed in the intestine, and mucins are known from nematodes. In molluscs, mucins are found in the matrix that contains calcite to form the shell.

a.

JUERGEN BERGER/SCIENCE PHOTO LIBRARY

b.

© Lonely Planet Images/Alamy

c.

carlo dapino/Shutterstock

FIGURE 1

Mucins act as lubricants on many membranes. *(a)* Staphylococcus aureus *bacteria (yellow) on human nasal epithelial cells adhering to mucus (blue) on the hairlike cilia that protrude from the epithelial cells. Mucins are also common in* **(b)** *saliva and* **(c)** *tears.*

between the ribs relax, and the elastic recoil of the lungs expels the air.

When physical activity increases the body's demand for O_2, contractions of other muscles help expel the air by forcefully reducing the volume of the chest cavity. That is, the abdominal wall muscles contract, which increases abdominal pressure. That pressure exerts an upward-directed force on the diaphragm, which is pushed upward. In addition,

internal intercostal muscles contract, pulling the chest wall inward and downward, causing it to flatten. As a result, the dimensions of the chest cavity decrease.

41.3c The Volume of Inhaled and Exhaled Air Varies over Wide Limits

The volume of air entering and leaving the lungs during inhalation and exhalation is called the **tidal volume.** In

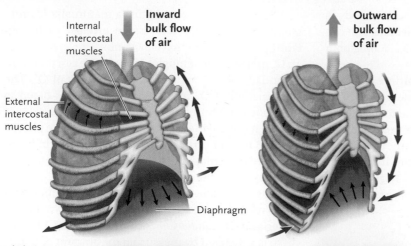

Internal intercostal muscles

Inward bulk flow of air

External intercostal muscles

Diaphragm

Outward bulk flow of air

Inhalation.
Diaphragm contracts and moves down. The external intercostal muscles contract and lift rib cage upward and outward. The lung volume expands.

SIU/Visuals Unlimited, Inc.

Exhalation during breathing or rest.
Diaphragm and external intercostal muscles return to the resting positions. Rib cage moves down. Lungs recoil passively.

SIU/Visuals Unlimited, Inc.

Figure 41.12
The respiratory movements of humans during breathing at rest. The movements of the rib-cage and diaphragm fill and empty the lungs. Inhalation is powered by contractions of the external intercostal muscles and diaphragm, and exhalation is passive. During exercise or other activities characterized by deeper and more rapid breathing, contractions of the internal intercostal muscles and the abdominal muscles add force to exhalation. The X-ray images show how the volume of the lungs increases during inhalation and decreases during exhalation.

a person at rest, the tidal volume amounts to about 500 mL. As physical activity increases, the tidal volume increases to match the body's demands for O_2; at maximal levels, the tidal volume reaches about 3400 mL in females and 4800 mL in males. This maximum tidal volume is called the **vital capacity** of an individual.

Even after the most forceful exhalation, about 1200 mL of air remains in the lungs in males and about 1000 mL in females; this is the **residual volume** of the lungs. In fact, the lungs cannot be deflated completely because small airways collapse during forced exhalation, blocking further outflow of air. Because air cannot be removed from the lungs completely, some gas exchange can always occur between blood flowing through the lungs and the air in the alveoli.

41.3d Ventilation Is Initiated and Controlled by Centres in the Brain

The respiratory movements are controlled by centres in the medulla and pons, part of the brain stem (see Chapter 37). Nerve signals from these centres to the muscles involved in breathing can vary the intake of air from as little as 5 to 6 L per minute to as much as 150 L per minute (for very brief periods). These centres integrate information about O_2 and CO_2 in the blood from O_2 and CO_2 receptors. These receptors are located in special sense organs (the carotid bodies) in the carotid arteries, which supply the brain, and in the aorta (the aortic body), which supplies blood to the rest of the body. These receptors are more sensitive to changes in CO_2: the P_{O_2} must drop below about 100 mm Hg before their activity increases significantly. The medulla integrates this information

with information coming from its own receptors, which monitor the pH of the cerebrospinal fluid. The pH of this fluid is determined mostly by the CO_2 concentration in the blood. (Remember that the pH decreases as CO_2 levels increase.) In general, the CO_2 level is most closely monitored. The O_2 receptors act as a backup system, which comes into play only when blood O_2 concentration falls to critically low levels. The level of CO_2 in the blood and body fluids is much more closely monitored and has a much greater effect on breathing than the O_2 level (see Section 41.1). This reflects the fact that air-breathing vertebrates have far more trouble eliminating CO_2 than obtaining O_2 under normal conditions, along with the fact that small changes in pH due to changes in the levels of CO_2 throughout the body profoundly affect the activity of all functional proteins, such as enzymes.

STUDY BREAK

1. Compare and contrast the ways in which bird and mammalian lungs are designed to enhance gas exchange in terms of the components of Fick's equation.
2. What is tidal volume and why is called by this name?

41.4 Mechanisms of Gas Transport

In this section, we consider the means by which gases are transported between the respiratory exchange surfaces and other body tissues. Recall that O_2 is not very soluble in fluids and so transport within the body is aided in most animals by pigment molecules that can bind and transport larger quantities of O_2. Hemoglobin is the vertebrate respiratory pigment.

At both the respiratory exchange surface and body tissues, gas exchange occurs when the gas diffuses from an area of higher partial pressure to an area of lower partial pressure. At the sites of gas exchange with the environment, the P_{O_2} in the environment is higher than the P_{O_2} in deoxygenated blood entering the network of capillaries in the gills or lungs (Figure 41.13). As a result, O_2 readily diffuses into the plasma solution in the capillaries.

41.4a Hemoglobin Greatly Increases the O_2-Carrying Capacity of the Blood

In vertebrates, after entering the plasma, O_2 diffuses into erythrocytes, where it combines with hemoglobin. The combination with hemoglobin removes O_2 from the plasma, lowering the P_{O_2} of the plasma and increasing ΔP between alveolar air and the blood. This increases the rate of diffusion of O_2 across the alveoli and into the plasma.

KEY

- ■ Partial pressure of O_2 (P_{O_2})
- ■ Partial pressure of CO_2 (P_{CO_2})

Figure 41.13
The partial pressures of O_2 (pink) and CO_2 (blue) in various locations in the body.

Recall from Chapter 32 that a mammalian hemoglobin molecule has four heme groups, each containing an iron atom that can combine reversibly with an O_2 molecule. A hemoglobin molecule can therefore potentially bind a total of four molecules of O_2. The combination of O_2 with hemoglobin allows blood to carry about 60 times as much O_2 (about 200 mL per litre) as it could if the O_2 simply dissolved in the plasma (about 3 mL per litre). About 98.5% of the O_2 in blood is carried by hemoglobin, and about 1.5% is carried in solution in the blood plasma.

The reversible combination of hemoglobin with O_2 is related to the P_{O_2} in a pattern shown by the *hemoglobin–O_2 equilibrium curve* in **Figure 41.14.** (The curve is generated by measuring the amount of hemoglobin saturated at a given P_{O_2}.) In air-breathing vertebrates, the curve is not linear but S-shaped, with a plateau region. As the P_{O_2} of the plasma increases, hemoglobin binds to the O_2 until every hemoglobin molecule is bound to four molecules of O_2. Once the hemoglobin is fully saturated, further increases in P_{O_2} lead to only a small extra amount of O_2 going into solution—the hemoglobin can hold no more. Note that over the steep part of the curve between 0 and 60 mm Hg (the range found in the capillaries throughout the bodies of most vertebrates), small changes in P_{O_2} result in large changes in the amount of O_2 bound to hemoglobin.

Because the P_{O_2} in alveolar air is about 100 mm Hg, most of the hemoglobin molecules in the blood leaving the alveolar networks are fully saturated, meaning that most of the hemoglobin molecules have bound four O_2 molecules (see Figure 41.14a). The P_{O_2} of the O_2 in solution in the blood plasma has risen to approximately the same level as in the alveolar air, about 100 mm Hg. This blood will also change colour, reflecting the bright red colour of oxygenated hemoglobin compared with the darker red colour of deoxygenated hemoglobin.

The oxygenated blood exiting from the alveoli collects in venules, which merge to form the pulmonary veins leaving the lungs. These veins carry the blood to the heart, which pumps the blood through the systemic circulation to all parts of the body.

As the oxygenated blood enters the capillary networks of body tissues, it encounters regions in which the P_{O_2} in the interstitial fluid and body cells is lower than that in the blood, ranging from about 40 mm Hg downward to 20 mm Hg or less (see Figure 41.14b). As a result, O_2 diffuses from the blood plasma into the interstitial fluid and from the fluid into body cells. As O_2 diffuses from the blood plasma into body tissues, it is replaced by O_2 released from hemoglobin.

Several factors contribute to the release of O_2 from hemoglobin, including increased acidity (lower pH) in active tissues. The acidity increases because oxidative reactions release CO_2, which combines with water to form carbonic acid (H_2CO_3). The lowered pH reduces

Enhancing Performance: Blood Doping 41.2

Because red blood cells (RBCs) greatly increase the ability of blood to transport oxygen, enhancing the number of RBCs in the bloodstream can enhance athletic performance. Initially, blood doping was achieved by the transfusion of blood, either from other individuals (homologous transfusion) or withdrawn earlier from the athlete and stored until just before a competition (autologous trans-fusion). Both types of transfusion can be dangerous for a host of reasons, including improperly stored blood,

risks of communication of infectious diseases, possibility of a transfusion reaction, and risk of infection. More recently, blood doping has been achieved by the use of the hormone erythropoietin (EPO). EPO is a naturally occurring growth factor that stimulates the formation of new RBCs. Injections of EPO can increase RBC counts for more than six months, and its use has become widespread in endurance sports. Again, it is not without risk since if the RBC count becomes too high, the blood

more viscous, increasing the work that must be done by the heart.

Becky Scott, now a retired Canadian cross-country skier, was originally awarded a bronze medal at the 2002 Salt Lake City Olympic Games for the 5 km pursuit. Scott's performance was all the more impressive given the nature of her competition. Her medal was later upgraded to a silver, then gold after both of the other medallists tested positive for darbepoetin, a pharmacological version of EPO that stimulates erythropoiesis.

the affinity of hemoglobin for O_2, which is released and used in cellular respiration.

The net diffusion of O_2 from blood to body cells continues until the blood leaves the capillary networks in the body tissues, at which point much of the O_2 has been removed from hemoglobin. The blood, now with a P_{O_2} of 40 mm Hg or less, returns in veins to the heart, which pumps it through the pulmonary arteries to the lungs for oxygenation.

41.4b Carbon Dioxide Diffuses down Partial Pressure Gradients from Body Tissues and into the Blood and Alveolar Air

The CO_2 produced by cellular oxidation diffuses from active cells into the interstitial fluid, where it reaches a partial pressure of about 46 mm Hg. Because this P_{CO_2} is higher than the 40 mm Hg P_{CO_2} in the blood entering the capillary networks of body tissues, CO_2 diffuses

a. Hemoglobin saturation level in lungs

b. Hemoglobin saturation range in body tissues

In the alveoli, in which the P_{O_2} is about 100 mm Hg and the pH is 7.4, most hemoglobin molecules are 100% saturated, meaning that almost all have bound four O_2 molecules.

In the capillaries of body tissues, where the P_{O_2} varies between about 20 and 40 mm Hg depending on the level of metabolic activity and the pH is about 7.2, hemoglobin can hold less O_2. As a result, most hemoglobin molecules release two or three of their O_2 molecules to become between 25% and 50% saturated. Note that the drop in pH to 7.2 (red line) in active body tissues reduces the amount of O_2 hemoglobin can hold as compared with pH 7.4. The reduction in binding affinity at lower pH increases the amount of O_2 released in active tissues.

Figure 41.14

Hemoglobin–O_2 equilibrium curves, which show the degree to which hemoglobin is saturated with O_2 at increasing P_{O_2}.

from the interstitial fluid into the blood plasma (**Figure 41.15a**).

Some of the CO_2 remains in solution as a gas in the plasma. In many organisms, however, significant amounts combine with water to produce carbonic acid (H_2CO_3), which dissociates into bicarbonate (HCO_3^-) and H^+ ions. In the erythrocyte, the enzyme carbonic anhydrase accelerates the reaction. This reaction maintains a maximal concentration gradient of CO_2 between the cells and the blood and is a means of temporarily storing the gas in a harmless form until it can be transported to the respiratory surface of the animal for release once more as a gas.

Most of the H^+ ions produced by the dissociation of carbonic acid combine with hemoglobin or with proteins in the blood. This combination, by removing excess H^+ from the blood solution, *buffers* the pH of the blood, helping to maintain it at the set point appropriate for the species, usually about 7.4.

CONCEPT FIX It is a common misconception that in mammals (including humans), exhaled air is depleted of oxygen. In actual fact, for most humans, exhaled air still contains 16% O_2 (inspired air contains 21%). For many animals under resting conditions, a very significant reserve of oxygen remains in the lung at the end of a breath. The exhaled air also contains 4% CO_2, however, and for air-breathing terrestrial vertebrates, it is the need to eliminate CO_2 that is the primary drive to breathe.

Figure 41.15
The reactions occurring during the transfer of CO_2 from body tissues to alveolar air.

a. Body tissues

In body tissues, some of the CO_2 released into the blood combines with water in the blood plasma to form HCO_3^- and H^+. However, most of the CO_2 diffuses into erythrocytes, where some combines directly with hemoglobin and some combines with water to form HCO_3^- and H^+. The H^+ formed by this reaction combines with hemoglobin; the HCO_3^- is transported out of erythrocytes to add to the HCO_3^- in the blood plasma.

b. Lungs

In the lungs, the reactions are reversed. Some of the HCO_3^- in the blood plasma combines with H^+ to form CO_2 and water. However, most of the HCO_3^- is transported into erythrocytes, where it combines with H^+ released from hemoglobin to form CO_2 and water. CO_2 is released from hemoglobin. The CO_2 diffuses from the erythrocytes and, with the CO_2 in the blood plasma, diffuses from the blood into the alveolar air.

Peter Hochachka, University of British Columbia

Dr. Peter Hochachka (1937–2002), of the University of British Columbia, spent his career exploring the various biochemical mechanisms that allow animals to exploit extreme environments. Among his interests were the metabolic characteristics of animals in environments low in O_2. He brought Sherpas from the Himalaya and Quechuas from the high Andes as volunteer research subjects to his lab and used positron emission tomography (PET) and magnetic resonance spectroscopy, two techniques that permit the non-invasive characterization of metabolic activity, as well as magnetic resonance imaging (MRI), to understand their metabolism. He and his collaborators showed that the brains of the volunteers living at high altitudes metabolized O_2 at lower rates. Their hearts relied more on glucose as a fuel, an arrangement that produces more work per O_2 molecule than the greater reliance on fatty acids characteristic of the hearts of people living nearer sea level. Thus, although the increased O_2-binding capacity of hemoglobin is important in animals that live at high altitudes, it is only one of a suite of genetic adaptations to living at high altitudes.

The discovery by Hochachka and others that there is a strong genetic component in humans and other animals and that this genetic component is not limited to the hemoglobin gene raises interesting questions. Which genes govern the improved performance at high altitudes? Did these genetic adaptations permit the astonishing feat of Rheinhold Messner, who, together with Peter Habeler in 1978, was the first human to climb to the pinnacle of Mount Everest without the use of supplementary O_2? A few others have matched this achievement, and, indeed, Messner repeated his feat alone in 1980.

Messner was born and raised in the mountainous Tyrol region of northern Italy. Although this in no way diminishes this extraordinary accomplishment, he may have had some genetic predisposition that permitted his survival, however agonizing, at an altitude where the atmospheric pressure is reduced from 760 mm Hg at sea level to 250 mm Hg and the P_{O_2} is only 53 mm Hg **(Figure 1)**.

FIGURE 1

Mount Everest. The barometric pressure at the summit is less than 250 mm Hg and the P_{O_2} is roughly 53 mm Hg, one-third of that found at sea level.

Most of the H^+ ions produced by the dissociation of carbonic acid combine with hemoglobin or with proteins in the plasma, so that the pH is maintained. Note, however, that if CO_2 levels are high, pH will fall, resulting in changes in breathing. The combination of solution in the plasma, conversion to bicarbonate, and combination with hemoglobin operate to maximize the ΔP of the gaseous CO_2 so that the rate of diffusion from the interstitial fluid into the blood is optimal.

The blood leaving the capillary networks of body tissues is collected in venules and veins and returned to the heart, which pumps it through the pulmonary arteries into the lungs. As the blood enters the capillary networks surrounding the alveoli, the entire process of CO_2 uptake is reversed **(Figure 41.15b)**. The P_{CO_2} in the blood, now about 46 mm Hg, is higher than the P_{CO_2} in the alveolar air, about 40 mm Hg (shown in Figure 41.13, p. 1044). As a result, CO_2 diffuses from the blood and into the air. The diminishing CO_2 concentrations in the plasma, along with the lower pH encountered in the lungs, promote the release of CO_2 from hemoglobin. As CO_2 diffuses away, bicarbonate ions in the blood combine with H^+ ions, forming carbonic acid molecules that break down into water and additional CO_2. This CO_2 adds to the quantities diffusing from the blood into the alveolar air. By the time the blood leaves the capillary networks in the lungs, its P_{CO_2} has been reduced to the same level as that of the alveolar air, about 40 mm Hg.

STUDY BREAK

1. Why is hemoglobin so important for O_2 transport in the blood?
2. Why is the pH of the blood different in the tissues and in the lungs? What is the effect of the change in pH between these two sites for O_2 binding to hemoglobin?

LIFE ON THE EDGE 41.4
Prospering in Thin Air

With increasing altitude, atmospheric pressure decreases, and with it, the P_{O_2} also decreases. At an elevation of 5000 m, the atmospheric pressure is about half that at sea level, and the P_{O_2} is thus 380×0.21 or 80 mm Hg, about half that at sea level. This reduces the ΔP between the alveolar air and the blood, and, in turn, the supply of O_2 to the tissues is reduced. Humans who normally live at or near sea level and move to higher elevations above about 2500 m experience fatigue, dizziness, and nausea until their systems produce additional erythrocytes, a physiological response to the stress of reduced O_2.

However, some animals live at high altitudes, such as the llama (*Lama glama*) from the Andes at about 4 000 m, or the bar-headed goose (*Anser indicus*), which migrates over the Himalaya mountains at elevations in excess of 8000 m. One of the factors that permits these animals to exploit what is a marginal environment for other animals is a genetic difference in the hemoglobin molecule that produces a higher affinity for O_2. The hemoglobin in these animals shifts the hemoglobin–oxygen dissociation curve in Figure 41.14, p. 1045 to the left so that the hemoglobin is closer to saturation at lower P_{O_2} levels.

Hemoglobin is particularly polymorphic: the gene has a number of alleles, and the alleles present in the animals that can live at very high altitudes produce the appropriate forms of hemoglobin. This is well illustrated by the deer mouse, *Peromyscus maniculatus*, which occupies an extreme range of altitudes from below sea level in Death Valley to above 4300 m in the Sierra Nevada mountains. The populations of deer mice at higher altitudes have alleles of the hemoglobin genes with higher affinities for O_2 than the alleles of mice at low altitudes.

Review

CourseMate
aplia™

Access an interactive eBook, chapter-specific interactive learning tools, including flashcards, quizzes, videos, and more in your Biology **CourseMate**, accessed through NelsonBrain.com Aplia™ is an online interactive learning solution that helps you improve comprehension—and your grade—by integrating a variety of mediums and tools such as videos, tutorials, practice tests, and an interactive eBook.

41.1 General Principles of Gas Exchange

- The percentage of a gas in a mixture of gases times the atmospheric pressure yields the partial pressure.
- Fick's equation describes the rate of diffusion across a biological membrane. The rate of diffusion is proportional to the product of the area over which diffusion occurs times the difference in partial pressures of the gas on either side of a membrane and is inversely proportional to the distance over which diffusion must occur.
- Gas exchange by simple diffusion is limited to small or flattened organisms.
- In larger animals, respiratory surfaces are increased, and the difference in partial pressures across a membrane is optimized by ventilation and perfusion.
- Water and air, as respiratory media, have different advantages and challenges. Water contains less oxygen, the rate of diffusion is greatly reduced, and its density requires greater energy for ventilation.

41.2 Adaptations for Gas Exchange

- Insects have a tracheal system that brings air directly to every cell.
- Gills are evaginations of the body surface. Water moves over gills by the beating of cilia or by muscular pumping.
- Water moves over the gills of sharks, bony fishes, and some arthropods, allowing countercurrent exchange to maximize the difference in partial pressure across the respiratory surface.
- Lungs are invaginated body surfaces with greatly expanded respiratory surfaces. They may be ventilated by positive pressure

breathing, in which air is forced into the lungs, or by negative pressure breathing. Negative pressure breathing relies on muscles that alternately increase and decrease the pressure within the body cavity.

41.3 The Mammalian Respiratory System

- Air enters and leaves the lungs via the nostrils and mouth leading to the trachea, which branch into two bronchi. The bronchi branch many times into bronchioles leading to alveoli, which are surrounded by blood capillaries.
- Mammals rely on a negative pressure mechanism. The tidal volume is the volume of air moved in and out of the lungs during normal breathing. The vital capacity is the volume that can be moved in and out by breathing as deeply as possible. The residual volume is the volume remaining in the lungs after exhaling as much as possible.
- Breathing is controlled by centres in the brain reacting to sensors for CO_2 and O_2 in the carotid arteries. The concentration of CO_2 has the greatest influence.

41.4 Mechanisms of Gas Transport

- The site of gas exchange in mammals is at the alveolar surface. The P_{O_2} in the alveolar air is greater than that in the blood, causing O_2 to diffuse into the blood and enter the erythrocytes, where it is bound by hemoglobin, thus maximizing the difference in partial pressure of that gas between the air and the blood.
- In the tissues, the reverse is true, and O_2 leaves the blood for the tissues.
- The P_{CO_2} is higher in the tissues than in the blood; CO_2 leaves the tissues and dissolves in the plasma and enters the erythrocytes, where most of it is converted into H^+ and HCO_3^- and released back into the plasma. This causes a slight drop in pH, promoting the release of O_2 from hemoglobin. The remaining CO_2 combines with hemoglobin. At the alveolar surface, the P_{CO_2} in the alveolar cells and the air in the lungs is lower than that in the blood, the HCO_3^- releases its CO_2, and CO_2 flows down the gradient.

Questions

Self-Test Questions

1. Which statement is correct concerning Fick's law of diffusion?
   a. The larger the partial pressure difference, the lower the rate of diffusion.
   b. The greater the surface area for exchange, the greater the rate of diffusion.
   c. The thinner the barrier, the higher the rate of diffusion.
   d. The lower the temperature, the higher the rate of diffusion.

2. Which statement is NOT true?
   a. The partial pressure of O_2 increases with altitude.
   b. Gases are in aqueous solution at respiratory surfaces.
   c. The solubility of O_2 decreases with an increase in temperature.
   d. Countercurrent flow optimizes the difference in partial pressures of a gas across a respiratory surface.
   e. The rate of diffusion of a gas increases with an increase in the difference of partial pressures on either side of a membrane.

3. Which of the following is a disadvantage associated with breathing water?
   a. low oxygen solubility
   b. dense respiratory medium
   c. must breathe a greater amount of the medium
   d. high oxygen content

4. Which of the following characterizes tracheal systems?
   a. positive pressure breathing
   b. closed tubes that circulate gases
   c. CO_2 sensors in the segmental ganglia
   d. the transport of respiratory gases directly to every cell
   e. uncontrolled diffusion of gases between the atmosphere and the tissues

5. Which of the following statements is correct?
   a. CO_2 receptors in the carotid body influence mammalian breathing.
   b. The concentration of O_2 in water rises with increasing temperature.
   c. Birds use a one-way flow of air through their lungs for gas exchange.
   d. O_2 receptors in the medulla have the greatest influence on mammalian breathing.
   e. An advantage of breathing in air (rather than water) is the reduced energy required to move the gases over the respiratory surface.

6. Countercurrent exchange
   a. is used by bony fish
   b. maximizes gas exchange by maintaining a diffusion gradient
   c. is described as the respiratory medium moving in the same direction as the blood flow
   d. is described as the respiratory medium moving in the opposite direction of the blood flow

7. Suppose Olympic speed skating champion Catriona Le May Doan is finishing her last lap. What occurs at this time?
   a. Her tidal volume is at vital capacity.
   b. Positive pressure brings air into her lungs.
   c. Her residual volume momentarily reaches zero.
   d. Her lungs undergo an elastic recoil when she inhales.
   e. Her diaphragm and rib muscles contract when she exhales.

8. The majority of CO_2 in the blood is
   a. bound to hemoglobin
   b. transported as HCO_3^-
   c. dissolved as CO_2 in the plasma
   d. dissolved as CO_2 in the red blood cells

9. You and your pet dog live at sea level. The atmospheric P_{O_2} is 150 mm Hg. Your dog's arterial P_{O_2} is 100 mm Hg, and his tissue P_{O_2} is 10 mm Hg. What would you expect your dog to do?
   a. die
   b. accumulate CO_2
   c. have a serious but nonlethal O_2 deficit
   d. become dizzy from too much O_2
   e. function normally

10. What does the hemoglobin–O_2 dissociation curve do?
    a. shows a shift to the left when pH rises
    b. shows a lack of dependence on CO_2 levels
    c. reflects about 50% dissociation in the alveoli
    d. shows that hemoglobin holds less O_2 when the pH rises
    e. explains how hemoglobin can bind more O_2 in the lungs and release it at the tissues where the pH is lower

Questions for Discussion

1. The ability to live at high elevations appears to have genetic components beyond the properties of the blood in many animals. What experiments can you devise to explore this possibility? (Hint: Some animals have high- and low-elevation populations.)

2. Hospital patients frequently have a small ring on the end of a finger that shines a red light from the pad of tissue to a detector on the fingernail. What do you think this apparatus measures, and why is it important to measure it continuously? What factors could change the value of this measurement?

3. The control of the spiracular opening in insects is assumed to be important in avoiding water loss during gas exchange. Suggest an experiment to test this hypothesis. How does this mechanism differ from that controlling the opening of the stomata in plants?

4. You have two patients, one with chronic obstructive pulmonary disease and one with reduced blood flow to the lungs. Which one will benefit the most from application of supplemental oxygen and why?

5. For an animal of your choice, use Fick's equation of diffusion to explain how it has become adapted for its lifestyle.

© Dennis Kunkel/Phototake

42 Regulating the Internal Environment

WHY IT MATTERS

In the Miramichi River of New Brunswick, an Atlantic salmon (*Salmo salar*) has spent two or three years growing from an egg to a fish about 10 to 25 cm in length. In the spring, as day length increases and the water temperature begins to rise, it undergoes a number of physiological, morphological, and behavioural changes. It loses some of its mottled coloration, becoming silvery in appearance, and joins other similar fish in migrating downstream. It may pause at the estuary of the river for a day or two, but then it abandons its freshwater environment and enters the sea, where it will remain for two or more years, feeding and growing to maturity. Eventually, it will return to the Miramichi to spawn **(Figure 42.1)**.

When the salmon leaves the fresh water of the river and enters the salt water of the North Atlantic Ocean, it moves from an environment in which the total concentration of solutes is about 0.1% to one with a concentration of about 3.5%. Its own body fluids contain about 1% solutes. Since water and many salts move freely across the gills of fish, which have a large surface area for gas exchange (see Chapter 41), the salmon moves, over the course of a few days, from a situation where it is constantly losing salts and taking up water from the environment to

Figure 42.1

Adult Atlantic salmon, ready to return to the river of their birth. The map and photo show the estuary of the Miramichi River in New Brunswick.

one in which the opposite occurs; it constantly takes up salts and loses water to its environment. Since all the cells of the body need to retain a relatively constant level of ions and water (neither shrinking nor swelling), dramatic changes must occur in the physiological processes that correct for these effects and maintain ion and water balance in body fluids. These physiological changes accompany its morphological changes and allow it to prosper in both environments.

All organisms may be subject to short-term fluctuations in their external environment that present challenges for them to maintain not only the integrity of their internal ions and fluids but also the functioning of all the systems that sustain life. Many are subject to seasonal changes that can also be challenging. The maintenance of a steady internal environment is called **homeostasis** (introduced in Chapter 31). In previous chapters, we have discussed why and how blood pressure (Chapter 32), blood glucose levels (Chapter 35), and blood oxygen levels (Chapter 41) are maintained relatively constant. In this chapter, we discuss the homeostatic control of ion, water, and temperature balance.

During evolution, a variety of physiological and behavioural mechanisms have appeared that have permitted organisms to exploit environments that may be highly variable. In the background are those mechanisms that accompanied the emergence from living in water to living on land. There are some important differences among marine, freshwater, and terrestrial environments. Organisms living in marine and terrestrial environments require mechanisms to obtain and conserve water; those in freshwater environments do not. On the other hand, obtaining salts and ions is relatively easy in marine environments but more difficult in freshwater and terrestrial ones. Finally, terrestrial

environments are subject to much greater variation in temperature than either aquatic environment. The temperature of aqueous environments is seldom greater than about 25°C, and the lower limit is a little above –2°C (salt water freezes at about this temperature). By contrast, terrestrial organisms in the northern temperate zone of Canada, for example, encounter temperatures that may range between approximately 40°C and –40°C. In this chapter, we explore the ways in which animals have adapted to overcome these challenges.

42.1 Introduction to Osmoregulation and Excretion

Living cells contain water, are surrounded by water, and constantly exchange water with their environment. The water of the external environment directly surrounds the cells of the simplest animals. For more complex animals, an aqueous extracellular fluid surrounds the cells and is separated from the external environment by a body covering. In animals with a circulatory system, the extracellular fluid includes both the blood and the interstitial fluid immediately surrounding the cells (see Chapter 31).

In this section, we review the mechanisms cells use to exchange water and solutes with the surrounding fluid through *osmosis*. We also look at how animals harness osmosis to regulate their internal *water balance*, the equilibrium between the inward and outward flow of water.

42.1a Osmosis Is Passive Diffusion

In osmosis (see Chapter 5), water molecules move across a selectively permeable membrane (one that lets water through but excludes most solutes) from a region of lesser solute concentration to a region of greater solute concentration. Selective permeability is a key factor in osmosis because it helps maintain differences in solute concentration on either side of biological membranes. Proteins are among the most important solutes in establishing the conditions producing osmosis. The passive transport of water occurs constantly in living cells (it will accompany any net ion transport), developing forces that lead to cell swelling or shrinking.

The total solute concentration of a solution may be measured in one of two ways. **Osmolarity** is measured in *osmoles*—the number of solute molecules and ions (in moles)—per litre of solution. **Osmolality** is measured in osmoles per kilogram of solution. Osmolality is used more frequently to measure the osmotic concentration of a solution, partly because the volume of water changes with temperature while the mass does not.

Because the total solute concentration in the body fluids of most animals is less than 1 osmole, osmolality is usually expressed in thousandths of an osmole, or *milliosmoles* (mOsm) per kilogram. As shown in **Figure 42.2**, the osmolality of body fluids in terrestrial vertebrates (including humans) is about 300 mOsm/kg. It is similar in freshwater organisms; in a goldfish, a freshwater teleost, it is about 290 mOsm/kg, while in freshwater invertebrates it is about 225 mOsm/kg. By contrast, sharks and many marine invertebrates, such as lobsters, have osmolalities close to that of sea water, about 1000 mOsm/kg, Interestingly, the osmolality in marine teleosts (bony fish such as the flounder) is only

about 330 mOsm/kg. The relatively low osmotic concentration in marine teleosts reflects their evolutionary history. Early marine teleosts invaded fresh water and prospered there. During the extensive radiation of the group in fresh water, many have reinvaded the marine habitat.

A solution of higher osmolality on one side of a selectively permeable membrane is said to be *hyperosmotic* to a solution of lower osmolality on the other side, and a solution of lower osmolality is said to be *hypoosmotic* to a solution of higher osmolality. If the solutions on either side of a membrane have the same osmotic concentrations, they are *isoosmotic*. Water moves across the membrane between solutions that differ in osmolality, whereas when two solutions are isoosmotic, no *net* water movement occurs, although water exchanges from one side to the other. (Compare this to the discussion of hypotonic, hypertonic, and isotonic in Section 5.4d, Chapter 5.)

The principles that determine osmotic concentration also determine the freezing point, boiling point, and vapour pressure of a solution. Increasing solute concentration (increasing osmolality) reduces the freezing point, increases the boiling point, and lowers the vapour pressure of a solution.

CONCEPT FIX It is a misconception that once a cell is killed, diffusion and osmosis stop. Diffusion and osmosis are passive processes and will occur as long as the cell membrane is intact, providing a selectively permeable barrier. Since ion transporters are no longer working, the ability of the cell to correct for passive movement will be gone, and, of course, with time, the cell membrane will break down. ⬡

42.1b Animals Use Different Approaches to Regulate Osmosis

Because even small differences in osmotic concentration can cause cells to swell or shrink, animals must keep their cellular and extracellular fluids isoosmotic. In some animals, called **osmoconformers**, the osmotic concentrations of the cellular and extracellular solutions simply match that of the environment.

Many marine invertebrates are osmoconformers: when placed in dilute sea water, the osmotic concentration of their body fluids decreases, and their weight increases as a result of the osmotic influx of water. Other animals, called **osmoregulators**, use control mechanisms to keep the osmolality of cellular and extracellular fluids constant (i.e., homeostatically controlled) but at levels that may differ from the osmolality of the surroundings. Most freshwater and terrestrial invertebrates, and almost all vertebrates, are osmoregulators. It is important to recognize that the various solutes contributing to the osmotic concentration may be at different concentrations inside the cell, in the extracellular fluids, and in the environment.

Figure 42.2
Osmolality of body fluids in some animal groups.

42.1c Excretion Is Closely Tied to Osmoregulation

Cells must control their ionic and pH balance as well as their osmotic concentration. This may require the removal of certain ions from cells and body fluids and their release into the environment. Animals excrete excess H^+ ions to keep the pH of body fluids near the neutral levels required by cells for survival. They also excrete toxic products of metabolism, such as nitrogenous (nitrogen-containing) compounds resulting from the breakdown of proteins and nucleic acids, and breakdown products of poisons and toxins. Excretion of ions and metabolic products is accompanied by water excretion because water serves as a solvent for those molecules. Animals that take in large amounts of water may also excrete water to maintain osmolality.

42.1d Microscopic Tubules Form the Basis of Excretion in Most Animals

Except in the simplest animals, minute tubular structures carry out osmoregulation and excretion **(Figure 42.3).** The tubules are immersed in body fluids at one end (called the *proximal end* of the tubules) and open directly or indirectly to the body exterior at the other end (called the *distal end* of the tubules). The tubules are formed from a **transport epithelium**—a layer of cells with specialized transport proteins in their plasma membranes. The transport proteins move specific molecules and ions into and out of the tubule by either active or passive transport, depending on the particular substance and its concentration gradient.

Typically, the tubules function in a four-step process:

1. **Filtration.** Filtration is the nonselective movement of water and a number of solutes—ions and small molecules, but not large molecules such as proteins—into the proximal end of the tubules through spaces between cells. In animals with an open circulatory system, the water and solutes come from body fluids, with movement into the tubules driven by the higher pressure of the body fluids compared with the fluid inside the tubule. In animals with a closed circulatory system, such as humans, the water and solutes come from the blood in capillaries that surround the tubules, with the movement into the tubules similarly driven by hydrostatic pressure. (Open and closed circulatory systems are described in Section 32.1, Chapter 32.)

2. **Reabsorption.** In reabsorption, some molecules (e.g., glucose and amino acids) and ions are transported by the transport epithelium back into the extracellular fluid and eventually into the blood (in animals with closed circulatory systems) as the filtered solution moves through the excretory tubule.

3. **Secretion.** Secretion is a selective process in which specific small molecules and ions are transported from the extracellular fluid and blood into the tubules. Secretion is the second and more important route for eliminating particular substances from the body fluid or blood, filtration being the first. The difference between the two processes is that filtration is nonselective whereas secretion is selective for substances transported.

4. **Release.** The fluid containing waste materials—urine—is released into the environment from the distal end of the tubule. In some animals, the fluid is stored in a bladder; in others, it is concentrated into a solid or semisolid form.

In all vertebrates and many invertebrates, the excretory tubules are concentrated in specialized organs, the *kidneys,* which are discussed in later sections.

42.1e Animals Excrete Nitrogen Compounds as Metabolic Wastes

The metabolism of ingested food is a source of both energy and molecules for the biosynthetic activities of an animal. Importantly, metabolism of ingested food produces *metabolic water,* which is used in chemical

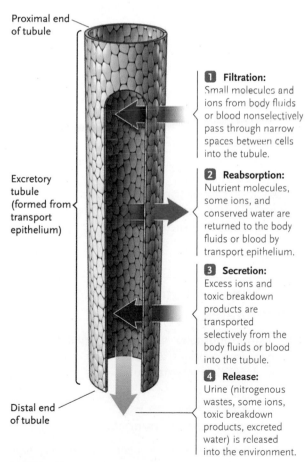

Proximal end of tubule

Excretory tubule (formed from transport epithelium)

Distal end of tubule

1 Filtration: Small molecules and ions from body fluids or blood nonselectively pass through narrow spaces between cells into the tubule.

2 Reabsorption: Nutrient molecules, some ions, and conserved water are returned to the body fluids or blood by transport epithelium.

3 Secretion: Excess ions and toxic breakdown products are transported selectively from the body fluids or blood into the tubule.

4 Release: Urine (nitrogenous wastes, some ions, toxic breakdown products, excreted water) is released into the environment.

Figure 42.3
Common structures and operations of the tubules carrying out osmoregulation and excretion in animals. The tubules are typically formed from a single layer of cells with transport functions.

reactions as well as being involved in physiological processes such as the excretion of wastes.

The proteins, amino acids, and nucleic acids in food are continually broken down as part of digestion (see Chapter 40) and by the constant turnover and replacement of these molecules in body cells. The nitrogenous products of this breakdown are excreted by most animals as *ammonia, urea,* or *uric acid* or a combination of these substances **(Figure 42.4).** The particular molecule or combination of molecules depends on a balance among toxicity, water conservation, and energy requirements.

Ammonia. Ammonia (NH_3) results from the metabolism of amino acids and proteins and is highly toxic: it can be safely transported and excreted from the body only in dilute solutions. Those animals with a plentiful supply of water, such as aquatic or marine invertebrates, teleost fish, and larval amphibians, excrete ammonia as their primary nitrogenous waste. Other animals detoxify ammonia by converting it to urea or uric acid.

Urea. All mammals, most amphibians, some reptiles, some marine fishes, and some terrestrial invertebrates combine ammonia with HCO_3^- and convert the product in a series of steps to *urea,* a soluble substance that is less toxic than ammonia. Although producing urea requires more energy than forming ammonia, excreting urea instead of ammonia requires much less water.

Uric Acid. Water is conserved further in some animals, including many terrestrial invertebrates, reptiles, and

birds, by the formation of uric acid instead of ammonia or urea. Uric acid is nontoxic, but its great advantage is its low solubility. During the concentration of the urine in the final stages of its formation, the uric acid precipitates as crystals that can be expelled with minimal water. (The white substance in bird droppings is uric acid.) The embryos of reptiles and birds, which develop within leathery or hard-shelled eggs that are impermeable to liquids, also conserve water by forming uric acid, which is stored as a waste product inside the shell. Similarly, the pupae of insects store uric acid in the rectum.

Many animals have the capacity to form all three products of nitrogen metabolism. Mammalian urine, for example, contains small amounts of uric acid, although urea predominates. Some tree frogs, such as *Phyllomedusa sauvagii,* have uric acid as their principal excretory product. This has enabled them to exploit the woodlands of South America, where the dry season is extremely arid. Conversely, the American cockroach, *Periplaneta americana,* an insect that normally lives in damp environments, uses ammonia as its primary excretory product and stores uric acid in special cells during periods when water is less available.

Sharks and rays maintain their osmotic concentration near that of their marine environment by retaining urea in their tissues and blood.

In the following sections, we look at the specifics of osmoregulation and excretion in different animal groups, beginning with the invertebrates.

STUDY BREAK

1. Define *osmolality.* What problems are associated with living in a high or low osmolar environment for a fish?
2. What are the sources of ammonia, urea, and uric acid in excretory products? Why do different species produce these different compounds? What are the advantages and disadvantages of each strategy?

42.2 Osmoregulation and Excretion in Invertebrates

Both osmoconformers and osmoregulators occur among the invertebrates, and most carry out excretion by specialized excretory structures.

42.2a Invertebrates Can Be Osmoconformers or Osmoregulators

Many marine invertebrates (sponges, cnidarians, some molluscs, and echinoderms) are osmoconformers. If placed in dilute solutions of sea water, they increase in weight because of the entry of water. They release nitrogenous wastes, usually in the form of ammonia, directly

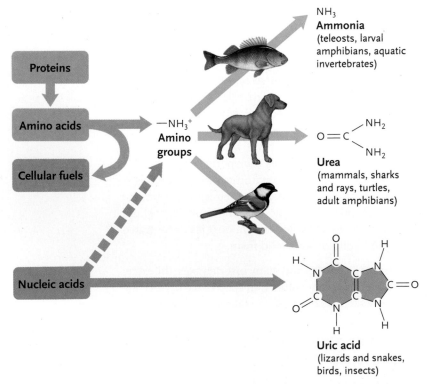

Figure 42.4
Nitrogenous wastes excreted by different animal groups. Although humans and other mammals primarily excrete urea, they also excrete small amounts of ammonia and uric acid.

from body cells to the surrounding sea water. The cells of these animals do not normally swell or shrink because the osmotic concentrations of their intracellular and extracellular fluids and the surrounding sea water are the same, about 1000 mOsm/kg. Although they do not expend energy to maintain their osmolality, osmoconformers do expend energy to keep some ions, such as Na^+, at concentrations different from the concentration in sea water.

In general, the invertebrates that spend their entire lives in the open sea, where the environment is osmotically stable, have very little capacity for osmoregulation. Thus, many marine molluscs, such as squid and octopus, are osmoconformers, as are most marine arthropods, such as lobsters.

Other marine invertebrates are more diverse in their responses to variations in the osmotic concentration of the environment. Invertebrates living in the intertidal zone or at the mouths of tidal rivers experience regular changes in the osmotic concentration of their environment. Some marine annelids and arthropods that live in such environments are capable of short-term osmoregulation, slowing or delaying the changes in osmotic concentration of their body fluids that result from dilution of sea water by the outflow from rivers **(Figure 42.5)**. Some animals that live in the intertidal zone use behavioural responses, such as closing their shells (mussels and clams) or retreating into burrows (some annelids) to avoid desiccation when the tide is out.

By contrast, all freshwater and terrestrial invertebrates are osmoregulators. Those that live in aquatic environments are faced with a potential influx of water, diluting their body fluids. Although osmoregulation is energetically expensive, these invertebrates can live in more varied habitats than osmoconformers can.

Freshwater osmoregulators such as flatworms and mussels are hyperosmotic relative to their environment, which causes water to move constantly from the surroundings into their bodies. This excess water must be excreted, at a considerable cost in energy, to maintain homeostasis. These animals obtain the salts they need from foods and by actively transporting salt ions from the water into their bodies (even fresh water contains some dissolved salts). This active ion transport occurs through the body surface or gills.

Terrestrial osmoregulators include annelids (earthworms), arthropods (insects, spiders and mites, millipedes, and centipedes), and molluscs (land snails and slugs). Although they do not have to excrete water entering by osmosis, they must constantly replace water lost from their bodies by evaporation and excretion. Most obtain water from their food, and some drink water. Like their freshwater relatives, these invertebrates must obtain salts from their surroundings, usually in their foods.

42.2b Specialized Excretory Tubules Participate in Osmoregulation

Most invertebrates (except marine osmoconformers) use specialized tubular structures to carry out excretion. These include *protonephridia* in flatworms and larval molluscs, *metanephridia* in annelids and most adult molluscs, and *Malpighian tubules* in insects and other arthropods. In protonephridia, the excretory tubules are open only at one end. Body fluids do not enter protonephridia directly. An *ultrafiltrate* enters the tubule through narrow extracellular spaces that permit only small molecules to enter and exclude larger molecules such as proteins. Metanephridia, by contrast, are open at both ends. They are characteristic of animals with coeloms, and the coelomic fluid is already an ultrafiltrate of the blood in the closed circulatory system.

Protonephridia. The flatworm *Dugesia* provides an example of the simplest form of invertebrate excretory tubule, the *protonephridium* (*proto* = before; *nephros* = kidney). In *Dugesia,* two branching networks of protonephridia run the length of the body **(Figure 42.6, p. 1056).** The cell at the blind end of each tubule has a bundle of cilia on its inner surface. The synchronous beating of the cilia resembles the flickering of a flame, so these cells are called *flame cells*. The cilia help draw a filtrate of body fluids through very small spaces between the cell membranes of the flame cell and those of the adjacent tubule cell and propel the filtrate along the tubule. As the fluids pass along the tubule, some molecules and ions are reabsorbed, whereas others are secreted into the tubules.

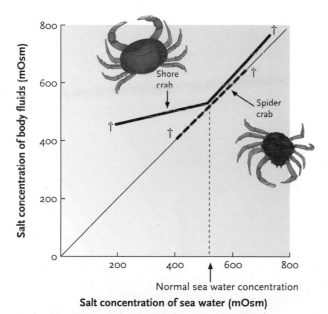

Figure 42.5

The concentration of the body fluids of two crabs when immersed in sea water of different concentrations. The spider crab lives in the sea, where it is not exposed to variation in the concentration of the water. The concentration of its fluids follows the 45° line that marks equivalency between the sea water concentration and the body fluid concentration. By contrast, the shore crab, which lives in the intertidal zone and in estuaries, can regulate its body fluids to some degree. The cross at the end of each line indicates the concentration at which each crab dies. Note that osmotic concentrations were not measured in this experiment.

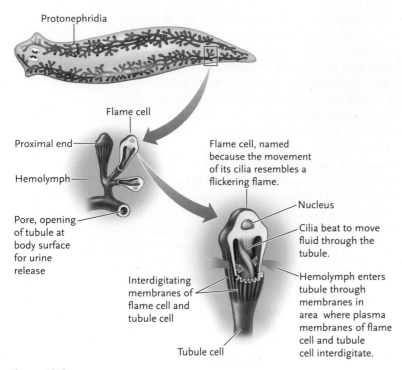

Figure 42.6

The protonephridia of the planarian *Dugesia*, showing the flame cells.

Labels in figure:
- Protonephridia
- Flame cell
- Proximal end
- Hemolymph
- Pore, opening of tubule at body surface for urine release
- Interdigitating membranes of flame cell and tubule cell
- Tubule cell
- Flame cell, named because the movement of its cilia resembles a flickering flame.
- Nucleus
- Cilia beat to move fluid through the tubule.
- Hemolymph enters tubule through membranes in area where plasma membranes of flame cell and tubule cell interdigitate.

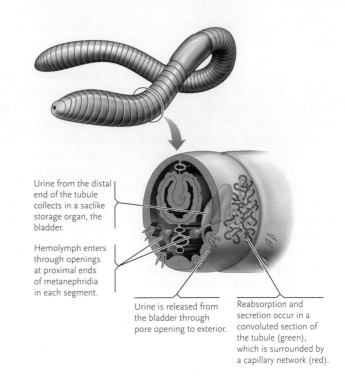

Figure 42.7

A metanephridium of an earthworm.

Labels in figure:
- Urine from the distal end of the tubule collects in a saclike storage organ, the bladder.
- Hemolymph enters through openings at proximal ends of metanephridia in each segment.
- Urine is released from the bladder through pore opening to exterior.
- Reabsorption and secretion occur in a convoluted section of the tubule (green), which is surrounded by a capillary network (red).

The urine resulting from this filtration system is released through pores that connect the network of protonephridia to the body surface. The principal nitrogenous excretory product is ammonia. Although some ammonia passes out in the urine, most of it passes through the body wall.

Metanephridia. Animals with metanephridia have coelomic cavities (see Chapter 25) that are separate from the circulatory system. The fluid in the coelom is a filtrate of the hemolymph or blood. Coelomic fluid enters the proximal end of the excretory tubule, and ions and other solutes are reabsorbed or secreted as the fluid moves along the tubule. In annelids, the metanephridium **(Figure 42.7)** is a segmental structure. The proximal ends of a pair of metanephridia are located in each body segment, one on each side of the animal. A funnel-like opening surrounded by cilia admits coelomic fluid. Each tubule of the pair extends into the following segment, where it bends and folds into a convoluted arrangement surrounded by a network of blood vessels. Reabsorption and secretion of specific molecules and ions take place in the convoluted section. Urine from the distal end of the tubule collects in a saclike storage organ, the *bladder,* from where it is released through a pore in the surface of the segment.

Malpighian Tubules. The excretory tubules of insects, the *Malpighian tubules,* have a closed proximal end that is immersed in the hemolymph **(Figure 42.8).** The distal ends of the tubules empty into the gut. The fluid in the tubules results primarily from secretion, although in some insects, an ultrafiltrate of the hemolymph may enter the upper part of the tubule through extracellular spaces. In particular, uric acid and several ions, including Na^+ and K^+, are actively secreted

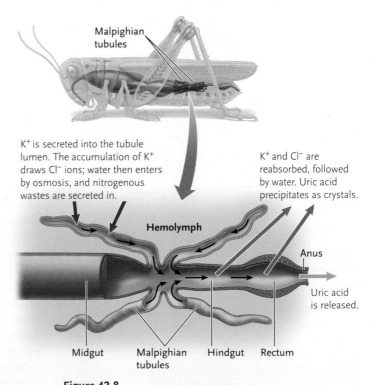

Labels in figure:
- Malpighian tubules
- K^+ is secreted into the tubule lumen. The accumulation of K^+ draws Cl^- ions; water then enters by osmosis, and nitrogenous wastes are secreted in.
- K^+ and Cl^- are reabsorbed, followed by water. Uric acid precipitates as crystals.
- Hemolymph
- Anus
- Uric acid is released.
- Midgut
- Malpighian tubules
- Hindgut
- Rectum

Figure 42.8

Excretion through Malpighian tubules in a grasshopper.

LIFE ON THE EDGE 42.1

Life Without Water

Some organisms live in temporary aquatic environments, consisting of ponds that dry up completely during periods of prolonged drought. One survival strategy involves complete desiccation of the animal, leading to anhydrobiosis (life without water). For example, the aquatic larvae of a midge (a small dipteran), *Polypedilum vanderplanki* **(Figure 1),** inhabit pools in Africa that can dry up completely for long periods. The larvae construct nests of mud, but within these nests, their water content is almost completely eliminated, and signs of life are absent. These desiccated larvae can withstand exposure to temperatures as low as −270°C and as high as +106°C. Immersed in water, the larvae recover within less than an hour, even after as long as 17 years of life without water. The precise mechanisms are

not fully understood, but the animals accumulate high concentrations of the disaccharide trehalose as they enter the anhydrobiotic state. This sugar is thought to form a glasslike structure that prevents the formation of crystals that would damage the cells. Similar mechanisms are known in yeasts and other microorganisms.

Courtesy of Takashi Okuda

FIGURE 1

The larva of Polypedilum vanderplanki *(a) in its active state and (b) during desiccation, showing the accumulation of trehalose. Optical and FTIR imaging data for a slowly dehydrated larva and a quickly dehydrated larva. Warm colours indicate higher intensity, i.e., larger amounts of trehalose. (Scale bar: 500 μm.)*
From: M. Sakurai et al. PNAS 2008; 105:5093–5098.

"Vitrification is essential for anhydrobiosis in an African chironomid, Polypedilum vanderplanki." Minoru Sakurai et al. PNAS April 1, 2008 vol. 105 no. 13 5093–5098. Copyright 2008 National Academy of Sciences, U.S.A.

---

into the tubules. As the concentration of these substances rises, water moves osmotically from the hemolymph into the tubule. The fluid then passes into the hindgut (intestine and rectum) of the insect as dilute urine. Cells in the hindgut wall actively reabsorb most of the Na$^+$ and K$^+$ back into the hemolymph, and water follows by osmosis. The uric acid left in the gut precipitates into crystals, which mix with the undigested matter in the rectum and are released with the feces. This arrangement is important in conserving water.

Besides these specialized tubular structures, the body wall is also important in osmoregulation in many invertebrates. Researchers have cut parasitic cod worms and made sausagelike sacs by removing the intestine and closing the cut ends with ligatures. The sacs are capable of maintaining the internal osmotic concentration in environments of different osmotic concentrations.

STUDY BREAK

1. How does a protonephridium differ from a metanephridium? In what ways are they similar? In which animal groups are each of these found?
2. What is the excretory product of most insects? How does it get into the urine?
3. Some insects feed on plants, such as tobacco, that contain poisons. Can you devise an experiment to test whether such poisons are eliminated by Malpighian tubules?

42.3 Osmoregulation and Excretion in Nonmammalian Vertebrates

In all vertebrates, specialized excretory tubules contribute to osmoregulation and excretion. The excretory tubules, called **nephrons,** are located in a specialized organ, the kidney. In all nonmammalian vertebrates, the kidneys produce a urine that is either hypoosmotic (dilute) or isoosmotic to body fluids, with the exception of some birds, which can produce urine that is weakly hyperosmotic. Mammals, on the other hand, can produce a very concentrated urine (up to 25 times the solute concentration of body fluids). This ability is unique to mammals and is discussed in the next section. The particular adaptations that maintain osmolality and water balance among the nonmammalian vertebrates vary depending on whether retention of water or of salts is the major issue.

42.3a Marine Fishes Conserve Water and Excrete Salts

Marine teleosts live in sea water, which is strongly hyperosmotic to their body fluids. As a result, they continually lose water to their environment by osmosis and must replace it by continual drinking. The kidneys of marine teleosts play little role in regulating salt in their body fluids because they cannot produce hyperosmotic urine that would both remove salt and conserve water. Instead, excess Na$^+$, K$^+$, and Cl$^-$ ions are eliminated from the body by specialized cells in the gills, called *chloride cells,* which actively transport Cl⁻ into the surrounding sea water; the Na⁺ and K⁺ ions are also actively transported to maintain electrical neutrality **(Figure 42.9a)**. Divalent ions in the ingested sea water, such as Ca^{2+} and Mg^{2+}, are removed by the kidneys in an isoosmotic urine. On balance, a marine teleost is able to retain most of the water it drinks and eliminate most of the salt, allowing its tissue fluids to remain hypoosmotic to the surrounding water without producing hyperosmotic urine. The kidneys play little role in the removal of nitrogenous wastes; these are released from the gills, primarily as ammonia, by simple diffusion.

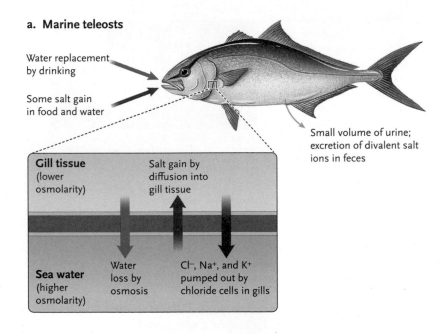

a. Marine teleosts

Water replacement by drinking

Some salt gain in food and water

Small volume of urine; excretion of divalent salt ions in feces

Gill tissue (lower osmolarity)

Salt gain by diffusion into gill tissue

Sea water (higher osmolarity)

Water loss by osmosis

Cl⁻, Na⁺, and K⁺ pumped out by chloride cells in gills

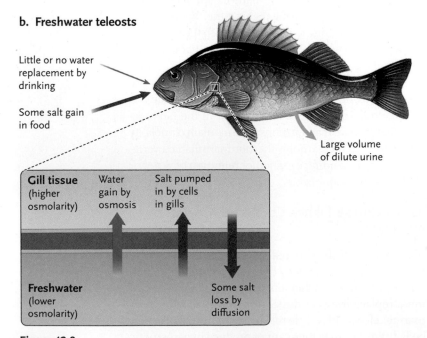

b. Freshwater teleosts

Little or no water replacement by drinking

Some salt gain in food

Large volume of dilute urine

Gill tissue (higher osmolarity)

Water gain by osmosis

Salt pumped in by cells in gills

Freshwater (lower osmolarity)

Some salt loss by diffusion

Figure 42.9

The mechanisms balancing the water and salt content of **(a)** marine teleosts and **(b)** freshwater teleosts.

Sharks and rays have a different adaptation to sea water—the osmolality of their body fluids is maintained close to that of sea water by retaining high levels of urea in body fluids, along with another nitrogenous waste, *trimethylamine oxide.* Elasmobranchs (see Chapter 26) may have concentrations of urea as high as 1300 mg per 100 mL of blood. The match in osmolality keeps sharks and rays from losing water to the surrounding sea by osmosis, and they do not have to drink sea water continually to maintain their water balance. Excess salts ingested with food are excreted in the kidney and by specialized secretory cells in a *rectal salt gland* located near the anal opening. The importance of urea as an osmolyte is illustrated by those species of stingrays that inhabit fresh water. In such species, the concentration of urea is reduced to about 2 to 3 mg per 100 mL of blood.

42.3b Freshwater Fishes and Amphibians Excrete Water and Conserve Salts

The body fluids of freshwater fishes and aquatic amphibians (no amphibians live in sea water, although the crab-eating frog (*Fejervarya cancrivora*) lives in mangrove swamps in Southeast Asia and can tolerate saltwater conditions) are hyperosmotic to the surrounding water, which usually ranges from about 1 to 10 mOsm/kg. Water therefore moves osmotically into their tissues. Such animals rarely drink, and they excrete large volumes of dilute urine to get rid of excess water **(Figure 42.9b)**. In freshwater fishes, salt ions lost with the urine are replaced by salt in foods and by active transport of Na⁺, K⁺, and Cl⁻ into the body by the gills. Aquatic amphibians obtain salt in the diet and by active transport across the skin from the surrounding water. Nitrogenous wastes are excreted from the gills as ammonia in both freshwater fishes and aquatic amphibians.

Terrestrial amphibians must conserve both water and salt, which is obtained primarily in foods. In these animals, the kidneys secrete salt into the urine, causing water to enter the urine by osmosis. In the bladder, the salt is reclaimed by active transport and returned to body fluids. The water remains in the bladder, making the urine very dilute; during times of drought, the water can be reabsorbed. Terrestrial amphibians also have behavioural adaptations that help minimize water loss, such as seeking shaded, moist environments and remaining inactive during the day. Larval amphibians, which are completely aquatic, excrete nitrogenous wastes from their gills as ammonia.

Most adult amphibians excrete nitrogenous wastes through their kidneys as urea. The leaf frog, *Phyllomedusa sauvagii* **(Figure 42.10)**, however, produces uric acid as the principal nitrogenous waste. In addition, it secretes a waxy substance from glands in its skin and uses its legs to smear this over the entire surface, thereby minimizing water loss.

Figure 42.10

Phyllomedusa sauvagii is a tree frog that prospers in the dry woodlands of South America. Among its many adaptations to a dry environment are the production of uric acid and the secretion from skin glands of a waterproofing waxy material.

Martin Fowler/Shutterstock

42.3c Reptiles and Birds Excrete Uric Acid to Conserve Water

Terrestrial reptiles and most birds conserve water by excreting nitrogenous wastes in the form of an almost water-free paste of uric acid crystals. Further water conservation occurs as the epithelial cells of the cloaca, the common exit for the digestive and excretory systems, absorb water from feces and urine before those wastes are eliminated. This arrangement is similar to the strategy used by insects, described earlier. In reptiles, the scales covering the skin allow almost no water to escape through the body surface.

Reptiles, such as crocodilians, sea snakes, and sea turtles, and birds, such as seagulls, penguins, and pelicans, that live in or around sea water take in large quantities of salt with their food and rarely or never drink fresh water. These animals typically excrete excess salt through specialized *salt glands* located in the head **(Figure 42.11)** that remove salts from the blood by

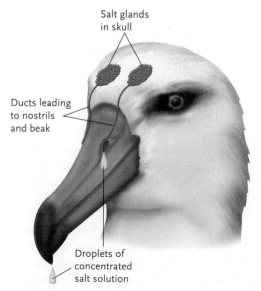

Figure 42.11

Salt glands in a bird living on a seacoast.

active transport. The salts are secreted to the environment as a water solution in which salts are two to three times as concentrated as in body fluids. The secretion exits through the nostrils of birds and lizards, through the mouth of marine snakes, and as salty tears from the eye sockets of sea turtles and crocodilians.

STUDY BREAK

1. What are the osmoregulatory problems faced by marine and freshwater teleosts, and how are they solved?
2. What excretory strategy is used by birds and reptiles to conserve water?
3. How do marine birds and reptiles excrete excess salts?

42.4 Osmoregulation and Excretion in Mammals

Since water moves by osmosis from areas of low solute concentration to areas of high solute concentration, it would seem impossible to produce a hyperosmotic urine, one in which water is reabsorbed into the body, leaving high concentrations of salt behind in the urine. We next describe of the structure and function of the mammalian kidney and the unique way in which "the impossible" has been achieved.

42.4a The Kidneys, Ureters, Bladder, and Urethra Constitute the Urinary System

Mammals have a pair of kidneys, located on each side of the vertebral column at the dorsal side of the abdominal cavity **(Figure 42.12, p. 1060)**. Internally, the mammalian kidney is divided into an outer **renal cortex** surrounding a central region, the **renal medulla.**

A **renal artery** carries blood to each kidney, where metabolic wastes and excess water and ions are excreted in the urine by the action of the nephrons. The blood is routed away from the kidney by the **renal vein.** The urine is produced in individual nephrons and is then processed further in **collecting ducts** that drain into a central cavity in the kidney called the **renal pelvis.**

From the renal pelvis, the urine flows through a tube called the **ureter** to the **urinary bladder,** a storage sac located outside the kidneys. Urine leaves the bladder through another tube, the **urethra,** which opens to the outside. Two sphincter muscles control the flow of urine from the bladder to the urethra. In human females, the opening of the urethra is just in front of the vagina; in males, the urethra opens at the tip of the penis. The two kidneys and two ureters, the urinary bladder, and the urethra constitute the mammalian urinary system.

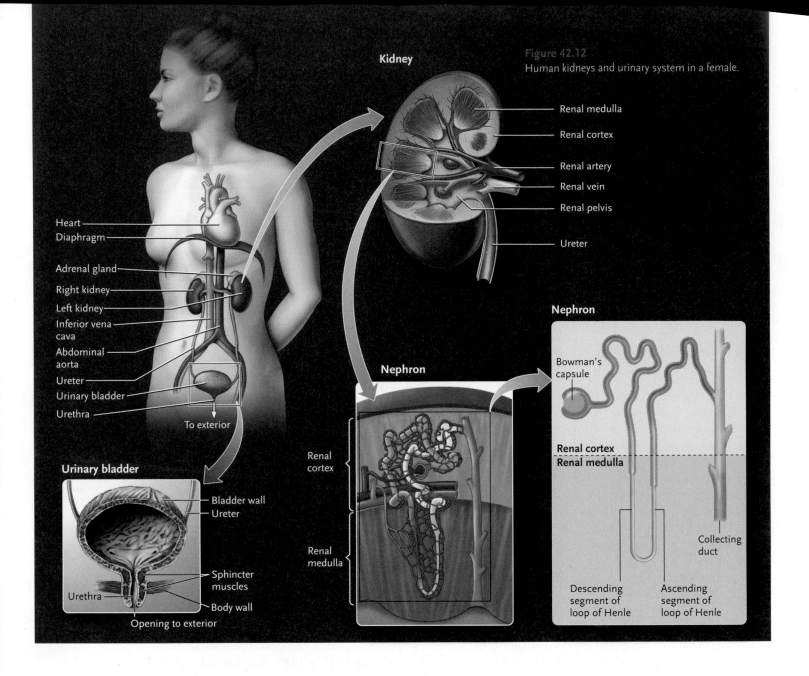

Figure 42.12
Human kidneys and urinary system in a female.

Kidney

- Renal medulla
- Renal cortex
- Renal artery
- Renal vein
- Renal pelvis
- Ureter

Heart
Diaphragm
Adrenal gland
Right kidney
Left kidney
Inferior vena cava
Abdominal aorta
Ureter
Urinary bladder
Urethra
To exterior

Nephron

Bowman's capsule

Renal cortex
Renal medulla

Collecting duct

Descending segment of loop of Henle
Ascending segment of loop of Henle

Nephron

Renal cortex

Renal medulla

Urinary bladder

Bladder wall
Ureter
Sphincter muscles
Urethra
Body wall
Opening to exterior

42.4b Regions of Nephrons Have Specialized Functions

Mammalian nephrons are differentiated into regions that perform successive steps in excretion. At its proximal end, a nephron forms **Bowman's capsule**, an infolded region that cups around a ball of blood capillaries called the **glomerulus (Figure 42.13).** The capsule and glomerulus are located in the renal cortex. Filtration takes place as fluids are forced into Bowman's capsule from the capillaries of the glomerulus.

Following Bowman's capsule, the nephron forms a **proximal convoluted tubule** in the renal cortex, which descends into the medulla in a U-shaped bend called the **loop of Henle** and then ascends again to form a **distal convoluted tubule.** The distal tubule drains the urine into a branching system of collecting ducts that lead to the renal pelvis. As many as eight nephrons may drain into a single branch of a

collecting duct. The combined activities of the proximal convoluted tubule, the loop of Henle, the distal convoluted tubule, and the collecting duct convert the filtrate that enters the nephron at the Bowman's capsule into urine.

Unlike most capillaries in the body, the capillaries in the glomerulus do not lead directly to venules. Instead, they form another arteriole that branches into a second capillary network called the **peritubular capillaries.** These capillaries thread around the proximal and distal convoluted tubules and the loop of Henle. Some molecules and ions are reabsorbed into the peritubular capillaries, whereas others are secreted from the blood into the nephron. However, because the capillaries and the tubules are not in physical contact due to the interstitial fluid between them, this transfer is not direct. Instead, the molecules or ions leave the tubule by passing through the one-cell-thick endothelial wall, diffuse through the

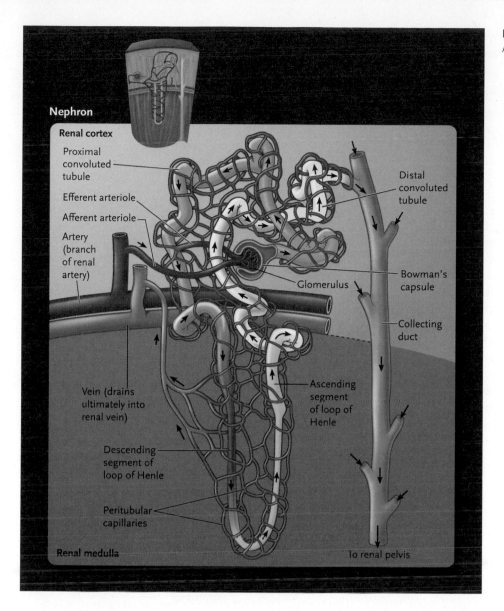

Figure 42.13
A nephron and its blood circulation.

Nephron

Renal cortex

Proximal convoluted tubule

Efferent arteriole

Afferent arteriole

Artery (branch of renal artery)

Glomerulus

Bowman's capsule

Distal convoluted tubule

Collecting duct

Vein (drains ultimately into renal vein)

Ascending segment of loop of Henle

Descending segment of loop of Henle

Peritubular capillaries

Renal medulla

To renal pelvis

interstitial fluid, and then pass into the capillary through its endothelial wall.

Each human kidney has more than a million nephrons. Of these, about 20% (the *juxtamedullary nephrons*) have long loops that descend deeply into the medulla of the kidney. The remaining 80% (the *cortical nephrons*) have shorter loops, most of which are located entirely in the cortex, and the remainder of which extend only partway into the medulla.

42.4c Nephrons and Other Kidney Structures Produce Hyperosmotic Urine

In mammals, urine is hyperosmotic to body fluids. Except for a few aquatic bird species, all other vertebrates produce urine that is hypoosmotic to body fluids or is at best isoosmotic. Production of hyperosmotic urine, a water-conserving adaptation, arises due to both structural (anatomical) and functional (physiological) features. Three features interact to conserve nutrients and water, balance salts, and concentrate wastes for excretion from the body:

- the structural arrangement of the loop of Henle, which descends into the medulla and returns to the cortex;
- differences in the permeability of successive regions of the nephron to water and ions, established by a specific group of membrane transport proteins in each region; and
- a gradient in the concentration of molecules and ions in the interstitial fluid of the kidney, established by these structural and functional processes, which increases gradually from the renal cortex to the deepest levels of the renal medulla.

Researchers determined the transport activities of specific regions of nephrons by dissecting them out of an animal and experimentally manipulating them *in vitro*. They placed segments in different buffered solutions and passed solutions containing various components of filtrates through the segment. By labelling specific molecules or ions radioactively, the scientists followed the movements of molecules in the solution surrounding the nephron segment or in the filtrate.

42.4d Filtration in Bowman's Capsule Begins the Process of Excretion

The mechanisms of excretion (**Figure 42.14**, and summarized in **Table 42.1**) begin in Bowman's capsule. The cells forming the walls of the capillaries of the glomerulus within Bowman's capsule and the cells of the capsule itself, are loosely connected leaving spaces just wide enough to allow water; ions; small nutrient molecules, such as glucose and amino acids; and nitrogenous waste molecules, primarily urea to pass into the lumen of the capsule. The higher pressure of the blood drives fluid containing these molecules and ions from the capillaries of the glomerulus into the capsule. A thin net of connective tissue between the capillary and Bowman's capsule epithelia contributes to the filtering process. Blood cells and plasma proteins are too large to pass and are retained inside the capillaries. The fluid entering the capsule is an ultrafiltrate of the blood.

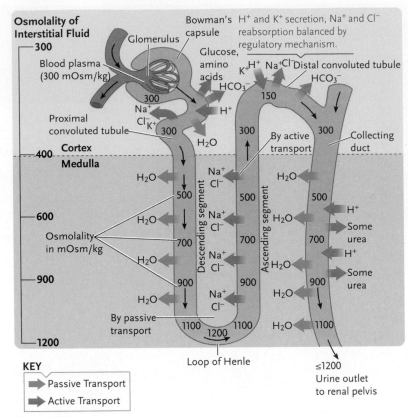

Figure 42.14

The movement of ions, water, and other molecules to and from nephrons and collecting tubules in the mammalian kidney. Nephrons in birds work in similar fashion. The numbers are osmolality values in milliosmoles per kilogram.

Table 42.1		Filtration, Reabsorption, and Secretion in Nephrons and Collecting Ducts		
Segment	Location	Permeability and Movement	Osmolality of Filtrate and Urine	Result of Passage
Bowman's capsule	Cortex	Water, ions, small nutrients, and nitrogenous wastes move through spaces between epithelia	300 mOsm/kg, same as surrounding interstitial fluid	Water and small substances, but not proteins, forced into nephron
Proximal convoluted tubule	Cortex	Na+ and K+ actively reabsorbed, Cl− follows; water leaves through aquaporins; H+ actively secreted; HCO3− actively reabsorbed into plasma of peritubular capillaries; glucose, amino acids, and other nutrients actively reabsorbed	300 mOsm/kg	67% of ions, 65% of water, 50% of urea, and all nutrients return to interstitial fluid; pH maintained
Descending segment of loop of Henle	Cortex into medulla	Water leaves through aquaporins; no movement of ions or urea	From 300 mOsm/kg at top to 1200 mOsm/kg at bottom of loop	Water drawn into interstitial fluid
Ascending segment of loop of Henle	Medulla into cortex	Na+ and Cl− actively transported out; no movement of water; no movement of urea	From 1200 mOsm/kg at bottom to 150 mOsm/kg at top of loop	Ions pumped into interstitial fluid creating osmotic gradient
Distal convoluted tubule	Cortex	K+ and Na+ secreted via active transport into urine; Na+ and Cl− actively reabsorbed; water moves out of urine through aquaporins; HCO3− actively reabsorbed into plasma of peritubular capillaries	From 150 mOsm/kg at beginning to 300 mOsm/kg at junction with collecting duct	Ions balanced, pH balanced
Collecting ducts	Cortex through medulla, empties into renal pelvis	Water moves out via aquaporins; some active secretion of ions; some urea leaves at bottom of duct	From 300 mOsm/kg to 1200 mOsm/kg at junction with renal pelvis	More water and some urea moves to interstitial fluid; some H+ added to urine

Aquaporins: Facilitating Osmotic Water Transport

Aquaporins are membrane proteins that form channels through which water can diffuse more rapidly than it would otherwise do. They are widely distributed, occurring in organisms from bacteria and yeast to mammals. In humans, at least 10 different aquaporins are known. The very narrow pores **(Figure 1)** permit water molecules to pass in single file, but because the molecules forming the channel are charged, other molecules of similar dimensions, such as H_3O^+, are excluded. The water moves in either direction in response to osmotic gradients: a single channel can permit as many as 3 billion molecules to cross the membrane per second.

Aquaporins are important in the functioning of mammalian kidneys.

For example, one aquaporin, aquaporin-2, resides on the membranes of vesicles within the cells of the collecting ducts. If the osmotic concentration of the body fluids increases, anti-diuretic hormone from the pituitary gland causes the aquaporins from the vesicles to be inserted into the membrane of the cells of the collecting ducts. The presence of more aquaporins in the membrane greatly increases the rate of osmotic reabsorption of water. The urine becomes more concentrated, and the osmotic concentration of body fluids is reduced.

FIGURE 1
An aquaporin channel.

Note that this ultrafiltrate contains many molecules (nutrients and ions) that the body does not want to loose. The fundamental process that occurs in the nephron consists of eliminating all small molecules and then taking back what is important, rather than actively secreting waste molecules and toxic substances. The advantage of producing urine in this manner is that animals have not had to evolve transport proteins for foreign and unwanted substances. They pass directly into the filtrate and are not reabsorbed.

Two factors help maintain the pressure driving fluid into Bowman's capsule. First, the diameters of the arteriole delivering blood to the glomerulus (called the **afferent arteriole**) and of the capillaries of the glomerulus itself are larger than that of arterioles and capillaries elsewhere in the body. The larger diameter maintains blood pressure by presenting less resistance to blood flow. Second, the diameter of the arteriole that receives blood from the glomerulus (called the **efferent arteriole**) is smaller than the diameter of the afferent arteriole, producing a damming effect that backs up the blood in the glomerulus and helps keep the pressure high.

In humans, Bowman's capsules collectively filter about 180 L of fluid each day, from a daily total of 1400 L of blood that passes through the kidneys. The human body contains only about 2.75 L of blood plasma, meaning that the kidneys filter a fluid volume equivalent to 65 times the volume of the blood plasma each day. On average, more than 99% of the filtrate, mostly water, is reabsorbed in the nephrons, leaving about 1.5 L to be excreted daily as urine.

42.4e Reabsorption and Secretion Occur in the Nephron

The fluid filtered into Bowman's capsule contains water, other small molecules, and ions at the same concentrations as the blood plasma. By the time the fluid reaches the distal end of the collecting duct, reabsorption out of and secretion into the tubules and collecting duct have markedly altered the concentrations of all components of the filtrate.

The Proximal Convoluted Tubule. This is the segment of the nephron where the valuable nutrients and ions that the body needs to retain are reabsorbed. Na^+/K^+ pumps in the epithelium of the proximal convoluted tubule move Na^+ and K^+ from the filtrate into the interstitial fluid surrounding the tubule (see Figure 42.14). The movement of positive charges sets up a voltage gradient that causes Cl^- ions to move out of the tubule with the positive ions. Specific active transport proteins move essentially all the glucose, amino acids, and other nutrient molecules out of the filtrate into the interstitial fluid, making the filtrate hypoosmotic to the interstitial fluid surrounding the tubule. As a result, water moves from the tubule into the interstitial fluid by osmosis. The osmotic movement is aided by *aquaporins,* proteins that form passages for water molecules in the transport epithelium of the tubule cells (see "Molecule behind Biology," Box 42.2). At this point, all of these substances that were filtered out of the blood into the filtrate in the tubule, have now been transported out of the filtrate into the interstitial fluid. The nutrients and water that entered the interstitial fluid then move into the capillaries of the peritubular network.

Some substances are secreted from the interstitial fluid into the tubule, primarily H^+ ions by active transport and the products of detoxified poisons by passive secretion (detoxification takes place in the liver). Small amounts of ammonia are also secreted into the tubule. The secretion of H^+ ions into the filtrate helps balance the acidity constantly generated in the body by metabolic reactions. H^+ secretion is coupled with HCO_3^- reabsorption from the filtrate in the tubule to the plasma in the peritubular capillaries.

In all, the proximal convoluted tubule reabsorbs about 67% of the Na^+, K^+, and Cl^- ions; 65% of the water; 50% of the urea; and essentially all the glucose, amino acids, and other nutrient molecules from the filtrate. The ions, nutrients, and water reabsorbed by the tubule are transported into the interstitial fluid and then into capillaries of the peritubular network. Although 50% of the urea is reabsorbed, the constant flow of filtrate through the tubules and the excretion of the remaining urea in the urine keep the concentration of nitrogenous wastes low in body fluids.

The proximal convoluted tubule has structural specializations that fit its function. The epithelial cells that make up its walls are carpeted on their inner surface by a brush border of microvilli. These microvilli greatly increase the surface area available for reabsorption and secretion.

The Descending Segment of the Loop of Henle. The filtrate flows from the proximal convoluted tubule into the descending segment of the loop of Henle. As this tubule segment descends, it passes through regions of increasingly higher solute concentrations in the interstitial fluid of the medulla (shown in Figure 42.14, p. 1062). (The generation of this concentration gradient is described later.) As a result, water moves out of the tubule by osmosis as the fluid travels through the descending segment.

The descending segment has aquaporins, which allow the rapid transport of water, but it has no other transport proteins. The outward movement of water concentrates the molecules and ions inside the tubule, gradually increasing the osmolality of the fluid to a peak of about 1200 mOsm/kg at the bottom of the loop. This is the same as the osmolality of the interstitial fluid at the bottom of the medulla.

The Ascending Segment of the Loop of Henle. The fluid then moves into the ascending segment of the loop of Henle, where Na^+ and Cl^- are actively transported into the interstitial fluid. The ascending segment has membrane proteins that transport salt ions but lacks aquaporins. Because water is trapped in the ascending segment, the osmolality of the urine is progressively reduced moving up this segment as salt ions, primarily Na^+ and Cl^-, are pumped out of the tubule.

The active transport of salt ions from the tubule into the interstitial fluid establishes the concentration gradient of the medulla, high near the renal pelvis, and low near the renal cortex. The energy required to transport NaCl from the ascending segment makes the kidneys one of the major ATP-consuming organs of the body.

By the time the fluid reaches the cortex at the top of the ascending loop, its osmolality has dropped to about 150 mOsm/kg. During the travel of fluid around the entire loop of Henle, water, nutrients, and ions have been conserved and returned to the peritubular capillaries, and the total volume of the filtrate in the nephron has been greatly reduced. Urea and other nitrogenous wastes have been concentrated in the filtrate. Little secretion into the tubule occurs in either the descending or ascending segments of the loop of Henle.

The Distal Convoluted Tubule. The transport epithelium of the distal convoluted tubule removes additional water from the filtrate in the tubule and works to balance the salt and bicarbonate concentrations of the filtrate against body fluids. In response to hormones triggered by changes in the body's salt concentrations, varying amounts of K^+ and H^+ ions are secreted into the filtrate, and varying amounts of Na^+ and Cl^- ions are reabsorbed. Bicarbonate ions are reabsorbed from the filtrate as in the proximal tubule.

In total, more ions move outward than inward in the distal tubule, and, as a consequence, water moves out of the tubule by osmosis through aquaporins. The amounts of urea and other nitrogenous wastes remain the same. By the time the filtrate, now urine, enters the collecting ducts at the end of the nephron, its osmolality is about 300 mOsm/kg.

The Collecting Ducts. The collecting ducts concentrate the urine. These ducts, which are permeable to water but not to salt ions, descend downward from the cortex through the medulla of the kidney. As the ducts descend, they travel through the gradient of increasing solute concentration in the medulla. This increase makes water move osmotically out of the ducts and greatly increases the concentration of the urine, which can become as high as 1200 mOsm/kg at the bottom of the medulla. Near the bottom of the medulla, the walls of the collecting ducts contain passive urea transporters that allow a portion of this nitrogenous waste to pass from the duct into the interstitial fluid. This urea adds significantly to the concentration gradient of solutes in the medulla.

In addition to these mechanisms, H^+ ions are actively secreted into the fluid by the same mechanism as in the proximal and distal convoluted tubules. The balance of the H^+ and bicarbonate ions established in the urine, interstitial fluid, and blood, achieved by secretion of H^+ into the urine by the nephrons and collecting ducts, is important for regulating the pH of blood and body fluids. The kidneys thus provide a safety valve if the acidity of body fluids rises beyond levels that can be controlled by the blood's buffer system (see Chapter 32).

At its maximum value of 1200 mOsm/kg, reached when water conservation is at its maximum, the urine reaching the bottom of the collecting ducts is about four times as concentrated as body fluids. But it can also be as low as 50 to 70 mOsm/kg when very dilute urine is produced in response to conditions such as excessive water intake.

The high osmolality of the interstitial fluid toward the bottom of the medulla would damage the medulla cells if they were not protected against osmotic water loss. The protection comes from high concentrations of otherwise inert organic molecules called *osmolytes* in these cells. The osmolytes, of which the most important is a sugar-alcohol called *sorbitol* (see "Molecule behind Biology," Box 40.6, Chapter 40), raise the osmolality of the cells to match that of the surrounding interstitial fluid. Urine flows from the end of the collecting ducts into the renal pelvis and then through the ureters into the urinary bladder, where it is stored. From the bladder, urine exits through the urethra to the outside.

42.4f Terrestrial Mammals Have Water-Conserving Adaptations

Terrestrial mammals have other adaptations that complement the water-conserving activities of the kidneys. One is the location of the lungs deep inside the body, which reduces water loss by evaporation during breathing (see Chapter 41). Another is a body covering of keratinized skin. Skin is so impermeable that it almost eliminates water loss by evaporation, except for the controlled loss through evaporation of sweat in mammals with sweat glands.

Among mammals, water-conserving adaptations reach their greatest efficiency in desert rodents such as the kangaroo rat (Figure 42.15). The proportion of nephrons with long loops extending deep into the kidney medulla of kangaroo rats is very high, allowing them to excrete urine that is 20 times as concentrated as body fluids. Further, most of the water in the feces is absorbed in the large intestine and rectum. Lacking sweat glands, they lose little water by evaporation from the body surface. Much of the moisture in their breath is condensed and recycled by specialized passages in the nasal cavities. They stay in burrows during the daytime and come out to feed only at night.

About 90% of the kangaroo rat's daily water supply is generated from oxidative reactions in its cells. (Humans, in contrast, can make up only about 12% of their daily water needs from this source.) The remaining 10% of the kangaroo rat's water comes from its food. These structural and behavioural adaptations are so effective that a kangaroo rat can survive in the desert without ever drinking water.

	Kangaroo Rat	Human
Water gain (millilitres)		
From ingesting food	6.0	850
From drinking liquids	0.0	1400
By metabolism	54.0	350
	60.0	2600
Water loss (millilitres)		
In urine	13.5	1500
In feces	2.6	200
By evaporation	43.9	900
	60.0	2600

Joe McDonald/Visuals Unlimited/Getty Images

Figure 42.15

A comparison of the sources of water for a human and a kangaroo rat (*Dipodomys* species). Water conservation in the kangaroo rat is so efficient that the animal never has to drink water.

Marine mammals, including whales, seals, and manatees, eat foods that are high in salt content. They are able to survive the high salt intake because they produce urine that is more concentrated than sea water. As a result, they are easily able to excrete all the excess salt they ingest in their diet.

The adaptations described in this section allow animals to maintain the concentration of body fluids at levels that keep cells from swelling or shrinking and permit excretion of toxic wastes. An equally important challenge is maintaining an internal temperature that allows the organ systems to function with maximum efficiency. We look at these processes in the next section.

STUDY BREAK

1. What can mammalian kidneys do that the kidneys of other vertebrates cannot?
2. Where does active transport of ions occur in the nephron?
3. What is the major event in the ascending segment of the loop of Henle? Why is this important?
4. What is the major event in the collecting duct?
5. Compare how marine birds and marine mammals deal with the problem of excreting the excess salt they take in with their food.

42.5 Introduction to Thermoregulation

Environmental temperatures vary enormously across Earth's surface. Temperatures in deserts in Australia, Africa, and the United States may reach 50°C, whereas temperatures across the Canadian prairies and the north can fall to –50°C in winter, and some locations in the Antarctic experience –80°C. There are also seasonal variations. A single location in the boreal forest of Canada might experience temperatures as low as –40°C in the winter and as high as 35°C in the summer. However, animal cells can function only within a temperature range from about 0 to 45°C. Not far below 0°C, the lipid bilayer of a biological membrane changes from a fluid to a frozen gel, which disrupts vital cell functions. Without protective measures, ice crystals will destroy the cell's organelles. At the other extreme, as temperatures approach 45°C, the kinetic motions of molecules become so great that most proteins and nucleic acids unfold from their functional form. Either condition leads quickly to cell death. Animals, therefore, usually maintain internal body temperatures somewhere within the 0 to 45°C limits, and most species can only operate over restricted portions of this range. As a consequence, most animals regulate their body temperatures to remain within their operable limits.

Temperature regulation (thermoregulation) is based on negative feedback pathways in which temperature receptors called *thermoreceptors* (see Chapter 37) monitor body temperature and integrate this information by comparing it to a temperature *set point* (see Section 31.4b, Chapter 31, for a description of the set point). Differences from the set point trigger physiological and behavioural responses that return the temperature to the set point. The responses triggered by negative feedback mechanisms (see Chapter 31) involve adjustments in the rate of heat-generating oxidative reactions within the body, coupled with adjustments in the rate of heat gain or loss at the body surface. The particular adaptations that accomplish these responses vary widely among species, however. And although body temperature is closely regulated around a set point in all endotherms, the set point itself may vary over the course of a day and between seasons (see Chapter 31).

In this section, we describe the structures, mechanisms, and behavioural adaptations that enable animals to regulate their temperature.

42.5a Thermoregulation Allows Animals to Reach Optimal Physiological Performance

Within the 0 to 45°C range of tolerable internal temperatures, an animal's *organismal performance* varies greatly. Organismal performance is a term that describes the rate and efficiency of an animal's biochemical, physiological, and whole-body processes. For instance, the speed at which a tropical fish can swim (one measure of organismal performance) is low when the animal's body temperature is cold, rises smoothly with body temperature until it levels to a fairly broad plateau, and then drops off dramatically with further increases in body temperature **(Figure 42.16a)**. The range of temperatures that provides optimal organismal performance varies from one species to another and may also vary within a species as a function of season **(Figure 42.16b)**. Similar patterns of temperature dependence are observed for numerous other body functions.

Animals that maintain their body temperature within the fairly narrow temperature range that corresponds to their optimal temperature can move quickly, digest food efficiently, and carry out necessary activities and processes rapidly and effectively (as shown in **Figure 42.16c**). Thus, in addition to keeping body temperatures within tolerable limits, thermoregulation allows animals to maintain an optimal level of organismal performance.

42.5b Animals Exchange Heat with Their Environment

As part of thermoregulation, animals exchange heat with their environment. Virtually all heat exchange occurs at surfaces where the body meets the external

a. Maximum running speed of a lizard at various body temperatures

b. Maximum swimming speed of a fish at various body temperatures in water and summer

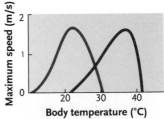
c. Range of optimal physiological performance

Figure 42.16

Body temperature and organismal performance. **(a)** The maximum swimming speed of a tropical fish changes dramatically with body temperature. **(b)** This relationship varies between species, as shown here for a temperate species of fish, and between seasons (winter = blue; summer = red). **(c)** An animal's other behavioural and physiological processes respond to temperature changes in similar ways. The advantage of regulating body temperature within the range indicated by the bar on the horizontal axis is a high level of organismal performance, indicated by the bar on the vertical axis.

environment. As with all physical bodies, heat flows into animals if they are cooler than their surroundings and flows outward if they are warmer. This heat exchange occurs by four mechanisms: *conduction, convection, radiation,* and *evaporation* **(Figure 42.17).**

Conduction is the flow of heat between atoms or molecules in direct contact. An animal loses heat by conduction when it contacts a cooler object and gains heat when it contacts an object that is warmer. **Convection** is the transfer of heat from a body to a fluid (air or water) that passes over its surface. The movement maximizes heat transfer by replacing fluid that has absorbed or released heat with fluid at the original temperature. **Radiation** is the transfer of heat energy as electromagnetic radiation. Any object warmer than absolute zero (–273°C) radiates heat; as the object's temperature rises, the amount of heat it loses as radiation increases as well. Animals also gain heat through radiation, particularly by absorbing radiation from the Sun. **Evaporation** is heat transfer through the energy required to change a liquid to a gas.

CONCEPT FIX Animals do not lose heat directly by sweating. Evaporation of water from a surface, however, is an efficient way to transfer heat; when the water in sweat evaporates from the body surface, the body cools down because heat is being transferred to the evaporated water in the surrounding air. In hot, humid regions where the air is saturated with water vapour, sweat does not evaporate and no heat can be lost in this manner. Thus, it is not the sweating that dissipates heat but the evaporation of the sweat. ⬡

All animals gain or lose heat by a combination of these four mechanisms. A moose struggling with the heat on a sunny summer day (Figure 42.17) loses heat by the evaporation of sweat from the skin and from the surface of the lungs, by convection as air flows over the skin, by conduction from the legs to the pond it is standing in, and by outward infrared radiation. It gains heat from internal biochemical reactions (especially oxidations), and by absorbing infrared and solar radiation. To maintain a constant body temperature, the heat gained and lost through these pathways must balance.

42.5c Animals Can Be Exothermic or Endothermic

Different animals use one of two major strategies to balance heat gain and loss. Animals that obtain heat primarily from the external environment are known as **ectotherms** (*ecto* = outside); those obtaining most of their heat from internal physiological sources are called **endotherms** (*endo* = inside). All ectotherms generate at least some heat from internal reactions, however, and endotherms can obtain heat from the environment under some circumstances.

Most invertebrates, fishes, amphibians, and reptiles are ectotherms. Although these animals are popularly described as cold-blooded, the body temperature of some, such as an active lizard, may be as high as or higher than ours on a sunny day. Ectotherms regulate body temperature by controlling the rate of heat exchange with the environment. Through behavioural and physiological mechanisms, they adjust body temperature toward a level that allows optimal physiological performance. However, most ectotherms are unable to maintain optimal body temperature when the temperature of their surroundings departs too far from that optimum, particularly when environmental temperatures fall. As a result, the body temperatures of ectotherms fluctuate with environmental temperatures, and ectotherms are typically less active when it is cold.

The endotherms—birds and mammals—keep their bodies at an optimal temperature by regulating two processes: (1) the amount of heat generated by internal oxidative reactions and (2) the amount of heat exchanged with the environment. Because endotherms use internal heat sources to maintain body temperature at optimal levels, they can remain active over a broader range of environmental temperatures than ectotherms. However, endotherms require a nearly constant supply of energy to maintain their body temperatures. And because that energy is provided by food,

Figure 42.17

Heat flows into and out of a moose on a hot, sunny day. Unlike conduction, convection, and evaporation, which take place through the kinetic movement of molecules, electromagnetic radiation (infrared) is transmitted through space as waves of energy.

CHAPTER 42 REGULATING THE INTERNAL ENVIRONMENT

endotherms must typically consume much more food than ectotherms of equivalent size. Some fishes, sea turtles, and invertebrates are also capable of generating significant amounts of internal heat.

The difference between ectotherms and endotherms is reflected in their metabolic responses to environmental temperature **(Figure 42.18)**. The metabolic rate of a resting mouse *increases* steadily as the environmental temperature falls from 25 to 10°C. This increase reflects the fact that to maintain a constant body temperature in a colder environment, endotherms must process progressively more food and generate more heat to compensate for their increased rate of heat loss.

By contrast, the metabolic rate of a resting lizard typically *decreases* steadily over the same temperature range. Because ectotherms do not maintain a constant body temperature, their biochemical and physiological functions, including oxidative reactions, slow down as environmental and body temperatures decrease. Thus, an ectotherm consumes less food and requires less energy when it is cold than when it is warm.

Ectothermy and endothermy represent different strategies for coping with the variations in environmental temperature that all animals encounter; neither strategy is inherently superior to the other. Endotherms can remain fully active over a wide temperature range. Cold weather does not prevent them from foraging, mating, or escaping from predators, but it does increase their energy and food needs—and to satisfy their need for food, they may not have the option of staying curled up safely in a warm burrow. Ectotherms do not have the capacity to be active when environmental temperatures drop too low; they move sluggishly and are unable to capture food or escape from predators.

However, because their metabolic rates are lower under such circumstances, so are their food needs, and they do not have to actively look for food and expose themselves to danger to the extent that endotherms do.

Having laid the ground rules of heat transfer and weighed the relative advantages and disadvantages of ectothermy and endothermy, we now begin a more detailed examination of how individual animals actually regulate their body temperatures within these overall strategies.

STUDY BREAK

What are the advantages and disadvantages of ectothermy and endothermy? Would these be different in tropical versus temperate regions?

42.6 Ectothermy

Because ectotherms obtain most of their body heat from their environment, they generally have body temperatures very similar to those of the ambient temperature that surrounds them. To change body temperature to improve performance, these species live in or seek warm or temperate environments, where temperatures fall within the range that produces optimal physiological performance. Ectotherms have some ability to regulate their body temperature by physiological, but mainly behavioural, means, and those with a greater ability to thermoregulate generally occupy more varied habitats.

42.6a Ectotherms Are Found in All Invertebrate Groups

Aquatic invertebrates are limited thermoregulators. Their body temperature closely follows the temperature of their surroundings. Intertidal marine invertebrates, however, that are routinely exposed to air, use behavioural responses to regulate body temperature. For example, a South American intertidal mollusc, *Echinolittorina peruviana,* is longer than it is wide. Researchers in Chile have shown that this animal orients itself as a means of thermoregulation. On sunny summer days, it faces the Sun, offering a smaller surface area for the Sun's rays. On overcast summer days, or during the winter, it orients itself with its side, which has the larger surface area, toward the Sun's rays.

Invertebrates living in terrestrial habitats regulate their body temperatures more closely. Many also use behavioural responses, such as moving between shaded and sunny regions, to regulate body temperature. Some winged arthropods, including bees, moths, butterflies, and dragonflies, use a combination of behavioural and heat-generating physiological mechanisms for thermoregulation. In cool weather, these animals warm up before taking flight by rapidly vibrating the large flight

Figure 42.18
Metabolic responses of ectotherms and endotherms to cooling environmental temperatures. At any temperature, the metabolic rates of endotherms are always higher than those of ectotherms of comparable size.

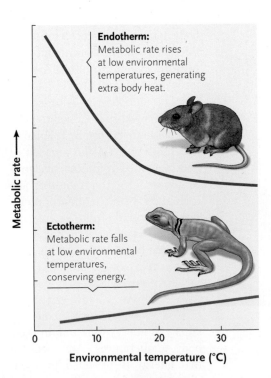

Endotherm: Metabolic rate rises at low environmental temperatures, generating extra body heat.

Ectotherm: Metabolic rate falls at low environmental temperatures, conserving energy.

Metabolic rate →

Environmental temperature (°C)

muscles in the thorax, in a mechanism similar to shivering in humans. The tobacco hawkmoth (*Manduca sexta*) vibrates its flight muscles until its thoracic temperature reaches about 36°C before flying. During flight, metabolic heat generated by the flight muscles sustains the elevated thoracic temperature, so much so that a flying sphinx moth produces more heat per gram of body weight than many mammals. Honeybees (*Apis mellifera*) form masses in the hive in winter and use the heat generated by vibrating their flight muscles to maintain temperature inside the hive. Even in a Manitoba winter, with external temperatures below −20°C, the temperature in the mass of bees is normally about 30°C, and the bees may continue to raise offspring, using food stored in the hive.

42.6b Most Fishes, Amphibians, and Reptiles Are Ectotherms

Vertebrate ectotherms (most fishes, amphibians, and reptiles) also vary widely in their ability to thermoregulate. Most aquatic species have a more limited thermoregulatory capacity than that found among terrestrial species, particularly the reptiles. Some fishes, however, are highly capable thermoregulators.

Fishes. The body temperatures of most fishes remain within one or two degrees of their aquatic environment. However, many fishes use behavioural mechanisms to keep body temperatures at levels that allow good physiological performance. Many freshwater species perform better at lower temperatures and may use opportunities provided by the thermal stratification of lakes and ponds to sustain optimal performance in the summer. They remain in deep, cool water during hot summer days, moving to the shallows to feed only during early morning and late evening when air and water temperatures are lower.

Some cold-water marine teleosts (such as tunas and mackerels) and some sharks (such as the great white), on the other hand, use endothermy in their aerobic swimming muscles to maintain muscle temperature as much as 10 to 12°C warmer than their surroundings to improve performance. These animals have in common the fact that they move over long distances, swimming continuously. The action of the muscles generates heat that permits the muscles and other organs to operate more efficiently. Much of this heat generated in other fish is lost at the gill–water interface. However, a *countercurrent heat exchanger* system between the arteries and the veins in the swimming muscles of these specialized fishes minimizes this loss (see Chapter 41). The anatomical details of the heat exchanger vary. In principle, however, the venules containing warm blood from the muscles form a network with arterioles containing cold blood coming from the gills. The heat from the venules is transferred to the arterioles and is returned to the muscles. This transfer

not only increases the temperature of the exercising muscle but reduces the temperature of the blood from the muscles returning to the heart on its way to the gills, and, thus, heat loss to the environment is minimized.

Amphibians and Reptiles. The body temperature of most amphibians also closely matches the environmental temperature. The tadpoles of foothill yellow-legged frogs (*Rana boylii*) regulate their body temperature to some degree by changing their location in ponds and lakes to take advantage of temperature differences between deep and shallow water or between sunny and shaded regions. Some terrestrial amphibians bask in the Sun to raise their body temperature and seek shade to lower body temperature. However, basking can be dangerous to amphibians because they lose water rapidly through their permeable skin. We have already noted that the leaf frog *Phyllomedusa sauvagii*, which often basks in sunlight, avoids this problem by coating itself with waterproofing lipids secreted by glands in its skin.

Thermoregulation is more pronounced among terrestrial reptiles. Some lizard species can maintain temperatures that are nearly as constant as those of endotherms **(Figure 42.19)**. For small lizards, the most common behavioural thermoregulatory mechanism is moving between sunny (warmer) and shady (cooler) regions. In the desert, lizards and other reptiles retreat into burrows during the hottest part of summer days. Some, such as the desert iguana (*Dipsosaurus dorsalis*), lose excess heat by *panting*—rapidly moving air in and out of the airways. The air movement increases heat loss by evaporation of water from the respiratory tract.

Lizards also frequently adjust their posture to foster heat exchange with the environment and control the angle of their body relative to the rays of the Sun. Horned lizards (genus *Phrynosoma*) often warm up by flattening themselves against warm, sunlit rocks to maximize their rate of heat gain by conduction from the rock and radiation from the Sun. Snakes and lizards can often be found on large rocks and on roads on chilly nights, taking advantage of the heat retained by

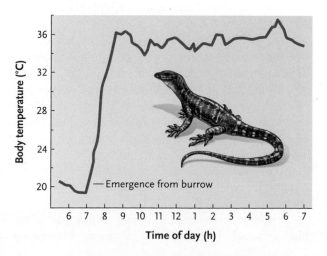

Figure 42.19
An example of excellent thermo-regulation in ectotherms. The body temperature of the Australian lizard *Varanus varius* rises quickly after the animal emerges from its burrow and remains relatively stable throughout the day.

PEOPLE BEHIND BIOLOGY 42.3
Ken Storey, Carleton University

Ken Storey, who leads a busy laboratory at Carleton University in Ottawa, explores the biochemical changes associated with hibernation and estivation in a wide range of animals, including both invertebrates and vertebrates. The wood frog, *Rana sylvatica,* is of particular interest because it spends the winter in a frozen state under the leaves on the forest floor. These frozen frogs have no heartbeat, breathing, or brain activity. Storey's research has shown that the wood frog's tolerance of freezing involves the liberation of glucose from glycogen stores in the liver and its accumulation at extremely high concentrations within the cells, resulting in a slurry of small ice crystals and glucose. This suggests a suspension of the function of insulin, which normally controls glucose concentrations (see "Life on the Edge," Box 42.4, page 1076). Although it may be obvious that the frogs freeze from the outside in and that heart and brain function will be the last to be suspended, it is also true that the frogs thaw from the inside out. The coordination of the events governing freezing and thawing involves a number of signal cascades, which Storey's lab has characterized. Storey is currently exploring gene expression during the process of freezing and thawing.

the stone or concrete. *Agama savignyi,* a lizard that lives in the Negev Desert in Israel, cools off at midday by climbing into shady bushes, moving away from the hot sand, and catching a cooling breeze.

Researchers have demonstrated experimentally that several lizard species couple physiological responses to behavioural mechanisms of thermoregulation. When a Galápagos marine iguana (*Amblyrhynchus cristatus*) is exposed to heat from infrared radiation, blood flow increases in the heated regions of the skin. The blood absorbs heat rapidly and carries it to critical organs in the core of the body. Conversely, when an area of skin is experimentally cooled, blood flow to it is restricted, thereby preventing the loss of heat to the external environment.

42.6c Ectotherms Can Compensate for Seasonal Variations in Environmental Temperature

Many ectotherms undergo seasonal physiological changes called **thermal acclimatization.** These changes allow the animals to attain good physiological performance at both winter and summer temperatures (see Figure 42.16, p. 1066).

For example, in the summer, bullhead catfish (*Ameiurus* species) can survive water temperatures as high as 36°C but cannot tolerate temperatures below 8°C. In the winter, however, the bullhead cannot survive water temperatures above 28°C but can tolerate temperatures near 0°C. Scientists have hypothesized that the production of different versions of some enzymes (perhaps encoded by different genes or produced as a result of alternative splicing) with optimal activity at cooler or warmer temperatures underlies such acclimatization.

Another acclimatizing change involves the phospholipids of biological membranes. Membrane phospholipids have higher proportions of double bonds in carp living in colder environments than in carp living in warmer environments. The higher proportion of double bonds makes it harder for the membrane to freeze. A higher proportion of cholesterol also protects membranes from freezing.

STUDY BREAK

1. Describe mechanisms an ectothermic animal can use to regulate its temperature.
2. What is thermal acclimatization? Why is it important?

42.7 Endothermy

Endotherms (mostly birds and mammals) have the most elaborate and extensive thermoregulatory adaptations of all animals. Set points (the core body temperatures that endotherms maintain homeostatically) vary with species and lie between about 39 and 42°C in birds and 32 and 39°C in mammals. We have already noted that the range of environmental temperatures that different organisms encounter is very great. A single species may encounter seasonal variations in environmental temperatures ranging over 70°C or more between winter and summer, yet their body temperatures do not vary.

We begin by describing the basic feedback mechanisms that maintain body temperature in this group.

42.7a The Hypothalamus Integrates Information from Thermoreceptors

Thermoreceptors are found in various locations in the bodies of endotherms, including the **integument** (skin), spinal cord, and hypothalamus. Two types of thermoreceptors occur in skin (see Chapters 36 and 37). In mammals, *warm receptors* send signals to the hypothalamus as the skin temperature rises above 30°C and reach maximum activity when the temperature rises above 40°C. Another type, the *cold receptor,* sends signals when skin temperature falls below about 35°C and reaches maximum activity at 25°C. By contrast, the highly sensitive thermoreceptors in the hypothalamus itself produce signals when the blood temperature shifts from the set point by as little as 0.01°C.

Signals from the thermoreceptors are integrated in the hypothalamus and other regions of the brain to bring about compensating physiological and behavioural responses (**Figure 42.20;** see also Figure 31.12, Chapter 31). The responses keep body temperature close to the set point, which varies normally in most mammals between 35 and 39°C for the head and trunk. The appendages may vary more widely in temperature. In very cold weather, for example, the legs, the feet, and especially the ears and nose are typically lower in temperature than the body core.

The hypothalamus was identified as a major thermoreceptor and response integrator in mammals by experiments on animals in which various regions of the brain were heated or cooled with a temperature probe. Within the brain, cooling and warming only the hypothalamus produced thermoregulatory responses such as shivering and panting. Later experiments revealed a similar response if regions of the spinal cord were cooled, indicating that thermoreceptors also occur in this location. The hypothalamus is also a major thermoreceptor and response integrator in fishes and reptiles. In birds, thermoreceptors in the spinal cord appear to be more significant in thermoregulation.

42.7b The Skin Controls Heat Transfer with the Environment

Besides its defensive role against infection, the skin of birds and mammals is an organ of heat transfer. It is a very large surface, in direct contact with the environment, across which heat can be transferred readily.

The outermost living tissue of human skin, the **epidermis,** consists of cells that divide and grow rapidly **(Figure 42.21, p. 1072),** becoming packed with fibres of a highly insoluble protein, *keratin*. When fully formed, the epidermal cells die and become compacted into a tough, impermeable layer.

Below the epidermis lies the **dermis,** a tissue layer packed with connective tissue fibres, such as collagen, that resist the compression, tearing, or puncture of the skin.

The dermis also contains thermoreceptors and a dense network of arterioles, capillaries, and venules. The arterioles delivering blood to the capillary networks of the skin constrict or dilate to control blood flow and with it the amount of heat transferred from the body core to the surface. Sweat glands and hair and feather follicles are also embedded in the dermis.

The innermost layer of the skin, the **hypodermis,** contains larger blood vessels and additional reinforcing connective tissue. The hypodermis also contains an insulating layer of fatty tissue below the dermal capillary network, which ensures that heat flows between the body core and the surface primarily through the blood. The insulating layer is thickest in mammals that live in cold environments, such as whales, seals, walruses, and polar bears, in which it is known as *blubber*.

Figure 42.20

The physiological and behavioural responses of birds and mammals to changes in skin and core temperature (see also Figure 31.12, Chapter 31).

The primary skin layers

Hair

Epidermis {

Dermis {

Hypodermis {

Oil gland

Hair follicle

Blood vessels

Sweat gland

Sensory neuron

Smooth muscle

Layering of the epidermis

Outer epidermal layer (dead cells)

Keratinized cells being compacted

Rapidly dividing cells of epidermis

Dermis

John D. Cunningham/Visuals Unlimited, Inc.

Figure 42.21
The structure of human skin.

42.7c The Body Reduces Heat Loss When Core Temperature Falls Below the Set Point

When thermoreceptors signal a fall in core temperature below the set point, the hypothalamus triggers compensating responses by sending signals through the autonomic nervous system (see Chapter 36). Among the immediate responses is constriction of the arterioles in the skin (vasoconstriction), which reduces the flow of blood to the skin's capillary networks. The reduced flow cuts down the amount of heat delivered to the skin and therefore lost from the body surface. The reduction in flow is most pronounced in the skin covering the extremities, where blood flow may be reduced by as much as 99% when core temperature falls. This is particularly important for animals in polar regions. In these animals, the veins and arteries to the legs may form a simple countercurrent heat exchange system in which cold blood returning from the foot takes heat from the arterial blood entering the foot **(Figure 42.22).** This minimizes heat loss from the foot while maintaining a nutritive flow of blood to the extremity.

In marine mammals such as whales and seals, heat loss is regulated by adjustments in the blood flow through the thick blubber layer to the skin. In cold water, blood flow is minimized by constriction of the vessels, making the skin temperature close to that of the surrounding water. In addition, heat loss in whales and seals is controlled by adjustments of the flow of blood to the flippers, which are not insulated by blubber and act as heat radiators. When heat must be conserved to maintain core temperature at the set point, blood flow to the flippers is reduced.

Another immediate response is contraction of the smooth muscles that erect the hair shafts in mammals and feather shafts in birds (*piloerection*). This traps air in pockets over the skin, reducing convective heat loss. The response is minimally effective in animals such as pigs and humans because hair is sparse on most parts of the body, but it produces the goose bumps we experience

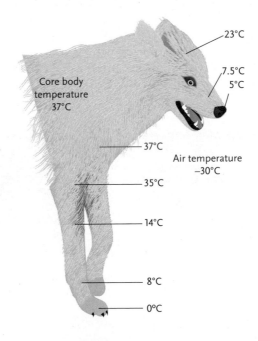

23°C

7.5°C
5°C

Core body temperature 37°C

37°C

Air temperature −30°C

35°C

14°C

8°C

0°C

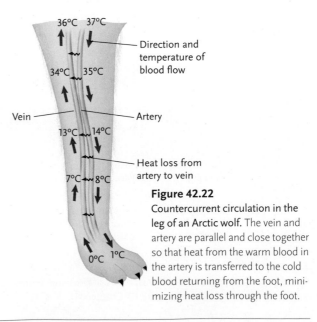

36°C 37°C

Direction and temperature of blood flow

34°C 35°C

Vein

Artery

13°C 14°C

Heat loss from artery to vein

7°C 8°C

Figure 42.22
Countercurrent circulation in the leg of an Arctic wolf. The vein and artery are parallel and close together so that heat from the warm blood in the artery is transferred to the cold blood returning from the foot, minimizing heat loss through the foot.

0°C 1°C

when the weather gets chilly. However, in mammals with fur coats or in birds, erection of the hair or feather shafts significantly increases the thickness of the insulating layer that covers the skin, trapping more air.

Immediate behavioural responses triggered by a reduction in skin temperature also help reduce heat loss from the body. Mammals may reduce heat loss by moving to a warmer locale or curling into a ball. Many mammals have an uneven distribution of fur that aids thermoregulation. In a dog, for example, the fur is thickest over the back and sides of the body and the tail and thinnest under the legs and over the belly. In cold weather, a dog will curl up, pull in its limbs, wrap its tail around its body, and bury its nose in its tail so that only body surfaces insulated by thick fur are exposed to the air **(Figure 42.23a)**. Many birds and mammals also huddle together to conserve heat. We have all seen puppies huddled together to keep warm; birds such as penguins also keep warm by huddling **(Figure 42.23b)**.

If these immediate responses do not return body temperature to the set point, the hypothalamus triggers further responses, most notably the rhythmic tremors of skeletal muscle we know as shivering. The heat released by the muscle contractions and the oxidative reactions powering them can raise the total heat production of the body substantially. At the same time, the hypothalamus triggers secretion of *epinephrine* (from the adrenal medulla) and *thyroid hormone* (see Chapter 35), both of which increase heat production by stimulating the oxidation of fats and other fuels. The generation of heat by oxidative mechanisms in nonmuscle tissue throughout the body is termed **nonshivering thermogenesis.**

In the young of many mammals (including newborn human infants), the most intense heat generation is by nonshivering thermogenesis that takes place in a specialized **brown adipose tissue** (also called brown fat), which can produce heat rapidly. Heat is generated by a mechanism that uncouples electron transport from ATP production in mitochondria (see Chapter 6); the heat is transferred throughout the body by the blood. Animals that hibernate or are active in cold regions contain larger amounts of brown adipose tissue. In most mammals, brown adipose tissue is concentrated between the shoulders in the back and around the neck where it preferentially warms the heart and the blood leaving the heart in arterial blood. In human newborns, this tissue accounts for about 5% of body weight. The tissue normally shrinks during late childhood and is absent or nearly so in most adults. However, if exposure to cold is ongoing, the tissue remains. Some Japanese and Korean divers who harvest shellfish in frigid waters and male Finns who work outside during the year have significant amounts of brown adipose tissue.

If none of these responses succeed in raising body temperature to the set point, the result is **hypothermia,** a condition in which the core temperature falls below normal for a prolonged period. In humans, a drop in core temperature of only a few degrees affects brain function and leads to confusion; progressive or continued hypothermia can lead to coma and death.

a.

Fredrik Broman/Iconica/Getty Images, Inc.

b.

© david tipling/Alamy

d.

Joe McDonald/Corbis

c.

Photos.com

Figure 42.23
Structural and behavioural adaptations controlling heat transfer at the body surface. **(a)** A husky (*Canis lupus familiaris*) conserving heat by curling up with the limbs under the body and the tail around the nose. **(b)** Penguins huddle together to conserve heat. **(c)** An elephant cools off by spraying itself with water. **(d)** A jackrabbit (*Lepus californicus*) dissipating heat from its ears on a hot summer day. Notice the dilated blood vessels in its large ears. Both the large surface area of the ears and the extensive network of blood vessels promote the dissipation of heat by convection and radiation.

42.7d The Body Increases Heat Loss When Core Temperature Rises above the Set Point

When the core temperature rises above the set point, the hypothalamus sends signals through the autonomic system that trigger responses that lower body temperature. As an immediate response, the signals relax smooth muscles of arterioles in the skin (vasodilation), increasing blood flow and with it the heat lost from the body surface. In marine mammals in warmer water, blood flow to the skin above the blubber increases, allowing excess heat to be lost from the body surface. In addition, when a whale generates excessive internal heat through the muscular activity of swimming, the flow of blood from the body core to the flippers increases.

The smooth muscles to feathers and fur in birds and mammals in hot climates also relax, and these layers are flattened, removing trapped air and decreasing their insulating capability. In addition, in mammals with sweat glands, such as antelopes, cows, humans, and horses, signals from the hypothalamus trigger the secretion of sweat, which absorbs heat as it evaporates from the surface of the skin. Some endotherms, including dogs (which have sweat glands only on their feet) and many birds (which have no sweat glands), use panting as a major way to release heat.

These physiological changes are reinforced by behavioural responses such as seeking shade or a cool burrow, plunging into cold water, wallowing in mud, or taking a cold drink. Elephants take up water in their trunks and spray it over their bodies to cool off in hot weather **(Figure 42.23c)**; dogs spread their limbs, turn on their side or back, and expose the relatively bare skin of the belly, which acts as a heat radiator. In hot weather, many birds fly with their legs extended so that heat flows from their legs into the passing air. Similarly, penguins expose featherless patches of skin under their wings to cool off on days when the weather is too warm. Jackrabbits **(Figure 42.23d)** and elephants dissipate heat from their large ears, which are richly supplied with blood vessels. In times of significant heat stress, kangaroos and rats spread saliva on their fur to increase heat loss by evaporation; some bats coat their fur with both saliva and urine.

When the heat gain of the body is too great to be counteracted by these responses, **hyperthermia** results. An increase of only a few degrees above normal for a prolonged period is enough to disrupt vital biochemical reactions and damage brain cells. Most adult humans become unconscious if their body temperature reaches 41°C and die if it goes above 43°C for more than a few minutes.

As with ectotherms, many mammals also undergo thermal acclimatization with seasonal temperature changes. Although in many cases a change in day length appears to be the actual trigger, the development of a thick fur coat in winter, which is shed in summer, enables them to adapt to seasonal temperatures. Some arctic and subarctic mammals develop a thicker layer of insulating fat in winter.

42.7e Birds and Mammals Have Daily and Seasonal Rhythms

The temperature set point in many birds and mammals varies in a regular cycle during the day. In some, the daily variations are relatively small. In others, larger variations are correlated with daily or seasonal temperature changes. These rhythms are a response to day length rather than temperature change.

Humans are among the endotherms for which daily variations in the temperature set point are small. Normally, human core temperature varies from a minimum of about 35.5°C in the morning to a maximum of about 37.7°C in the evening. Women also show a monthly variation keyed to the menstrual cycle, with temperatures rising about 0.5°C from the time of ovulation until menstruation begins. The physiological significance of these variations is unknown.

Camels undergo a daily variation of as much as 7°C in set point temperature. During the day, a camel's set point gradually resets upward, an adaptation that allows its body to absorb a large amount of heat. The heat absorption conserves water that would otherwise be lost by evaporation to keep the body at a lower set point. At night, when the desert is cooler, the thermostat resets again, allowing the body temperature to cool several degrees, releasing the excess heat absorbed during the day.

When the environmental temperature is cool, having a lowered temperature set point greatly reduces the energy required to maintain body temperature. In many animals, the lowered set point is accompanied by reductions in metabolic, nervous, and physical activity (including slower respiration and heartbeat), producing a sleeplike state known as **torpor.**

Entry into **daily torpor,** a period of inactivity keyed to variations in daily temperature, is typical of many small mammals and birds. These animals typically expend more energy per unit of body weight to keep warm than larger animals because the ratio of body surface area to volume increases as body size decreases; that is, the ratio of surface area across which they lose heat increases while the volume of cells producing heat decreases. Hummingbirds feed actively during the daytime, when their set point is close to 40°C. During the cool of night, however, the set point drops to as low as 13°C. This allows the birds to conserve enough energy to survive overnight when they are unable to feed and would otherwise be unable to obtain enough fuel to produce heat; they would literally starve to death. Some nocturnal animals, including bats and small rodents, such as the deer mouse, become torpid in cool locations during daylight hours when they do not actively feed. At night, their temperature set point rises and they become fully active **(Figure 42.24)**.

Many animals enter a prolonged state of torpor tied to the seasons, triggered in most cases by a change in day length that signals the transition between summer and winter. The importance of day length has been demonstrated by laboratory experiments in which animals have been induced to enter seasonal torpor by changing the period of artificial light to match the winter or summer day length.

Many mammals during winter enter a more extreme state of metabolic suppression called **hibernation** (*hiberna* = winter), greatly reducing metabolic expenditures when food is unobtainable. Hibernators must store large quantities of fats to serve as energy reserves. The drop in body temperature during hibernation varies with the mammal. In some, such as hedgehogs, groundhogs, and squirrels, body temperature falls to within 1°C of environmental temperatures down to just above freezing. In some species of hedgehogs, body temperature falls from about 38°C in the summer to as low as 5 to 6°C during winter hibernation. The Arctic ground squirrel's body supercools (goes to a below-freezing, unfrozen state) during hibernation, with its body temperature dropping to about −3°C. Hibernating mammals may experience brief periods of arousal during the course of the winter.

In larger mammals, such as bears, the degree of metabolic suppression and fall in body temperature is less pronounced. The core temperature of bears drops only 5 to 10°C. Although sluggish, hibernating bears will waken readily if disturbed. They also waken normally from time to time, as when females wake to give birth during the winter season.

Some ectotherms, including amphibians and reptiles living in northern latitudes, also become torpid during winter. The Antarctic codfish, *Notothenia cordiceps*, spends the summer feeding on phytoplankton. In the winter, however, phytoplankton are reduced as a result of the low levels of light. The fish enter a state similar to hibernation. They remain relatively immobile in refuges, and their metabolic rate drops by about one-third. Because the temperature of the water remains constant over the seasons, the fish clearly have the capacity to control their metabolic rate independent of temperature.

Some mammals enter seasonal torpor during summer, called **estivation** (*aestivalis* = of summer), when environmental temperatures are high and water is scarce. Some ground squirrels remain inactive in the cooler temperatures of their burrows during extreme summer heat. Many ectotherms, among them land snails, lungfishes, many toads and frogs, and some desert-living lizards, weather such climates by digging into the soil and entering a state of estivation that lasts throughout the hot, dry season.

STUDY BREAK

1. What can birds and mammals do to dissipate heat on very hot days? How would this be affected by high humidity?
2. Mammals that live in the desert are often nocturnal. What advantages are there in terms of thermoregulation?

Figure 42.24

Cycle of daily torpor in a deer mouse (*Peromyscus maniculatus*).

Inga Spence/Visuals Unlimited, Inc.

LIFE ON THE EDGE 42.4
Surviving Freezing

For birds and mammals, freezing temperatures lead to the formation of ice crystals that disrupt cell membranes and kill cells. Many ectotherms, however, encounter temperatures in winter that are well below the freezing point of their body fluids and yet their cells do not die. The tiny second-stage caterpillar of the spruce budworm (*Choristoneura fumiferana*) spends the winter at the tips of spruce trees in Canada, where temperatures may reach −40°C **(Figure 1)**. Their ability to survive depends on the production of an antifreeze protein. Antifreeze proteins also occur in marine fishes that occupy habitats where the water temperature may be below the freezing point of their body fluids, and they occur in some amphibians, such as the wood frog (*Rana sylvatica*, see "People behind Biology," Box 42.3, Figure 1). Research led by Peter Davies at Queen's University has shown that these proteins bond with forming ice crystals, limiting their growth, so although the water freezes, the crystals remain small enough that cell structure is not disrupted.

The molecular structure of the antifreeze proteins is diverse, and at least four types are known. This diversity appears even within a single species: work in Garth Fletcher's laboratory at Memorial University in St. John's, Newfoundland, has shown that the protein found in plasma of several species of marine teleosts is different from that in the skin cells or gill cells. This diversity suggests that genes for the various types of antifreeze proteins in fish arose independently during the relatively recent cooling of the polar oceans.

Figure 1
(a) The effects of spruce budworm on stands of western Douglas fir. *(b) Spruce budworm* (Choristoneura fumiferana). *(c) The icefish* Trematomus bernacchi. *(d) Frozen specimens of the wood frog* Rana sylvatica.

Review

Access an interactive eBook, chapter-specific interactive learning tools, including flashcards, quizzes, videos, and more in your Biology **CourseMate**, accessed through NelsonBrain.com **Aplia™** is an online interactive learning solution that helps you improve comprehension—and your grade—by integrating a variety of mediums and tools such as videos, tutorials, practice tests, and an interactive eBook.

42.1 Introduction to Osmoregulation and Excretion

- Osmotic concentration of a solution is measured as osmolality in milliosmoles per kilogram (mOsm/kg) of solute. Both molecules and ions contribute to osmolality. Water moves osmotically from a solution of lower osmolality to one of higher osmolality. When comparing two solutions of different osmolality, the solution of higher osmolality is hyperosmotic and the solution of lower osmolality is hypoosmotic. Solutions of the same osmolality are isoosmotic.

- Osmoregulation describes the mechanisms that keep the osmolality of intracellular and extracellular fluids isotonic. Osmoregulators keep the osmolality of body fluids different from that of the environment. Osmoconformers allow the osmolality of their body fluids to match that of the environment.

- Osmoregulation is closely related to excretion because molecules and ions must be removed from the body to maintain the isotonicity of cells and extracellular fluids. Excretion also removes excess water, nitrogenous wastes, excess acid, and toxic molecules from the body.

- In most animals, tubules formed from a transport epithelium carry out the combined processes of osmoregulation and excretion. Extracellular fluids are filtered into the proximal end of the tubules; as the fluid moves through the tubules, some ions and molecules are reabsorbed from the fluid, and others are secreted into the fluid. Water is added or removed from the fluid to maintain the animal's water balance. The processed fluid is released to the exterior of the animal as urine.

- Nitrogenous wastes from the metabolism of amino acids and nucleic acids are excreted as ammonia, urea, or uric acid or as a combination of these substances.

42.2 Osmoregulation and Excretion in Invertebrates

- Most marine invertebrates are osmoconformers, whereas the invertebrates living in freshwater or terrestrial environments are osmoregulators.

- Because the body fluids of marine osmoconformers are isoosmotic to sea water, they expend little or no energy on maintaining water balance. Body fluids in osmoregulators living in freshwater and terrestrial environments are hyperosmotic to their surroundings. They must therefore expend energy to excrete water moving into their cells by osmosis and to obtain the salts required to maintain osmolality.

- Most invertebrates have specialized excretory tubules such as protonephridia, metanephridia, or Malpighian tubules that eliminate nitrogenous wastes and may assist in osmoregulation. A few groups eliminate wastes by diffusion.

- Protonephridia are blind tubes that produce an ultrafiltrate of the body fluids and adjust its ionic composition by secretion and reabsorption. Metanephridia are open tubes that take in coelomic fluid and adjust the ionic concentration.

- Malpighian tubules are blind tubes, and ions, uric acid, and other compounds enter by secretion.

42.3 Kidney Function in Nonmammalian Vertebrates

- Marine teleosts must continually drink sea water to replace body water lost by osmosis to their hyperosmotic environment. The Na^+, K^+, and Cl^- in the ingested sea water are excreted from the gills. Nitrogenous wastes are excreted by the gills as ammonia.

- Sharks use urea and trimethylamine oxide as osmolytes to maintain their body fluids isoosmotic with sea water. As a result, sharks and rays do not lose water by osmosis and do not drink sea water. Excess salts ingested in foods are excreted in the kidney and by a rectal salt gland.

- Body fluids of freshwater fishes and amphibians are hyperosmotic to their environment, and these animals must excrete the excess water that enters by osmosis. Body salts are obtained from food and, in fishes, by active transport through the gills. Nitrogenous wastes are excreted from the gills of fish and larval amphibians as ammonia and through the kidneys of adult amphibians as urea.

- Most reptiles and birds conserve water by secreting nitrogenous wastes as uric acid. Water is also absorbed from the urine and the feces in the cloaca.

- Marine birds and reptiles secrete excess salts through a gland in the head.

42.4 Osmoregulation and Excretion in Mammals

- In mammals and other vertebrates, excretory tubules are concentrated in a specialized excretory organ, the kidney. Each of the pair of mammalian kidneys is divided into an outer renal cortex surrounding a central renal medulla. The mammalian excretory tubule, the nephron, has a proximal end at which filtration takes place, a middle region in which reabsorption and secretion occur, and a distal end that releases urine.

- The interstitial fluid reabsorbs ions, water, and other molecules from the nephron. A network of capillaries surrounding the nephron absorbs these materials. The urine leaving individual nephrons is processed further in collecting ducts and then pools in the renal pelvis. From there it flows through the ureter to the urinary bladder and through the urethra from the bladder to the exterior of the animal.

- At its proximal end, the mammalian nephron forms a cuplike Bowman's capsule around a cluster of capillaries, the glomerulus. A filtrate consisting of water, other small molecules, and ions is forced from the glomerulus into Bowman's capsule, from which it travels through the nephron and drains into the collecting ducts and renal pelvis.

- The proximal convoluted tubule of the nephron secretes H^+ into the filtrate and actively reabsorbs Na^+, K^+, HCO_3^-, and nutrients such as glucose and amino acids.

- In the descending segment of the loop of Henle, water is reabsorbed by osmosis.

- In the ascending segment of the loop of Henle, Na^+ and Cl^- move from the tubule by active transport. This establishes the osmotic gradient in the medulla of the kidney that is essential for water conservation.

- In the distal convoluted tubule, regulatory mechanisms operate to balance the concentrations of H^+ and salts between the urine and the interstitial fluid surrounding the nephron. K^+ and Na^+ move by active transport.

- In the collecting ducts, additional H^+ is secreted into the urine and water is reabsorbed; some urea is also reabsorbed at the bottom of the ducts.

42.5 Introduction to Thermoregulation

- Animals maintain body temperature at a level that provides optimal physiological performance. Heat flows between animals and their environment by conduction, convection, radiation, and evaporation.

- Ectothermic animals obtain heat energy primarily from the environment, and endothermic animals obtain heat energy primarily from internal reactions.

42.6 Ectothermy

- Ectotherms, including all invertebrates and amphibians, reptiles, and most fishes among the vertebrates, control body temperature by regulating heat exchange with the environment. Their thermoregulatory responses may be physiological or behavioural. For most ectotherms, the ability to thermoregulate is limited, and body temperature does not differ widely from environmental temperature.

- Many animals undergo thermal acclimatization, a change in the limits of tolerable temperatures as the environment alternates between warm and cool seasons or between day and night. The acclimatization may involve structural changes and/or metabolic alterations.

42.7 Endothermy

- Endotherms, mostly birds and mammals, maintain body temperature over a narrow range by balancing internal heat production against heat loss from the body surface.

- Internal heat production is controlled by negative feedback pathways triggered by thermoreceptors in the skin, hypothalamus, and spinal cord.

- Signals from the receptors are integrated in the hypothalamus to bring about compensating responses by activating the autonomic nervous system, the endocrine system, and the motor nerves. These responses return the core temperature to a set point when deviations occur.

- When body temperature falls below a set point, responses include an increase in heat-generating metabolic reactions and a reduction of blood flow to the body surface. Behavioural responses also reduce heat loss.

- When body temperature rises above the set point, blood flow to the skin increases and sweating is induced in mammals with sweat glands. Mammals with no or few sweat glands and birds, which have no sweat glands, release heat by panting. Behavioural responses also contribute to heat loss.

- The skin of endotherms is water impermeable, reducing heat loss by direct evaporation of body fluids. Mammals with sweat glands regulate evaporative heat loss by releasing moisture to the skin surface when body temperature rises.

The blood vessels of the skin regulate heat loss by constricting or dilating. A layer of insulating fatty tissue under the vessels limits losses to the heat carried by the blood. The hair of mammals and feathers of birds also insulate the skin. Erection of the hair or feathers reduces heat loss by thickening the insulating layer.

- The temperature set point in many birds and mammals varies in daily and seasonal patterns. During cooler conditions, a lowered set point is accompanied by torpor: a reduction in metabolic, nervous, and physical activity. Seasonal torpor includes winter hibernation and summer estivation.

- Some animals, such as certain cold-water marine fishes, exhibit a form of endothermy in which part, but not all, of their core is maintained at a temperature significantly higher than the surrounding environment.

Questions

Self-Test Questions

1. In terms of osmoregulation, why are most sharks like freshwater fish?
   a. They are osmoregulators.
   b. They are osmoconformers.
   c. They are more concentrated than the water in which they live.
   d. They are less concentrated than the water in which they live.

2. Which structure can carry out filtration and/or excretion?
   a. ciliated metanephridia in insects
   b. a nephron and a bladder in insects
   c. the hindgut of earthworms
   d. protonephridia containing flame cells in flatworms

3. If an animal secretes uric acid crystals, in which environment could you conclude that the animal most likely lives?
   a. fresh water
   b. marine
   c. terrestrial and very dry
   d. terrestrial and very wet

4. Which statement describes what happens in the kidneys?
   a. In the descending loop of Henle, water leaves the tubule.
   b. In the collecting duct, water enters the tubule via aquaporins.
   c. The fluid that enters Bowman's capsule is an ultrafiltrate of the blood.
   d. In the ascending loop of Henle, Na^+ and K^+ enter the tubule by simple diffusion.

5. Substances that are NOT reabsorbed will do the following:
   a. be excreted from the body in urine
   b. remain in the nephron
   c. leave the kidney through the renal vein
   d. return to the glomerulus

6. What is unique to endotherms?
   a. torpor
   b. thermal acclimatization
   c. thermoregulation by the hypothalamus
   d. a body temperature that does not change

7. Boa constrictors wrap themselves around their eggs and shiver. Which term refers to this warming mechanism?
   a. evaporation
   b. conduction
   c. convection
   d. radiation

8. Thermal acclimatization can be described as follows:
   a. It involves regulation of body temperature in response to information provided by a thermoreceptor.
   b. It is the change in an animal's physiology that accompanies seasonal changes.
   c. It occurs when core body temperature is below normal for an extended period of time.
   d. It occurs when core temperature is above normal for an extended period of time.

9. If the set point for temperature regulation were increased, which would you expect to occur?
   a. decreased epinephrine
   b. shivering
   c. vasodilation
   d. both a and c

10. Which statement best exemplifies ectotherms?
    a. All invertebrates are ectotherms.
    b. Food demand decreases when environmental temperatures decrease.
    c. The metabolic rate increases as the environmental temperature decreases.
    d. Body temperature remains constant when environmental temperatures change.

Questions for Discussion

1. Compare and contrast the challenges for salt and water balance of animals living in marine, freshwater, and terrestrial environments.

2. Describe how the structure of aquaporins allows water to pass through a membrane but not protons.

3. Hockey players are often advised to consume sports drinks containing salt before, during, and after a game. Why do you think this is?

4. Mammals that live in the desert are often nocturnal. What advantages are there in terms of thermoregulation?

5. The internal temperature of a reptile, such as a crocodile, varies with its developmental stage. Adult crocodiles tend to have a higher internal temperature less subject to change due to environmental variation in temperature. Why do you think this is?

Death of a cancer cell. A cytotoxic T cell (orange) induces a cancer cell (mauve) to undergo apoptosis (programmed cell death). Cytotoxic T cells are part of the body's immune response system and are programmed to seek out, attach to, and kill cancer cells and pathogen-infected host cells.

© Dr. Andrejs Liepins/Science Photo Library/Photo Researchers, Inc.

43 Defences against Disease

WHY IT MATTERS

Diseases have plagued all organisms, including humans, for billions of years. All animals, even insects, starfish, worms, and organisms too small to see with the naked eye, can suffer from some sort of disease. In humans, acquired immune deficiency syndrome (AIDS), first identified in the early 1980s, now affects about 40 million people worldwide and continues to spread. Malaria affects around 500 million people. Similar diseases in other organisms, such as avian influenza and avian malaria, may significantly reduce bird populations, and insect populations may be killed by outbreaks of specific viruses. Overall, bacteria, viruses, and parasites can all cause disease in their hosts. However, immune systems are able to regulate or eliminate the majority of pathogens that cause disease. We combat the other pathogens by developing effective drug treatments that eliminate the disease-causing organism or developing vaccines that provide protection from infection.

The development of vaccines began with efforts to control smallpox, a dangerous and disfiguring viral disease that once infected millions of people worldwide, killing more than one-third of its victims. As early as the twelfth century, healthy individuals in China sought out people who were recovering from mild smallpox infections, ground up scabs from their lesions, and inhaled the powder or pushed it into their skin. Variations on this treatment were effective in protecting many people against smallpox infection.

In 1796, an English country doctor, Edward Jenner, used a more scientific approach. He knew that milk-maids never got smallpox if they had contracted cowpox, a similar but mild disease of cows that can be transmitted to humans. Jenner decided to see if a deliberate infection with cowpox would protect humans from smallpox. He scratched material from a cowpox sore into a boy's arm. Six weeks later, after the cowpox infection had subsided, he scratched fluid from human smallpox sores into the boy's skin. (Jenner's use of the boy as an experimental subject would now be considered highly unethical.) Remarkably, the boy remained free from smallpox. Jenner carried out additional, carefully documented case studies with other patients with the same results. His technique became the basis for worldwide **vaccination** (*vacca* = cow) against smallpox. With improved vaccines, smallpox has now been eradicated from the human population.

Vaccination takes advantage of the **immune system** (*immunis* = exempt), the natural protection that is our main defence against infectious disease. This chapter focuses on the roles of the different components of the immune system that deal with infection. We describe aspects of immune systems in different organisms, from insects to humans, to examine their similarities and differences.

CONCEPT FIX Some people think that *disease* and *parasites* are synonymous. A disease and a parasite are not the same thing. A parasite or pathogen is an organism that may infect us, whereas a disease is the manifestation of symptoms we show (sneezing, diarrhea, swollen liver, fever). Many individuals in a group may become infected with the same pathogen or parasite. Some of us will have genetic factors that prevent the foreign organism from developing, multiplying, and causing disease, while others will come down with full-blown symptoms. Sometimes parasites can develop and be transmitted from one individual to another without the infected person knowing they have an infection. These asymptomatic carriers can be important in maintaining an outbreak of disease as it is difficult to identify them as infected individuals and then treat them to eliminate the problem. ⬡

43.1 Three Lines of Defence against Invasion

Every organism is constantly exposed to *pathogens* and *parasites,* potentially disease-causing organisms such as viruses, bacteria, fungi, protists, and larger parasites such as trematodes, cestodes, and nematodes. Humans and other animals have three lines of defence against these threats. The first line of defence involves physical barriers that prevent the entry of pathogens. The second is the *innate immune system*—inherited mechanisms that protect the body from pathogens in a nonspecific way. The third is the *adaptive immune system,* found only in vertebrates, which involves inherited mechanisms that lead to the synthesis of molecules such as antibodies that target pathogens in a specific way. Reaction to an infection takes minutes in the case of the innate immunity system versus several days for the adaptive immune system.

43.1a The Epithelium Is a Barrier to Infection

An organism's first line of defence is the body surface—the skin covering the body exterior, the cuticle of an arthropod, the outer layer of a plant, and the epithelial surfaces covering internal body cavities and ducts, such as the lungs and intestinal tract. The body surface forms a barrier of tight junctions between epithelial cells that keeps most parasites and pathogens (as well as toxic substances) from entering the body.

In the respiratory tract, ciliated cells constantly sweep the mucus with its trapped bacteria and other foreign matter into the throat, where it is coughed out or swallowed. Many of the body cavities lined by mucus membranes have environments that are hostile to pathogens. For example, the strongly acidic environment inside the stomach kills most ingested bacteria and destroys many viruses, including those trapped in swallowed mucus from the respiratory tract. Most of the pathogens that survive the stomach acid are destroyed by the digestive enzymes and bile secreted into the small intestine. Reproductive tracts may be acidic or basic, preventing many pathogens from surviving there, and many epithelial tissues secrete proteins such as defensins or lysozymes that are lethal to many bacteria.

43.1b Immune Systems Protect the Body

The body's second line of defence is a series of generalized internal chemical, physical, and cellular reactions that attack pathogens that have breached the first line. These defences include inflammation, which creates internal conditions that inhibit or kill many pathogens, and specialized cells that engulf or kill pathogens or infected body cells. These initial nonspecific responses to pathogens are components of the **innate immune system.**

The innate immune response relies on germ-line-encoded receptors that recognize a set of highly conserved molecular patterns that are present on the surface of pathogens but not found on host cells. Innate immunity provides an immediate, *nonspecific* response; that is, it targets any invading pathogen and has no memory of prior exposure to that specific pathogen.

Invertebrates, fungi, and plants rely solely on innate immune responses, whereas vertebrates use the innate immune system in conjunction with the adaptive response for a more powerful overall response. This most complex line of defence, found only in vertebrates, is called **adaptive** (or **acquired**) **immunity.** Adaptive immunity is *specific:* it recognizes individual pathogens and mounts an attack that directly neutralizes or eliminates them. It is stimulated and shaped by the presence of a specific pathogen or foreign molecule in the body. This mechanism, which takes several days to become protective, is triggered by specific molecules on pathogens that are recognized as being foreign to the body. The body retains a memory of the first exposure to a foreign molecule, enabling it to respond more quickly if the same pathogen is encountered again in the future. This is the basis of the vaccination programs we will discuss later.

Innate immunity and adaptive immunity together constitute the immune system, and the defensive reactions of the system are termed the **immune response.** Functionally, all components of the immune system interconnect and communicate at the chemical and molecular levels. The immune system is the product of long-term coevolutionary interactions between pathogens and their hosts. Over millions of years, the mechanisms by which pathogens attack and invade have become more efficient, but the defences of organisms against the invaders have kept pace.

43.1c Organisms Can Recognize Pathogens

The basic tenet of immunity is that an organism can recognize a pathogen as being different from the host. This is often termed recognition of *nonself* and is the essential first step before any immune response can be initiated. Different organisms do this in different ways. Most organisms recognize unique *pathogen-associated molecular patterns* (PAMPs) found on many microbial organisms, using host molecules called *pattern recognition receptors* (PRRs). Common PAMPs include carbohydrates, glycoproteins, lipids, and nucleic acids. Two classic examples of PAMPs are the bacterial cell wall components lipoteichoic acid, found on Gram-positive bacteria, and lipopolysaccharide, found on Gram-negative bacteria. Major invertebrate PRRs include the Gram-negative bacteria binding protein and β 1,3-glucan recognition proteins that recognize and bind to common molecules found on many groups of pathogenic organisms rather than recognizing each pathogen species individually. For example, lipopolysaccharide is found on the outer surface of all Gram-negative bacteria and serves as a general PAMP to which a PRR can bind. Once specific PRRs are activated by the presence of the PAMP, signalling cascades are initiated that activate various components of the innate or acquired immune responses.

Plants respond to pathogens in a similar manner. They have two branches of immune responses: a system that uses transmembrane PRRs that respond to the PAMPs described for invertebrates and an intracellular response that uses protein products encoded by *R* genes that respond to infection and systemic signals from nearby infected cells. Damage to the plant cells by pathogens is believed to be the signal that activates the expression of plant R proteins.

Different PAMPs may activate the same or different signalling pathways and elicit different responses. This has been studied best in the fruit fly, *Drosophila melanogaster.* Infection of *Drosophila* with fungi and bacteria activates the Toll, JAK-STAT, and immune deficiency signalling (IMD) pathways that result in nuclear factor (NF)-κB-like transcription factors being translocated to the nucleus, activating many components of the innate immune response. Many similar pathways and molecules are found in humans. Researchers who discovered the Toll-receptors in Drosophila, which allowed for the discovery of Toll-like receptors in humans, received the Nobel Prize in Medicine and Physiology in 2011.

CONCEPT FIX The implication in this chapter is that all associations between viruses, bacteria, fungi, and parasites with vertebrate or invertebrate hosts have a negative impact on the hosts. Negative impacts are caused by many organisms, such as those that cause human disease. In other cases, however, these associations are beneficial to one or both organisms. Symbiotic relationships (two organisms living together) include **phoresis**, in which one organism uses another to be transported to new areas; **mutualism**, often an obligate relationship in which both symbionts benefit, such as the relationship between termites and their intestinal protozoans, or cows and their symbiotic bacteria that help digest cellulose, or the gut microflora in humans that help prevent pathogen invasion and produce nutrients we cannot obtain from our diet; and **commensalism**, where one symbiont benefits with no effect on the other, such as epiphytic plants or ciliates on crustaceans. Not all associations between different organisms cause problems. The immune systems of each organism must be able to recognize and differentiate between friend and foe and learn not to attack and eliminate beneficial symbionts. ◙

Study Break

1. What features of epithelial surfaces protect against pathogens?
2. What are the key differences between innate immunity and adaptive immunity?
3. How are pathogens recognized as nonself?

43.2 Nonspecific Defences: Innate Immunity

Invertebrates have only an innate response, and the PAMP–PRR interactions activate the signalling pathways described above. These activate processes such as

phagocytosis (the internalization and destruction of particulate matter) of small pathogens by hemocytes (blood cells) and the coagulation of the hemolymph (invertebrate blood). Larger pathogens may be encapsulated by hemocytes and covered in a melanin-like material that kills them **(melanotic encapsulation)**. This may be helped by the release of reactive intermediates of nitrogen and oxygen. The third component of the innate response involves the production of small **antimicrobial peptides** that kill pathogens not eliminated by the other responses. Some intracellular pathogens, such as viruses, are inaccessible to these immune factors. These often are eliminated through apoptosis, a form of programmed cell death (see Section 43.2a). This coordinated, multifaceted, and integrated approach eliminates potential pathogens, preventing them from harming or killing the host.

The study of invertebrate immunology began when a Russian scientist poked a rose thorn into the body of a starfish (see "People behind Biology," Box 43.6, p. 1101) and watched how the hemocytes surrounded the thorn **(Figure 43.1)**. The innate immune responses of invertebrates, now a rapidly developing field of research, have allowed us to understand how the innate system works in both invertebrates and vertebrates, as well as what molecules are activated in response to different stimuli. Plants respond in a similar manner. They can wall off cells that are infected, undergo cell death to prevent pathogen development, and produce several small antimicrobial peptides that kill microbial pathogens.

Figure 43.1

Innate immune responses demonstrated by the role of starfish blood cells responding to a thorn that has penetrated the cuticle.

Vertebrates use similar types of specific host cell-surface receptors that recognize the various PAMPs found on microbial pathogens. Some receptors activate signalling pathways that bring about the secretion of lethal antimicrobial peptides that kill the pathogen. Other receptors trigger the host cell to engulf the pathogen, as was described for phagocytosis in invertebrates, but in vertebrates, this may also initiate an inflammation response and activate the soluble receptors of the *complement system* described below. The innate responses that recognize and initiate immune pathways in plants, invertebrates, and vertebrates are strikingly similar.

Antimicrobial Peptides. All epithelial surfaces, namely skin; the lining of the gastrointestinal tract; the lining of the nasal passages, gills, and lungs; and the lining of the genitourinary tracts, are protected by antimicrobial peptides, such as the *defensins* (see "Molecule behind Biology," Box 43.1). These epithelial cells secrete defensins upon attack by a microbial pathogen. The defensins attack the plasma membranes of the pathogens, eventually disrupting them and thereby killing the cells. In particular, defensins play a significant role in the innate immunity of the intestinal tracts of vertebrates and invertebrates. Antimicrobial peptides such as the defensins are highly conserved in plants, invertebrates, vertebrates, and even single-celled organisms, indicating their important role in immunity throughout evolution. Other antimicrobial peptides are found only in specific groups, suggesting a more specialized role that has maintained their existence.

Inflammation. A tissue's rapid response to injury, including infection by most pathogens, involves **inflammation** (*inflammare* = to set on fire): the heat, pain, redness, and swelling that occur at the site of an infection.

Several interconnecting mechanisms initiate inflammation **(Figure 43.2, p. 1084)**. Consider bacteria entering a tissue as a result of a wound. **Monocytes** (a type of leukocyte) enter the damaged tissue from the bloodstream through the endothelial wall of the capillary. Once in the damaged tissue, the monocytes differentiate into **macrophages** (= big eaters), which are phagocytes that are usually the first to recognize pathogens at the cellular level. (**Table 43.1, p. 1084**, lists the major types of leukocytes, including macrophages; see also **Figure 43.3, p. 1085**) Cell-surface receptors on the macrophages recognize and bind to surface molecules on the pathogen, activating the macrophage to phagocytize (engulf) the pathogen (see Figure 43.2, step 1, p. 1084). There may not be enough macrophages present at the site of infection to eliminate all the pathogens. Activated macrophages also secrete **cytokines**, molecules that signal, activate, and recruit more immune cells to increase the system's response to the pathogen.

MOLECULE BEHIND BIOLOGY 43.1

Defensins

Defensins are ubiquitous cationic molecules used in the defences of essentially all organisms. Defensins have been isolated from several orders of the higher insects, such as the Diptera (flies) and Coleoptera (beetles), and from ancient insects, such as the Odonata (dragonflies). Functional analogues have been isolated and characterized from amoebas, nematodes, scorpions, molluscs, mammals (including humans), and plants. In some organisms, these molecules are secreted into the body cavity, whereas in others, they are intracellular and are released only at a wound site.

This strong conservation suggests that this molecule is of ancient origin and has been maintained throughout evolution due to its importance in limiting the growth of microbial pathogens. Defensins are composed of a series of structures: an N-terminal loop; an α-helix; and twisted, antiparallel β-sheets **(Figure 1).** The three-dimensional shape of defensins is stabilized by the presence of three disulfide bridges. Defensins are active against many Gram-positive bacteria, some Gram-negative bacteria, and some fungi. The lethality occurs as the one region of the peptide binds to the outer surface of the bacteria, allowing other regions to form pores in the microbial membranes, causing a permeabilization that causes a loss of cytoplasmic potassium, a depolarization of the inner membrane, reduced amounts of cytoplasmic ATP, and a reduction in respiration. This can occur in single-celled organisms, in the body cavity of an insect, in plant tissues, or in the white blood cells of a vertebrate. Defensins represent one family of molecules conserved throughout all taxa for the same function and are truly universal immune molecules.

FIGURE 1

Computer-generated model of a defensin molecule showing the arrangement of the coiled α-helix (red) and the β-sheets (blue) that are held together by disulfide bridges (yellow).

The death of cells caused by the pathogen at the infection site activates cells that are dispersed throughout the connective tissue, called **mast cells**, which then release histamine (see Figure 43.2, step 2, p. 1084). This histamine, along with the cytokines from activated macrophages, dilates local blood vessels around the infection site and increases their permeability. This increases blood flow and leakage of fluid from the vessels into body tissues (step 3). The response initiated by cytokines directly causes the heat, redness, and swelling of inflammation.

Cytokines also make the endothelial cells of the blood vessel wall stickier, causing circulating **neutrophils** (another type of phagocytic leukocyte) to attach to them in massive numbers. From there, the neutrophils are attracted to the infection site by **chemokines**, proteins also secreted by activated macrophages (see Figure 43.2, step 4, p. 1084). To get to the infection site, the neutrophils pass between endothelial cells of the blood vessel wall. Neutrophils may also be attracted directly to the pathogen by molecules released from the pathogens themselves. Like macrophages, neutrophils have cell-surface receptors that enable them to recognize and engulf pathogens (step 5).

Once a macrophage or neutrophil has engulfed the pathogen, it uses a variety of mechanisms to destroy it. These mechanisms include the secretion of enzymes and defensins located in lysosomes and the production of toxic compounds. The harshness of these attacks usually kills the neutrophils as well, whereas macrophages usually survive to continue their pathogen-scavenging activities. Dead and dying neutrophils, in fact, are a major component of the pus formed at infection sites. The pain of inflammation is caused by the migration of macrophages and neutrophils to the infection site and their activities there.

Some parasitic worms are too large to be engulfed by macrophages or neutrophils. In that case, macrophages, neutrophils, and **eosinophils** (another type of leukocyte) cluster around the worm and secrete lysosomal enzymes in amounts usually sufficient to kill the parasite.

The Complement System. Another nonspecific defence mechanism activated by invading pathogens is the **complement system**, a group of more than 30 interacting soluble plasma proteins that circulate in the blood and interstitial fluid. Normally inactive, the proteins are activated when they recognize molecules

Figure 43.2

The steps producing inflammation. The colourized micrograph on the left shows a macrophage engulfing a yeast cell.

Biology Media/Photo Researchers, Inc.

Bacteria at injury site

Macrophages

Mast cells

Cytokines

Chemokines

Neutrophils

Capillary

Histamine

Neutrophils sticking to wall

Endothelial cell of capillary

1 A break in the skin introduces bacteria, which reproduce at the wound site. Activated macrophages engulf the pathogens and secrete cytokines and chemokines.

2 Activated mast cells release histamine.

3 Histamine and cytokines dilate local blood vessels and increase their permeability. The cytokines also make the blood vessel wall sticky, causing neutrophils to attach.

4 Chemokines attract neutrophils, which pass between cells of the blood vessel wall and migrate to the infection site.

5 Neutrophils engulf the pathogens and destroy them.

Table 43.1	Major Types of Leukocytes and Their Functions
Type of Leukocyte	**Function**
Monocyte	Differentiates into a macrophage when released from blood into damaged tissue
Macrophage	Phagocyte that engulfs infected cells, pathogens, and cellular debris in damaged tissues; helps activate lymphocytes in carrying out immune response
Neutrophil	Phagocyte that engulfs pathogens and tissue debris in damaged tissues
Eosinophil	Secretes substances that kill eukaryotic parasites such as worms
Lymphocyte	Main subtypes involved in innate and adaptive immunity are natural killer (NK) cells, B cells, plasma cells, helper T cells, and cytotoxic T cells. NK cells function as part of innate immunity to kill virus-infected cells and some cancerous cells of the host. The other cell types function as part of adaptive immunity: they produce antibodies, destroy infected and cancerous body cells, and stimulate macrophages and other leukocyte types to engulf infected cells, pathogens, and cellular debris.
Basophil	Responds to IgE antibodies in an allergy response by secreting histamine, which stimulates inflammation

Figure 43.3
Major cellular components of mammalian blood and their origins from stem cells.

Labels on figure:
Leukocytes
Monocyte/macrophage
Eosinophil
Basophil
B lymphocyte
Platelets
Neutrophil
T lymphocyte
Natural killer (NK) cell
Erythrocyte
Myeloid stem cell
Lymphoid stem cell
Pluripotent stem cell

on the surfaces of pathogens. Activated complement proteins participate in a cascade of reactions on pathogen surfaces, producing large numbers of different complement proteins, some of which assemble into *membrane attack complexes*. These complexes insert into the plasma membrane of many types of bacterial cells and create pores that allow ions and small molecules to pass readily through the membrane. As a result, the bacteria can no longer maintain osmotic balance, and they swell and lyse. For other types of bacterial cells, the cascade of reactions coats the pathogen with fragments of the complement proteins. Cell-surface receptors on phagocytes then recognize these fragments and engulf and destroy the pathogen.

Several activated proteins in the complement cascade also act individually to enhance the inflammatory response. For example, some of the proteins stimulate mast cells to enhance histamine release, whereas others increase the blood vessel permeability.

43.2a Three Main Strategies Are Used to Combat Pathogenic Viruses

Specific molecules on pathogens such as bacteria are key to initiating innate immune responses. In contrast, the innate immune system often cannot distinguish between surface molecules of viral pathogens and host cells or cannot enter host cells to eliminate intracellular pathogens. The host must, therefore, use other strategies to provide some immediate protection against these infections until the adaptive immune system, which can discriminate between pathogen and host proteins, is effective. Three main strategies in this regard involve RNA interference, interferon, and natural killer cells.

RNA Interference. *RNA interference (RNAi)* is a cellular mechanism that is triggered by double-stranded (ds) RNA molecules. The dsRNA interferes with the ability of a cell to transcribe specific genes. Because dsRNA is a natural part of the life cycle of many viruses, the use of RNAi can inhibit the dsRNA found in many viruses and eliminate the infection.

Similarly, the virus can interfere with the host immune machinery, including RNAi pathways. Thus, the activities within a cell, and the success of a pathogen such as a virus, depend on the interplay between pro- and anti-infection responses. The only well-established antiviral mechanisms reported in insects such as the fruit fly, *D. melanogaster*, are RNAi and apoptosis. To combat this host response, many viruses contain genes that encode RNAi suppressors or inhibitors of apoptosis that help them survive.

Interferon. Viral dsRNA may also cause the infected host cell to produce two cytokines, interferon-α and interferon-β. **Interferons** can be produced by most cells of the body. Interferons act both on the infected cell that produced them, an autocrine effect, and on neighbouring uninfected cells, a paracrine effect (see Chapter 35). Interferons bind to cell-surface receptors, triggering a signal transduction pathway that changes the gene expression pattern of the cells. Key changes include the activation of a ribonuclease enzyme that degrades most cellular RNA and the inactivation of a key protein required for protein synthesis, thereby inhibiting most protein synthesis in the cell. These effects on RNA and protein synthesis inhibit pathogen replication while putting the cell in a weakened state from which it can often recover.

Apoptosis. Apoptosis, or programmed cell death, is a process inherent to all eukaryotic cells that has been highly conserved through evolution. It represents an intrinsic form of cell death that is tightly regulated by a variety of internal and external cellular signals to avoid killing healthy, productive cells. During development, apoptosis is required to sculpt tissues, remove old and dying cells, and eliminate embryonic cells with damaged DNA. Throughout life, apoptosis is also used as an immune response against intracellular pathogens and parasites. These organisms often trigger abnormal cellular activity, which induces intrinsic apoptotic pathways, activating initiator and effector caspases that dismantle the cell's structure. Once effector caspases have been activated, the cell is destined to die. Apoptotic cells fragment into membrane-bound apoptotic bodies that are readily phagocytosed and digested by macrophages or by neighbouring cells without generating an inflammatory response. If the pathogen is recognized as nonself and the apoptotic response is initiated in time, both the infected cell and the pathogen are eliminated, and no disease is seen. However, as discussed in Section 43.6, some pathogens have developed mechanisms to inactivate this response.

Natural Killer Cells. Cells that have been infected with a virus must be destroyed. That is the role of *natural killer (NK) cells*. NK cells are a type of *lymphocyte,* a leukocyte that carries out most of its activities in the tissues and organs of the blood and lymphatic circulatory systems (see Figure 32.17, Chapter 32). NK cells circulate in the blood and kill target host cells—not only cells that are infected with virus but also some cells that have become cancerous.

NK cells can be activated by cell-surface receptors or by interferons secreted by virus-infected cells. NK cells are not phagocytes; instead, they secrete granules containing *perforin,* a protein that creates pores in the target cell's membrane. Unregulated diffusion of ions and molecules through the pores causes osmotic imbalance, swelling, and rupture of the infected cell. NK cells also kill target cells indirectly through the secretion of *proteases* (protein-degrading enzymes) that pass through the pores. The proteases trigger apoptosis (see Section 8.5f, Chapter 8). That is, the proteases activate other enzymes that cause the degradation of DNA, which, in turn, induces pathways leading to the cell's death.

How does an NK cell distinguish a target cell from a normal cell? The surfaces of most vertebrate cells contain particular *major histocompatibility complex (MHC) proteins.* You will learn about the role of these proteins in adaptive immunity in the next section. NK cells monitor the level of MHC proteins and respond differently depending on their level. An appropriately high level, as occurs in normal cells, inhibits the killing activity of NK cells. Because intracellular pathogens often inhibit the synthesis of MHC proteins in the cells they infect, these cells are recognized by NK cells.

Cancer cells also have low or, in some cases, no MHC proteins on their surfaces, which makes them a target for destruction by NK cells.

STUDY BREAK

1. What are the usual characteristics of the inflammatory response?
2. What processes specifically cause each characteristic of the inflammatory response?
3. What is the complement system?
4. Why does combating viral pathogens require a different response by the innate immune system than combating bacterial pathogens? What are the four main strategies a host uses to protect against viral infections?

43.3 Specific Defences: Adaptive Immunity

Adaptive immunity is a defence mechanism that recognizes specific molecules as being foreign and clears these molecules from the body. The foreign or abnormal molecules that are recognized may be free, as in the case of toxins, or found on the surface of a virus or cell, including pathogenic bacteria, cancer cells, virus- or pathogen-infected cells, pollen, and cells of transplanted organs. Adaptive immunity develops specifically in response to the presence of foreign molecules and therefore takes several days to become effective. This time delay to mount an adaptive response would be a significant problem in eliminating pathogens were it not for the innate immune system, which combats the invading pathogens in its nonspecific way within minutes after they enter the body.

There are two key distinctions between innate and adaptive immunity:

- innate immunity is nonspecific, whereas adaptive immunity is specific, and
- innate immunity retains no memory of exposure to the pathogen, whereas adaptive immunity retains a memory of the foreign molecule that triggered the response, enabling a rapid, more powerful response if that pathogen is encountered again.

43.3a Antigens Can Be Cleared by B Cells or T Cells

A foreign molecule that triggers an adaptive immunity response is called an **antigen** (= *anti*body *gen*erator). Antigens are macromolecules; most are large proteins (including glycoproteins and lipoproteins) or polysaccharides (including lipopolysaccharides). Some types of nucleic acids can also act as antigens, as can various large, artificially synthesized molecules.

Antigens may be *exogenous,* meaning that they enter the body from the environment, or *endogenous,* meaning that they are generated within the body. Exogenous antigens include antigens on pathogens introduced beneath the skin, antigens in vaccinations, and inhaled and ingested macromolecules such as toxins. Endogenous antigens include proteins encoded by viruses that have infected cells and abnormal proteins produced by mutated genes, such as those produced in cancer cells.

Antigens are recognized in the body by two types of lymphocytes, B cells and T cells. **B cells** differentiate from stem cells in the bone marrow (see Chapter 31). It is easy to remember this as "B for bone." However, the "B" actually refers to the *bursa of Fabricius,* a lymphatic organ found only in birds, where B cells were first discovered. After their differentiation, B cells are released into the blood and circulate throughout the body in the blood and lymphatic circulatory systems.

Hematopoietic stem cells in the bone marrow migrate through the circulatory system to the thymus where they differentiate into **T cells.** The T cells enter the circulation and peripheral lymphoid tissues, including the thymus (the "T" in "T cell" refers to the thymus).

The role of lymphocytes in adaptive immunity was demonstrated by experiments in which all of the leukocytes in mice were killed by irradiation. These mice were unable to develop adaptive immunity. Injecting lymphocytes from normal mice into the irradiated mice restored the response; other body cells extracted from normal mice and injected could not restore the response. (For more on the use of mice as an experimental organism in biology, see "Research Organisms: The Mighty Mouse and the Lowly Fruit Fly," Box 43.2.)

Research Organisms: The Mighty Mouse and the Lowly Fruit Fly 43.2

The house mouse (*Mus musculus*) **(Figure 1a)** and its cells have been used as models for research on mammalian developmental genetics, immunology, and cancer and have enabled scientists to carry out experiments that would not be practical or ethical with humans. Mice are small, are easy to maintain in the laboratory, and have been used extensively as experimental animals. Gregor Mendel, the founder of genetics, kept mice as part of his studies. More recently, mouse genetic experiments have revealed more than 500 mutants that cause hereditary diseases, immunological defects, and cancer in mammals, including humans. The mouse has also been the model used to introduce and modify genes through genetic engineering, producing giant mice by introducing a human growth hormone gene, or "knockout" mice, in which a gene of interest is rendered nonfunctional (see Chapter 15, and "Knockouts: Genes and Behaviour," Box 39.1, Chapter 39) to determine its normal function. By knocking out mouse genes that are homologous to human genes involved in diseases such as cystic fibrosis, researchers can study human diseases in these model organisms, opening pathways to cure

human genetic diseases. In 2002, the sequence of the mouse genome was published, enabling researchers to refine and expand their use of the mouse as a model organism for studies of mammalian biology and mammalian diseases.

Similarly, the fruit fly (*Drosophila melanogaster*) **(Figure 1b)** has become a major organism to study basic genetics, aspects of gene regulation, developmental biology, and especially the role of innate immunity against pathogens. This insect can be raised quickly, cheaply, and in massive numbers. *Drosophila* has been instrumental to our understanding of dorsal–ventral patterning during development and has been one of the major organisms used to identify pathways of immune signalling. Because insects do not have an adaptive immune system, the innate immune system can be studied by itself without the interaction with components of the adaptive system. Toll receptors, important in immune signalling, were first found in *Drosophila* and subsequently used to identify similar molecules in vertebrates, called toll-like receptors. Mutant lines lacking specific functional

genes have been generated in *Drosophila* to study the roles of these genes in all organisms. Because the signalling pathways of the innate immune pathways are highly conserved, information learned on how fruit flies recognize and eliminate pathogens can be transferred to similar studies in other organisms. The genome of *Drosophila* was completed in 2000, allowing for comparisons among and between the genomes of vertebrates and invertebrates.

The mighty mouse and the common fruit fly have provided researchers with amazing amounts of information to understand how our bodies work, how similar genes function in different groups of animals, and how we can apply what we learn about one animal to another.

a. b.

Peter Skinner/Photo Researchers, Inc.

Watercolor illustration of Drosophila by Edith M. Wallace, Thomas Hunt Morgan's illustrator. This image was published in C.B. Bridges and T.H. Morgan, Contributions to the Genetics of Drosophila melanogaster (Washington, DC: Carnegie Institution; 1919), CIW publication #278.

FIGURE 1
Two common research organisms: a mouse and a fruit fly.

There are two types of adaptive immune responses: **antibody-mediated immunity** (also called *humoral immunity*) and **cell-mediated immunity.** The steps involved in the adaptive immune response are similar for antibody-mediated immunity and cell-mediated immunity:

1. **Lymphocyte encounter.** The lymphocytes encounter, recognize, and bind to an antigen.
2. **Lymphocyte activation.** The lymphocytes are activated by binding to the antigen and proliferate by cell division to produce large numbers of clones.
3. **Antigen clearance.** The activated lymphocytes are responsible for clearing the antigen from the body.
4. **Development of immunological memory.** Some of the activated lymphocytes differentiate into **memory cells,** which circulate in the blood and lymph, ready to initiate a rapid immune response on subsequent exposure to the same antigen.

These steps are explained in more detail in the following discussions of antibody-mediated immunity and cell-mediated immunity.

43.3b Immunity Can Be Mediated by Antibodies or Antibody-Mediated Immunity

An adaptive immune response begins as soon as an antigen is encountered in the body and is recognized as foreign.

Antigen Encounter and Recognition by Lymphocytes. Exogenous antigens are encountered by lymphocytes in the blood or lymphatic systems. As already mentioned, the two key lymphocytes that recognize antigens are B cells and T cells. Each B cell and each T cell is specific for a particular antigen, meaning that the cell can bind to only one particular molecular structure. The binding is so specific because the plasma membrane of each B cell and T cell is studded with thousands of identical receptors for the antigen; in B cells, they are called **B-cell receptors (BCRs)**, and in T cells, they are called **T-cell receptors (TCRs) (Figure 43.4).** The populations of B cells and T cells contain cells capable of recognizing any antigen, and each antigen can be recognized by multiple cells. For example, each of us has about 10 trillion B cells that collectively have about 100 million different kinds of BCRs. And all of these cells are present *before* the body has encountered the antigens.

The binding between antigen and receptor is an interaction between two molecules that fit together like an enzyme and its substrate. A given BCR or TCR typically does not bind to the whole antigen molecule but to small regions of it called **epitopes** or *antigenic determinants*. Therefore, several different B cells and T cells may bind to the population of a particular antigen they encounter.

BCRs and TCRs are encoded by different genes and thus have different structures (see "The Generation of Antibody Diversity," Box 43.3). When the BCR on a naive B cell matches a detected antigen, it is activated and may differentiate into a plasma cell that proliferates and secretes antibodies that recognize the same antigen (see Figure 43.4a).

As you will learn in more detail, an antibody molecule is a protein consisting of four polypeptide chains.

Figure 43.4
(a) Antigen-binding receptor on a B cell and the arrangement of light and heavy polypeptide chains in the antibody molecule. As shown, two sites, one at the tip of each arm of the Y, bind the same antigen.
(b) Antigen-binding receptor on a T cell.

a. B-cell receptor (BCR)

Identical antigen-binding sites

Identical light chains

Light chain

V
V
C
C

Identical heavy chains

Heavy chain

Disulfide linkage

KEY
V = variable region
C = constant region

Plasma membrane

Transmembrane domains

b. T-cell receptor (TCR)

Antigen-binding site

α chain
β chain

Plasma membrane

Transmembrane domains

The Generation of Antibody Diversity 43.3

The human genome has approximately 20 000 to 25 000 genes, far fewer than necessary to encode 100 million different antibodies if two genes encoded one antibody, one gene for the heavy chain and one for the light chain. The great diversity in antigen-binding capability of these receptors is generated in a different way from one gene per chain. During B-cell differentiation, the DNA segments that encode parts of the light and heavy chains undergo three rearrangements. The genes for the two different subunits of the T-cell receptor undergo similar rearrangements. The Nobel Prize for Medicine or Physiology in 1987 was awarded to Dr. Susumu Tonegawa for discovering the genetic basis for the generation of antibody diversity.

The light chain expressed by an undifferentiated B cell is encoded by three types of DNA segments, and one of each type is needed to make a complete, functional light-chain gene. In humans, about 40 different V segments encode most of the variable regions of the chain, 5 different J (joining) segments encode the rest of the variable region, and only 1 copy of the segment makes up the constant (C) part of the chain. Thus, a complete light chain comprises one V segment, adjacent to one J segment, adjacent to the C region, which is the same for all light chains regardless of V or J segment usage (see Figure 43.4).

During B-cell differentiation, a DNA rearrangement occurs in which one random V segment and one random J segment join with the C segment to form a functional light-chain gene. During this assembly, there is a deletion of DNA between the V and J segments, and the positions at which the DNA breaks and rejoins in the V- and J-joining reaction occur randomly over a distance of several nucleotides, which adds greatly to the variability of the final gene assembly. The DNA between the J segment and the C segment becomes an intron in the final assembled gene. Transcription of this newly assembled gene produces a typical pre-mRNA molecule (see Chapter 13). The introns are removed during the production of the mRNA by RNA processing. Translation of the mRNA produces the light chain with both the variable and the constant regions.

The assembly of functional heavy-chain genes occurs similarly. However, whereas light-chain genes have one C segment, heavy-chain genes have five types of C segments, each of which encodes one of the constant regions of IgM, IgD, IgG, IgE, and IgA. The inclusion of one of the five C-segment types in the functional heavy-chain gene therefore specifies the class of antibody that will be made by the B cell.

At one end is a region that embeds in a plasma membrane, whereas at the other end are two identical *antigen-binding sites*, regions that bind to a specific antigen. TCRs are simpler than BCRs, consisting of a protein made up of two different polypeptides (see Figure 43.4b). Like BCRs, TCRs have an antigen-binding site at one end and a membrane-embedded region at the other end.

Antibodies. Antibodies are the core molecules of antibody-mediated immunity. Antibodies are large, complex proteins that belong to a class of proteins known as *immunoglobulins* (Ig). Each antibody molecule consists of four polypeptide chains: two identical *light chains* and two identical *heavy chains* about twice or more the size of the light chain (see Figure 43.4a). The chains are held together in the complete protein by disulfide (–S–S–) linkages and fold into a Y-shaped structure. The bonds between the two arms of the Y form a hinge that allows the arms to flex independently of one another.

Each polypeptide chain of an antibody molecule has a *constant region* and a *variable region*. Each antibody type has the same amino acid sequence in the constant region of the heavy chain and likewise for the constant region of the light chain. The variable regions of both the heavy and the light chains, by contrast, have different amino acid sequences for each antibody molecule

in a population. Structurally, the variable regions are the top halves of the polypeptides in the arms of the Y-shaped molecule. The three-dimensional folding of the heavy chain and light chain variable regions of each arm creates the antigen-binding site. The antigen-binding site is identical on both arms of the same antibody molecule because both ends of the Y have the same amino acid sequences in their variable regions. However, the antigen-binding sites are different from antibody molecule to antibody molecule (produced by different B-cell clones) because of the amino acid differences in the variable regions of the two chain types.

The constant regions of the heavy chains in the tail part of the Y-shaped structure determine the *class* of the antibody, that is, its location and function. Humans have five different classes of antibodies: IgM, IgG, IgA, IgE, and IgD **(Table 43.2, p. 1090)**.

IgM antibodies are the first antibodies produced in the early stages of an antibody-mediated response after BCRs are activated and B cells differentiate into plasma cells. When they bind an antigen, IgM antibodies activate the complement system and stimulate the phagocytic activity of macrophages.

IgG antibodies circulate in the highest concentration in the blood and lymphatic system, where they also stimulate phagocytosis and activate the complement system when it binds an antigen. IgG is produced

Table 43.2 Five Classes of Antibodies

Class	Structure	Location	Functions
IgM		Surfaces of unstimulated B cells; free in circulation	First antibodies to be secreted by B cells in primary response; when bound to antigen, promotes agglutination reaction, activates complement system, and stimulates phagocytic activity of macrophages
IgG		Blood and lymphatic circulation	Most abundant antibody in primary and secondary responses; crosses placenta, conferring passive immunity to fetus; stimulates phagocytosis and activates complement system
IgA		Body secretions such as tears, breast milk, saliva, and mucus	Blocks attachment of pathogens to mucus membranes; confers passive immunity for breast-fed infants
IgE		Skin and tissues lining gastrointestinal and respiratory tracts (secreted by plasma cells)	Stimulates mast cells and basophils to release histamine; triggers allergic responses
IgD		Surface of unstimulated B cells	Membrane receptor for mature B cells; probably important in B-cell activation (clonal selection)

in large amounts when the body is exposed a second time to the same antigen and can cross the placenta to provide protection to the fetus.

IgA is found mainly in body secretions such as saliva, tears, breast milk, and the mucus coating of body cavities such as the lungs, digestive tract, and vagina. In these locations, the antibodies bind to surface groups on pathogens and block their attachment to body surfaces. Breast milk transfers IgA antibodies, and thus immunity, to a nursing infant.

IgE is secreted by plasma cells of the skin and the tissues lining the gastrointestinal tract and respiratory tract. IgE binds to basophils and mast cells, where it mediates many allergic responses, such as hay fever, asthma, and hives. When its specific antigen binds to IgE, the basophils or mast cells release histamine, which triggers an inflammatory response. IgE also contributes to mechanisms that combat infection by parasitic worms.

IgD occurs with IgM as a receptor on the surfaces of B cells; its function is not well understood but may be involved in B-cell activation.

T-Cell Activation. We now follow the development of an antibody-mediated immune response by linking the recognition of an antigen by lymphocytes, the activation of lymphocytes by antigen binding, and the production of antibodies. Typically, the pathway begins when a type of T cell becomes activated and follows the steps outlined in **Figure 43.5,** which determine the fate

Antibody-mediated immune response: T-cell activation

Dendritic cell (a phagocyte) is activated by engulfing a pathogen such as a bacterium.

↓

Pathogen macromolecules are degraded in dendritic cell, producing antigens.

↓

Dendritic cell becomes an antigen-presenting cell (APC) by displaying antigens on surface bound to class II MHC proteins.

↓

APC presents antigen to CD4+ T cell and activates the T cell.

↓

CD4+ T cell proliferates to produce a clone of cells.

↓

Clonal cells differentiate into helper T cells, which aid in effecting the specific immune response to the antigen.

Figure 43.5

An outline of T-cell activation in antibody-mediated immunity.

of pathogenic bacteria that have been introduced under the skin. Circulating viruses in the blood follow the same pathway.

First, a type of phagocyte called a **dendritic cell** engulfs a bacterium in the infected tissue by phagocytosis (**Figure 43.6,** step 1). Dendritic cells are so named because they have many surface projections resembling the dendrites of neurons. They have the same origin as leukocytes and recognize a bacterium as foreign by the same recognition mechanism used by macrophages in the innate immune system. In essence, the dendritic cell is part of the innate immune system, but its primary role is to stimulate the development of an adaptive immune response.

Engulfing a bacterium activates the dendritic cell; the cell now migrates to a nearby lymph node. Within the dendritic cell, the endocytic vesicle containing the bacterium fuses with a lysosome. In the lysosome, the bacterium's proteins are degraded into short peptides, which are antigens (see Figure 43.6, step 2). The antigens bind to **class II major histocompatibility complex (MHC)** proteins (step 3), and the interacting molecules then migrate to the cell surface, where the antigen is displayed (step 4). These steps in the lymph node, which are recapped in **Figure 43.7, p. 1092,** step 1, have converted the cell into an **antigen-presenting cell (APC)**, ready to present the antigen to T cells in the next step of antibody-mediated immunity.

MHC proteins are named for the large cluster of genes encoding them, called the **major histocompatibility complex.** The complex spans 4 million base pairs and contains 128 genes. Many of these genes play important roles in the immune system. Each individual of each vertebrate species has a unique combination of MHC proteins on almost all body cells, meaning that no two individuals of a species,

except identical twins, are likely to have exactly the same MHC proteins on their cells. There are two classes of MHC proteins, class I and class II, which have different functions in adaptive immunity, as we will see.

The key function of an APC is to present the antigen to a lymphocyte. In the antibody-mediated immune response, the APC presents the antigen, bound to a class II MHC protein, to a type of T cell in the lymphatic system called a **CD4⁺ T cell** because it has receptors named CD4 on its surface. A specific CD4⁺ T cell, which has a TCR with an antigen-binding site that recognizes the antigen, binds to the antigen on the APC (see Figure 43.7, step 2, p. 1092). The CD4 receptor on the T cell helps link the two cells together by binding to the MHCII.

When the APC binds to the CD4⁺ T cell, the APC secretes an *interleukin* (= between leukocytes), a type of cytokine, which activates the T cell (see Figure 43.7, step 3, p. 1092). The activated T cell then secretes cytokines (step 4), which act in an autocrine manner (see Chapter 35) to stimulate **clonal expansion**, the proliferation of the activated CD4⁺ T cell by cell division to produce a clone of cells. These clonal cells differentiate into **helper T cells** (step 5), so named because they assist with the activation of B cells. A helper T cell is an example of an **effector T cell**, meaning that it is involved in effecting—bringing about—the specific immune response to the antigen.

B-Cell Activation. Antibodies are produced and secreted by B cells. The activation of a B cell that makes the specific antibody against an antigen requires the B cell to present the antigen on its surface and then to link with a helper T cell that has differentiated as a result of encountering and recognizing the same antigen. The process is outlined in Figure 43.7, p. 1092, and **Figure 43.8, p. 1092.**

The process of antigen presentation on a B-cell surface begins when BCRs on the B cell interact directly with soluble bacterial (in our example) antigens in the blood or lymph. Once the antigen binds to a BCR, the complex is taken into the cell and the antigen is processed in the same way as in dendritic cells, being broken down into smaller fragments, culminating with a presentation of each antigen-derived peptide fragment on the B-cell surface in a complex with class II MHC proteins (see Figure 43.7, step 6, p. 1092).

When one of the helper T cells produced above encounters a B cell displaying the same antigen, usually in a lymph node or in the spleen, the T and B cells become tightly

1 A dendritic cell engulfs a bacterium.

2 Large molecules of engulfed bacterium are broken down to produce antigens.

3 Antigens bind to class II MHC proteins.

4 Antigen is displayed on cell surface bound to MHC protein—the cell is now an antigen-presenting cell (APC).

Antigen

Class II MHC protein

Dendritic cell

Antigen-class II MHC protein on cell surface

Figure 43.6
Generation of an antigen-presenting cell after a dendritic cell engulfs a bacterium.

a. T-cell activation

1 The bacterium is taken up by phagocytosis and degraded in a lysosome.

2 Bacterial antigens are displayed on the APC cell surface bound to class II MHC proteins and presented to CD4⁺ T cells with TCRs that recognize the antigen.

3 The APC secretes an interleukin, which activates the T cell.

4 Activated T cell secretes cytokines, which stimulate the T cell to proliferate to produce a clone of cells.

5 The cloned cells differentiate into helper T cells.

Figure 43.7
The antibody-mediated immune response.

Antibody-mediated immune response: B-cell activation

A BCR on a B cell recognizes an antigen on the surface of a bacterium and the bacterium is engulfed.

Pathogen macromolecules are degraded in the B cell, producing antigens.

B cell displays antigens on its surface bound to class II MHC proteins.

Helper T cell with TCR that recognizes the same antigen links to the B cell.

Helper T cell secretes interleukins that activate the B cell.

B cell proliferates to produce a clone of cells.

Some B-cell clones differentiate into plasma cells, which secrete antibodies specific to the antigen, and others differentiate into memory B cells.

Figure 43.8
An outline of B-cell activation in antibody-mediated immunity.

linked (see Figure 43.7, step 7). The linkage depends on the TCRs, which recognize and bind the antigen displayed by the class II MHC molecules on the surface of the B cell, and on CD4, which stabilizes the binding as it did for T-cell binding to the dendritic cell. The linkage between the cells first stimulates the helper T cell to secrete interleukins that activate the B cell and then stimulates the B cell to proliferate, producing a clone of these B cells with identical B-cell receptors (step 8). Some of the cloned cells differentiate into relatively short-lived **plasma cells**, which now secrete the same antibody that was displayed on the parental B cell's surface to circulate in lymph and blood. Others differentiate into **memory B cells**, which are long-lived cells that set the stage for a much more rapid response should the same antigen be encountered later in life (step 9).

Clonal selection is the process by which a lymphocyte is specifically selected for cloning when it encounters a foreign antigen from among a randomly generated, enormous diversity of lymphocytes with receptors that specifically recognize the antigen **(Figure 43.9)**. The process of clonal selection was proposed in the 1950s by several scientists, most notably F. Macfarlane Burnet, Niels Jerne, and David Talmage. Their proposals, made long before the mechanism was understood, described clonal selection as a form of natural selection operating in miniature: antigens select the cells recognizing them, which reproduce and become dominant in the B-cell population. Burnet received the Nobel Prize in 1960 for his research in immunology.

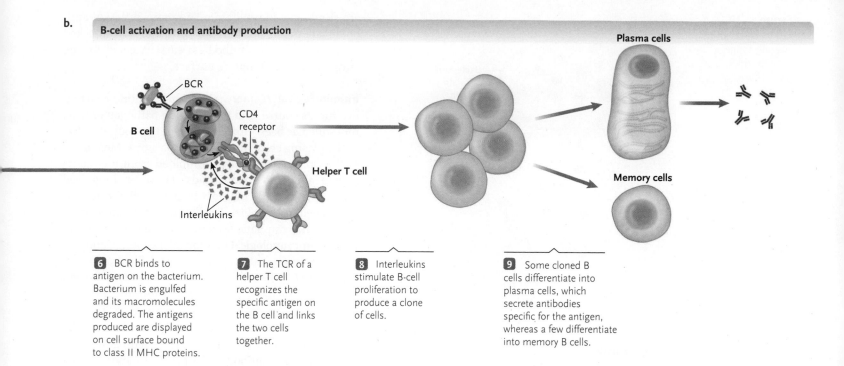

b.

B-cell activation and antibody production

Plasma cells

BCR

B cell

CD4 receptor

Helper T cell

Interleukins

Memory cells

6 BCR binds to antigen on the bacterium. Bacterium is engulfed and its macromolecules degraded. The antigens produced are displayed on cell surface bound to class II MHC proteins.

7 The TCR of a helper T cell recognizes the specific antigen on the B cell and links the two cells together.

8 Interleukins stimulate B-cell proliferation to produce a clone of cells.

9 Some cloned B cells differentiate into plasma cells, which secrete antibodies specific for the antigen, whereas a few differentiate into memory B cells.

Clearing the Body of Foreign Antigens. How do the antibodies produced in an antibody-mediated immune response clear different types of foreign antigens from the body? Toxins produced by invading bacteria, such as tetanus toxin, can be *neutralized* by antibodies **(Figure 43.10a, p. 1094)**. The antibodies bind to the toxin molecules, inactivating them.

Antibodies bind to antigens on the surfaces of intact bacteria at an infection site or in the circulatory system. Because the two arms of an antibody molecule bind to different copies of the antigen molecule, an antibody molecule may bind to two bacteria with the same antigen. A population of antibodies can link many bacteria together into a lattice, causing *agglutination,* or clumping of the bacteria **(Figure 43.10b, p. 1094)**. Agglutination immobilizes the bacteria, preventing them from infecting cells. Antibodies can also agglutinate viruses to prevent them from infecting cells.

More importantly, antibodies bound to antigens aid the innate immune response that was initially set off by the pathogens by stimulating the complement system. Membrane attack complexes are formed and insert themselves into the plasma membranes of the bacteria, leading to their lysis and death. In the case of virus infections, membrane attack complexes can insert themselves into the membranes surrounding enveloped viruses, which disrupts the membrane and prevents the viruses from infecting cells.

Antibodies also enhance phagocytosis of bacteria and viruses. Phagocytic cells have receptors on their surfaces that recognize the heavy-chain end of antibodies (the end of the molecule opposite the antigen-binding sites). Antibodies bound to bacteria or viruses

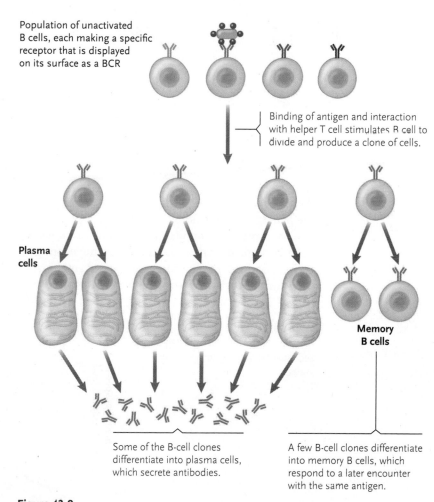

Population of unactivated B cells, each making a specific receptor that is displayed on its surface as a BCR

Binding of antigen and interaction with helper T cell stimulates B cell to divide and produce a clone of cells.

Plasma cells

Memory B cells

Some of the B-cell clones differentiate into plasma cells, which secrete antibodies.

A few B-cell clones differentiate into memory B cells, which respond to a later encounter with the same antigen.

Figure 43.9

Clonal selection. The binding of an antigen to a B cell that already displays a specific antibody to that antigen stimulates the B cell to divide and differentiate into plasma cells, which secrete the antibody, and memory cells, which remain in the circulation ready to mount a response against the antigen at a later time.

Figure 43.10

Examples of
clearing antigens
from the body.

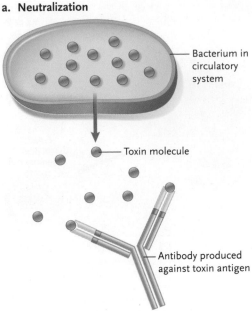

a. Neutralization

Bacterium in
circulatory
system

Toxin molecule

Antibody produced
against toxin antigen

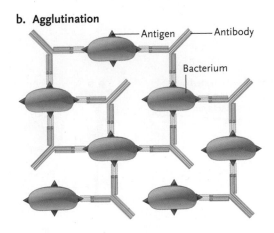

b. Agglutination

Antigen — Antibody

Bacterium

therefore bind to phagocytic cells, which then engulf the pathogens and destroy them.

For simplicity, the adaptive immune response has been described here in terms of a single antigen. Pathogens have many different types of antigens on their surfaces, which means that many different B cells are stimulated to proliferate and many different antibodies are produced. Pathogens are therefore attacked by many different antibodies, each targeted to one antigen on the pathogen's surface.

Immunological Memory. Once an immune reaction has run its course, and the invading pathogen or toxic molecule has been eliminated from the body, division of the plasma cells and T-cell clones stops. Most or all of the clones die and are eliminated from the bloodstream and other body fluids. However, long-lived memory B cells and **memory helper T cells** (which differentiated from helper T cells) remain in an inactive state in the lymphatic system. Their persistence provides an **immunological memory** of the foreign antigen.

Immunological memory is illustrated in **Figure 43.11.** When the body is exposed to a foreign antigen for the first time, a **primary immune response** results, following the steps already described. The first antibodies appear in the blood in 3 to 14 days, and by week 4, the primary response has essentially gone away. IgM is the first antibody type produced and secreted into the bloodstream in a primary immune response. This primary immune response curve is followed whenever a new foreign antigen enters the body.

When a foreign antigen enters the body for a second time, a **secondary immune response** results (see Figure 43.11). The secondary response is more rapid than the primary response because it involves the memory B cells and memory T cells that have been stored. It does not have to initiate the clonal selection of a new B cell and T cell. Moreover, less antigen is needed to elicit a secondary response than a primary response, and many more antibodies are produced. The predominant antibody produced in a secondary immune response is IgG; the switch occurs at the gene level in the memory B cells.

Immunological memory forms the basis of vaccinations, in which antigens in the form of living or dead pathogens or antigenic molecules themselves are introduced into the body. After the immune response,

Figure 43.11

Immunological memory: primary and
secondary responses to the same
antigen.

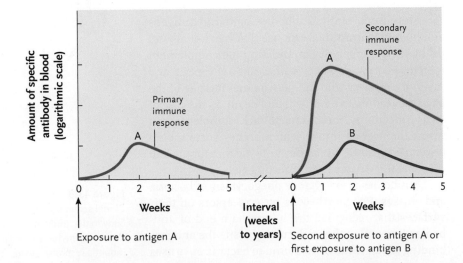

Amount of specific
antibody in blood
(logarithmic scale)

Primary
immune
response

A

Secondary
immune
response

A

B

Weeks

Interval
(weeks
to years)

Weeks

Exposure to antigen A

Second exposure to antigen A or
first exposure to antigen B

memory B cells and memory T cells remaining in the body can mount an immediate and intense immune reaction against similar antigens. As mentioned in "Why It Matters," Edward Jenner introduced the cowpox virus—a virus closely related to, but less virulent than, the smallpox virus—into healthy individuals who initiated a primary immune response. After the response ran its course, a bank of memory B cells and memory T cells remained in the body, able to quickly recognize the similar antigens of the smallpox virus and initiate a secondary immune response. Similarly, the polio vaccine developed by Jonas Salk uses polioviruses that have been inactivated by exposing them to formaldehyde. Although the viruses are inactive, their surface groups can still act as antigens. The antigens trigger an immune response, leaving memory B and T cells able to mount an intense immune response against active polioviruses.

Active and Passive Immunity. **Active immunity** is the production of antibodies in response to exposure to a foreign antigen, as has just been described. **Passive immunity** is the acquisition of antibodies as a result of direct transfer from another person. This form of immunity provides immediate protection against the antigens that the antibodies recognize without the person receiving the antibodies having developed a primary immune response. Examples of passive immunity include the transfer of IgG antibodies from the mother to the fetus through the placenta and the transfer of IgA antibodies in the first breast milk fed from the mother to the baby. We can use this passive immunity to our advantage by injecting intravenous immunoglobulin (IVIG) that contains IgG from many donors as treatment for specific conditions (see p. 1102). Compared with active immunity, passive immunity is a short-lived phenomenon with no memory, in that the antibodies typically break down within a month. However, in that time, the protection plays an important role. For example, a breast-fed baby is protected until it is able to mount an immune response itself, an ability that is not present until about a month after birth.

Drug Effects on Antibody-Mediated Immunity. Several drugs used to reduce the rejection of transplanted organs target helper T cells. Cyclosporin A, used routinely after organ transplants, blocks the activation of helper T cells and, in turn, the activation of B cells. Although very successful, cyclosporin and other immunosuppressive drugs also leave the treated individual more susceptible to infection by pathogens.

43.3c Immunity Can Be Mediated by Cells

In cell-mediated immunity, cytotoxic T cells directly destroy host cells infected by intracellular pathogens **(Figure 43.12)**. The killing process begins when some of the pathogens are broken down by cytoplasmic

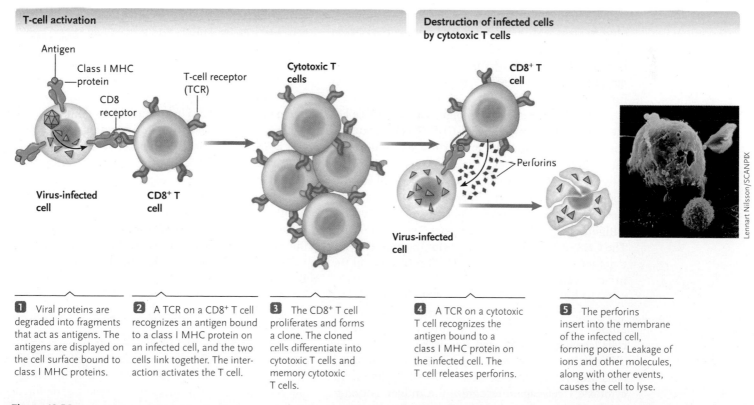

T-cell activation			Destruction of infected cells by cytotoxic T cells	

1 Viral proteins are degraded into fragments that act as antigens. The antigens are displayed on the cell surface bound to class I MHC proteins.

2 A TCR on a CD8⁺ T cell recognizes an antigen bound to a class I MHC protein on an infected cell, and the two cells link together. The interaction activates the T cell.

3 The CD8⁺ T cell proliferates and forms a clone. The cloned cells differentiate into cytotoxic T cells and memory cytotoxic T cells.

4 A TCR on a cytotoxic T cell recognizes the antigen bound to a class I MHC protein on the infected cell. The T cell releases perforins.

5 The perforins insert into the membrane of the infected cell, forming pores. Leakage of ions and other molecules, along with other events, causes the cell to lyse.

Figure 43.12
The cell-mediated immune response.

Some Cancer Cells Kill Cytotoxic T Cells to Defeat the Immune System 43.4

Among the arsenal of weapons employed by cytotoxic T cells to eliminate abnormal, infected, or cancerous body cells is apoptosis mediated by the *Fas–FasL* system. Fas is a receptor that occurs on the surfaces of many cells; FasL is a ligand displayed on the surfaces of some cell types, including cytotoxic T cells. If a cell carrying the Fas receptor contacts a cytotoxic T cell with the FasL signal displayed on its surface, a cascade of internal reactions initiates apoptosis and kills the cell with the Fas receptor.

Surprisingly, cytotoxic T cells also carry the Fas receptor, so they can kill each other by displaying the FasL signal. This mutual killing plays an important role in reducing the level of an immune reaction after a pathogen has been eliminated. In the case of immune privilege, cells in specific regions such as the cornea, nervous tissue, and testes express FasL to induce the apoptosis of infiltrating cytotoxic T cells and reduce inflammation.

Some cancer cells survive elimination by the immune system by making and displaying FasL and killing any cytotoxic T cells that attack the tumour. This was found first in patients suffering from malignant melanoma, a dangerous skin cancer, who had a breakdown product associated with FasL in their bloodstream.

Proteins extracted from melanoma cells, or sections made from melanoma tissue, tested positive (using antibodies) for the presence of FasL, indicating that FasL was present in the tumour cells. Similarly, the expression of FasL mRNA was also detected in the tumour cells. However, no Fas receptor was found in these samples, suggesting that Fas synthesis was turned off in the tumour cells.

FasL in melanoma cells kills cytotoxic T cells that invade the tumour, whereas the absence of Fas receptors ensures that the tumour cells do not kill each other. The presence of FasL and absence of the Fas receptor may explain why melanomas, and many other types of cancer, are rarely destroyed by the immune system.

Melanoma cells originate from pigment cells in the skin called *melanocytes.* Normal melanocytes do not contain FasL, indicating that synthesis of the protein is turned on as part of the transformation from normal melanocytes into cancer cells.

This research could lead to an effective treatment for cancer using the Fas–FasL system. If melanoma cells could be induced to make Fas as well as FasL, for example, they might eliminate a tumour by killing each other!

---

enzymes inside infected host cells, and the smaller protein fragments (or antigen-derived peptide fragments) themselves act as antigens. These antigens bind to class I MHC proteins, which are delivered to the cell surface by essentially the same mechanisms as in B cells (step 1). At the surface, the antigens are displayed by the class I MHC protein and the cell then functions as an APC.

The APC presents the antigen to a type of T cell in the lymphatic system called a **CD8⁺ T cell** because it has receptors named CD8 on its surface in addition to the TCRs. The presence of a CD8 receptor distinguishes this type of T cell from that involved in antibody-mediated immunity. A specific CD8⁺ T cell that has a TCR that recognizes the antigen binds to that antigen on the APC (see Figure 43.12, step 2, p. 1095). The CD8 receptor on the T cell helps the two cells link together by binding to the MHC II molecule on the infected cell.

The link between the APC and the CD8⁺ T cell activates the T cell, which then proliferates to form a clone. Some of the cells differentiate to become **cytotoxic T cells** (see Figure 43.12, step 3, p. 1095), whereas a few differentiate into *memory cytotoxic T cells*. Cytotoxic T cells are another type of effector T cell. TCRs on the cytotoxic T cells again recognize the antigen bound to class I MHC proteins on the infected cells (the APCs) (step 4). The cytotoxic T cell then destroys the infected cell using mechanisms similar to those used by NK cells. That is, an activated cytotoxic T cell releases perforin, which creates pores in the membrane of the target cell. The leakage of ions and other molecules through the pores causes the infected cell to rupture. The cytotoxic T cell also secretes proteases that enter infected cells through the newly created pores and cause it to self-destruct by apoptosis (see Figure 43.12, step 5 and photo inset, p. 1095). The rupture of dead infected cells releases the pathogens to the interstitial fluid, where they are open to attack by antibodies and phagocytes.

Cytotoxic T cells can also kill cancer cells if their class I MHC molecules display fragments of altered cellular proteins that do not normally occur in the body. Another mechanism used by cytotoxic T cells to kill cells, and a process used by some cancer cells to defeat the mechanism, is described in "Some Cancer Cells Kill Cytotoxic T Cells to Defeat the Immune System," Box 43.4.

43.3d How Antibodies Are Used in Research

The ability to generate antibodies against essentially any antigen provides an invaluable research tool for scientists. Most antibodies are obtained by injecting a molecule into a test animal such as a mouse, rabbit, or goat and collecting and purifying the antibodies from the blood. Scientists can then attach a visible marker such as a dye molecule or heavy metal atom to the antibody and determine when and where specific biological molecules are found in cells or tissues. Antibodies can also be used to "grab" a molecule of interest from a mixture of molecules by attaching antibodies generated against that molecule to plastic beads that are packed into a glass column. When the mixture is poured through the column, the molecule remains bound to the antibody in the column. The molecules can then be obtained from the column in purified form by adding a reagent that breaks the antigen–antibody bonds.

Injecting a molecule of interest into a test animal typically produces a wide spectrum of antibodies that react with different parts of the antigen. Some antibodies may cross-react with other similar antigens, producing false results that can complicate the research. These problems have been solved by producing **monoclonal antibodies,** each of which reacts only against the same segment (epitope) of a single antigen. In addition to their use in scientific research, monoclonal antibodies are also widely used in medical applications such as pregnancy tests, screening for prostate cancer, and testing for HIV and other sexually transmitted diseases.

STUDY BREAK

1. How, in general, do the antibody-mediated and cell-mediated immune responses help clear the body of antigens?
2. Describe the general structure of an antibody molecule.
3. What is clonal selection?
4. How does immunological memory work?

43.4 Malfunctions and Failures of the Immune System

The immune system is highly effective, but it is not foolproof. Some malfunctions of the immune system cause the body to react against its own proteins or cells, producing *autoimmune diseases*. In addition, some viruses and other pathogens have evolved means of avoiding destruction by the immune system. A number of these pathogens, including the AIDS virus, even use parts of the immune response to promote infection. Another malfunction causes the *allergic reactions* that many of us experience from time to time.

43.4a The Immune System Normally Protects against Attack

B cells and T cells are involved in the development of **immunological tolerance,** which protects the body's own molecules from attack by the immune system. Although the process is not understood, molecules present in an individual from birth are not recognized

as foreign by circulating B and T cells and do not elicit an immune response. During their initial differentiation in the bone marrow and thymus, any B and T cells that react with *self* molecules carried by MHC proteins become suppressed or are induced to kill themselves by apoptosis. The process of excluding self-reactive B and T cells goes on throughout the life of an individual.

Evidence that immunological tolerance is established early in life comes from experiments with mice. For example, if a foreign protein is injected into a mouse at birth, during the period in which tolerance is established, the mouse will not develop antibodies against the protein if it is injected later in life. Similarly, if mutant mice are produced that lack a given complement protein, so that the protein is absent during embryonic development, they will produce antibodies against that protein if it is injected during adult life. Normal mice do not produce antibodies if the protein is injected.

43.4b Immunological Tolerance Sometimes Fails

The mechanisms setting up immunological tolerance sometimes fail, leading to an **autoimmune reaction—** the production of antibodies against molecules of the body. In most cases, the effects of such antiself antibodies are not serious enough to produce recognizable disease. However, in some individuals—about 5 to 10% of the human population—antiself antibodies cause serious problems.

For example, *type 1 diabetes* (see Chapter 35) is an autoimmune reaction against the pancreatic beta cells that produce insulin. The antiself antibodies gradually eliminate the beta cells until the individual is incapable of producing insulin. *Systemic lupus erythematosus (lupus)* is caused by production of a wide variety of antiself antibodies against blood cells, blood platelets, and internal cell structures and molecules such as mitochondria and proteins associated with DNA in the cell nucleus. People with lupus often become anemic and have problems with blood circulation and kidney function because the antibodies, combined with body molecules, accumulate and clog capillaries and the microscopic filtering tubules of the kidneys. Lupus patients may also develop antiself antibodies against the heart and kidneys. *Rheumatoid arthritis* is caused by a self-attack on connective tissues, particularly in the joints, causing pain and inflammation. *Multiple sclerosis* results from an autoimmune attack against a protein of the myelin sheaths that insulate the surfaces of neurons. Multiple sclerosis can seriously disrupt nervous function, producing such symptoms as muscle weakness and paralysis, impaired coordination, and pain.

The causes of most autoimmune diseases are unknown. In some cases, an autoimmune reaction can be traced to injuries that expose body cells or proteins that are normally inaccessible to the immune system, such as the lens protein of the eye, to B and T cells. In other cases, as in type 1 diabetes, an invading virus stimulates the production of antibodies that can also react with self proteins. Antibodies against the Epstein-Barr and hepatitis B viruses can react against myelin basic protein, the protein attacked in multiple sclerosis. Sometimes, environmental chemicals, drugs, or mutations alter body proteins so that they appear foreign to the immune system and come under attack.

Some viruses use parts of the immune system to get a free ride to the cell interior. For example, the HIV virus has a surface molecule that is recognized and bound by the CD4 receptor on the surface of helper T cells. Binding to CD4 locks the virus to the cell surface and stimulates the membrane covering the virus to fuse with the plasma membrane of the helper T cell. (The protein coat of the virus is wrapped in a membrane derived from the plasma membrane of the host cell in which it was produced.) The fusion introduces the virus into the cell, initiating the infection and leading to the destruction and death of the T cell. (Further details on human immunodeficiency virus (HIV) infection and AIDS are presented in "Applied Research: HIV and AIDS," Box 43.5.)

43.4c Allergies Result from Overactivity of the Immune System

The substances responsible for allergic reactions form a distinct class of antigens called **allergens**, which induce B cells to secrete an overabundance of IgE antibodies (**Figure 43.13**). IgE antibodies, in turn, bind to receptors on mast cells in connective tissue and on **basophils**, a type of leukocyte in the blood (see Table 43.1, p. 1084), inducing them to secrete histamine, which produces a severe inflammation. Most of the inflammation occurs in tissues directly exposed to the allergen, such as the surfaces of the eyes, the lining of the nasal passages, and the air passages of the lungs. Signal molecules released by activated mast cells also stimulate mucosal cells to secrete floods of mucus and cause smooth muscle in airways to constrict (histamine also causes airway constriction). The resulting allergic reaction can vary in severity from a mild irritation to serious and even life-threatening debilitation. *Asthma* is a severe response to allergens involving constriction of airways in the lungs. Antihistamines, medications that block histamine receptors, are usually effective in countering the effects of the histamine released by mast cells.

An individual is *sensitized* by a first exposure to an allergen, which may produce only mild allergic symptoms or no reaction at all (see Figure 43.13a). However, the sensitization produces memory B and T cells. At subsequent exposures, the system is poised to produce a greatly intensified allergic response (see Figure 43.13b).

In some persons, inflammation stimulated by an allergen is so severe that the reaction brings on a life-threatening condition called **anaphylactic shock**. Extreme swelling of air passages in the lungs interferes with breathing, and massive leakage of fluid from capillaries causes the blood pressure to drop precipitously. Death may result in minutes if the condition is not treated promptly. In individuals who have become

a. Initial exposure to allergen

1 Allergen (antigen) enters the body.

IgE antibodies

Mast cell

IgE antibodies

B cell

Nucleus

Histamine granules

Mitochondrion

2 Allergen binds B-cell surface antibodies; the B cell now processes the allergen and, with stimulation by a helper T cell (not shown), proceeds through the steps leading to cell division and antibody production.

3 Activated B-cell clone produces and secretes IgE antibodies active against the allergen.

4 IgE antibodies attach to mast cells in tissues, which have granules containing histamine molecules. Memory B and T cells capable of recognizing the allergen are also produced.

b. Further exposures to allergen

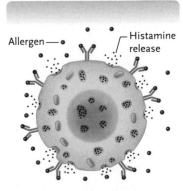

Allergen

Histamine release

5 After the first exposure, when the allergen enters the body, it binds with IgE antibodies on mast cells; binding stimulates the mast cell to release histamine and other substances.

Figure 43.13

The response of the body to allergens. **(a)** The steps in sensitization after initial exposure to an allergen. **(b)** Production of an allergic response by further exposures to the allergen.

Applied Research: HIV and AIDS 43.5

Acquired immune deficiency syndrome (AIDS) is a result of infection by the human immunodeficiency virus, HIV **(Figure 1),** and is defined as having a very specific level of immune deficiency. First reported in the late 1970s, HIV now infects more than 40 million people worldwide, 64% of them in Africa. AIDS is a potentially lethal disease, although drug therapy has reduced the death rate for HIV-infected individuals.

HIV is transmitted when an infected person's body fluids, especially blood or semen, enter the blood or tissue fluids of another person. The entry may occur during vaginal, anal, or oral intercourse, or the virus may be transmitted via contaminated needles shared by intravenous drug users or from infected mothers to their infants during pregnancy, birth, and nursing. HIV is rarely transmitted through casual contact; food; or body products such as saliva, tears, urine, or feces.

The primary cellular hosts for HIV are macrophages and helper T cells, which are ultimately destroyed by the virus. Infection makes helper T cells unavailable for the stimulation and proliferation of B cells and cytotoxic T cells. The assault on lymphocytes and macrophages cripples the immune system and makes the body highly vulnerable to otherwise non-life-threatening infections.

In 1996, researchers confirmed the process by which HIV initially infects its primary target, the helper T cells. First, a glycoprotein of the viral coat, called *gp120,* attaches the virus to a helper T cell by binding to its CD4 receptor. Another viral protein triggers fusion of the viral surface membrane with the T-cell plasma membrane, releasing the virus into the cell. Once inside, a viral enzyme, *reverse transcriptase,* uses the viral RNA as a template for making a DNA copy. (When it is outside a host cell, the genetic material of HIV is RNA rather than DNA.) Another viral enzyme, *integrase,* then splices the viral DNA into the host cell's DNA **(Figure 2).**

Reverse transcriptase

Viral coat proteins

gp120

Viral RNA

Integrase

Membrane coat derived from host cell

FIGURE 1
Structure of a free HIV viral particle.

1 Viral particle enters cell.

Viral RNA genome

2 Viral reverse transcriptase makes DNA copy of viral RNA genome.

Viral DNA

Nucleus

3 DNA copy of viral genome is integrated into host DNA.

Transcription · Transcription

Viral RNA genome

Viral mRNA

Translation

Viral proteins

4 Viral DNA is transcribed into viral RNA genomes and into viral mRNAs, which are translated into viral proteins.

5 Viral RNAs and proteins assemble into new viral particles, which bud from cell.

FIGURE 2
The steps in HIV infection of a host cell.

(continued)

Applied Research: HIV and AIDS 43.5 (continued)

Once it is part of the host cell DNA, the viral DNA is replicated and passed on as the cell divides. As part of the host cell DNA, the virus is effectively hidden in the helper T cell and protected from attack by the immune system.

When the infected helper T cell is stimulated by an antigen, the viral DNA is copied into new viral RNA molecules and into mRNAs that direct host cell ribosomes to make viral proteins. The viral RNAs are added to the viral proteins to make infective HIV particles, which are released from the host cell by budding **(Figure 3).** The infection also leads uninfected helper T cells to destroy themselves in large numbers by apoptosis, through mechanisms that are still unknown.

Initially, infected people suffer a mild fever and other symptoms that may be mistaken for the flu or the common cold. The symptoms disappear as antibodies against viral proteins appear in the body, and the number of viral particles drops in the bloodstream. An infected person may remain apparently healthy for years yet can infect others. Both the transmitter and the recipient of the virus may be unaware that the virus is present, making it difficult to control the spread of HIV.

Eventually, more and more helper T cells and macrophages are destroyed, wiping out the body's immune response. The infected person becomes susceptible to secondary, opportunistic infections, such as a pneumonia caused by a fungus (*Pneumocystis carinii*); tuberculosis; persistent yeast (*Candida albicans*) infections of the mouth, throat, rectum, or vagina; and infection by many common bacteria and viruses that rarely infect healthy humans. These infections signal the appearance of full-blown AIDS, the characteristic very low lymphocyte count and immune function that allow these opportunistic pathogens to establish and proliferate. If untreated, this results in steady debilitation and death, typically within 5 years.

Currently, there is no cure for HIV and no vaccine that can prevent infection. The viral envelope proteins (gp120 and gp41) of HIV mutate constantly, making a vaccine

Z. Salahuddin, National Institutes of Health

Z. Salahuddin, National Institutes of Health

150 nm

FIGURE 3
An HIV particle budding from a host cell. As it passes from the host cell, it acquires a membrane coat derived from the host cell plasma membrane.

developed against one form of the virus useless when the next form appears. Most mutations occur during replication of the virus during reverse transcription of viral RNA.

The development of AIDS can be greatly slowed by drugs that interfere with reverse transcription of the viral RNA. Infected people may be treated with a "cocktail" of several drugs, including *reverse transcriptase inhibitors* that inhibit viral reproduction and destruction of helper T cells, or compounds that inhibit fusion of the virus to host cells, thus extending their lives. Drug cocktails are not a cure, however, because the virus is still present. If the therapy is stopped, the virus again replicates and the T-cell population drops.

---

sensitized to the venom of wasps and bees, for example, a single sting may bring on anaphylactic shock within minutes. Allergies developed against drugs such as penicillin and certain foods can have the same drastic effects. Anaphylactic shock can be controlled by immediate injection of epinephrine (adrenaline), which reverses the condition by constricting blood vessels and dilating air passages in the lungs.

CONCEPT FIX From reading this chapter you may believe that all parasites are bad for us. There is newer evidence that some "autoimmune" diseases are a result of our cleanliness and the relatively sterile environments in which we live, no longer exposed to dirt and parasites that used to infect us. Through the millennia we were exposed routinely to and maintained a constant fauna of parasites within our bodies. Research suggests that when parasites are present, components of the immune system, whose purpose is to reduce or suppress activities of other immune cells, are activated. When these parasites are absent, no suppression takes place, and the activated immune system attacks our own bodies. While the subject is still controversial, there are studies that treat people suffering from Crohn's disease, irritable bowel syndrome, inflammatory bowel disease, multiple sclerosis, and some allergies with intestinal parasitic worms. The presence of the worms serves to regulate some aspects of our immune systems, and in some people reduce their symptoms, which emphasizes the mutualistic relationships and interactions between gut microorganisms and the immune system. How this works, which molecules are involved, and how the interactions between immune cells are regulated is currently under study. ●

STUDY BREAK

1. What is immunological tolerance?
2. Explain how a failure in the immune system can result in an allergy.

PEOPLE BEHIND BIOLOGY 43.6
Élie Metchnikoff, Pasteur Institute

In 1882, a Russian zoologist named Élie Metchnikoff, working in Italy, pierced a larva of the common starfish with a rose thorn. Later he observed cells collecting around the thorn. He recognized that these cells were trying to isolate and eliminate the thorn through what we now term phagocytosis. Although phagocytosis was known to occur in human bacterial infections, Metchnikoff's initial studies with the starfish, and later with animal models injected with human pathogens, demonstrated that this response was used universally by animals to eliminate pathogens. These initial experiments have led to scientific disciplines such as cellular immunology, innate immunity, and comparative immunology and have contributed to our understanding of the evolution of immune responses. For this pioneering work and keen observation, Metchnikoff shared the Nobel Prize in medicine in 1908 with Paul Ehrlich.

43.5 Defences in Other Organisms

All organisms must be able to defend themselves, and we can compare what we know in mammals with what we know about the immune systems of other organisms. Molecular studies in sharks and rays have revealed DNA sequences that are clearly related to the sequences coding for antibodies in mammals, and sharks produce antibodies capable of recognizing and binding specific antigens. Antibody diversity is produced by the same kinds of genetic rearrangements in both sharks and mammals, although the embryonic gene segments for the two polypeptides are arranged differently in these organisms. Sharks also mount nonspecific defences, including the production of a steroid that appears to kill bacteria and neutralizes viruses nonspecifically and with high efficiency.

We have demonstrated that invertebrates lack the adaptive immune system and instead rely on innate responses that allow them to eliminate pathogens via phagocytosis, encapsulation, or the expression of antimicrobial peptides. Similarly, plants rely on innate responses only to recognize and eliminate the pathogens or infected cells, often using plant antimicrobial peptides.

The significant similarities between the innate immune responses of vertebrates, invertebrates, and plants, as described earlier in this chapter, and the similarities and differences in immune responses in "primitive" and "advanced" organisms, allow us to look at the evolution of immune responses and the production of specific molecules to eliminate parasites and pathogens in very diverse types of organisms.

STUDY BREAK

1. How can studies on primitive organisms help us understand immune responses in more advanced organisms such as humans?
2. Why is understanding the evolution of immune responses important?

43.6 How Do Parasites and Pathogens Circumvent Host Responses?

The immune systems of all organisms arose to recognize and eliminate pathogens. Some of the complexities of these systems have been detailed in this chapter. However, the fact that all organisms still suffer from diseases indicates that as strong as our immune systems are, pathogens and parasites are always looking for weak points to exploit.

43.6a Parasites and Pathogens Hide in, Confuse, and Manipulate the Host

Disease-causing organisms can develop in regions of the host's body that do not have a strong immune response, hide in host defence cells, confuse the immune response, or directly manipulate host responses.

Many bacteria, nematodes, trematodes, and other parasites enter via the mouth, establish in some region of the alimentary tract, and allow their eggs or offspring to exit with the feces. Although the alimentary tract of most organisms has some level of immune activity, the immune response is not as strong as it is in other regions. Thus, these organisms develop where the immune response is limited. We do not recognize broccoli as foreign and generate antibodies against broccoli in our guts. Organisms do not normally produce immune responses to gut contents; in fact, this might be counterproductive. Many organisms rely on symbiotic microbial organisms to help digest food and produce vitamins. Killing these organisms could kill the host.

Some pathogens enter the cerebrospinal fluid, which often shows a reduced immune response. Although relatively protected here, the pathogens have a problem in dispersing their offspring to subsequent hosts.

Many pathogens make themselves look like the host. They invade the body cavities of vertebrates or invertebrates or the circulatory system of vertebrates and coat themselves with host factors to confuse the immune response. Trematodes, such as *Schistosoma* species, that live in our blood/lymphatic system cover themselves in host proteins so that they are hidden from the antibody response of the host and then use host factors to stimulate their development: tumour necrosis factor (TNF) stimulates egg production, and growth is stimulated by the cytokine interleukin-7. Much of the pathology caused by this parasite is due to the immune response of the host rather than to any direct damage by the parasite.

Intracellular pathogens such as *Leishmania* species live and reproduce in the macrophages that normally eliminate pathogens, developing in the last place the host would look. They survive by producing anti-oxidant enzymes to detoxify superoxide molecules, they downregulate the signal transduction pathways that produce lethal molecules, and they produce surface glycoproteins that are refractory to host lysosomal enzymes. Therefore, the very cells the host relies on to eliminate parasites serve as incubators for these organisms. Because infected cells are considered self, they are not eliminated by other host immune responses.

Infections with the bacterium *Listeria monocytogenes,* an opportunistic food-borne bacterium that has been found to contaminate deli meats and cold cuts, soft-ripened cheese, and undercooked meats, can cause severe disease in humans. In the past few years in Canada there have been large recalls of processed (ready-to-eat) meats from manufacturers whose products were found contaminated with *L. monocytogenes.* This bacterium is ubiquitous and can continue to grow slowly even at refrigeration temperatures. Listeriosis can be very serious in pregnant women, newborns, the elderly, and individuals who have a compromised immune system due to chronic infection (e.g., HIV, cancer, diabetes). *L. monocytogenes* directly penetrates the intestinal mucosa through enterocytes by binding directly to host cells using listerial internalins and host cell adhesion factors. Alternatively, *L. monocytogenes* can invade or be phagocytosed by human macrophages that normally eliminate human pathogens. By reproducing within these cells, *L. monocytogenes* can avoid host immune molecules and may become inaccessible to antibiotics. This bacterium is also an important animal model of disease to study how bacteria invade intestinal tissues and move from cell to cell, which immune mechanisms are best at eliminating the pathogen, and which aspects of the bacterium we might target with new drugs.

Another potent bacterial disease in Canada is "flesh-eating bacteria" or necrotizing fasciitis. This infection is rare, but in severe cases can destroy the deeper layers of muscles, skin, and underlying soft tissue and can spread within the subcutaneous tissue. This disease is caused by several bacteria, such as *Streptococcus pyogenes, Staphylococcus aureus, Vibrio vulnificus, Clostridium perfringens,* and *Bacteroides fragilis,* although the most common cause is *S. pyogenes.* These bacteria usually enter the body through minor cuts or scrapes and produce toxins that directly kill host tissues,

affect blood flow to the afflicted region, and break down and kill host tissues, producing expanding regions of dead tissue. While anyone can be infected and suffer symptoms, people who suffer from chronic health problems (diabetes, cancer, liver and kidney disease) or have a compromised immune system have a greater chance of developing severe illness. Once established in the body, the infection may spread rapidly and can become life-threatening through major organ failure. *S. pyogenes* has evolved numerous molecular mechanisms to modulate both the adaptive and innate immune responses by humans including the secretion of proteolytic enzymes that degrade immunoglobulins. Treatment with broad-spectrum antibiotics and in some cases surgery is required to eliminate the bacteria and remove dead tissue. Intravenous treatment with immunoglobulin (IVIG) to boost the immune system and neutralize the bacterial toxins may be used in addition to surgery and antibiotics to treat necrotizing fasciitis. In some instances amputation of a limb is required to stop the spread of infection. In 1994, Lucien Bouchard, a charismatic politician and lawyer from Québec, suffered from necrotizing fasciitis. He was treated with antibiotics and IVIG but still had a leg amputated. His illness and treatment brought much publicity to the disease.

Some pathogens regularly change their surface coats to avoid recognition and destruction by the immune system. When the host develops antibodies against one version of the surface proteins, the pathogens produce different surface proteins, and the host produces new antibodies. These changes continue indefinitely, allowing the pathogens to keep one step ahead of the immune system. This strategy, called **antigenic variation,** is used by organisms such as the protozoan parasite that causes African sleeping sickness; the bacterium that causes gonorrhea; and the viruses that cause influenza, the common cold, and AIDS.

In insect vectors of viruses such as dengue, the virus manipulates the insect's immune response. Normally, intracellular pathogens are eliminated via apoptosis (see Section 43.2). The dengue virus, however, induces the expression of *inhibitors of apoptosis* (IAPs) to prevent cell degradation until it has established and replicated, after which it allows the cells to rupture, releasing virus particles that then enter new cells.

Many viruses also produce RNAi suppressors that prevent the host cells from preventing the viruses' multiplication using RNAi strategies, as described in Section 43.2.

43.6b Parasites and Pathogens Engage in Symbiotic Partnerships to Evade Host Immune Responses

Several very different groups of organisms work together symbiotically to overcome the response of a host. Whereas individually they would be eliminated by the host, the combination overwhelms the ability of the host to eliminate either organism.

Nematodes + Bacteria. Soil-living nematodes that enter the body cavity of insects are killed by the combination of encapsulation and melanization described previously, and many soil bacteria cannot enter the insects. Some nematodes have teamed up with specific bacteria in a symbiotic relationship to overcome host defences. Nematodes penetrate the insect and release bacteria that are phagocytosed but not killed. These bacteria multiply within hours and produce compounds that inactivate the insect's immune response. The nematodes feed and reproduce using the bacteria and host tissues as food. When resources for growth and reproduction become limited, millions of infective nematodes store some of these specific bacteria and leave the dead insect en masse in search of new hosts.

Wasps and Viruses. Some insect *parasitoids*, such as wasps, lay their eggs in other insects. Normally, these would be eliminated via encapsulation. However, some parasitoid wasps have formed an allegiance with a polyDNA virus. The virus is injected into the host insect along with the wasp egg. This virus inactivates the host's immune response, allowing the wasp larva to develop, mature, and emerge from the host, carrying some of the virus within its reproductive tract.

In the continuing battle between host and parasite/pathogen, there are constant interactions and feedback mechanisms. Each development by the host to eliminate the pathogen is countered by pathogen factors to ensure the pathogen's survival. And some of the mechanisms used are very ingenious!

STUDY BREAK

1. Compare invertebrate and mammalian immune defences.
2. How do pathogens avoid the immune responses of their hosts?
3. What mechanisms can pathogens use to avoid detection by the host?
4. How can different organisms work together to overcome host defences?
5. How can we compare immune responses between animals, and what benefit would such comparisons provide?

Review

Access an interactive eBook, chapter-specific interactive learning tools, including flashcards, quizzes, videos, and more in your Biology **CourseMate**, accessed through NelsonBrain.com
Aplia™ is an online interactive learning solution that helps you improve comprehension—and your grade—by integrating a variety of mediums and tools such as videos, tutorials, practice tests, and an interactive eBook.

43.1 Three Lines of Defence against Invasion

- Humans and other vertebrates have three lines of defence against pathogens. The first, which is nonspecific, is the barrier set up by the skin and mucus membranes.

- The second line of defence, also nonspecific, is innate immunity, an innate system that defends the body against pathogens and toxins penetrating the first line. This is the only kind of immune system found in invertebrates.

- The third line of defence, adaptive immunity, is specific: it recognizes and eliminates particular pathogens and retains a memory of that exposure so as to respond rapidly if the pathogen is encountered again. The response is carried out by lymphocytes, a specialized group of leukocytes.

43.2 Nonspecific Defences: Innate Immunity

- In the innate immune system, molecules on the surfaces of pathogens are recognized as foreign by receptors on host cells. This is common to all animals and plants. In invertebrates, this activates systems to remove the pathogen via phagocytosis, encapsulation, or the production of antimicrobial peptides. In vertebrates, the pathogen is combated by the inflammation and complement systems.

- In both vertebrates and invertebrates, epithelial surfaces and specific tissues secrete antimicrobial peptides in response to attack by microbial pathogens. These disrupt the plasma membranes of pathogens, killing them.

- Inflammation is characterized by heat, pain, redness, and swelling at the infection site. Several interconnecting mechanisms initiate inflammation, including pathogen engulfment; histamine secretion; and cytokine release, which dilates the local blood vessels, increases their permeability, and allows for leakage into body tissues.

- Large arrays of complement proteins are activated when they recognize molecules on the surfaces of pathogens. Some complement proteins form membrane attack complexes, which insert themselves into the plasma membrane of many types of bacteria and cause their lysis. Fragments of other complement proteins coat pathogens, stimulating phagocytes to engulf them.

- Four nonspecific defences are used to combat viral pathogens: RNA interference, interferons, natural killer cells, and apoptosis.

43.3 Specific Defences: Adaptive Immunity

- Adaptive immunity, which is carried out by B and T cells, targets particular pathogens or toxin molecules.

- Antibodies consist of two light and two heavy polypeptide chains, each with variable and constant regions. The variable regions of the chains combine to form the specific antigen-binding site.

- Antibodies occur in five different classes: IgM, IgD, IgG, IgA, and IgE. Each class is determined by its constant region.

- Antibody diversity is produced by genetic rearrangements in developing B cells that combine gene segments into intact genes encoding the light and heavy chains. The rearrangements producing heavy-chain genes and T-cell receptor genes are similar. The light- and heavy-chain genes are transcribed into precursor mRNAs, which are processed into finished mRNAs, which are translated on ribosomes into the antibody polypeptides.

- The antibody-mediated immune response has two general phases: (1) T-cell activation and (2) B-cell activation and antibody production. T-cell activation begins when a dendritic cell engulfs a pathogen and produces antigens, making the cell an antigen-presenting cell (APC). The APC secretes interleukins, which activate the T cell. The T cell then secretes cytokines, which stimulate the T cell to proliferate, producing a clone of cells. The clonal cells differentiate into helper T cells.

- B-cell receptors (BCRs) on B cells recognize antigens on a pathogen and engulf it. The B cells then display the antigens. The TCR on a helper T cell activated by the same antigen binds to the antigen on the B cell. Interleukins from the T cell stimulate the B cell to produce a clone of cells with identical BCRs. The clonal cells differentiate into plasma cells, which secrete antibodies specific for the antigen, and memory B cells, which provide immunological memory of the antigen encounter.

- Clonal expansion is the process of selecting a lymphocyte specifically for cloning when it encounters an antigen from among a randomly generated, large population of lymphocytes with receptors that specifically recognize the antigen.

- Antibodies clear the body of antigens by neutralizing or agglutinating them or by aiding the innate immune response.

- In immunological memory, the first encounter of an antigen elicits a primary immune response. Later exposure to the same antigen elicits a more rapid secondary response with a greater production of antibodies.

- Active immunity is the production of antibodies in response to an antigen. Passive immunity is the acquisition of antibodies by direct transfer from another person.

- In cell-mediated immunity, cytotoxic T cells recognize and bind to antigens displayed on the surfaces of infected body cells or to cancer cells. They then kill the infected cell.

- Antibodies are widely used in research to identify, locate, and determine the functions of molecules in biological systems.

43.4 Malfunctions and Failures of the Immune System

- In immunological tolerance, molecules present in an individual at birth normally do not elicit an immune response.

- In some people, the immune system malfunctions and reacts against the body's own proteins or cells, producing autoimmune disease.

- The first exposure to an allergen sensitizes an individual by leading to the production of memory B and T cells, which cause a greatly intensified response to subsequent exposures.

- Most allergies result when antigens act as allergens by stimulating B cells to produce IgE antibodies, which lead to the release of histamine. Histamines induce the symptoms characteristic of allergies (see Figure 43.13).

43.5 Defences in Other Organisms

- Antibodies, complement proteins, and other molecules with defensive functions have been identified in all vertebrates.

- Invertebrates and plants rely on nonspecific defences, including surface barriers, phagocytes, encapsulation, melanization, and antimicrobial molecules.

43.6 How Do Parasites and Pathogens Circumvent Host Responses?

- Pathogens develop in regions of the host where the immune response is limited.

- Parasites and pathogens cover themselves with host material so that they are not recognized as nonself.

- Parasites and pathogens develop in host immune cells by inactivating the immune response.

- Some pathogens use antigenic variation to keep one step ahead of the host response.

- Some pathogens manipulate the gene expression of host molecules.

- Pathogens may work together to overcome host responses that would kill either of the participants.

Questions

Self-Test Questions

1. Viruses are controlled by
   a. $CD8^+$ T cells that bind class I MHC proteins holding viral antigens
   b. $CD4^+$ T cells that bind free viruses in the blood
   c. B cells secreting perforin
   d. antibodies that bind the viruses with their constant ends
   e. natural killer cells secreting antiviral antibodies

2. Which of the following is not a component of the inflammatory response?
   a. macrophages
   b. neutrophils
   c. B cells
   d. mast cells
   e. eosinophils

3. When a person resists infection by a pathogen after being vaccinated against it, this is the result of
   a. innate immunity
   b. immunological memory
   c. a response with defensins
   d. an autoimmune reaction
   e. an allergy

4. Which of the following is among the characteristics of a B cell?
   a. It has the same structure in both invertebrates and vertebrates.
   b. It recognizes antigens held on class I MHC proteins.
   c. It binds viral infected cells and directly kills them.
   d. It makes many different BCRs on its surface.
   e. It has a BCR on its surface, which is the IgM molecule.

5. Antibodies
   a. are each composed of four heavy and four light chains
   b. display a variable end, which determines the antibody's location in the body
   c. that belong to the IgE group are the major antibody class in the blood
   d. that are found in large numbers in the mucous membranes belong to class IgG
   e. function primarily to identify and bind antigens free in body fluids

6. The generation of antibody diversity includes the
   a. joining of V to C to J segments to make a functional light-chain gene
   b. choice from several different types of C segments to make a functional light-chain gene
   c. deletion of the J segment to make a functional light-chain gene
   d. joining of V to J to C segments to make a functional light-chain gene
   e. initial generation of IgG followed later by IgM on a given cell

7. An APC
   a. can be a CD8⁺ T cell
   b. derives from a phagocytic cell and is lymphocyte stimulating
   c. secretes antibodies
   d. cannot be a B cell
   e. cannot stimulate helper T cells

8. Which one of the following is a function of antibodies?
   a. deactivate the complement system
   b. neutralize natural killer cells
   c. clump bacteria and viruses for easy phagocytosis by macrophages
   d. eliminate the chance for a secondary response
   e. kill viruses inside of cells

9. Suppose Jen punctured her hand with a muddy nail. In the emergency room, she received both a vaccine and someone else's antibodies against tetanus toxin. Which of the following describes the immunity conferred here?
   a. both active and passive
   b. active only
   c. passive only
   d. first active and later passive
   e. innate

10. Medicine attempts to enhance the immune response when treating
    a. organ transplant recipients
    b. anaphylactic shock
    c. rheumatoid arthritis
    d. HIV infection
    e. type 1 diabetes

Questions for Discussion

1. HIV wreaks havoc with the immune system by attacking helper T cells and macrophages. Would the impact be altered if the virus attacked only macrophages? Explain.

2. Given what you know about how foreign invaders trigger immune responses, explain why mutated forms of viruses, which have altered surface proteins, pose a monitoring problem for memory cells.

3. Cats, dogs, and humans may develop myasthenia gravis, an autoimmune disease in which antibodies develop against acetylcholine receptors in the synapses between neurons and skeletal muscle fibres. Based on what you know of the biochemistry of muscle contraction (see Chapter 38), explain why people with this disease typically experience severe fatigue with even small levels of exertion, drooping of facial muscles, and trouble keeping their eyelids open.

The large number of gulls (*Larus* species) is obvious at a landfill site near Thunder Bay, Ontario. The population of gulls reflects the local population of humans.

M.B. Fenton

44 Population Ecology

WHY IT MATTERS

Controlling rabies in wildlife involves understanding many aspects of biology, from populations to epidemiology and behaviour. Rabies, from the Latin *rabere* (to rage or rave), affects the nervous system of terrestrial mammals. Caused by a **Lyssavirus**, rabies is usually spread by bites because the virus accumulates in the saliva of infected animals. Before 1885, when Louis Pasteur in France developed a vaccine for it, rabies was common in Europe, and many people died from it every year. In 2007, the World Health Organization estimated that worldwide, more than 50 000 people die annually from rabies, usually people in the developing world. Between 1980 and the end of 2000, 43 people in the United States and Canada died of rabies.

Animals with *furious* rabies become berserk, attacking anything and everything in their path, a behaviour that spreads the virus and helps ensure its survival. Animals with paralytic rabies (*dumb rabies*) suffer from increasing paralysis that progresses forward from the hindlimbs. Animals with either manifestation of rabies can spread the disease by biting when there is virus in their saliva. Paralysis of the throat muscles means that rabid animals cannot swallow the saliva they produce, so they appear to foam at the mouth.

Rabies is almost invariably fatal once an animal or a human shows clinical symptoms of the disease, so immunization of someone exposed to the disease should start as soon as possible after exposure. Since 1980, human diploid vaccines have been commonly available, raising the level of protection against rabies.

From the 1960s to the 1990s, a visit to almost any rural hospital in southern Ontario (Canada) would have revealed at least one farmer receiving postexposure rabies shots. During that time, red foxes (*Vulpes vulpes*) were the main vector for rabies in Ontario, and cows (*Bos taurus*) exposed to rabies through fox bites in turn exposed farmers to the virus. Many farmers are accustomed to treating choking cows by reaching into the cow's gullet to clear an obstruction. A farmer dealing with a rabid cow could have been scratched and exposed to the virus, and then, after the cow died of rabies, the farmer would have received postexposure rabies shots. Rabies transmitted to cows from foxes posed a threat to human lives and was a significant drain on the economy through compensation paid to farmers whose cattle succumbed to the disease.

In 1967, 4-year-old Donna Featherstone of Richmond Hill, Ontario, died of rabies after being bitten by a stray cat. The resulting public outcry set the stage for a rabies eradication program in Ontario. Controlling fox rabies in southern Ontario was achieved by a combination of innovation and knowledge of basic biology. There were three phases: (a) developing an oral vaccine, (b) developing a means of vaccinating foxes, and (c) monitoring the impact of the program on the fox population.

First, two main baits for the oral vaccine were developed, and one, Evelyn, Rocketniki, Abelseth (ERA), was a modified live virus replicated in tissues of the mouth and throat. ERA successfully stimulated seroconversion in red foxes and vaccinated them against rabies. Second, foxes were vaccinated by eating ERA-containing baits scented with chicken. The baits were small, the size of restaurant packets of jam, and easy to distribute widely from low-flying aircraft, allowing vaccination of foxes across large areas of southern Ontario. Third, each bait contained tetracycline, a biomarker absorbed into the system of any mammal that ate the bait. Once in the body, some tetracycline penetrated the dentine of the animals' teeth, especially in younger individuals. Biologists sectioned and stained teeth from foxes taken by trappers. In the sections, bands of tetracycline in tooth rings (Figure 44.1) identified foxes that had taken baits, and biologists established that over 70% of red foxes had been vaccinated by this method.

Before the bait vaccination program, on average 211 cattle annually died of rabies in southern Ontario. The baiting program started in 1989, and by 1996, rabies in cattle dropped to an average of 11 cases a year and the levels of rabies in foxes in Ontario were dramatically reduced. The example demonstrates

Figure 44.1

Tetracycline rings in carnivore teeth. Yellow fluorescent lines from ingestion of rabies baits with tetracycline as a biomarker. The sections are undecalcified, ultraviolet fluorescent × 100. **(a)** Coyote (*Canis latrans*) tooth with seven daily tetracycline lines from vaccine baits. **(b)** Canine tooth of a four-year-old raccoon (*Procyon lotor*) with yearly tetracycline lines in cementum. af = autofluorescent collagen; Fa = fall baits, 1998; pl = periodontal ligament; Sp = spring baits, 1998 and 1999.

Reprinted from Rabies, Alan C. Jackson, "Rabies Control in Wildlife" by David H. Johnston, Rowland R. Tinline, Pages No. 445–471, Copyright 2003, with permission from Elsevier.

how problems in biology are solved by combined approaches, from population biology, behaviour, immunology, and epidemiology.

The purpose of this chapter is to introduce you to ecology in general and population ecology in particular.

Ecology is the study of the relationships among species and between species and the environments in which they occur. Studies of populations are fundamental to ecology and involve everything from the numbers of individuals to their age structure and patterns of reproduction. This connects with work on the life histories of species, often with a focus on reproduction and survival. Changes in the numbers of individuals of a species may lead to an explosion in numbers or to extinction, and both biotic and abiotic factors can influence changes in populations. The basics of population biology and ecology apply as much to our own species as they do to others.

44.1 The Science of Ecology

Ecology encompasses two related disciplines. In **basic ecology**, major research questions relate to the distribution and abundance of species and how they interact with each other and the physical environment. Using these data as a baseline, workers in **applied ecology** develop conservation plans and amelioration programs to limit, repair, and mitigate ecological damage caused by human activities (see also Chapter 47). Ecology has its roots in descriptive natural history dating back to the ancient Greeks. Modern ecology was born in 1870 when the German biologist Ernst Haeckel coined the term (from *oikos* = house). Contemporary researchers still gather descriptive information about ecological relationships, often as the starting point for other studies. Although ecological research is dominated by hypothetico-deductive approaches, initial inductive approaches allow biologists to generate appropriate hypotheses about how systems function. Research in ecology is often linked to work in genetics, physiology, anatomy, behaviour, paleontology, and evolution, as well as geology, geography, and environmental science. Many ecological phenomena, such as climate change, occur over huge areas and long time spans, so ecologists must devise ways to determine how environments influence organisms and how organisms change the environments in which they live.

Ecology can be divided into four increasingly complex and inclusive levels of organization. First, in **organismal ecology**, researchers study organisms to determine the genetic, biochemical, physiological, morphological, and behavioural adaptations to the abiotic environment (see *The Purple Pages*). Second, in **population ecology**, researchers focus on groups of individuals of the same species that live together. Population ecologists study how the size and other characteristics of populations change in space and time. Third, in **community ecology**, biologists examine populations of different species that occur together in one area (are sympatric). Community ecologists study interactions between species, analyzing how predation, competition, and environmental disturbances influence a community's development, organization, and structure (see Chapter 46). Fourth, those studying **ecosystem ecology** explore how nutrients cycle and energy flows between the biotic components of an ecological community and the abiotic environment (see Chapter 46).

Ecologists can create hypotheses about ecological relationships and how they change through time or differ from place to place. Some formalize these ideas in mathematical models that express clearly defined, but hypothetical, relationships among important variables in a system. Manipulation of a model, usually with the help of a computer, can allow researchers to ask what would happen if some of the variables or their relationships changed. Thus, researchers can simulate natural events and large-scale experiments before investing time, energy, and money in fieldwork and laboratory work. Bear in mind that mathematical models are no better than the ideas and assumptions they embody, and useful models are constructed only after basic observations have defined the relevant variables.

Ecologists use field or laboratory studies to test predictions of their hypotheses about relationships among variables in systems. In controlled experiments, researchers compare data from an experimental treatment (involving manipulation of one or more variables) with data from a control (in which nothing is changed). In some cases, *natural experiments* can be conducted because of the patterns of distribution and/or behaviour of species. This has the advantage of allowing ecologists to test predictions about how systems are operating without manipulating variables. Two species of fish, cutthroat trout (*Oncorhynchus clarki*) and Dolly Varden char (*Salvelinus*

malma), live in coastal lakes of British Columbia. Some lakes have either trout or char, but others contain both species. The natural distributions of these fishes allowed researchers to measure the effect of each species on the other. In lakes in which both species live, each restricts its activities to fewer areas and eats a smaller variety of prey than it does in lakes in which it occurs alone.

STUDY BREAK

1. What are the four levels of organization in ecology? Give a brief description of each.
2. What is a mathematical model? Why are such models important in ecology?
3. What two treatments are important when doing experiments? Why?

44.2 Population Characteristics

CONCEPT FIX Many people believe that the sizes of populations of animals and plants will increase until net demands for food (and other resources) exceed the supply. This crisis of carrying capacity leads to crashes in populations and even to extinction. Under natural conditions, however, interactions among individuals (of the same or different species) usually cause populations to stop growing well before they reach carrying capacity. In many populations, there are natural cycles of numbers. ⬡

Seven characteristics can be described for any population.

44.2a Geographic Range Is Determined by the Boundaries of Distribution

Populations have characteristics that transcend those of the individuals making up the populations. Every population has a **geographic range**, the overall spatial boundaries within which it lives. Geographic ranges vary enormously. A population of snails might inhabit a small tide pool, whereas a population of marine phytoplankton might occupy an area that is orders of magnitude as large. Every population also occupies a **habitat**, the specific environment in which it lives, as characterized by its biotic and abiotic features. Ecologists also measure other population characteristics, such as size, distribution in space, and age structure.

44.2b Population Density Is Based on the Number of Individuals per Unit Area

Population size is the number of individuals making up the population at a specified time (N_t). **Population density** is the number of individuals per unit area or per unit volume of habitat. Species with a large body size

Figure 44.2

Population density and body size. Population density generally declines with increasing body size among animal species. There are similar trends for other organisms.

KEY
- Aquatic invertebrates
- Terrestrial invertebrates
- Mammals
- Birds
- Vertebrate ectotherms

(y-axis: Density (animals/km²), values 10^{12}, 10^8, 10^4, 1.0, 10^{-4}; x-axis: Body mass (kg), values 10^{-9}, 10^{-6}, 10^{-3}, 1.0, 10^3)

generally have lower population densities than those with a small body size **(Figure 44.2)**. Although population size and density are related measures, knowing a population's density provides more information about its relationship to the resources it uses. If a population of 200 oak trees occupies 1 hectare (ha; 10 000 m²), the population density is 200 × 10 000 m⁻² or 1 tree per 50 m². But if 200 oaks are spread over 5 ha, the density is 1 tree per 250 m². Clearly, the second population is less dense than the first, and its members will have greater access to sunlight, water, and other resources.

Ecologists measure population size and density to monitor and manage populations of endangered species, economically important species, and agricultural pests. For large-bodied species, a simple head count could provide accurate information. For example, ecologists survey the size and density of African elephant populations by flying over herds and counting individuals **(Figure 44.3)**. Researchers use a variation on that technique to **estimate** population size in tiny organisms that live at high population densities. To estimate the density of aquatic phytoplankton, for example, you might collect water samples of known volume from

representative areas in a lake and count them by looking through a microscope. These data allow you to estimate population size and density based on the estimated volume of the entire lake. In other cases, researchers use the mark–release–recapture sampling technique (see "Capture–Recapture," Box 44.1, p. 1110). One ongoing challenge is measuring population size in organisms that are clones, for example, stands of poplar trees (*Populus* spp.).

44.2c Population Dispersion Is the Distribution of Individuals in Space

Populations can vary in their **dispersion**, the spatial distribution of individuals within the geographic range. Ecologists define three theoretical patterns of dispersion: *clumped, uniform,* and *random* **(Figure 44.4, p. 1110)**.

Clumped dispersion (see Figure 44.4a, p. 1110) is common and occurs in three situations. First, suitable conditions are often patchily distributed. Certain pasture plants, for instance, may be clumped in small, scattered areas where cowpats had fallen for

a.

b.

Figure 44.3

Counting elephants. It is easy to think that large animals such as African elephants (*Loxodonta africana*) would be easy to count from the air **(a)**. This may or may not be true, depending on vegetation. But it can be easy to overlook animals, particularly young ones **(b)**, in the shade.

Capture–Recapture 44.1

Ecologists use the mark–release–recapture technique to estimate the population size of mobile animals that live within a restricted geographic range. To do this, a sample of organisms (n_1) is captured, marked, and released. Ideally, the marks (or tags) are permanent and do not harm the tagged animal. Insects and reptiles are often marked with ink or paint, birds with rings (bands) on their legs, and mammals with ear tags or collars.

Later, a second sample (n_2) of the population is captured. In the second sample, the proportion of marked (n_{2m}) to unmarked individuals is used to estimate the total population (x) of the study area by solving the following equation for x:

$$n_1/x = n_{2m}/n_2$$

Assume that you capture a sample of 120 butterflies **(Figure 1)**, mark each one, and release them. A week later, you capture a sample of 150 butter-

FIGURE 1
This butterfly has been captured and marked before release in a capture–recapture experiment.

M.B. Fenton

flies, 30 that you marked. Thus, you had marked 30 of 150, or 1 of every 5 butterflies, on your first field trip. Because you captured 120 individuals on that first excursion, you would estimate that the total population size is $120 \times (150/30) = 600$ butterflies.

The capture–recapture technique is based on several assumptions that are critical to its accuracy: (1) being marked has no effect on survival, (2) marked and unmarked animals mix randomly in the population, (3) no migration into or out of the population takes place during the estimating period, and (4) marked individuals are just as likely to be captured as unmarked individuals. (Sometimes animals become "trap shy" or "trap happy," a violation of the fourth assumption.)

© Amos Nachoum/CORBIS

Dan Suzio/Photo Researchers, Inc.

a. Clumped
b. Random
c. Uniform

A clumped dispersion pattern is one in which individuals are grouped more closely to each other than if they are randomly dispersed.

A random dispersion pattern, in which organisms are distributed independently of each other, serves as a statistical yardstick for evaluating other dispersion patterns.

A uniform dispersion pattern is one in which individuals are more widely separated from each other than they are if they are randomly dispersed.

Figure 44.4
Dispersion patterns. A clumped pattern **(a)** is evident in fish that live in social groups. A random pattern **(b)** of dispersion appears to be rare in nature, where it occurs in organisms that are neither attracted to nor repelled by conspecifics. Nearly uniform patterns **(c)** are demonstrated by creosote bushes (*Larrea tridentata*) near Death Valley, California.

months, locally enriching the soil. Second, populations of some social animals (see Chapter 39) are clumped because mates are easy to locate within groups, and individuals may cooperate in rearing offspring, feeding, or defending themselves from predators. Third, populations can be clumped when species reproduce by asexual clones that remain attached to the parents. Aspen trees and sea anemones reproduce this way and often occur in large aggregations (see Chapter 19). Clumping may also occur in species in which seeds, eggs, or larvae lack dispersal mechanisms and offspring grow and settle near their parents.

Uniform distributions can occur when individuals repel one another because resources are in short supply. Creosote bushes are uniformly distributed in the dry scrub deserts of the American Southwest (see Figure 44.4c). Mature bushes deplete the surrounding soil of water and secrete toxic chemicals, making it impossible for seedlings to grow. This chemical warfare is called *allelopathy*. Moreover, seed-eating ants and rodents living at the bases of mature bushes eat any seeds that fall nearby. In these situations, the distributions of species of plants and animals can be uniform and interrelated. Territorial behaviour, the defence of an area and its resources, can also produce uniform dispersion in some species of animals, such as nests in colonies of colonial birds (see Chapter 39).

Black-Footed Ferret, *Mustela nigripes* 44.2

Black-footed ferrets **(Figure 1)** are crepuscular and nocturnal hunters of the prairie. Weighing 0.6 to 1.1 kg, these weasel relatives (family Mustelidae, order Carnivora) were once abundant in western North America, from Texas in the United States to Saskatchewan and Alberta in Canada. Like other mustelids, males are larger than females. In the wild, these predators probably fed mainly on prairie dogs (*Cynomys* species) and lived around prairie dog towns. Litters range in size from one to five. Females bear a single litter a year, and males and females are sexually mature at age one year.

By 1987, *M. nigripes* was probably extinct in the wild. The last known wild population was discovered near Meeteetse, Wyoming, in 1981. Seven animals from this population were captured and brought into captivity and served as the genetic founders for a captive breeding program. Over 4800 juvenile black-footed ferrets were produced by this program, and wildlife officials began to release captive-bred animals into suitable habitats.

At Shirley Basin, Wyoming, 228 captive-born black-footed ferrets were received between 1991 and 1994. By 1996, only 25 were observed in the wild and by 1997, only 5. This decline reflected the impact of diseases, specifically canine distemper and plague. In 1996, it seemed that the reintroductions would fail, and *M. nigripes* would again be extinct in the wild.

In 2003, however, 52 black-footed ferrets were observed in the field at Shirley Basin, and, since then, the population has increased significantly **(Figure 2)**. The increase reflects an intrinsic rate of increase (*r*) of 0.47, which reflects success in the first year of life and derives from a combination of survival and fertility.

There appears to be hope for the future of *M. nigripes*. It remains to be determined if the genetic bottleneck (see Chapter 19) that the species has endured will prove to be an important handicap to long-term survival.

FIGURE 1

Mustela nigripes, *the black-footed ferret. This critically endangered carnivore from the North American prairie shows evidence of a comeback.*

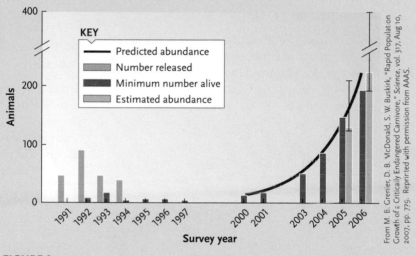

FIGURE 2

Population growth. Black-footed ferrets in Shirley Basin, Wyoming, have shown rapid population growth. The 95% confidence limits suggest a population of 192 to 401 in 2006.

From M. B. Grenier, D. B. McDonald, S. W. Buskirk, "Rapid Population Growth of a Critically Endangered Carnivore," *Science*, vol. 317, Aug 10, 2007, pp. 779. Reprinted with permission from AAAS.

Random dispersion (see Figure 44.4b) occurs when environmental conditions do not vary much within a habitat, and individuals are neither attracted to nor repelled by others of their species (conspecifics). Ecologists use formal statistical definitions of *random* to establish a theoretical baseline for assessing the pattern of distribution. In cases of random dispersion, individuals are distributed unpredictably. Some spiders, burrowing clams, and rainforest trees exhibit random dispersion.

Whether the spatial distribution of a population appears to be clumped, uniform, or random depends partly on the size of the organisms and of the study area.

Oak seedlings may be randomly dispersed on a spatial scale of a few square metres, but over an entire mixed hardwood forest, they are clumped under the parent trees. Therefore, dispersion of a population depends partly on the researcher's scale of observation.

In addition, the dispersion of animal populations often varies through time in response to natural environmental rhythms. Few habitats provide a constant supply of resources throughout the year, and many animals move from one habitat to another on a seasonal cycle, reflecting the distribution of resources such as food. Tropical birds and mammals are often widely dispersed in deciduous forests during the wet season, when food is widely available. During the dry season, these species crowd into narrow *gallery forests* along watercourses, where evergreen trees provide food and shelter.

44.2d Age Structure Is the Numbers of Individuals of Different Ages

All populations have an **age structure**, a statistical description of the relative numbers of individuals in each age class (discussed further in Chapter 45). Individuals can be categorized roughly as prereproductive (younger than the age of sexual maturity), reproductive, or postreproductive (older than the maximum age of reproduction). A population's age structure reflects its recent growth history and predicts its future growth potential. Populations composed of many prereproductive individuals obviously grew rapidly in the recent past. These populations will continue to grow as young individuals mature and reproduce.

44.2e Generation Time Is the Average Time between Birth and Death

Another characteristic that influences a population's growth is its **generation time**, the average time between the birth of an organism and the birth of its offspring. Generation time is usually short in species that reach sexual maturity at a small body size **(Figure 44.5).** Their

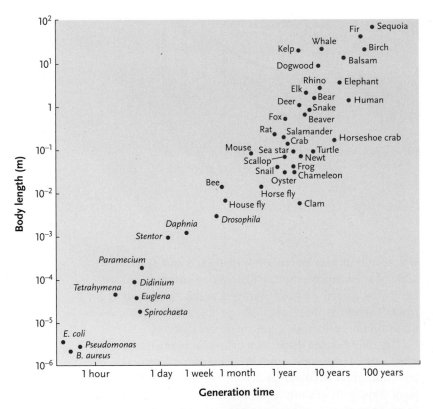

Figure 44.5

Generation time and body size. Generation time increases with body size among bacteria, protists, plants, and animals. The logarithmic scale on both axes compresses the data into a straight line.

populations often grow rapidly because of the speedy accumulation of reproductive individuals.

44.2f Sex Ratio: Females:Males

Populations of sexually reproducing organisms also vary in their **sex ratio**, the relative proportions of males and females. In general, the number of females in a population has a bigger impact on population growth than the number of males because only females actually produce offspring. Moreover, in many species, one male can mate with several females, and the number of males may have little effect on the population's reproductive output. In northern elephant seals (see Chapter 16), mature bulls fight for dominance on the beaches where the seals mate. Only a few males may ultimately inseminate a hundred or more females. Thus, the presence of other males in the group may have little effect on the size of future generations. In animals that form lifelong pair bonds, such as geese and swans, the numbers of males and females influence reproduction in the population.

44.2g The Proportion Reproducing Is the Incidence of Reproducing Individuals in a Population

Population ecologists try to determine the proportion of individuals in a population that are reproducing. This issue is particularly relevant to the conservation of any species in which individuals are rare or widely dispersed in the habitat (see Chapter 47).

STUDY BREAK

1. What is the difference between geographic range and habitat?
2. What are the three types of dispersion? What is the most common pattern found in nature? Why?
3. What is the common pattern of generation time among bacteria, protists, plants, and animals?

44.3 Demography

Populations grow larger through the birth of individuals and the **immigration** (movement into the population) of organisms from neighbouring populations. Conversely, death and **emigration** (movement out of the population) reduce population size. **Demography** is the statistical study of the processes that change a population's size and density through time.

Ecologists use demographic analysis to predict a population's growth. For human populations, these data help governments anticipate the need for social services such as schools, hospitals, and chronic care facilities. Demographic data allow conservation ecologists to develop plans to protect endangered species. Demographic data on northern spotted owls (*Strix occidentalis caurina*) helped convince the courts to restrict logging in the owl's primary habitat, the old growth forests of the Pacific Northwest. Life tables and survivorship curves are among the tools ecologists use to analyze demographic data.

44.3a Life Tables Show the Number of Individuals in Each Age Group

Although every species has a characteristic lifespan, few individuals survive to the maximum age possible. Mortality results from starvation, disease, accidents, predation, or inability to find a suitable habitat. Life insurance companies first developed techniques for measuring mortality rates (known as actuarial science), and ecologists adapted these approaches to the study of nonhuman populations.

A **life table** summarizes the demographic characteristics of a population **(Table 44.1)**. To collect life table data for short-lived organisms, demographers typically mark a **cohort**, a group of individuals of similar age, at birth and monitor their survival until all members of the cohort die. For organisms that live more than a few years, a researcher might sample the population for one or two years, recording the ages at which individuals die and then extrapolating these results over the species' lifespan. The approach to the timing of collection of data about reproduction and longevity will depend on the details of the species under study.

In any life table, lifespans of organisms are divided into age intervals of appropriate length. For short-lived species, days, weeks, or months are useful, whereas for longer-lived species, years or groups of years will be better. Mortality can be expressed in two complementary ways. **Age-specific mortality** is the proportion of individuals alive at the start of an age interval that died during that age interval. Its more cheerful reflection, **age-specific survivorship**, is the proportion of individuals alive at the start of an age interval that survived until the start of the next age interval. Thus, for the data shown in Table 44.1, the age-specific mortality rate during the 3- to 6-month age interval is 195/722 = 0.270, and the age-specific survivorship rate is 527/722 = 0.730. For any age interval, the sum of age-specific mortality and age-specific survivorship must equal 1. Life tables also summarize the proportion of the cohort that survived to a particular age, a statistic identifying the probability that any randomly selected newborn will still be alive at that age. For the 3- to 6-month age interval in Table 44.1, this probability is 722/843 = 0.856.

Life tables also include data on **age-specific fecundity**, the average number of offspring produced by surviving females during each age interval. Table 44.1 shows that plants in the 3- to 6-month age interval produced an average of 300 seeds each. In some species, including humans, fecundity is highest in individuals of intermediate age. Younger individuals have not yet reached sexual maturity, and older individuals are past their reproductive prime. However, fecundity increases steadily with age in some plants and animals.

44.3b Survivorship Curves Graph the Timing of Deaths of Individuals in a Population

Survivorship data are depicted graphically in a **survivorship curve**, which displays the rate of survival for individuals over the species' average lifespan.

Table 44.1	Life Table for a Cohort of 843 Individuals of the Grass *Poa annua* (Annual Bluegrass)					
Age Interval (in months)	Number Alive at Start of Age Interval	Number Dying during Age Interval	Age-Specific Mortality Rate	Age-Specific Survivorship Rate	Proportion of Original Cohort Alive at Start of Age Interval	Age-Specific Fecundity (Seed Production)
0–3	843	121	0.144	0.856	1.000	0
3–6	722	195	0.270	0.730	0.856	300
6–9	527	211	0.400	0.600	0.625	620
9–12	316	172	0.544	0.456	0.375	430
12–15	144	90	0.625	0.375	0.171	210
15–18	54	39	0.722	0.278	0.064	60
18–21	15	12	0.800	0.200	0.018	30
21–24	3	3	1.000	0.000	0.004	10
24–	0	—	—	—	—	—

Source: Begon, M., and M. Mortimer. *Population Ecology.* Sunderland, MA: Sinauer Associates, 1981. Adapted from R. Law, 1975.

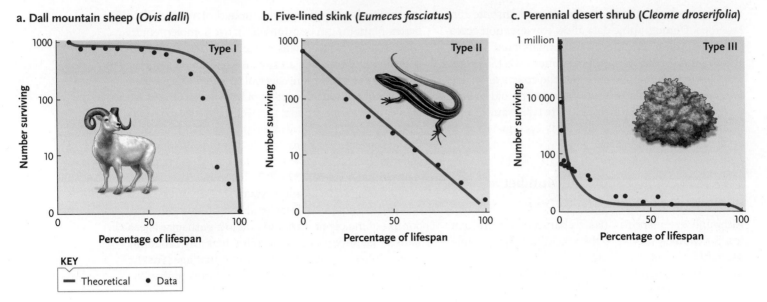

a. Dall mountain sheep (*Ovis dalli*)
Type I

Number surviving
1000
100
10
0
0   50   100
Percentage of lifespan

b. Five-lined skink (*Eumeces fasciatus*)
Type II

Number surviving
1000
100
10
0
0   50   100
Percentage of lifespan

c. Perennial desert shrub (*Cleome droserifolia*)
Type III

Number surviving
1 million
10 000
100
0
0   50   100
Percentage of lifespan

KEY
— Theoretical   • Data

Figure 44.6

Survivorship curves. The survivorship curves of many organisms (pink) roughly match one of three idealized patterns (blue).

Ecologists have identified three generalized survivorship curves (blue lines in **Figure 44.6**), although most organisms exhibit survivorship patterns falling between these idealized patterns.

Type I curves reflect high survivorship until late in life (see Figure 44.6a). They are typical of large animals that produce few young and provide them with extended care, which reduces juvenile mortality. Large mammals, such as Dall mountain sheep, produce only one or two offspring at a time and nurture them through their vulnerable first year. At that time, the young are better able to fend for themselves and are at lower risk for mortality (compared with younger animals). The picture of survivorship in mammals could change if one starts with the time of conception, as opposed to birth. The change would reflect problems of pregnancy (see Chapter 19) and health of mothers.

Type II curves reflect a relatively constant rate of mortality in all age classes, a pattern that produces steadily declining survivorship (see Figure 44.6b). Many lizards, such as the five-lined skink, as well as songbirds and small mammals, face a constant probability of mortality from predation, disease, and starvation and show a type II pattern.

Type III curves reflect high juvenile mortality, followed by a period of low mortality once offspring reach a critical age and size (see Figure 44.6c, in which the vertical scale is logarithmic). *Cleome droserifolia*, a desert shrub from the Middle East, experiences extraordinarily high mortality in its seed and seedling stages. Researchers estimate that for every 1 million seeds produced, fewer than 1000 germinate, and only about 40 individuals survive their first year. Once a plant becomes established, however, its likelihood of future survival is higher, and the survivorship curve flattens out. Many plants, insects, marine invertebrates, and fishes exhibit type III survivorship.

STUDY BREAK

1. What is the relationship between age-specific mortality and age-specific survivorship? If the age-specific mortality is 0.384, what is the age-specific survivorship?
2. What is age-specific fecundity?
3. Describe three survivorship curves. Which curve describes humans? Songbirds? Insects?

44.4 The Evolution of Life Histories

Analysis of life tables reveals how natural selection affects an organism's **life history**, which includes the lifetime patterns of growth, maturation, and reproduction. Ecologists study life histories to understand tradeoffs in the allocation of resources to these three activities. The results of their research suggest that natural selection adjusts the allocation of resources to maximize an individual's number of surviving offspring.

Every organism is constrained by a finite **energy budget**, the total amount of energy it can accumulate and use to fuel its activities. An organism's energy budget is like a savings account. When the individual accumulates more energy than it needs, it makes deposits to this account, storing energy as starch, glycogen, or fat. When the individual expends more energy than it harvests, it makes withdrawals from its energy stores. But unlike a bank account, an organism's energy budget cannot be overdrawn, and no loans against future "earnings" are possible.

Just as humans find clever ways to finance their schemes, many organisms use different ways to mortgage their operations. Organisms that enter states of inactivity or dormancy can maximize the time over which they use stored energy. An extreme example would be animals and plants that can survive freezing, an obvious strategy for conserving energy. Hibernation and estivation in animals are other examples (see Chapter 42). Hibernating animals use periods of reduced body temperature to survive prolonged periods of cold weather. Estivation is inactivity during prolonged periods of high temperatures. Specialized spores can be resistant to heat and desiccation. Migrating birds on long flights get energy by metabolizing fat as well as other body structures, such as muscle or digestive tissue. Organisms use the energy they harvest for three broadly defined functions: maintenance (the preservation of good physiological condition), growth, and reproduction. When an organism devotes energy to any one of these functions, the balance in its energy budget is reduced, leaving less energy for other functions.

A fish, a deciduous tree, and a mammal illustrate the dramatic variations existing in life history patterns. Larval coho salmon (*Oncorhynchus kisutch*) hatch in the headwaters of a stream, where they feed and grow for about a year before assuming their adult body form and swimming to the ocean. They remain at sea for a year or two, feeding voraciously and growing rapidly. Eventually, using a Sun compass and geomagnetic and chemical cues, salmon return to the rivers and streams where they hatched. The fishes swim upstream. Males prepare nests and try to attract females. Each female lays hundreds or thousands of relatively small eggs. After breeding, the body condition of males and females deteriorates, and they die.

Most deciduous trees in the temperate zone, such as oaks (genus *Quercus*), begin their lives as seeds (acorns) in late summer. The seeds remain metabolically inactive until the following spring or a later year. After germinating, seedling trees collect nutrients and energy and continue to grow throughout their lives. Once they achieve a critical size, they may produce thousands of acorns annually for many years. Thus, growth and reproduction occur simultaneously through much of the trees' life.

European red deer (*Cervus elaphus*) are born in spring, and the young remain with their mothers for an extended period, nursing and growing rapidly. After weaning, the young feed on their own. Female red deer begin to breed after reaching adult size in their third year, producing one or two offspring annually until they are about 16 years old, when they reach their maximum lifespan and die.

How can we summarize the similarities and differences in the life histories of these organisms? All three species harvest energy throughout their lives. Salmon and deciduous trees continue to grow until old age, whereas deer reach adult size fairly early in life. Salmon produce many offspring in a single reproductive episode, whereas deciduous trees and deer reproduce repeatedly. However, most trees produce thousands of seeds annually, whereas deer produce only one or two young each spring.

What factors have produced these variations in life history patterns? Life history traits, like all population characteristics, are modified by natural selection. Thus, organisms exhibit evolutionary adaptations that increase the fitness of individuals. Each species' life history is, in fact, a highly integrated "strategy" or suite of selection-driven adaptations.

In analyzing life histories, ecologists compare the number of offspring with the amount of care provided to each by the parents. They also determine the number of reproductive episodes in the organism's lifetime and the timing of first reproduction. Because these characteristics evolve together, a change in one trait is likely to influence others.

44.4a Fecundity versus Parental Care: Cutting Your Losses

If a female has a fixed amount of energy for reproduction, she can package that energy in various ways. A female duck with 1000 units of energy for reproduction might lay 10 eggs with 100 units of energy per egg. A salmon, which has higher fecundity, might lay 1000 eggs with 1 unit of energy in each. The amount of energy invested in each offspring before it is born is **passive parental care** provided by the female. Passive parental care is provided through yolk in an egg; endosperm in a seed; or, in mammals, nutrients that cross the placenta.

Many animals also provide **active parental care** to offspring after their birth. In general, species producing many offspring in a reproductive episode (e.g., the coho salmon) provide relatively little active parental care to each offspring. In fact, female coho salmon, each producing 2400 to 4500 eggs, die before their eggs even hatch. Conversely, species producing few offspring at a time (e.g., European red deer) provide much more care to each one. A red deer doe nurses its single fawn for up to eight months before weaning it.

44.4b How Often to Breed: Once or Repeatedly?

The number of reproductive episodes in an organism's lifespan is a second life history characteristic adjusted by natural selection. Some organisms, such as coho salmon, devote all of their stored energy to a single reproductive event. Any adult that survives the upstream migration is likely to leave some surviving offspring. Other species, such as deciduous trees and red deer, reproduce more than once. In contrast to salmon, individuals of these species devote only some of their energy budget to reproduction at any time, with the balance allocated to maintenance and growth. Moreover, in some plants, invertebrates, fishes, and reptiles, larger individuals produce more offspring than smaller ones. Thus, one advantage of using only part of the energy budget for reproduction is that continued growth may result in greater fecundity at a later age. However, if an organism does not survive until the next breeding season, the potential advantage of putting energy into maintenance and growth is lost.

44.4c Age at First Reproduction: When to Start Reproducing

Individuals that first reproduce at the earliest possible age may stand a good chance of leaving some surviving offspring. But the energy they use in reproduction is not available for maintenance and growth. Thus, early reproducers may be smaller and less healthy than individuals that delay reproduction in favour of other functions. Conversely, an individual that delays reproduction may increase its chance of survival and its future fecundity by becoming larger or more experienced. But there is always some chance that it will die before the next breeding season, leaving no offspring at all. Therefore, a finite energy budget and the risk of mortality establish a tradeoff in the timing of first reproduction. Mathematical models suggest that delayed reproduction will be favoured by natural selection if a sexually mature individual has a good chance of surviving to an older age, if organisms grow larger as they age, and if larger organisms have higher fecundity. Early reproduction will be favoured if adult survival rates are low, if animals do not grow larger as they age, or if larger size does not increase fecundity. These characteristics apply more readily to some animals and plants than they do to others. Among animals, the features discussed above apply more readily to vertebrate than to invertebrate animals. Parasitic organisms may have quite different patterns of life history.

Life history characteristics vary from one species to another, and they can vary among populations of a single species. Predation differentially influences life history characteristics in natural populations of guppies (*Poecilia reticulata*) in Trinidad (see "Life Histories of Guppies," Box 44.3).

Life Histories of Guppies 44.3

Some years ago, drenched with sweat and with fishnets in hand, two ecologists were engaged in fieldwork on the Caribbean island of Trinidad. They were after guppies (*Poecilia reticulata*), small fish most of us see in pet shops. In their native habitats, guppies bear live young in shallow mountain streams **(Figure 1),** and John Endler and David Reznick were studying the environmental variables influencing the evolution of their life history patterns.

Male guppies are easy to distinguish from females. Males stop growing at sexual maturity. They are smaller, and their scales have bright colours that serve as visual signals in intricate courtship displays. Females are drably coloured and continue to grow larger throughout their lives. In the mountains of Trinidad, guppies live in different streams, even in different parts of the same stream. Two other species of fish eat guppies **(Figure 2).** In some streams, a small killifish (*Rivulus hartii*) preys on immature guppies but does not have much success with the larger adults. In other streams, a

FIGURE 1

David Reznick surveys a shallow stream in the mountains of Trinidad.

Male guppy (right) that shared a stream with pike–cichlids (below)

Male guppy (right) that shared a stream with killifish (below)

FIGURE 2

Male guppies from streams where pike–cichlids live (top) are smaller and more streamlined and have duller colours than those from streams where killifish live (bottom). The pike–cichlid prefers to eat large guppies, and the killifish feeds on small guppies. Guppies are shown approximately life sized; adult pike–cichlids grow to 16 cm in length, and adult killifish grow to 10 cm. (Guppy photos: David Reznick/University of California, Riverside: computer enhanced by Lisa Starr; predator photos: Hippocampus Bildarchiv.)

(continued)

Life Histories of Guppies 44.3 (*continued*)

large pike–cichlid (*Crenicichla alta*) prefers mature guppies and rarely hunts small, immature ones.

Reznick and Endler found that the life history patterns of guppies vary among streams with different predators. In streams with pike–cichlids, male and female guppies mature faster and begin to reproduce at a smaller size and younger age than their counterparts in streams where killifish live. Female guppies from pike–cichlid streams reproduce more often, producing smaller and more numerous young. These differences allow guppies to avoid some predation. Those in pike–cichlid streams begin to reproduce when they are smaller than the size preferred by that predator. Those from killifish streams grow quickly to a size that is too large to be consumed by killifish **(Figure 3).**

Although these life history differences were correlated with the distributions of the two predatory fishes, they might result from some other, unknown differences between the streams. Endler and Reznick investigated this possibility with controlled laboratory experiments. They shipped groups of live guppies to California, where they bred guppies from each kind of stream for two generations. Both types of experimental populations were raised under identical conditions in the absence of predators. Even in the absence of predators, the two types of experimental populations retained their life history differences. These results provided evidence of a genetic (heritable) basis for the observed life history differences.

Endler and Reznick also examined the role of predators in the *evolution* of the size differences **(Figure 4).** They raised guppies for many generations in the laboratory under three experimental conditions: some alone, some with killifish, and some with pike–cichlids. As predicted, the guppy lineage subjected to predation by killifish became larger at maturity. Individuals that were small at maturity were frequently eaten, and their reproduction was limited. The lineage raised with pike–cichlids showed a trend toward earlier maturity. Individuals that matured at a larger size faced a greater likelihood of being eaten before they had reproduced.

When they first visited Trinidad, Endler and Reznick had introduced guppies from a pike–cichlid stream to another stream that contained killifish but no pike–cichlids or guppies. There, 11 years later, guppy populations had changed. As the researchers predicted, the guppies became larger and reproduced more slowly, characteristics typical of natural guppy populations that live and die with killifish.

FIGURE 3

Guppies in streams occupied by pike–cichlids are smaller than those in streams occupied by killifish.

FIGURE 4

Female guppies from streams occupied by pike–cichlids reproduce more often (shorter time between broods) and produce more young per brood and smaller young (lower embryo mass) than females living in streams occupied by killifish.

STUDY BREAK

1. Organisms use energy for what three main operations?
2. Explain passive and active parental care in humans.
3. When would early reproduction be favoured?

44.5 Models of Population Growth

We now examine two mathematical models of population growth, exponential and logistic. **Exponential** models apply when populations experience unlimited growth. **Logistic** models apply when population growth is limited, often because available resources are finite. These simple models are tools that help ecologists refine their hypotheses, but neither provides entirely accurate predictions of population growth in nature. In the simplest versions of these models, ecologists define births as the production of offspring by any form of reproduction and ignore the effects of immigration and emigration.

44.5a Exponential Models: Populations Taking Off

Populations sometimes increase in size for a period of time with no apparent limits on their growth. In models of exponential growth, population size increases steadily by a constant ratio. Populations of bacteria and prokaryotes provide the most obvious examples, but multicellular organisms also sometimes exhibit exponential population growth.

Bacteria reproduce by binary fission. A parent cell divides in half, producing two daughter cells, and each can divide to produce two granddaughter cells. Generation time in a bacterial population is simply the time between successive cell divisions. If no bacteria in the population die, the population doubles in size each generation.

Bacterial populations grow quickly under ideal temperatures and with unlimited space and food. Consider a population of the human intestinal bacterium *Escherichia coli*, for which the generation time can be as short as 20 minutes. If we start with a population of one bacterium, the population doubles to two cells after one generation, to four cells after two generations, and to eight cells after three generations **(Figure 44.7)**. After only 8 hours (24 generations), the population will number more than 16 million. And after a single day (72 generations), the population will number nearly 5×10^{21} cells. Although other bacteria grow more slowly

than *E. coli*, it is no wonder that pathogenic bacteria, such as those causing cholera or plague, can quickly overtake the defences of an infected animal.

When populations of multicellular organisms are large, they have the potential for exponential growth, as we shall see below for our own species. In any event, over a given time period,

change in population size = number of births − number of deaths.

We express this relationship mathematically by defining N as the population size; ΔN (pronounced "delta N") as the change in population size; Δt as the time period during which the change occurs; and B and D as the numbers of births and deaths, respectively, during that time period. Thus, $\Delta N/\Delta t$ symbolizes the change in population size over time, and

$$\Delta N/\Delta t = B - D.$$

The above equation applies to any population for which we know the exact numbers of births and deaths. Ecologists usually express births and deaths as per capita (per individual) rates, allowing them to apply the model to a population of any size. The per capita birth rate (b) is the number of births in the population during the specified time period divided by the population size: $b = (B/N)$. Similarly, the per capita death rate, d, is the number of deaths divided by the population size: $d = (D/N)$.

If in a population of 2000 field mice, 1000 mice are born and 200 mice die during 1 month, $b = 1000/2000 = 0.5$ births per individual per month, and $d = 200/2000 = 0.1$ deaths per individual per month. Of course, no mouse can give birth to half an offspring, and no individual can die one-tenth of a death. But these rates tell us the per capita birth and death rates *averaged over all mice in the population*. Per capita birth and death rates are always expressed over a specified time period. For long-lived organisms, such as humans, time is measured in years. For short-lived organisms, such as fruit flies, time is measured in days. We can calculate per capita birth and death rates from data in a life table.

Now we can revise the population growth equation to use per capita birth and death rates instead of the actual numbers of births and deaths. The change in a population's size during a given time period ($\Delta N/\Delta t$) depends on the per capita birth and death rates, as well as on the number of individuals in the population. Mathematically, we can write

$$\Delta N/\Delta t = B - D = bN - dN = (b - d)N$$

or, in the notation of calculus,

$$dN/dt = (b - d)N.$$

This equation describes the **exponential model of population growth.** (Note that in calculus, dN/dt is the notation for the population growth rate. The d in dN/dt is *not* the same d we use to symbolize the per capita death rate.)

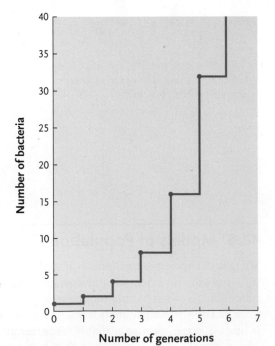

Figure 44.7

Bacterial population growth. If all members of a bacterial population divide simultaneously, a plot of population size over time forms a stair-stepped curve in which the steps get larger as the number of dividing cells increases.

The difference between the per capita birth rate and the per capita death rate, $b - d$, is the **per capita growth rate** of the population, symbolized by r. Like b and d, r is always expressed per individual per unit time. Using the per capita growth rate, r, in place of $b - d$, the exponential growth equation is written

$$dN/dt = rN.$$

If the birth rate exceeds the death rate, r has a positive value ($r > 0$), and the population is growing. In our example with field mice, r is 0.5 − 0.1 = 0.4 mice per mouse per month. If, on the other hand, the birth rate is lower than the death rate, r has a negative value ($r < 0$), and the population is shrinking. In populations in which the birth rate equals the death rate, r is zero, and the population's size is not changing—a situation known as **zero population growth**, or ZPG. Even under ZPG, births and deaths still occur, but the numbers of births and deaths cancel each other out.

Populations will grow as long as the per capita growth rate is positive ($r > 0$). In our hypothetical population of field mice, we started with $N = 2000$ mice and calculated a per capita growth rate of 0.4 mice per individual per month. In the first month, the population grows by 0.4 × 2000 = 800 mice **(Figure 44.8).** At the start of the second month, $N = 2800$ and r is still 0.4. Thus, in the second month, the population grows by 0.4 × 2800 = 1120 mice. Notice that even though r remains constant, the *increase* in population size grows each month because more individuals are reproducing. In less than two years, the mouse population will increase to more than one million! A graph of exponential population growth has a characteristic J shape, getting steeper through time. The population grows at an ever-increasing pace because the change in a population's size depends on the number of individuals in the population and its per capita growth rate.

Imagine a hypothetical population living in an ideal environment with unlimited food and shelter; no predators, parasites, or disease; and a comfortable abiotic environment. Under such circumstances (admittedly unrealistic), the per capita birth rate is very high, the per capita death rate is very low, and the per capita growth rate, r, is as high as it can be. This maximum per capita growth rate, symbolized r_{max}, is the population's **intrinsic rate of increase.** Under these ideal conditions, our exponential growth equation is

$$dN/dt = r_{max}N.$$

When populations grow at their intrinsic rate of increase, population size increases very rapidly. Across a wide variety of protists and animals, r_{max} varies inversely with generation time: species with a short generation time have higher intrinsic rates of increase than those with a long generation time **(Figure 44.9, p. 1120).**

The exponential model predicts unlimited population growth. But we know from even casual observations that population sizes of most species are somehow limited. We are not knee-deep in bacteria, rosebushes, or garter snakes. What factors limit the growth of populations? As a population gets larger, it uses more vital resources, perhaps leading to a shortage of resources. In this situation, individuals may have less energy available for maintenance and reproduction, causing decreases in per capita birth rates and increases in per capita death rates. Energy in food is not always equally available, and when an animal spends time handling food to eat it, the ratio of cost (handling) to benefit (energy in the food) diminishes, affecting return on investment. Such rate changes can affect a population's per capita growth rate, causing population growth to slow or stop.

Month	Old Population Size		Net Monthly Increase		New Population Size
1	2000	+	800	=	2800
2	2800	+	1120	=	3920
3	3920	+	1568	=	5488
4	5488	+	2195	=	7683
5	7683	+	3073	=	10 756
6	10 756	+	4302	=	15 058
7	15 058	+	6023	=	21 081
8	21 081	+	8432	=	29 513
9	29 513	+	11 805	=	41 318
10	41 318	+	16 527	=	57 845
11	57 845	+	23 138	=	80 983
12	80 983	+	32 393	=	113 376
13	113 376	+	45 350	=	158 726
14	158 726	+	63 490	=	222 216
15	222 216	+	88 887	=	311 103
16	311 103	+	124 441	=	435 544
17	435 544	+	174 218	=	609 762
18	609 762	+	243 905	=	853 667
19	853 677	+	341 467	=	1 195 134

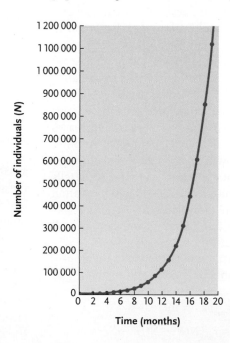

Figure 44.8

Exponential population growth. Exponential population growth produces a J-shaped curve when population size is plotted against time. Although the per capita growth rate (r) remains constant, the increase in population size gets larger every month because more individuals are reproducing.

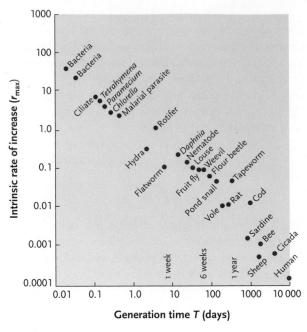

Figure 44.9

Generation time and r_{max}. The intrinsic rate of increase (r_{max}) is high for protists and animals with short generation times and low for those with long generation times.

44.5b Logistic Models: Populations and Carrying Capacity (K)

Environments provide enough resources to sustain only a finite population of any species. The maximum number of individuals that an environment can support indefinitely is termed its **carrying capacity**, symbolized as *K*. *K* is defined for each population. It is a property of the environment that can vary from one habitat to another and in a single habitat over time. The spring and summer flush of insects in temperate habitats supports large populations of insectivorous birds. But fewer insects are available in autumn and winter, causing a seasonal decline in *K* for birds, so autumnal migrations occur in birds seeking more food and less inclement weather. Other cycles are annual, such as variation in water levels in wetlands from year to year.

The **logistic model of population growth** assumes that a population's per capita growth rate, *r*, decreases as the population gets larger **(Figure 44.10)**. In other words, population growth slows as the population size approaches *K*. The mathematical expression *K* − *N* tells us how many individuals can be added to a population before it reaches *K*. The expression (K − N)/K indicates what percentage of the carrying capacity is still available.

To create the logistic model, we factor the impact of *K* into the exponential model by multiplying r_{max} by (K − N)/K to reduce the per capita growth rate (*r*) from its maximum value (r_{max}) as *N* increases:

$$dN/dt = r_{max}N(K - N)/K.$$

a. The predicted effect of *N* on *r*

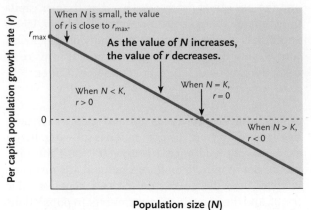

b. Population size through time

Figure 44.10

The logistic model of population growth. The logistic model **(a)** assumes that the per capita population growth rate (*r*) decreases linearly as population size (*N*) increases. The logistic model also predicts that population size **(b)** increases quickly at first but then slowly approaches carrying capacity (*K*).

The calculation of how *r* varies with population size is straightforward **(Table 44.2)**. In a very small population (*N* much smaller than *K*), plenty of resources are available; the value of (K − N)/K is close to 1. Here the per capita growth rate (*r*) approaches the maximum possible (r_{max}). Under these conditions, population growth is close to exponential. If a population is large (*N* close to *K*), few additional resources are available. Now the value of (K − N)/K is small, and the per capita growth rate (*r*) is very low. When the size of the population exactly equals *K*, (K − N)/K becomes 0, as does the population growth rate, the situation defined as ZPG.

The logistic model of population growth predicts an S-shaped graph of population size over time, with the population slowly approaching *K* and remaining at that level **(Figure 44.11)**. According to this model, the population grows slowly when the population size is small because few individuals are reproducing. It also grows slowly when the population size is large because the per capita population growth rate is low. The population grows quickly (*dN*/*dt* is highest) at intermediate population sizes, when a sizable number of individuals are breeding and the per capita population growth rate (*r*) is still fairly high (see Table 44.2).

The logistic model assumes that vital resources become increasingly limited as a population grows. Thus, the model is a mathematical portrait of **intraspecific** (within species) **competition,** the dependence of two or more individuals in a population on the same limiting resource. For mobile animals, limiting resources could be food, water, nesting sites, and refuges from predators. For sessile species, space can be a limiting resource. For plants, sunlight, water, inorganic nutrients, and growing space can be limiting. The pattern of uniform dispersion described earlier often reflects intraspecific competition for limited resources.

In some very dense populations, accumulation of poisonous waste products may reduce survivorship and reproduction. Most natural populations live in open systems where wastes are consumed by other organisms or flushed away. But the buildup of toxic wastes is common in laboratory cultures of microorganisms. For example, yeast cells ferment sugar and produce ethanol as a waste product. Thus, the alcohol content of wine usually does not exceed 13% by volume, the ethanol concentration that poisons yeasts that are vital to the wine-making process.

How well do species conform to the predictions of the logistic model? In simple laboratory cultures, relatively small organisms, such as *Paramecium,* some crustaceans, and flour beetles, often show an S-shaped pattern of population growth (Figure 44.11 left, middle). Moreover, large animals introduced into new environments sometimes exhibit a pattern of population growth that matches the predictions of the logistic model (Figure 44.11 right).

Nevertheless, some assumptions of the logistic model are unrealistic. For example, the model

| Table 44.2 | The Effect of N on r and ΔN^* in a Hypothetical Population Exhibiting Logistic Growth in which K equals 2000 and r_{max} is 0.04 per capita per year |

N (population size)	$(K - N)/K$ (% of K available)	$r = r_{max}(K - N/K)$ (per capita growth rate)	$\Delta N = rN$ (change in N)
50	0.975	0.0390	2
100	0.950	0.0380	4
250	0.875	0.0350	9
500	0.750	0.0300	15
750	0.625	0.0250	19
1000	0.500	0.0200	20
1250	0.375	0.0150	19
1500	0.250	0.0100	15
1750	0.125	0.0050	9
1900	0.050	0.0020	4
1950	0.025	0.0010	2
2000	0.000	0.0000	0

*ΔN rounded to the nearest whole number.

predicts that survivorship and fecundity respond immediately to changes in a population's density. Many organisms exhibit a delayed response (a **time lag**) because fecundity has been determined by resource availability at some time in the past. This may reflect conditions that prevailed when individuals were adding yolk to eggs or endosperm to seeds. Moreover, when food resources become scarce, individuals may use stored energy reserves to survive and reproduce. This delays the impact of crowding

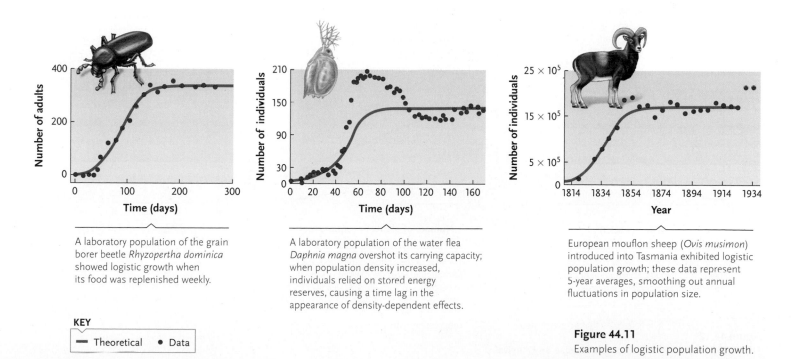

A laboratory population of the grain borer beetle *Rhyzopertha dominica* showed logistic growth when its food was replenished weekly.

A laboratory population of the water flea *Daphnia magna* overshot its carrying capacity; when population density increased, individuals relied on stored energy reserves, causing a time lag in the appearance of density-dependent effects.

European mouflon sheep (*Ovis musimon*) introduced into Tasmania exhibited logistic population growth; these data represent 5-year averages, smoothing out annual fluctuations in population size.

KEY

— Theoretical   • Data

Figure 44.11
Examples of logistic population growth.

until stored reserves are depleted and means that population size may overshoot *K* (see Figure 44.11 middle, p. 1121). Deaths may then outnumber births, causing the population size to drop below *K*, at least temporarily. Time lags often cause a population to oscillate around *K*.

The assumption that the addition of new individuals to a population always decreases survivorship and fecundity is unrealistic. In small populations, modest population growth may not have much impact on survivorship and fecundity. In fact, most organisms probably require a minimum population density to survive and reproduce. Some plants flourish in small clumps that buffer them from physical stresses, whereas a single individual living in the open would suffer adverse effects. In some animal populations, a minimum population density is necessary for individuals to find mates. Determining the minimum viable population for a species is an important issue in conservation biology (see Chapter 47).

STUDY BREAK

1. When do you use an exponential model rather than a logistic one?
2. Define the terms in the equation $dN/dt = (b - d)N$.
3. What does it mean when $r < 0$, $r > 0$, or $r = 0$? What is r_{max}, and how does it vary with generation time?

44.6 Population Regulation

What environmental factors influence population growth rates and control fluctuations in population size? Some factors affecting population size are **density dependent** because their influence increases or decreases with the density of the population. Intraspecific competition and predation are examples of density-dependent environmental factors. The logistic model includes the effects of density dependence in its assumption that per capita birth and death rates change with population density.

Numerous laboratory and field studies have shown that crowding (high population density) decreases individual growth rate, adult size, and survival of plants and animals **(Figure 44.12)**. Organisms living in extremely dense populations are unable to harvest enough resources. They grow slowly and tend to be small, weak, and less likely to survive. Gardeners understand this relationship and thin their plants to achieve a density that maximizes the number of vigorous individuals that survive to be harvested.

Crowding has a negative effect on reproduction **(Figure 44.13)**. When resources are in short supply, each individual has less energy for reproduction after meeting its basic maintenance needs. Hence, females in crowded populations produce either fewer offspring or smaller offspring that are less likely to survive.

In some species, crowding stimulates developmental and behavioural changes that may influence the density of a population. Migratory locusts can

Tadpoles of the frog *Rana tigrina* grew faster and reached larger adult body size at low densities than at high densities.

The size of the annual dune grass *Vulpia fasciculata* decreased markedly when plants were grown at high density. Density effects became more accentuated through time as the plants grew larger (indicated by the progressively steeper slopes of the lines).

The water flea *Daphnia pulex* had higher survivorship at a density of 8/mL than at densities of 16/mL or 32/mL.

Figure 44.12
Effects of crowding on individual growth, size, and survival.

The number of seeds produced by shepherd's purse (*Capsella bursa-pastoris*) decreased dramatically with increasing density in experimental plots.

The mean number of eggs produced by the Great Tit (*Parus major*), a woodland bird, declined as the number of breeding pairs in Marley Wood increased.

Figure 44.13

Effects of crowding on fecundity.

develop into either solitary or migratory forms in the same population. Migratory individuals have longer wings and more body fat, characteristics that allow long-distance dispersal. High population density increases the frequency of the migratory form. Thus, many locusts move away from the area of high density **(Figure 44.14)**, reducing the size and thus the density of the original population.

Although these data about locusts confirm the assumptions of the logistic equation, they do not prove that natural populations are regulated by density-dependent factors. Experimental evidence is necessary to provide a convincing demonstration that an increase in population density causes population size to decrease, whereas a decrease in density causes it to increase.

In the 1960s, Robert Eisenberg experimentally increased the numbers of aquatic snails (*Lymnaea elodes*) in some ponds, decreased them in others, and maintained natural densities in control ponds. Adult survivorship did not differ between experimental and control treatments. But there was a gradient in egg production from few eggs (snails in high-density ponds), to more (control density), to most (control density). Furthermore, survival rates of young snails

Figure 44.14

A swarm of locusts. Migratory locusts (*Locusta migratoria*) moving across an African landscape can devour their own weight in plant material every day.

declined as density increased. After four months, densities in the two experimental groups converged on those in the control, providing strong evidence of density-dependent population regulation.

At this stage, intraspecific competition appears to be the primary density-dependent factor regulating population size. Competition between populations of different species can also exert density-dependent effects on population growth (see Chapter 45).

But predation can also cause density-dependent population regulation. As a particular prey species becomes more numerous, predators may consume more of it because it is easier to find and catch. Once a prey species exceeds some threshold density, predators may consume a larger percentage of its population, a density-dependent effect. On rocky shores in California, sea stars feed mainly on the most abundant invertebrate there. When one prey species becomes common, predators feed on it disproportionately, drastically reducing its numbers. Then they switch to now more abundant alternative prey.

Sometimes several density-dependent factors influence a population at the same time. On small islands in the West Indies, spiders are rare wherever lizards (*Ameiva festiva, Anolis carolinensis,* and *Anolis sagrei*) are abundant but common where the lizards are rare or absent. To test whether the presence of lizards limits the abundance of spiders, David Spiller and Tom Schoener built fences around plots on islands where these species occur. They eliminated lizards from experimental plots but left them in control plots. After two years, spider populations in some experimental plots were five times as dense as those in control plots, suggesting a strong impact of lizard populations on spider populations **(Figure 44.15, p. 1124)**. In this situation, lizards had two density-dependent effects on spider populations. First, lizards ate spiders, and, second, they competed with them for food. Experimental evidence made it possible for biologists to better understand the situation.

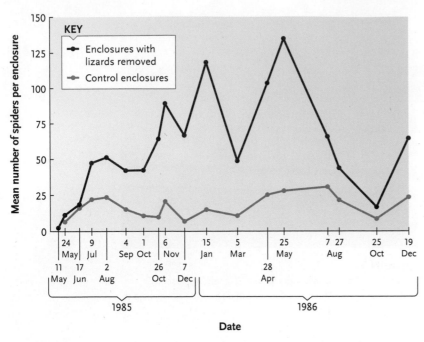

Figure 44.15
Populations of spiders (*Metepeira daytona*) on a small island in the Bahamas are influenced by the presence of lizards. Note how much higher the population densities of spiders are in the absence than in the presence of lizards.

Predation, parasitism, and disease can cause density-dependent regulation of plant and animal populations. Infectious microorganisms (e.g., rabies) spread quickly in a crowded population. In addition, if crowded individuals are weak or malnourished, they are more susceptible to infection and may die from diseases that healthy organisms would survive. Effects on survival can be direct or indirect.

44.6a Density-Independent Factors: Reducing Population in Spite of Density

Some populations are affected by **density-independent** factors that reduce population size regardless of its density. If an insect population is not physiologically adapted to high temperature, a sudden hot spell may kill 80% of them whether they number 100 or 100 000. Fires, earthquakes, storms, and other natural disturbances can contribute directly or indirectly to density-independent mortality. Because such factors do not cause a population to fluctuate around its *K*, these density-independent factors can reduce but do not **regulate** population size.

Density-independent factors have a particularly strong effect on populations of small-bodied species that cannot buffer themselves against environmental change. Their populations grow exponentially for a time, but shifts in climate or random events cause high mortality before populations reach a size at which density-dependent factors would regulate their numbers. When conditions improve, populations grow exponentially, at least until another density-independent factor causes them to crash again. A small Australian insect, a thrip (*Thrips imaginis*), eats the pollen and flowers of plants in the rose family. These thrips can be abundant enough to damage blooms. Populations of thrips grow exponentially in spring, when many flowers are available and the weather is warm and moist **(Figure 44.16)**. But their populations crash predictably during summer because thrips do not tolerate hot and dry conditions. After the crash, a few individuals survive in remaining flowers, and they are the stock from which the population grows exponentially the following spring.

44.6b Interactions between Density-Dependent and Density-Independent Factors: Sometimes Population Density Affects Mortality

Density-dependent factors can interact with density-independent factors and limit population growth. Food shortage caused by high population density (a density-dependent factor) may lead to malnourishment. Malnourished individuals may be more likely to succumb to the stress of extreme weather (a density-independent factor).

Populations can be affected by density-independent factors in a density-dependent manner. Some animals retreat into shelters to escape environmental stresses, such as floods or severe heat. If a population is small, most individuals can be accommodated in available refuges. But if a population is large (exceeds the capacity of shelters), only a proportion will find suitable shelter. The larger the population, the greater the percentage of individuals exposed to the stress(es). Thus, although the density-independent effects of weather limit populations of thrips, the availability of flowers in summer (a density-dependent factor) regulates the size of the starting populations of thrips the following spring. Hence, both density-dependent and density-independent factors influence the size of populations of thrips.

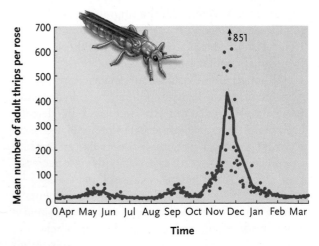

Figure 44.16
Booms and busts in a thrips population. Populations of the Australian insect *Thrips imaginis* grow exponentially when conditions are favourable during spring (which begins in September in the southern hemisphere). But the populations crash in summer when hot and dry conditions cause high mortality.

44.6c Life History Characteristics: Evolution of Strategies for Population Growth

Even casual observation reveals tremendous variation in how rapidly population sizes change in different species. New weeds often appear in a vegetable garden overnight, whereas the number of oak trees in a forest may remain relatively stable for years. Why do only some species have the potential for explosive population growth? The answer lies in how natural selection has moulded life history strategies adapted to different ecological conditions. Some ecologists recognize two quite different life history patterns, **r-selected** species and **K-selected** species **(Table 44.3; Figure 44.17)**.

On the face of it, *r*-selected species are adapted to rapidly changing environments, and many have at least some of the features outlined in Table 44.3. The success of an *r*-selected life history depends on flooding the environment with a *large quantity* of young because only some may be successful. Small body size means that compared with larger-bodied species, *r*-selected species lack physiological mechanisms to buffer them from environmental variation. Populations of *r*-selected species can be so reduced by changes in abiotic environmental factors (e.g., temperature or moisture) that they never grow large enough to reach *K* and face a shortage of limiting resources. In these cases, *K* cannot be estimated by researchers, and changes in population size are not accurately described by the logistic model of population growth. Although *r*-selected species appear to have poor tolerance of environmental change, they are said to be adapted to rapidly changing environments.

At the same time, *K*-selected species have at least some of the features outlined for them in Table 44.3. These organisms survive the early stages of life (type I or type II survivorship), and a low r_{max} means that their populations grow slowly. The success of a *K*-selected life history is linked to the production of a relatively small number of **high-quality** offspring that join an already well-established population. Generalizations about *r*-selected and *K*-selected species are misleading. We can recognize this by comparing two species of mammals.

Peromyscus maniculatus, deer mice, occur widely in North America. In southern Ontario, adults weigh 12 to 31 g, females produce average litters of four (range two to eight), and each can have four or five litters a year. Females become sexually mature at age two months and breed in their first year. Occasionally, deer mice live to age three years in the wild. Throughout their extensive range in North America, *Myotis lucifugus,* little brown bats, weigh 7 to 12 g; females bear a single young per litter and have one litter per year. Females may breed a year after they are born, but many may wait until they are two years old. In the wild, little brown bats can live over 30 years. Using these data, one small mammal (deer mouse) is an *r*-strategist, whereas another (little brown bat) is a *K*-strategist. To complicate matters, deer mice living in Kananaskis in the mountains near Calgary, Alberta, mature at one year and may have two litters per year, typically five young per litter. Compared to little brown bats, Kananaskis deer mice are *r*-strategists. Compared with Ontario deer mice, they are more like *K*-strategists.

Biologists may find the idea of *r*-strategists and *K*-strategists useful, but too often the idea means imposing some human view of the world on a natural system. *K*-strategists and *r*-strategists may be more like beauty, defined by the eye of the beholder. Elephants (*Loxodonta africana, Loxodonta cyclotis, Elephas maximus*) are big and meet all *K*-strategist criteria. Many insects are small but in all other respects meet the criteria considered typical of *K*-strategists because of their patterns of reproduction. Codfish (*Gadus morhua*) are big (compared to insects or bats) but meet most of the criteria used to identify *r*-strategists, such as their patterns of reproduction.

Table 44.3	Characteristics of *r*-Selected and *K*-Selected Species	
Characteristic	**r-Selected Species**	**K-Selected Species**
Maturation time	Short	Long
Life span	Short	Long
Mortality rate	Usually high	Usually low
Reproductive episodes	Usually one	Usually several
Time of first reproduction	Early	Late
Clutch or brood size	Usually large	Usually small
Size of offspring	Small	Large
Active parental care	Little or none	Often extensive
Population size	Fluctuating	Relatively stable
Tolerance of environmental change	Generally poor	Generally good

a. An r-selected species

b. A K-selected species

Figure 44.17

Life history differences. An *r*-selected species, **(a)** *Chenopodium quinoa*, matures in one growing season and produces many tiny seeds. Quinoa was a traditional food staple for indigenous people of North and South America. A *K*-selected species, **(b)** *Cocos nucifera*, a coconut palm, grows slowly and produces a few large seeds repeatedly during its long life.

44.6d Population Cycles: Ups and Downs in Numbers of Individuals

Population densities of many insects, birds, and mammals in the northern hemisphere fluctuate between species-specific lows and highs in a multiyear cycle. Arctic populations of small rodents (*Lemmus lemmus*) vary in size over a 4-year cycle, whereas snowshoe hares (*Lepus americanus*), ruffed grouse (*Bonasa umbellus*), and lynx have 10-year cycles. Ecologists documented these cyclic fluctuations more than a century ago, but none of the general hypotheses proposed to date explain cycles in all species. Availability and quality of food, abundance of predators, prevalence of disease-causing microorganisms, and variations in weather can influence population growth and declines. Furthermore, food supply and predators for a cycling population are themselves influenced by a population's size.

Theories of **intrinsic control** suggest that as an animal population grows, individuals undergo hormonal changes that increase aggressiveness, reduce reproduction, and foster dispersal. The dispersal phase of the cycle may be dramatic. When populations of Norway lemming (*Lemmus lemmus*), a rodent that lives in the Scandinavian Arctic, reach their peak density, aggressive interactions drive younger and weaker individuals to disperse. The dispersal of many thousands of lemmings during periods of population growth has sometimes been incorrectly portrayed in nature films as a suicidal mass migration.

Other explanations focus on extrinsic control, such as the relationship between a cycling species and its food or predators. A dense population may exhaust its food supply, increasing mortality and decreasing reproduction. The die-off of large numbers of African elephants in Tsavo National Park in Kenya is an example of the impact of overpopulation. There elephants overgrazed vegetation in most of the park habitat. In 1970, the combination of overgrazing and a drought caused high mortality of elephants. The picture is not always clear because experimental food supplementation does not always prevent decline in mammal populations. This suggests some level of intrinsic control.

Cycles in populations of predators could be induced by time lags between populations of predators and prey and vice versa **(Figure 44.18).** The 10-year cycles of snowshoe hares and their feline predators, Canada lynx, were often cited as a classic example of such an interaction. But snowshoe hare populations

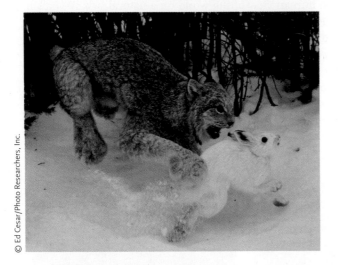

© Ed Cesar/Photo Researchers, Inc.

Figure 44.18

The predator–prey model. Predator–prey interactions may contribute to density-dependent regulation of both populations. A mathematical model **(a)** predicts cycles in the numbers of predators and prey because of time lags in each species' responses to changes in the density of the other. (Predator population size is exaggerated in this graph.) **(b)** Canada lynx (*Lynx canadensis*) and snowshoe hare (*Lepus americanus*) were often described as a typical cyclic predator–prey interaction. The abundances of lynx (red line) and snowshoe hare (blue line) are based on counts of pelts trappers sold to the Hudson's Bay Company over a 90-year period. Recent research shows that population cycles in snowshoe hares are caused by complex interactions between the snowshoe hares, its food plants, and its predators.

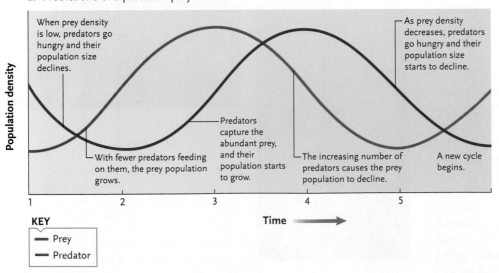

a. Predictions of a predator–prey model

When prey density is low, predators go hungry and their population size declines.

With fewer predators feeding on them, the prey population grows.

Predators capture the abundant prey, and their population starts to grow.

The increasing number of predators causes the prey population to decline.

As prey density decreases, predators go hungry and their population size starts to decline.

A new cycle begins.

Population density

Time

KEY
— Prey
— Predator

b. Lynx and hare population sizes through time

Number of hare pelts taken (× 1000)

Number of lynx pelts taken (× 1000)

Time (years)

KEY
— Hare
— Lynx

can exhibit a 10-year fluctuation even on islands where lynx are absent. Thus, lynx are not solely responsible for population cycles in snowshoe hares. To further complicate matters, the database demonstrating fluctuations was often the numbers of pelts purchased by the Hudson's Bay Company. Here, fur price influenced the trapping effort and the numbers of animals harvested. This economic reality brought into question the relationship between the numbers of pelts and actual population densities of lynx and snowshoe hares.

Charles Krebs and his colleagues studied hare and lynx interactions with a large-scale, multiyear experiment in Kluane in the southern Yukon. Using fenced experimental areas, they could add food for snowshoe hares, exclude mammalian predators, or apply both experimental treatments while monitoring unmanipulated control plots. When mammalian predators were excluded, densities of snowshoe hares approximately doubled relative to controls. Where food was added, densities of snowshoe hares tripled relative to controls. In plots where food was added and predators were excluded, densities of snowshoe hares increased 11-fold compared with controls. Krebs and his colleagues concluded that neither food availability nor predation is solely responsible for population cycles in snowshoe hares. They postulated that complex interactions between snowshoe hares, their food plants, and their predators generate cyclic fluctuations in populations of snowshoe hares.

STUDY BREAK

1. What are density-dependent factors? Why do dense populations tend to decrease in size?
2. Define density-independent factors and give some examples.
3. Describe two key differences between *r*-selected species and *K*-selected species.

44.7 Human Population Growth

How do human populations compare with those of other species? The worldwide human population was expected to pass 7 billion by the end of 2011. Like many other species, humans live in somewhat isolated populations that vary in their demographic traits and access to resources. Although many of us live comfortably, at least a billion people are malnourished or starving, lack access to clean drinking water, and live without adequate shelter or health care.

For most of human history, our population grew slowly, reflecting the impact of a range of restraints. Over the past two centuries, the worldwide human population has grown exponentially **(Figure 44.19)**. Demographers identified three ways in which we have avoided the effects of density-dependent regulating factors.

First, humans have expanded their geographic range into virtually every terrestrial habitat, alleviating competition for space. Our early ancestors lived in tropical and subtropical grasslands, but by 40 000 years ago, they had dispersed through much of the world. Their success resulted from their ability to solve ecological problems by building fires, assembling shelters, making clothing and tools, planning community hunts, and sharing information. Vital survival skills spread from generation to generation and from one population to another because language allowed communication of complex ideas and knowledge.

Second, we have increased *K* in habitats we occupy, isolating us, as a species, from restrictions associated with access to resources. This change began to occur about 11 000 years ago, when populations in different parts of the world began to shift from hunting and gathering to agriculture (see Chapter 48). At that time, our ancestors cultivated wild grasses and other

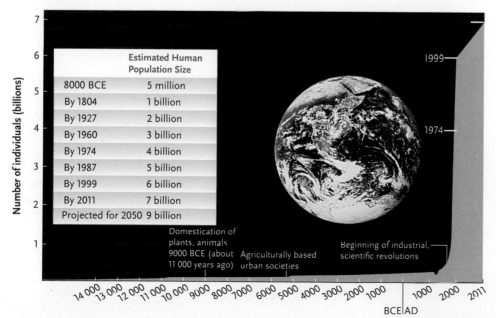

Figure 44.19

Human population growth. The worldwide human population grew slowly until 200 years ago, when it began to increase explosively. The dip in the mid-fourteenth century represents the death of 60 million Asians and Europeans from the bubonic plague. The table shows how long it took for the human population to add each billion people. (Photo: NASA.)

Estimated Human Population Size	
8000 BCE	5 million
By 1804	1 billion
By 1927	2 billion
By 1960	3 billion
By 1974	4 billion
By 1987	5 billion
By 1999	6 billion
By 2011	7 billion
Projected for 2050	9 billion

plants, diverted water to irrigate crops, and used domesticated animals for food and labour. Innovations such as these increased the availability of food, raising both K and rates of population growth. In the mid-eighteenth century, people harnessed the energy in fossil fuels, and industrialization began in Western Europe and North America. Food supplies and K increased again, at least in industrialized countries, largely through the use of synthetic fertilizers, pesticides, and efficient methods of transportation and food distribution.

Third, advances in public health reduced the effects of critical population-limiting factors such as malnutrition, contagious diseases, and poor hygiene. Over the past 300 years, modern plumbing and sewage treatment, removal of garbage, and improvements in food handling and processing, as well as medical discoveries, have reduced death rates sharply. Births now greatly exceed deaths, especially in less industrialized countries, resulting in rapid population growth. Note, however, that problems of hygiene and access to fresh water and food had been solved in some societies at least hundreds of years ago. Rome, for example, had a population of about 1 million people by 2 CE, and this was supported by an excellent infrastructure for importing and distributing food, providing fresh water, and dealing with human wastes.

44.7a Age Structure and Economic Growth: Phases of Development

Where have our migrations and technological developments taken us? It took about 2.5 million years for the human population to reach 1 billion, 80 years to reach the second billion, and only 12 years to jump from 5 billion to 6 billion and another 12 years to reach 7 billion (see the inset table in Figure 44.19, p. 1127). Rapid population growth now appears to be an inevitable consequence of our demographic structure and economic development.

44.7b Population Growth and Age Structure: Not All Populations Are the Same

In 2011, the worldwide annual growth rate for the human population averaged about 1.15% ($r = 0.0115$ new individuals per individual per year). Population experts expect that rate to decline, but even so, the human population will probably exceed 9 billion before 2050.

In 2000, population growth rates of individual nations varied widely, ranging from much less than 1% to more than 3% **(Figure 44.20a)**. Industrialized countries of Western Europe have achieved nearly ZPG, but other countries, particularly those in Africa, Latin America, and Asia, will experience huge increases over the next 20 or 25 years **(Figure 44.20b)**.

For all long-lived species, differences in age structure are a major determinant of differences in population growth rates **(Figure 44.21)**. There are three basic patterns in the graphs in Figure 44.21. In the first, in countries with ZPG, there are approximately equal numbers of people of reproductive and prereproductive ages. The ZPG situation is exacerbated when reproductives have very few offspring, meaning that prereproductives may not even replace themselves in the population. Second, in countries with negative growth (without immigration), postreproductives outnumber reproductives, and these populations will not experience a growth spurt when today's children reach

a. Mean annual population growth rates

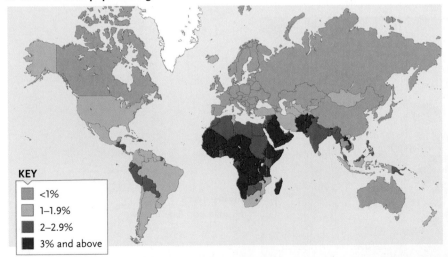

KEY
- <1%
- 1–1.9%
- 2–2.9%
- 3% and above

b. Projected population sizes for 2025

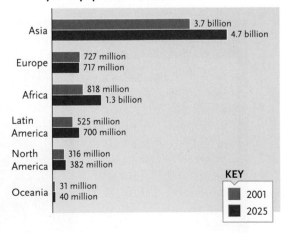

Asia — 3.7 billion / 4.7 billion
Europe — 727 million / 717 million
Africa — 818 million / 1.3 billion
Latin America — 525 million / 700 million
North America — 316 million / 382 million
Oceania — 31 million / 40 million

KEY
- 2001
- 2025

Figure 44.20

Local variation in human population growth rates. In 2001, **(a)** average annual population growth rates varied among countries and continents. In some regions **(b),** the population is projected to increase greatly by 2025 (red) compared with the population size in 2001 (orange). The population of Europe is likely to decline.

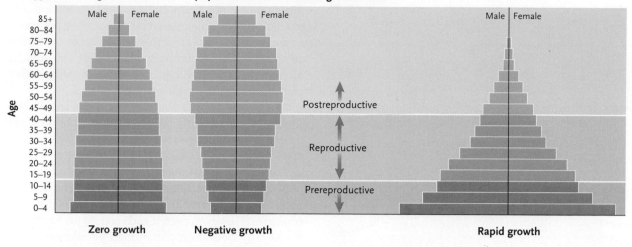

a. Hypothetical age distributions for populations with different growth rates

Zero growth   Negative growth   Rapid growth

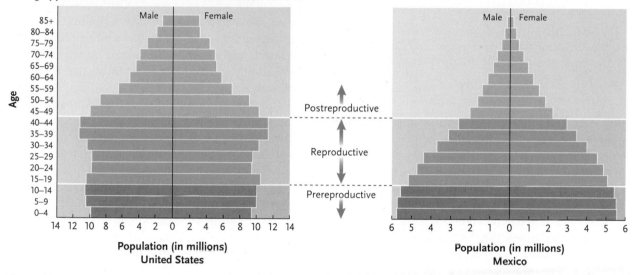

b. Age pyramids for the United States and Mexico in 2000

Population (in millions)
United States

Population (in millions)
Mexico

Figure 44.21

Age structure diagrams. Age structure diagrams **(a)** differ for countries with zero, negative, and rapid population growth rates. The width of each bar represents the proportion of the population in each age class. Age structure diagrams for the United States and Mexico **(b)** in 2000 (measured in millions of people) suggest that these countries will experience different growth rates.

reproductive age. Third are countries where reproductives vastly outnumber postreproductives.

Countries with rapid growth have a broad-based age structure (pattern three, above), with many youngsters born during the previous 15 years. Worldwide, more than one-third of the human population falls within this prereproductive base. This age class will soon reach sexual maturity. Even if each woman produces only two offspring, populations will continue to grow rapidly because so many individuals are reproducing. This situation can be described as a *population bomb*.

The age structures of the United States and Mexico differ, which has consequences for population growth in the two jurisdictions. Remember the potential importance of immigration and emigration when considering the longer-term impact of the population bomb.

44.7c Population Growth and Economic Development: Interconnections

The relationship between a country's population growth and its economic development can be depicted by the **demographic transition model (Figure 44.22, p. 1130).** This model describes historical changes in demographic patterns in the industrialized countries of Western Europe. Today, we do not know if it accurately predicts the future for developing nations.

According to this model, during a country's **preindustrial** stage, birth and death rates are high, and the population grows slowly. Industrialization begins a *transitional* stage, when food production rises, and health care and sanitation improve. Death rates decline, resulting in increased rates of population growth. Later, as living conditions improve, birth rates decline, causing a drop in rates of population growth.

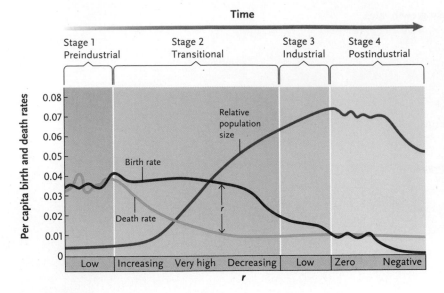

Figure 44.22

The demographic transition. The demographic transition model describes changes in the birth and death rates and relative population size as a country passes through four stages of economic development. The bottom bar describes the net population growth rate, *r*.

When the **industrial** stage is in full swing, population growth slows dramatically. Now people move from countryside to cities, and urban couples often choose to accumulate material goods instead of having large families. ZPG is reached in the *postindustrial* stage. Eventually, the birth rate falls below the death rate, *r* falls below zero, and population size begins to decrease.

Today, the United States, Canada, Australia, Japan, Russia, and most of Western Europe are in the industrial stage. Their growth rates are slowly decreasing. In Germany, Bulgaria, and Hungary (and other European countries), birth rates are lower than death rates, and populations are shrinking, indicating entry into the postindustrial stage. Kenya and other less industrialized countries are in the transitional stage, but they may not have enough skilled workers or enough capital to make the transition to an industrialized economy. For these reasons, many poorer nations may be stuck in the transitional stage. Developing countries experience rapid population increase because they experience declines in death rates associated with the transitional stage without the decreases in birth rates typical of industrial and postindustrial stages.

44.7d Controlling Reproductive Output: Planned Reproduction

Most governments realize that increased population size is now the major factor causing resource depletion, excessive pollution, and an overall decline in quality of life. The principles of population ecology demonstrate that slowing the rate of population growth and effecting an actual decline in population size can be achieved only by decreasing the birth rate or increasing the death rate. Increasing mortality is neither a rational nor a humane means of population control. Some governments use family planning programs in an attempt to lower birth rates. In other countries, any form of family planning is unlawful. This topic is discussed further in Chapter 47, where we will see that education of women is a vital undertaking.

To achieve ZPG, the average **replacement rate** should be just slightly higher than two children per couple. This is necessary because some female children die before reaching reproductive age. Today's replacement rate averages about 2.5 children in less industrialized countries with higher mortality rates in prereproductive cohorts and 2.1 in more industrialized countries. However, even if each couple on Earth produced only 2 children, the human population would continue to grow for at least another 60 years (the impact of the population bomb). Continued population growth is inevitable because today's children, who outnumber adults, will soon mature and reproduce. The worldwide population will stabilize only when the age distributions of all countries resemble that for countries with ZPG.

Family planning efforts encourage women to delay their first reproduction. Doing so reduces the average family size and slows population growth by increasing generation time (see Figure 44.9, p. 1120). Imagine two populations in which each woman produces two offspring. In the first population, women begin reproducing at age 32 years, and in the second, they begin reproducing at age 16 years. We can begin with a cohort of newborn baby girls in each population. After 32 years, women in the first population will be giving birth to their first offspring, but women in the second population will be new grandmothers. After 64 years, women in the first population will be new grandmothers, but women in the second population will witness the birth of their first great-great grandchildren (if their daughters also bear their first children at age 16 years). Obviously, the first population will grow much more slowly than the second.

44.7e The Future: Where Are We Going?

Homo sapiens has arrived at a turning point in our cultural evolution and in our ecological relationship with Earth. Hard decisions await us, and we must make them soon. All species face limits to their population growth, and it is naive to assume that our unique abilities exempt us from the laws of population growth. We have postponed the action of most factors that limit population growth, but no amount of invention and intervention can expand the ultimate limits set by resource depletion and a damaged environment. We now face two options for limiting human population growth: we can make a global effort to limit our population growth, or we can wait until the environment does it for us.

Jack Millar, a professor of biology at the University of Western Ontario in London, and his students study the life histories of small mammals such as mice, voles, and wood rats. They do most of this work in the field, mainly at sites in the Kananaskis Valley in southwestern Alberta. The work involves trapping the small mammals and marking them so that they can recognize them later. Recaptures of known individuals allow the researchers to track the performances of individuals. Millar and his students have been following populations of deer mice for over 20 years, and their records have allowed them to ask basic questions about life history.

Most deer mice born in any year in the Kananaskis Valley are dead by the end of September of that year. Although a few females are able to bear two litters in a year, most do not. Compared with deer mice living in southwestern Ontario (see Section 44.6c), the mice in Kananaskis are barely hanging on. But Millar and his students were interested to learn what factors limit age at first reproduction and the ability of a female to breed more than once a year. Female mice given protein-rich diets (cat food) were sometimes able to breed in their first summer, suggesting a strong influence of food quality on life history traits.

With data on deer mice covering a span of more than 20 years, Millar was able to explore the possible effects of climate change on deer mice living in the Kananaskis Valley. Specifically, between 1985 and 2003, female deer mice typically conceived their first litters on May 2, and the first births occurred on May 26. There were no statistically significant changes in the timing of first births, although the average temperatures in early May had declined by about 2°C during this period. Spring breeding of the deer mice was not related to temperatures or snowfall. The decline in temperature had no effect on the mice's reproductive success. Changes in photoperiod appear to be responsible for initiating reproductive activity in the mice. Their access to protein did affect their reproductive output.

Discoveries about diseases associated with wildlife are a side benefit of Millar's endeavours. The work that Millar and his students have done provided a different view of the role of beavers in the spread of giardiasis, also known as "beaver fever." Giardiasis is caused by infections of a protozoan species in the genus *Giardia*. Humans can be infected if they drink water containing spores or trophozoites of *Giardia* species. Humans with giardiasis suffer from intestinal distress. As the name beaver fever implies, these aquatic rodents have been presumed to be the source of human infections. Using specimens, some provided by Millar and his students, P.M. Wallis and colleagues determined that 20 of 21 red-backed voles (*Clethrionomys gapperi*) were infected by *Giardia* at a much higher rate of infection than any other small mammals and also higher than beavers (2 of 50 infected).

Millar's work has demonstrated how long-term experimental research involving both observations and experiments can shed light on life history strategies.

Return to Figure 44.19, p. 1127 and observe that only the Plague (also known as the Black Death) caused any deflection from the trajectory of the curve tracking growth in the human population. The Plague appears to have been spread into Europe by the Mongols. The Plague, long established in China, arrived in the Mongol summer capital of Shangdu in 1332. By 1351, the population of China had been reduced by 50 to 66%. By 1345, the Plague had reached Feodosija in Ukraine (then Kaffa). Between 1340 and 1400, it is estimated that the population of Africa declined from 80 million to 68 million and the world population from 450 million to between 350 million and 375 million. These data do not include the Americas because the Plague did not reach there until about 1600.

To put these percentages in context, consider human deaths associated with World War II. In this conflict, Great Britain lost less than 1% of its population, France about 1.5%, and Germany 9.1%. In Poland and Ukraine, where there was a postwar famine, 19% of the human populations there are said to have died.

These sobering figures remind us that we are animals, vulnerable to many of the factors that affect other species on Earth. Now, look back at the chapter-opening image and note the large numbers of gulls at a landfill site. The gulls and the landfill illustrate a fundamental point in population biology, namely, the ability of populations to reach large numbers and have large environmental impacts whether the species are gulls or people.

STUDY BREAK

1. In what three ways have humans avoided the effects of density-dependent regulation factors?
2. What is a population bomb?
3. What does family planning encourage women to do?

Progesterone

The advent of birth control pills **(Figure 1)** had a great impact on the behaviour of people. Women using birth control pills had more control over their fertility than others. Central to the development of an effective oral contraceptive was a change in the molecular structure of progesterone **(Figure 2a)**. Specifically, the addition of a CH$_3$ group **(Figure 2b)** meant that the new molecule, megestrol, had the same effect on a woman's reproductive system, but it was not quickly metabolized and remained in the system long enough to have the desired effect (suppressing ovulation). Similarly, slight modifications to the estradiol molecule turned it into ethinylestradiol **(Figure 3)**. Megestrol is an analogue of progesterone, and ethinylestradiol is an analogue of estradiol.

Today, biologists working in zoos use a variety of birth control methods to control the fertility of animals in their collections. For critically endangered species such as black-footed ferrets (see "Black-Footed Ferret, *Mustela nigripes*," Box 44.2, p. 1111), this means using information about cycles of fertility to maximize reproductive output.

For animals whose populations are growing at a rapid pace, birth control gives keepers the chance to control growth of the populations. The same principles apply to working with organisms in the wild, but getting African elephants to take their birth control pills has not proven to be easy.

Hormones and their analogues are common in untreated municipal wastewaters. In some cases, male fish exposed to these wastewaters are becoming feminized. Specifically, some male fish produce vitellogenin mRNA and protein, substances normally associated with the maturation of oocytes in females. Males thus exposed produce early-stage eggs in their testes. This feminization occurs in the presence of estrogenic substances, including natural estrogen (17b-estradiol) and the synthetic estrogen 17a-ethinylestradiol.

Do a few feminized male fish in the population matter? Karen A. Kidd and six colleagues conducted a seven-year whole-lake experiment in northwestern Ontario (the Experimental Lakes Area). Male fathead minnows (*Pimephales promelas*) **(Figure 4)** chronically exposed to low levels (5–6 ng·L^{-1}) of estrogenic substances showed feminizing effects and the development of intersex males, whereas females had altered oogenesis. The situation led to the near-extinction of fathead minnows in the experimental lake.

FIGURE 1
Birth control pills, a selection of products.

M.B. Fenton

a.

Progesterone

b.

Professor John Wiebe

CH$_3$

Megestrol

FIGURE 2
Progesterone and the synthetic megestrol.

Estradiol

a.

b.

Ethinylestradiol

Professor John Wiebe

FIGURE 3
Estradiol and the synthetic ethinylestradiol.

Konrad P. Schmidt

FIGURE 4
Pimphales promelas, the fathead minnow.

44.8 Sisyphean Problems in Population Biology

According to the myth, Sisyphus revealed a secret of Zeus, the supreme Greek god, so in Hades, Sisyphus faced a life of eternal frustration because the boulder he had to push up a hill always rolled back down. The equivalent of this situation is a recurring theme in population biology. For example, on many oceanic islands, eradication of rats and cats is a Sisyphean problem because when either introduced pest is at levels of high populations, it can be easy to kill them with a relatively small investment per cat or per rat. Control or, better still, eradication of cats and rats may reduce the threat to native species (see also Chapter 47). When their populations diminish, the effort and cost per kill increases. In difficult financial times, it may be easy to relent on control measures and use the funds elsewhere. But as soon as the pressure is removed from the populations of rats and cats, the numbers increase, starting the cycle anew.

Sisyphean problems also occur in disease control. The prevalence rates of malaria in children (ages 2 to 10 years) in Zanzibar illustrates this problem **(Figure 44.23)**. Zanzibar, an archipelago consisting of several islands off the east coast of Africa, has a population of 1.2 million people, compared to 678 million in Africa. Today the annual antimalarial efforts in Zanzibar prevent about 600 000 cases of and about 3300 deaths from malaria. The cost is about US$1183 per death averted and US$34.50 per impact of reducing the incidence of the disease.

The data on the prevalence of the malarial parasite in children demonstrate the importance of maintaining antimalarial programmes even in the face of success measured as fewer cases of malaria and fewer deaths from it. Arrival of people already infected with the malarial parasite in Zanzibar is part of the problem. The same situation applies to the control of measles, which, unlike malaria, can be controlled by vaccination.

Infestations of bedbugs are yet another Sisyphean problem. The population biology roots of such problems lie in the patterns of population growth: the impact of r (intrinsic rate of increase), N (population size), and K (carrying capacity). Perhaps Sisyphus's challenge was modest compared to that posed by some problems in population biology!

STUDY BREAK

1. Why is it appropriate to consider malaria control as a Sisyphean problem?
2. Why is the malaria situation different between Zanzibar and continental Africa?

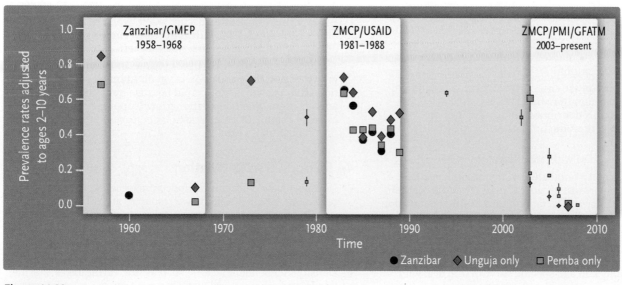

From Smith, D.L., J.M. Cohen, B. Moonen, A.J. Tatem, O.J. Sabot, F. Ali and S.M. Mugheiry. 2011. "Solving the Sisyphean problem of malaria in Zanzibar." *Science*, vol. 332: 1384–1385. Reprinted with permission from AAAS.

Figure 44.23

The incidence of malaria parasites in children between 1958 and 2010. During periods of concerted efforts to reduce or eliminate malaria, the incidence of parasites in children drops, only to rebound when control measures are stopped. Large symbols represent regional and national surveys; smaller symbols, smaller-scale surveys. GMEP was part of the Global Malaria Eradication Programme, ZMCP was the Zanzibar Malaria Control Programme assisted by USAID, and ZMCP/PMI/GFATM is the Zanzibar Malaria Control Programme assisted by the U.S. President's Malaria Initiative and the Global Fund to Fight AIDS, Tuberculosis, and Malaria. Here Zanzibar refers to all of the islands; Pemba and Unguja are specific islands included in the archipelago.

Review

Access an interactive eBook, chapter-specific interactive learning tools, including flashcards, quizzes, videos, and more in your Biology **CourseMate**, accessed through NelsonBrain.com **Aplia™** is an online interactive learning solution that helps you improve comprehension—and your grade—by integrating a variety of mediums and tools such as videos, tutorials, practice tests, and an interactive eBook.

44.1 The Science of Ecology

- Organismal ecology is the study of organisms to determine adaptations to the abiotic environment, including morphological, physiological, biochemical, behavioural, and genetic adaptations. Population ecologists document changes in size and other characteristics of populations of species over space and time. Community ecologists study sympatric populations, the interactions among them, and how these interactions affect the community's growth. Interactions may include predation and competition. Ecosystem ecologists study nutrient cycling and energy flow through the biotic and the abiotic environment.

- Mathematical models express hypotheses about ecological relationships and different variables, allowing researchers to manipulate the model and document resulting changes. In this way, researchers can simulate natural events before investing in lab work.

- Experimental and control treatments are necessary because they allow ecologists to separate cause and effect.

44.2 Population Characteristics

- Geographic range is the overall spatial boundary around a population. Individuals in the population often live in a specific habitat within the range.

- A lower population density means that individuals have greater access to resources such as sunlight and water. The capture–mark–recapture technique assumes that (1) a mark has no effect on an individual's survival, (2) marked and unmarked individuals mix randomly, (3) there is no migration throughout the estimation period, and (4) marked and unmarked individuals are equally likely to be caught.

- Three types of dispersion are clumped, uniform, and random. Clumped is most common in nature because suitable conditions are usually patchily distributed and animals often live in social groups. Asexual reproduction patterns can also lead to clumped aggregations.

- Generation time increases with body size.

- The number of males in a population of mammals has little impact on population growth because females bear the costs of reproduction (pregnancy and lactation), thus limiting population growth. Sea horses are different because males get pregnant.

44.3 Demography

- Age-specific mortality and age-specific survivorship deal with age intervals. In any one interval, age-specific mortality is the proportion of individuals that died during that time. Age-specific survivorship is the number surviving during the interval. The two values must sum to 1. For example, if age-specific survivorship is 0.616, then age-specific mortality is 1 – 0.616 or 0.384.

- Age-specific fecundity is the average number of offspring produced by surviving females during each age interval.

- In a type I curve, high survivorship at a young age decreases rapidly later in life. Type I curves are common for large animals, including humans. In a type II curve, the relationship is linear because there is a constant rate of mortality across the lifespan. Songbirds fit in this category. A type III curve shows high mortality at a young age that stabilizes as individuals grow older and larger. Insects fall into this category.

44.4 The Evolution of Life Histories

- Maintenance, growth, and reproduction are the three main energy-consuming processes.

- Passive care occurs in animals that simply lay eggs and leave them or, in mammals, as nutrients cross the placenta from the mother to the developing baby. Active care involves nursing and other care provided after birth.

- Salmon have a short lifespan and devote a great deal of energy to reproduction. Deciduous trees may reproduce more than once and use only some energy in any reproductive event, balancing reproduction and growth.

- Early reproduction is favoured if adult survival rates are low or if, when animals age, they do not increase in size. In this case, fecundity does not increase with size.

44.5 Models of Population Growth

- An exponential model is used when a population has unlimited growth.

- dN/dt = change in a population's size during a given time period; b = per capita birth rate; d = per capita death rate; N = number of individuals in the population; $b - d$ = per capita growth rate = r.

- When $r > 0$, the birth rate exceeds the death rate, and the population is growing. When $r < 0$, the birth rate is less than the death rate, and the population is shrinking. When $r = 0$, the birth and death rates are equal, and the population is neither growing nor shrinking. The intrinsic rate of increase (r_{max}) is the maximum per capita growth rate. This value usually varies inversely with generation time, so a shorter generation time means a higher r_{max}.

- Intraspecific competition occurs when two or more individuals of the same species depend on the same limiting resource. For deer, this could include food, water, or refuge from predators.

- A logistic model has the following pattern: when the population growth is low, the population is small. At intermediate population sizes, growth is more rapid because more individuals breed and r is high. When population growth approaches K (carrying capacity), competition increases, r decreases, and the growth of the population is reduced.

44.6 Population Regulation

- Density-dependent factors include intraspecific competition and predation. At high density, fewer resources are available for individuals, which, in turn, use more energy in maintenance needs and less in reproduction. Offspring produced at higher population densities are often smaller in number or size and less likely to survive. At high population levels, adults may be smaller and weaker.

- Density-independent factors, such as fire, earthquakes, storms, floods, and other natural disturbances, reduce a population size regardless of density.

- r-selected species often have large numbers of small young, whereas K-selected species usually have small numbers of larger young. Other possibilities may include characteristics from Table 44.3.

- Extrinsic control includes interactions between individuals in a population and their food and predators. Once a food supply is exhausted, reproduction will decrease and mortality will increase. Intrinsic control can be hormonal changes within a population that cause increased aggressiveness, faster dispersal, and reduced reproduction. Aggression can cause weaker individuals to be forced to disperse to reduce the population density.

44.7 Human Population Growth

- Humans have avoided the effects of density-dependent regulation factors by expanding their geographic range into virtually every habitat, increasing K through agriculture, and reducing population-limiting factors resulting from poor hygiene, malnutrition, and contagious diseases.

- A population bomb is when many offspring are born in one time period, first forming the prereproductive base. At sexual maturity, populations can grow rapidly because of the large number of individuals in this cohort.

- The preindustrial stage is characterized by slow population growth, as birth and death rates are high. The transitional stage has better health care and sanitation, as well as increased food production. In the transitional stage, there is a decline in death rates, allowing population growth, but birth rates eventually decline as living conditions improve. In the industrial stage, there is slow population growth as family size decreases because couples choose to have fewer children and accumulate more material goods. In the postindustrial stage, the population size decreases as the birth rate falls below the death rate.

- Family planning encourages families to delay first reproduction, decreasing the size of the average family and, in turn, reducing the population size as generation time has increased. Decisions about reproduction should involve couples.

44.8 Sisyphean Problems in Population Biology

- Sisyphean problems in biology range from the challenge of eradicating pests (such as introduced rats and cats) to the problem of controlling diseases such as malaria. In either case, when the incidence of the pests or the disease drops below some level and control operations stop, the populations of pests and the incidence of disease rebound.

Questions

Self-Test Questions

1. Ecologists sometimes use mathematical models to do which of the following tasks?
   a. simulate natural events before conducting detailed field studies
   b. make basic observations about ecological relationships in nature
   c. collect survivorship and fecundity data to construct life tables
   d. determine the geographic ranges of populations

2. Which term can be used to describe the number of individuals per unit area or volume of habitat?
   a. dispersion pattern
   b. density
   c. size
   d. age structure

3. Suppose that one day you caught and marked 90 butterflies in a population. A week later, you returned to the population and caught 80 butterflies, including 16 that had been marked previously. What is the size of the butterfly population?
   a. 170
   b. 450
   c. 154
   d. 186

4. What does a uniform dispersion pattern imply about the members of a population?
   a. They work together to escape from predators.
   b. They use resources that are patchily distributed.
   c. They may experience intraspecific competition for vital resources.
   d. They have no ecological interactions with each other.

5. What does the model of exponential population growth predict about the per capita population growth rate (r)?
   a. r does not change as a population gets larger.
   b. r gets larger as a population gets larger.
   c. r gets smaller as a population gets larger.
   d. r is always at its maximum level (r_{max}).

6. If a population of 1000 individuals experiences 452 births and 380 deaths in 1 year, what is the value of r for this population?
   a. 0.072/individual/year
   b. 0.452/individual/year
   c. 0.380/individual/year
   d. 0.820/individual/year

7. According to the logistic model of population growth, what happens to the absolute number of individuals by which a population grows during a given time period?
   a. It gets steadily larger as the population size increases.
   b. It gets steadily smaller as the population size increases.
   c. It remains constant as the population size increases.
   d. It is highest when the population is at an intermediate size.

8. Which example might reflect density-dependent regulation of population size?
   a. An exterminator uses a pesticide to eliminate carpenter ants from a home.
   b. Mosquitoes disappear from an area after the first frost.
   c. Northeast storms blow over and kill all willow trees along a lake.
   d. A clam population declines in numbers in a bay as the number of predatory herring gulls increases.

9. Which pattern is a K-selected species likely to exhibit?
   a. a type I survivorship curve and a short generation time
   b. a type II survivorship curve and a short generation time
   c. a type III survivorship curve and a short generation time
   d. a type I survivorship curve and a long generation time

10. Which one of the following is a reason that human populations have sidestepped factors that usually control population growth?
   a. Agriculture and industrialization have increased the carrying capacity for our species.
   b. The population growth rate (r) for the human population has always been small.
   c. The age structure of human populations has no impact on its population growth.
   d. Plagues have killed off large numbers of humans at certain times in the past.

Questions for Discussion

1. Do you expect to see a genetic bottleneck effect in *Mustela nigripes* populations in the wild in the future? If so, how long will they take to appear?

2. Design an income tax policy and social services plan that would encourage people to have either larger or smaller families.

3. Many city-dwellers have noted that the density of cockroaches in apartment kitchens appears to vary with the habits of the occupants. People who wrap food carefully and clean their kitchen frequently tend to have fewer arthropod roommates than those who leave food on kitchen counters and clean less often. Interpret these observations from the viewpoint of a population ecologist.

4. Why have bedbugs reemerged as all-too-common pests in many dwellings? How can they be controlled?

5. How could the use of composting by urban gardeners affect local populations of raccoons? Is there a "green" solution to the perceived problem posed by urban raccoons?

Grasshopper feeding on a leaf.

Jeremy N. McNeil

45 Population Interactions and Community Ecology

WHY IT MATTERS

It is easy to believe that there are many more species (much more species richness) in the tropics than there are in temperate zones. On a visit to tropical locations, it is not hard to be impressed by the diversity of life, whether you snorkel at a coral reef, go for a boat ride along a tropical river, or hike through a rainforest. Is there really such a difference between the two zones? Does it matter what organisms you look for? Consider herbivorous insects (those eating leaves), of which there are more species in the tropics than in temperate zones. Why is this so?

Ecological theory suggests that in the tropics, greater uniformity in climate is associated with increased ecological specialization of species, that is, more niches, where a *niche* is a species' place in nature. For plant-eating insects in the tropics, more species means that each species tends to eat a narrower range of plant species compared with the fewer species of herbivorous insects in temperate areas. In other words, each species occupies a narrower niche in the tropics, so there are more niches and hence more species.

In animals such as insects with different life stages (see Chapter 25), the niche changes over time. Each life cycle stage (in some insects, egg, larva (caterpillar), pupa, and adult) fills a different niche and plays a different role in the species' life history. The eggs are development machines, the larvae are eating machines, the pupae are metamorphosis machines, and the adults are mating machines.

Biologists can obtain a picture of the feeding niche of a species of butterfly or moth by documenting the food habits of caterpillars. In this way, L. A. Dyer and 12 colleagues studied the diets of moth and butterfly (Lepidoptera) caterpillars at 8 forest sites in the New World (North, South, and Central America) between latitudes 15° S and 55° N. On average, tropical species are more specialized in their diets than temperate ones **(Figure 45.1)**. Each species of caterpillar in the tropics ate fewer species of plants than its temperate counterpart. The prediction that tropical herbivorous insects occupy narrower feeding niches than temperate ones is supported by these data for Lepidoptera. One consequence of specialization is that there are more species of Lepidoptera in the tropics than in temperate zones.

Other tropical locations may have many species but perhaps less local variation. On the island of Papua New Guinea, many species of butterflies and moths (with herbivorous caterpillars) live in extensive geographic ranges across 75 000 km² tracts of rainforest **(Figure 45.2, p. 1138)**. Vojtech Novotny and 15 colleagues reported that consistency of diversity is typical of herbivorous insects, including Lepidoptera, beetles eating wood, and fruit flies and other flies eating fruit.

Exploring the details of communities of organisms can allow us to make sense of the patterns of life's diversity. Diversity is the watchword, and it can support almost as many theories as there are ecologists. The purpose of this chapter is to explore interactions between species of organisms and place the interactions in an ecological context.

Interactions among species form the basis of biotic communities. Many of the interactions revolve around eating and avoiding being eaten and involve a diversity of ploys and strategies. While some interactions are antagonistic (eating and avoiding being eaten), others are mutualistic, such as animals pollinating flowers, where the actions of one species benefit others. Competition for resources may occur within and between species. Biologists use a variety of approaches to assess interactions within biotic communities and to assess the impact of disturbances that may be natural or artificial.

45.1 Interspecific Interactions

Interactions between species typically benefit or harm the organisms involved, although they may be neutral **(Table 45.1, p. 1138)**. Furthermore, where interactions with other species affect individuals' survival and reproduction, many of the relationships we witness today are the products of long-term evolutionary modification. Good examples range from predator–prey interactions to those associated with pollination or dispersal of seeds.

Interactions between species can change constantly, but remember that the interactions occur at the individual level. Some individuals of a species may be better adapted when another species exerts selection pressure on that species. This adaptation can, in turn, help these individuals exert selection pressure on the other species, which can exert selection pressure on the first species in the chain. The situation, known as **coevolution**, is defined as genetically based reciprocal adaptation in two or more interacting species. A good example is provided by the arms race between echolocating bats and insects with bat-detecting ears (see "Echolocation: Communication," Box 39.2, Chapter 39).

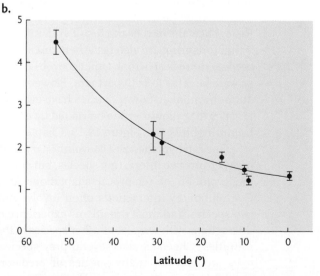

Figure 45.1

Caterpillar diet breadth. Numbers of host plant genera per caterpillar species at seven sites along a latitudinal gradient: **(a)** shows box plots of the number of host plant genera per caterpillar species, **(b)** shows a quadratic regression of diet breadth across latitude.

Figure 45.2

Papua New Guinea: different patterns of food specialization and distribution. Geographic distribution of **(a)** a caterpillar, **(b)** an ambrosia beetle, and **(c)** fruit fly species in the lowlands. Caterpillar and beetle species are classified as generalists (orange; feeding on more than one genus), clade specialists (blue; feeding on more than one species from a single genus), or monophagous (green; feeding on a single plant species). Note the differences between the caterpillars, beetles, and fruit flies.

Table 45.1		Population Interactions and Their Effects
Interaction		**Effects on Interacting Populations**
Predation	+/−	Predators gain nutrients and energy; prey are killed or injured.
Herbivory	+/−	Herbivores gain nutrients and energy; plants are killed or injured.
Competition	−/−	Both competing populations lose access to some resources.
Commensalism	+/0	One population benefits; the other population is unaffected.
Mutualism	+/+	Both populations benefit.
Parasitism	+/−	Parasites gain nutrients and energy; hosts are injured or killed.

Some coevolutionary relationships are straightforward. Ecologists describe the coevolutionary interactions between some predators and their prey as a race in which each species evolves adaptations that temporarily allow it to outpace the other. When antelope populations suffer predation by cheetahs, natural selection fosters the evolution of faster antelopes. Faster cheetahs may be the result of this situation, and if their offspring are also fast, then antelopes will also become more fleet of foot. Other coevolved interactions provide benefits to both partners. Flower structures of different monkey-flower species have evolved characteristics that allow them to be visited by either bees or hummingbirds (see Figure 19.15, Chapter 19).

One can hypothesize a coevolutionary relationship between any two interacting species, but documenting the evolution of reciprocal adaptations is difficult. Coevolutionary interactions often involve more than two species, and most organisms experience complex interactions with numerous other species in their communities. Cheetahs take several prey species. Antelopes are prey for many species of predators, from cheetahs to lions, leopards, and hyenas, as well as some larger birds of prey. Not all predators use the same hunting strategy. Therefore, the simple portrayal of coevolution as taking place between two species rarely does justice to the complexity of these relationships.

STUDY BREAK

What is coevolution? Is it usually restricted to two species?

45.2 Getting Food

Because animals typically acquire nutrients and energy by consuming other organisms, **predation** (the interaction between predatory animals and the animal prey they consume) and **herbivory** (the interaction between herbivorous animals and the plants they eat) can be the most conspicuous relationships in ecological communities.

Both predators and herbivores have evolved characteristics allowing them to feed effectively. Carnivores use sensory systems to locate animal prey and specialized behaviours and anatomical structures to capture and consume it. Herbivores use sensory systems to identify preferred food or to avoid food that is toxic.

Rattlesnakes, such as species in the genus *Crotalus,* use heat sensors on pits in their faces (see Figure 37.26, Chapter 37) to detect warm-blooded prey. The snakes deliver venom through fangs (hollow teeth) by open-mouthed strikes on prey. After striking, the snakes wait for the venom to take effect and then use chemical sensors also on the roofs of their mouths to follow the scent trail left by the dying prey. The venom is produced in the snakes' salivary glands. It contains neurotoxins that paralyze prey and protease enzymes that begin to digest it. Elastic ligaments connecting the bones of the snakes' jaws (mandibles) to one another and the mandibles to the skull allow snakes to open their mouths very wide to swallow prey larger than their heads (see Figure 40.32, Chapter 40).

Herbivores have comparable adaptations for locating and processing their food plants. Insects use chemical sensors on their legs and mouthparts to identify edible plants and sharp mandibles or sucking mouthparts to consume plant tissues or sap. Herbivorous mammals have specialized teeth to harvest and grind tough vegetation (see Figure 26.57, Chapter 26). Herbivores, such as farmer ants (see Chapter 48), ruminants, or termites (see "Digesting Cellulose: Fermentation," Box 40.2, Chapter 40), may also coopt other species to gain access to nutrients locked up in plant materials.

All animals select food from a variety of potential items. Some species, described as *specialists,* feed on one or just a few types of food. Among birds, Everglades Kites (*Rostrhamus sociabilis*) eat only apple snails (*Pomacea paludosa*). Koalas (see Figure 26.51, Chapter 26) eat the leaves of only a few of the many available species of *Eucalyptus*. Other species, described as **generalists**, have broader tastes. Crows (genus *Corvus*) take food ranging from grain to insects to carrion. Bears (genus *Ursus*) and pigs (genus *Sus*) are as omnivorous as humans.

How does an animal select its food? Why pizza rather than salad? Mathematical models, collectively described as **optimal foraging theory**, predict that an animal's diet is a compromise between the costs and benefits associated with different types of food. Assuming that animals try to maximize their energy intake at any meal, their diets should be determined by the ratio of costs to benefits: the costs of obtaining the food versus the benefits of consuming it. Costs are the time and energy it takes to pursue, capture, and consume a particular kind of food. Benefits are the energy provided by that food. A cougar (*Felis concolor*) will invest more time and energy hunting a mountain goat (*Oreamnos americanus*) than a jackrabbit (*Lepus townsendii*), but the payoff for the cat is a bigger meal. One important element in food choice is the relative abundance of prey. *Encounter rate* is usually influenced by population density and can influence a predator's diet. For the cougar, encounter rate determines the time between jackrabbits, and when they are abundant, they can be a more economical target than larger, scarcer prey.

Food abundance affects food choice. When prey are scarce, animals often take what they can get, settling for food that has a higher cost-to-benefit ratio. When food is abundant, they may specialize, selecting types that provide the largest energetic return. Bluegill sunfishes eat *Daphnia* and other small crustaceans. When crustacean density is high, these fishes hunt mostly large *Daphnia,* which provide more energy for their effort. When prey density is low, bluegills eat *Daphnia* of all sizes **(Figure 45.3)**.

Think of yourself at a buffet. The array of food can be impressive, if not overwhelming. But your state of hunger, the foods you like, the ones you do not like, and any to which you are allergic all influence your

Figure 45.3

An experiment demonstrating that prey density affects predator food choice. Bluegill sunfishes (*Lepomis macrochirus*) were offered equal numbers of small, medium, and large prey (*Daphnia magna*) at three different total densities of prey. Because large prey are easy to find, the fishes encountered them more often, especially at the highest prey densities, than either medium-sized or small prey. The fishes' choice of prey varied with prey density, but they always chose the largest prey available.

selection. You may also be influenced by choices made by others. In your feeding behaviour, you betray your animal heritage.

STUDY BREAK

1. How do predators differ from herbivores? How are they similar?
2. Is a koala a generalist or a specialist? What is the difference?
3. What does optimal foraging theory predict? Describe the costs and benefits central to this theory.

45.3 Defence

CONCEPT FIX Some people believe that "natural" products (chemicals) are beneficial to us, while artificial ones are potentially harmful. In reality, many plants produce chemicals (natural products) that are dangerous and even deadly—to humans and to other animals and to some plants. Contact with the leaves (or stems, roots, flowers, or berries) of poison ivy may be enough to convince you that not all plant products are beneficial. If not, you can read about conine (see Figure 48.31, Chapter 48), an active ingredient in poison hemlock, the poison that killed Socrates. ⬡
Predation and herbivory negatively affect the species being eaten, so it is no surprise that animals and plants have evolved mechanisms to avoid being caught and eaten. Some plants use spines, thorns, and irritating

hairs to protect themselves from herbivores. Plant tissues often contain poisonous chemicals that deter herbivores from feeding. When damaged, milkweed plants (family Asclepiadaceae) exude a milky, irritating sap **(Figure 45.4)** that contains poisons that affect the heart (cardiac glycosides). Even small amounts of cardiac glycosides are toxic to the heart muscles of some vertebrates. Other plants have compounds that mimic the structure of insect hormones, disrupting the development of insects that eat them. Most of these poisonous compounds are volatile, giving plants their typical aromas. Some herbivores have developed the ability to recognize these odours and avoid toxic plants. Some plants increase their production of toxic compounds in response to herbivore feeding. Potato and tomato plants damaged by herbivores have higher levels of protease-inhibiting chemicals. These compounds prevent herbivores from digesting the proteins they have eaten, reducing the food value of these plants.

45.3a Be Too Big to Tackle

Size can be a defence. At one end of the spectrum, this means being too small to be considered food. At the other end, it means being so big that few, if any, predators can succeed in attacking and killing the prey. Today, elephants and some other large herbivores (megaherbivores) are species with few predators (other than humans). But 50 000 years ago, there were larger predators (see Figure 17.1, Chapter 17), including one species of "lion" that was one-third larger than an African lion.

45.3b Eternal Vigilance: Always Be Alert

A first line of defence of many animals is avoiding detection. This often means not moving, but it also

means keeping a sharp lookout for approaching predators and the danger they represent **(Figure 45.5)**. Animals that live in groups benefit from the multitude of eyes and ears that can detect approaching danger, so the risk of predation can influence group size and social interactions.

45.3c Avoid Detection: Freeze—Movement Invites Discovery

Many animals are cryptic, camouflaged so that a predator does not distinguish them from the background. Patterns such as the stripes of a zebra (*Equus burchellii*) make the animal conspicuous at close range, but at a distance, patterns break up the outline, rendering the animals almost invisible. Many other animals look like something that is not edible. Some caterpillars look like bird droppings, whereas other insects look like thorns or sticks. Neither bird droppings nor thorns are usually eaten by insectivores.

45.3d Thwarting Attacks: Take Evasive Action

Animals resort to other defensive tactics once they have been discovered and recognized. Running away

Figure 45.5
Eternally vigilant. The sentry of a group of meerkats (*Suricata suricatta*).

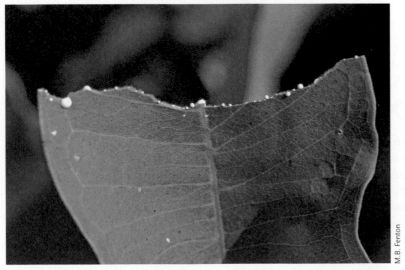

Figure 45.4
Protective latex sap. Milky sap laced with cardiac glycosides oozes from a cut milkweed (*Asclepias* species) leaf. Milky sap does not always mean dangerous chemicals; for example, the sap of dandelions is benign.

is a typical next line of defence. Taking refuge in a shelter and getting out of a predator's reach is an alternative. African pancake tortoises (*Malacochersus tornieri*) are flat, as the name implies. When threatened, they retreat into rocky crevices and puff themselves up with air, becoming so tightly wedged that predators cannot extract them.

If cornered by a predator, offence becomes the next line of defence. This can involve displays intended to startle or intimidate by making the prey appear large and/or ferocious. Such a display might dissuade a predator or confuse it long enough to allow the potential victim to escape. Many animals use direct attack in these situations, engaging whatever weapons they have (biting, scratching, stinging, etc.). Direct attacks are not usually a good primary defence because they involve getting very close to the predator, something prey usually avoid doing.

45.3e Spines and Armour: Be Dangerous or Impossible to Attack

Other organisms use active defence in the form of spines or thorns **(Figure 45.6)**. North American porcupines (genus *Erethizon*) release hairs modified into sharp, barbed quills that, when stuck into a predator, cause severe pain and swelling. The spines detach easily from the porcupine, and the nose, lips, and tongue of an attacker are particularly vulnerable. There are records of leopards (*Panthera pardus*) being killed by porcupine spines. In these instances, the damage to the leopards' mouths, combined with infection, was probably the immediate cause of death. Many other mammals, from monotremes (spiny anteaters) to tenrecs (insectivores from Madagascar, *Tenrec* species and *Hemicentetes* species), hedgehogs (*Erinaceus* species), and porcupines in the Old World use the same defence. So do some fishes and many plants.

Other organisms are armoured **(Figure 45.7)**. Examples include bivalve and gastropod molluscs, chambered nautiluses, arthropods such as horseshoe crabs (*Limulus* species), trilobites (see Chapter 25), fishes such as catfish (*Siluriformes*), reptiles (turtles; see Figure 26.38, Chapter 26), and mammals (armadillos, scaly anteaters). We know a great deal about extinct species that were armoured (see Chapter 17) because they often made good fossils.

45.3f Chemical Defence Ranges from Bad Taste to Deadly

Like plants that produce chemicals to repel herbivores, many animals make themselves chemically unattractive.

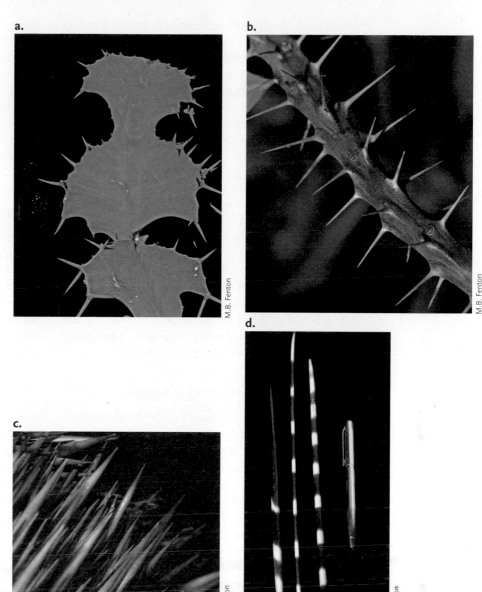

Figure 45.6

Defensive spines. Plants such as **(a)** the cowhorn euphorb (*Euphorbia grandicornis*) and **(b)** crown of thorns (*Euphorbia milli*) and animals such as **(c)** spiny anteaters (*Tachyglossus* species) and **(d)** porcupines (*Hystrix* species) use thorns or spines in defence. Pen shown for scale with quills in **(d)**.

Figure 45.7
Armour. Turtles and their allies (see Chapter 26) live inside shells. This leopard tortoise (*Geochelone pardalis*) is inspecting the remains of a conspecific. Armour does not guarantee survival.

At one level, this can be as simple as smelling or tasting bad. Have you ever had a dog or a cat that was sprayed by a skunk (*Mephitis mephitis*)? Many animals vomit and defecate on their attackers. Skunks and bombardier beetles escalate this strategy by producing and spraying a noxious chemical. Other animals go beyond spraying. Many species of cnidarians, annelids, arthropods, and chordates produce dangerous toxins and deliver them directly into their attackers. These toxins may be synthesized by the user (e.g., snake venom; see "Molecule behind Biology," Box 45.1, p. 1144) or sequestered from other sources, often plants or other animals (see "Nematocysts," Box 45.2, p. 1146). Caterpillars of monarch butterflies are immune to the cardiac glycosides in the milkweed leaves they eat. They extract, concentrate, and store these chemicals, making the caterpillars themselves (and the adult butterflies) poisonous to potential predators. The concentrations of defensive chemicals may be higher in the animal than they were in its food. Cardiac glycosides persist through metamorphosis, making adult monarchs poisonous to vertebrate predators.

45.3g Warnings Are Danger Signals

Many animals that are noxious or dangerous are **aposematic**: they advertise their unpalatability with an appropriate display (**Figure 45.8**; see Chapter 16). Aposematic displays are designed to "teach" predators to avoid the signaller, reducing the chances of harm to would-be predators and prey. Predators that attack a brightly coloured bee or wasp and are stung learn to associate the aposematic pattern with the sting. Many predators quickly learn to avoid black-and-white skunks, yellow-banded wasps, or orange monarch butterflies because they associate the warning display with pain, illness, or severe indigestion.

But for every ploy there is a counterploy, and some predators eat mainly dangerous prey. Bee-eaters (family Meropidae) are birds that eat hymenopterans (bees and wasps). Some individual African lions specialize on porcupines, and animals such as hedgehogs (genus *Erinaceus*) seem able to eat almost anything and show no ill effects. Indeed, some hedgehogs first lick toads and then their own spines, anointing them with toad venom. Hedgehog spines treated with toad venom are more irritating (at least to people) than untreated ones, enhancing their defensive impact.

45.3h Mimicry Is Advertising, Whether True or False

If predators learn to recognize warning signals, it is no surprise that many harmless animals' defences are based on imitating (mimicking) species that are dangerous or distasteful. **Mimicry** occurs when one species evolves to resemble another (**Figure 45.9**). **Batesian mimicry**, named for English naturalist Henry W. Bates, occurs when a palatable or harmless species (the **mimic**) resembles an unpalatable or poisonous one (the **model**). Any predator that eats the poisonous model and suffers accordingly will subsequently avoid other organisms that resemble it. However, the predator must survive the encounter. **Müllerian mimicry**, named for German zoologist Fritz Müller, involves two or more unpalatable species looking the same, presumably to reinforce lessons learned by a predator that attacks any species in the mimicry complex.

For mimicry to work, the predator must learn (see Chapter 39) to recognize and then avoid the prey. The more deadly the toxin, the less likely an individual predator is to learn by its experience. In many cases, predators learn by watching the discomfort of a conspecific that has eaten or attacked an aposematic prey.

Plants often use toxins to protect themselves against herbivores. Is this also true of toxins in mushrooms (see Chapter 19)?

45.3i There Is No Perfect Defence

Helmets protect soldiers, skiers, motorcyclists, and cyclists, but not completely because no defence provides perfect protection. Some predators learn to circumvent defences. Many predators learn to deal with a diversity of prey species and a variety of defensive tactics. Orb web spiders confronting a captive in a web adjust their behaviour according to the prey. They treat moths differently from beetles, and they treat bees in yet another way. When threatened by a predator, headstand beetles raise their rear ends and spray a noxious chemical from a gland at the tip of the abdomen. This behaviour deters many would-be predators. But experienced grasshopper mice from western North America circumvent this defence. An experienced mouse grabs the beetle, averts its face (to avoid the spray), turns the beetle upside down so that the gland discharges into the ground, and eats the beetle from the head down (**Figure 45.10**).

Figure 45.8
Warning colours. This arrowhead frog gets its name from toxins in its skin that were used to poison arrowheads.

M.B. Fenton

a. Batesian mimicry

Drone fly (*Eristalis tenax*), the mimic

Honeybee (*Apis mellifera*), the model

b. Müllerian mimicry

Heliconius erato

Heliconius melpomene

Figure 45.9

Mimicry. **(a)** Batesian mimics are harmless animals that mimic a dangerous one. The harmless drone fly (*Eristalis tenax*) is a Batesian mimic of the stinging honeybee (*Apis mellifera*). **(b)** Müllerian mimics are poisonous species that share a similar appearance. Two distantly related species of butterfly, *Heliconius erata* and *Heliconius melpomene*, have nearly indistinguishable patterns on their wings.

STUDY BREAK

1. List the eight defence techniques used by animals and/or plants. Provide an example of each.
2. How do animals obtain the chemicals they use in chemical defences?
3. What is the purpose of aposematic displays?

a. *Eleodes* **beetle**

b. Grasshopper mouse

Figure 45.10

Defence and learning. When confronted by a predator, **(a)** the headstand beetle (*Eleodes longicollis*) raises its abdomen and sprays a noxious chemical from its hind end. Experienced grasshopper mice (*Onychomys leucogaster*) **(b)** thwart the beetle's defence by grabbing it, turning it upside down, and eating it headfirst.

45.4 Competition

Different species using the same limiting resources experience **interspecific competition** (competition between species). Competing individuals may experience increased mortality and decreased reproduction, responses similar to the effects of intraspecific competition. Interspecific competition can reduce the size and population growth rate of one or more of the competing populations.

Community ecologists identify two main forms of interspecific competition. In **interference competition**, individuals of one species harm individuals of another species directly. Here animals may fight for access to resources, as when lions chase smaller predators such as hyenas, jackals, and vultures from their kills. Many plant species, including creosote bushes (see Figure 44.4, Chapter 44), release toxic chemicals into the soil, preventing other plants from growing nearby.

In **exploitative competition**, two or more populations use (*exploit*) the same limiting resource, and the presence of one species reduces resource availability for others. Exploitative competition need not involve snout-to-snout or root-to-root confrontations. In the deserts of the American Southwest, many bird and ant species eat mainly seeds, and each seed-eating species may deplete the food supply available to others without necessarily encountering each other.

Taipoxin: Snake Presynaptic Phospholipase A₂ Neurotoxins

Snake venoms are typically a concoction of ingredients designed to immobilize and digest prey. Like those of the venom of nematocysts, the effects of snake venom can include symptoms associated with neurotoxins, cardiotoxins, hemolytic actions, and digestion (necrosis) of tissues. Not all snakes (or other venomous animals) have the same venom.

Snake presynaptic phospholipase A₂ neurotoxins, or SPANs, have neurotoxic effects and work by blocking neuromuscular junctions. Phospholipase A₂ activity varies greatly among SPANs. Using mouse neuromuscular junction hemidiaphragm preparations and neurons in culture, M. Rigoni and seven colleagues explored the way in which SPANs work. They used SPANs from single-chain notexin (from *Notechis scutatus*, the eastern tiger snake); a two-subunit B-bungarotoxin (from *Bungarus multicinctus*, the many-banded krait); the three-subunit taipoxin (from *Oxyuranus scutellatus*, the taipan; **Figure 1**); and the five-unit textilotoxin (from *Pseudonaja textilis*, the eastern brown snake).

The results showed that administration of SPANs to neuromuscular junctions causes enlargement of the junctions and reduction in the contents of synaptic vesicles. SPANs also induce exocytosis of neurotransmitters. In other words, SPANs bind nerve terminals via receptors **(Figure 2)**; the

FIGURE 1

The Taipan (*Oxyuranus spp*) is an extremely venomous snake from northern Australia and southern New Guinea.

BMCL/Shutterstock

FIGURE 2

Taipoxin paralyzes the neuromuscular junction by causing membrane fusion between the plasma membranes (tan colour) of presynaptic ganglia and synaptic vesicles, forming a pore that allows mixing of lipids from inner (purple) and outer (green) leaflets. Although this is probably restricted by proteins (yellow ribbons) around the pore, phospholipase A₂ changes the curvature at the junction, resulting in the paralysis noted above.

From Joshua Zimmerberg, Leonid V. Chernomordik, "Synaptic Membranes Bend to the Will of a Neurotoxin", *Science*, vol. 310, Dec 9, 2005, pp. 1626–1627. Reprinted with permission from AAAS.

(continued)

Taipoxin: Snake Presynaptic Phospholipase A₂ Neurotoxins

results indicate that venoms can be used to further our understanding of what happens at neuromuscular junctions.

Among extant lepidosauran reptiles (snakes and lizards), two lineages have venom delivery systems, advanced snakes and helodermatid (gila monster) lizards. The view that the evolution of venom systems is fundamental to the radiation of snakes has been supported by the prevalence of venom among snakes and its restriction to just two species of lizards. Using tools of molecular genetics, B. G. Fry and 13 colleagues explored the early evolution of venom systems in lizards and snakes. The ancestral condition, in venomous lizards, is lobed, venom-secreting glands on upper and lower jaws. Advanced snakes and two lizards have more derived venom systems. They have one pair of venom glands, either upper or lower glands. Analysis of venoms indicates that snakes, iguanians (monitor lizards), and anguimorphs form a single clade (**Figure 3**), suggesting that venom is an ancestral trait in this evolutionary line of reptiles.

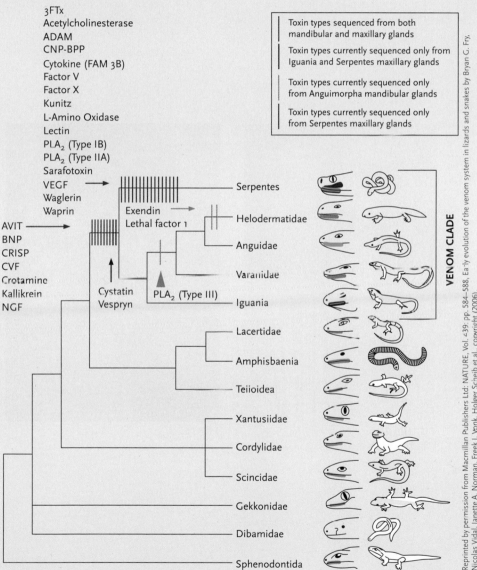

FIGURE 3

Snake and lizard phylogeny based on the appearance of venom. Shown here are the relative glandular development and appearance of toxin recruitment in squamate reptile phylogeny. Glands secreting mucus are blue, ancestral venom glands are red, and derived venom is orange. Elements in venom include the following: three-finger toxins (3FTx); a disintegrin and metalloproteinase (ADAM); C-type natriuretic peptide–bradykinin–potentiating peptide (CNP-BPP); cobra venom factor (CVF); nerve growth factor (NGF); and vascular endothelial growth factor (VEGF).

Nematocysts 45.2

Swimmers at ocean beaches in warmer parts of the world can be exposed to stings from the Portuguese man-o'-war. In the United States, at least three human deaths have been caused by exposure to the venom of its nematocysts **(Figure 1).** First aid for someone who has been stung includes (a) using sea water to flush away any tentacles still clinging to the victim (or picking them off if necessary), (b) applying ice or cold packs to the area of the sting(s) and leaving them in place for 5 to 15 minutes, (3) using an inhaled analgesic to reduce pain, and (4) seeking additional medical aid.

Beaches where Portuguese man-o'-war and other jellyfish may occur must be supervised by lifeguards who understand the danger. The inflatable bladders (sails; see **Figure 2**) make Portuguese man-o'-war easy to see in the water, and swimming is not permitted when they are near.

In 1968, lifeguards and others at a beach at Port Stephens, New South Wales, in Australia were surprised and concerned when they realized that some people had been stung by Portuguese man-o'-war when none of these animals had been spotted near the beach. The stinging animals turned out to be sea slugs, *Glaucus* species. Since 1903, it had been known that sea slugs use nematocysts as a defence.

Glaucus atlanticus **(Figure 3)** feed on the cnidosacs that contain the nematocysts, preferentially selecting and storing those of Portuguese man-o'-war, which have two sizes of nematocysts. The sea slugs take the larger nematocysts that, when discharged, have the longest penetrants. It is likely that the same digestive processes other sea slugs use to extract chloroplasts can be used to extract nematocysts.

This situation demonstrates the versatility of defensive systems in animals.

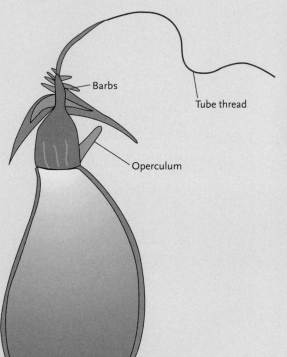

FIGURE 2
Physalia physalis, *Portuguese man-o'-war.*

FIGURE 3
Glaucus atlanticus, *a sea slug that ingests nematocysts from Physalia physalis.*

Barbs

Tube thread

Operculum

FIGURE 1
Nematocyst. Nematocysts are stinging cells occurring in animals in the phylum Cnidaria (see Chapter 25). Nematocysts of Physalia physalis (Portuguese man-o'-war; Figure 2) contain toxic proteins and at least six or seven enzymes that can be injurious. Unpurified nematocyst venoms have several effects, some of which can be lethal. The venoms can be neurotoxic, cardiotoxic, or myotoxic or cause lysis of red blood cells or mitochondria. Like other venoms, nematocyst venom from the Portuguese man-o'-war can interfere with the transport of Na+ and Ca²⁺ ions.

D.P. Wilson/FLPA/Photo Researchers, Inc.

DR T.E. THOMPSON/SCIENCE PHOTO LIBRARY

45.4a Competition and Niches: When Resources Are Limited

In the 1920s, the Russian mathematician Alfred J. Lotka and the Italian biologist Vito Volterra independently proposed a model of interspecific competition, modifying the logistic equation (see Chapter 44) to describe the effects of competition between two species. In their model, an increase in the size of one population reduces the population growth rate of the other.

In the 1930s, a Russian biologist, G. F. Gause, tested the model experimentally. He grew cultures of two *Paramecium* species (ciliate protozoans) under constant laboratory conditions, regularly renewing food and removing wastes. Both species feed on bacteria suspended in the culture medium. When grown alone, each species exhibited logistic growth. When grown together in the same dish, *Paramecium aurelia* persisted at high density, but *Paramecium caudatum* was almost eliminated (**Figure 45.11**). These results inspired Gause to define the competitive exclusion principle. Populations of two or more species cannot coexist indefinitely if they rely on the same limiting resources and exploit them in the same way. One species inevitably harvests resources more efficiently; produces more offspring than the other; and, by its actions, negatively affects the other species.

Ecologists developed the concept of the **ecological niche** to visualize resource use and the potential for interspecific competition in nature. They define a population's niche by the resources it uses and the environmental conditions it requires over its lifetime. In this context, niche includes food, shelter, and nutrients, as well as nondepletable abiotic conditions such as light intensity and temperature. In theory, an almost infinite variety of conditions and resources could contribute to a population's niche. In practice, ecologists usually identify the critical resources for which populations might compete. Sunlight, soil moisture, and inorganic nutrients are important resources for plants, so differences in leaf height and root depth, for example, can affect plants' access to these resources. Food type, food size, and nesting sites are important for animals. When several species coexist, they often use food and nest resources in different ways.

Ecologists distinguish the **fundamental niche** of a species, the range of conditions and resources it could tolerate and use, from its **realized niche**, the range of conditions and resources it actually uses in nature. Realized niches are smaller than fundamental niches, partly because all tolerable conditions are not always present in a habitat and partly because some resources are used by other species. We can visualize competition between two populations by plotting their fundamental and realized niches with respect to one or more resources (**Figure 45.12**). If the fundamental niches of two populations overlap, they *might* compete in nature.

Observing that several species use the same resource does not demonstrate that competition occurs (or does not occur). All terrestrial animals consume

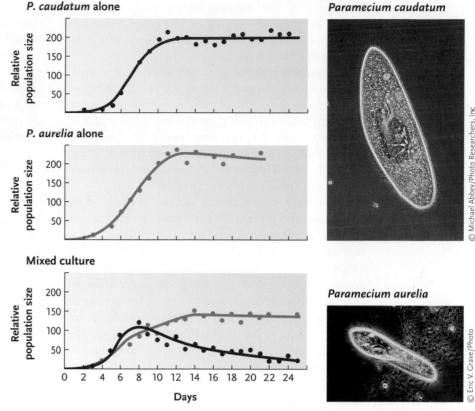

Figure 45.11
Gause's experiments on interspecific competition in *Paramecium*.

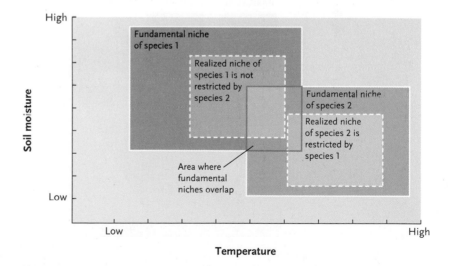

Figure 45.12
Fundamental versus realized niches. In this hypothetical example, both species 1 and species 2 can survive intermediate temperature conditions, as indicated by the shading where their fundamental niches overlap. Because species 1 actually occupies most of this overlap zone, its realized niche is not much affected by the presence of species 2. In contrast, the realized niche of species 2 is restricted by the presence of species 1, and species 2 occupies warmer and drier parts of the habitat.

oxygen but do not compete for oxygen because it is usually plentiful. Nevertheless, two general observations provide *indirect* evidence that interspecific competition may have important effects.

Resource partitioning occurs when several sympatric (living in the same place) species use different resources or the same resources in different ways. Although plants might compete for water and dissolved nutrients, they may avoid competition by partitioning these resources, collecting them from different depths in the soil **(Figure 45.13)**. This allows coexistence of different species.

Character displacement can be evident when comparing species that are sometimes sympatric and sometimes allopatric (living in different places). Allopatric populations of some animal species are morphologically similar and use similar resources, whereas sympatric populations are morphologically different and use different resources. Differences between sympatric species allow them to coexist without competing. Allen Keast studied honey-eaters (family Meliphagidae), a group of birds from Australia, to illustrate this situation. In mainland Australia, up to six species in the genus *Melithreptus* occur in some habitats. Just off the coast of Kangaroo Island, there are two species. When two species are sympatric, each feeds in a wider range of situations than when six species live in the same area, reflecting the use of broader niches. Behavioural and morphological differences are evident when species are compared between the different situations.

Data on resource partitioning and character displacement suggest, but do not prove, that interspecific competition is an important selective force in nature. To demonstrate *conclusively* that interspecific competition limits natural populations, one must show that the presence of one population reduces the population size or density of its presumed competitor. In a classic field experiment, Joseph Connell examined competition between two barnacle species **(Figure 45.14)**. Connell first observed the distributions of both species of barnacles in undisturbed habitats to establish a reference baseline. *Chthamalus stellatus* is generally found in shallow water on rocky coasts, where it is periodically exposed to air. *Balanus balanoides* typically lives in deeper water, where it is usually submerged.

In the absence of *Balanus* on rocks in deep water, larval *Chthamalus* colonized the area and produced a flourishing population of adults. *Balanus* physically displaced *Chthamalus* from these rocks. Thus, interference competition from *Balanus* prevents *Chthamalus* from occupying areas where it would otherwise live. Removal of *Chthamalus* from rocks in shallow water did not result in colonization by *Balanus*. *Balanus* apparently cannot live in habitats that are frequently exposed to air. Connell concluded that there was competition between the two species. But competition was asymmetrical because *Chthamalus* did not affect the distribution of *Balanus*, whereas *Balanus* had a substantial effect on *Chthamalus*.

45.4b Symbiosis: Close Associations

Symbiosis occurs when one species has a physically close ecological association with another (*sym* = together; *bio* = life; *sis* = process). Biologists define three types of symbiotic interactions: commensalism, mutualism, and parasitism (see Table 45.1, p. 1138).

In **commensalism**, one species benefits from and the other is unaffected by the interactions. Commensalism appears to be rare in nature because few species are unaffected by interactions with another. One possible example is the relationship between Cattle Egrets (*Bubulcus ibis*, birds in the heron family) and the large grazing mammals with which they associate **(Figure 45.15)**. Cattle Egrets eat insects and other small animals that their commensal partners flush from grass. Feeding rates of Cattle Egrets are higher when they associate with large grazers than when they do not. The birds clearly benefit from this interaction, but the presence of birds has no apparent positive or negative impact on the mammals.

In **mutualism**, both partners benefit. Mutualism appears to be common and includes coevolved relationships between flowering plants and animal pollinators. Animals that feed on a plants' nectar or

Figure 45.13

Resource partitioning. The root systems of three plant species that grow in abandoned fields partition water and nutrient resources in soil. Bristly foxtail grass (*Setaria faberi*) has a shallow root system, Indian mallow (*Abutilon theophrasti*) has a moderately deep taproot, and smartweed (*Polygonum pennsylvanicum*) has a deep taproot that branches at many depths.

Photos: left, © Tony Wharton, Frank Lane Picture Agency/Corbis; middle, © Hal Horwitz/ Corbis; right, © Joe McDonald/Corbis.

Treatment 1: Remove *Balanus*
In the absence of *Balanus*, *Chthamalus*
occupies both shallow water and deep water.

Treatment 2: Remove *Chthamalus*
In the absence of *Chthamalus*, *Balanus*
still occupies only deep water.

High tide

Chthamalus

Low tide

Balanus

Fundamental
niche of
Chthamalus

Fundamental
niche of
Balanus

Figure 45.14
Demonstration of competition between two species of barnacles.

M.B. Fenton

Figure 45.15
Commensalism. Cattle Egrets (*Bubulcus ibis*) feed on insects and other small animals flushed by the movements of large grazing animals such as African elephants (*Loxodonta africana*).

pollen carry the plants' gametes from one flower to another **(Figure 45.16, p. 1150)**. Similarly, animals that eat fruits disperse the seeds and "plant" them in piles of nutrient-rich feces. Mutualistic relationships between plants and animals do not require active cooperation, as each species simply exploits the other for its own benefit. Some associations between bacteria and plants are mutualistic. Perhaps the most important of these associations is between *Rhizobium* and leguminous plants such as peas, beans, and clover (see Chapter 40).

Mutualistic relationships between animal species are common. Cleaner fishes, small marine species,

feed on parasites attached to the mouths, gills, and bodies of larger fishes **(Figure 45.17, p. 1150)**. Parasitized fishes hover motionless while cleaners remove their ectoparasites. The relationship is mutualistic because cleaner fishes get a meal, and larger fishes are relieved of parasites.

The relationship between the bull's horn acacia tree (*Acacia cornigera*) of Central America and a species of small ants (*Pseudomyrmex ferruginea*) is a highly coevolved mutualism **(Figure 45.18, p. 1151)**. Each acacia is inhabited by an ant colony that lives in the tree's swollen thorns. Ants swarm out of the thorns to sting, and sometimes kill, herbivores that touch the tree. Ants also clip any vegetation that grows nearby. Acacia trees colonized by ants grow in a space free of herbivores and competitors, and occupied trees grow faster and produce more seeds than unoccupied trees. In return, the plants produce sugar-rich nectar consumed by adult ants and protein-rich structures that the ants feed to their larvae. Ecologists describe the coevolved mutualism between these species as *obligatory,* at least for the ants, because they cannot subsist on any other food sources.

Many animals eat honey and sometimes also the bees that produce it. In Africa, Greater Honey-Guides (*Indicator indicator*) are birds that use a special guiding display to lead humans to beehives. In one tribe of Kenyans, the honey-gathering Borans use a special whistle to call *I. indicator*. Boran honey-gatherers that work with Greater Honey-Guides are much more efficient at finding beehives than those working alone. When the honey-gatherer goes to the hive and raids it to obtain honey, Greater Honey-Guides help themselves to bee larvae, left-over honey, and wax. Although *I. indicator*

a. Flowering yucca plant

b. Female yucca moth

c. Yucca moth larva

A female yucca moth uses highly modified mouthparts to gather the sticky pollen and roll it into a ball. She carries the pollen to another flower, and after piercing its ovary wall, she lays her eggs. She then places the pollen ball into the opening of the stigma.

When moth larvae hatch from the eggs, they eat some of the yucca seeds and gnaw their way out of the ovary to complete their life cycle. Enough seeds remain undamaged to produce a new generation of yuccas.

Figure 45.16

Mutualism between plants and animals. Several species of yucca plants (*Yucca* species) are each pollinated exclusively by one species of moth (*Tegeticula* species). The adult moth appears at the time of year when the plants are flowering. These species are so mutually interdependent that the larvae of each moth species can feed on only one species of yucca, and each yucca plant can be pollinated by only one species of moth. Extinction of the pollinator will usually lead to extinction of the plant. Most plant–animal mutualisms are less specific.

are said also to guide ratels (honey badgers, *Mellivora capensis*) to beehives, there are no firm data supporting this assumption.

In **parasitism**, one species—the parasite—uses another—the host—in a way that is harmful to the host. Parasite–host relationships are often considered to be specialized predator–prey relationships because one population of organisms feeds on another. But parasites rarely kill their hosts because a dead host is not a continuing source of nourishment.

— Cleaner wrasse

Figure 45.17

Mutualism between animal species. A large potato cod (*Epinephelus tukula*) from the Great Barrier Reef in Australia remains nearly motionless in the water while a striped cleaner wrasse (*Labroides dimidiatus*) carefully removes and eats ectoparasites attached to its lip. The potato cod is a predator; the striped cleaner wrasse is a potential prey. Here the mutualistic relationship supersedes the possible predator–prey interaction.

Endoparasites, such as tapeworms, flukes, and roundworms, live *within* a host. Many endoparasites acquire their hosts passively when a host accidentally ingests the parasites' eggs or larvae. Endoparasites generally complete their life cycle in one or two host individuals. Ectoparasites, such as leeches, aphids, and mosquitoes, feed on the exterior of the host. Most animal ectoparasites have elaborate sensory and behavioural mechanisms, allowing them to locate specific hosts, and they feed on numerous host individuals during their lifetimes. Plants such as mistletoes (genus *Phoradendron*) live as ectoparasites on the trunks and branches of trees; their roots penetrate the host's xylem and extract water and nutrients. These differ from epiphytes such as bromeliads or Spanish moss that use the host only as a base. Other plants are root parasites, for example, *Conopholis americana*.

Not all parasites feed directly on a host's tissues. Some bird species are brood parasites, laying their eggs in the host's nest. It is quite common for female birds such as Canvasback Ducks, Brown-headed Cowbirds, and Kirtland's Warblers (*Aythya valisineria*) to lay their eggs in the nests of conspecifics (members of the same species). Some species of songbirds often lay some eggs in the nests of others, a variation on hedging of genetic bets and on extra-pair copulations (see Chapters 33 and 39, respectively). Brood parasitism is the next level of escalation in this spectrum of parasitism. Brown-headed Cowbirds (*Molothrus ater*), like other brood parasites, always lay their eggs in the nest of other species, leaving it to the host parents to raise their young. This behaviour can have drastic repercussions for host species. Brown-headed Cowbirds, for instance, have played a large role in the near-extinction of Kirtland's Warblers (*Dendroica kirtlandii*).

The feeding habits of insects called parasitoids fall somewhere between true parasitism and predation. A female parasitoid lays her eggs in a larva or pupa of another insect species, and her young consume the tissues of the living host. Because the hosts chosen by most parasitoids are highly specific, agricultural ecologists often try to use parasitoids to control populations of insect pests.

STUDY BREAK

1. What is interspecific competition? What two types of interspecific competition have been identified by community ecologists?
2. Describe the competitive exclusion principle.
3. What is a species' ecological niche? How does a fundamental niche differ from a realized niche?

Figure 45.18

Highly coevolved mutualisms. **(a)** Bull's horn acacia trees (*Acacia cornigera*) provide colonies for small ants (*Pseudomyrmex ferruginea*). In addition to providing homes (domatia—yellow arrow in **(b)** in hollow thorns, the acacia also provides food for the ants (nectar—yellow arrow in **(c)**. In the same area in the New World tropics, a cowhorn orchid **(d)** is patrolled by ants (yellow arrow) that are also housed in **(c)** domatia (yellow arrow in **(e)** on the plant.

45.5 The Nature of Ecological Communities

The interactions that occur among species in an ecological community can be broadly categorized as antagonistic or mutually beneficial **(Figure 45.19)**. Trophic interactions are those associated with consumption (antagonistic)—one species eating another—the usual situation portrayed in food webs. Mutually beneficial interactions include, for example, those between flowering plants and their insect pollinators. Understanding the dynamics of community dynamics requires knowledge of the structure of community networks (e.g., food webs; see Chapter 46) as well as information about how structure influences the extinction or persistence of species. An overview of the dynamics of an ecological community is obtained through a combination of fieldwork and attendant statistical analysis of data to document ecosystem architecture. The second element, knowledge of the influence of architecture on species persistence, emerges from mathematical modelling.

To explore the nature of ecosystems, Elisa Thebault and Colin Fontaine examined pollination (mutualistic) and plant–herbivore (trophic) systems **(Figure 45.20, p. 1152)**. They found that the structure of the network favouring ecosystem stability differs between trophic (herbivore) and mutually beneficial (pollination) networks. In pollination networks, the elements are highly connected and nested, promoting stability of communities.

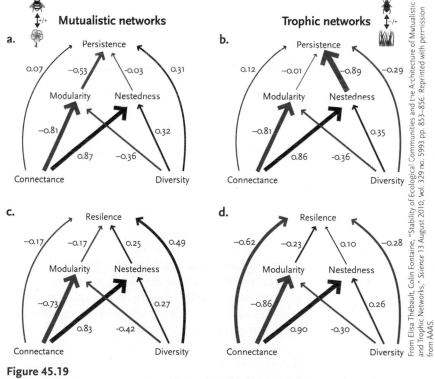

Figure 45.19

The persistence (a, b) and resilience (c, d) of pollinating and herbivore ecosystem patterns are summarized, revealing important differences. The thickness of arrows, scaled to standardized coefficients, illustrates the relative strength of the effects. Red identifies negative effects; black, positive ones. There is a further comparison of the effects of connectance and diversity, comparing direct and indirect effects, considering modularity and nestedness. The numbers in each diagram indicate the coefficients along the path.

From Elisa Thebault, Colin Fontaine, "Stability of Ecological Communities and the Architecture of Mutualistic and Trophic Networks," *Science* 13 August 2010, vol. 329 no. 5993 pp. 853–856. Reprinted with permission from AAAS.

a. Interactive hypothesis

The interactive hypothesis predicts that species within communities exhibit similar distributions along environmental gradients (indicated by the close alignment of several curves over each section of the gradient) and that boundaries between communities (indicated by arrows) are sharp.

b. Individualistic hypothesis

The individualistic hypothesis predicts that species distributions along the gradient are independent (indicated by the lack of alignment of the curves) and that sharp boundaries do not separate communities.

c. Siskiyou Mountains

d. Santa Catalina Mountains

Most gradient analyses support the individualistic hypothesis, as illustrated by distributions of tree species along moisture gradients in Oregon's Siskiyou Mountains and Arizona's Santa Catalina Mountains.

Figure 45.20
Two views of ecological communities. Each graph line indicates a different species.

In herbivore networks, stability is greater in structures that are compartmentalized and weakly connected. The work identifies features that affect the stability of ecosystems, potentially informing those working to effect conservation at the system level.

Ecotones, the borders between communities, are sometimes wide transition zones. Ecotones are generally species rich because they include plants and animals from both neighbouring communities, as well as some species that thrive only under transitional conditions. Although ecotones are usually relatively broad, places where there is a discontinuity in a critical resource or important abiotic factor may have a sharp community boundary. Chemical differences between soils derived from serpentine rock and sandstone establish sharp boundaries between communities of native California wildflowers and introduced European grasses **(Figure 45.21)**.

STUDY BREAK

1. Distinguish between antagonistic and mutualistic architectural structures in ecosystems.
2. Are ecotones generally species rich or species poor?

Jasper Ridge Biological Preserve

Figure 45.21
Sharp community boundaries. Soils derived from serpentine rock have high magnesium and heavy metal content, which many plants cannot tolerate. Although native California wildflowers (bright yellow in this photograph) thrive on serpentine soil at the Jasper Ridge Preserve of Stanford University, introduced European grasses (green in this photograph) competitively exclude them from adjacent soils derived from sandstones.

Living organisms offer many examples of mutualistic interactions in which one species (or group of species) shows varying levels of dependence on another or others. Mutualistic situations can place species on the edge of survival. Where one species depends entirely on another, the extinction of one must lead to change or the extinction of both (e.g., Dodos—see Chapter 47—and yucca plants and their moths). There are many other examples of close relationships, including a desert melon (*Cucumis humifructus*) that depends perhaps entirely on aardvarks (*Orycteropus afer*) for dispersal of its seeds. Aardvarks can sniff out the underground melons, dig them up, and eat them to obtain water. When aardvarks bury their dung, they plant the melon's seeds and fertilize them. The survival of the melon depends on the aardvark but not vice versa.

Mutualistic interactions between species can be even more complex. In the African savannah, ants often live in mutualistic relationships with trees. In east Africa, whistling thorn acacia trees (*Acacia drepanolobium*) are host to four species of ants (see Figure 45.18, p. 1151). One species of ant (*Cremat-ogaster mimosae*) in particular depends on room (hollows in swollen thorns, called domatia) and board (carbohy-drates secreted from extrafloral glands and the bases of leaves) provided by the trees. Another species of ant (*Cremat-ogaster sjostedti*) also lives on the trees but usually nests in holes made by cerambycid beetles that burrow into and harm the trees.

The ants, particularly *C. mimosae*, attack animals that attempt to browse on the foliage or branches of *A. drepanolo-bium*. They deter many herbivores, from large mammals to wood-boring beetles (such as cerambycids). If large, browsing mammals are excluded from the area, *A. drepanolobium* produce fewer domatia and fewer carbohydrates for *C. mimosae*. The decline in this species of ant leads to higher damage by cerambycid beetles and increases in populations of *C. sjostedti*.

Many other plants also use ants as mercenaries (see Figure 45.18, p. 1151), and it is becoming clear that survival of these systems depends on the con-tinued presence of participating species.

45.6 Community Characteristics

Growth forms (sizes and shapes) of plants vary mark-edly in different environments, so the appearances of plants can often be used to characterize communities. Warm, moist environments support complex vegeta-tion with multiple vertical layers. Tropical forests include a canopy formed by the tallest trees, an under-storey of shorter trees and shrubs, and a herb layer under openings in the canopy. Vinelike lianas and epi-phytes grow on the trunks and branches of trees **(Figure 45.22)**. In contrast, physically harsh environ-ments are occupied by low vegetation with simple structure. Trees on mountainsides buffeted by cold winds are short, and the plants below them cling to rocks and soil. Other environments support growth forms between these extremes.

Communities differ greatly in species richness, the number of species that live within them. The harsh environment on a low desert island may support just a few species of microorganisms, fungi, algae, plants, and arthropods. In contrast, tropical forests that grow under milder physical conditions include many thou-sands of species. Ecologists have studied global pat-terns of species richness (see Chapter 47) for decades. Today, as human disturbance of natural communities has reached a crisis point, conservation biologists try to understand global patterns of species richness to determine which regions of Earth are most in need of preservation.

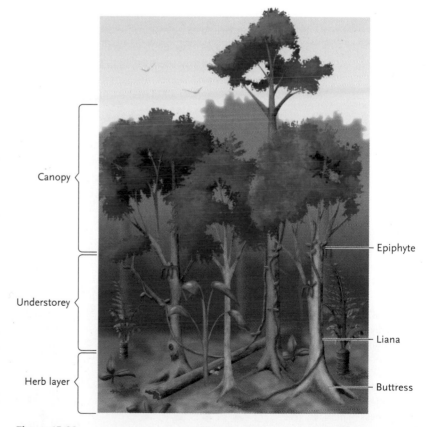

Figure 45.22

Layered forests. Tropical forests, such as one near the Mazaruni River in Guyana (South America), include a canopy of tall trees and an understorey of short trees and shrubs. Huge vines (lianas) climb through the trees, eventually reaching sunlight in the canopy. Epiphytic plants grow on trunks and branches, increasing the structural complexity of the habitat.

The relative abundances of species vary across communities. Some communities have one or two abundant species and a number of rare species. In others, the species are represented by more equal numbers of individuals. In a temperate deciduous forest in southern Québec, red oak trees (*Quercus rubra*) and sugar maples (*Acer saccharum*) might together account for nearly 85% of the trees. A tropical forest in Costa Rica may have more than 200 tree species, each making up a small percentage of the total.

The factors underlying diversity and community structure can be expected to vary among groups of organisms, and the interactions between very different groups of organisms can have positive effects on both. Using an experimental mycorrhizal plant system (see Chapter 23), H. Maherali and J. N. Klironomos found that after one year, the species richness of mycorrhizal fungi correlated with higher plant productivity. In turn, the diversity and species richness of mycorrhizal fungi were highest when their starting community had more distinct evolutionary lineages. This example illustrates the importance of diversity and interactions.

45.6a Measuring Species Diversity and Evenness: Calculating Indices

The number of species is the simplest measure of diversity, so a forest with four tree species has higher diversity than one with two tree species. But there can be more to measuring diversity than just counting species. Biologists use indices of diversity to facilitate comparison of data sets documenting the numbers of species and of individuals. Shannon's index of diversity (H'), one commonly used measure, is calculated using the formula

$$H' = -\sum_{i=1}^{S} p_i \ln p_i$$

where S is the total number of species in the community (richness), p_i is the proportion of S made up by species I, and ln is the natural logarithm.

Another index, Shannon's evenness index (E_H), is calculated using the formula

$$E_H = \frac{H'}{\ln S}$$

where ln S is the natural logarithm of the number of species. Evenness is an indication of the mixture of species. Indices of diversity and evenness allow population biologists to objectively portray and compare the diversity of communities.

Use the two indices to compare the 3 forests of 50 trees each **(Figure 45.23)**. The number of species and number of individuals of each species in each forest are shown in **Table 45.2**. In Table 45.2, the values of H' and E_H provide an indication of the diversity of the three hypothetical forests and the evenness of species representations. Lower values of H' and E_H suggest communities with few species (low H' values) or uneven distribution (low E_H values). Higher values of H' and E_H suggest a richer array of species with evenly distributed individuals.

Measures of diversity can be used to advantage. Ecologists refer to α diversity to represent the numbers of sympatric species in one community and β

Table 45.2	Shannon's Indices for Measuring Diversity and Evenness		
Numbers of Individuals Per Species			
	Forest A*	Forest B*	Forest C*
Species 1	39	5	25
Species 2	2	5	25
Species 3	2	5	0
Species 4	1	5	0
Species 5	1	5	0
Species 6	1	5	0
Species 7	1	5	0
Species 8	1	5	0
Species 9	1	5	0
Species 10	1	5	0
Shannon Indices			
H' diversity	0.6	2.3	0.7
E_h evenness	0.26	1.0	1.0

*Forests from Figure 45.23.

Figure 45.23

Species diversity. In this hypothetical example, each of three samples of forest communities (A, B, and C) contains 50 trees. Indices allow biologists to express the diversity of species and evenness of numbers (see Table 45.2).

Forest A

Forest B

Forest C

diversity to depict the numbers in a collection of communities. The number of herbivorous Lepidoptera species in one national park is α diversity, whereas β diversity is the number of species in the country in which the park is located. The trend to establish parks that cross international boundaries is a step toward recognizing the reality that political and biological boundaries can be quite different. Measures of diversity can be used directly in some conservation plans (see Chapter 47).

45.6b Trophic Interactions: Between Nourishment Levels

Every ecological community has trophic structure (*troph* = nourishment), comprising all plant–herbivore, predator–prey, host–parasite, and potential competitive interactions **(Figure 45.24)**. We can visualize the trophic structure of a community as a hierarchy of trophic levels, defined by the feeding relationships among its species (see Figure 45.24a).

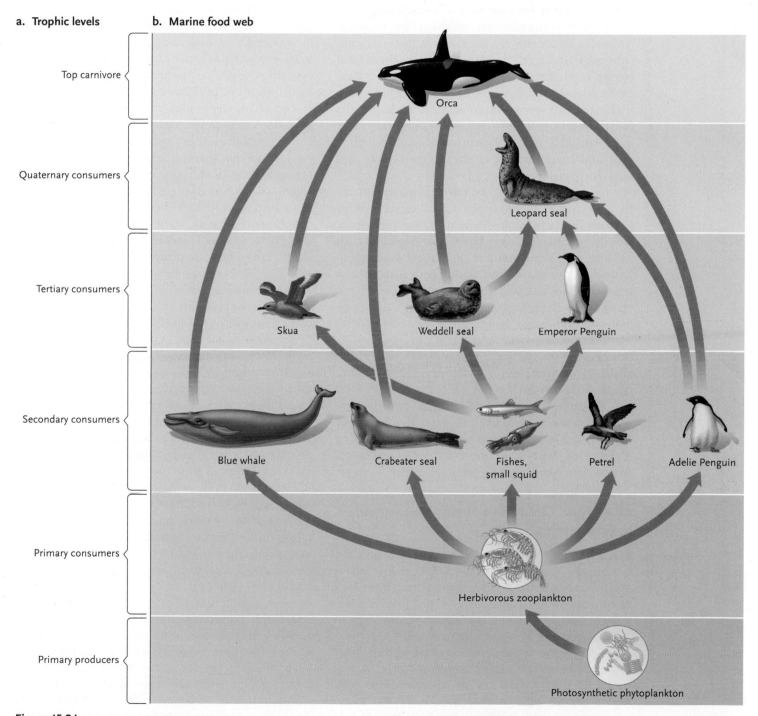

a. Trophic levels   **b. Marine food web**

Figure 45.24
The marine food web off the coast of Antarctica.

Photosynthetic organisms are primary producers, the first trophic level. Primary producers are photoautotrophs (*auto* = self) because they capture sunlight and convert it into chemical energy that is used to make larger organic molecules that plants can use directly. Plants are the main primary producers in terrestrial communities. Multicellular algae and plants are the major primary producers in shallow freshwater and marine environments, whereas photosynthetic protists and cyanobacteria play that role in deep, open water.

All consumers in a community (animals, fungi, and diverse microorganisms) are heterotrophs (*hetero* = other) because they acquire energy and nutrients by eating other organisms or their remains. Animals are consumers. Herbivores (primary consumers) feed directly on plants and form the second trophic level. Secondary consumers (mesopredators) eat herbivores and form the third trophic level. Animals that eat secondary consumers make up the fourth trophic level, the tertiary consumers. At one meal, animals that are omnivores (e.g., humans, pigs, and bears) can act as primary, secondary, and tertiary consumers.

Detritivores (scavengers) form a separate and distinct trophic level. These organisms extract energy from organic detritus produced at other trophic levels. Detritivores include fungi, bacteria, and animals such as earthworms and vultures that ingest dead organisms, digestive wastes, and cast-off body parts such as leaves and exoskeletons. Decomposers, a type of detritivore, are small organisms, such as bacteria and fungi, that feed on dead or dying organic material. Detritivores and decomposers serve a critical ecological function because their activity reduces organic material to small inorganic molecules that producers can assimilate (see Chapter 20).

Although omnivores obviously do not fit exclusively into one trophic level, this can also be true of other organisms. Sea slugs that use chloroplasts or carnivorous plants are examples of species that do not fit readily into trophic categories.

45.6c Food Chains and Webs: Connections in Ecosystems

Ecologists use food chains and webs to illustrate the trophic structure of a community. Each link in a food chain is represented by an arrow pointing from food to consumer (see Figure 45.24b, p. 1155). Simple, straight-line food chains are rare in nature because most consumers feed on more than one type of food and because most organisms are eaten by more than one type of consumer. Complex relationships are portrayed as food webs—sets of interconnected food chains with multiple links.

In the food web for the waters off the coast of Antarctica (see Figure 45.24, p. 1155), primary producers and primary consumers are small organisms occurring in vast numbers. Microscopic diatoms (phytoplankton) are responsible for most photosynthesis, and small shrimplike krill (zooplankton) are the major primary consumers. These tiny organisms, in turn, are eaten by larger species such as fish and seabirds, as well as by suspension-feeding baleen whales. Some secondary consumers are eaten by birds and mammals at higher trophic levels. The top carnivore in this ecosystem, the orca, feeds on carnivorous birds and mammals.

Ideally, depictions of food webs would include all species in a community, from microorganisms to top consumer. But most ecologists simply cannot collect data on every species, particularly those that are rare or very small. Instead, they study links between the most important species and simplify analysis by grouping together trophically similar species. Figure 45.24, p. 1155 categorizes the many different species of primary producers and primary consumers as phytoplankton and zooplankton, respectively.

Many biological *hot spots* (areas with many species) exist, from thermal vents on the floor of some oceans to deposits of bat guano in some caves. A more recently described example is icebergs drifting north from Antarctica. The icebergs can be hot spots of enrichment because of the nutrients and other materials they shed into surrounding waters. The water around two free-drifting icebergs (0.1 km^2 and 30.8 km^2 in area) was sampled in the Weddell Sea. High concentrations of chlorophyll, krill, and seabirds extended about 3.7 km around each iceberg. These data, reported by K. L. Smith Jr. and seven colleagues, demonstrate that icebergs can have substantial effects on pelagic ecosystems.

In the late 1950s, Robert MacArthur analyzed food webs to determine how the many links between trophic levels may contribute to a community's stability. The stability of a community is defined as its ability to maintain species composition and relative abundances when environmental disturbances eliminate some species from the community. MacArthur hypothesized that in species-rich communities, where animals feed on many food sources, the absence of one or two species would have only minor effects on the structure and stability of the community as a whole. He proposed a connection between species diversity, food web complexity, and community stability.

Subsequent research has confirmed MacArthur's reasoning. The average number of links per species generally increases with increasing species richness. Comparative food web analysis reveals that the relative proportions of species at the highest, middle, and lowest trophic levels are reasonably constant across communities. In 92 communities, MacArthur found two or three prey species per predator species, regardless of species richness.

Barcode of Life 45.4

To calculate the diversity of organisms using an index such as the Shannon–Weaver one described in the text, you need to know how many different species are in your sample. The diversity of species can be overwhelming, so it is difficult to provide a confident estimate of how many species remain undescribed. For many groups of organisms, there may be very few authorities able to identify species and provide descriptions of "new" species, the ones not yet described and therefore nameless. The Barcode of Life Data Systems, based in Guelph, Ontario, offers one alternative to the challenge of knowing how many species are in the sample you have just acquired, or the origin of a mysterious mouse found in a shipment of frozen chickens from Thailand.

The Barcode of Life project depends upon variation in the mitochondrial cytochrome *c oxidase 1* (*CO1*) gene consisting of about 650 nucleotides. This genetic barcode is embedded in almost every cell and offers biologists a chance to identify a species even if they have only a small sample of feathers or fur, a leaf, a seed, or a caterpillar. Since identification of some species depends upon having a whole adult specimen, being able to make an identification from an egg, a larva, or a hair offers enormous potential. Identification of organisms with different life stages can be particularly challenging. Using morphology, it can be easy to identify a

butterfly or a frog, but much more difficult to identify its caterpillar or its tadpole.

The Barcode of Life project is based on polymerase chain reaction (PCR) technology, which allowed biologists to process 100 samples every three hours. Subsequent advances in genomic technology have increased our capacity for efficient sequencing of DNA. The combination of this potential and an army of researchers collecting specimens and global positioning satellite (GPS) technology to document locations means that the Barcode of Life project can deliver accurate (to 97.5%) identifications of specimens in a short time. Further developments could see biologists and naturalists armed with appropriately programmed handheld devices to obtain in-field identifications.

One important consequence of this project is that biologists will have a fighting chance to document more fully the diversity of life on Earth. On one hand, this means realizing that 1 species of the butterfly *Astraptes fulgerator* is actually 10 species, or that what people had thought were several species is, in fact, one. Protecting species through CITES, the Convention on International Trade in Endangered Species, means being able to name them so that they can be

placed on a protected list. The Barcode of Life project should allow a merchant to be sure that the ivory being sold in her shop is from an extinct mammoth, rather than a living species said to be endangered (Chapter 47). The same applies to food species in a market—is that fish really what the label says?

Everyone has experience with barcode operations because they are used in many retail outlets and therefore we all know that barcodes and readers do not always work. These limitations, as well as biological ones associated with genetics of different species, make some organisms more appropriate for Barcode of Life approaches than others.

a.

International Barcode of Life

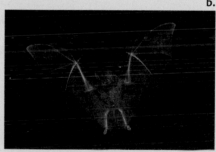

b.

M. B. Fenton

Shown here is (a) the bar code of (b) a flying fringe-lipped bat (**Trachops cirrhosus**).

Interactions among species in most food webs can be complex, indirect, and hard to unravel. In contrast, rodents and ants living in desert communities of the American Southwest potentially compete for seeds, their main food source. Plants that produce the seeds compete for water, nutrients, and space. Rodents generally prefer to eat large seeds, whereas ants prefer small seeds. Thus, feeding by rodents reduces the potential population sizes of plants that produce large seeds. As a result, the population sizes of plants that produce small seeds may increase, ultimately providing more food for ants (see Chapter 40). Compared with the

Antarctic system described above (see Figure 45.24), this community is not particularly complex.

STUDY BREAK

1. Why are indices important for population biologists? What do Shannon's indices measure?
2. Differentiate between α and β diversity.
3. Are herbivores primary or secondary consumers? Which trophic level do they form? Where do omnivores belong?

45.7 Effects of Population Interactions on Community Structure

Observations of resource partitioning and character displacement suggested that some process had fostered differences in resource use among coexisting species, and competition provided the most straightforward explanation of these patterns.

Interspecific competition can cause local extinction of species or prevent new species from becoming established in a community, reducing its species richness. During the 1960s and early 1970s, ecologists emphasized competition as the primary factor structuring communities.

45.7a Competition: More Than One Species Competing for a Resource

To further explore the role of competition, ecologists undertook field experiments on competition in natural populations. The experiment on barnacles (see Figure 45.14, p. 1149) is typical of this approach—the impact on one species' potential competitors of adding or removing another species changed patterns of distribution or population size. The picture that emerges from the results of these experiments is not clear, even to ecologists. In the early 1980s, Joseph Connell surveyed 527 published experiments on 215 species. He found that competition was demonstrated in roughly 40% of the experiments and more than 50% of species. At the same time, Thomas W. Schoener used different criteria to evaluate 164 experiments on approximately 400 species. He found that competition affected more than 75% of species.

It is not surprising that there is no single answer to the question about how competition works in and influences communities. Plant and vertebrate ecologists working with K-selected species generally believe that competition has a profound effect on species distributions and resource use. Insect and marine ecologists working with r-selected species argue that competition is not the major force governing community structure, pointing instead to predation or parasitism and physical disturbance. We know that even categorizing a species as r- or K-selected is open to discussion (see Chapter 44).

45.7b Feeding: You Are What You Eat

Predators can influence the species richness and structure of communities by reducing the sizes of prey populations. On the rocky coast of British Columbia, different species that fill different trophic roles compete for attachment sites on rocks, a requirement for life on a wave-swept shore. Mussels are the strongest competitors for space, eliminating other species from the community (see "Effect of a Predator on the Species Richness of Its Prey," Box 45.5). At some sites, predatory sea stars preferentially eat mussels, reducing

their numbers and creating space for other species to grow. Because the interaction between *Pisaster* and *Mytilus* affects other species as well, it qualifies as a strong interaction.

In the 1960s, Robert Paine used removal experiments to evaluate the effects of predation by *Pisaster* (see "Effect of a Predator on the Species Richness of Its Prey," Box 45.5). In predator-free experimental plots, mussels outcompeted barnacles, chitons, limpets, and other invertebrate herbivores, reducing species richness from 15 species to 8. In control plots containing predators, all 15 species persisted. Ecologists describe predators such as *Pisaster* as **keystone species**, defined as species with a greater effect on community structure than their numbers might suggest.

Herbivores also exert complex effects on communities. In the 1970s, Jane Lubchenco studied herbivory in a periwinkle snail, believed to be a keystone species on rocky shores in Massachusetts (see "The Complex Effects of a Herbivorous Snail on Algal Species Richness," Box 45.6, p. 1160). The features of plants and algae and the food preferences of animals that eat them can influence community structure.

STUDY BREAK

1. How does the importance of competition vary between K-selected and r-selected species?
2. Does predation or herbivory increase or decrease species richness? Explain.
3. What is a keystone species?

45.8 Effects of Disturbance on Community Characteristics

Recent research tends to support the individualistic view that many communities are not in equilibrium and that species composition changes frequently. Environmental disturbances such as storms, landslides, fires, floods, avalanches, and cold spells often eliminate some species and provide opportunities for others to become established. Frequent disturbances keep some ecological communities in a constant state of flux.

Physical disturbances are common in some environments. Lightning-induced fires commonly sweep through grasslands, powerful hurricanes often demolish patches of forest and coastal habitats, and waves wash over communities at the edge of the sea and sweep away organisms as well as landforms and other structures.

Joseph Connell and his colleagues conducted an ambitious long-term study of the effects of disturbance on coral reefs, shallow tropical marine habitats that are among the most species-rich communities on Earth. In some parts of the world, reefs are routinely battered by violent storms that wash corals off the substrate,

Effect of a Predator on the Species Richness of Its Prey 45.5

Biologists used a predatory sea star (*Pisaster ochraceus*) to assess the influence a predator can have on species richness and relative abundance of prey **(Figure 1)**. *P. ochraceus* preferentially eats mussels (*Mytilus californicus*), one of the strongest competitors for space in rocky intertidal pools. Robert Paine removed *Pisaster* from caged experimental study plots, leaving control study plots undisturbed, and then monitored the species richness of *Pisaster*'s invertebrate prey over many years.

Paine documented an increase in mussel populations in the experimental plots as well as complex changes in the feeding relationships among species in the intertidal food web **(Figure 2)**. When he removed *P. ochraceus*, the top predator in this food web, he observed a rapid decrease in the species richness of invertebrates and algae. Species richness on control plots did not change over the course of the experiment.

Predation by *P. ochraceus* prevents mussels from outcompeting other invertebrates on rocky shores.

FIGURE 1

A predatory sea star (Pisaster ochraceus) *feeding on a mussel* (Mytilus californicus).

© Nancy Rotenberg/maXximages.com

FIGURE 2

Changes in the species richness of invertebrates and algal species according to changes in populations of sea stars.

creating bare patches in the reef. The scouring action of storms creates opportunities for coral larvae to settle on bare substrates and start new colonies.

From 1963 to 1992, Connell and his colleagues tracked the fate of the Heron Island Reef at the south end of Australia's Great Barrier Reef **(Figure 45.25)**. The inner flat and protected crests of the reef are sheltered from severe wave action during storms, whereas some pools and crests are routinely exposed to physical disturbance. Because corals live in colonies of variable

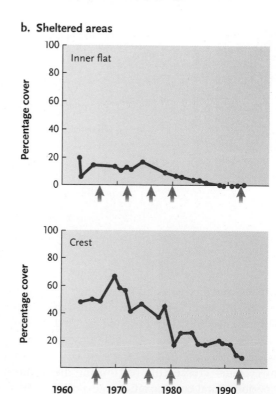

Figure 45.25

Major hydrodynamic disturbances to coral reefs, such as tsunamis and severe storms, have important impacts on coral reefs. Using oceanographic and engineering models, it is possible to predict the degree of dislodgement of benthic reef corals and, in this way, predict how coral shape and size indicate vulnerability to major disturbances. The use of these models is particularly important during times of climate change. The effects of storms on corals. Five tropical cyclones (marked by grey arrows) damaged corals on the Heron Island Reef during a 30-year period. Storms reduced the percentage cover of corals in **(a)** exposed parts of the reef much more than in **(b)** sheltered parts of it.

The Complex Effects of a Herbivorous Snail on Algal Species Richness 45.6

Jane Lubchenco made enclosures that prevented periwinkle snails (*Littorina littorea*) from entering or leaving study plots in tide pools and on exposed rocks in rocky intertidal habitat **(Figure 1)**. She then monitored the algal species composition in the plots, comparing them to the density of the periwinkles. In this way, she examined the influence of the periwinkles on the species richness of algae in intertidal communities.

The results varied dramatically between the study plots in tide pools and on exposed rocks. In tide pools, periwinkle snails preferentially ate *Enteromorpha*, the competitively dominant alga. At intermediate densities of *Enteromorpha*, the periwinkles remove some of these algae, allowing weakly competitive species to grow. The snails' grazing increases species richness. But

grazing by periwinkles when *Enteromorpha* is at low or high densities reduces the species richness of algae in tide pools. On exposed rocks, where periwinkle snails rarely eat the competitively dominant alga *Chondrus*, feeding by snails reduces algal species richness **(Figure 2)**.

Periwinkle snails (*Littorina littorea*)

Enteromorpha growing in tide pools

Chondrus growing on exposed rocks

FIGURE 1

The distribution of periwinkle snails and two kinds of algae.

In tide pools

Periwinkles per square metre

In tide pools, snails at low densities eat little algae and *Enteromorpha* competitively excludes other algal species, reducing species richness. At high snail densities, heavy feeding on all species reduces algal species richness. At intermediate snail densities, grazing eliminates some *Enteromorpha*, allowing other species to grow.

On exposed rocks

Periwinkles per square metre

On exposed rocks, periwinkles never eat much *Chondrus*, but they consume the tender, less successful competitors. Thus, feeding by periwinkles reinforces the competitive superiority of *Chondrus*: as periwinkle density increases, algal species richness declines.

FIGURE 2

Density of periwinkles versus algal species richness in tide pools and on exposed rocks.

size, the researchers monitored coral abundance by measuring the percentage of the substrate (i.e., the sea floor) that colonies covered. They revisited marked study plots at intervals, photographing and identifying individual coral colonies.

Five major cyclones crossed the reef during the 30 year study period. Coral communities in exposed

areas of the reef were in a nearly continual state of flux. In exposed pools, four of the five cyclones reduced the percentage of cover, often drastically. On exposed crests, the cyclone of 1972 eliminated virtually all corals, and subsequent storms slowed the recovery of these areas for more than 20 years. In contrast, corals in sheltered areas suffered much less storm damage.

Nevertheless, their coverage also declined steadily during the study as a natural consequence of the corals' growth. As colonies grew taller and closer to the ocean's surface, their increased exposure to air resulted in substantial mortality.

Connell and his colleagues also documented *recruitment,* the growth of new colonies from settling larvae, in their study plots. They discovered that the rate at which new colonies developed was almost always higher in sheltered than in exposed areas. Recruitment rates were extremely variable, depending in part on the amount of space that storms or coral growth had made available.

This long-term study of coral reefs illustrates that frequent disturbances prevent some communities from reaching an equilibrium determined by interspecific interactions. Changes in the coral reef community at Heron Island result from the effects of external disturbances that remove coral colonies from the reef, as well as internal processes (growth and recruitment) that either eliminate colonies or establish new ones. In this community, growth and recruitment are slow processes and disturbances are frequent. Thus, the community never attains equilibrium, and moderate levels of disturbance can foster high species richness.

The intermediate disturbance hypothesis, proposed by Connell in 1978, suggests that species richness is greatest in communities experiencing fairly frequent disturbances of moderate intensity. Moderate disturbances create openings for *r*-selected species to arrive and join the community while allowing *K*-selected species to survive. Thus, communities that experience intermediate levels of disturbance contain a rich mixture of species. Where disturbances are severe and frequent, communities include only *r*-selected species that complete their life cycles between catastrophes. Where disturbances are mild and rare, communities are dominated by long-lived *K*-selected species that competitively exclude other species from the community.

Several studies in diverse habitats have confirmed the predictions of the intermediate disturbance hypothesis. Colin R. Townsend and his colleagues studied the effects of disturbance at 54 stream sites in the Taieri River system in New Zealand. Disturbance occurs in these communities when water flow from heavy rains moves rocks, soil, and sand in the streambed, disrupting animal habitats. Townsend and his colleagues measured how much the substrate moved in different streambeds to develop an index of the intensity of disturbance. Their results indicate that species richness is highest in areas that experience intermediate levels of disturbance **(Figure 45.26)**.

Some ecologists have suggested that species-rich communities recover from disturbances more readily than less diverse communities. In the United States, David Tilman and his colleagues conducted large-scale

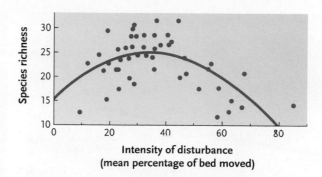

Figure 45.26
An observational study that supports the intermediate disturbance hypothesis. In the Taieri River system in New Zealand, species richness was highest in stream communities that experienced an intermediate level of disturbance.

experiments in midwestern grasslands. They examined relationships between species number and the ability of communities to recover from disturbance. Grassland plots with high species richness recover from drought faster than plots with fewer species.

STUDY BREAK

1. What did Connell's 30 year study of coral reefs illustrate about the ability of communities to reach a state of equilibrium?
2. What is the intermediate disturbance hypothesis? Describe one study that supports this hypothesis.
3. How does species richness affect the rate of recovery following a disturbance?

45.9 Succession

Ecosystems change over time in a process called **succession**, the change from one community type to another.

45.9a Primary Succession: The First Steps

Primary succession begins when organisms first colonize habitats without soil, such as those created by erupting volcanoes and retreating glaciers **(Figure 45.27, p. 1162)**. Lichens are often among the very first colonists (see Chapter 23), deriving nutrients from rain and bare rock. They secrete mild acids that erode rock surfaces, initiating the slow development of soil, which is enriched by the organic material lichens produce. After lichens modify a site, mosses (see Chapter 24) colonize patches of soil and grow quickly.

As soil accumulates, hardy, opportunistic plants (grasses, ferns, and broad-leaved herbs) colonize the site from surrounding areas. Their roots break up rock, and when they die, their decaying remains enrich the soil. Detritivores and decomposers facilitate these processes. As the soil becomes deeper and richer, increased moisture and nutrients support bushes and, eventually, trees. Late successional stages are often dominated by *K*-selected species with woody trunks and branches

1 The glacier has retreated about 8 m per year since 1794.

2 This site was covered with ice less than 10 years before this photo was taken. When a glacier retreats, a constant flow of melt water leaches minerals, especially nitrogen, from the newly exposed substrate.

3 Once lichens and mosses have established themselves, mountain avens (genus *Dryas*) grows on the nutrient-poor soil. This pioneer species benefits from the activity of mutualistic nitrogen-fixing bacteria, spreading rapidly over glacial till.

4 Within 20 years, shrubby willows (genus *Salix*), cottonwoods (genus *Populus*), and alders (genus *Alnus*) take hold in drainage channels. These species are also symbiotic with nitrogen-fixing microorganisms.

5 In time, young conifers, mostly hemlocks (genus *Tsuga*) and spruce (genus *Picea*), join the community.

6 After 80 to 100 years, dense forests of Sitka spruce (*Picea stichensis*) and western hemlock (*Tsuga heterophylla*) have crowded out the other species.

Figure 45.27
Primary succession following glacial retreat. The retreat of glaciers at Glacier Bay, Alaska, has allowed ecologists to document primary succession on newly exposed rocks and soil.

© ER Degginger/Color-Pic, Inc. ALL RIGHTS RESERVED.

that position leaves in sunlight and large root systems that acquire water and nutrients from soil.

In the classical view of ecological succession, long-lived species, which replace themselves over time, eventually dominate a community, and new species join it only rarely. This relatively stable, late successional stage is called a **climax community** because the dominant vegetation replaces itself and persists until an environmental disturbance eliminates it and allows other species to invade. Local climate and soil conditions, the surrounding communities where colonizing species originate, and chance events determine the species composition of climax communities. We now know that even climax communities change slowly in response to environmental fluctuations.

45.9b Secondary Succession: Changes after Destruction

Secondary succession occurs after existing vegetation is destroyed or disrupted by an environmental disturbance, such as a fire, a storm, or human activity. The presence of soil makes disturbed sites ripe for colonization and may contain numerous seeds that germinate after disturbance. Early stages of secondary succession proceed rapidly, but later stages parallel those of primary succession.

45.9c Climax Communities: The Ultimate Ecosystems Until Something Changes

Similar climax communities can arise from several different successional sequences. Hardwood forests can also develop in sites that were once ponds. During **aquatic succession**, debris from rivers and runoff accumulates in a pond, filling it to its margins. Ponds are first transformed into swamps, inhabited by plants adapted to a semisolid substrate. As larger plants get established, their high transpiration rates dry the soil, allowing other plant species to colonize. Given enough time, the site may become a meadow or forest in which an area of moist, low-lying ground is the only remnant of the original pond.

Because several characteristics of communities can change during succession, ecologists try to document how patterns change. First, because r-selected species are short lived and K-selected species are long lived, species composition changes rapidly in the early stages and more slowly in later stages of succession. Second, species richness increases rapidly during early stages because new species join the community faster than resident species become extinct. In later stages, species richness stabilizes or may even decline. Third, in terrestrial communities receiving sufficient rainfall, the maximum height and total mass of the vegetation increase steadily as large species replace small ones, creating the complex structure of the climax community.

Because plants influence the physical environment below them, the community itself increasingly moderates its microclimate. The shade cast by a forest canopy helps retain soil moisture and reduce temperature fluctuations. The trunks and canopy also reduce wind speed. In contrast, the short vegetation in an early successional stage does not effectively shelter the space below it.

Although ecologists usually describe succession in terms of vegetation, animals can show similar patterns. As the vegetation shifts, new resources become available, and animal species replace each other over time. Herbivorous insects, often with strict food preferences, undergo succession along with their food plants. And as herbivores change, so do their predators, parasites, and parasitoids. In old-field succession in eastern North America, different vegetation stages harbour a changing assortment of bird species **(Figure 45.28)**.

Differences in dispersal abilities (see "Dispersal," Box 45.7, p. 1164), maturation rates, and lifespans among species are partly responsible for ecological succession. Early successional stages harbour many r-selected species because they produce numerous small seeds that colonize open habitats and grow quickly. Mature successional stages are dominated by K-selected species because they are long lived. Nevertheless, coexisting populations inevitably affect one another. Although the role of population interactions in succession is generally acknowledged, ecologists debate the relative importance of processes that either facilitate or inhibit the turnover of species in a community.

45.9d Facilitation Hypothesis: One Species Makes Changes That Help Others

The facilitation hypothesis suggests that species modify the local environment in ways that make it less

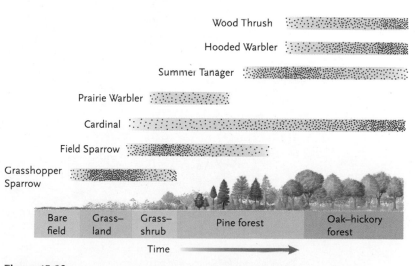

Figure 45.28

Succession in animals. Successional changes in bird species composition in an abandoned agricultural field in eastern North America parallel the changes in plant species composition. The residence times of several representative species are illustrated. The density of stippling inside each bar illustrates the density of each species through time.

Dispersal 45.7

Organisms often show astonishing dispersal abilities. In some cases, long-distance dispersal by plants in the Arctic is effected by the combination of strong winds and extensive expanses of ice and snow. The Svalbard Archipelago **(Figure 1)** is an interesting location for the study of plant dispersal. The islands were glaciated 20 000 years ago, and it is likely that plants did not survive this condition. The fossil record indicates that plants have been present on Svalbard for fewer than 10 000 years, although between 4000 and 9500 years ago, the climate was warmer there (by 1 to 2°C) than it is now.

Using DNA fingerprinting, I. G. Alsos and eight colleagues demonstrated that plant colonization of the Svalbard Archipelago has involved the arrival of plants from all possible adjacent regions **(Figure 2).** In eight of nine species, genetic evidence

From Inger Greve Alsos, Pernille Bronken Eidesen, Dorothee Ehrich, Inger Skrede, Kristine Westergaard, Gro Hilde Jacobsen, Jon Y. Landvik, Pierre Taberlet, Christian Brochmann, "Frequent Long-Distance Plant Colonization in the Changing Arctic", *Science*, vol. 316, Jun 15, 2007, pp. 1606–1609. Reprinted with permission from AAAS.

FIGURE 1

The location of the Svalbard Archipelago.

From Inger Greve Alsos, Pernille Bronken Eidesen, Dorothee Ehrich, Inger Skrede, Kristine Westergaard, Gro Hilde Jacobsen, Jon Y. Landvik, Pierre Taberlet, Christian Brochmann, "Frequent Long-Distance Plant Colonization in the Changing Arctic", *Science*, vol. 316, Jun 15, 2007, pp. 1606–1609. Reprinted with permission from AAAS.

FIGURE 2

Source regions for Svalbard plants. *Shading shows the geographic distribution of nine species of plants, and dotted lines show the distributions of related species. The main genetic groups are represented by colours, although some populations (*) could not be assigned to a genetic group. Arrows identify source populations, and the numbers indicate the percentage allocation by source region.*

(continued)

Dispersal 45.7 (continued)

indicates multiple colonization events. Plants can obviously disperse without assistance from animals.

In other situations, plants disperse with the assistance of animals through pollination and seeds. Using *Prunus mahaleb*, the mahaleb cherry **(Figure 3),** and genetic techniques, P. Jordano and two colleagues examined the role of birds and mammals in pollination and dispersing seeds. Small Passerine Birds dispersed seeds short distances (most less than 50 m) from the parent tree, whereas medium-sized birds (*Corvus corone* and *Turdus viscivorus*) usually dispersed seeds over longer distances (more than 110 m). Mammals (usually *Martes foina* and *Vulpes vulpes* but sometimes *Meles meles*) dispersed seeds about 500 m. The genetic work also provided an indication of the extent of gene flow during pollination.

It is obvious that plants capable of self-fertilization or vegetative reproduction can be more effective colonists than those depending on outcrossing, especially with the help of animal pollinators.

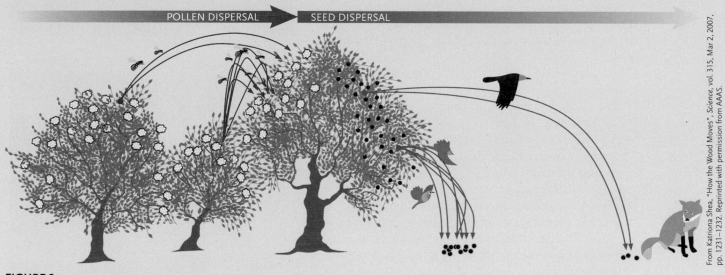

POLLEN DISPERSAL → SEED DISPERSAL

From Katriona Shea, "How the Wood Moves", *Science*, vol. 315, Mar 2, 2007, pp. 1231–1232. Reprinted with permission from AAAS.

FIGURE 3

The movement of pollen and seeds from mahaleb cherry trees. Gene flow occurs through pollination and seed dispersal (see Chapter 19).

suitable for themselves but more suitable for colonization by species typical of the next successional stage. When lichens first colonize bare rock, they produce a small quantity of soil that is required by mosses and grasses that grow there later. According to this hypothesis, changes in species composition are both orderly and predictable because the presence of each stage facilitates the success of the next one. Facilitation is important in primary succession, but it may not be the best model of interactions that influence secondary succession.

45.9e Inhibition Hypothesis: One Species Negatively Affects Others

The inhibition hypothesis suggests that new species are prevented from occupying a community by species that are already present. According to this hypothesis, succession is neither orderly nor predictable because each stage is dominated by the species that happened to have colonized the site first. Species replacements occur only when individuals of dominant species die of old age or when an environmental disturbance reduces their numbers. Eventually, long-lived species replace short-lived species, but the precise species composition of a mature community is open to question. Inhibition appears to play a role in some secondary successions. The interactions among early successional species in an old field are highly competitive. Horseweed inhibits the growth of asters that follow them in succession by shading aster seedlings and releasing toxic substances from their roots. Experimental removal of horseweed enhances the growth of asters, confirming the inhibitory effect.

45.9f Tolerance Hypothesis: Species Tolerate One Another

The tolerance hypothesis asserts that succession proceeds because competitively superior species replace competitively inferior ones. According to this model, early-stage species neither facilitate nor inhibit the growth of later-stage species. Instead, as more species arrive at a site and resources become limiting, competition eliminates species that cannot harvest scarce resources successfully. In the Piedmont region of North

America, young hardwood trees are more tolerant of shade than are young pine trees, and hardwoods gradually replace pines during succession. Thus, the climax community includes only strong competitors. Tolerance may explain the species composition of many transitional and mature communities.

At most sites, succession probably results from some combination of facilitation, inhibition, and tolerance, coupled with interspecific differences in dispersal, growth, and maturation rates. Moreover, within a community, the patchiness of abiotic factors strongly influences plant distributions and species composition. In deciduous forests of eastern North America, maples (*Acer* species) predominate on wet, low-lying ground, but oaks (*Quercus* species) are more abundant at higher and drier sites. Thus, a mature deciduous forest is often a mosaic of species and not a uniform stand of trees.

Disturbance and density-independent factors play important roles, in some cases speeding successional change. Moose (*Alces alces*) prefer to feed on deciduous shrubs in northern forests. This disturbance accelerates the rate at which conifers replace deciduous shrubs. On Isle Royale in Lake Superior, however, grazing by moose strongly affects balsam fir (*Abies balsamea*), their preferred food there. The net effect is a severe reduction in conifers and an increase in deciduous shrubs. Disturbance can also inhibit successional change, establishing a **disturbance climax** or **disclimax community**. In many grassland communities, periodic fires and grazing by large mammals kill seedlings of trees that would otherwise become established. Thus, disturbance prevents the succession from grassland to forest, and grassland persists as a disclimax community.

Animals such as moose can alter patterns of succession and vegetation in some communities, but the effect also extends to small mammals. Removal experiments involving kangaroo rats and plots of shrubland in the Chihuahuan Desert (southeastern Arizona) allowed J. H. Brown and E. J. Heske to demonstrate that these rodents were keystones in some systems where they occur. Kangaroo rats affect the plants in several ways. They are seed predators, and their burrowing activities disturb soils. Excluding kangaroo rats from experimental plots led to a threefold increase in the density of tall perennials and annual grasses **(Figure 45.29)**, suggesting that by predation on seeds and burrowing, these rodents affected the vegetation in the experimental areas.

On a local scale, disturbances often destroy small patches of vegetation, returning them to an earlier successional stage. A hurricane, tornado, or avalanche may topple trees in a forest, creating small, sunny patches of open ground. Locally occurring *r*-selected species take advantage of newly available resources and quickly colonize the openings. These local patches then undergo succession that is out of

From James H. Brown, Edward J. Heske, "Control of a Desert-Grassland Transition by a Keystone Rodent Guild", *Science*, vol. 250, Dec 21, 1990, pp. 1705–1707. Reprinted with permission from AAAS.

Figure 45.29

Predation and succession. Kangaroo rats (*Dipodomys*) were removed from the left side of the fence, which excluded them from the plot on the left. The top photograph was taken 5 years after the removal and the bottom one 13 years after. A large-seeded annual (after 5 years) and tall grasses are present in the *Dipodomys*-free plots.

step with the immediately surrounding forest. Thus, moderate disturbance, accompanied by succession in local patches, can increase species richness in many communities.

STUDY BREAK

1. What are the two types of succession? How do they differ?
2. What is a climax community? What determines the species composition of a climax community?
3. Identify and briefly describe the three hypotheses used to explain how succession proceeds.

45.10 Variations in Species Richness among Communities

Species richness often varies among communities according to a recognizable pattern. Two large-scale patterns of species richness—latitudinal trends and island patterns—have captured the attention of ecologists for more than a century.

45.10a Latitudinal Effects: From South to North

Ever since Darwin and Wallace travelled the globe (see Chapter 17), ecologists have recognized broad latitudinal trends in species richness. For many but not all plant and animal groups, species richness follows a latitudinal gradient, with the most species in the tropics and a steady decline in numbers toward the poles **(Figure 45.30)**. Several general hypotheses may explain these striking patterns.

Some hypotheses propose historical explanations for the *origin* of high species richness in the tropics. The benign climate in tropical regions allows some tropical organisms to have more generations per year than their temperate counterparts. Small seasonal changes in temperature mean that tropical species may be less likely than temperate species to migrate from one habitat to another, reducing gene flow between geographically isolated populations (see Chapter 19). These factors may have fostered higher speciation rates in the tropics, accelerating the accumulation of species. Tropical communities may also have experienced severe disturbance less often than communities at higher latitudes, where periodic glaciations have caused repeated extinctions. Thus, new species may have accumulated in the tropics over longer periods of time.

Other hypotheses focus on ecological explanations for the *maintenance* of high species richness in the tropics. Some resources are more abundant, predictable, and diverse in tropical communities. Tropical regions experience more intense sunlight, warmer temperatures in most months, and higher annual rainfall than temperate and polar regions (see *The Purple Pages*). These factors provide a long and predictable growing season for the lush tropical vegetation, which supports a rich assemblage of herbivores, and through them many carnivores and parasites. Furthermore, the abundance, predictability, and year-round availability of resources allow some tropical animals to have specialized diets. Tropical forests support many species of fruit-eating bats and birds that could not survive in temperate forests where fruits are not available year-round.

Species richness may be a self-reinforcing phenomenon in tropical communities. Complex webs of population interactions and interdependency have coevolved in relatively stable and predictable tropical climates. Predator–prey, competitive, and symbiotic interactions may prevent individual species from dominating communities and reducing species richness.

45.10b Equilibrium Theory of Island Biogeography

In 1883, a volcanic eruption virtually obliterated the island of Krakatoa. Within 50 years, what was left of Krakatoa had been recolonized by plants and animals, providing biologists with a clear demonstration of the dispersal powers of many living species. The colonization of islands and the establishment of biological communities there have provided many natural experiments that have advanced our knowledge of ecology and populations. Islands are attractive sites for experiments because although the species richness of communities may be stable over time, the species composition is often in flux as new species join a community and others drop out. In the 1960s, Robert MacArthur and Edward O. Wilson used islands as model systems to address the question of why communities vary in species richness. Islands provide natural laboratories for studying ecological phenomena, just as they do for evolution (see Chapter 17). Island communities can be small, with well-defined boundaries, and are isolated from surrounding communities.

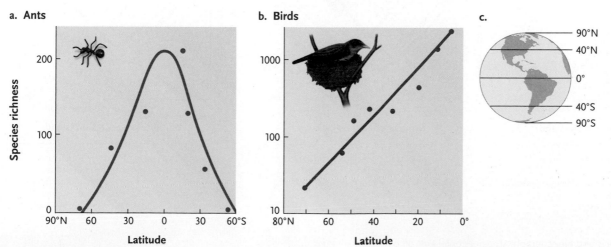

a. Ants **b. Birds** **c.**

Figure 45.30

Latitudinal trends in species richness. The species richness of many animals and plants varies with latitude **(c)** as illustrated here for **(a)** ants in North, Central, and South America and **(b)** birds in North and Central America. The species richness data used in **(b)** are based on records of where these birds breed.

MacArthur and Wilson developed the equilibrium theory of island biogeography to explain variations in species richness on islands of different size and different levels of isolation from other landmasses. They hypothesized that the number of species on any island was governed by give and take between two processes: the immigration of new species to an island and the extinction of species already there **(Figure 45.31)**.

According to their model, the mainland harbours a *species pool* from which species immigrate to offshore islands. Seeds and small arthropods are carried by wind or floating debris. Animals such as birds arrive under their own power. When only a few species are on an island, the rate at which new species immigrate to the island is high. But as more species inhabit the island over time, the immigration rate declines because fewer species in the mainland pool can still arrive on the island as *new* colonizers (see Chapter 17). Once some species arrive on an island, their populations grow and persist for variable lengths of time. Other immigrants die without reproducing. As the number of species on an island increases, the rate of species extinction also rises. Extinction rates increase over time partly because more species can go extinct there. In addition, as the number of species on the island increases, competition and predator–prey interactions can reduce the population sizes of some species and drive them to extinction.

According to MacArthur and Wilson's theory, an equilibrium between immigration and extinction determines the number of species that ultimately occupy an island (see Figure 45.31a). Once that equilibrium has been reached, the number of species remains relatively constant because one species already on the island becomes extinct in about the same time it takes a new one to arrive. The model does not specify which species immigrate or which ones already on the island become extinct. It simply predicts that the number of species on the island is in equilibrium, although species composition is not. The ongoing processes of immigration and extinction establish a constant turnover in the roster of species that live on any island.

The MacArthur–Wilson model also explains why some islands harbour more species than others. Large islands have higher immigration rates than small islands because they are larger targets for dispersing organisms. Moreover, large islands have lower extinction rates because they can support larger populations and provide a greater range of habitats and resources. At equilibrium, large islands have more species than small islands do (see Figure 45.31b). Islands near the mainland have higher immigration rates than distant islands because dispersing organisms are more likely to arrive at islands close to their point of departure. Distance does not affect extinction rates, so, at equilibrium, nearby islands have more species than distant islands (see Figure 45.31c).

The equilibrium theory's predictions about the effects of area and distance are generally supported by data on plants and animals **(Figure 45.32)**. Experimental work has verified some of its basic assumptions. Amy Schoener found that more than 200 species of marine organisms colonized tiny artificial islands (plastic kitchen scrubbers) within 30 days after she placed them in a Bahamian lagoon. Her research also confirmed that immigration rate increases with island size. Daniel Simberloff and Edward O. Wilson exterminated insects on tiny islands in the Florida Keys and monitored subsequent immigration and extinction (see "Experimenting with Islands," Box 45.9, p. 1170).

a. Immigration and extinction rates

The number of species on an island at equilibrium (indicated by the arrow) is determined by the rate at which new species immigrate and the rate at which species already on the island go extinct.

b. Effect of island size

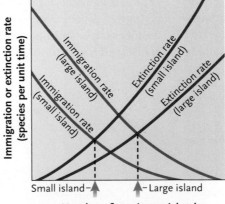

Immigration rates are higher and extinction rates lower on large islands than on small islands. Thus, at equilibrium, large islands have more species.

c. Effect of distance from mainland

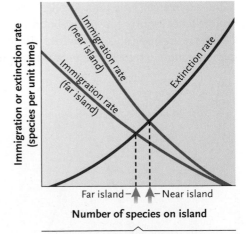

Organisms leaving the mainland locate nearby islands more easily than distant islands, causing higher immigration rates on near islands. Thus, near islands support more species than far ones.

Figure 45.31
Predictions of the theory of island biogeography. The horizontal axes of the graphs are time.

PEOPLE BEHIND BIOLOGY 45.8
Bridget J. Stutchbury, York University

Bridget Stutchbury studies the behaviour and ecology of songbirds, working at sites in eastern North America (United States and Canada), as well as sites in the Neotropics. One aspect of her research is documenting the reproductive behaviour of birds. Although songbirds were thought to be monogamous over at least a breeding season, using genetic techniques, Stutchbury and others are discovering that both males and females often mate with a bird that is not their mate. This behaviour is called extrapair copulation if it is just mating or extrapair fertilization

when young result from the matings.

Using radio tracking to follow individual birds combined with DNA fingerprinting, Stutchbury and her colleagues were able to look at the movement patterns of Acadian Flycatchers (*Empidonax virescens*) and determine how far males and females travelled to meet their extrapair partners. Males travelled 50 to 1500 m from their nests to meet partners.

Work with other species, such as Hooded Warblers (*Wilsonia citrina*), demonstrated that when these birds lived in small forest fragments, their

mating behaviours were disturbed compared with the behaviours of those nesting in larger tracts of forest.

Overall, her research has demonstrated that whereas some songbirds in the eastern United States and eastern Canada depend on corridors connecting habitat fragments, other species cross open habitats to use different patches of forest.

In 2007, her book *Silence of the Songbirds* reported declines in numbers of migrating songbirds and raised concerns about their future.

a. Distance effect

The number of lowland bird species on islands of the South Pacific declines with the islands' distance from the species source, the large island of New Guinea. Data in this graph were corrected for differences in the sizes of the islands. The number of bird species on each island is expressed as a percentage of the number of bird species on an island of equivalent size close to New Guinea.

b. Area effect

The number of bird species on tropical and subtropical islands throughout the world increases dramatically with island area. The data for islands near to a source and islands far from a mainland source are presented separately to minimize the effect of distance. Notice that the distance effect reduces the number of bird species on islands that are more than 300 km from a mainland source.

Figure 45.32

Factors that influence bird species richness on islands. **(a)** Evidence that fewer bird species colonize islands that are distant from the mainland source. **(b)** Evidence that more bird species colonize large islands than small ones.

Experimenting with Islands 45.9

Shortly after Robert MacArthur and Edward O. Wilson published the equilibrium theory of island biogeography in the 1960s, Wilson and Daniel Simberloff, one of Wilson's graduate students at Harvard University, undertook an ambitious experiment in community ecology. Simberloff reasoned that the best way to test the theory's predictions was to monitor immigration and extinction on barren islands.

Simberloff and Wilson devised a system for removing all the animals from individual red mangrove trees in the Florida Keys. The trees, with canopies that spread from 11 to 18 m in diameter, grow in shallow water and are isolated from their neighbours. Thus, each tree is an island that harbours an arthropod community. The species pool on the Florida mainland includes about 1000 species of arthropods, but each mangrove island contains no more than 40 species at one time.

After cataloguing the species on each island, Simberloff and Wilson hired an extermination company to erect large tents over each mangrove island and fumigate them to eliminate all arthropods on them **(Figure 1).** The exterminators used methylbromide, a pesticide that does not harm trees or leave any residue. The tents were then removed.

Simberloff then monitored both the immigration of arthropods to the islands and the extinction of species that became established on them. He surveyed four islands regularly for two years and at intervals thereafter.

The results of this experiment confirm several predictions of MacArthur and Wilson's theory **(Figure 2).** Arthropods rapidly recolonized the islands, and within eight or nine months, the number of species living on each island had reached an equilibrium that was close to the original species number. The island nearest the mainland had more

Daniel Simberloff, University of Tennessee

FIGURE 1

After cataloguing the arthropods, Simberloff and Wilson hired an extermination company to eliminate all living arthropods.

species than the most distant island. However, immigration and extinction were rapid, and Simberloff and Wilson suspected that some species went extinct even before they had noted their presence. The researchers also discovered that three years after the experimental treatments, the species composition of the islands was still changing constantly and did not remotely resemble the species composition on the islands before they were defaunated.

Simberloff and Wilson's research was a landmark study in ecology because it tested the predictions of an important theory using a field experiment. Although such efforts are now almost routine in ecological studies, this project was one of the first to demonstrate that large-scale experimental manipulations of natural systems are feasible and that they often produce clear results.

FIGURE 2

On three of four islands, species richness slowly returned to the predefaunation level (indicated by colour-coded dotted lines). The most distant island had not reached its predefaunation species richness after two years.

Their research confirmed the equilibrium theory's predictions that an island's size and distance from the mainland influence how many species will occupy it.

The equilibrial view of species richness can also apply to mainland communities that exist as islands in a metaphorical sea of dissimilar habitat. Lakes are "islands" in a "sea" of dry land, and mountaintops are habitat "islands" in a "sea" of low terrain. Species richness in these communities is partly governed by the immigration of new species from distant sources and the extinction of species already present. As human activities disrupt environments across the globe, undisturbed sites function as islandlike refuges for threatened and endangered species. Conservation biologists apply the general lessons of MacArthur and Wilson's theory to the design of nature preserves (see Chapter 47).

The study of community ecology promises to keep biologists busy for some time to come.

STUDY BREAK

1. How does species richness change with increasing latitude?
2. In the island biogeography model proposed by MacArthur and Wilson, what processes govern the number of species on an island? What happens to the number of species once equilibrium is reached?
3. What effect do island size and distance from the mainland have on immigration and extinction of colonizing species?

Review

Access an interactive eBook, chapter-specific interactive learning tools, including flashcards, quizzes, videos, and more in your Biology **CourseMate**, accessed through NelsonBrain.com **Aplia™** is an online interactive learning solution that helps you improve comprehension—and your grade—by integrating a variety of mediums and tools such as videos, tutorials, practice tests, and an interactive eBook.

45.1 Interspecific Interactions

- Coevolution involves genetically based, reciprocal adaptations in two or more interacting species. Coevolution is not restricted to two species but often involves complex interactions among several species in a community.

45.2 Getting Food

- Predators eat animal prey, whereas herbivores eat plants. Predators and herbivores are animals with characteristics allowing them to feed efficiently. Predation and herbivory are the most conspicuous relationships in ecological communities.
- A koala is a specialist because it eats the leaves of only a few of the available species of *Eucalyptus*. Specialists tend to eat only a few types of food, whereas generalists take a broader diet.
- Optimal foraging theory predicts that an animal's diet is a compromise between the costs and the benefits associated with different types of food. Costs include the time and energy it takes to pursue, capture, and consume a particular kind of food. Benefits are the energy that the food provides.

45.3 Defence

- Animals use seven types of defence: size, eternal vigilance, avoiding detection, counterattack, chemical defence, warnings, and mimicry. Below are examples of each.
- The large size of elephants means that they have few natural predators.
- Meerkats are constantly on the lookout for potential predators.

- Caterpillars that look like bird droppings are not recognized as edible.
- A bee or a scorpion has a sting, and porcupines and other mammals have spines.
- Skunks spray a noxious chemical at potential predators.
- Skunks have black and white colouration and monarch butterflies have orange and black colouration.
- The harmless drone fly mimics the colouration and behaviour of the stinging bee or wasp.
- Animals using chemical defences either synthesize the chemicals themselves or sequester them from other sources. This can include plants that the organism eats.
- Aposematic displays teach would-be predators to avoid the signaller.
- Batesian mimicry occurs when an edible or harmless species mimics an inedible or a poisonous one. In Müllerian mimicry, two or more unpalatable or poisonous species have a similar appearance.

45.4 Competition

- Intraspecific competition can occur between two different species. Two types of competition are interference and exploitation. The competitive exclusion principle states that two or more species cannot coexist indefinitely if both rely on the same limiting resources and exploit them in the same way. One species will be able to harvest the available resources better and eventually outcompete the other species.
- A population's ecological niche is defined as the resources it uses and the environmental conditions it requires over its lifetime. A fundamental niche, larger than a realized niche, includes all conditions and resources a population can tolerate. A realized niche is the range of conditions and resources that a population actually encounters in nature.
- Resource partitioning occurs when sympatric species use different resources or the same resources in different ways. Plants

may position their root systems at different levels, which avoids competition for water and nutrients.

- Character displacement results in sympatric species that differ in morphology and use different resources even though they would not do so in allopatric situations. An example of character displacement is the honey-eaters of Australia.

45.5 The Nature of Ecological Communities

Type of Interaction	Effect on Species Involved	Example
Commensalism	One species benefits; the other is unaffected (+/0)	Egrets and the large grazers that flush insects out of grasses during feeding
Mutualism	Both species benefit (+/+)	Bull's horn acacia tree and a species of small ants
Parasitism	One species benefits (parasite); the other is harmed (host) (+/−)	Ectoparasites such as mosquitoes and leeches and their mammalian hosts

- Two hypotheses about ecological communities have been developed by ecologists. The interactive hypothesis predicts that mature communities are at equilibrium and, if disturbed, will return to the predisturbed state. The individualistic hypothesis predicts that communities do not achieve equilibrium but rather are in a steady state of flux in response to disturbance and environmental change.
- Ecotones are generally species rich because they contain species from both communities, as well as species that occur only in transition zones.

45.6 Community Characteristics

- Indices allow population biologists to objectively compare the diversity of communities. Shannon's indices provide a measure of diversity (H') and evenness (E_H).
- Alpha (α) diversity is the number of species living in a single community. Beta (β) diversity is the number of species living in a collection of communities.
- Herbivores are primary consumers and form the second trophic level. Omnivores can be primary, secondary, and tertiary consumers (second, third, and fourth trophic levels, respectively) in a single meal.
- Generally, communities that support complex food webs are more stable. The disappearance of one or even two species does not have a major impact on the food web and thus community structure.

45.7 Effects of Population Interactions on Community Structure

- Species distribution and resource use in K-selected species are profoundly affected by competition. However, competition seems to have little effect on the community structure of r-selected species.
- Predation and herbivory can increase and/or decrease species richness, depending on the circumstances. Species richness can increase if a predator eliminates a strong competitor, allowing

other organisms to exploit the available resources, for example, predatory sea stars reducing populations of mussels. Species richness can decrease when a predator eats less abundant species, further reducing their numbers.

- A keystone species has a much greater effect on the community than its numbers might suggest. Only a few individuals can have a profound impact on community structure.

45.8 Effects of Disturbance on Community Characteristics

- A community may never attain equilibrium because of disturbances such as cyclones, mortality caused by internal processes, and the recruitment of new colonies.
- The intermediate disturbance hypothesis states that species richness is greatest in communities experiencing fairly frequent disturbances of moderate intensity. Data gathered about a river system in New Zealand revealed that areas with moderate disturbance (e.g., moved rocks, soil, and sand in the streambed) had the highest species diversity.
- Generally, communities with a higher species richness recover from disturbance much more quickly than those with a low species richness.

45.9 Succession

- Primary succession begins when organisms first colonize habitats without soil, whereas secondary succession occurs after existing vegetation is destroyed or disrupted by an environmental disturbance.
- A climax community is a late successional stage that can be found in both primary and secondary succession. Climax communities are dominated by a few species that replace themselves and persist until a disturbance eliminates them. Species composition of a climax community is determined by local climate and soil conditions, surrounding vegetation, and chance events.
- The facilitation hypothesis holds that species modify the environment in a way that makes it less suitable for themselves but more suitable for those species that follow them in succession. The inhibition hypothesis contends that species currently occupying a successional stage prevent new species from occupying the same community. The tolerance hypothesis holds that early-stage species neither facilitate nor inhibit the growth of new species. Instead, succession proceeds because new species are able to outcompete and replace early-stage species.

45.10 Variance in Species Richness among Communities

- Species richness generally decreases with increasing latitude.
- The numbers of species on an island is governed by immigration of new species and extinction of species already there. Once equilibrium between immigration and extinction is reached, the number of species on an island remains relatively constant. As one species goes extinct, it is replaced by a newly arrived immigrant species.
- Large islands have higher immigration rates and lower extinction rates than small islands. Islands near the mainland have higher immigration rates than distant islands. Distance does not affect extinction rates. As a result, at equilibrium, near islands have more species than far islands.

Questions

Self-Test Questions

1. According to optimal foraging theory, what do predators do?
   a. always eat the largest prey possible
   b. always eat the prey that are easiest to catch
   c. choose prey based on the costs of consuming it compared to the energy it provides
   d. eat plants when animal prey are scarce
   e. have coevolved mechanisms to overcome prey defences

2. What term refers to the use of the same limiting resource by two species?
   a. brood parasitism
   b. interference competition
   c. exploitative competition
   d. mutualism

3. What is the range of resources that a population of one species can possibly use called?
   a. its fundamental niche
   b. its realized niche
   c. resource partitioning
   d. its relative abundance

4. Differences in molar (tooth) structure of sympatric mammals may reflect which of the following?
   a. predation
   b. character displacement
   c. interference competition
   d. cryptic colouration

5. Bacteria that live in the human intestine assist human digestion and eat nutrients that the human consumes. Which term best describes this relationship?
   a. commensalism
   b. mutualism
   c. endoparasitism
   d. ectoparasitism

6. In the table below, the letters refer to four communities, and the numbers indicate how many individuals were recorded for each of five species. Which community has the highest species diversity?

	Species 1	Species 2	Species 3	Species 4	Species 5
a.	80	10	10	0	0
b.	25	25	25	25	0
c.		4	6	8	80
d.	20	20	20	20	20

7. Which phrase best describes a keystone species?
   a. is usually a primary producer
   b. has a critically important role in determining the species composition of its community
   c. is always a predator
   d. usually exhibits aposematic colouration

8. Species richness can be highest in communities with this type of disturbances.
   a. very frequent and severe
   b. very frequent and of moderate intensity
   c. very rare and severe
   d. of intermediate frequency and moderate intensity

9. Which term refers to a community's change in species composition from bare and lifeless rock to climax vegetation?
   a. competition
   b. secondary succession
   c. primary succession
   d. facilitation

10. What does the equilibrium theory of island biogeography predict about the number of species found on an island?
    a. It increases steadily until it equals the number in the mainland species pool.
    b. It is greater on large islands than on small ones.
    c. It is smaller on islands near the mainland than on distant islands.
    d. It is greater for islands near the equator than for islands near the poles.

Questions for Discussion

1. Many landscapes dominated by agricultural activities also have patches of forest of various sizes. What is the minimum amount of habitat required by different species? Focus on 10 species—5 animals and 5 plants. For each species, can you estimate the minimum viable population?

2. Using the terms and concepts introduced in this chapter, describe the interactions that humans have with 10 other species. Try to choose at least 8 species that we do not eat.

3. After reading about the two potential biases in the scientific literature on competition, describe how future studies of competition might avoid such biases.

4. What are the primary producers in a community of parasites?

5. What influence does agriculture have on population interactions and community development?

Among the fastest growing ecosystems in the world—shopping malls and residential areas sprawl in the north part of London, Ontario.

M.B. Fenton

46 Ecosystems

WHY IT MATTERS

As shown in the chapter-opening photograph, urban ecosystems are the most rapidly growing habitat on the planet, replacing existing habitats at an astonishing rate partly because of growth in populations and in economies. The system portrayed in the photograph is low-density housing with services (water and electricity), but in many parts of the world, housing expansions are high density, with few, if any, services. Apart from humans and our domesticated plant and animal species, which components of the original flora and fauna persist? Walk around your neighbourhood and check it out.

How does the urban ecosystem differ from what was there before? In what ways does it differ? Think of runoff from rain and snow, of the heat-absorbing and reflecting properties of buildings, concrete, and asphalt. What are the effects of gardeners and landscapers, however well meaning? The urban ecosystem offers people in general, and biologists in particular, many opportunities for research and study. We must determine what changes we can effect in the construction and design of neighbourhoods to maximize their compatibility with native organisms. How can we make urban neighbourhoods more useful to migrating songbirds?

Archaeological evidence indicates that urban sprawl occurred around 6000 years ago around the site of Tell Brak in what is now northern Syria. Then the "city" that stood at Tell Brak occupied about 55 ha when other contemporary settlements rarely exceeded 3 ha and the largest of its neighbours was just 15 ha. There is evidence of spatial separation between subcommunities at Tell Brak, where neighbourhoods were divided by walls and limited points of access.

Urban sprawl may not be new, but the current scale makes it a frontier for action to achieve conservation of biodiversity. The purpose of this chapter is to explore some aspects of ecosystems and introduce them as objects of biological study.

Ecosystems are often studied by following the movement of energy from one level to another. Photosynthetic organisms form the energetic basis for ecosystems, providing sources of food for other organisms (usually animals). Levels of biomass at different trophic levels (primary producers; primary, secondary, and tertiary consumers) generally reflect the movement of energy. The movement of markers such as DDT (see "Molecule behind Biology," Box 46.2, p. 1184) through ecosystems provided an all-too-sobering view of the connectedness among the ecosystems of the globe.

46.1 Energy Flow and Ecosystem Energetics

Ecosystems receive a steady input of energy from an external source, usually the Sun. Energy flows through an ecosystem, but, as dictated by the laws of thermodynamics, much of that energy is lost without being used by organisms. In contrast, materials cycle between living and nonliving reservoirs, both locally and on a global scale. The flow of energy through and the cycling of materials around an ecosystem make resident organisms highly dependent on one another and on their physical surroundings.

Food webs define the pathways by which energy and nutrients move through an ecosystem's biotic components. In most ecosystems, nutrients and energy move simultaneously through a grazing food web and a detrital food web **(Figure 46.1).** The grazing food web includes the producer, herbivore, and secondary consumer trophic levels. The detrital food web includes

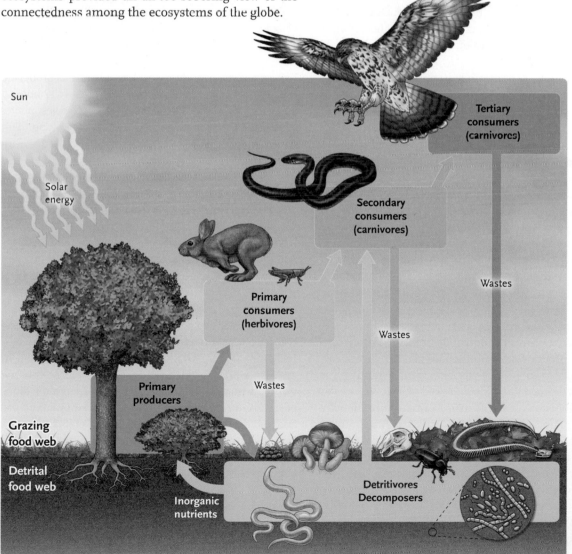

Figure 46.1

Grazing and detrital food webs. Energy and nutrients move through two parallel food webs in most ecosystems. The grazing food web includes producers, herbivores, and carnivores. The detrital food web includes detritivores and decomposers. Each box in this diagram represents many species, and each arrow represents many arrows.

detritivores and decomposers. Because detritivores and decomposers subsist on the remains and waste products of organisms at every trophic level, the two food webs are closely interconnected. Detritivores also contribute to the grazing food web when carnivores eat them.

All organisms in a particular trophic level are the same number of energy transfers from the ecosystem's ultimate energy source. Photosynthetic plants are one energy transfer removed from sunlight, herbivores (primary consumers) are two, secondary consumers are three, and tertiary consumers are four.

46.1a Primary Productivity Involves Fixing Carbon

Virtually all life on Earth depends on the input of solar energy. Every minute of every day, Earth's atmosphere intercepts roughly 80 kJ (kilojoules) of energy per square metre (see Chapter 1). About half of that energy is absorbed, scattered, or reflected by gases, dust, water vapour, and clouds before it reaches the planet's surface (see *The Purple Pages*). Most energy reaching the surface falls on bodies of water or bare ground, where it is absorbed as heat or reflected back into the atmosphere. Reflected energy warms the atmosphere. Only a small percentage contacts primary producers, and most of that energy evaporates water, driving transpiration in plants (see Chapter 7).

Ultimately, photosynthesis converts less than 1% of the solar energy arriving at Earth's surface into chemical energy. But primary producers still capture enough energy to produce an average of several kilograms of dry plant material per square metre per year. On a global scale, they produce more than 150 billion tonnes of new biological material annually. Some of the solar energy that producers convert into chemical energy is transferred to consumers at higher trophic levels.

The rate at which producers convert solar energy into chemical energy is an ecosystem's **gross primary productivity**. But like other organisms, producers use energy for their own maintenance functions. After deducting energy used for these functions (see Chapter 6), whatever chemical energy remains is the ecosystem's **net primary productivity**. In most ecosystems, net primary productivity is 50 to 90% of gross primary productivity. In other words, producers use between 10 and 50% of the energy they capture for their own respiration.

Ecologists usually measure primary productivity in units of energy captured ($kJ \cdot m^{-2} \cdot year^{-1}$) or in units of biomass created ($kg \cdot m^{-2} \cdot year^{-1}$). **Biomass** is the dry mass of biological material per unit area or volume of habitat. (We measure biomass as the *dry* mass of organisms because their water content, which fluctuates with water uptake or loss, has no energetic or nutritional value.) Do not confuse an ecosystem's productivity with its **standing crop biomass**, the total dry mass of plants present at a given time. Net primary productivity is the *rate* at which the standing crop produces *new* biomass (see Chapter 7).

Energy captured by plants is stored in biological molecules, mostly carbohydrates, lipids, and proteins. Ecologists can convert units of biomass into units of energy or vice versa as long as they know how much carbohydrate, protein, and lipid a sample of biological material contains. For reference, 1 g of carbohydrate and 1 g of protein each contains about 17.5 kJ of energy. Thus, net primary productivity indexes the rate at which producers accumulate energy as well as the rate at which new biomass is added to an ecosystem. Ecologists measure changes in biomass to estimate productivity because it is far easier to measure biomass than energy content. New biomass takes several forms, including

- growth of existing producers,
- creation of new producers by reproduction, and
- storage of energy as carbohydrates.

Because herbivores eat all three forms of new biomass, net primary productivity also measures how much new energy is available for primary consumers.

The potential rate of photosynthesis in any ecosystem is proportional to the intensity and duration of sunlight, which varies geographically and seasonally (see Chapter 6, Chapter 7, and *The Purple Pages*). Sunlight is most intense and day length is least variable near the equator. In contrast, the intensity of sunlight is weakest and day length is most variable near the poles. This means that producers at the equator can photosynthesize for nearly 12 hours a day, every day of the year, whereas near the poles, photosynthesis is virtually impossible during the long, dark winter. In summer, however, photosynthesis occurs virtually around the clock.

Sunlight is not the only factor influencing the rate of primary productivity. Temperature and availability of water and nutrients also affect this rate. Many of the world's deserts receive plenty of sunshine but have low rates of productivity because water is in short supply and the soil is poor in nutrients. Mean annual primary productivity varies greatly on a global scale **(Figure 46.2)**, reflecting variations in these environmental factors (see *The Purple Pages*).

On a finer geographic scale, within a particular terrestrial ecosystem, mean annual net productivity often increases with the availability of water **(Figure 46.3).** In systems with sufficient water, a shortage of mineral nutrients may be limiting. All plants need specific ratios of macronutrients and micronutrients for maintenance and photosynthesis (see Chapter 7). But plants withdraw nutrients from soil, and if nutrient concentration drops below a critical level, photosynthesis may decrease or stop altogether. In every ecosystem, one nutrient inevitably runs out before the supplies of other nutrients are exhausted. The element in shortest supply is called a **limiting nutrient** because its absence curtails productivity. Productivity in agricultural fields is subject to the same constraints as productivity in natural ecosystems.

SeaWiFS Project, NASA/Goddard Space Flight Center and ORBIMAGE

Figure 46.2
Global variation in primary productivity. Satellite data from 2002 provide a visual portrait of net primary productivity across Earth's surface. High-productivity regions on land are dark green; low-productivity regions are yellow. For aquatic environments, the highest productivity is red, down through orange, yellow, green, blue, and purple (lowest).

Figure 46.3
Water and net primary productivity. Mean annual precipitation among 100 sites in the Great Plains of North America. These data include only above-ground productivity.

Table 46.1	Standing Crop Biomass and Net Primary Productivity of Different Ecosystems	
Ecosystem	Mean Standing Crop Biomass (kg/m²)	Mean Net Primary Productivity (kg/m²/y¹)
Terrestrial Ecosystems		
Tropical rainforest	450	22.0
Tropical deciduous forest	350	16.0
Temperate rainforest	350	13.0
Temperate deciduous forest	300	12.0
Savanna	40	9.0
Boreal forest (taiga)	200	8.0
Woodland and shrubland	60	7.0
Agricultural land	10	6.5
Temperate grassland	16	6.0
Tundra and alpine tundra	6.0	1.4
Desert and thornwoods	7.0	0.9
Extreme desert, rock, sand, ice	0.2	0.03
Freshwater Ecosystems		
Swamp and marsh	150	20
Lake and stream	0.2	2.5
Marine Ecosystems		
Open ocean	0.03	1.3
Upwelling zones	0.2	5.0
Continental shelf	0.1	3.6
Kelp beds and reefs	20	25
Estuaries	10	15
World Total	**36**	**3.3**

From Whittaker, R.H. 1975. *Communities and Ecosystems.* 2nd ed. Macmillan.

Farmers increase productivity by irrigating (adding water to) and fertilizing (adding nutrients to) their crops.

In freshwater and marine ecosystems, where water is always readily available, the depth of water and combined availability of sunlight and nutrients govern the rate of primary productivity. Productivity is high in near-shore ecosystems, where sunlight penetrates shallow, nutrient-rich waters. Kelp beds and coral reefs along temperate and tropical marine coastlines, respectively, are among the most productive ecosystems on Earth (**Table 46.1**; see also Figure 46.2). In contrast, productivity is low in the open waters of a large lake or ocean. There sunlight penetrates only the upper layers, and nutrients sink to the bottom; thus, the two requirements for photosynthesis—sunlight and nutrients—are available in different places.

Although ecosystems vary in their rates of primary productivity, these differences are not always proportional to variations in their standing crop biomass (see Table 46.1). For example, biomass amounts in temperate deciduous forests and temperate grasslands differ by a factor of 20, but the difference in their rates of net primary productivity is much smaller. Most biomass in trees is present in nonphotosynthetic tissues such as wood, so their ratio of productivity to biomass is low $(12 \text{ kg} \cdot \text{m}^{-2}/300 \text{ kg}(\text{m} - 2 = 0.04)$. By contrast, grasslands do not accumulate much biomass because annual mortality, herbivores, and fires remove plant material as it is produced, so their productivity to biomass ratio is much higher (6.0 kg(m–2/16 kg(m–2 = 0.375).

Some ecosystems contribute more than others to overall net primary productivity **(Figure 46.4)**. Ecosystems covering large areas make substantial total contributions, even if their productivity per unit area is low. Conversely, geographically restricted ecosystems make large contributions if their productivity is high. Open ocean and tropical rainforests contribute about equally to total global productivity, but for different reasons. Open oceans have low productivity, but they cover nearly two-thirds of Earth's surface. Tropical rainforests are highly productive but cover only a relatively small area.

Net primary productivity ultimately supports all consumers in grazing and detrital food webs. Consumers in the grazing food web eat some biomass at every trophic level except the highest. Uneaten biomass eventually dies and passes into detrital food webs. Moreover, consumers assimilate only a portion of the material they ingest, and unassimilated material passed as feces also supports detritivores and decomposers.

46.1b Secondary Productivity Involves Animals Eating Plants, Thus Moving Up the Trophic Scale

As energy is transferred from producers to consumers, some is stored in new consumer biomass, called **secondary productivity**. Nevertheless, two factors cause

energy to be lost from the ecosystem every time it flows from one trophic level to another. First, animals use much of the energy they assimilate for maintenance and locomotion rather than for production of new biomass. Second, as dictated by the second law of thermodynamics, no biochemical reaction is 100% efficient, so some of the chemical energy liberated by cellular respiration is converted to heat, which most organisms do not use.

46.1c Ecological Efficiency Is Measured by Use of Energy

Ecological efficiency is the ratio of net productivity at one trophic level to net productivity at the trophic level below. If plants in an ecosystem have a net primary productivity of $1.0 \text{ kg} \cdot \text{m}^{-2} \cdot \text{year}^{-1}$ of new tissue, and the herbivores that eat those plants produce 0.1 kg of new tissue per square metre per year, the ecological efficiency of the herbivores is 10%. The efficiencies of three processes (harvesting food, assimilating ingested energy, and producing new biomass) determine the ecological efficiencies of consumers.

Harvesting efficiency is the ratio of the energy content of food consumed compared with the energy content of food available. Predators harvest food efficiently when prey are abundant and easy to capture (see Chapter 45).

Assimilation efficiency is the ratio of the energy absorbed from consumed food to the total energy

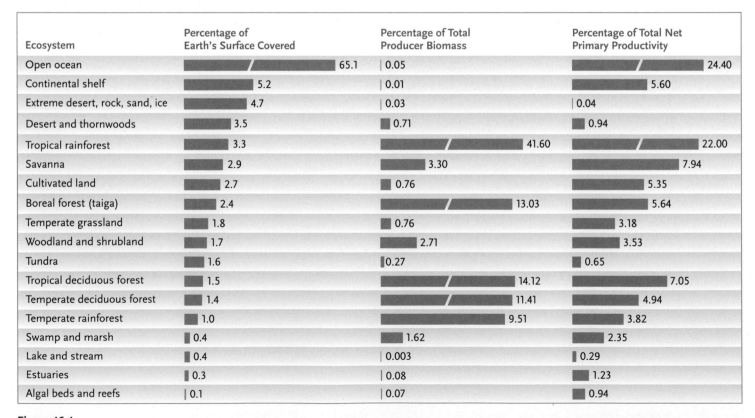

Ecosystem	Percentage of Earth's Surface Covered	Percentage of Total Producer Biomass	Percentage of Total Net Primary Productivity
Open ocean	65.1	0.05	24.40
Continental shelf	5.2	0.01	5.60
Extreme desert, rock, sand, ice	4.7	0.03	0.04
Desert and thornwoods	3.5	0.71	0.94
Tropical rainforest	3.3	41.60	22.00
Savanna	2.9	3.30	7.94
Cultivated land	2.7	0.76	5.35
Boreal forest (taiga)	2.4	13.03	5.64
Temperate grassland	1.8	0.76	3.18
Woodland and shrubland	1.7	2.71	3.53
Tundra	1.6	0.27	0.65
Tropical deciduous forest	1.5	14.12	7.05
Temperate deciduous forest	1.4	11.41	4.94
Temperate rainforest	1.0	9.51	3.82
Swamp and marsh	0.4	1.62	2.35
Lake and stream	0.4	0.003	0.29
Estuaries	0.3	0.08	1.23
Algal beds and reefs	0.1	0.07	0.94

Figure 46.4

Biomass and net primary productivity. An ecosystem's percentage coverage of Earth's surface is not proportional to its contribution to total biomass of producers or its contribution to the total net primary productivity.

content of the food. Because animal prey is relatively easy to digest, carnivores absorb between 60 and 90% of the energy in their food. Assimilation efficiency is lower for prey with indigestible parts such as bones or exoskeletons. Herbivores assimilate only 15 to 80% of the energy they consume because cellulose is not very digestible. Herbivores lacking cellulose-digesting systems are on the low end of the scale, whereas those that can digest cellulose are at the higher end.

Production efficiency is the ratio of the energy content of new tissue produced to the energy assimilated from food. Production efficiency varies with maintenance costs. Endothermic animals often use less than 10% of their assimilated energy for growth and reproduction because they use energy to generate body heat (see Chapter 42). Ectothermic animals channel more than 50% of their assimilated energy into new biomass.

The overall ecological efficiency of most organisms is 5 to 20%. As a rule of thumb, only about 10% of energy accumulated at one trophic level is converted into biomass at the next higher trophic level, as illustrated by energy transfers at Silver Springs, Florida **(Figure 46.5)**. Silver Springs is an ecosystem that has been studied for many years. Producers in the Silver Springs ecosystem convert 1.2% of the solar energy they intercept into chemical energy (represented by 86 986 kJ·m^{-2}·year^{-1} of gross primary productivity). However, plants use about two-thirds of this energy for respiration, leaving a net primary productivity, one-third of which is to be included in new plant biomass,. All consumers in the grazing food web (on the right in Figure 46.5) ultimately depend on this energy source, which diminishes with each transfer between trophic levels. Energy is lost to respiration and export at each

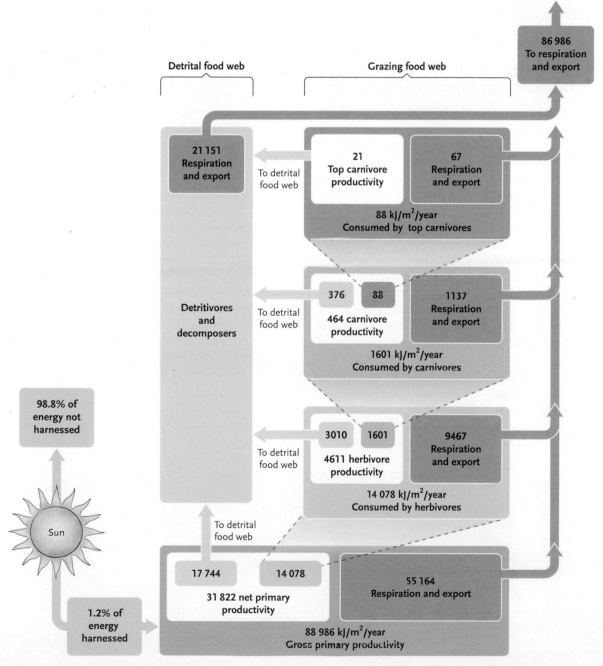

Figure 46.5
Energy flow through the Silver Springs ecosystem.

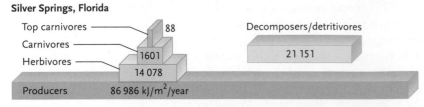

Silver Springs, Florida

Figure 46.6

Pyramids of energy. The pyramid of energy for Silver Springs, Florida, shows that the amount of energy (kJ·m^{-2}·year^{-1}) passing through each trophic level decreases as it moves up the food web.

trophic level. In addition, organic wastes and uneaten biomass represent substantial energy that flows into the detrital food web (on the left in Figure 46.5). To determine the ecological efficiency of any trophic level, we divide its productivity by the productivity of the level below it. The ecological efficiency of midlevel carnivores at Silver Springs is 10.06%, 464 kJ·m^{-2}·year^{-1}/4611 kJ·m^{-2}·year^{-1}.

46.1d Three Types of Pyramids Describe Ecosystems: Energy, Biomass, and Numbers

As energy works its way up a food web, energy losses are multiplied in successive energy transfers, greatly reducing the energy available to support the highest trophic levels (see Figure 46.5). Consider a hypothetical example in which ecological efficiency is 10% for all consumers. Assume that the plants in a small field annually produce new tissues containing 100 kJ of energy. Because only 10% of that energy is transferred to new herbivore biomass, the 100 kJ in plants produces 10 kJ of new herbivorous insects, 1 kJ of new songbirds that eat insects, and only 0.1 kJ of new falcons that eat songbirds. About 0.1% of the energy from primary productivity remains after three trophic levels of transfer. If the energy available to each trophic level is depicted graphically, the result is a **pyramid of energy**, with primary producers on the bottom and higher-level consumers on the top **(Figure 46.6)**.

The low ecological efficiencies that characterize most energy transfers illustrate one advantage of eating "lower on the food chain." This reality is reflected by major adaptive radiations of lineages of

animals whose ancestors were secondary consumers when they switched to being primary consumers. Good examples of such radiations occur, for example, among insects, fish, dinosaurs, and mammals.

Even though humans digest and assimilate meat more efficiently than vegetables, we could feed more people if we all ate more primary producers directly instead of first passing them through another trophic level, such as cattle or chickens, to produce meat. Production of animal protein is costly because much of the energy fed to livestock is used for their own maintenance rather than production of new biomass. But despite the economic and health-related logic of a more vegetarian diet, changing our eating habits alone will not eliminate food shortages or the frequency of malnutrition. Many regions of Africa, Australia, North America, and South America support vegetation that is suitable only for grazing by large herbivores. These areas could not produce significant quantities of edible grains and vegetables without significant additions of water and fertilizer (see Chapter 48).

Inefficiency of energy transfer from one trophic level to the next has profound effects on ecosystem structure. Ecologists illustrate these effects in diagrams called **ecological pyramids**. Trophic levels are drawn as stacked blocks, with the size of each block proportional to the energy, biomass, or numbers of organisms present. Pyramids of energy typically have wide bases and narrow tops (see Figure 46.6) because each trophic level contains only about 10% as much energy as the trophic level below it.

Progressive reduction in productivity at higher trophic levels usually establishes a **pyramid of biomass (Figure 46.7)**. The biomass at each trophic level is proportional to the amount of chemical energy temporarily stored there. Thus, in terrestrial ecosystems, the total mass of producers is generally greater than the total mass of herbivores, which is, in turn, greater than the total mass of predators (see Figure 46.7a). Populations of top predators, from killer whales to lions and crocodiles, contain too little biomass and energy to support another trophic level; thus, they have no nonhuman predators.

Freshwater and marine ecosystems sometimes exhibit inverted pyramids of biomass (see Figure 46.7b). In the open waters of a lake or ocean, primary

Figure 46.7

Pyramids of biomass. (a) The pyramid of standing crop biomass for Silver Springs is bottom heavy, as it is for most ecosystems. **(b)** Some marine ecosystems, such as that in the English Channel, have an inverted pyramid of biomass because producers are quickly eaten by primary consumers. Only the producer and herbivore trophic levels are illustrated here. The data for both pyramids are given in kilograms per square metre of dry biomass.

a. Grassland (summer)

b. Temperate forest (summer)

Top carnivores · Carnivores · Herbivores · Producers

Grassland: 1 / 90 000 / 200 000 / 1 500 000

Temperate forest: 2 / 120 000 / 150 000 / 200

Figure 46.8

Pyramids of numbers. **(a)** The pyramid of numbers (numbers of individuals per 1000 m²) for temperate grasslands is bottom heavy because individual producers are small and very numerous. **(b)** The pyramid of numbers for forests may have a narrow base because herbivorous insects usually outnumber the producers, many of which are large trees. Data for both pyramids were collected in summer. Detritivores and decomposers (soil animals and microorganisms) are not included because they are difficult to count.

consumers (zooplankton) eat primary producers (phytoplankton) almost as soon as they are produced. As a result, the standing crop of primary consumers at any moment in time is actually larger than the standing crop of primary producers. Food webs in these ecosystems are stable because producers have exceptionally high **turnover rates.** In other words, producers divide and their populations grow so quickly that feeding by zooplankton does not endanger their populations or reduce their productivity. However, on an annual basis, the *cumulative total* biomass of primary producers far outweighs that of primary consumers.

The reduction of energy and biomass affects population sizes of organisms at the top of a food web. Top predators can be relatively large animals, so the limited biomass present in the highest trophic levels is concentrated in relatively few animals **(Figure 46.8).** The extremely narrow top of this **pyramid of numbers** has grave implications for conservation biology (see Chapter 47). Top predators tend to be large animals with small population sizes. And because each individual must patrol a large area to find sufficient food, members of a population are often widely dispersed within their habitats. As a result, they are subject to genetic drift (see Chapter 19) and are highly sensitive to hunting, habitat destruction, and random events that can lead to extinction. Top predators may also suffer from the accumulation of poisonous materials that move through food webs (see the next section). Even predators that feed below the top trophic level often suffer the ill effects of human activities. Consumers sometimes regulate ecosystem processes.

Numerous abiotic factors, such as the intensity and duration of sunlight, rainfall, temperature, and the availability of nutrients, have significant effects on primary productivity. Primary productivity, in turn, profoundly affects the populations of herbivores and predators that feed on them. But what effect does feeding by these consumers have on primary productivity?

Consumers sometimes influence rates of primary productivity, especially in ecosystems with low species diversity and relatively few trophic levels. Food webs in lake ecosystems depend primarily on the productivity of phytoplankton **(Figure 46.9).** Phytoplankton are, in

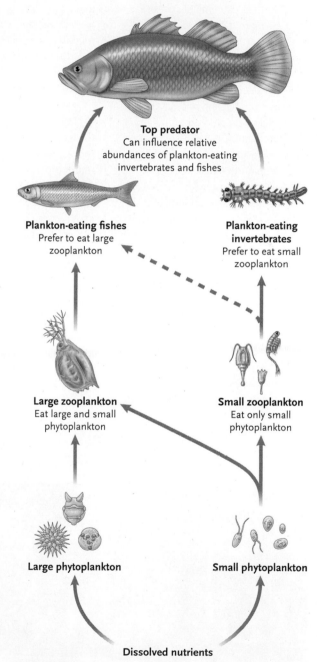

Top predator
Can influence relative abundances of plankton-eating invertebrates and fishes

Plankton-eating fishes
Prefer to eat large zooplankton

Plankton-eating invertebrates
Prefer to eat small zooplankton

Large zooplankton
Eat large and small phytoplankton

Small zooplankton
Eat only small phytoplankton

Large phytoplankton

Small phytoplankton

Dissolved nutrients

Figure 46.9

Consumer regulation of primary productivity. A simplified food web illustrates that lake ecosystems have relatively few trophic levels. The effects of feeding by top carnivores can cascade downward, exerting an indirect effect on the phytoplankton and thus on primary productivity.

Fishing Fleets at Loggerheads with Sea Turtles Box 46.1

Populations of loggerhead sea turtles (*Caretta caretta*) that nest on Western Pacific beaches in Australia and Japan have been in decline. Like other sea turtles, *C. caretta* hatch from eggs that females bury on sandy beaches. Immediately after hatching, the young turtles rush to the surf and the open ocean. Turtles mature at sea and return to their hatching beaches to lay eggs. Using mitochondrial DNA (mtDNA), Bruce Bowen and colleagues explored the situation sea turtles face.

The researchers took mtDNA samples from nesting populations in Australia and Japan, from populations of turtles feeding in Baja California, and from turtles drowned in fishing nets in the north Pacific. One 350-base-pair segment of mtDNA included sequence variations that are characteristic of different loggerhead populations. After samples were amplified by the polymerase chain reaction, sequencing revealed three major variants of mtDNA, which the researchers designated as sequences A, B, and C. The sequences were distributed among loggerhead turtles, as shown in **Table 1.**

The mtDNA of most *C. caretta* found in Baja California and in fishing nets in the north Pacific matched that of turtles from the Japanese nesting areas. These data support the idea that loggerhead turtles hatched in Japan make the 10 000-km-long migration across the North Pacific to Baja California. The data also indicate that a few turtles that hatched in Australia may follow the same migratory route.

This migration could be aided by the North Pacific Current, which moves from west to east, whereas the return trip from Baja to Japan could be made via the North Equatorial Current, which runs from east to west just north of the equator. Loggerhead turtles have been found in these currents, and further tests will reveal whether they have the mtDNA sequence characteristic of the individuals nesting in Japan and feeding in Baja California.

The nesting population of *C. caretta* in Japan is 2000 to 3000 females. It is uncertain if this population can survive the loss of thousands of offspring to fishing in the North Pacific. The number of female loggerhead turtles nesting in Australia has declined by 50 to 80% in the last decade, so the loss of only a few individuals in fishing nets could also have a drastic impact on this population. To save the loggerhead turtles, wildlife managers and international agencies must establish and enforce limits on the number of migrating individuals trapped and killed in the ocean fisheries.

Like other sea turtles, the loggerheads are severely impacted by fishing. As many as 4000 loggerheads drown in nets every year, and others are caught in longline fisheries. Adoption of a new fish hook **(Figure 1)** could reduce the turtle catch in longline fishing operations.

Table 1	Sources of Turtles by Nesting Grounds		
Number of Turtles			
Location	Sequence A	Sequence B	Sequence C
Australian nesting areas	26	0	0
Japanese nesting areas	0	23	3
Baja California feeding grounds	2	19	5
North Pacific	1	28	5

M. B. Fenton

FIGURE 1

Sea turtles and longlining. Conventional longline hooks (left) readily catch sea turtles, whereas the hook on the right does not. The World Wildlife Fund is promoting the use of hooks (right) that are friendly to sea turtles in an effort to reduce their losses to longline fishing.

turn, eaten by herbivorous zooplankton, themselves consumed by predatory invertebrates and fishes. The top nonhuman carnivore in these food webs is usually a predatory fish.

Herbivorous zooplankton play a central role in regulation of lake ecosystems. Small zooplankton species consume only small phytoplankton. Thus, when *small* zooplankton are especially abundant, large phytoplankton escape predation and survive, and the lake's primary productivity is high. By contrast, large zooplankton are voracious, eating both small and large phytoplankton. When large zooplankton are especially abundant, they reduce the overall biomass of phytoplankton, lowering the ecosystem's primary productivity.

In this trophic cascade, predator–prey effects reverberate through population interactions at two or more trophic levels in an ecosystem. Feeding by plankton-eating invertebrates and fishes has a *direct* impact on herbivorous zooplankton populations and an *indirect* impact on phytoplankton populations (the ecosystem's primary producers). Invertebrate predators prefer small zooplankton. And when the invertebrates that eat small zooplankton are the dominant predators in the ecosystem, large zooplankton become more abundant; they consume many phytoplankton, causing a decrease in productivity. But plankton-eating fishes prefer to eat large zooplankton (see Figure 46.9, p. 1181), so when they are abundant, small zooplankton become the dominant herbivores, leading large phytoplankton to become more numerous, which raises the lake's productivity.

Large predatory fishes may add an additional level of control to the system because they feed on and regulate the population sizes of plankton-eating invertebrates and fishes. Thus, the effects of feeding by the top predator can cascade downward through the food web, affecting the densities of plankton-eating invertebrates and fishes, herbivorous zooplankton, and phytoplankton. Research in Norway with brown trout (*Salmo trutta*), a top predator, and Arctic char (*Salvelinus alpinus*), the prey, demonstrated how culling prey can promote the recovery of top predators. In this case, Lake Takvatn was the scene of a large-scale experiment. Older, stunted prey species (*S. alpinus*) were removed. These fish had eaten small prey, so an increase in the availability of prey and recovery of the predator resulted. In this case, *S. trutta* was the top predator, and *S. alpinus,* an introduced species, was culled to rejuvenate the system. Another process of bioremediation, the addition of piscivorous fish to a lake, has also been successful in restoring ecosystem balance in other parts of the world.

46.1e Biological Magnification Is the Movement of Contaminants Up the Food Chain

DDT (a formerly popular insecticide; see "Molecule behind Biology," Box 46.2, p. 1184) provided a clear demonstration of the interconnectedness of organisms. Consumers accumulate DDT from all the organisms they eat in their lifetimes. Primary consumers, such as herbivorous insects, may ingest relatively small amounts of DDT, but a songbird that eats many of these insects accumulates all the collected DDT consumed by its prey. A predator such as a raptor, perhaps a Sharp-shinned Hawk (*Accipiter striatus*) that eats songbirds, accumulates even more. Whether the food chain (web) is aquatic or terrestrial, the net effect on higher-level consumers is the same **(Figure 46.10)**.

Natural systems have provided many examples of biological magnification. In cities where DDT was used in an effort to control the spread of Dutch elm disease, songbirds died from DDT poisoning after eating insects that had been sprayed (whether or not they were involved in spreading the disease). In forests, DDT was used in an effort to control spruce budworm moths (*Choristoneura occidentalis*), and salmon died because runoff carried DDT into their streams and rivers, where their herbivorous prey consumed it.

Despite the ban on the use of DDT in the United States in 1973, in 1990, the California State Department of Health recommended closing a fishery off the coast of California because of DDT accumulating there. DDT discharged in industrial waste 20 years earlier was still moving through the ecosystem. The

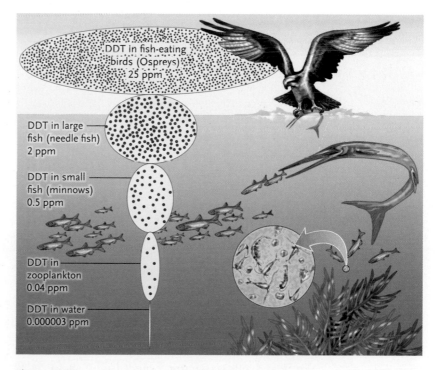

Figure 46.10

Biological magnification. In this marine food web in northeastern North America, DDT concentration (measured in parts per million, ppm) was magnified nearly 10 million times between zooplankton and the Osprey (*Pandion haliaetus*).

MOLECULE BEHIND BIOLOGY 46.2
DDT: Dichloro-Diphenyl-Trichloroethane

FIGURE 1
A molecule of DDT.

Originally formulated in 1873, DDT's potential as an insecticide was only recognized in 1939 by Paul Muller of Geigy Pharmaceutical in Switzerland. DDT **(Figure 1),** the first of the chlorinated insecticides, was used extensively in some theatres of World War II, notably in Burma (now Myanmar) in 1944, when the Japanese forces were on the brink of moving into India. There Allied forces suffered from "three m's": mud, morale, and malaria. Meanwhile, in 1943 in southern Italy, DDT was instrumental in controlling populations of lice that plagued Canadian troops there. Widespread application of DDT in Burma reduced the incidence of malaria by killing mosquitoes, the vectors for the disease (see Chapter 25). After World War II, the use of DDT spread rapidly, and the World Health Organization (WHO) credited this molecule with saving 25 million human lives (mainly through control of mosquitoes that carry malaria).

At first, DDT appeared to be an ideal insecticide. In addition to being inexpensive to produce, it had low toxicity to mammals (300 to 500 mg·kg⁻¹is the LD_{50}, the amount required to kill half of the target population). But many insects subsequently developed immunity to DDT, reducing its effectiveness.

DDT is chemically stable and soluble in fat, so instead of being metabolized by mammals, it is stored in their fat. The biological half-life of DDT is approximately eight years (it takes about eight years for a mammal to metabolize half the amount of DDT it has assimilated). DDT is released when fat is metabolized, so when mammals metabolize fat (for example, when humans go on a diet), they are exposed to higher concentrations of DDT in their blood. DDT also had dramatic effects on some birds, notably those higher up the food chain. Eggshell thinning was a consequence of exposure to DDT. Populations of birds such as Peregrine Falcons (*Falco peregrinus*) plummeted.

Since 1985, the use of DDT has been totally banned in Canada, and it is now banned in many other countries. But DDT is still produced in countries such as the United States and still used in countries where malaria is a prominent problem because the ecological costs of DDT are considered secondary to the importance of controlling the mosquitoes. WHO estimates that every 30 seconds, a child dies of malaria. Approximately 40% of the world's population of humans is at risk of contracting malaria where they live, mainly in Africa. Malaria also remains a problem in tropical and subtropical Asia and Central and South America. People in southern Europe and the Middle East may also be at risk.

By the early 1970s, cetaceans in the waters around Antarctica had DDT in their body fat even though DDT had never been used there. The movement of DDT up the food chain and through food webs demonstrated the interconnections in biological systems. The movement of DDT also provides a graphic demonstration of the transfer of materials from one trophic level to another.

Removing DDT from the arsenal of products used to control insects has had other impacts. For example, there has been an upsurge recently in the number of houses and apartments infested by bedbugs (*Cimex lectularius*). DDT had been very effective in the control of bedbugs, but in its absence, populations of these insects have rebounded, renewing old challenges that our grandparents had experienced.

half-life of DDT in an organism's body fat is eight years.

Other contaminants emulate DDT. Mercury contamination is common in many parts of the world, often as a by-product of the pulp and paper industry. Minamata, the disease humans get from mercury poisoning, is usually linked to the consumption of fish taken from contaminated watersheds. Eating fish contaminated with mercury can result in mercury concentrations in people's hair (0.9 to 94 mg·kg⁻¹) and otters (*Lontra canadensis;* 0.49 to 54.37 mg·kg⁻¹). In southern Ontario, the hair of bats that eat insects that emerge from mercury-contaminated sediments contains concentrations up to 13 mg·kg⁻¹.

Fish are obviously not essential to this chain of biomagnification.

STUDY BREAK

1. What is net primary productivity? How does it differ from standing crop biomass? Are the pyramids useful?
2. Many deserts have low levels of productivity despite receiving a lot of sunlight. Why?
3. What are assimilation efficiency and production efficiency?

46.2 Nutrient Cycling in Ecosystems

The availability of nutrients is as important to ecosystem function as the input of energy. Photosynthesis requires carbon, hydrogen, and oxygen, which producers acquire from water and air. Primary producers also need nitrogen, phosphorus, and other minerals (see Chapter 40). A deficiency in any of these minerals can reduce primary productivity.

Earth is essentially a closed system with respect to matter, even though cosmic dust enters the atmosphere. Thus, unlike energy, for which there is a constant cosmic input, virtually all of the nutrients that will ever be available for biological systems are already present. Nutrient ions and molecules constantly circulate between the abiotic environment and living organisms in **biogeochemical cycles.** And, unlike energy, which flows through ecosystems and is gradually lost as heat, matter is conserved in biogeochemical cycles. Although there may be local shortages of specific nutrients, Earth's overall supplies of these chemical elements are never depleted or increased.

Nutrients take various forms as they pass through biogeochemical cycles. Materials such as carbon, nitrogen, and oxygen form gases that move through global *atmospheric cycles.* Geologic processes move other materials, such as phosphorus, through local *sedimentary cycles,* carrying them between dry land and the sea floor. Rocks, soil, water, and air are the reservoirs where mineral nutrients accumulate, sometimes for many years.

Ecologists use a **generalized compartment model** to describe nutrient cycling **(Figure 46.11).** Two criteria divide ecosystems into four compartments in which nutrients accumulate. First, nutrient molecules and ions are either *available* or *unavailable,* depending on whether they can be assimilated by organisms. Second, nutrients are present in either *organic* material, living or dead tissues of organisms, or *inorganic* material, such as rocks and soil. Minerals in dead leaves on the forest floor are in the available-organic compartment because they are in the remains of organisms that can be eaten by detritivores. Calcium ions in limestone rocks are in the unavailable-inorganic compartment because they are in a nonbiological form that producers cannot assimilate.

Nutrients move rapidly within and between the available compartments. Living organisms are in the available-organic compartment, and whenever heterotrophs consume food, they recycle nutrients within that reservoir (indicated by the circular arrow in the upper left of Figure 46.11). Producers acquire nutrients from the air, soil, and water of the available-inorganic compartment. Consumers acquire nutrients from the available-inorganic compartment when they drink water or absorb mineral ions through their

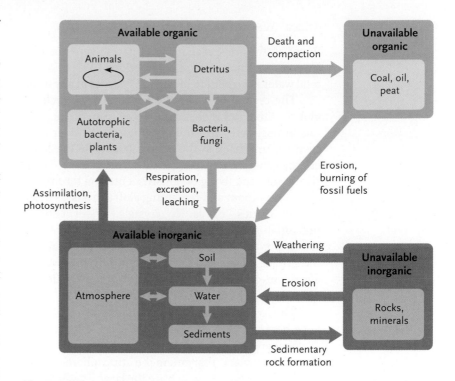

Figure 46.11

A generalized compartment model of nutrient cycling. Nutrients cycle through four major compartments within ecosystems. Processes that move nutrients from one compartment to another are indicated on the arrows. The circular arrow under "Animals" represents animal predation on other animals.

integument. Several processes routinely transfer nutrients from organisms to the available-inorganic compartment. Respiration releases carbon dioxide, moving both carbon and oxygen from the available-organic compartment to the available-inorganic compartment.

By contrast, the exchange of materials into and out of the unavailable compartments is generally slow. Sedimentation, a long-term geologic process, converts ions and particles of the available-inorganic compartment into rocks of the unavailable-inorganic compartment. Materials are gradually returned to the available-inorganic compartment when rocks are uplifted and eroded or weathered. Similarly, over millions of years, the remains of organisms in the available-organic compartment were converted into the coal, oil, and peat of the unavailable-organic compartment.

Except for the input of solar energy, we have described energy flow and nutrient cycling as though ecosystems were closed systems. In reality, most ecosystems exchange energy and nutrients with neighbouring ecosystems. Rainfall carries nutrients into a forest ecosystem, and runoff carries nutrients from a forest into a lake or river. Ecologists have mapped biogeochemical cycles of important elements, often by using radioactively labelled molecules that they can follow in the environment.

46.2a Water Is the Staff of Life

Water is the universal intracellular solvent for biochemical reactions, but only a fraction of 1% of Earth's total water is present in biological systems at any time.

The cycling of water, the **hydrogeologic cycle**, is global, with water molecules moving from oceans into the atmosphere, to land, through freshwater ecosystems, and back to the oceans **(Figure 46.12)**. Solar energy causes water to evaporate from oceans, lakes, rivers, soil, and living organisms, entering the atmosphere as a vapour and remaining aloft as a gas, as droplets in clouds, or as ice crystals. Water falls as precipitation, mostly in the form of rain and snow. When precipitation falls on land, water flows across the surface or percolates to great depths in soil, eventually re-entering the ocean reservoir through the flow of streams and rivers.

The hydrogeologic cycle maintains its global balance because the total amount of water entering the atmosphere is equal to the amount that falls as precipitation. Most water that enters the atmosphere evaporates from the oceans, which are the largest reservoir of water on the planet. A much smaller fraction evaporates from terrestrial ecosystems, and most of that is through transpiration by green plants.

Constant recirculation provides fresh water to terrestrial organisms and maintains freshwater ecosystems such as lakes and rivers. Water also serves as a transport medium that moves nutrients within and between ecosystems, as demonstrated in a series of classic experiments in the Hubbard Brook Experimental Forest (see "Studies of the Hubbard Brook Watershed," Box 46.3).

46.2b Carbon Is the Backbone of Life

Carbon atoms provide the backbone of most biological molecules, and carbon compounds store the energy captured by photosynthesis (see Chapter 7). Carbon enters food webs when producers convert atmospheric carbon dioxide (CO_2) into carbohydrates. Heterotrophs acquire carbon by eating other organisms or detritus. Although carbon moves somewhat independently in sea and on land, a common atmospheric pool of CO_2 creates a global **carbon cycle** **(Figure 46.13, p. 1188)**.

The largest reservoir of carbon is sedimentary rock, such as limestone. Rocks are in the unavailable-inorganic compartment, and they exchange carbon with living organisms at an exceedingly slow pace. Most *available* carbon is present as dissolved bicarbonate

a. The water cycle

Figure 46.12

The hydrogeologic cycle. Water cycles through marine, atmospheric, and terrestrial reservoirs. **(a)** Data next to the arrows list the amount of water (in km³·year⁻¹) moved among the reservoirs by various processes. **(b)** The oceans are by far the largest of the six major reservoirs of water on Earth.

b. Volume of water reservoirs

Water reservoirs	Volume (10^3 km³)
Oceans	1 370 000
Polar ice, glaciers	29 000
Groundwater	4 000
Lakes, rivers	230
Soil moisture	67
Atmosphere (water vapour)	14

Studies of the Hubbard Brook Watershed Box 46.3

Water flows downhill, so local topography affects the movement of dissolved nutrients in terrestrial ecosystems. A **watershed** is an area of land from which precipitation drains into a single stream or river. Each watershed represents a part of an ecosystem from which nutrients exit through a single outlet. When several streams join to form a river, the watershed drained by the river encompasses the smaller watersheds drained by the streams. The Mackenzie River watershed covers roughly 20% of Canada and includes the watersheds of the Peace and Athabasca rivers, as well as many other watersheds drained by smaller streams and rivers.

Watersheds are ideal for large-scale field experiments about nutrient flow in ecosystems because they are relatively self-contained units. Herbert Bormann and Gene Likens conducted a classic experiment on nutrients in watersheds in the 1960s. Bormann and Likens manipulated small watersheds of temperate deciduous forest in the Hubbard Brook Experimental Forest in the White Mountain National Forest of New Hampshire. They measured precipitation and nutrient input into the watersheds, the uptake of nutrients by vegetation, and the amount of nutrients leaving the watershed via streamflow. They monitored nutrients exported in streamflow by collecting water samples from V-shaped concrete weirs built into bedrock below the streams that drained the watersheds **(Figure 1)**. Impermeable bedrock underlies the soil, preventing water from leaving the system by deep seepage.

Bormann and Likens collected several years of baseline data on six undisturbed watersheds. Then, in 1965 and 1966, they felled all of the trees in one small watershed and used herbicides to prevent regrowth. After

Gene E. Likens, from Gene E. Likens et al., *Ecology Monograph*, 40(1): 23–47, 1970

FIGURE 1

A weir used to measure the volume and nutrient content of water leaving a watershed by streamflow.

these manipulations, they monitored the output of nutrients in streams that drained experimental and control watersheds. They attributed differences in nutrient export between undisturbed watersheds (controls) and the clear-cut watershed (experimental treatment) to the effects of deforestation.

Bormann and Likens determined that vegetation absorbed substantial water and conserved nutrients in undisturbed watersheds. Plants used about 40% of the precipitation for transpiration. The rest contributed to

runoff and groundwater. Control watersheds lost only about 8 to 10 kg of calcium per hectare each year, an amount replaced by erosion of bedrock and input from rain. Moreover, control watersheds actually accumulated about 2 kg of nitrogen per hectare per year and slightly smaller amounts of potassium.

The experimentally deforested watershed experienced a 40% annual increase in runoff, including a 300% increase during a four-month period in summer. Some mineral losses were similarly large. The net loss of calcium was 10 times as high **(Figure 2)** as in the control watersheds and of potassium was 21 times as high. Phosphorus losses did not increase because this mineral was apparently retained by the soil. The loss of nitrogen, however, was very large— 120 kg·ha^{-1}×year^{-1}. The washing out of nitrogen meant that the stream draining the experimental watershed became choked with algae and cyanobacteria. The Hubbard Brook experiment demonstrated that deforestation increases flooding and decreases the fertility of ecosystems.

FIGURE 2

Calcium losses from the deforested watershed were much greater than those from controls. The arrow indicates the time of deforestation in early winter. Mineral losses did not increase until after the ground thawed the following spring. Increased runoff also caused large water losses from the watershed.

c. The global carbon cycle

a. Amount of carbon in major reservoirs

Carbon reservoirs	Mass (10^{12} g)
Sediments and rocks	770 000 000
Ocean (dissolved forms)	397 000
Soil	15 000
Atmosphere	7 500
Biomass on land	7 150

b. Annual global carbon movement between reservoirs

Direction of movement	Mass (10^{12} kg)
From atmosphere to plants (carbon fixation)	1200
From atmosphere to ocean	1070
To atmosphere from ocean	1050
To atmosphere from plants	600
To atmosphere from soil	600
To atmosphere from burning fossil fuel	50
To atmosphere from burning plants	20
To ocean from runoff	4
Burial in ocean sediments	1

Labels within figure: Diffusion between atmosphere and ocean; Combustion of fossil fuels; Dissolved in ocean water (bicarbonate and carbonate); Photosynthesis; Aerobic respiration; Marine food webs; Incorporation into sediments; Death, sedimentation; Uplifting over geological time; Marine sediments, including formations with fossil fuels; Sedimentation

Figure 46.13

The carbon cycle. Marine and terrestrial components of the global carbon cycle are linked through an atmospheric reservoir of carbon dioxide. **(a)** By far the largest amount of Earth's carbon is found in sediments and rocks. **(b)** Earth's atmosphere mediates most of the movement of carbon. **(c)** In this illustration of the carbon cycle, boxes identify major reservoirs and labels on arrows identify the processes that cause carbon to move between reservoirs.

ions (HCO_3^-) in the ocean. Soil, atmosphere, and plant biomass are significant, but much smaller, reservoirs of available carbon. Atmospheric carbon is mostly in the form of molecular CO_2, a product of aerobic respiration. Volcanic eruptions also release small quantities of CO_2 into the atmosphere.

Carbon atoms sometimes leave organic compartments for long periods of time. Some organisms in marine food webs build shells and other hard parts by incorporating dissolved carbon into calcium carbonate ($CaCO_3$) and other insoluble salts. When shelled organisms die, they sink to the bottom and are buried in sediments. Other animals, notably vertebrates, store calcium in bone. Insoluble carbon that accumulates as rock in deep sediments may remain buried for millions of years before tectonic uplifting brings it to the surface, where erosion and weathering dissolve sedimentary rocks and return carbon to an available form.

Carbon atoms are also transferred to the unavailable-organic compartment when soft-bodied organisms die and are buried in habitats where low oxygen concentration prevents decomposition. In the past, under suitable geologic conditions, these carbon-rich tissues were slowly converted to gas, petroleum, or coal, which we now use as fossil fuels. Human activities,

especially burning fossil fuels, are transferring carbon into the atmosphere at an unnaturally high rate. The resulting change in the worldwide distribution of carbon is having profound consequences for Earth's atmosphere and climate, including a general warming of the climate and a rise in sea level (see "Disruption of the Carbon Cycle," Box 46.4, p. 1190).

46.2c Nitrogen Is a Limiting Element

All organisms require nitrogen to construct nucleic acids, proteins, and other biological molecules (see Chapter 40). Earth's atmosphere had a high nitrogen concentration long before life began. Today, a global **nitrogen cycle** moves this element between the huge atmospheric pool of gaseous molecular nitrogen (N_2) and several much smaller pools of nitrogen-containing compounds in soils, marine and freshwater ecosystems, and living organisms **(Figure 46.14)**.

Molecular nitrogen is abundant in the atmosphere, but triple covalent bonds bind its two atoms so tightly that most organisms cannot use it. Only certain microorganisms, volcanic action, and lightning can convert N_2 into ammonium (NH_4^+) and nitrate (NO_3^-) ions. This conversion is called **nitrogen fixation** (see Chapter 20).

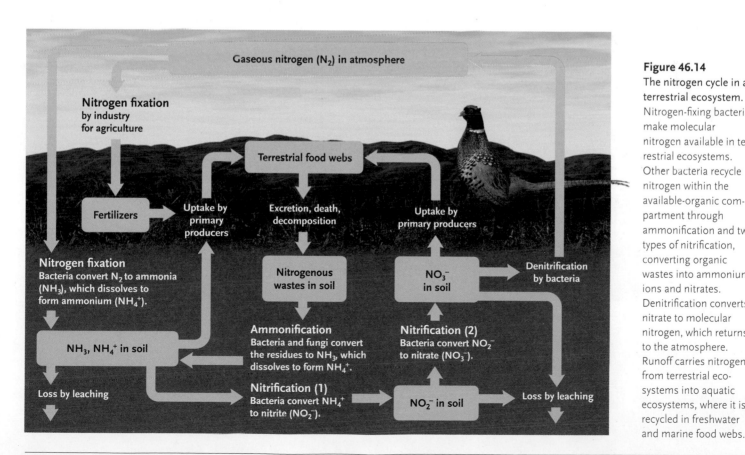

Figure 46.14

The nitrogen cycle in a terrestrial ecosystem. Nitrogen-fixing bacteria make molecular nitrogen available in terrestrial ecosystems. Other bacteria recycle nitrogen within the available-organic compartment through ammonification and two types of nitrification, converting organic wastes into ammonium ions and nitrates. Denitrification converts nitrate to molecular nitrogen, which returns to the atmosphere. Runoff carries nitrogen from terrestrial ecosystems into aquatic ecosystems, where it is recycled in freshwater and marine food webs.

Disruption of the Carbon Cycle 46.4

The concentrations of gases in the lower atmosphere have a profound effect on global temperature, in turn affecting global climate. Molecules of CO_2, water vapour, ozone, methane, nitrous oxide, and other compounds collectively act like a pane of glass in a greenhouse (hence the term *greenhouse gases*). They allow short wavelengths of visible light to reach Earth's surface while impeding the escape of longer, infrared wavelengths into space, trapping much of their energy as heat **(Figure 1)**. Greenhouse gases foster the accumulation of heat in the lower atmosphere, a warming action known as the **greenhouse effect.** This natural process prevents Earth from being a cold and lifeless planet.

Data from air bubbles trapped in glacial ice indicate that atmospheric CO_2 concentrations have fluctuated widely over Earth's history **(Figure 2).** Since the late 1950s, scientists have measured atmospheric concentrations of CO_2 and other greenhouse gases at remote sampling sites such as the top of Mauna Loa in the Hawaiian Islands. These sites are free of local contamination and reflect average global conditions. Concentrations of greenhouse gases have increased steadily for as long as they have been monitored **(Figure 3).**

The graph for atmospheric CO_2 concentration has a regular zigzag pattern that follows the annual cycle of plant growth (see Figure 3). The concentration of CO_2 decreases during the summer because photosynthesis withdraws so much from the atmospheric available-inorganic pool. The concentration of CO_2 is higher during the winter when photosynthesis slows while aerobic respiration continues, returning carbon to the atmospheric available-inorganic pool. Whereas the zigs and zags in the data for CO_2 represent seasonal highs and lows, the midpoint of the annual peaks and troughs has increased steadily for 40 years. These data are evidence of a rapid buildup of atmospheric CO_2, representing a shift in the distribution of carbon in the major reservoirs on Earth. The best estimates suggest that CO_2 concentration has increased by 35% in the last 150 years and by more than 10% in the last 30 years.

The increase in the atmospheric concentration of CO_2 appears to result from combustion, whether we burn fossil fuels or wood. Today, humans burn more wood and fossil fuels than ever before. Vast tracts of tropical forests are being cleared and burned (see Chapter 47). To make matters worse, deforestation reduces the world's biomass of plants that assimilate CO_2 and help maintain the carbon cycle as it existed before human activities disrupted it.

The increase in the concentration of atmospheric CO_2 is alarming because plants with C_3 metabolism respond to increased CO_2 concentrations with increased growth rates. This is not true of C_4 plants (see Chapter 7). Thus, rising atmospheric levels of CO_2 will probably alter the relative abundances of many plant species, changing the composition and dynamics of their communities.

Simulation models suggest that increasing concentrations of any greenhouse gas may intensify the greenhouse effect, contributing to a trend of global warming. Should we be alarmed about the prospect of a warmer planet? Some models predict that the mean temperature of the lower atmosphere will rise by 4°C, enough to increase ocean surface temperatures. In some areas, such as the Canadian Arctic and the Antarctic, warming has occurred much more rapidly than predicted or expected.

FIGURE 1
The greenhouse effect.

Sunlight penetrates the atmosphere and warms Earth's surface.

Earth's surface radiates heat (infrared wavelengths) to the atmosphere. Some heat escapes into space. Greenhouse gases and water vapour absorb some infrared energy and reradiate the rest of it back toward Earth.

When atmospheric concentrations of greenhouse gases increase, the atmosphere near Earth's surface traps more heat. The warming causes a positive feedback cycle in which rising ocean temperatures cause increased evaporation of water, which further enhances the greenhouse effect.

FIGURE 2

Carbon dioxide levels over time. The amount of atmospheric CO_2 has risen dramatically since about 1850 (arrow).

Water expands when heated, and global sea level could rise as much as 0.6 m just from this expansion. In addition, atmospheric temperature is rising fastest near the poles. Thus, global warming may also foster melting of glaciers and the Antarctic ice sheet, which might raise sea level as much as 50 to 100 m, inundating low coastal regions. Waterfronts in Vancouver, Los Angeles, Hong Kong, Durban, Rio de Janeiro, Sydney, New York, and London would be sub-merged. So would agricultural lands in India, China, and Bangladesh, where much of the world's rice is grown. Moreover, global warming could disturb regional patterns of precipitation and temperature. Areas that now produce much of the world's grains would become arid scrub or deserts, and the now-forested areas to their north would become dry grasslands.

Many scientists believe that atmospheric levels of greenhouse gases will continue to increase at least until the middle of the twenty-first century and that global temperature may rise by several degrees. At the Earth Summit in 1992, leaders of the industrialized countries agreed to try to stabilize CO_2 emissions by the end of the twentieth century. We have already missed that target, and some countries, including the United States (then the largest producer of greenhouse gases), have now forsaken that goal as too costly. Stabilizing emissions at current levels will not reverse the damage already done, nor will it stop the trend toward global warming. We should begin preparing for the consequences of global warming now. We might increase reforestation efforts because a large tract of forest can withdraw significant amounts of CO_2 from the atmosphere. We might also step up genetic engineering studies to develop heat-resistant and drought-resistant crop plants, which may provide crucial food reserves in regions of climate change.

Carbon dioxide (CO_2) from fossil fuel combustion, factory emissions, car exhaust, and deforestation contributes to an overall increase in atmospheric levels of the gas.

Methane (CH_4) is produced by anaerobic bacteria in swamps, landfills, and termite mounds. The microorgan-isms in the digestive tracts of cattle and other ruminants also produce large quantities of this gas.

Nitrous oxide (N_2O) is a natural gaseous by-product of denitrifying bacteria. Large quantities are also released from synthetic fertilizers and the wastes of animals in feedlots.

FIGURE 3

Increases in atmospheric concentrations of three greenhouse gases, mid-1970s through 2004. The data were collected at a remote monitoring station in Australia (Cape Grim, Tasmania) and compiled by scientists at the Commonwealth Scientific and Industrial Research Organization, an agency of the Australian government.

Once nitrogen is fixed, primary producers can incorporate it into biological molecules such as proteins and nucleic acids. Secondary consumers obtain nitrogen by consuming these molecules.

Several biochemical processes produce different nitrogen-containing compounds and thus move nitrogen through ecosystems. These processes are nitrogen fixation, ammonification, nitrification, and denitrification **(Table 46.2)**.

In nitrogen fixation, several kinds of microorganisms convert molecular nitrogen (N_2) to ammonium ions (NH_4^+). Certain bacteria, which collect molecular nitrogen from the air between soil particles, are the major nitrogen fixers in terrestrial ecosystems (see Table 46.2). The cyanobacteria partners in some lichens (see Chapter 23) also fix molecular nitrogen. Other cyanobacteria are important nitrogen fixers in aquatic ecosystems, whereas the water fern (genus *Azolla*) plays that role in rice paddies. Collectively, these organisms fix an astounding 200 million tonnes of nitrogen each year. Plants and other primary producers assimilate and use this nitrogen in the biosynthesis of amino acids, proteins, and nucleic acids, which then circulate through food webs.

Some plants, including legumes (such as beans and clover), alders (*Alnus* species), and some members of the rose family (Rosaceae), are mutualists with nitrogen-fixing bacteria. These plants acquire nitrogen from soils much more readily than plants that lack such mutualists. Although these plants have the competitive edge in nitrogen-poor soil, non-mutualistic species often displace them in nitrogen-rich soil. In an interesting twist on the usual predator–prey relationships, several species of flowering plants living in nitrogen-poor soils capture and digest insects (see "Pitcher Plant Ecosystems," Box 46.5, p. 1193–1194).

In addition to nitrogen fixation, other biochemical processes make large quantities of nitrogen available to producers. **Ammonification** of detritus by bacteria and fungi converts organic nitrogen into ammonia (NH_3), which dissolves in water to produce ammonium ions (NH_4^+) that plants can assimilate. Some ammonia escapes into the atmosphere as a gas. **Nitrification** by certain bacteria produces nitrites (NO_2^-), which are then converted by other bacteria to usable nitrates (NO_3^-). All of these compounds are water soluble, and water rapidly leaches them from soil into streams, lakes, and oceans.

Under conditions of low oxygen availability, **denitrification** by still other bacteria converts nitrites or nitrates into nitrous oxide (N_2O) and then into molecular nitrogen (N_2), which enters the atmosphere (see Table 46.2). This action can deplete supplies of soil nitrogen in waterlogged or otherwise poorly aerated environments, such as bogs and swamps.

In 1909, Fritz Haber developed a process for fixing nitrogen, and with the help of Carl Bosch, the process was commercialized for fertilizer production. The Haber–Bosch process has altered Earth's nitrogen cycles and is said to be responsible for the existence of 40% of the people on Earth. Before the implementation of the Haber–Bosch process, the amount of nitrogen available for life was limited by the rates at which N_2 was fixed by bacteria or generated by lightning strikes. Today, spreading fertilizers rich in nitrogen is the basis for most of agriculture's productivity. This practice has quadrupled some yields over the past 50 years (see Chapter 48). Of all nutrients required for primary production, nitrogen is often the least abundant. Agriculture routinely depletes soil nitrogen, which is removed from fields through the harvesting of plants that have accumulated nitrogen in their tissues. Soil erosion and leaching remove more. Traditionally, farmers rotated their crops, alternately planting legumes and other crops in the same fields. In combination with other soil conservation practices, crop rotation stabilized soils and kept them productive, sometimes for hundreds of years. Some of the most arable land in New York State was farmed by members of the Mohawk Iroquois First Nations. The evidence of this comes from the locations of palisaded villages. The people moved their villages

Table 46.2	Biochemical Processes That Influence Nitrogen Cycling in Ecosystems		
Process	Organisms Responsible	Products	Outcome
Nitrogen fixation	Bacteria: *Rhizobium, Azotobacter, Frankia*	Ammonia (NH_3), ammonium ions (NH_4^+)	Assimilated by primary producers
	Cyanobacteria: *Anabaena, Nostoc*		
Ammonification of organic detritus	Soil bacteria and fungi	Ammonia (NH_3), ammonium ions (NH_4^+)	Assimilated by primary producers
Nitrification			
(1) Oxidation of NH_3	Bacteria: *Nitrosomonas, Nitrococcus*	Nitrite (NO_2^-)	Used by nitrifying bacteria
(2) Oxidation of NO_2^-	Bacteria: *Nitrobacter*	Nitrate (NO_3^-)	Assimilated by primary producers
Denitrification of NO_3^-	Soil bacteria	Nitrous oxide (N_2O), molecular nitrogen (N_2)	Released to atmosphere

Pitcher Plant Ecosystems 46.5

Pitcher plants have modified leaves (pitchers) that act as pitfall traps for drowning and digesting insect prey. Pitchers have developed in at least five different evolutionary lines of vascular plants (see Chapter 28). Throughout much of North America, pitcher plants (the provincial flower of Newfoundland and Labrador; **Figure 1**) are common in bogs. *Sarracenia purpurea*, like other carnivorous plants, obtain much of their nitrogen from the insects they capture.

The captured arthropod prey, mainly ants and flies, is the base of a food web inside the pitchers. These are shredded and partly consumed by larvae of midges (*Metriocnemus knabi*) and sarcophagid flies (*Fletcherimyia fletcheri*; **Figure 2**). A subweb of bacteria and protozoa processes shredded prey, which are eaten by filter-feeding rotifers (*Habrotrocha rosa*; **Figure 3, p. 1194**) and mites (*Sarraceniopus gibsonii*). Mosquito larvae (*Wyeomyia smithii*) eat the bacteria, protozoa, and rotifers, whereas the larger sarcophagid fly larvae eat the rotifers and smaller mosquito larvae. Populations of bacteria, protozoa, and rotifers grow much more rapidly than populations of mosquito or midge larvae, making the system sustainable.

Pitchers are essential to the life cycles of two species of insects whose larvae live in them. A mosquito and a midge coexist in the same pitchers, and their populations are limited by

M.B. Fenton

FIGURE 1
Sarracenia purpurea, a pitcher plant. The flower on a long stalk extends above the pitchers. One pitcher is shown in the photo on the left.

M.B. Fenton

the availability of insect carcasses. In any pitcher, growth in populations of the midge larvae is not affected by increases in the numbers of mosquito larvae. But populations of mosquito larvae increase as populations of midge larvae increase (see Figure 2).

The situation is an example of processing-chain commensalism because the action of one species creates opportunities for another. In this case, midge larvae feed on the

hard parts of insect carcasses and break them up in the process. Mosquito larvae are filter-feeders, consuming particles derived from the decaying matter. The feeding of the midges generates additional food for the mosquito larvae. Although the populations of midge and mosquito larvae can be large in any pitcher, only a single sarcophagid fly larva occurs in any pitcher. *F. fletcheri* is a *K*-strategist (see Chapter 44) and gives birth to

a.

KEY
- 8 midges
- 30 midges

Mosquito number (per tube)

5 mosquitoes — 15 mosquitoes

b.

KEY
- 8 midges
- 30 midges

Total mosquito mass (mg)

5 mosquitoes — 15 mosquitoes

FIGURE 2
Midge and mosquito larvae in pitchers. (a) The density and (b) total dry mass of mosquito larvae are the same whether the population of midges is low (8 midges) or high (30 midges). FH = high food availability; FL = low food availability. Error bars show standard errors of the mean.

(continued)

Pitcher Plant Ecosystems 46.5 (continued)

FIGURE 3

A bdelloid rotifer, Habrotrocha rosa, *from a* Sarracenia purpurea *pitcher.*

a.

Courtesy of the Biodiversity Institute of Ontario

b.

Courtesy of Daniel Handfield

D. Liane Cochran-Stafira/Saint Xavier University

FIGURE 4

Moths whose caterpillars eat Sarracenia purpurea. *The caterpillars of* **(a)** Exyra fax *and* **(b)** Papaipema appassionata *feed on pitcher plants, either* **(a)** *the lining of pitchers or* **(b)** *the rhizomes.*

larvae. If you place more than one *F. fletcheri* larva in a pitcher, a fight ensues. The larger larva either wins or leaves the pitcher to pupate in the sphagnum around it.

These insects do not appear to compete with their hosts, the pitcher plants. The abundance of rotifers living in the pitchers of *S. purpurea* is negatively associated with the presence of midge and mosquito larvae (which eat the rotifers). Rotifers are detritivores, and their excretory products (NO_3-N, NH_4OH, P) account for a major portion of the N acquired by the plants from their insect prey.

Two species of moths also exploit *Sarracenia purpurea* **(Figure 4)**. *Exyra fax* and *Papaipema appassionata* do not live in the pitchers. *E. fax* caterpillars eat the interior surface of the pitcher chambers, whereas *P. appassionata* caterpillars consume the rhizomes. Although predation by *E. fax* caterpillars does not kill the plants, predation by *P. appassionata* does. To what trophic level does one assign moths whose caterpillars are herbivores feeding on primary producers that eat insects?

---

and farming operations every 10 to 20 years, changing fields repeatedly over hundreds of years.

The production of synthetic fertilizers is expensive, using fossil fuels as both raw material and an energy source. Fertilizer becomes increasingly costly as supplies of fossil fuels dwindle. Furthermore, rain and runoff leach excess fertilizer from agricultural fields and carry it into aquatic ecosystems. Nitrogen has become a major pollutant of freshwater ecosystems, artificially enriching the waters and allowing producers to expand their populations. Human activities have disrupted the global nitrogen cycle **(Figure 46.15)**.

46.2d Phosphorus Is Another Essential Element

Phosphorus compounds lack a gaseous phase, and this element moves between terrestrial and marine ecosystems in a sedimentary cycle **(Figure 46.16)**. Earth's crust is the main reservoir of phosphorus, as it is for other minerals, such as calcium and potassium, that also undergo sedimentary cycles.

Phosphorus is present in terrestrial rocks in the form of phosphates (PO_4^{3-}). In the **phosphorus cycle**, weathering and erosion add phosphate ions to soil and carry them into streams and rivers, which eventually transport them to the ocean. Once there, some phosphorus enters marine food webs, but most of it precipitates out of solution and accumulates for millions of years as insoluble deposits, mainly on continental shelves. When parts of the sea floor are uplifted and exposed, weathering releases the phosphates.

Plants absorb and assimilate dissolved phosphates directly, and phosphorus moves easily to higher trophic levels. All heterotrophs excrete some phosphorus as a waste product in urine and feces; the phosphorus becomes available after decomposition. Primary producers readily absorb the phosphate ions, so phosphorus cycles rapidly *within* terrestrial communities.

Supplies of available phosphate are generally limited, however, and plants acquire it so efficiently that they reduce soil phosphate concentration to extremely low levels. Thus, like nitrogen, phosphorus is a common ingredient in agricultural fertilizers, and excess phosphates are pollutants of freshwater

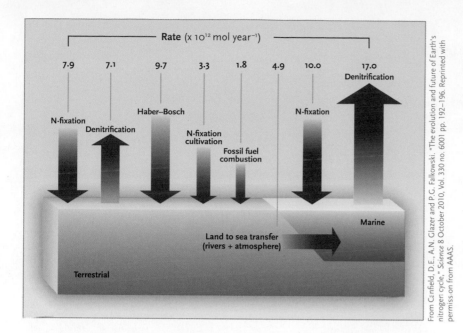

From Canfield, D.E., A.N. Glazer and P.G. Falkowski. "The evolution and future of Earth's nitrogen cycle," *Science* 8 October 2010, Vol. 330 no. 6001 pp. 192–196. Reprinted with permiss on from AAAS.

Figure 46.15
Modern global nitrogen flux depends upon the efficiency of transfer of N between reservoirs. Thickness of arrows indicates relative size of flux. Anthropogenic inputs are shown as dark brown arrows.

ecosystems. A particularly good example is Lake Erie, a Great Lake that was heavily affected by accumulations of phosphorus. The example here is more convincing because the problem has largely been resolved over the years.

For many years, phosphate for fertilizers was obtained from **guano** (the droppings of seabirds that consume phosphorus-rich food), which was mined on small islands that hosted seabird colonies, for example, in Polynesia and Micronesia. We now obtain most phosphate for fertilizer from phosphate rock mined in places such as Saskatchewan that have abundant marine deposits.

STUDY BREAK

1. How is balance maintained in the hydrogeologic cycle?
2. How do consumers obtain carbon?
3. What is the role of cyanobacteria in the nitrogen cycle? Why is their role important?

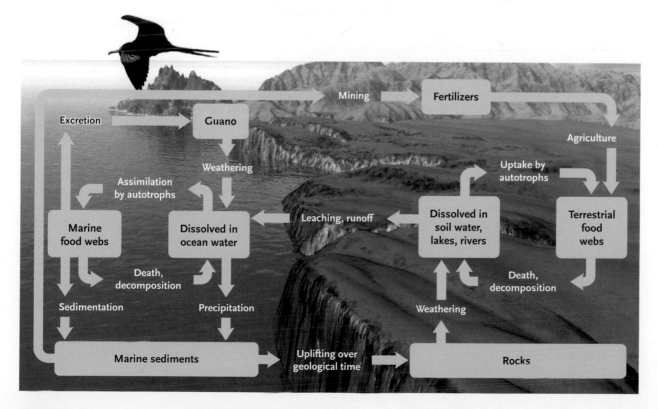

Figure 46.16
The phosphorus cycle. Phosphorus becomes available to biological systems when wind and rainfall dissolve phosphates in rocks and carry them into adjacent soil and freshwater ecosystems. Runoff carries dissolved phosphorus into marine ecosystems, where it precipitates out of solution and is incorporated into marine sediments.

The fragmentation of habitats is a ubiquitous effect of human activity on landscapes. In many parts of the world, land areas that used to be continuous forest are now large expanses of agricultural or urban landscapes dotted with small fragments of forest **(Figure 1)**. Lenore Fahrig examines the impact of landscape structure on the abundance, distribution, and persistence of organisms.

In her research, Fahrig uses a variety of organisms, from beetles to plants and birds. She considers habitats and the impacts of roads and fence lines. She and her students try to identify the habitat features associated with the persistence of species after fragmentation and the role of connectivity between fragments in the persistence of populations in the fragments.

Using a combination of theoretical work and fieldwork, she has assessed the responses of species in different trophic roles to the fragmentation of habitat. Her work demonstrates that

not all species respond in the same way and that some benefit from fragmentation.

The connections between theoretical work and reality emerge

clearly from her research, and the implications for conservation of biodiversity (see Chapter 47) are clear.

FIGURE 1

An aerial view of farmland in southwestern Ontario illustrates isolated patches of forest (woodlots) and bands of woodland (riparian) along the edges of a creek. The woodlots are varied in their size and shape and in the degree of their isolation or connection to other woodlots.

46.3 Ecosystem Modelling

Ecologists use modelling to make predictions about how an ecosystem will respond to specific changes in physical factors, energy flow, or nutrient availability. Analyses of energy flow and nutrient cycling allow us to create a *conceptual model* of how ecosystems function **(Figure 46.17).** Energy that enters ecosystems is gradually dissipated as it flows through a food web. By contrast, nutrients are conserved and recycled among the system's living and nonliving components. This general model does not include processes that carry nutrients and energy out of one ecosystem and into another.

More importantly, the model ignores the nuts-and-bolts details of exactly how specific ecosystems function. Although it is a useful tool, a conceptual model does not really help us predict what would happen, say, if we harvested 10 million tonnes of introduced salmon from Lake Erie every year. We could simply harvest the fishes and see what happens. But ecologists prefer less

intrusive approaches to studying the potential effects of disturbances.

One approach to predicting "what would happen if ..." is **simulation modelling.** Using this approach, researchers gather detailed information about a specific ecosystem. They then derive a series of mathematical equations that define its most important relationships. One set of equations might describe how nutrient availability limits productivity at various trophic levels. Another might relate the population growth of zooplankton to the productivity of phytoplankton. Other equations would relate the population dynamics of primary carnivores to the availability of their food, and still others would describe how the densities of primary carnivores influence reproduction in populations at both lower and higher trophic levels. Thus, a complete simulation model is a set of interlocking equations that collectively predict how changes in one feature of an ecosystem might influence other features.

Creating a simulation model is a challenge because the relationships within every ecosystem are

Figure 46.17

A conceptual ecosystem model. A simple conceptual model of an ecosystem illustrates how energy flows through the system and is lost from both detrital and grazing food webs. Nutrients are recycled and conserved.

KEY

- Nutrients in organic matter
- Nutrients in inorganic state
- Energy flow

complex. First, you must identify the important species, estimate their population sizes, and measure the average energy and nutrient content of each. Next, you must describe the food webs in which they participate, measure the quantity of food each species consumes, and estimate the productivity of each population. And, for the sake of completeness, you must determine the ecosystem's energy and nutrient gains and losses caused by erosion, weathering, precipitation, and runoff. You must repeat these measurements seasonally to identify annual variation in these factors. Finally, you might repeat the measurements over several years to determine the effects of year-to-year variation in climate and chance events.

After collecting these data, you must write equations that quantify the relationships in the ecosystem, including information about how temperature and other abiotic factors influence the ecology of each species. Having completed that job, you would begin to predict, for example, possibly in great detail, the effects of adding 1000 new housing units to an area of native prairie or boreal forest. Of course, you must refine the model whenever new data become available.

Some ecologists devote their professional lives to studying ecosystem processes and creating simulation models. The long-term initiative at the Hubbard Brook Forest provides a good example (see "Studies of the Hubbard Brook Watershed," Box 46.3). As we attempt to understand larger and more complex ecosystems (and as we create larger and more complex environmental problems), modelling becomes an increasingly important tool. If a model is based on well-defined ecological relationships and good empirical data, it can allow us to make accurate predictions about ecosystem changes without the need for costly and environmentally damaging experiments. But, like all ideas in science, a model is only as good as its assumptions, and models must constantly be adjusted to incorporate new ideas and recently discovered facts.

STUDY BREAK

1. Briefly describe the process of simulation modelling.
2. Why is simulation modelling necessary?

46.4 Scale, Ecosystems, Species

As we have seen, the complex interactions between and among species combine with abiotic and biotic factors to produce even more complex situations. Several questions emerge from this situation, including: What determines which species occur in an ecosystem? What controls the size of the populations of species in an ecosystem? How do species in an ecosystem interact? What effect does scale have on the situation?

Ecosystems span scales from millimetres to kilometres. Consider the microorganisms in a biofilm of water compared to the species, some of them microorganisms, in the water contained in the pitcher of a pitcher plant. Furthermore, the community of organisms may vary among pitchers on one plant. Like the pitcher-based community, terrestrial organisms living on an island may be relatively isolated. Consider the differences among islands, such as the British Isles, the Hawaiian Islands, or the Galapagos Islands, with respect to the combination of size (area), degree of isolation (distance from mainland), and range of habitats.

Variations in the scale of interactions **(Figure 46.18, p. 1198)** help to put the nature of ecosystems in context.

Compare Figure 46.18, p. 1198, to Figure 3 in "Dispersal," Box 45.7, Chapter 45, about pollen and seed dispersal. More obvious in the latter is the influence of mobility on patterns of dispersal and connections. Large animals disperse seeds farther than small ones. Animals that can fly have greater potential as dispersers of seeds and pollen than those that walk or run. Data

Figure 46.18

Climate, species interactions, habitat, and dispersal are four main factors controlling the distribution of species (vertical axis). Note the variation in scale (horizontal axis) across which these factors can act.

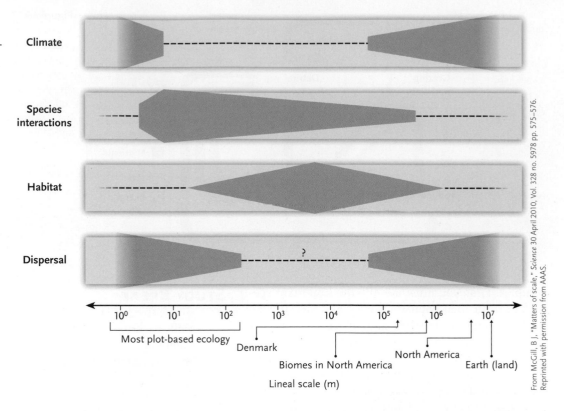

From McGill, B J., "Matters of scale," *Science* 30 April 2010, Vol. 328 no. 5978 pp. 575–576. Reprinted with permission from AAAS.

on the distribution and habitat associations of terrestrial birds in Denmark reveal how species in the same genus and those filling similar niches have more influence on the patterns of distribution of one another than less similar species.

Studies of salmon along the northwest coast of North America (Great Bear Rainforest in British Columbia and sites around Bristol Bay in Alaska) reveal how species in the genus *Oncorhynchus* can influence the plant communities bordering the streams in which they spawn. Nutrients from salmon enter these communities when salmon die after spawning, or when they are taken and eaten by predators such as bears. Healthy populations of salmon affect the nutrient loading in terrestrial plants along the rivers and streams. The density of salmon and the characteristics of the watershed (steep versus shallow banks) influence the situation. Nutrient input from salmon leads to an increase in plants such as salmonberry, associated with nutrient-rich soils. Lower input from salmon is associated with plants associated with nutrient-poor soils (e.g., blueberries). Increases in nutrient-rich soils coincide with decreases in plant diversity **(Figure 46.19)**.

The above data from salmon at sites along 50 watersheds in British Columbia demonstrate the local impact that species in one genus can have. Work from sites in Alaska shows how the inherent diversity of

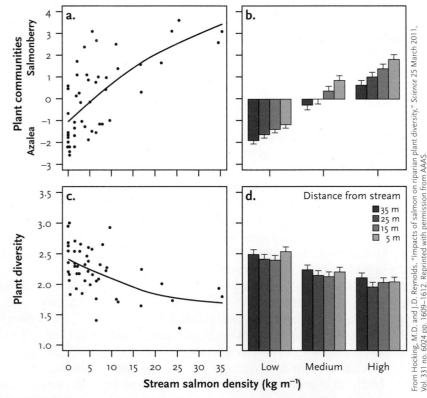

From Hocking, M.D. and J.D. Reynolds, "Impacts of salmon on riparian plant diversity," *Science* 25 March 2011, Vol. 331 no. 6024 pp. 1609–1612. Reprinted with permission from AAAS.

Figure 46.19

The influence of stream level density of spawning salmon (horizontal axis) on the structure of the community of understorey plants (a, b), and on the diversity of plants (c, d) (vertical axis). Note the impact of distance from the stream.

populations of sockeye salmon (*O. nerka*) is vital to the survival of the species and, by extension, the ecosystem. The data from sockeye salmon show how damping variance in the population provides stability. One example of variance is the timing of returns of salmon to the streams in which they hatched. The diversity is part of the *portfolio effect,* named because it is analogous to the impact of asset diversity on the stability of financial portfolios.

The diversity inherent in several hundred discrete watershed-based populations of sockeye is less than half the diversity that would occur if the sockeye were a single homogeneous population. The diversity also makes the sockeye more resilient to pressures of fishing. Studies of food webs in the watersheds provide further evidence of diversity and extend the portfolio effect.

In short, work with salmon advances our knowledge of the fundamental nature of ecosystems and helps us to appreciate the importance of maintaining biodiversity, setting the stage for Chapter 47.

STUDY BREAK

1. Why do ecosystems range so greatly in scale?
2. How do salmon have such a great influence on ecosystems around the streams in which they spawn?

Review

  Access an interactive eBook, chapter-specific interactive learning tools, including flashcards, quizzes, videos, and more in your Biology **CourseMate**, accessed through NelsonBrain.com **Aplia™** is an online interactive learning solution that helps you improve comprehension—and your grade—by integrating a variety of mediums and tools such as videos, tutorials, practice tests, and an interactive eBook.

46.1 Energy Flow and Ecosystem Energetics

- Net primary productivity is the chemical energy remaining in a system after energy has been used by producers to complete life processes and cellular respiration. Net primary productivity differs from standing crop biomass in that net primary productivity is a measure of energy, whereas standing crop biomass is a measure of dry mass.

- Other factors affect primary productivity, such as water and access to nutrients.

- Assimilation efficiency refers to energy absorbed from eating compared with the total energy in the food. Production efficiency is the energy content of new tissue material compared with the energy absorbed from food intake.

- Some energy is lost during transfer by consumption. The process becomes less efficient as the number of transfers increases, meaning that less energy is transferred to the final consumer.

- Biological magnification occurs when material (e.g., DDT) present in small amounts in a producer or low-level organism is consumed by another organism, transferring the material to the predator. DDT accumulates with each successive transfer. Top predators exhibit the highest concentrations of contaminants such as DDT.

46.2 Nutrient Cycling in Ecosystems

- The amount of water that leaves Earth and enters the atmosphere through evaporation is equal to the amount of water reaching Earth by precipitation.

- Producers transform atmospheric carbon (CO_2) into carbohydrates. Consumers then eat the producers and take in the carbohydrates.

- Cyanobacteria can fix nitrogen, which is crucial because although atmospheric nitrogen levels are high, this nitrogen is not accessible to plants or animals. Atmospheric nitrogen must be converted or fixed into a usable form such as ammonium or nitrate.

- Phosphate ions are carried to bodies of water through weathering and erosion, where most of it precipitates. Eventually, weathering releases phosphates, which are then directly absorbed by plants.

46.3 Ecosystem Modelling

- Modelling involves collecting data about an ecosystem and deriving mathematical equations about the relationships in the ecosystem. Data collected over different seasons and different years can be used to simulate the effects of a disruption on various levels of the ecosystem in question.

- Simulation modelling helps us understand and predict the impact of influences on certain ecosystems without actually conducting an experiment. Altering anything in an ecosystem without knowledge of its possible effects can be devastating on many or all levels.

46.4 Scale, Ecosystems, Species

- Biotic and abiotic factors interact in ecosystems, and these can occur across scales from millimetres to kilometres.

- At one end, the microorganisms in a biofilm of water provide an example of ecological interactions, as do the organisms living in the water in a pitcher plant.

- Islands provide another example of a range of scales and interactions from the Galápagos Islands as a group to individual islands.

- Plants disperse using different mechanisms, from wind to the activities of animals.

- In the west coast rainforest of North America, salmon (*Oncorhynchus*) influence plant communities along the rivers and streams in which they spawn.

Questions

Self-Test Questions

1. Which of the following events moves energy and material from a detrital food web into a grazing food web?
   a. an earthworm eating dead leaves on the forest floor
   b. a robin catching and eating an earthworm
   c. a crow eating a dead robin
   d. a bacterium decomposing the feces of an earthworm

2. What is the definition of the total dry mass of plant material in a forest?
   a. a measure of the forest's gross primary productivity
   b. a measure of the forest's net primary productivity
   c. a measure of the forest's standing crop biomass
   d. a measure of the forest's ecological efficiency

3. Which ecosystem has the highest rate of net primary productivity?
   a. open ocean
   b. temperate deciduous forest
   c. tropical rainforest
   d. agricultural land

4. Endothermic animals exhibit a lower ecological efficiency than ectothermic animals for which reason?
   a. Endotherms are less successful hunters than ectotherms.
   b. Endotherms eat more plant material than ectotherms.
   c. Endotherms are larger than ectotherms.
   d. Endotherms use more of their energy to maintain body temperature than ectotherms.

5. What determines the amount of energy available at the highest trophic level in an ecosystem?
   a. only the gross primary productivity of the ecosystem
   b. only the net primary productivity of the ecosystem
   c. the net primary productivity and the ecological efficiencies of herbivores
   d. the net primary productivity and the ecological efficiencies at all lower trophic levels

6. Which pyramid is inverted in some freshwater and marine ecosystems exhibit?
   a. biomass
   b. energy
   c. numbers
   d. ecological efficiency

7. Which process moves nutrients from the available-organic compartment to the available-inorganic compartment?
   a. respiration
   b. assimilation
   c. sedimentation
   d. photosynthesis

8. Which of the following materials has a sedimentary cycle?
   a. oxygen
   b. nitrogen
   c. phosphorus
   d. carbon

9. Which statement is supported by the results of studies at the Hubbard Brook Experimental Forest?
   a. Most energy captured by primary producers is lost before reaching the highest trophic level in an ecosystem.
   b. Deforested watersheds experience a more significant decrease in runoff than undisturbed watersheds.
   c. Deforested watersheds lose more calcium and nitrogen in runoff than undisturbed watersheds.
   d. Nutrients generally move through biogeochemical cycles very quickly.

10. Biological magnification describes which phenomenon?
    a. Certain materials become increasingly concentrated in the tissues of animals at higher trophic levels.
    b. Certain materials become most concentrated in the tissues of animals at the lowest trophic levels.
    c. Certain materials accumulate only in the tissues of tertiary consumers.
    d. Certain materials accumulate only in the tissues of detritivores.

Questions for Discussion

1. Identify 12 ecosystem changes associated with hydroelectric power projects. Consider upstream and downstream changes as well as those associated with transmission of generated power. How does preparing your answers draw on information presented in this chapter?

2. A lake near your home becomes overgrown with algae and pondweeds a few months after a new housing development is built nearby. What kind of data would you collect to determine whether the housing development might be responsible for the changes in the lake?

3. Some politicians question whether recent increases in atmospheric temperature result from our release of greenhouse gases into the atmosphere. They argue that atmospheric temperature has fluctuated widely over Earth's history, and the changing temperature is just part of a historical trend. What information would allow you to refute or confirm their hypothesis? From another perspective, describe the pros and cons of reducing greenhouse gases as soon as possible versus taking a "wait-and-see" approach to this question.

4. What are the ecological consequences of converting crops from food to biofuels?

5. Look at the birds in your neighbourhood. How many have been introduced? How does their behaviour differ from those of native species of birds living in the same immediate areas?

A leopard photographed in the wild in South Africa.

Laura Erin Barclay

47 Conservation of Biodiversity

WHY IT MATTERS

Achieving preservation of Earth's biodiversity is one of the most pressing challenges facing our species today. Numbers of species are a simple indicator of biodiversity, perhaps the most apparent and easy to grasp. But as we have seen, many species of organisms remain undescribed and unnamed. Without names and descriptions, how can we recognize or count them? As we shall see shortly, being unnamed means being unprotected. The Barcode of Life project (see Box 45.4, Chapter 45) is one promising effort to better catalogue biodiversity by identifying and allowing us to name its components.

Research on ecosystems shows repeatedly how the numbers of species are associated with stability and productivity, and, as we have seen (Chapter 45), antagonistic and mutualistic systems differ in community composition. The natural order (association between productivity and biodiversity), however, does not coincide with the productivity that our own species must achieve to feed our ever-expanding populations. Creating and maintaining agricultural monocultures is a way for us to maximize food production and efficiency of harvest. In many areas, this approach leads to the disappearance of family-operated farms. Is this progress justified by efforts to increase efficiency and yield? Humans also use genetically modified organisms to increase productivity and marketability, as well as other features, such as shelf life and portability. All too often, increased agricultural productivity is achieved by the use of more fertilizer, water, and energy. Does agriculture have to be the enemy of biodiversity?

Some people have connected humans' attitude to Earth and its riches with religious teachings. In 1967, Lynn White Jr., a professor of medieval history, explored the historical roots of our ecological crisis. He focused on the Christian view of creation, the importance of science, and the separation of humans from their environmental roots. A dualism between humans and nature had emerged in some Christian societies more than in others. Inherent in these societies was the prevailing idea that it is God's will that humans exploit nature for their own ends. White nominated St. Francis of Assisi **(Figure 47.1)** as the patron saint of ecologists. He said that appreciating the virtue of humility was key to understanding the teachings of St. Francis. His point was that as soon as an animal or a plant (or a meadow, lake, or grove of trees) has its own place in nature (in God's eyes), then it can become as important as we believe we are.

The onus is on us as citizens of the planet to conserve biodiversity, whether the focus is species or habitats. One of the main problems we must overcome is the attitude of many humans, as reviewed by White.

Today a common reflection of this attitude is that being able to do something (afford to, have the means to) is justification enough for doing it—whether the project involves making space for a shopping mall by draining a wetland or cutting down the trees in a woodlot.

If we as a species can recognize the importance of biodiversity and accept that the world is not ours to do with as we please, what is the best route to protecting and conserving biodiversity? Should we focus on species? On genetic diversity? On ecosystems? How should we blend these approaches to achieve the best support for the endeavour? How can we engage people in this important activity and perhaps move them away from a human-centric view of the world?

As we shall see, at almost every turn there are examples of human activities driving other species to extinction. The motivations for human actions range from little more than greed to the daily effort to survive. The purpose of this chapter is to introduce you to a range of situations and examples associated with the reduction of biodiversity by extinction and the threat of extinction. We also consider steps that can be taken to protect biodiversity, including some successes and some failures.

Although extinction has been a recurring phenomenon in the history of life on Earth, the current extinction of species as a result of human activities is of grave concern to biologists and others concerned about our future. Changes wrought by humans include introduction of alien species and overharvesting of natural resources. These changes often have unexpected impacts on other species. Adoption of standardized criteria for identifying species at risk is an important part of conservation. Efforts to conserve biodiversity are focused at the species and/or habitat levels. In the final analysis, many of them depend upon taking steps to control the population of our own species and the related consumption of resources and habitat. We also need to change our attitudes and recognize that we are but one of millions of species on the planet and that, ultimately, our survival will depend upon theirs.

47.1 Extinction

Extinction is part of the process of evolution. Given that life has been on Earth for about 3 billion years, today there are more extinct than living species. Occasionally, the fossil record demonstrates a continuum in time from one species to another, sometimes blurring the boundaries between taxa (see Chapter 29). In this case, one could argue that the original species in a series lives on in its descendants. For example, the discovery that the genome of *Homo sapiens sapiens* contains some genes from *Homo sapiens neanderthalensis* leaves open the question about the distinctness of the two taxa. Although data for fossil species usually do not permit us to assess the levels of gene flow between

Figure 47.1
St. Francis of Assisi.

M.B. Fenton

populations, the Neanderthals provide an interesting exception. The difficulties inherent in applying the species concept to fossil material are familiar to paleontologists but less so to biologists.

Species and lineages have been going extinct since life first appeared. We should expect species to disappear at some low rate, the **background extinction rate**; as environments change, poorly adapted organisms do not survive or reproduce. In all likelihood, more than 99.9% of the species that have ever lived are now extinct. David Raup has suggested that, on average, as many as 10% of species go extinct every million years and more than 50% go extinct every 100 million years. Thus, the history of life has been characterized by an ongoing turnover of species.

The fossil record indicates that extinction rates rose well above the background rate at least five times in Earth's history. These events are referred to as mass extinctions. One extinction occurred at the end of the Ordovician and the beginning of the Devonian, the next at the end of the Devonian, then the end of the Permian, the end of the Triassic, and the end of the Cretaceous. The Permian extinction was the most severe, and more than 85% of the species alive at that time disappeared forever. This extinction was the end of the trilobites, many amphibians, and the trees of the coal swamp forests. During the last mass extinction, at the end of the Cretaceous, half of the species on Earth, including most dinosaurs, disappeared. A sixth mass extinction, potentially the largest of all, is occurring now as a result of human degradation of the environment.

Different factors were responsible for the five mass extinctions. Some were probably caused by tectonic activity and associated changes in climate. For example, the Ordovician extinction occurred after Gondwana moved toward the South Pole, triggering a glaciation that cooled the world's climate and lowered sea levels. The Permian extinction coincided with a major glaciation and a decline in sea level induced by the formation of Pangaea (see Chapter 19).

Many researchers believe that an asteroid impact caused the Cretaceous mass extinction. The resulting dust cloud may have blocked the sunlight necessary for photosynthesis, setting up a chain reaction of extinctions that began with microscopic marine organisms. Geologic evidence supports this hypothesis. Rocks dating to the end of the Cretaceous period (65 million years ago) contain a highly concentrated layer of iridium, a metal that is rare on Earth but common in asteroids. The impact from an iridium-laden asteroid only 10 km in diameter could have caused an explosion—equivalent to a billion tonnes of TNT—that scattered iridium dust around the world. Geologists have identified the submarine Chicxulub crater, 180 km in diameter, off Mexico's Yucatán peninsula as the likely site of the impact.

Although scientists agree that an asteroid struck Earth at that time, many question its precise relationship to the mass extinction. Dinosaurs had begun their decline at least 8 million years earlier, but many persisted for at least 40 000 years after the impact. Moreover, other groups of organisms did not suddenly disappear, as one would expect after a global calamity. The Cretaceous extinction took place over tens of thousands of years. Furthermore, some organisms survived periods of extinction, such as ginkgo trees (*Ginkgo biloba*), horseshoe crabs (*Limulus polyphemus*), and coelocanths (*Latimeria chalumnae*).

Even today we cannot blame the extinctions of most species on the activities of humans. But our increasing technological capability and prowess coincide with a burgeoning population of people. This situation is exacerbated by the philosophical view that humans are disconnected from nature. Thus, we are becoming better and better at destroying the biota of the planet. Taking action requires identifying root causes and then trying to make changes that will alleviate the problems.

First, we consider extinctions not linked to humans, and then we review examples of situations in which our actions have either directly or indirectly led to the extinction of species. The fact that extinction is integral to the process of evolution is hardly justification or rationalization for our driving so many species there. Put another way, invoking "survival of the fittest" may not be adequate justification for eradicating other species.

47.1a Dinosaurs: A Most Notable Extinction

Why do species go extinct? There could be as many theories as there are extinct species! The disappearance of the dinosaurs is one of the best-known extinction events in Earth's history. At the end of the Cretaceous about 65.5 million years ago, the dinosaurs disappeared. The ancestors of dinosaurs had appeared in the Triassic, and the group underwent extensive adaptive radiation reflected in body size, lifestyle, and distribution. Although people think of large and spectacular carnivorous dinosaurs such as *Tyrannosaurus rex* or the huge herbivore *Apatosaurus* (previously known as *Brontosaurus*), in reality, many species of dinosaurs were small and delicate.

Evidence from deposits in Alberta suggests that the carnivorous dinosaur *Albertosaurus* **(Figure 47.2, p. 1204)** showed age-specific mortality and high juvenile survival **(Figure 47.3a, p. 1204)**. Indeed, the survivorship curves (see Chapter 44) for *Albertosaurus* resemble those for humans **(Figure 47.3b, p. 1204)**. The data do not provide any indication of a flaw that predisposed dinosaurs to extinction. This is sobering, given the similarity between some aspects of dinosaur population biology and those of our own. The prevailing view today is that the disappearance of the dinosaurs is linked to the impact of an asteroid. Many other theories have been proposed to explain extinction, but the fact that birds and mammals and many other groups of organisms showed widespread extinctions

Figure 47.2
Mounted skeleton of *Albertosaurus* on display in the Royal Tyrrell Museum, Drumheller, Alberta. This late Cretaceous carnivore is abundant in fossil beds in Alberta and elsewhere.

As a group, multituberculates were prominent and persisted for 100 million years (compared with 150 million years for dinosaurs), making them the most successful mammals to date.

Multituberculates ranged from small (~20 g) to medium (5 to 10 kg) in size and exhibited both terrestrial and arboreal lifestyles. We can only speculate what happened to them, and why they became extinct. The widespread success of rodents almost worldwide could lend credibility to competition as the reason for the multituberculates' demise. However, the fossil record does not tell us what rodents and multituberculates competed for: food? nest sites?

STUDY BREAK

1. What is extinction?
2. What were multituberculates?

at the end of the Cretaceous implies a pervasive catastrophic event.

47.1b Multituberculates Are a Mammalian Example of Extinction

There is more to extinction than dinosaurs. Competition (see Chapter 45) has been proposed as a mechanism that can lead to extinction. Among mammals, the adaptive radiation of rodents (order Rodentia; **Figure 47.4a**) in the early Oligocene coincides with the disappearance of multituberculates (order Multituberculata; **Figure 47.4b**).

47.2 The Impact of Humans

When it comes to extinctions, we know most about those resulting from our activities, usually because these records are relatively recent and accessible. If you recently visited Mauritius, you might have noticed that the few remaining Mauritian calvaria trees are slowly dying of old age. Their passing will mark the extinction of this species, which has occurred even though the trees continued to bloom and produce seeds. The key to the pending extinction of *Sideroxylon majus* is the

a.

b.

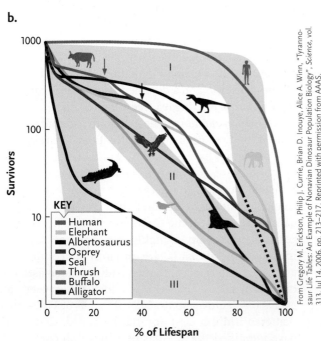

From Gregory M. Erickson, Philip J. Currie, Brian D. Inouye, Alice A. Winn, "Tyrannosaur Life Tables: An Example of Nonavian Dinosaur Population Biology", *Science*, vol. 313, Jul 14, 2006, pp. 213–217. Reprinted with permission from AAAS.

Figure 47.3
(a) Survivorship curve for a hypothetical cohort of 1000 *Albertosaurus* with presumed neonatal mortality of 60%. **(b)** Survivorship of *Albertosaurus* compared with that of other animals, including humans from developed countries, short-lived birds, mammals, and lizards, as well as crocodilians and some captive mammals.

LIFE ON THE EDGE 47.1
Sex Determination and Global Warming

Failure to reproduce puts the survival of a species on the edge, so anything that interferes with reproduction can be threatening. Genetic recombination is a fundamental benefit of sexual reproduction, enabling increases in genetic diversity and elimination of deleterious mutants. Effective sexual reproduction means having male and female systems, sometimes in one individual (hermaphrodites) and perhaps more often in different individuals. Males and females differ in many fundamental ways—genetically, hormonally, physiologically, and anatomically.

In humans and many other animals, gender is determined by genotype, with males having an X and a Y chromosome and females having two X chromosomes. The reverse is true in many other animals, for example birds. But in many reptiles gender is determined environmentally. Eggs incubated at some temperatures develop into males; when incubated at other temperatures, they produce females.

In 2008, D. A. Warner and R. Shine reported the results of experiments done with jacky dragons

(*Amphibolurus muricatus*), an Australian lizard in which gender is determined by temperature. Eggs incubated at 23 to 26°C or 30 to 33°C produce females; those incubated from 27 to 29°C produce males. Warner and Shine tested the hypothesis that temperature-dependent sex determination ensured production of females when they had an advantage and males when the advantage was to them. Using a combination of temperature and hormonal manipulations, Warner and Shine could produce males or females at any temperature. They analyzed paternity to assess the reproductive output of these males and observed eggs laid and hatched to document these females' reproductive output.

In female jacky dragons, larger body sizes occur at higher temperatures, and larger females have higher fecundity than smaller ones. Higher temperatures also correlate with larger body size in males. However, males hatched from eggs incubated between 27 and 29°C sired more offspring than those hatched from eggs incubated at lower or higher temperatures.

Change in climate, such as global warming, could put species with temperature-dependent sex determination at risk by effectively eliminating males or females from the population. Eggs incubated at the wrong temperatures would fail to hatch. The importance of variation in temperature during development in ectothermic organisms could explain the prevalence of genotypic-dependent sex determination in euthermic (homeothermic) viviparous animals. Viviparous or ovoviviparous ectotherms (fish, amphibians, reptiles, other animals) could also rely on temperature-dependent gender determination, provided that their developing young experience an appropriate range of temperatures.

Recent work from Mexico reveals that since 1975, 12% of local populations of lizards have disappeared, likewise 4% of worldwide local populations. Like other ectotherms, lizards have a narrow thermal range in which they thrive, and climate change has altered the thermal niches available to them. This and temperature-dependent gender determination put lizards in double jeopardy.

a.

DigiMorph.org

b.

M.B. Fenton

Figure 47.4

(a) The skull of a multituberculate (*Kryptobaatar dashzevegi*) from the Mongolian late Cretaceous **(b)** the skull of a groundhog (*Marmota monax*), a North American rodent, compared with.

earlier extinction of Dodos. To germinate, seeds of Mauritian calvaria trees had to pass through the Dodo's digestive tract. The Dodo **(Figure 47.5, p. 1206)** was a medium-sized flightless bird that lived on the island of Mauritius. When European sailors first visited the island, they used Dodos as a source of fresh meat. Then,

as the island was settled, the birds were exposed to introduced predators (cats, dogs, rats) and an expanding human population. Dodos vanished by 1690.

Species confined to islands often have small populations and are unaccustomed to terrestrial predators, making them vulnerable to extinction. The fossil and

PEOPLE BEHIND BIOLOGY 47.2
Amanda Vincent, University of British Columbia

Sea horses are a central focus for Amanda Vincent's research. She holds a Canada Research Chair in marine conservation and is the director of Project Seahorse. Sea horses are notable for the details of their biology (see Chapter 40) and because they are big business.

Vincent has studied the behaviour of sea horses. During mating, the male's sperm fertilizes the female's eggs, but the female then transfers the fertilized eggs to the male's brood pouch; thus, the male gets "pregnant." Males and females are in regular contact during the period of pregnancy. These contact behaviours may be key to the monogamy that appears to be typical of male–female relationships in sea horses.

The world trade in sea horses involves an estimated 20 million of them each year. In Asia, millions of dried sea horses are traded each year, mainly for use in traditional Chinese medicines. Remedies that include sea horses are said to be useful in treating symptoms from asthma and skin problems to incontinence and disorders of the thyroid. Dried sea horses may also be ingredients in aphrodisiacs.

Vincent has been very active in efforts to conserve sea horses, including working with local fishing communities to conserve them and maintain a sustainable harvest. This means establishing local protected areas and growing some sea horses in controlled conditions so that they, rather than wild stock, are harvested.

Vincent is an example of a biologist who combines an academic interest with its practical applications. Her work in conservation connects the realities of harvesting animals with the demands for their conservation.

a.

Raphus cucullatus by Roelandt Savery, 1626

b.

ISLAND OF THE DODOS
(Black dots indicate places where dodo remains have been found)

Reprinted by permission from Macmillan Publishers Ltd: NATURE, Vol. 443: pp. 138–140, "Ornithology: Digging for dodo" by Henry Nicholls, copyright (2006).

Figure 47.5

(a) A reconstruction of a *Raphus cucullatus*, the Dodo, an extinct flightless bird from **(b)** Mauritius.

species disappeared soon after people settled there. These examples demonstrate that humans do not have to be industrial or "high tech" to effect extinctions.

Meanwhile, in the North Atlantic, people hunted *Pinguinus impennis,* the Great Auk, to extinction. However, land birds with large distributions and huge populations have also disappeared, such as *Ectopistes migratorius,* the Passenger Pigeon in eastern North America. Large-scale harvesting of these birds, combined with their low reproductive rate (clutch size: one egg), made the birds vulnerable in spite of their enormous populations. Animals that produce one young per year and suffer "normal" mortality must live at least 10 years to replace themselves in the population (see Chapter 44).

STUDY BREAK

1. When did the five mass extinctions occur? Which was the most severe? Which extinction affected the dinosaurs?
2. What caused these extinctions?
3. Why are island animals and plants particularly susceptible to extinction due to human impacts?

CONCEPT FIX It is easy to believe that we must focus conservation efforts on large, charismatic animals and plants because these can be the poster images of conservation. We now realize that it is often more important to protect ecosystems, recognizing that the many components of ecosystems play a vital role in maintaining biodiversity, including the large and charismatic members of ecological communities.

subfossil records show that many species of birds disappeared from islands in the South Pacific as Polynesians arrived there from the west. This occurred from Tonga to Easter Island and beyond **(Figure 47.6)**. The Galápagos, only discovered by people in 1535, was sheltered from the wave of human-induced extinctions. On Easter Island, endemic species of sea birds and other

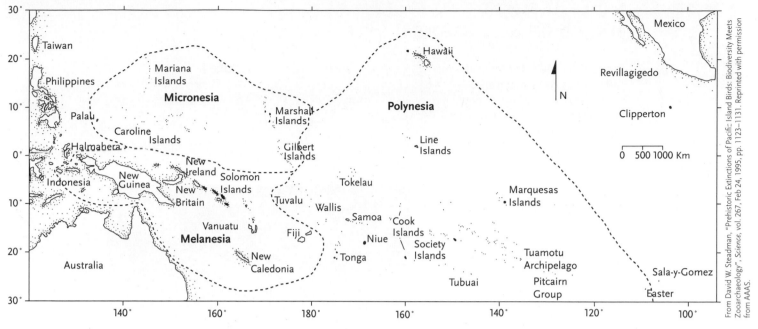

Figure 47.6
Islands in the South Pacific where the arrival of Polynesians coincided with the extinction of many island species of birds.

47.3 Introduced and Invasive Species

Humans cause extinction through hunting and by the introduction of other species. House cats, *Felis domesticus,* are among the worst introductions people have made. Anecdotal records suggest that in 1894, one house cat (named Tibbles) exterminated an entire population of flightless wrens **(Figure 47.7)** on Stephen's Island, a 2.6 km² island off the north shore of New Zealand. Fossils indicate that the wrens had occurred widely in New Zealand. This record stands for one individual, Tibbles, taking out the remaining approximately 10 pairs and exterminating the species.

It should be obvious that moving species from one part of the world to another, whether done willfully or by accident, can have calamitous impacts. The invaders, once arrived and established, may outcompete resident species, laying waste to species and ecosystems. The list of introduced organisms is very long and includes many domesticated or commensal species of animals and plants. The arrival of zebra mussels **(Figure 47.8a)** in the Great Lakes is the main reason for the decline of the now endangered eastern pond mussels **(Figure 47.8b)**

Figure 47.8
(a) Zebra mussels, *Dressina polymorpha*, were introduced to the Great Lakes in North America, where they have spread rapidly. **(b)** They are directly responsible for the declines in eastern pond mussels (*Lampsilis radiata*), a local mussel species.

Figure 47.7
Stephen's Island Wren, *Xenicus lyalli*. This species was exterminated by one cat.

MOLECULE BEHIND BIOLOGY 47.3

The 2,4-D Molecule and Resiliency

Resiliency is one of the most impressive features of life at the species and/or ecosystem levels. In one respect, this feature complicates the challenges of conserving biodiversity because introduced species can be so invasive, reflecting their adaptability.

Humans first identified 2,4-D (2,4-dichlorophenoxyacetic acid; **Figure 1**) in 1942, and from 1944, it was marketed as a herbicide more effective against broad-leaved plants than against grasses. Technically, 2,4-D is a hormone absorbed by the plant and translocated to the growing points of roots and shoots. 2,4-D kills weeds by inhibiting growth. The global market for 2,4-D is probably more than U.S.$300 million, and it is mainly used to control broad-leaved weeds in cereal crops. According to the World Health Organization (WHO), 2,4-D is a "moderately hazardous pesticide" known to affect a variety of animals (e.g., dogs but not rats). Curiously, it turns out that other animals may use 2,4-D for their own ends.

In 1971, Thomas Eisner and colleagues reported that a grasshopper (*Romalea microptera;* **Figure 2**) produced a froth of chemicals **(Figure 3)** for protection against ants. One of the main ingredients in the froth was 2,5-dichlorophenol, apparently derived from 2,4-D. This is an astonishing demonstration of adaptability that can underlie resiliency.

Resiliency and the recuperative powers of ecosystems are demonstrated by stories of "lost cities," for example, structures built by Maya in Central America, being found in a jungle. Archaeological evidence reveals that in some habitats, these buildings and pyramids were overgrown by the rainforest in about 100 years. The Great Zimbabwe Ruins in southern Africa were overgrown by savanna woodland in a period of 100 to 200 years and only latterly "discovered" by European explorers.

FIGURE 1
2,4-dichlorophenoxyacetic acid, 2,4-D.

2, 4-D

(2, 4-dichlorophenoxy)acetic acid

FIGURE 2
Romalea microptera, *a grasshopper that uses an ant repellent with a 2,4-D derivative.*

I (500) II (50) III (40)

IV (30) V (14) VI (7)

VII (4) VIII (2) IX (1)

FIGURE 3
Active ingredients in the defensive froth of the grasshopper, Romalea microptera. *2,5-dichlorophenol (boxed) is apparently derived from 2,4-D.*

© KHALED KASSEM/Alamy

The immigrant mussels outcompeted and overgrew the native ones, reducing their range and populations to levels that resulted in eastern pond mussels being recommended for listing as endangered in Canada in 2007.

Meanwhile, in parts of the British Isles, flatworms (*Arthurdendyus triangulatus*; **Figure 47.9**; see also Chapters 25 and 40, respectively) introduced from New Zealand are deadly predators of earthworms. Since their arrival in garden pots, the flatworms have thrived and spread rapidly, coinciding with the demise of earthworms. Ironically, although we often think of gardeners as individuals in touch with nature, their propensity to introduce exotic species may not be compatible with conservation. Earthworms themselves have been introduced widely to places around the world.

Some organisms move about in ballast water. Since about 1880, ships have regularly used water for ballast. In the early 1990s, a survey of ballast water in 159 cargo ships in Coos Bay, Oregon, revealed 367 taxa representing 16 animal and 3 protist phyla, as well as 3 plant divisions. The samples included all major and most minor phyla. Organisms in the ballast water included carnivores, herbivores, omnivores, deposit feeders, scavengers, suspension feeders, primary producers, and parasites. Ballast water is taken on in one port and discharged in another, providing many species with almost open access to waters around the world.

Meanwhile, introduced diseases (and the organisms that cause them) have decimated, if not obliterated, resident species. When Europeans arrived in the New World, *Castanea dentata,* the American chestnut tree, was widespread in forests from southern Ontario to Alabama. This large tree of the forest canopy grew to heights of 30 m. Often most abundant on prime agricultural soils, the species' distribution and density were reduced as settlers from Europe cleared more and

more land for agriculture. *Endothia parasitica,* the chestnut blight, was introduced perhaps around 1904 from Asian nursery stock. This introduced blight killed the American chestnut trees by the 1930s. By 2000, only scattered American chestnut trees remained, most of them stump sprouts.

Why are invading species so successful? Does the spread of Starlings (*Sturnus vulgaris*) or dandelions (*Taraxacum officinale*) after introduction to new continents suggest that they moved into vacant niches? Does it mean that they are better competitors? In the case of Starlings, 13 birds were introduced to Central Park in New York City in 1890, and they have spread far and wide. Once they are established, invading or introduced species can pose huge conservation problems because of their effects on ecosystems and diversity.

Although many invaders arrive, only a few are widely successful and become large-scale problems in their new settings. Invading plants are most often successful in nutrient-rich habitats, where they can achieve high growth rates, early reproduction, and maximal production of offspring. What happens in resource-poor settings? In the past, conventional wisdom has suggested that low-resource settings could be reservoirs for native species that could outcompete invaders.

However, an experimental examination of the responses of native and introduced species to challenging conditions revealed that invasive plant species almost always fared better **(Figure 47.10)**. Resource use

Figure 47.9
This earthworm-eating planarian (*Arthurdendyus triangulatus*) was introduced to the British Isles from New Zealand. It has had a devastating effect on local populations of earthworms.

Figure 47.10
(a) Photosynthetic rates (RUE) and **(b)** light-use efficiency of invasive plant species (blue bars) make them more competitive than native ones (yellow bars). The plants were from three different habitats in Hawaii.

efficiency (RUE), calculated by measuring carbon assimilation per unit of resource, provides an indicator of success. Many invasive species, such as ferns, C₃ and C₄ grasses, herbs, shrubs, and trees, were more successful in low-resource systems than native species were.

This research was conducted in Hawaii, an excellent place for studying invasive species because so many are there. Among the invaders were *Bromus tectorum* (cheatgrass), *Heracleum mantegazzianum* (cartwheel flower or giant hogweed), and *Pinus radiata* (Monterey pine). Humans have introduced these plants for gardening (cheatgrass and cartwheel flower) or commercial timber production (Monterey pine). The data demonstrate that attempting to restore ecosystems and exclude invading species by reducing resource availability does not succeed because of the efficiency with which some species use resources.

STUDY BREAK

1. Give two examples of invasive species, one animal and one plant. Describe the history of the invasion.
2. Are invasive species more apt to be successful than native species? Why or why not?
3. What is ballast water? Why does it figure in transporting species from one place to another?

47.4 How We Got/Get There

Lamentably, we know that humans can exterminate species that are populous and widespread as well as ones that have small populations and occur in a small area.

47.4a Poaching Caused the Demise of the Black Rhinoceros

It is estimated that 60 000 black rhinos (*Diceros bicornis*) lived in the wild in Africa in 1960 **(Figure 47.11a)**. This large (1.5 m at the shoulder, 1400 kg) browsing mammal was widespread in sub-Saharan Africa **(Figure 47.11b)**. Adult males and females have two distinctive "horns" **(Figure 47.12a;** see also Figure 47.11a), actually formed from hair. Rhinos use the horns to protect themselves and their young from predators and other rhinos. By 1981, the populations in the wild had been reduced to between 10 000 and 15 000, and again reduced to about 3500 by 1987. Today only a few individuals survive in some protected areas in Africa. In less than 30 years, the species was almost exterminated in the wild.

In 1960, black rhinos were one of the "big five" on the list of big game for which hunters made safaris to Africa to shoot as trophies. Others on the list included the African lion, African elephant, Cape buffalo (*Syncerus caffer*), and leopard. Safari hunters then paid

Figure 47.11
(a) Black rhinos (*Diceros bicornis*) were widespread and common in Africa in 1960 (orange area on the map in (b)). **(b)** Today their range (dark spots in orange areas) is much reduced, reflecting diminished populations. Note the oxpecker (*Buphagus africanus*) sitting on the rhino.

a.

b.

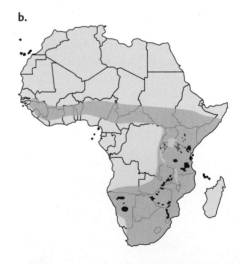

M.B. Fenton

Figure 47.12
(a) A horn from a black rhino in Zimbabwe is shown with **(b)** a rhino horn bowl from China and **(c)** a jambiya with a rhino horn handle.

a.

M.B. Fenton

b.

M.B. Fenton

c.

M.B. Fenton

large sums of money to go to Africa and obtain licences to kill trophy specimens of each of the big five. But this hunting pressure, which has since stopped, did not lead to the extermination of black rhinos.

People have long used the horns of all species of rhino in different ways. In China, bowls made from rhino horn **(Figure 47.12b)** were believed to have magical properties in that they could remove or neutralize poisons. Travelling nobles were served wine in their own rhino horn bowls to minimize the chances of their being poisoned. In India and some other areas from India to Korea, powdered rhino horn was used as a fever suppressant. Contrary to popular belief, rhino horn does not appear to have been used as an aphrodisiac, an early version of Viagra.

A tradition among some people of the Arabian Peninsula is the carrying of a jambiya or ceremonial dagger. Jambiyas with rhino horn handles **(Figure 47.12c)** were highly prized. In 1973, when the price of oil jumped from U.S.$4 to U.S.$12 a barrel, the ensuing "energy crisis" meant a larger market for jambiyas because more people could afford them. Increased cash flow and easy access to military weapons such as Kalashnikov assault rifles **(Figure 47.13)** provided an incentive and a means to kill rhinos. The epidemic of poaching started in northern Kenya and spread southward throughout the continent. Thus, poaching for their horns led to the catastrophic reduction in the populations of black rhinos. The large population of rhinos that had long survived in the presence of predators, including *Homo sapiens,* was not protected from extermination. In 1984, going for a walk at night around the headquarters of Mana Pools National Park in Zimbabwe almost always meant meeting a black rhino. By 1987, the rhinos were very scarce, and by 1990 they did not exist in the area.

The demise of black rhinos can only be attributed to human greed.

47.4b The Barndoor Skate Is a Victim of By-catch

Our harvesting of food organisms can affect more than just the target species on land and at sea. Barndoor skates (*Dipturus laevis;* **Figure 47.14**) are elasmobranchs that used to occur widely in the northwest Atlantic. With a maximum body width of about 1 m, this is one

Figure 47.13
A Kalashnikov assault rifle (an AK), a weapon widely used in the poaching of animals in many parts of the world.

Figure 47.14
The barndoor skate (*Dipturus laevis*) was once widespread in the northwestern Atlantic Ocean. Mortality associated with by-catch has severely reduced its populations.

of the largest skates. Dramatic reductions in the biomass of barndoor skates are obvious from locations ranging from the southern Grand Bank to southern New England **(Figure 47.15, p. 1212)**.

Recent captures of barndoor skates have been at depths greater than 1000 m, which may be one of the last refuges for this distinctive species. A combination of directed fishing for skates off the coasts of Newfoundland and Nova Scotia and by-catch of barndoor skates may spell the end for this species. In fishing terms, "by-catch" occurs when nontarget species are taken by fishers. Victims of by-catch include other species of fish, as well as sea turtles and marine mammals.

Removing species from ecosystems or depleting their numbers can also affect many other species in the ecosystem.

47.4c The Bay Scallop Is Affected by Overfishing of Sharks

Populations of organisms we harvest for food often show marked declines. The annual harvest of bivalve molluscs has been a local fishery in Chesapeake Bay in the United States and elsewhere along the eastern seaboard for hundreds of years. In 1999, populations of bay scallops (*Argopecten irradians;* **Figures 47.16 and 47.17, p. 1212**), a main target of the fishery, were very low. The immediate reason for the low populations was the impact of predation by skates and rays that feed heavily on bivalve molluscs. Skates and rays are tertiary consumers and in turn are eaten by larger elasmobranchs, specifically various species of sharks.

Among tertiary consumers, the cownose ray **(Figure 47.18, p. 1212)** showed a marked increase in population. Evidence from surveys on the U.S. Atlantic coast estimates an order-of-magnitude increase in populations of cownose rays, and the total population of 14 species of rays and skates exceeds 40 million. So the decline in scallop (and other bivalve) populations can be explained by the increase in predation by tertiary consumers, especially skates and rays.

The picture becomes clearer when the population data for the local great sharks are added to the mix

a.

Figure 47.16
A handful of bay scallops (*Argopecten irradians*).

b.

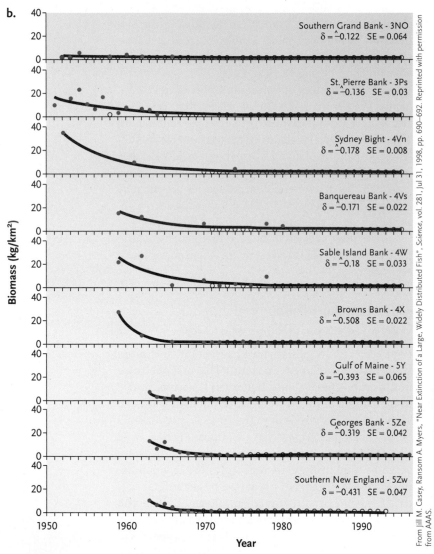

From Jill M. Casey, Ransom A. Myers, "Near Extinction of a Large, Widely Distributed Fish", *Science*, vol. 281, Jul 31, 1998, pp. 690–692. Reprinted with permission from AAAS.

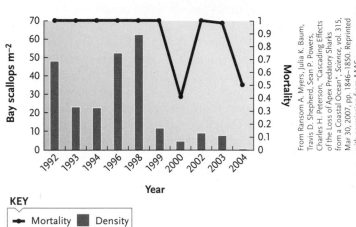

KEY
— Mortality   ■ Density

From Ransom A. Myers, Julia K. Baum, Travis D. Shepherd, Sean P. Powers, Charles H. Peterson, "Cascading Effects of the Loss of Apex Predatory Sharks from a Coastal Ocean", *Science*, vol. 315, Mar 30, 2007, pp. 1846–1850. Reprinted with permission from AAAS.

Figure 47.17
Numbers of bay scallops off the east coast of the United States.

From Jill M. Casey, Ransom A. Myers, "Near Extinction of a Large, Widely Distributed Fish", *Science*, vol. 281, Jul 31, 1998, pp. 690–692. Reprinted with permission from AAAS.

Figure 47.15
(a) Fishery subdivisions off the east coast of Canada and the United States providing data about the abundances of barndoor skates. **(b)** Catch records of barndoor skates from these fishing subdivisions.

Figure 47.18
A cownose ray (*Rhinoptera bonasus*).

(Figure 47.19). Prolonged and intensive fishing of 12 species of sharks accounts for a 35 year decline in their populations (see Figure 47.19, top row). The sharks have been taken primarily for their fins and meat. In some parts of the world, shark fins sell for

around U.S.$700 per kilogram and are used to make shark fin soup.

The data demonstrate how a century-old scallop fishery was effectively destroyed because of predation by tertiary consumers, whose populations, in turn,

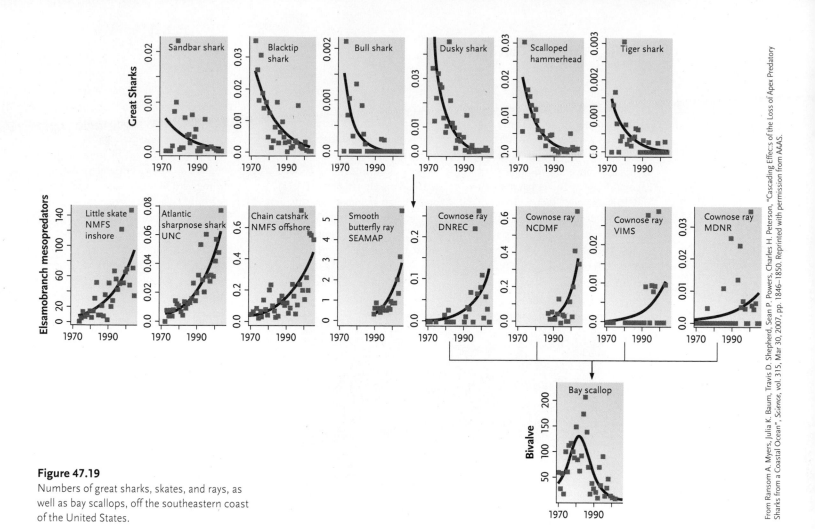

Figure 47.19

Numbers of great sharks, skates, and rays, as well as bay scallops, off the southeastern coast of the United States.

From Ransom A. Myers, Julia K. Baum, Travis D. Shepherd, Sean P. Powers, Charles H. Peterson, "Cascading Effects of the Loss of Apex Predatory Sharks from a Coastal Ocean", *Science*, vol. 315, Mar 30, 2007, pp. 1846–1850. Reprinted with permission from AAAS.

had been enhanced (see Figure 47.19, middle row) by the removal of top predators, the great sharks. The data illustrate a cascading ecological effect and demonstrate the potential long-term harm that our species can do to ecosystems and the species inhabiting them. The demise of bay scallops and other bivalves can be attributed to the impact of large-scale harvesting of marine resources. The late Ransome Myers and his colleagues documented this cascade of effects.

The examples above are merely samples from a long list of species. Evidence of declines of populations of native species can be found almost everywhere. Whether the root cause is overharvesting, introduced species, or destruction of habitat, species from whales to songbirds are threatened by human activity. What can we do about it?

STUDY BREAK

1. What is the significance of rhino horn in the conservation of these animals?
2. What connects the decline in the scallop fishery to sharks?
3. What is by-catch?

47.5 Protecting Species

The widespread recognition of trademarks such as the World Wildlife Fund (WWF) panda demonstrates how associating a cause with an icon can be very successful. It is not surprising that many conservation efforts began with a focus on one species—such as giant pandas (*Ailuropoda melanoleuca*), polar bears (*Ursus maritimus*), or redwood trees (*Sequoia sempervirens*). The lure of conservation movements that focus on charismatic species is very strong. But charismatic organisms may not need protection, whereas some species that are unattractive, dangerous, or mundane are in desperate need of our assistance. Unfortunately, mundane, ugly, and dangerous (to us) species are unlikely to serve as a call to arms (or to attract financial support). Worldwide, the WWF panda is one of the most recognized logos, whether or not pandas are in the neighbourhood.

A critical first step toward conservation is the development and adoption of objective, data-based criteria for assessing the risk posed to different species. This process has been developed on several fronts around the world. The criteria and assessment procedures perfected by the International Union for

We saw earlier (see Chapter 18) how the Linnaean system of nomenclature is used to name species. Once a species has a name, however acquired, it may benefit from protection under CITES, the Convention on International Trade in Endangered Species of Wild Fauna and Flora. But will data-based decisions about what counts as endangered be consistent and predictable? The answer is "yes" and "no." The example of black rhinos showed one situation in which protection under CITES did not work. There are others.

Also in Africa, the leopard (see the chapter-opening photograph) was accorded protection under CITES. The passing of the Endangered Species Act (ESA) in the United States (1972) precipitated an interesting situation: it obliged Americans to "obey" the listing of leopards on CITES Appendix 1, which banned the importation of leopard skins, including those shot on safari hunts. The rationale for the listing was the belief that leopards were endangered and their survival was threatened by hunting.

There were quick, negative responses to the ban on importing leopard skins into the United States from two different groups. First were the hunting and related associations and lobbies whose members were anxious to be able to bring home trophies. Second, leaders and governments in many African countries that benefited from the hunts objected to the ban because safaris were (and still are) an important source of foreign exchange. In many of these countries, "safari hunting areas" were set aside to accommodate visitors, and these large tracts of land also protected populations of nongame species and appropriate habitat.

What do the data show? Leopards are 40 to 80 kg, solitary cats that hunt by stealth. They are widespread in Africa but have been little studied. The estimate is that there are more than 700 000 leopards in the wild in Africa, with resident populations in all but very small countries with high human population densities. In 2000, Zimbabwe alone had a population of more than 16 000 leopards in the wild. The 1969 safari harvest of 6100 leopards throughout Africa and the export of their skins were not a threat to the population in Zimbabwe, let alone to leopards in the whole continent.

Ecologists studied the population of leopards in the Matetsi Safari Area in Zimbabwe. Before 1974, the 4300 km² area was a cattle ranch whose operators made strong efforts to eradicate leopards to protect their livestock. After conversion to a hunting area, people on the first safaris rarely succeeded in shooting leopards. By 1984, the leopard population in the Matetsi Safari Area was 800 to 1000, and in 1988, the annual safari quota there was 3.6% (12 to 28 leopards). When leopards shot in the mid-1980s were compared with those taken in the

FIGURE 1
Polar bear, Ursus maritimus.

M.B. Fenton

a.

FIGURE 2
(a) Saola (Pseudoryx nghetinhensis) *and (b) its distribution.*

Bill Robichaud, Saola Working Group.

b.

Pu Mat
Nghe An
Thua Thien Hue
Quang Nam
LAOS
THAILAND
VIETNAM
CAMBODIA

● Presumed saola distribution

From Richard Stone, "The Saola's Last Stand", *Science*, vol. 314, Dec 1, 2006, pp. 1380–1383. Reprinted with permission from AAAS.

(continued)

Hunting: Threat or Salvation? 47.4 (*continued*)

1970s, no change in leopard size was found. But by 1986, the average age of leopards taken as trophies was 5.4 years, compared with 3.2 years from the earlier period. These data show that leopards can persist even when subjected to heavy hunting pressure. On average, leopards live longer in a safari hunting regime than when they are being hunted in the context of predator control operations. Other evidence suggests that populations of leopards persist even in urban areas—trapping evidence suggests that resident leopards live in Nairobi, the capital of Kenya.

Leopards are an interesting example of human responses to conservation. Hunting or some other form of harvesting is not necessarily a threat to the survival of some species. Indeed, some harvesting may be critical to the livelihood of some people and can advance efforts to protect some species. But decisions about harvesting made in one part of

the world can influence what happens elsewhere.

Today there are quotas for the numbers of leopards that can be harvested in different countries in Africa. Safari hunters must obtain licences to take trophies, and skins exported must be accompanied by paperwork showing that the harvest was legal. The documentation allows a citizen, for example, of Canada or of a European Union country, to import a leopard skin. This was not possible in the United States in the 1970s, but it is now. In Africa, local farmers are permitted to kill "problem" animals that threaten their livestock or themselves and their families and may be supported in this by government officials.

Key elements in the success of harvesting include having data about the population of organisms, the rates of reproduction, and the rates of harvest. Enforcement of quotas is essential if this approach is to

succeed. Legal harvest quotas do not require people who object to hunting to be hunters. Trophy hunting is not the exclusive preserve of countries in Africa. On April 3, 2007, *The Globe and Mail* reported that the economy of Nunavut received C$2.9 million from polar bear **(Figure 1)** hunting. Hunters can pay U.S.$20 000 for a polar bear hunt.

In 1992, saola **(Figure 2)** made the news as one of the first "new" species of large mammals to be discovered in recent times. These goatlike animals live in a restricted area of Vietnam, where they have been and are hunted by local people. Saolas are rare, and little is known about them. There are no quotas for the local hunters, and it is not practical to enforce a ban on their harvest. In reality, we probably lack critical information about the biology of many species of wildlife today. However, once they have names, they have a chance of being protected.

Conservation of Nature (IUCN) are used widely. There are many records of success, but there also are many examples of species with which and situations in which we have failed. Making arguments based on data does not guarantee success. Using a data-based approach, some species emerge as being in need of protection, but others do not. Being rare or unusual, by itself, will not warrant protection. The species concept and the Linnaean system of nomenclature (see Chapter 18) are fundamental to conservation.

In Canada, recommendations about the conservation status of species involve the Committee on the Status of Endangered Wildlife in Canada (COSEWIC). The definition of wildlife includes plants and animals. Like IUCN, COSEWIC recognizes six categories for assessing species at risk:

- *Extinct* wildlife species no longer exist.
- *Extirpated* species no longer exist in one location in the wild but occur elsewhere.
- *Endangered* species face imminent extirpation or extinction.
- *Threatened* species are likely to become endangered if limiting factors are not reversed.
- *Special concern* species may become threatened or endangered because of a combination of biological characteristics and identified threats.
- *Data deficient* is a category used when available information is insufficient either to resolve a

wildlife species' eligibility of assessment or to permit an assessment of its risk of extinction.

A seventh category—*not at risk*—is used to identify species not at risk of extinction under current circumstances.

COSEWIC members vote on the appropriate conservation category for each species whose status they review. The members consider the area of occupancy, which is an indication of the range of a species and the availability of suitable habitat. They take into consideration population information, including trends in the numbers of organisms, correcting for species that show extreme fluctuations in numbers from year to year. They consider the demographics of the species and the variability in the habitat where the species occurs. Generation time is also considered, along with specific habitat features that may be essential for the species' survival. Data on population size, particularly the numbers of reproducing adults, are important, as well as risks to the species' survival.

In a biological context, the criteria used by COSEWIC (and similar agencies elsewhere) are familiar to population biologists (see Chapter 44). The data describe the numbers of individuals in the population, fecundity, mortality, and the intrinsic rate of increase. Carrying capacity is also important, as is the area (range) over which the species occurs. These criteria are designed to promote data-based decisions about the conservation status of species.

47.6 Protecting What?

Before data are used to address questions of species-at-risk status, conservation biologists must decide about eligibility. The conservation jargon for this is "designatable unit." Are the organisms "real" species? Are they subspecies? Are they distinct populations? Are they really Canadian? Do they regularly occur in Canada or perhaps turn up here by accident? If the species does not breed here, is the habitat they use in Canada essential to their survival? Most species of wildlife in Canada occur close to the border with the United States, and many species widespread in the United States just make it into Canada. In some cases, a distinct population is treated as a designatable unit. Distinct populations may be recognized by their geographic distribution and/or their genetic structure.

Questions about what units are designatable hearken back to the definition of species (see Chapter 19). Off the west coast of Canada, striking differences in behaviour can be used to distinguish between two "kinds" of killer whales. The *resident* killer whales eat mainly fish and often echolocate. The *transient* killer whales eat mainly marine mammals and rarely produce echolocation signals. Furthermore, repeated sightings of recognizable individual whales indicate that different groups of these animals live in different areas along the coast **(Figure 47.20)**.

In reviewing the conservation status of killer whales, COSEWIC recognized different designatable units based on behaviour and geography **(Figure 47.21, p. 1217)**. The different units faced different threats to their survival.

Questions about what to protect often reflect different realities of biology. Migrating birds may be blown off course and end up in southern Ontario instead of their usual habitat much farther south. Marine birds or mammals may feed in Canadian waters but breed elsewhere. Many organisms commonly hitchhike, using ocean vessels, aircraft, or automobiles as vehicles of dispersal. But some hitchhikers, for example, some snails, travel with birds, making the association and the dispersal more "natural."

People can be quick to try to protect species they consider to be important or distinctive. In 2003, the Ontario Ministry of Natural Resources reported four to six white-coloured moose (*Alces alces*) among the approximately 1900 moose in two wildlife management areas near Foleyet in northeastern Ontario. Should white-coloured moose be protected? There was local support for protecting the moose, animals that have cultural and spiritual significance for First Nations communities. White moose have been reported from other places in northern Ontario, Newfoundland and Labrador, and elsewhere. Although the population of white moose is small and widespread, there is no evidence that they are a designatable unit. In Canada, they have not been accorded special protection.

There is protection at the international level. CITES, the Convention on International Trade in Endangered Species of Wild Fauna and Flora, plays a

a.

b.

c.

Figure 47.20

Three views of a killer whale (*Orcinus orca*). **(a)** A captive animal in Vancouver, **(b)** a wild orca swimming off the Queen Charlotte Islands, and **(c)** a Haida representation.

An Endangered Species 47.5

Banff Springs snails, *Physella johnsoni* **(Figure 1),** live and eat algae in five hot springs on Sulphur Mountain in Banff National Park, Alberta. Not very long ago, Banff Springs snails were found in nine springs. In 1996, the total population of snails was about 5000. Water temperatures in the springs occupied by the snails range from 26 to 48°C, but temperatures less than 44°C seem best for them. Their very limited occurrence makes them vulnerable to extinction (COSEWIC, 2000).

Humans appear to be the main threat to the survival of Banff Springs snails. By discarding unsightly (to humans) accumulations of algae from pools, people have killed some snails that were in the algal mats. Changes in the patterns of water circulation may subject some snails to high temperatures that could be lethal. Well-wishers that throw copper coins into the pools may have harmed snails because of contamination arising from the interaction of copper with sulfurous water in the springs.

Other impacts of people are not clear, but one threat is entertaining to contemplate—people "skinny-dipping" in the pools are thought to threaten the snails. Some skinny-dippers have been caught and charged. Bathers in the pools, clad or unclad, may have crushed snails while getting into or out of the water. Bathers doused in sunscreen or insect repellents may have introduced chemicals into the snails' habitat and further reduced their populations.

Banff Springs snails are neither charismatic nor prominent, but the data-based approach to decision making has provided the basis for identifying them as endangered.

FIGURE 1

Banff Springs snail, Physella johnsoni.

Degner, M. & L., used with permission of Parks Canada

pivotal role in protecting species. In 2010, international trade in wildlife is a leading threat to conserving biodiversity because in addition to directly affecting local populations of threatened species, it can also spread infectious diseases and promote the spread of invasive species. Membership in CITES includes 175 countries, and CITES tries to regulate trade in almost 34 000 species. Basic, accurate, and reliable biological data about species are essential for informing decisions about which species should be protected. Yet, decisions about what species are protected by CITES are political and not necessarily uniformly acclaimed. Between 2009 and 2011, the annual budget of the secretariat of CITES was U.S.$5.2 million, coming from donations.

Recovery Strategy for the Northern and Southern Resident Killer Whales (Orcinus orca), in Canada, Fig. 1 p.4, from http://dsp-psd.pwgsc.gc.ca/collection_2008/ec/En3-4-46-2007E.pdf. Fisheries and Oceans Canada. Reproduced with the permission of Her Majesty the Queen in Right of Canada, 2011.

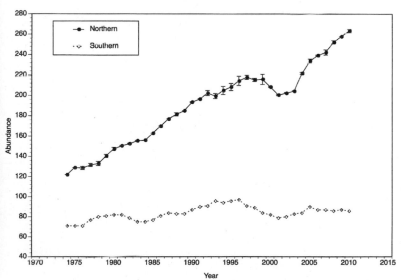

Northern Resident Killer Whales of British Columbia: Photo-identification Catalogue and Population Status to 2010, Figure 2, p. 8, from http://www. dfo-mpo.gc.ca/Library/343523.pdf Fisheries and Oceans Canada. Reproduced with the permission of Her Majesty the Queen in Right of Canada, 2011.

Figure 47.21

(a) The population distribution (designatable units) of killer whales off the coast of British Columbia and **(b)** estimates of population sizes of northern and southern resident killer whales (British Columbia).

Who Gets Protection? 47.6

Being recognized as rare and considered to be endangered does not necessarily translate into protection.

Because the Endangered Species Act (ESA) in the United States does not protect hybrids, this can affect the conservation of, for example, the Florida panther **(Figure 1),** a subspecies of cougar. Cougars, also known as panthers, used to occur widely in North, South, and Central America. Although still widespread in some areas, the current range of cougars in most of the United States and Canada is much less than it was when Columbus arrived in the New World in 1492. Florida panthers, a small population recognized as a subspecies, occur mainly in the Florida keys. Florida panthers were protected under the ESA.

Using techniques of molecular genetics, biologists determined that Florida panthers carried the genes of cougars from South America. This situation probably arose when panthers originally caught in South America were brought to the United States as zoo animals or for display in circuses or animal shows. Some of these animals escaped and interbred with local Florida panthers. Florida panthers with genes from South American cougars are technically hybrids and are therefore not protected by the ESA.

There are many other examples of situations in which genetic tools allow clearer delineation of boundaries between populations (designatable units) and species. In some cases, however, removal of protection from other "species" because of their genetic status can lead to their extinction. *Ammodramus maritimus nigrescens,* or the Dusky Seaside Sparrow, was previously considered to be a distinct form living in Florida. When genetic evidence showed that these darker animals were not genetically distinct, they lost their protected status and have virtually disappeared.

Other species, such as round-nosed grenadier, have suffered calamitous declines in population. These codlike fish **(Figure 2)** were taken in large numbers after cod populations had declined **(Figure 3).** The species was on the verge of extinction even before much was known about it. We do know that round-nosed grenadiers are late to mature, and their populations are slow to recover.

Although round-nosed grenadiers and at least four other species meet the IUCN criteria for listing as endangered, these fish have not been and are not protected. Fisheries and Oceans Canada has not supported a move to protect round-nosed grenadiers. Changing fishing practices to avoid catching the few remaining round-nosed grenadiers is not economically feasible when other species are still being caught in sufficient numbers to justify a continued fishery. The situation differs only from that facing the barndoor skate in that the round-nosed grenadiers have been the targets of an active fishery.

We have seen that the hunt for polar bears can bring significant income to the economy of Nunavut, and the same is true of other jurisdictions within the bear's range.

(continued)

FIGURE 2
Coryphaenoides rupestris, a round-nosed grenadier.

FIGURE 3
Captures of round-nosed grenadiers.

FIGURE 1
A Florida panther (Felis concolor coryi).

Who Gets Protection? 47.6 (*continued*)

There are distinct populations of polar bears **(Table 1)** within Canada's jurisdiction. The occurrence of bears in political jurisdictions including Canada, the United States, Russia, Iceland, Denmark (Greenland), Norway, Finland, and Sweden makes it more difficult to protect them. The apparent vulnerability of the bears to climate change and their value as trophies may combine to hasten their demise.

Table 1   **Status of Canadian Polar Bear Populations (January 1997).**

Population	% Females in harvest	Number	Sustainable Annual Kill	Mean Annual Kill	Environ. Concern	Status[1]	Quality of Estimate	Degree of Bias	Age of Estimate	Harvest/ Capture Data
Western Hudson Bay	31	1200	54	44	None	S[a]	Good	None	Current	Good (>15 yr)
Southern Hudson Bay	35	1000	43	45	None	S[a]	Fair	Moderate	Old	Fair (5–10 yr)
Foxe Basin	38	2300	91	118	None	S[a]	Good	None	Current	Good (>15 yr)
Lancaster Sound	25	1700	77	81	None	S[a]	Fair	None	Current	Good (>15 yr)
Baffin Bay	35	2200	94	122	None	D?[b]	Fair	None	Current	Fair (>15 yr)
Norwegian Bay	30	100	4	4	None	S[a]	Fair	None	Current	Good (>15 yr)
Kane Basin	37	200	8	6	None	S	Fair	None	Current	Fair (>15 yr)
Queen Elizabeth	–	(200?)	9?	0	Possible	S?[b]	None	–	–	–
Davis Strait	36	1400	58	57	None	S?[b]	Fair	Moderate	Outdated	Good (>15 yr)
Gulf of Boothia	42	900	32	37	None	S[a]	Poor	Moderate	Outdated	Good (>15 yr)
M'Clintock Channel	33	700	32	25	None	S[a]	Poor	Moderate	Outdated	Good (>15 yr)
Viscount Melville sound	0	230	4	0	None	I	Good	None	Current	Good (>15 yr)
Northern Beaufort Sea	43	1200	42	29	None	S	Good	None	Recent	Good (>15 yr)
Southern Beaufort Sea	36	1800	75	56	None	S	Good	Moderate	Recent	Good (>15 yr)

■ D = decreasing; I = increasing; S = stationary; ? = indicated trend uncertain

■ [a]Population is managed with a flexible quota system in which overharvesting in a given year results in a fully compensatory reduction to the following year's quota

■ [b]See text, "Population Size and Trend," for discussion.

COSEWIC Assessment and Update Status Report on the Polar Bear Ursus maritimus in Canada, 2002. http://www.sararegistry.gc.ca/document/default_e.cfm?documentID=248. Reproduced with the permission of the Minister of Public Works and Government Services, 2011.

Budget restrictions influence the effectiveness of CITES at the secretariat level by affecting the capacity for detailed collection and analysis of basic data.

At local levels, however, unmonitored trade in wildlife continues to occur openly, often in clear violation of CITES. Orchids are a clear example. In a period when CITES records showed 20 cases of orchids listed by CITES coming into Thailand from four neighbouring countries (Lao People's Democratic Republic, Myanmar, Cambodia, and Vietnam), 168 cases were observed in local markets. At one market in the Mekong Delta, one trader can sell more orchids in one day than reported by CITES over a period of 9 years!

STUDY BREAK

1. Give an example of a designatable unit that is a species.
2. Give an example of a designatable unit that is a population.
3. Is *designatable unit* synonymous with *species*?

47.7 The Downside of Being Rare

Whether the commodity is coins, stamps, antiques, or endangered species, as soon as something is rare enough, there is a market for it. This "get them while they last" attitude is exemplified by trade in *Leucopsar rothschildi,* Bali Starlings **(Figure 47.22a)**. This bird, another island species, faces immediate extinction, but it is in high demand as an exotic pet. In 1982, when there were fewer than 150 individuals in the wild, 35 were for sale as pets, 19 in Singapore and 16 in Bali.

Rare species may also be in demand for use of their body parts in traditional medicine. One stark example is the swim bladders of *Bahaba taipingensis,* the Chinese bahaba **(Figure 47.22b)**. At a time when fewer than 6 individuals are caught each year, more than 100 boats are trying to catch them. The swim bladders are used in traditional medicine. They are worth at least seven times their weight in gold. Shark fins are even more valuable. These are extreme examples similar to the earlier story about rhino horns and jambiyas.

Before criticizing and condemning the users or consumers of jambiyas or Chinese bahaba swim bladders, think about the overall impact of our lifestyle on other species of animals and plants. Of particular note is an insatiable demand for energy. Are sport utility vehicles necessary? Personal watercraft? Snowmobiles? All-terrain vehicles? The list goes on. Is a Canadian as justified in buying a large SUV as a North Yemenese a jambiya with a rhino horn handle? Once again, might (the ability or capacity to do something) may not be right.

Figure 47.22

(a) A Bali Starling (*Leucopsar rothschildi*) and **(b)** Chinese bahaba (*Bahaba taipingensis*).

STUDY BREAK

1. What is the value of the International Union for Conservation of Nature (IUCN)?
2. Why do species description and formal naming affect the Convention on International Trade in Endangered Species of Wild Fauna and Flora (CITES)?
3. What is the difference between an extinct species and an extirpated species? Give an example of each.

47.8 Protecting Habitat

It is obvious from many of the examples above that protecting species has not been entirely successful as a conservation strategy. As a species, we are much better at killing than we are at conserving. Whether this is direct or indirect, the end result can be the same. It is also clear that destruction of habitat is an effective way to remove a species. For example, populations of mosquitoes can be limited by denying them places to lay their eggs. This is a common theme in public education programs designed to reduce the incidence of West Nile virus (or other mosquito-borne diseases).

Is protection of habitat an effective strategy? The answer can be "yes," particularly for species that are not motile. Many species of plants have specific habitat requirements. From trees to shrubs, forbs, ferns, and mosses, we know that we can protect species by protecting habitat. Furthermore, protecting large tracts of habitat can also protect large, mobile species. Rainforests, whether tropical or temperate, are examples of habitats that can be flagships for protection and conservation. They are also considered by many to be storehouses of wealth associated with biodiversity, from building materials to compounds of pharmacological value.

The case of the black rhino demonstrated how a species targeted for harvesting can be driven to the brink of extinction even when it is protected (or lives in national parks or game reserves). *Panax quinquefolius,* American ginseng, is another target species, now endangered in Canada because of harvesting. The species used to grow wild from southwestern Québec and southern Ontario south to Louisiana and Georgia. This 20- to 70-cm-tall perennial is long lived in rich, moist, mature, sugar maple-dominated woods. Although the species has been listed on Appendix II of COSEWIC since 1973, populations have continued to decline. In 2000, there were 22 viable populations in Ontario and Québec, but none were secure. Black rhinos and ginseng were common about 50 years ago, but by 2008, both demonstrated the risks of being rare and expensive. They are also examples of the need for immediate on-the-ground enforcement of regulations and laws protecting species and habitats.

Protecting habitats can be most challenging in areas with larger human populations. All of the viable populations of American ginseng in Ontario and Québec were close to roads, making the plants vulnerable to anyone who knew about them and wished to take advantage of the economic opportunity they presented. *Sorex bendirii,* the Pacific water shrew, is another example of a species whose future in Canada is threatened by expanding human populations and the associated value of real estate **(Figure 47.23, p. 1222)**.

In British Columbia, expanding human population and the wine industry in the southern Okanagan Valley have combined to dramatically reduce a local ecosystem dominated by antelope bush **(Figure 47.24, p. 1223)**. The antelope bush system, one of the most endangered ecosystems in Canada, is home to a number of species of plants and animals whose future is now threatened by the demise of the habitat they require. The boom in real estate for people looking for retirement properties, more than just the density of human populations, is a key factor in this situation. Meanwhile, in southern Ontario, the demand for real estate to accommodate the expanding housing and business market is reducing both the available natural habitats and farmland.

STUDY BREAK

1. Give examples of how protecting a habitat can work.
2. How do market forces influence the abundance of species?

47.9 Effecting Conservation

Today we face many challenges when trying to protect biodiversity. Too many of the immediate threats are the direct or indirect consequences of human activities. We must protect species by acting at levels ranging from species to populations and habitats.

47.9a Human Population Is a Root Problem in Conservation

One fundamental root cause of declining biodiversity is the human population and the energy and habitat consumed in trying to feed, house, and protect our flourishing species. Visit the website http://www.ined.fr/en/everything_about_population/world_population_me/ and use it to determine the estimated human population in the year you were born and then for the years in which your parents and grandparents were born. Even when many people are killed, the momentum of our population increase does not slow down. The December 2004 tsunami killed approximately 250 000 people, at a time when the world population was estimated at 6 billion. By comparison, the 1883 explosion of Krakatoa (and resulting tsunamis) is thought to have killed 35 000 people when the global human population was about 1.5 billion. If these estimates are correct, $4.1 \times 10^{-3}\%$ of the human population at the time was killed by the 2004 tsunami and $2.3 \times 10^{-3}\%$ by the explosion of Krakatoa. Neither calamity caused the human population growth curve (see Chapter 44) to waver.

If human population growth continues at the same rate as it grows now, it will double in 40 years. However, studies show that our population is not growing as quickly as it did during much of the twentieth century. The United Nations Development Program (UNDP) has released data on human fertility (the total number of births per woman) for 162 countries **(Table 47.1, p. 1223)**. Compared with 1970–75, 152 countries had lower human fertility in 2000–05, 3 countries showed increases in fertility, and 7 showed no change.

Concerned about the global population and its effect on Earth, world leaders adopted the United Nations Millennium Development Goals in 2000, committing their nations to achieving the following goals by 2015:

Figure 47.23
(a) The distribution of *Sorex bendiri*. **(b)** Lower Fraser Valley locations where it was found (solid circles) or not found (open circles). **(c)** For comparison, the same area is shown with changes in the availability of urban lands in 1992 and 1998. Data on the map is from 2004.

SOURCE: Baseline Thematic Mapping Present Land Use Mapping at 1:220 000

- ending poverty and hunger,
- universal education,
- gender equality,
- child health,
- maternal health,
- combating HIV/AIDS,
- environmental sustainability, and
- global partnerships.

These goals can be achieved only if reproduction is controlled (see Chapter 37). In 1994, the United Nations held the International Conference on Population and Development (ICPD), which set a target for global investment in family planning. By 2004, the amount spent had fallen to 13% of this target. Consequently, family planning information and devices (usually for fertility control) are not readily available in many of the

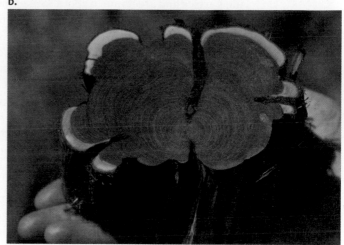

Figure 47.24

Antelope bush, *Purshia tridentata,* showing (a) the bush and (b) a cross section of the stem. These woody shrubs have long lifespans, and the ecosystem they typify is home to a variety of species.

lowest-income countries. In 1950, Sri Lanka and Afghanistan had the same population. Sri Lanka began strong efforts to make family planning available in culturally acceptable ways. This did not happen in Afghanistan. By 2050, Afghanistan will have four times as many people as Sri Lanka. The solution centres around controlling the fertility of women, but more particularly on giving them the power to control their own fertility in culturally acceptable ways. As seen in Chapter 44, the growth potential of a population is determined by the numbers of females of reproductive age. Why females? Because females are the limiting step in reproduction—the ones who produce the eggs or young.

47.9b Signs of Stress Show up on Systems and on Species

People's demand for food, water, and energy puts thousands of other species at risk. We do not have to look far to see examples of species and ecosystems under stress (see Chapter 46). For example, we are losing birds. We know this because for years, birdwatchers and ornithologists have counted them and monitored their behaviour and activity. Locally, birds are affected by changes in habitat availability as cities and towns and their suburbs expand into adjoining land. Birds also lose habitat when agricultural operations expand to increase productivity. Birds that make annual migrations from temperate areas of the world to tropical and subtropical ones must survive the changes that accumulate across their entire circuit of habitats, each one essential to their survival.

Avian influenza (also called bird flu) is a looming crisis for humans, one that appears to involve birds as central players. The issue here is another one involving basic biology, namely the outcome when a disease-causing organism jumps from one species (host) to another. Bird flu could have as much to do with our insatiable demand for poultry as food as it does with birds. In 2006, 12 billion chickens were farmed in China. Worldwide, poultry farms housed over 100 billion broiler chickens. Raising organisms at very high densities (see Chapter 44) provides an ideal setting for the spread of disease. Humans have responded to the threat of bird flu by wholesale slaughter of fowl, raising concerns about the roles played by migrating birds, and trying to develop a vaccine that will protect humans from bird flu. All involve basic biology.

Drylands are arid, semiarid, and subhumid areas where precipitation is scarce and more or less unpredictable. In drylands, the combination of high temperatures, low relative humidities, and abundant solar radiation means high potential evapotranspiration. Drylands cover approximately 41% of Earth's

Table 47.1	Variations in Fertility Rate (Total Births per Woman): A Sample of UNDP Data for 162 Countries		
Country	Human Development Index (HDI) rank	1970–75	2000–05
Norway	2	2.2	1.8
Canada	4	2.0	1.5
U.S.A.	12	2.0	2.0
Portugal	29	2.7	1.5
Brazil	70	4.7	2.3
China	81	4.9	1.7
Indonesia	107	5.2	2.4
India	128	5.4	3.1

land surface and are home to about 38% of the human population. Drylands are not just a problem of deserts but cover large expanses, for example, of Canada's prairie provinces. However, between 10 and 20% of the drylands are subject to some form of severe land degradation, directly affecting the lives of at least 250 million people. Climate change, combined with increasing pressure on water resources for these people, their crops, and their animals, compound the problems that confront them. Competition for limited resources, such as water, can generate local and international strife.

We have seen that complexity is an important and pervasive feature of ecosystems. Biodiversity is intimately associated with complexity, and disruption of this complexity often translates into reduced biodiversity and decay of ecosystems. Ironically, many social and economic systems that humans have developed are also subject to disruption by stress. This places the onus on our species to develop sustainable operations, whether in the area of agriculture, resource use and exploitation, or conservation.

STUDY BREAK

1. How is reproductive effort different between males and females in birds and in mammals?
2. List the United Nations Millennium Development Goals.
3. How are drylands at risk?

47.10 Taking Action

It is easy to believe that nothing can change, that as individuals we have no power. Yet we can also think of things that have changed dramatically in a relatively short time. Two good examples are the abolition of slavery and the emancipation of women, proving humans' capacity for effecting change. On a more local level, the acceptance of the use of tobacco in public has declined remarkably in the last 20 years—in Canada and elsewhere. We also have seen the abolition of capital punishment and much more ready access to abortion in Canada.

But none of these changes is universal. In the daily news we find stories about people living in virtual slavery, of people executed in public, of women with few or no rights in their home countries. We need only travel short distances to learn that not everyone in Canada can eat in a smoke-free restaurant. To complicate the matter, not everyone agrees that the changes listed above are for the better.

Effecting changes in our approach to conservation means identifying the root causes for the erosion of biodiversity and the things that are impediments to conservation. This means starting by changing our own lifestyles, including the food we eat and our use of energy. We must be wary of simple, and often misleading, solutions and avoid blaming someone else as a way of self-exoneration. We must respect the rights of others; use education and training to become informed; and learn to be objective, to examine and evaluate data or evidence. The outpouring of support for victims of the 2004 tsunami demonstrated that humans have great empathy for their fellows, and we need to extend this concern to the other species with whom we share the planet.

We have seen that action is needed at the species and the habitat level, and there is a propensity to focus more on species. But in the human view, all species are not equal. The 2006 IUCN list of threatened species shows that whereas 20% of the described species of mammals were listed as threatened, only 0.07% of the insect species received this level of attention. Other interesting numbers from this table are 12% of described species of birds listed as threatened, 4% of fish species, 3.5% of dicotyledonous plants, and 0.006% of species of mushrooms. In Canada, the same situation prevails, with mammals and birds dominating the list of threatened species, with other taxa receiving less attention. Do these data about threatened species mean that mammals are more vulnerable than insects? That we care more about mammals than about insects? Or does it mean that there are more "experts" to offer opinions and data about mammals than about insects? Are the possibilities mutually exclusive?

Biology can be at the centre of the movement to achieve conservation of biodiversity while being part of our efforts to achieve sustainable use of the resources we need as a species **(Figure 47.25)**. Conservation begins at home when we modify our lifestyles and become active on any front, from protecting local habitat and species to protecting charismatic species elsewhere. To better appreciate the situation, try to answer the questions posed in **Figure 47.26**. Elephants are an excellent example of how the objectivity that can be inherent in data is vulnerable to emotional responses.

STUDY BREAK

1. How can you change your lifestyle to promote conservation?
2. How is education critical to conservation?

Figure 47.25
Eat yourself out of house and home—like this African elephant (*Loxodonta africana*) trekking across the shore to Lake Kariba.

M.B. Fenton

a.

M.B. Fenton

b.

M.B. Fenton

c.

M.B. Fenton

Figure 47.26
To understand some of the dilemmas facing conservationists, use the Internet to explore the situation of African elephants.
(a) How many species are there? What are the populations in the wild? What products from elephants do we use **(b)** and **(c)**? Are elephants endangered? How can they be protected? What are the main threats to their survival?

Review

CourseMate Access an interactive eBook, chapter-specific interactive learning tools, including flashcards, quizzes, videos, and more in your Biology **CourseMate**, accessed through NelsonBrain.com

aplia **Aplia™** is an online interactive learning solution that helps you improve comprehension—and your grade—by integrating a variety of mediums and tools such as videos, tutorials, practice tests, and an interactive eBook.

47.1 Extinction

- A species is said to be extinct when there are no living representatives known on Earth. Conservation organizations usually say that a species is extinct when it has not been seen or recorded for 50 years.

- Mass extinctions occurred at the end of the Ordovician and the beginning of the Devonian, at the end of the Devonian, at the end of the Permian, at the end of the Triassic, and at the end of the Cretaceous. The Permian extinction was the most severe, and more than 85% of the species alive at that time disappeared forever, including the trilobites, many amphibians, and the trees of the coal swamp forests. Dinosaurs did not survive the extinction that occurred at the end of the Cretaceous.

- The extinction at the end of the Cretaceous is believed to have been caused by an asteroid impact. Dust clouds resulting from the impact blocked the sunlight necessary for photosynthesis, setting up a chain reaction of extinctions that began with microscopic marine organisms and finished with dinosaurs (as well as many birds and mammals).

- Measured by time on Earth, multituberculates were the most successful mammals.

47.2 The Impact of Humans

- Species (particularly flightless birds) that are confined to islands often have small populations and are unaccustomed to introduced terrestrial predators (such as cats, dogs, rats, etc.), making them vulnerable to extinction when human populations settle and expand.

- The demise of the calvaria trees (*Sideroxylum majus*) on the island of Mauritius will occur even though the trees continue to bloom and produce seeds. The extinction of the tree is linked to the earlier extinction of Dodos since *S. majus* seeds had to pass through the Dodo's digestive tract to germinate.

47.3 Introduced and Invasive Species

- Stephen's Island wrens were flightless and unaccustomed to predators. The population on the island was small, and it was easy for Tibbles the cat to catch and kill the remaining 20 birds.

- Since about 1880, ships have regularly used ballast water. A survey of ballast water in 159 ships in Coos Bay, Oregon, revealed 367 species of organisms representing 19 animal phyla and 3 plant divisions. When ships empty their ballast, the organisms in it are introduced to the system where the ship is anchored.

- RUE, resource use efficiency, is measured as carbon assimilation per unit resource. Many invasive plant species in Hawaii are more efficient than native species. This means that conserving native biodiversity in the face of invasive and introduced organisms is a pervasive problem.

47.4 How We Got/Get There

- Horns of rhinos, particularly black rhinos (*Diceros bicornis*), have been used to make handles for ornamental daggers (jambiyas) in some parts of the Arabian peninsula. Increasing oil prices in the early 1970s increased the demand for jambiyas. The main source of rhino horn was from poaching rhinos in Africa.

- During fishing operations, nontarget species are often caught in nets. They are by-catch. Barndoor skates once occurred across the North Atlantic. Today these skates are almost gone, although they were never the targets of a fishery.

- The demise of the bay scallops occurred because of an increase in the populations of skates and rays that are predators of bay scallops. The increase in skates and rays was attributed to the decline in populations of their predators, sharks. The sharks were extensively fished for their fins. Large-scale harvesting of the scallops for human consumption also compounded the impacts and contributed to their demise.

47.5 Protecting Species and 47.6 Protecting What?

- The International Union for Conservation of Nature (IUCN) has established objective criteria identifying species that are at risk. Extinct means the species no longer exists, extirpated means the species is locally extinct, endangered means the species is facing imminent extirpation or extinction, threatened means the species is likely to become endangered if limiting factors are not reversed, and special concern means the species may become threatened or endangered because of biological characteristics and identified threats. The criteria take into account data on populations, their patterns of distribution, and their population status.

- The Convention on International Trade in Endangered Species of Wild Fauna and Flora (CITES) attempts to prohibit international trade in endangered species. Newly described and as yet undescribed (and therefore unnamed) species are not protected because they have no legal identity.

- Species such as passenger pigeons or Dodos that have been exterminated are extinct. Extirpated species are locally extinct. Black-footed ferrets (see "Black-Footed Ferret, *Mustela nigripes*," Box 44.2, Chapter 44) have been extirpated in Canada but still occur in the United States.

- In Canada, recommendations about the conservation status of species involve the Committee on the Status of Endangered Wildlife in Canada (COSEWIC). COSEWIC members vote on the appropriate conservation category for each species whose status they review and use IUCN criteria to assess the status of species.

47.7 The Downside of Being Rare

- An animal on the list of endangered species is more likely to become a commodity in high demand because it has become rare. The Bali Starling is an example.

47.8 Protecting Habitat

- Protecting habitat can be particularly difficult.
- Networks of protected areas can influence conservation.

47.9 Effecting Conservation

- In 1994, the International Conference on Population and Development (ICPD) outlined a plan for investing in family planning.

- The United Nations Millennium Development Goals of 2000 are ending poverty and hunger, universal education, gender equality, child and maternal health, combating HIV/AIDS, environmental sustainability, and global partnerships.

- Drylands cover 41% of Earth's land surface, and 10 to 20% of drylands are subject to severe land degradation, affecting, in 2008, the lives of at least 250 million people.
- Climate change and increasing pressure on water supplies negatively affect drylands.
- The case of leopards (*Panthera pardus*) demonstrates how some species persist even in the face of considerable hunting pressure.
- Targeted hunting—selection of trophy or spectacular specimens—can be less threatening to a species' survival than by-catch or eradication programs (bounties on predators such as wolves). Extensive killing, even of species with large populations, can drive them to the brink of extinction. Black rhinos are a telling example.
- The overgrowth of Mayan cities or ruins in Africa demonstrates the resiliency of ecosystems. A grasshopper's use of 2,4-D to synthesize an ant repellent demonstrates the resiliency of individuals.
- Hybrids are not protected by the U.S. Endangered Species Act, putting species such as Florida panthers at risk because their populations have been genetically contaminated.

47.10 Taking Action

- African elephants epitomize some of the challenges involved in taking action to protect a species and its habitats.
- This species also illustrates the potential importance of hunting and poaching.

Questions

Self-Test Questions

1. Extinction is a natural part of the process of speciation. What do some estimates suggest is the percentage of the species that have ever lived that are now extinct?
   a. more than 20%
   b. more than 30%
   c. more than 50%
   d. more than 80%

2. Some researchers use evidence from a variety of sources to support the suggestion that an asteroid striking Earth in this period largely explains the extinction of the dinosaurs.
   a. Ordovician
   b. Triassic
   c. Cretaceous
   d. Pleistocene

3. If our species first appeared 200 000 years before present, the multituberculates survived this many times as long as we have to date.
   a. 50
   b. 100
   c. 500
   d. 1000

4. Hunting by people is largely responsible for the extinction of which of the following?
   a. multituberculates, Dodos, and passenger pigeons
   b. barndoor skates, black-footed ferrets, and giant auks
   c. passenger pigeons, giant auks, and Dodos
   d. black rhinos, Bali starlings, and ginseng

5. The ballast water of ships is responsible for the spread of which species?
   a. *Arthurdendyus triangulatus*
   b. *Dressina polymorpha*
   c. *Rattus norvegicus*
   d. *Lampsilis radiata*

6. In Hawaii, high resource use efficiency (RUE), measured as carbon use, partly explains the success of these invading species.
   a. ferns
   b. C_3 and C_4 grasses
   c. flatworms
   d. Both b and c are correct.

7. Which tertiary consumers have experienced increases in populations, which may explain the demise of scallops off the southeastern coast of the United States?
   a. skates and rays
   b. sharks
   c. killer whales
   d. pelagic seabirds

8. Species such as black-footed ferrets (*Mustela nigripes*) no longer occur in Canada but still live in the United States. Which term describes their status?
   a. extinct
   b. extirpated
   c. highly endangered
   d. not at risk

9. CITES is designed to stop international trade in which of the following species, among others?
   a. passenger pigeons
   b. black rhinos
   c. Canada geese
   d. leopards

10. Differences in government support for family planning explain the differences in the growth of human populations in which two countries?
    a. Great Britain and France
    b. Afghanistan and Sri Lanka
    c. Mexico and Germany
    d. India and South Africa

Questions for Discussion

1. Should gardeners and farmers be exempt from rules concerning the introduction of foreign species? Why or why not?

2. In situations where the behaviour of one endangered species threatens the survival of another (or others), how should authorities proceed?

3. What species are "rare" on your campus? What is a good working definition of rare? What steps can you take to protect rare species?

4. How will the cost of food influence efforts to conserve species at risk?

5. How does the biological definition of species influence our efforts to conserve species?

Sunflowers. Originally from the New World, sunflowers (*Helianthus annuus*) are grown as a source of oil. In terms of harvest and area under cultivation, in 1998, sunflowers ranked twelfth in importance among domesticated plants in the world. Domesticated sunflowers often hybridize with local wild species, creating a challenge for those concerned about biodiversity.

M.B. Fenton

48 Putting Selection to Work

WHY IT MATTERS

In 1960, an estimated 1.8 billion people in the world (60% of the population) did not receive enough food every day to sustain themselves fully over the longer period—they were hungry. This number was reduced to 1.1 billion (17%) in 2000. Even though the world population had grown by 3 billion in the intervening period, about 700 million fewer people were hungry in 2000.

Worldwide in 2000, subsistence farmers accounted for about 66% of the hungry people. The reduction in the numbers of hungry people can be tied to changes in agriculture that have increased yields. Specifically, the combination of new genetic strains, better fertilizers, better irrigation, more effective pest control, and more efficient harvesting and processing means more productivity. One indication of this change is provided by data about corn yields. In Iowa in 1935, corn yields were about 1600 kg·ha^{-1} compared with about 10 700 kg·ha^{-1} in 2000. Changes in crop yield are part of the "green revolution." Agriculture in general and the green revolution in particular have allowed humans to continue to redefine one element of carrying capacity (see Chapter 44): the amount of food available to our populations.

But agricultural improvements are not enough. Climate also influences crop yield. In 2006 in southwestern Ontario (~42° N in Canada), the corn yield was about 10 000 kg · ha⁻¹, whereas in Zimbabwe (~18° S), on commercial farms, it was about 5500 to 6600 kg · ha⁻¹, compared with about 500 to 1000 kg · ha⁻¹ on communal lands where farming was low tech. Irrigation also influences yield: in Zimbabwe, irrigated cornfields produce 8500 to 10 000 kg · ha⁻¹, much more than nonirrigated commercial farms.

Although increases in crop yield and a reduced incidence of malnutrition and starvation sound like good news, in 2007, hunger still claimed the lives of about 20 000 children a day. Worldwide, one child in three is underweight and malnourished. Ironically, at the same time in some developed countries, obesity in children reached almost epidemic proportions.

In addition to the *biology* of domestication and increasing crop yields, the *security* of food sources plays a vital role in the survival of tens of thousands of people. In this context, security refers to social and political factors and stability. In 2011, changes in the political structure of several countries in North Africa and the Middle East may have been as attributable to rising costs of food and their impact on average people as to any other single factor. Availability of fresh water is inextricably associated with agriculture and the global food supply.

Changes in diet may have been fundamental to the origin and adaptive radiation of species in the genus *Homo*. The use of fire and tools influenced our ancestors' abilities to obtain food. Diets rich in "brain food," such as many aquatic animals, as well as in starches **(Figure 48.1)** could have heralded important changes in our ancestors.

Our species has turned natural selection to its advantage by domesticating other species, selectively breeding strains with traits that provide us with more food or other desirable commodities. Domestication emerged from cultivation of wild forms, probably in association with a more sedentary lifestyle, and has occurred in different parts of the world, from central Asia to the Far East, from the Middle East to the New World and southeast Asia. We depend on the productivity of many domesticated food plants to sustain our populations, and on domesticated animals for labour, hides, and food. Domestication provides repeated examples of how our species has benefited from selection, and unravelling the history of the process depends heavily on genetic tools.

48.1 Domestication

The purpose of this chapter is to explore how humans have used selection to put biodiversity to work. Biologists and anthropologists believe that our ancestors originally gathered plants and hunted animals in the wild for use as food, building products, or fuel (see "Molecule behind Biology," Box 48.1, p. 1231). From gathering, our ancestors progressed to cultivating plants, a process involving the systematic sowing of wild plant seeds. Over time, cultivation improved when people provided more care to their crops and eventually involved repetitive cycles of sowing, collecting, and sowing wild stock **(Figure 48.2, p. 1230). Domestication** is more than just taming. It occurs when people selectively breed individuals of other species (plants and animals) to increase the desirable characteristics in the progeny (e.g., in plants: yield, taste, colour, shelf life). This marked the birth of agriculture. The progression from gathering to cultivation to domestication of plants occurred independently at several locations around the world. The beginning of the Neolithic Period is often

HOMININ COOKBOOK

Evolution of our diets and food preparation techniques

●●⬤ Estimated cranial capacity (range: 385–1350 cm³)

A – Australopithecus
H – Homo

H. sapiens (200 000 yr–) ⬤
H. neanderthalensis (250 000–28 000 yr) ●
H. heidelbergensis (0.6–0.1 Myr) ●
H. ergaster (1.9 Myr–30 000 yr) ●
A. afarensis (4–3 Myr) ●
A. africanus (3–2.4 Myr) •
A. afarensis (4–3 Myr) •

Time scale (Myr): 4.0 3.8 3.6 3.4 3.2 3.0 2.8 2.6 2.4 2.2 2.0 1.8 1.6 1.4 1.2 1.0 0.8 0.6 0.4 0.2 0

Early tool use for meat consumption—oldest such evidence to date (Afar, Ethiopia)

Tool use for meat consumption (Middle Awash Valley, Ethiopia)

Stone tool–facilitated consumption of turtle, fish, and crocodile (Kenya)

Burnt remains at Swarthrans cave (South Africa) and charred sediment at other African sites suggest an ancient hearth, but whether these fires represent routine, controlled use remains uncertain.

Earliest widely accepted evidence for controlled fire (Gesher Benot Ya'aqov, Israel)

Strong evidence of controlled fire (numerous sites in Europe)

Consumption of aquatic animals mainly catfish (South Africa)

Evidence of starch consumption, including granules of sorghum and African potato (Mozambique)

Figure 48.1

A diagrammatic presentation of the progression in diet and brain size across 4 million years of hominin history.

Reprinted by permission from Macmillan Publishers Ltd: NATURE, Volume: 468, Pages: S8–S9, "Evolution: The first supper," Michael Eisenstein, copyright 2010.

Figure 48.2

The way in which garlic (*Allium sativum*) is grown influences the size and development of the bulbs. From left to right, **(a)** one domesticated, **(b)** two cultivated, and **(c)** two wild garlic bulbs.

humans were exploiting and continue to exploit many species without actually domesticating them.

48.1a When and Where Did Domestication Take Place?

Once they were domesticated, many domesticated plants and animals became widely used, becoming staple foods carried with humans as they moved to occupy many of the land areas on the planet. Data provided by the tools of molecular genetics (see Chapter 17) have made it easier to determine where and when domestication events took place. In the past, archaeologists had to try to recognize the remains of domesticated species and distinguish them from wild species. This was often impossible because individual bones or pieces of plant did not always provide a clear indication of domestication. In 1973, radiocarbon dates suggested that the first dogs (*Canis familiaris*) were domesticated by 9500 years B.P., based on remains found in England and elsewhere in Europe. In 2002, mitochondrial DNA (mtDNA) evidence suggested an East Asian origin of domestication of dogs dating from 15 000 years B.P. But pictures based on genetic evidence can also change. In 2003, morphological and genetic evidence suggested a southeast Asian origin of domesticated pigs (*Sus scrofa*), whereas in 2005, new genetic data indicated multiple origins of domestication of pigs across Eurasia **(Figure 48.3)**.

Worldwide, domestication of aquatic species has lagged behind that of terrestrial ones. Although there are about 180 species of domesticated freshwater animals, about 250 species of marine animals, and about 19 species of marine plants, all were domesticated in the last 1000 years, most in the last 100 years **(Figure 48.4, p. 1232)**.

48.1b How Long Did Domestication Take? Archaeological Evidence

The time it takes to progress from harvesting tended wild crops to cultivating them and then to domesticating them varies with species and situation. When there are clear morphological or chemical differences between cultivated and domesticated stocks, determining the place and time of domestication is possible. Wheat is an example of such a morphological change. Wheat and other cereal crops are grasses that disperse their seed explosively by shattering. The process of domestication of wheat and cereal crops meant developing stocks that

defined by the domestication of other species, and this period started at different times in different parts of the world.

But agriculture is not the exclusive domain of humans. Recall that about 50 million years ago, ants of the tribe Attini were the first to manipulate other species (fungi) to increase food availability (see Chapter 23). Today at least 200 species of ants in this tribe are obligate farmers. These early farmers have lost their own digestive enzymes and rely on fungal enzymes to digest the food for them. The ant farmers propagate their fungal crops asexually, with each colony working with one species. Therefore, any single species of farmer ant may propagate several different species of fungi. These ants have been involved in at least five domestication events, and there are a number of interesting parallels between these ants and people.

The list of species that humans have domesticated is long. It includes many land plants (~250 species), some yeasts, and terrestrial animals from insects to birds and mammals (~44 species). Biogeographic and genetic evidence shows that domestication of some species by humans occurred in different places and at different times. Domestication was not a one-time (or one-location) event and appears to have arisen independently in 8 to 10 environmentally and biotically diverse areas in the world.

As intriguing as which species were domesticated is the fact that very few available species of animals, plants, and fungi were domesticable. At the same time,

Salicylic Acid 48.1

FIGURE 1
The molecular structure of salicylic acid.

Salicylic acid
2-OH-$C_6C_4CO_2H$

The precursor of the main active ingredient in aspirin is salicylic acid, which is obtained from the bark of willow trees (*Salix* species). Over 2500 years B.P., Chinese medical practitioners used an extract of willow bark to relieve pain and fever. The same kinds of extracts were used in medicine as practised in Greece and in Assyria. In Iceland 500 years ago, willow bark extracts were used to treat the symptoms of colds and headaches. Willow extract was widely used among First Nations people in North America, who commonly used it to stanch bleeding. They also used the supple willow twigs in other applications, from snares for catching mammals to nets for catching fish. This is not an example of domestication, but it demonstrates how the spread of traditional knowledge about plants and their products among peoples is pervasive.

do not shatter (**indehisence**) from stocks that shattered (**dehiscence**) (**Figure 48.5, p. 1232**). Ripe indehiscent grains are easily gathered (harvested) compared with dehiscent ones that naturally scatter. Indehiscence in wheat results from a naturally occurring mutation.

But, in addition to selecting indehiscent stock, the early farms also had to select for plants whose seeds did not go through a period of dormancy. This change would allow repeated sowing of crops when conditions were appropriate. Material recovered from sites in

Figure 48.3
Origins of domestication of pigs. Mitochondrial DNA obtained from pigs indicates 14 clusters of related lineages, each identified by a different colour. The geographic relationships are shown with the phylogeny. Pigs were domesticated in numerous centres.

From Greger Larson, Keith Dobney, Umberto Albarella, Meiying Fang, Elizabeth Matisoo-Smith, Judith Robins, Stewart Lowden, Heather Finlayson, Tina Brand, Eske Willerslev, Peter Rowley-Conwy, Leif Andersson, Alan Cooper, "Worldwide Phylogeography of Wild Boar Reveals Multiple Centers of Pig Domestication", *Science*, vol. 307, Mar 11, 2005, pp. 1618–1621. Reprinted with permission from AAAS.

To warthog

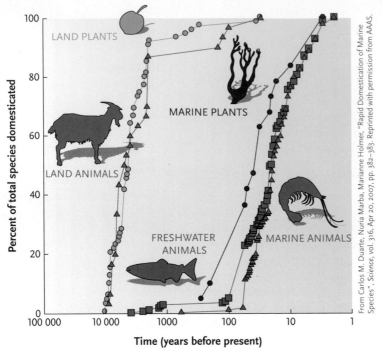

From Carlos M. Duarte, Nuria Marba, Marianne Holmer, "Rapid Domestication of Marine Species", *Science*, vol. 316, Apr 20, 2007, pp. 382–383. Reprinted with permission from AAAS.

Figure 48.4

Most land species were domesticated much earlier than most aquatic ones.

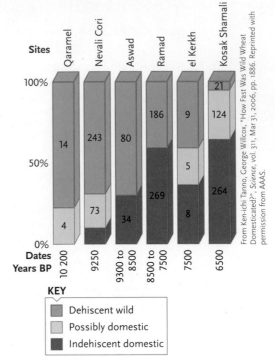

From Ken-ichi Tanno, George Willcox, "How Fast Was Wild Wheat Domesticated?", *Science*, vol. 311, Mar 31, 2006, pp. 1886. Reprinted with permission from AAAS.

KEY

- Dehiscent wild
- Possibly domestic
- Indehiscent domestic

Figure 48.6

Timing of domestication of wheat. Data from archaeological digs at six locations in the Middle East demonstrate the transition from wild (dehiscent) to domesticated (indehiscent) wheat from 10 200 to 6500 years B.P.

M.B. Fenton

Figure 48.5

(a) Some plants readily shed ripe seeds from the inflorescence; these plants show dehiscence. **(b)** Indehiscence is the propensity to hold seeds. These two herbarium specimens, (a) bottle brush grass (*Elymus hystrix*) and (b) riverbank wild rye (*Elymus riparius*), illustrate dehiscence and indehiscence, respectively.

northeastern Syria and Turkey has been radiocarbon dated and shows that wild varieties of wheat were cultivated for at least 1000 years before domestication **(Figure 48.6)**. When sexual reproduction is involved in the breeding process, the time to domestication is partly determined by life cycle, so finding stock that can self-fertilize can accelerate the domestication process.

When organisms reproduce asexually, domestication may occur more rapidly. Common figs (*Ficus carica* var. *domestica*) are gynodioecious and provide an example of more rapid domestication. In parthenocarpic female figs, ovaries develop without pollination and fertilization. Parthenocarpic figs can be propagated by cutting branches, sticking them in the ground, and waiting for them to grow into trees. When figs reproduce sexually, symbiotic fig wasps (*Blastophaga psenes;* **Figure 48.7**) serve as pollinators. The absence of access holes for wasps in fossil figs allows biologists to recognize parthenocarpic figs and date early incidences of fig domestication. At one site in the lower Jordan Valley (Middle East), parthenocarpic figs date to between 10 500 and 11 400 years B.P., perhaps preceding the domestication of cereal crops by about 1000 years.

CEFE–UMR 5175. Photo courtesy of Finn Kjellberg.

Figure 48.7

Female flowers on some fig trees (*Ficus carica*) are fertilized by symbiotic wasps, *Blastophaga psenes*.

48.1c In Which Habitats Did Domestication Occur?

The transition from nomadic hunters and gatherers to people living more localized lives in more permanent dwellings appears to have been a prelude to cultivation and domestication. These changes meant that people would have been available to care for their "crops," whether grown from seeds or from parthenocarpic plants, and whether cultivated or domesticated.

Although controlled burning has been documented at many sites in the last 10 000 years, there is evidence of it 50 000 to 55 000 years ago at sites near Mossel Bay in South Africa, and it still occurs today **(Figure 48.8)**. Archaeological evidence indicates that some humans were increasingly using some plant resources and using local burning to increase productivity. The increased use of plant resources and fire occurred during a period of harsh environmental conditions. These changes in human behaviour coincided with the appearance of more sophisticated tools, the use of marine organisms as food, and the first use of ochre for decoration. These modifications suggest differences in human behaviour that may have assisted the emergence of domestication.

Were changes in habitat associated with domestication? Evidence from pollen shows that from 7500 years B.P. in the lower Yangtze region of China, people used fire to clear alders, which are small woody bushes

Figure 48.8

In Ghana (West Africa), fire is still used in slash and burn to clear the underbrush from an area where forest trees have been felled.

(*Alnus* species). This element in the process of domestication is called *niche construction* or *ecosystem engineering*, modifying the environment and setting the stage for domestication. At the lower Yangtze Neolithic site, people used fire first to prepare and then to maintain sites in lowland swamps, where they cultivated rice **(Figure 48.9)**. This region in China was a major centre of rice domestication. The evidence suggests

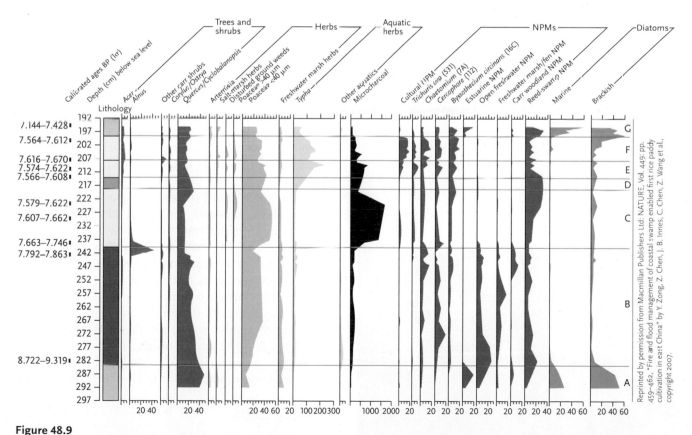

Figure 48.9

The climatic setting for rice domestication at Kuahugiao in China. Shown here are generalized stratigraphic units and their associated pollen (shown in colours) and microscopic charcoal (black) that indicate conditions of climate and habitat. The data support the use of fire to establish favourable conditions for growing rice. NPMs are nonpollen microfossils that provide paleoecological data. The increases in charcoal, grasses (Poaceae), and reed-swamp microfossils in phases C, E, and F (right edge) indicate the use of fire to establish favourable conditions for growing rice.

Reprinted by permission from Macmillan Publishers Ltd: NATURE, Vol. 449: pp. 459–462, "Fire and flood management of coastal swamp enabled first rice paddy cultivation in east China" by Y. Zong, Z. Chen, J. B. Innes, C. Chen, Z. Wang et al., copyright 2007.

that rice cultivation began in coastal wetlands in an ecosystem vulnerable to coastal change. This system was very fertile and productive and used for at least 200 years before the land was inundated by sea water.

Meanwhile, at sites on the coast of Peru, occupied between 3800 and 3500 years B.P., people ate marine organisms as the main animal food, combined with cultivated plants (squashes, *Cucurbita* species; beans, *Phaseolus lunatus* and *P. vulgaris;* peppers, *Capsicum* species; jicama, *Pachyrhizus tuberosus*) and wild plants (guava, *Psidium guajava;* lacuma, *Lucuma bifera;* and pacay, *Inga feuillei*). Cotton was an important crop used for making fishing tackle and clothing. The findings from these Peruvian sites and many other sites around the world suggest a progression toward domestication, including the range of foods consumed, the development of more sophisticated tools, and the use of materials from plants and animals as tools, as well as in food. Domestication, therefore, involved the spread among peoples of the practice of using plants and animals to advantage.

48.1d Abu Hureyra on the Euphrates Is an Example of a Setting for Domestication

This prehistoric settlement (a recent photograph is shown in **Figure 48.10**) on the south side of the Euphrates River (35° 52 N, 38° 24 E) about 130 km from Aleppo (a modern Syrian city) also illustrates progression toward domestication. The first habitations that we know of in Abu Hureyra date from about 12 000 years ago. Its population was estimated at 100 to 200 people who lived in semisubterranean pit dwellings clustered together on a low promontory overlooking the river. By 7000 to 9400 years ago, 4000 to 6000 people lived at the same site, now in multiroomed family dwellings made of mud and brick. This settlement was built over the remains of the earlier one.

People living at Abu Hureyra about 12 000 years B.P. ate the fruits and seeds of over 100 species of local plants as well as local animals such as gazelles. Many

Figure 48.10

Abu Hureyra in Syria, the site of an early village.

The Tell of Abu Hureyra from the West. From *Village on the Euphrates: From Foraging to Farming at Abu Hureyra* by A. M. T. Moore, G. C. Hillman, A. J. Legge (2006). By permission of Oxford University Press, Inc.

of the plants and animals appear to have come from the adjoining oak-dominated park woodland. It appears to have been a time of plentiful food. The situation changed, however, and by 9400 years ago, the climate was cooler and drier, and the people relied more on cultivated plants and less on wild ones. By this time, there was little evidence of use of plants from the oak-dominated parkland, which by then was at least 14 km from the settlement. These changes were evident in pollen records and in plant and animal remains associated with the dwellings. The climate change likely triggered the start of cultivation of foods that could serve as caloric staples. Despite the changing climate and the focus on fewer food staples, the human population at the site dramatically increased.

STUDY BREAK

1. Explain the benefits of the green revolution. What is responsible for it?
2. Why did domestication develop?
3. Why can domestication take place more rapidly in asexually reproducing organisms?

48.2 Why Some Organisms Were Domesticated

We can surmise, perhaps accurately, that securing a sustainable food supply provided an initial motivation for cultivation and domestication. It is certainly true that cultivated plants from beans to squash, corn to rice and cereal grains all help feed many, many people worldwide. People eat different parts of plants, from flowers and fruits to seeds, leaves, stems, roots, and tubers. Plants may be a source of energy (calories), or their products may be used to enhance flavours, to control and repel pests, or as medicines. Still others, such as the bottle gourd (*Lagenaria siceraria*), are used as containers. Domesticated cereal grains have been derived from variants (local varieties, sometimes known as breeds, cultivars, or landraces) with four important features: (a) nonshattering, (b) large seeds, (c) self-compatibility, and (d) no required dormancy. This suite of characters makes them valuable because they can be readily fertilized, harvested, and planted whenever conditions permit. Domesticated animals provide food, but many are also used as a source of labour. The following are examples of four very different domesticated species and how people use them.

48.2a Cattle

Cattle were among the first of the large herd mammals to be domesticated, at least 9000 years B.P. One theory proposes that the domesticators of cattle were sedentary farmers, not nomadic hunters. Some anthropologists

a.

b.

Tom McHugh/Photo Researchers, Inc.

M. B. Fenton

Figure 48.11

Today there are two varieties of domesticated cattle: **(a)** the humped *Bos indicus* and **(b)** the humpless *Bos taurus*.

maintain that a religious motivation was behind the domestication of cattle because the curve of their horns resembled the crescent of the Moon and hence the mother-goddess. Imposing horns were particularly prominent in some male *Bos primigenius* (called *urus*), the apparent Pleistocene ancestor of domesticated cattle. Whatever the original impetus, today there are two basic stocks of cattle **(Figure 48.11)**, the humped *Bos indicus* and the humpless *Bos taurus*. Cattle provide us with labour, milk, meat, hides, and blood, and in some societies, they are symbols of wealth. At the root of the domestication of cattle are some biological realities: they are relatively docile animals that live in herds and can be useful in many ways.

48.2b Honeybees

Domestic honeybees provide us with honey and pollination services. Steps to domestication of honeybees included changes in their behaviour compatible with large population size in hives. Features of honeybees that make them suitable for domestication are their colonial and food-storing behaviours, unlike other species of bees that are solitary and do not store honey. The changes could have involved hygiene, aggression, and foraging. Although everyone recognizes honey as a product of bees, the service provided by bees is often overlooked. In 2000 in the United States, it is estimated that bees contributed about U.S.$14.5 billion through their role as pollinators. Plants such as alfalfa, apples, almonds, onions, broccoli, and sunflowers are exclusively pollinated by insects, usually more than 90% by honeybees. Many beekeepers earn significant income by moving their bees from location to location, thus providing a mobile pollinator service for farmers. Declines in populations of honeybees have serious economic implications throughout the world, but many

conservationists are also concerned about the impact of populations of honeybees on native bee species.

48.2c Cotton

At least four species of cotton **(Figure 48.12)** have been domesticated: two diploid species from the Old World (*Gossypium arboreum*, *G. herbaceum*) and two tetraploids from the New World (*G. hirsutum* and *G. barbadense*). The domestication events appear to have been independent, and one site on the Mexican gulf coast of Tabasco shows evidence of people growing

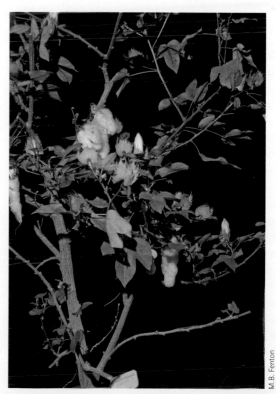

Figure 48.12

Cotton, *Gossypium herbaceum*, showing flowers and cotton bolls.

M. B. Fenton

![image of hands holding photographic film]

PEOPLE BEHIND BIOLOGY 48.2
Richard Keith Downey, Research Scientist, Agriculture and Agri-Food Canada

Richard Keith Downey was born in 1927 in Saskatchewan and attended the University of Saskatchewan and Cornell University. He is best known for his work on rapeseed. In 1928, rapeseed had been brought to Shellbrook, Saskatchewan, by Fred and Olga Solovonuk when they immigrated to Canada from their native Poland. They had brought seeds of *Brassica rapa*, although *Brassica napus* from Argentina was the main traditional source of rapeseed oil. During World War II, rapeseed was grown as a source of industrial lubricants because erucic acid and glucosinolates in the oil precluded its use as food for people and livestock.

Downey was the leader of a team of researchers at Agriculture and Agrifoods Canada that developed canola (the name comes from "Canada" and "oil"), an edible, high-value crop that is high in proteins. Canola is well known as a vegetable oil, but the meal derived from the plants is the source of protein, making canola useful as animal feed. The team's work resulted in a crop that went from 2600 to 4.25 million hectares under cultivation in Canada. Canola is now grown around the world, and the high crop is used in cooking oils and feed for livestock.

Downey and his team developed the *half-seed* method, partitioning a seed so that half could be tested for composition using gas–liquid chromatography. The researchers could then select and germinate the half-seeds with the most promising features. Using this approach, Downey and his team developed 18 varieties of canola and several of table mustard. This work had a huge impact on the economy of Canada in general and the prairies in particular, as well as an influence on food availability throughout the world.

Downey is also known for a program that introduced children in elementary school to the scientific method. The approach involved using canola seeds that had travelled into space aboard the space shuttle *Columbia* in 1996. Children in over 2000 classrooms in Canada received space seeds along with control seeds and germinated them. Downey helped analyze the results of the experiments. Space seeds germinated faster and at higher rates than control seeds and grew more rapidly. In this way, Downey introduced elementary students to plant science and the space environment.

---

cotton by 4400 years B.P. Cotton seeds were a source of oil, whereas fibre was and is still used in applications ranging from clothing to implements such as ropes and nets.

48.2d Yeast

Strains of the yeast *Saccharomyces cerevisiae* have been used by people in bread making beginning at least 6000 years B.P. Evidence of this is in archaeological finds in Egypt, indicating the presence of bakeries and breweries, two yeast-based operations. Analysis of 12 DNA microsatellites obtained from 651 strains of *S. cerevisiae* collected at 56 locations around the world revealed 575 distinct genotypes. Yeasts associated with bread were intermediate between wild types and those used in making beer and wine, whereas those used in the production of rice wine and sake were more similar to those used for beer. About 28% of the genetic variation in yeast genotypes was associated with geographic location. The basal group of these 12 DNA microsatellites was samples from Lebanon, suggesting a Mesopotamian origin and a spread of yeast types along the Danube River and around the Mediterranean. Different strains of yeast have different capacities for maltose fermentation. Commercial bakers' yeast strains are more effective at maltose fermentation than nonindustrial strains. Domesticated yeast makes

important contributions to providing humans with food and drink and supports lucrative industries.

48.2e Rice

Rice (*Oryza sativa*) is one of the world's most important food crops, and its domestication depended on the change from dehiscence (shattering) to indehiscence (nonshattering). Domesticated rice is derived from two wild species: *Oryza rufipogon* and *Oryza indica*. In 2006, Changbao Li and his colleagues reported that three quantitative trait loci (QTL) in F_1 hybrids between these two species were responsible for a reduction of grain shattering (dehiscence) in rice. Specifically, *sh3*, *sh4*, and *sh8* were involved, with *sh4* explaining 64% of the phenotypic variance. In the wild species, *sh4* was dominant and caused the shattering. The genetic changes in *sh3*, *sh4*, and *sh8* affected normal development of the abscission layer, explaining the change to indehiscence **(Figure 48.13)**. We can now better understand the genetics of changes associated with the domestication of rice.

These changes occur in the two major varieties of domesticated rice, *Oryza sativa japonica* and *Oryza sativa indica*. Jason Londo and his colleagues used DNA sequence variation to demonstrate multiple independent domestication events. Although *O. sativa indica* was probably domesticated in eastern India,

From Changbao Li, Ailing Zhou, Tao Sarg, "Rice Domestication by Reducing Shattering", *Science*, vol. 311, Mar 31, 2006, pp. 1936–1939. Reprinted with permission from AAAS.

Figure 48.13

Rice dehiscence and indehiscence. Under a fluorescence microscope, a longitudinal section of the junction between the rice flower and its pedicel shows a complete abscission layer (al in **(a)**) and an incomplete one (al in **(b)**). In these figures, f = flower side; p = pedicel side; and v = vascular bundles. *Oryza nivara* is shown in **(a)**, *O. sativa* in **(b)**, *O. sativa japonica* in **(c)**, and transformed *O. sativa japonica* in **(d)**.

Myanmar, and Thailand south of the Himalayan mountains, *O. sativa japonica* was domesticated in southern China **(Figure 48.14)**.

48.2f Wheat

Other major domestications appear to stem from single domestication events, including wheat, barley **(Figure 48.15, p. 1238)**, and corn. DNA fingerprinting was used by Manfred Heun and his colleagues to identify the Karacadağ mountains **(Figure 48.16, p. 1238)** in today's Turkey as *the* site of domestication of einkorn wheat. Einkorn wheat is derived from the wild *Triticum*

monococcum boeoticum. Einkorn wheat is selfing and nonshattering and has a firm stalk, heavier seeds, and denser seed masses than its progenitor (see Figure 19.24, Chapter 19), all contributing to the ease and efficiency of harvest. The genetic changes between einkorn wheat and the wild stock from which it was derived were relatively minor, and domestication probably occurred in a short period of time.

Archaeological evidence reveals that einkorn wheat spread rapidly throughout the immediate area and beyond. The same single domestication event and rapid spread of the new crop also appear to be true of barley **(Figure 48.17b, p. 1239;** *Hordeum vulgare* derived from *Hordeum spontaneum*). More recent wheat domestication is discussed in "Marquis Wheat," Box 48.3, p. 1240.

48.2g Lentils

Lentils (*Lens culinaris* from *Lens orientalis;* **Figure 48.17a, p. 1239**) were more difficult to domesticate than wheat or rice. Wild lentils are small plants, producing, on average, 10 seeds per plant. Furthermore, these seeds go through a period of programmed dormancy. The combination of low yield and dormancy means that relatively few seeds germinate. Lentils could have been cultivated only after a dormancy-free mutant had appeared. Archaeological evidence suggests that the first stages of lentil domestication (loss of dormancy) occurred in what is now southeastern Turkey and northern Syria, suggesting a single initial domestication event. The second phase was selection for strains that produced large numbers of seeds. This change may have occurred some distance (hundreds or even thousands of kilometres) from the original sites of domestication.

Haplotype	B	C	D	E
p-VATPase				
indica	21%	16%	**94%**	**77%**
japonica	**79%**	**84%**	6%	23%

Haplotype	BB	CC	DD	EE	FF
SAM					
indica	7%	17%	**80%**	**73%**	**84%**
japonica	**93%**	**83%**	20%	27%	16%

Figure 48.14

Geography of rice domestication. Genetic haplotype information allows identification of major domestication regions for rice. The haplotype network of the neutral nuclear p-VATPase region is shown in **(a)**, compared with **(b)**, the haplotype of the functional nuclear SAM region. In this diagram, orange represents *Oryza japonica;* blue, *O. indica* (Aus cultivar); and yellow, *O. indica.* Lines joining haplotypes represent mutational steps.

Londo, J. Y-C Chiang, K-H Hung, T-Y Chiang, and B. Schaal. (2006) "Phylogeography of Asian wild rice, Oryza rufipogon reveals multiple independent domestications of cultivated rice, Oryza sativa." *Proc. Natl. Acad. Sci.* 103: 9578–9583. Copyright 2006 National Academy of Sciences, U.S.A.

Figure 48.15
A barley field near London, Ontario, illustrates the consistency of a monoculture, one plant dominating an area, in this case for artificial reasons.

From Manfred Heun, Ralf Schafer-Pregl, Dieter Klawan, Renato Castagna, Monica Accerbi, Basilio Borghi, Francesco Salamini, "Site of Einkorn Wheat Domestication Identified by DNA Fingerprinting", *Science*, vol. 278, Nov 14, 1997, pp. 1312–1314. Reprinted with permission from AAAS.

Figure 48.16
Site of wheat domestication. A phylogenetic analysis based on allelic frequency at 288 amplified fragment length polymorphism marker loci revealed that the progenitor of *T. m. boeoticum* came from what is now southeastern Turkey.

Figure 48.17

Two important domesticated crops are (a) lentils (*Lens culinaris*) and (b) barley (*Hordeum vulgare*). In each case, individual grains are about 6 mm long.

48.2h Corn

Corn (*Zea mays*), like wheat and barley, appears to have been domesticated at one location. Unlike wheat or barley, domestication of corn required drastic changes from the ancestral teosinte (*Zea mays parviglumis;* **Figure 48.18**). Corn kernels do not disassociate from the cob, presumably reflecting changes associated with domestication (and analogous to indehiscence). Analysis of some of the most ancient inflorescences of teosinte indicates that by 6250 years B.P. the kernels did not disassociate, suggesting that domestication was

Figure 48.18

Teosinte and domesticated corn. Ears of domesticated corn (*Zea mays*, right) are larger than those of one species of its wild relative teosinte (*Zea diploperennis*, left). Crossing domesticated corn and teosinte produces intermediate forms (centre).

under way at that time. Corn appears to have been domesticated in the Central Balsas Valley of south central Mexico or in the Mexican State of Puebla at altitudes of 1000 to 1500 m. The deposits that contained the undissociated teosinte kernels also had the remains of squash (*Cucurbita pepo*). Although squash appears to have been domesticated in the same area, remains from a cave in Puebla and Oxa States in Mexico suggest that the people there were cultivating it by about 4000 years before corn. These data again demonstrate that some people were responsible for multiple domestication events. Corn, beans, and squash, the "three sisters" of early farmers in the New World, together provided different foods. The beans climbed on the corn stalks and provided nitrogen fixation services (see Chapter 46), while the squash leaves shaded out the weeds.

48.2i Grapes

The Eurasian grape (*Vitis vinifera sylvestris*), a dioecious plant, is widespread from the Atlantic coasts of Europe to the western Himalayas, and its fruits were often eaten by Paleolithic hunter–gatherers. Domestication of *V. vinifera* involved the selection of hermaphroditic genotypes that produced larger, more colourful fruit, along with the development of techniques for vegetative propagation. Grafting, attaching parts of one plant to another, further increased the capacity for vegetative propagation. Domesticated grapes have a higher sugar content than wild ones, ensuring better fermentation, greater yield, and more regular production. Domestication of grapes is associated with the production of wine, which also required storage in containers made of pottery, which appeared only about 10 500 years B.P.

Genetic analyses suggest at least two important origins of grape domestication: one in the near East and the other in the region of the western Mediterranean. Many wine-grape cultivars from Europe can be traced to western Mediterranean stock, as can over 70% of the cultivars on the Iberian Peninsula. It is possible that the original wild stock of *V. vinifera* has vanished due to genetic contamination by various cultivars.

48.2j Plants in the Family Solonaceae

Solanaceous plants include species such as deadly nightshade (*Atropa belladonna*) that produce virulent poisons, as well as food species (tomatoes, *Solanum lycopersicum;* potatoes, *Solanum tuberosum;* and eggplant, *Solanum melongena*) that are staples of many meals worldwide (**Figure 48.19, p. 1240**).

Potatoes originated in western South America, specifically in areas of what is now Chile. Today, local varieties (also known as breeds, cultivars, or landraces) of potatoes are adapted to the local conditions where they grow. These landraces form the *Solanum brevicaule* complex. Genotypes from multilocus amplified fragment length polymorphisms were determined from 261 wild

Figure 48.19

Solonaceae. Domesticated species include **(a)** capsicum peppers, **(b)** eggplant, **(c)** potato, and **(d)** tomato.

M.B. Fenton

(see Chapter 19). They vary noticeably in leaf shape, floral patterns, and tuber colour. Domesticated potatoes have been selected for short stolons, large tubers, and various colours of tubers from white to yellow to black. After being introduced to Europe, potatoes became an important food staple, supplanting traditional crops such as grains, and millions of people were adversely affected when a blight caused widespread failure of the potato crop. The blight was caused by the oomycete protist, *Phytophthora infestans*. The "potato famine" in Ireland had huge social repercussions: many people died, and others emigrated to Canada, the United States, and Australia.

Tomatoes (*Solanum lycopersicum*) were domesticated from plants that grew in South and Central America, but there is considerable debate about when they were domesticated. Two modern forms, wild cherry tomatoes and currant tomatoes, were recently domesticated from stock native to eastern Mexico. Eaten raw or cooked, tomatoes come in different sizes, shapes, and colours. Different strains grow well in a variety of situations, meaning that tomatoes can be grown in many different climate zones. When grown in greenhouses, tomatoes are often pollinated by resident bumblebees, although many cultivars are self-pollinating.

Eggplants include three closely related cultivated species: *Solanum melongena*, the brinjal eggplant or aubergine; *Solanum aethiopicum*, the scarlet eggplant; and *Solanum macrocarpum*, the gboma eggplant. All cultivated species are native to the Old World, with

and 98 landrace samples. The resulting data suggest that potatoes (*S. tuberosum*) arose from one domestication event. Today, wild potatoes still occur in Chile, along with eight cultivar groups of potatoes—some diploid and some triploid, others tetraploid or pentaploid

Marquis Wheat 48.3

Different strains of domesticated crops, such as wheat and corn, have different features that make them better suited to some areas (climates) than to others. But wheat crops provide both flour for bread and straw for thatching and animal bedding. Whereas Red Fife wheat matures in 130 days and produces 3270 kg·ha⁻¹, Hard Red Calcutta wheat matures in 110 days but yields only 1240 kg·ha⁻¹. In an effort to find a wheat variety that would grow well and produce a good yield in the Canadian Prairies, Sir Charles E. Saunders made extensive crosses and developed Marquis wheat by 1906. To do this involved selective breeding: a planned program of hybridization of different wheat varieties, rigid selection of the best available material, preliminary and final evaluations of the results from

replicated trials, and extensive testing of the new varieties. In the 1880s, Dr. William Saunders (Sir Charles's father) had introduced and tested many strains of wheat, often from Russia and India.

Crosses that led to the emergence of Marquis wheat were mainly focused on Hard Red Calcutta and Red Fife. The products of the crosses were tested at stations near Agassiz, British Columbia; Indian Head, Saskatchewan; and Brandon, Manitoba. At the latter two locations, these two varieties differed by three weeks in reaching maturity.

Sir Charles is famous for the "chewing test" he used to test the products of the crosses. He observed that chewing allowed him to determine the elasticity of the gummy substance produced (gluten). Other

tests included baking bread with flour ground from the different strains to ensure that the product was satisfactory.

In 1906, Marquis wheat emerged as the product of a cross between a Hard Red Calcutta female and a Red Fife male. The kernels were dark red and hard, medium in size, and short. Heads were medium in length and bearded. Marquis ripens a few days before Red Fife and produces flour that is strong and of good colour. Tested at Brandon in 1908, Marquis wheat was the earliest to ripen and yielded 4336 kg·ha⁻¹—the best among the strains compared. Note that in Ottawa, Marquis wheat was not as productive, yielding only 2522 kg·ha⁻¹, reflecting the effect of climate and conditions on yield.

S. macrocarpum and *S. aethiopicum* having been domesticated in Africa. The origin of the brinjal eggplant is less certain, but it may have originated in Africa and been domesticated in India and southeast China. During the Arab conquests, it spread from there to the Mediterranean and today is cultivated around the world. Brinjal eggplants and tomatoes are autogamous diploids.

Chilli peppers, *Capsicum* species, are another member of the Solonaceae that originated in the New World. Known as producers of capsaicin ("Molecule behind Biology," Box 33.1, Chapter 33), chilli peppers are often used to spice food. Cultivation of *Capsicum* species was well advanced and widespread in the Americas by 6000 years B.P. Then, as now, they were used as condiments.

People use other members of this family as the source of hallucinogenic compounds. Notable examples are tobacco and species in the genus *Datura*. Jimson weed or locoweed (*Datura stramonium*) contains strong poisons, including belladonna alkaloids, atropine, and scopalamine. It grows in many parts of the world and has often been used as a hallucinogenic drug because one active ingredient interferes with neurotransmitters (see Chapter 36) and can induce violent hallucinations. The name "locoweed" is a useful, important warning.

Stepping outside the Solonaceae to the family Brassicaceae, species in the genus *Brassica* also include many varieties seen on dinner tables worldwide (see "Domesticated Plants in the Genus *Brassica*," Box 48.4, p. 1244).

48.2k Squash

In the family Cucurbitaceae, at least five species of squash (*Cucurbita*; **Figure 48.20**) were domesticated in

Figure 48.20
Many cultivars of squash, *Cucurbita* species, are New World domesticates, some first domesticated in southwestern Mexico at least 10 000 years B.P.

the Americas before European settlers arrived, some of them at least 10 000 years B.P. Squash, beans, and corn were the "three sisters," staple foods farmed by many First Nations peoples in the New World (see Section 48.2h). Genetic data obtained from an intron region of the mitochondrial *nad1* gene suggest that at least six independent domestication events occurred. *Cucurbita argyrosperma* appears to have been domesticated from *C. sororia*, a wild Mexican gourd that grew in the general area of Mexico as teosinte. *C. moschata* was probably domesticated somewhere in lowland South America and *C. maxima* in the humid lowlands of Bolivia from *C. andreana*. The *Cucurbita pepo* complex seems to be derived from at least two domestication events, one in eastern North America and one in northeastern Mexico.

Many people are familiar with *C. pepo* as the pumpkin, but the species also includes summer squashes and zucchinis. *Cucurbita maxima* is the Hubbard and other winter squashes, which also include some *C. pepo* and *C. moshata*. The diversity of these cultivars is astonishing. The intraspecific variations provide another example of the difficulty of applying the species concept to the diversity of life (see Chapter 19).

48.2l Dogs

Behaviour provides clues to important aspects about the domestication of dogs. Researchers assessed the abilities of dogs, chimps, and wolves to read human signals indicating the location of food. Even young puppies with little human contact were more skillful at these social cognition skills than chimpanzees and wolves. Interspecific communication appears to have been strongly selected for during the domestication of dogs, building on the evolutionary history of social skills associated with cooperative hunting inherited from their wolf ancestors.

Dogs were among the first animals to have been domesticated, presumably to help people with hunting. Genetic, behavioural, and morphological evidence indicates that dogs were derived from wolves. The earliest morphological evidence suggests domestication of dogs by 14 500 years B.P. whereas mtDNA data suggest a date of 15 000 years B.P. Genetic data suggest an East Asian origin for dogs. Other mtDNA data from specimens in Latin American and Alaska indicate that dogs crossed into North America via the Bering Land Bridge, with people producing a group (clade) of dogs unique to the New World. The mtDNA data imply that either European colonists or native aboriginals actively prevented dogs that they brought with them from interbreeding with dogs already present in the New World.

48.2m *Salmo salar*, Atlantic Salmon

Atlantic salmon naturally occurs around the North Atlantic (locations in North America, Greenland, and Europe), but intensive fishing has reduced its natural stocks to the brink of extinction in some areas. However, Atlantic salmon have also been introduced to many sites around the world, from Jordan and Greece to Australia, New Zealand, Chile, Argentina, Brazil, and the Falkland Islands. There are both landlocked natural and introduced freshwater populations of Atlantic salmon. This species has been a traditional target of subsistence, sport, and commercial fishing and more recently the focus of aquaculture operations. The farmed fish have been selectively bred; thus, they are domesticated. Farmed fish are larger and more aggressive than those from wild stock, and they mature later.

Aquaculture operations have proven to be very lucrative, leading to a proliferation of these facilities in many areas. But some aquacultural operations have negative impacts. For example, escaped fish are thought to interbreed with local species (on the west coast of North America), threatening their genetic survival. This threat may be reduced by using sterile triploid Atlantic salmon for aquaculture. Sterile triploids can be mass produced, making it relatively feasible to use them in many areas. But concerns about the productivity and survival of triploid fish compared with diploid individuals have slowed the spread of their use.

Aquaculture can bring other problems. Sea lice, such as *Lepeophtheirus salmonis,* are parasitic copepod crustaceans that can cause serious problems for salmon aquacultural facilities. Recurrent sea lice infestations of aquacultured populations have spread to and decimated some wild salmon populations. Infestations by sea lice originating from cultured salmon have also caused a 99% collapse of some wild populations of pink salmon (*Oncorhynchus gorbuscha*) in coastal British Columbia.

The scale of aquaculture operations involving Atlantic salmon is astounding. In 2006, in the province of Nova Scotia alone, 35 000 tonnes of Atlantic salmon were produced by aquaculture. Atlantic salmon also dominate farmed stock in British Columbia. The scale of production has wide environmental, social, and economic implications for human nutrition and employment.

48.2n Some Organisms Were Domesticated for More than One Use

Some animals and plants provide more than one crop. Cotton, as noted above, provides oilseed and fibre. Cattle are sources of meat, milk, blood, hides, and labour. Sheep provide wool, milk, meat, and hides. Sheepskins with the wool attached are used to make clothing.

48.2o Some Organisms Were Cultivated but Not Domesticated

People cultivate many species that have not been domesticated because there is no evidence of selective

M.B. Fenton

Figure 48.21
Pearls for sale in the Pearl Market in Beijing, China.

breeding. Mushrooms are examples because they have been cultivated and used as a source of protein for several thousand years without selective breeding of specific lines (= domestication).

Ostriches (*Struthio camelus*) are ranched (= cultivated) for their meat, hides, feathers, and eggs, but they are not domesticated. Crocodiles (*Crocodylus* species) are also ranched for their hides and meat. Oysters (*Pinctada fucata*) and other species of molluscs have been cultivated for hundreds of years mainly for pearls **(Figure 48.21)**. Other animals, such as *Python regius* (ball pythons), are bred and sold to snake fanciers. Breeders may select individuals with specific traits in their breeding programs, technically making the animals domesticated because the definition does not speak to use.

STUDY BREAK

1. Distinguish between cultivation and domestication. Give examples.
2. How has domestication affected K, the carrying capacity?
3. Use two of the examples to compare the timing, location, and path of domestication. Be sure to explain how the domesticated organisms are used.
4. How did the domestication of rice, wheat, barley, and lentils differ from that of squash and potatoes?
5. Use an example to show how domestication of animals depends on their behaviour.

48.3 Yields

In his book *The Upside of Down: Catastrophe, Creativity and the Renewal of Civilization,* Thomas Homer-Dixon calculated the amount of energy it would have taken to build the Coliseum in Rome. He estimated that it would have taken 44 billion kilocalories of energy: 34 billion for oxen and 10 billion for human workers (assuming that both worked 220 days a year for 5 years and that the humans received 12 500 kJ·day⁻¹). The Roman workers would have eaten grain, mainly wheat, as well as legumes, vegetables, wine, and a little meat. The oxen would have been fed hay, mainly alfalfa, as well as legumes, millet, clover, tree foliage, and wheat chaff. Records from the time indicate a yield of wheat of about 1160 kg·ha⁻¹ and alfalfa of about 2600 kg·ha⁻¹. Wheat delivers 1.0×10^7 kJ·ha⁻¹ and alfalfa 1.6×10^7 kJ·ha⁻¹. Growing wheat would have required 58 days of slave labour per hectare per year. If farmers had had to pay labourers, the cost of production would have been higher.

Based on these data, Homer-Dixon calculated that building the Coliseum would have required the wheat grown on 19.8 km² of land and the alfalfa on 35.2 km². At its peak around 1 and 2 CE the population of the city of Rome was 1 million, and that number would have required the food produced on 8800 km² of land, equivalent to the area of Lebanon today. Much of the wheat that fed Rome came from North Africa, as well as Sicily and other parts of Italy.

On average, one adult human needs 8300 kJ·day⁻¹ or 3.0×10^6 kJ·yr⁻¹ to maintain a stable body mass. This assumes a much lower level of exercise and physical exertion than the Roman worker in Homer-Dixon's calculations. If people were to meet their caloric demands from wheat alone, and if wheat delivers about 8700 kJ·kg⁻¹, at 8300 kJ·day⁻¹, each person would need to consume about 350 kg of wheat a year. In 2007 in southwestern Ontario, a wheat yield of 6600 kg·ha⁻¹ meant that 1 ha of land would support 18.8 people for a year. A city of 50 000, eating only wheat, would need the wheat produced on 2660 ha **(Figures 48.22 and 48.23)**.

Source: Based on drawing courtesy of University of Western Ontario

M.B. Fenton

Figure 48.23
Envisioning 20 ha. Two views of the same area: a drawing **(a)** in which the coloured area represents 20 ha and an aerial photograph **(b)** showing the same football stadium on the campus of the University of Western Ontario, in London, Ontario.

M.B. Fenton

Figure 48.22
The field marked with the * is 20 ha and, if planted in wheat, should yield 13 200 kg in southwestern Ontario. Note that the area is also being used to harvest wind energy.

The data in **Table 48.1, p. 1245** demonstrate that it takes energy input to generate energy, in this case food. So variations in crop yields noted at the beginning of this chapter have huge repercussions. From a farmer's perspective, the difference in farm income would be substantial if the yield of corn were 1600 kg·ha⁻¹ versus 10 000 kg·ha⁻¹ (Table 48.1, p. 1245). But, even without considering the costs of transportation (from farm to market), the data illustrate the impact of the cost of fuel. Spraying, planting, and trucking all require diesel fuel, so any change in the price of this commodity influences the costs of farm operations.

Domesticated Plants in the Genus *Brassica* 48.4

Some plants have provided humans with an embarrassment of riches. Imagine plants in one genus (*Brassica*) whose flowers, roots, stems, leaves, and seeds are all important food crops **(Figure 1)**. Foods from these vegetables are high in vitamin C and soluble fibre. They contain a rich mixture of nutrients, including some (diindolylmethane, sulforaphane, and selenium) thought to have anticancer effects.

A sample of an all-*Brassica* meal could include broccoli, cauliflower, Brussels sprouts, kale, and cabbage, all variations of one species, *Brassica oleracea*. You could add rutabaga (*Brassica napus*) along with turnip and rapini (*Brassica rapa*) to the menu and use canola oil (see "People behind Biology," Box 48.2) and mustard (*B. rapa, B. carinata, B. elongata, B. juncea, B. nigra, B. ruprestris*) to dress the parts of the meal presented as salad.

Nuclear restriction fragment length polymorphisms (RFLPs) obtained from

M. B. Fenton

FIGURE 1

*Brassicas in our diets. Shown here are cultivars of brassicas that commonly appear in people's diets, including **(a)** radishes, **(b)** Brussels sprouts, **(c)** cauliflower, **(d)** broccoli, **(e)** turnip, **(f)** rutabaga, **(g)** mustard, **(h)** cabbage, and **(i)** canola oil.*

10 different *Brassica rapa*, 9 cultivated types of *B. oleracea*, and 6 other species in *Brassica* and related genera suggest two basic evolutionary pathways **(Figure 2)** for diploid species: one that gave rise to *B. fruticulosa, B. nigra*, and

FIGURE 2

The shortest phylogenetic tree showing the relationships between different species of Brassica, *including cultivars and wild species.* A1–A5 B. rapa *cultivars: 1 = flowering pak choi; 2 = pak choi; 3 = B. narinosa; 4 = Chinese cabbage; 5 = turnip; A6–A10 B. rapa wild: Bal = B. alboglabra; Bc 1–4 = B. cretica; Bd = B. drepanensis; Bia = B. incana; Bis = B. isularis Bma = B. macrocarpa; Bmo = B. montana; Bol = B. oleracea; Br = B Rupestris; BBv = B. villosa; C2–C23 B. oleracea cultivars: 2 = broccoli; 3 = broccoli (packman); 4 = cabbage; 8 = Portuguese tree kale; 12 = Chinese kale; 15 = kohlrabi; 19 = borecole; 23 = cauliflower; Bf = B. fruticulosa; Bn = B. nigra; Bt = B. tournefortii; De = Diplotaxis erucoides; Es = Eruca sativa; Rs = Raphanus sativus.*

With kind permission from Springer Science+Business Media: *Theoretical and Applied Genetics*, "Brassica: taxonomy based on nuclear restriction fragment length polymorphisms (RFLPs)", volume 79, Apr 1, 1990, pp. 497–506, K. Song.

a) Data from Song et al. 1988a
b) Outgroup

(continued)

Terrain influences the level of technology that can be used in farming practices. Small terraced plots **(Figure 48.24, p. 1245)** must be worked by hand or with the help of animals. Large expanses of relatively flat land can be worked effectively and efficiently with machinery **(Figure 48.25, p. 1246)**, increasing the energy consumption associated with farming but also the yield. Modern agriculture relies on energy from petroleum products, so increases in the price of oil can undermine food production, especially if crops originally grown for food are used in the production of biofuels.

There are many factors to consider when determining sustainability.

STUDY BREAK

1. How must crop yield be balanced against the cost of achieving it? Does this apply to a kitchen garden (as opposed to a functioning farm)?
2. What factors were fundamental in allowing the city of Rome to have a population of over 1 million people in 2 CE?

Sinapis arvensis (Brassica adpressa is a close relative), and the other to B. oleracea and B. rapa **(Figure 3)**. Raphanus sativus and Eruca sativa appear to be intermediate between the two lineages (see Figure 2). Europe and East Asia appear to have been centres of domestication for Brassica species.

The related Arabidopsis is an important experimental tool used in understanding the genetics and selection of desirable traits in Brassica.

With kind permission from Springer Science+Business Media: Theoretical and Applied Genetics, "Brassica taxonomy based on nuclear restriction fragment 'ength polymorphisms (RFLPs)", volume 79, Apr 1, 1990, pp. 497–506. K. Song.

FIGURE 3

Geographic distribution and hypothetical origins and evolutionary pathways of Brassica oleracea and B. rapa, which may have shared a common ancestor in Europe. Please note that the political divisions on the map are no longer current.

Legend:
- ◼ Possible common ancestor of A and C genomes
- ◻ Distribution of wild relatives of B. oleracea
- ◼ Distribution of different kales
- ◼ Regions of B. oleracea domestication
- ◼ Regions of B. rapa domestication

Table 48.1	Balancing Cost and Yield, a Farm in Southwestern Ontario (Costs as of Autumn, 2007)	
Crop/Material/Process	Yield kg·ha⁻¹	C$·ha⁻¹
Corn	10 000	1650
Soy beans	3500	1300
Wheat	6600	900
Costs		
Seed		150
Fertilizer		125–225
Spray		50–100
Planting		38
Labour		40–190
Combine		100
Trucking		25
Crop insurance		20
Field rental		325

M.B. Fenton

Figure 48.24

A series of rock walls creates terraced areas for growing crops near Beijing in China. The terraces hold soil, but the setting precludes extensive use of mechanized farming equipment.

Figure 48.25
Large expanses of relatively flat land lend themselves to mechanized farming, allowing more uniform conditions and crops.

48.4 Complications

As anyone who has ever gardened or worked a farm knows well, there is more to growing crops than putting seeds or small plants in the ground and then harvesting the crops.

48.4a Fertilizer, Water, Yield, and Pests Are Factors in the Care of Crops

In the course of operating an experimental farm in the Negev Desert in southern Israel **(Figure 48.26)**, researchers established several basic truths. By providing 20 m³ of

Figure 48.26
An experimental farm plot near Avdot in the Negev Desert in southern Israel. The green areas are irrigated with water stored in an underground cistern. The experimental farm was established on an ancient farm site. Other fields previously under cultivation are shown. By collecting runoff during and after rainfall, farmers have stored water for their families and crops for hundreds of years.

manure (sheep and goat) and 600 kg of ammonium sulfate per hectare, they could obtain good yields: 4800 kg·ha⁻¹ of barley (where less tended crops yielded 400 to 600 kg·ha⁻¹) and 4400 kg·ha⁻¹ (nanasit strain) or 2700 kg·ha⁻¹ (Florence strain) of wheat. They were able to produce 750 kg·ha⁻¹ of carrots and 650 kg·ha⁻¹ of onions. Achieving these yields required cultivation of the soil, irrigation, and dealing with a variety of pests. Their farm became an oasis of green that attracted hares, gazelles, porcupines, desert partridges, and a host of insects, meaning that control of pest species had to be routine.

Irrigation was a key to good crops, and the experiment had been designed to test the prediction that by collecting runoff water and storing it in cisterns, the people there could farm in an area with little and highly seasonal rainfall. In 2006–07, the 60 mm total rainfall in the area occurred between November 20 and April 16. Water collected as runoff and stored in a 1400 m³ cistern could last the farm (people, animals, and crops) over two years.

48.4b Cats Are Sometimes Workers

The need to control rodent pests in areas where grain is stored **(Figure 48.27)** might be one factor explaining

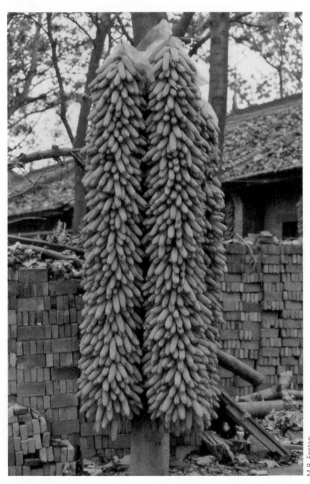

Figure 48.27
Harvested crops can be stored in different ways. Near Tien in China, farmers hang collections of corn cobs after harvest. This approach to crop storage suggests a dearth of local birds and rodents that might consume the corn.

the domestication of cats, *Felis silvestris catus*. Carlos A. Driscoll and colleagues examined short tandem repeat (STR) and mtDNA data from 979 cats and wild progenitors to examine relationships among them. The evidence suggested at least five founder populations, including the European wildcat (*Felis silvestris silvestris*), near Eastern wildcat (*F. s. lybica*), central Asian wildcat (*F. s. ornata*), southern African wildcat (*F. s. cafra*), and Chinese desert cat (*F. s. bieti*). Each of these populations represents a distinct subspecies. Cats were thought to have been domesticated in the Near East, and their descendants were transported across the world with assistance from humans **(Figure 48.28)**. Driscoll and his colleagues proposed that the domestication of cats coincided with the development of agriculture in different locations.

Figure 48.28

The origins of domestic cats. **(a)** Genetic assessment of 979 cats (*Felis silvestris catus*) based on short tandem repeats (STR) and mtDNA identifies different contributors to cat genotypes. **(b)** The accompanying phenogram of 851 domesticated and wild cats illustrates the relationships between domestic cats and wild genetic contributors.

From Carlos A. Driscoll, Marilyn Menotti-Raymond, Alfred L. Roca, Karsten Hupe, Warren E. Johnson, Eli Geffen, Eric H. Harley, Miguel Delibes, Dominique Pontier, Andrew C. Kitchener, Nobuyuki Yamaguchi, Stephen J. O'Brien, David W. Macdonald, "The Near Eastern Origin of Cat Domestication", *Science*, vol. 317, Jul 27, 2007, pp. 519–523. Reprinted with permission from AAAS.

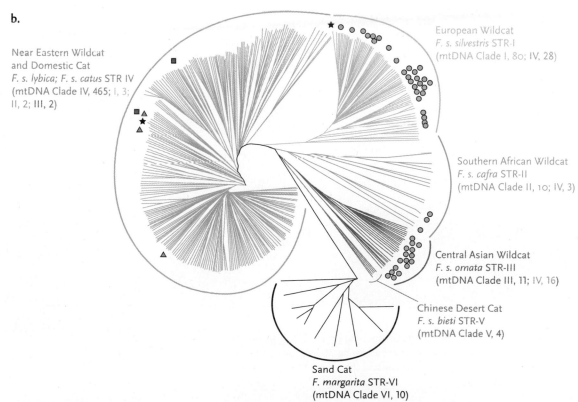

48.4c Crops Can Become Contaminated

People living in rural parts of Bosnia, Bulgaria, Croatia, Romania, and Serbia exhibit a high incidence of a devastating renal disease termed *endemic Balkan nephropathy* (EN). People afflicted with EN progress from chronic renal failure to a high incidence of cancer of the upper urinary tract. EN and its associated cancer can be related to chronic dietary poisoning by aristolochic acid. The source of the poisoning is contamination of grain crops with the plant *Aristolochia clematitis*. A clue to this situation came from horses that developed renal failure after being fed hay contaminated with *A. clematitis*. The presence of weeds or other contaminants in crops **(Figure 48.29)** poses an important challenge to farmers, one that goes beyond how the productivity of the crop is affected by weeds' needs for water and nutrients.

Ironically, the medicinal virtues of extracts of *A. clematitis* are extolled on some websites selling homeopathic remedies. A first step in solving the mystery of EN came from case studies of some Belgian women who had developed renal problems after taking extracts of *A. clematitis* as part of a weight loss program.

STUDY BREAK

1. What factors influence crop yield?
2. How does crop yield vary?
3. What are some of the problems associated with crops?

48.5 Chemicals, Good and Bad

Plants are often treasured as much for the chemicals they produce as for their use as food, and until the time of Linnaeus (Chapter 18), plants were mainly classified by their medicinal properties. The chef who adds rosemary (*Rosmarinus officinalis;* **Figure 48.30**) to a dish as it is cooking knows that the flavour will enhance the final product. Other plant products are used as medicines. Phenolic compounds are responsible for the distinctive flavours of coffee, cinnamon, cloves, and nutmeg, which add flavour and aroma to food. Some of these compounds, such as caffeine, can be addictive.

The secondary compounds of plants may add taste to our food but can also be lethal. Consider how the plants use these compounds. Ginsenosides (obtained from ginseng, *Panax quinquefolius*), for example, appear to be used by ginseng plants as fungicides, whereas humans take them to stimulate the immune system. Other plant products are toxic. Conine, produced by poison hemlock (*Conium maculatum;* not to be confused with the hemlock tree), is an active ingredient used by the plant to defend against herbivores **(Figure 48.31)**. It was the hemlock used to kill Socrates. Plants that look the same often produce quite different chemicals. Poison hemlock, for example, superficially resembles Queen Anne's lace (*Daucus carota*), a common weed. It can also be confused with fennel (*Foeniculum vulgare*) and parsley (*Petroselinum crispum*), two herbs often used in cooking.

Figure 48.29
Weeds, such as the milkweeds (*Asclepias* species) growing in this barley field in south-western Ontario, can pose a problem at harvesting. If the weeds are toxic, they must be extracted from the harvested crop to ensure the safety of animals and people that consume the barley.

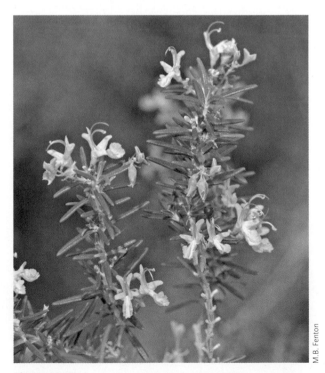

Figure 48.30
Herbs such as rosemary (*Rosmarinus officinalis*) are used to add flavour during cooking.

Figure 48.31
Conine, the poison from poison hemlock.

The speed with which changes can occur in biological systems can be astonishing, exemplified by the assimilation of new foods into our own diets whether the product is natural or synthetic. This is not a feature unique to humans. Work on ant farmers revealed that one species (*Cyphomyrmex rimosus*) introduced to Florida quickly acquired a crop cultivated by another species of ant indigenous there (*Cyphomyrmex minutus*). Also in Florida, the grasshopper *Romalea microptera* uses a mix of chemicals to repel ants (see "Molecule behind Biology," Box 47.3, Chapter 47). Soon after people began to use 2,4-D (2,4-dichlorophenoxyacetic acid) to kill weeds, the grasshopper added 2,5-dichlorophenol to its ant-repellent mixture. This situation is analogous to humans cultivating and domesticating new crop species.

The pharmacological potential of plant products for treating and preventing human ailments has not been lost on three groups of people: those interested in conserving biodiversity, those concerned about alleviating human suffering, and those anxious to make money by selling biopharmaceuticals to others.

Study Break

1. Why do humans use 2,4-D? What other uses could it have?
2. Why are spices important?
3. What is poison hemlock?

48.6 Molecular Farming

CONCEPT FIX Some people believe that genetically modified organisms pose a serious risk to those who consume them. The reality is that genetically modified food organisms, such as rice, are not dangerous and may be beneficial (e.g., golden rice with enriched Vitamin A). The other reality is that some genetically modified organisms pose a risk to wild stock of the same species. ◖

Many native peoples in the New World used tobacco (*Nicotiana tabacum*) as a traditional medicine to ease the pain of childbirth, stave off hunger, and treat various ailments **(Figure 48.32)**. Tobacco was dried and smoked in ceremonies; used in poultices; brewed as a tea; and used as an emetic, an expectorant, and a laxative. By 1540, tobacco reached Europe, where it was

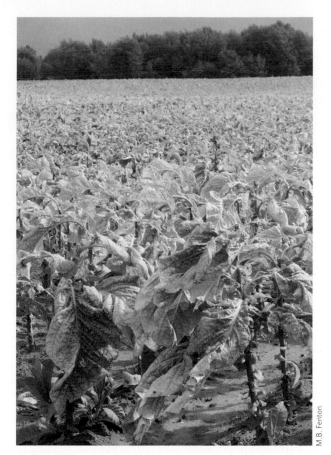

Figure 48.32
A tobacco field in southwestern Ontario.

said to cure illnesses ranging from epilepsy to plague. People have also used nicotine, an alkaloid in tobacco, in the same way as tobacco plants do, as an insecticide. The recreational use of tobacco has given the plant a bad name, even though other *Nicotiana* species are commonly used in gardens for their aromatic white or pink flowers.

Tobacco, however, is undergoing a rebirth as a positive contributor. *Molecular farming* involves the use of plants as producers of specific proteins useful as human medications. Plants can be genetically modified to produce large amounts of these proteins at low cost. Concerns about using plants as molecular farms reflect the possibility of biologically active products entering ecosystems and dispersing through food webs, via pollen or seeds, all of which could negatively affect existing crops. Enter tobacco, a non-food plant that is harvested before flowering. Tobacco is not cold hardy (in Canada), but it is easy to genetically modify and is highly productive (40-day production cycle). Using appropriate DNA technology (see Chapter 15), T-DNA containing the human *IL-10* gene was inserted into the tobacco genome by connecting it to a plant promoter and an *Agrobacterium* terminator. In this way, tobacco plants are modified to produce interleukin-10 (*IL-10*), which can be used to treat irritable bowel disease in humans. Interleukin is a cytokine involved in the regulation of inflammatory diseases, reducing the production of necrosis factor by tumours. The IL-10 was found not to enter the soil in which the tobacco was grown or the aphids or other insects that fed on the tobacco plants. The vast amount of agricultural land that was used to grow tobacco for recreational use can now be used for molecular farming. This change to molecular farming of tobacco could produce many different useful compounds.

STUDY BREAK

1. How are plant products used in addition to their role as food?
2. What is molecular farming?
3. What conservation risks are associated with molecular farming? With agriculture in general?

48.7 The Future

It is tempting to believe that the diversity of life will continue to provide humans with solutions to many of their problems in the world: food for the hungry, poisons to selectively control pests, and biopharmaceuticals to cure diseases. Molecular farming potentially allows new approaches to solving old problems. Although we can continue to domesticate other species, effectively taking evolution in directions that suit us, we must remember that when new forms require higher investments in energy and fertilizer, costs can outweigh benefits.

In 2008, global increases in the price of food were partly due to our using traditional food crops (e.g., corn) to produce ethanol to fuel vehicles. In 2007, the energy return on investment (EROI) for biofuel (ethanol, or food for internal combustion engines) from corn was about 1. This means that every litre of ethanol produced from corn consumes about a litre of petroleum fuel. Other crops, for example, poplar trees, have much better EROIs. Although biofuels are potentially low-carbon-emitting energy sources, the means of production dramatically influences their "greenness." In many cases, production of biofuels generates a *biofuel carbon debt*. In Brazil, Southeast Asia, and the United States, converting native habitat (rainforest, peatlands, savanna, and grasslands) to produce biofuels generates 17 to 420 times as much CO_2 as the habitats normally produce. When these costs are taken into account, biofuels are not feasible environmentally friendly alternatives.

Calculating EROI and tracking it over time helps put energy use in perspective. In Rome in 1 C.E., the EROI for wheat was 12:1, and for alfalfa, it was 27:1. In 2007, the EROI value for gasoline was about 17:1, whereas in the 1930s, it was about 100:1. The values of EROI speak to the sustainability of a process, so Canadians must be concerned that the EROI on the tar sands is less than 4:1 without taking into consideration the water consumed by the process.

The development of resistance to toxins, whether of bacteria to antibiotics or of insect pests to insecticides or of weeds to herbicides, demonstrates that evolution works both ways. Perfecting genetic strains of crops protected by resistance to a pathogen or pest and using them exclusively can make the crops vulnerable to pathogens or pests that are resistant to the defence(s). The potato famine, discussed in Section 48.2j, was exacerbated by the lack of genetic diversity of the potatoes used in Europe: they were vulnerable to blight.

Over evolutionary history, individuals able to exploit other species had an advantage over those that did not, whether within a society or between societies. The same principles apply to our own species. Our advantages of exploiting other species include increased access to food (quantity and quality), labour, materials for constructing things, and chemicals for treating disorders or controlling pests. These advantages were amplified through domestication, which meant increasing control over the other species, leading to several net effects. One effect was achieving larger populations of humans because of better access to food and/or protection from disease. Ironically, living closer to more animals also exposes us to diseases such as avian flu, swine flu, and smallpox. Another factor was probably the increase in available time for the development and perfection of new tools and techniques and the emergence of groups of people in society who did not contribute directly by gathering or processing food. Such people could have contributed to society through their talents as artisans, soldiers, or even politicians.

The range of possibilities seems endless, particularly with the advent of the ability to directly modify genotypes and thus phenotypes. Perhaps we should be glad that the Attine ants have domesticated only fungi.

STUDY BREAK

What is artemisinin? What is golden rice? Why are they important?

LIFE ON THE EDGE 48.5

Feeding People and Keeping Them Healthy

We have seen how humans' ability to harness nature has allowed us to reduce the number of hungry people in the world. Nevertheless, in 2008, converting food crops to biofuels in the interest of being "green" meant less food. This development coincided with climate change, which further reduced the availability of food worldwide. This impact was amplified by increases in the prices of food crops, in turn making food less accessible to many poor people. This brings us back to the price of oil, the energy used in agriculture to produce food, and the cost of food.

We use plants for more than food. In 2008, over 1 million people died from malaria, caused by a blood parasite (see Chapter 25). Some 300 to 500 million people worldwide suffer from malaria. Most (over 75%) of the deaths were of children under 5 years of age and living in Africa. For years, alkaloids (quinine, quinidine, cichonidine, and cinchonine) extracted from the bark of four species of tree in the genus *Cinchona* have been used to treat agues and periodic fevers. Cinchona alkaloids have been particularly effective against malaria, but some strains of malaria are resistant to quinines and other treatments, suggesting that they are not the solution to malaria.

Enter qinghao, also known as huang hua hao, an extract from a ubiquitous shrub, *Artemisia annua*. Extracts of qinghao (artemisinin) have long been used in traditional Chinese medicine. In 1971, Chinese scientists discovered its effectiveness in treating malaria and reported it to the world in 1979. In 2008, artemisinin combination treatments became first-line drugs for some forms of malaria (uncomplicated falciparum malaria), but they were not available worldwide. Using improved agriculture techniques—selection of high-yielding hybrids, microbial production, and synthetic peroxidases—could lower prices, increase the availability of artemisinin, and save many lives.

In 2007, about one-third of the annual U.S.$30 billion worldwide investment in agriculture research was aimed at solving the problems of agriculture in developing countries—home to about 80% of the global population. This investment is less than 3% of the amount that countries of the Organization for Economic Co-operation and Development (OECD) spend to subsidize their own agricultural production. To ensure continued reduction of human hunger, OECD countries must invest more to solve the agriculture problems in the developing world. One important first step in this process is recognizing the energy input required to grow enough food to feed the human population (see Section 48.3).

We know that our agricultural prowess can be used to increase production of food and medicines such as artemisinin. Golden rice provides another example. In 1984, the World Health Organization estimated that 250 000 to 500 000 children a year had diets lacking in vitamin A. This deficiency damaged their retinas and corneas, so many of them went blind and half of them died.

By the early 2000s, Ingo Potrykus and Peter Byer had used genetic engineering to splice two daffodil genes and a bacterial gene into the rice genome. The genetically modified rice, *golden rice,* was golden in colour and produced precursors to vitamin A in its endosperm. Golden rice offered a way to address the results of vitamin A deficiency. Growing golden rice was field tested in Louisiana in 2004 and 2005.

In 2008, it appeared that even though golden rice offered the ability to prevent the suffering arising from vitamin A deficiency, it was unlikely that any would be planted before 2012. The delay reflects a combination of widespread public suspicion about genetically modified organisms (GMOs) and the high cost of obtaining approval to use GMOs. The costs associated with getting approval mean that only large companies with large budgets are likely to succeed in getting GMO products approved.

Moving more people away from "the edge" means investing more in finding solutions to agricultural operations in the developing world to ensure that discoveries such as artemisinin and golden rice are used to advantage. This requires policies and investments that support small-scale operations, probably subsidizing the costs of energy and water necessary to grow enough food. Our ancestors who domesticated crops such as wheat and corn, lentils and squash, and potatoes and rice changed the world for us. We should ensure that their legacy lives on.

Review

CourseMate Access an interactive eBook, chapter-specific interactive learning tools, including flashcards, quizzes, videos, and more in your Biology **CourseMate**, accessed through NelsonBrain.com **Aplia™** is an online interactive learning solution that helps you improve comprehension—and your grade—by integrating a variety of mediums and tools such as videos, tutorials, practice tests, and an interactive eBook.

48.1 Domestication

- The green revolution is credited with reducing the number of hungry people in the world by increasing agricultural productivity. Increased productivity reflects the use of improved strains of crops, increased applications of fertilizers, and more extensive irrigation. Higher productivity (crop yields) also reflects more dependence on mechanized (fossil fuel-based) farming operations.

- There are three stages in the exploitation of biodiversity for human benefit. The initial stage involves hunting and gathering, collecting organisms in the wild. The second stage is cultivation or caring for organisms under progressively controlled conditions. The third stage, domestication, involves selective breeding to enhance desired characteristics and features. The domestication process can apply to animals; plants; or other organisms, such as yeast and fungi.

- Domestication of asexually reproducing organisms does not involve selective breeding, which provides more control, allows shorter generation times, or speeds up the process of selection.

- Sexually reproducing organisms that are successfully domesticated are usually capable of self-fertilization and/or readily propagated by grafting.

- Living in the same sites year-round allowed people to tend and protect their crops. Increased time in one place would also have facilitated the process of selective breeding.

- At least 200 species of ants in the tribe Attini are obligate farmers. Other ants also tend seed gardens.

- The first evidence of domestication appears to be figs by about 12 000 years B.P. Cultivation may have been practised for 1000 years before domestication. Many crops had been domesticated by 6000 years B.P.

48.2 Why Some Organisms Were Domesticated

- Yeast appears to have been domesticated in Egypt by 6000 years B.P. when it was used in making bread and beer. Cotton may have been domesticated in at least four sites, two in the Old World and two in the New World. Cotton is used as a source of oil seed and fibre, and some domestication had occurred by 4400 years B.P.

- The change from dehiscence (shattering) to indehiscence (non-shattering) was critical in the domestication of plants, such as grasses, whose seeds were the crop to be harvested.

- Squash and potatoes provide carbohydrates from fruits or tubers; the seeds are not the target of domestication.

- The domestication of dogs appears to have been based, in part, on their social behaviour, including their ability to communicate with people. Some experiments show that dogs are better at reading communication signals from people than other animals, such as chimps.

- Some animals are farmed for meat and hides (and for feathers and eggs), but there is no evidence of selective breeding.

48.3 Yields

- The level of farming intensity, the strains of crops, the application of fertilizers, and irrigation affect crop yields. Terrain can influence the level of mechanization.

- The data on corn and wheat yields clearly demonstrate variation over time and location.

48.4 Complications

- Rich patches of food reflect higher productivity but can attract pests.

48.5 Chemicals, Good and Bad

- Various plant chemicals are used as stimulants, medicines, hallucinogens, pesticides, and flavourings.

48.6 Molecular Farming

- Molecular farming is the use of plants to produce various useful proteins in large amounts at lower cost. Molecular farming may prove to be an inexpensive way to manufacture medicines and other substances.

48.7 The Future

- Energy return on investment (EROI) is an important concept whether the topic is crops or oil. When the cost of seeing a crop from planting to harvest exceeds the return, there is little point in continuing to use the crop. The same should be true for harvesting energy, for example, oil from the tar sands.

Questions

Self-Test Questions

1. According to available evidence, when did humans first domesticate other organisms?
   a. 6000
   b. 8000
   c. 12 000
   d. 20 000

2. The process of moving from cultivation to domestication involved dehiscence (shattering) to indehiscence (nonshattering) in the following way.
   a. rice
   b. wheat
   c. squash
   d. Both a and b are correct.

3. Parthenocarpy was important in the domestication of which species?
   a. dogs
   b. figs
   c. lentils
   d. cotton

4. At Abu Hureyra, which of the following did settlers domesticate?
   a. olives
   b. some grains
   c. cattle
   d. hot peppers

5. Which group includes only domesticated organisms?
   a. yeast, mushrooms, pigs, and oysters
   b. honeybees, yeast, rice, and ostriches
   c. cattle, pigs, cats, and dogs
   d. lentils, mushrooms, yeast, and crocodiles

6. Plants in the family Solonaceae include which of the following?
   a. tomatoes, potatoes, and eggplant
   b. potatoes, hot peppers, and deadly nightshade
   c. corn, tobacco, and hot peppers
   d. Both a and b are correct.

7. If a person needs 8300 kJ·day^{-1}, and wheat yields 6638 kg·ha^{-1}, how much land would be needed to produce enough wheat for 1 year for a city of 20 000 people who eat only wheat?
   a. 155 ha
   b. 1055 ha
   c. 2055 ha
   d. 5055 ha

8. Endemic Balkan nephropathy is an example of a disorder arising when people eat crops which have been subjected to the following.
   a. irrigation with polluted water
   b. contamination with *Aristolochia clematitis*
   c. contamination with *Rosmarinus officinalis*
   d. contamination with *Asclepias exultata*

9. *Nicotiana tabacum* is being used to produce which of the following medications?
   a. nicotine
   b. interleukin
   c. acetylcholine
   d. conine

10. EROI, energy return on investment, suggests that alfalfa in Roman times was this many times as efficient at energy production as the tar sands in Alberta in 2008.
    a. 4
    b. 6
    c. 10
    d. 50

Questions for Discussion

1. When is domestication complete? At what point is a domesticated stock a separate species? Is domestication ever complete?

2. Why have so few aquatic species been domesticated? Why has there been a recent increase in the numbers of domesticated aquatic organisms?

3. How do domesticated populations threaten native species? Should this be a concern for conservation biologists? What can be done to minimize this threat to native species?

4. Why is the price of oil so important in food production?

5. How can we ensure continued supplies of water for food production?

Glossary

accommodation A process by which the lens changes to enable the eye to focus on objects at different distances. p. 916

acid precipitation Rainfall with low pH, primarily created when gaseous sulfur dioxide (SO_2) dissolves in water vapour in the atmosphere, forming sulfuric acid. p. 1005

acrosome A specialized secretory vesicle on the head of an animal sperm, which helps the sperm penetrate the egg. p. 802

acrosome reaction The process in which enzymes contained in the acrosome are released from an animal sperm and digest a path through the egg coats. p. 817

active immunity The production of antibodies in the body in response to exposure to a foreign antigen. p. 1095

active parental care Parents' investment of time and energy in caring for offspring after they are born or hatched. p. 1115

adaptation, sensory *See* sensory adaptation. p. 906

adaptive (acquired) immunity A specific line of defence against invasion of the body in which individual pathogens are recognized and attacked to neutralize and eliminate them. p. 1081

adipose tissue Connective tissue containing large, densely clustered cells called adipocytes that are specialized for fat storage. p. 764

adrenal cortex The outer region of the adrenal glands, which contains endocrine cells that secrete two major types of steroid hormones, the glucocorticoids and the mineralocorticoids. p. 867

adrenal medulla The central region of the adrenal glands, which contains neurosecretory neurons that secrete the catecholamine hormones epinephrine and norepinephrine. p. 867

adrenocorticotropic hormone (ACTH) A hormone that triggers hormone secretion by cells in the adrenal cortex. p. 864

afferent arteriole The vessel that delivers blood to the glomerulus of the kidney. p. 1063

age structure A statistical description or graph of the relative numbers of individuals in each age class in a population. p. 1112

age-specific fecundity The average number of offspring produced by surviving females of a particular age. p. 1113

age-specific mortality The proportion of individuals alive at the start of an age interval that died during that age interval. p. 1113

age-specific survivorship The proportion of individuals alive at the start of an age interval that survived until the start of the next age interval. p. 1113

agonist A muscle that causes movement in a joint when it contracts. p. 958

aldosterone A mineralocorticoid hormone released from the adrenal cortex that increases the amount of Na reabsorbed from the urine in the kidneys and absorbed from foods in the intestine, reduces the amount of Na secreted by salivary and sweat glands, and increases the rate of K excretion by the kidneys, keeping Na and K balanced at the levels required for normal cellular function. p. 868

allantoic membrane Forms from mesoderm and endoderm that has bulged outward from the gut and encloses the allantois. p. 831

allantois In an amniote egg, an extraembryonic membrane sac that fills much of the space between the chorion and the yolk sac and stores the embryo's nitrogenous wastes. p. 831

allergen A type of antigen responsible for allergic reactions, which induces B cells to secrete an overabundance of IgE antibodies. p. 1098

all-or-nothing principle The principle that an action potential is produced only if the stimulus is strong enough to cause depolarization to reach the threshold. p. 883

altruism A behavioural phenomenon in which individuals appear to sacrifice their own reproductive success to help other individuals. p. 960

alveolus (plural, alveoli) One of the millions of tiny air pockets in mammalian lungs, each surrounded by dense capillary networks. p. 1039

amacrine cell A type of neuron that forms lateral connections in the retina of the eye, connecting bipolar cells and ganglion cells. p. 918

ammonification A metabolic process in which bacteria and fungi convert organic nitrogen compounds into ammonia and ammonium ions; part of the nitrogen cycle. p. 1192

amnion In an amniote egg, an extraembryonic membrane that encloses the embryo, forming the amniotic cavity and secreting amniotic fluid, which provides an aquatic environment in which the embryo develops. p. 830

Amniota The monophyletic group of vertebrates that have an amnion during embryonic development. p. 831

amplification An increase in the magnitude of each step as a signal transduction pathway proceeds. p. 858

amygdala A grey-matter centre of the brain that works as a switchboard, routing information about experiences that have an emotional component through the limbic system. p. 932

anabolic steroid A steroid hormone that stimulates muscle development. p. 869

anaphylactic shock A severe inflammation stimulated by an allergen, involving extreme swelling of air passages in the lungs that interferes with breathing and massive leakage of fluid from capillaries that causes blood pressure to drop precipitously. p. 1098

anatomy The study of the structures of organisms. p. 757

androgen One of a family of hormones that promote the development and maintenance of sex characteristics. pp. 813, 868

angiotensin A peptide hormone that raises blood pressure quickly by constricting arterioles in most parts of the body; it also stimulates release of the steroid hormone aldosterone. p. 858

animal behaviour The responses of animals to specific internal and external stimuli. p. 960

animal pole The end of the egg where the egg nucleus is located, which typically gives rise to surface structures and the anterior end of the embryo. p. 825

anion A negatively charged ion. p. 882

antagonistic pair Two skeletal muscles, one of which flexes as the other extends to move joints. p. 954

anterior pituitary The glandular part of the pituitary, composed of endocrine cells that synthesize and secrete several tropic and nontropic hormones. p. 862

antibody-mediated immunity Adaptive immune response in which plasma cells secrete antibodies. p. 1088

antidiuretic hormone (ADH) A hormone secreted by the posterior pituitary that increases water absorption in the kidneys, thereby increasing the volume of the blood. p. 865

antigen A foreign molecule that triggers an adaptive immunity response. p. 1086

antigen-presenting cell (APC) A cell that presents an antigen to T cells in antibody-mediated immunity and cell-mediated immunity. p. 1091

antigenic variation The process by which an infectious organism alters its surface proteins to evade a host immune response. Parasites such as the trypanosomes that cause sleeping sickness in humans have 10% of their genes dedicated to generating new surface glycoproteins. p. 1102

antimicrobial peptides Small, potent, broad-spectrum antibiotic peptides that are used by hosts collectively to - eliminate bacterial and fungal pathogens. Some antimicrobial peptides also may act as immunomodulators. p. 1082

anti-Müllerian hormone p. 839

aorta A large artery from the heart that branches into arteries leading to all body regions except the lungs. p. 784

aortic body One of several small clusters of chemoreceptors, baroreceptors, and supporting cells located along the aortic arch that measures changes in blood pressure and the composition of arterial blood flowing past it. p. 1043

apical surface p. 759

aposematic Refers to bright, contrasting patterns that advertise the unpalatability of poisonous or repellent species. p. 1142

appendicular skeleton The bones comprising the pectoral (shoulder) and pelvic (hip) girdles and limbs of a vertebrate. p. 952

appendix A fingerlike sac that extends from the cecum of the large intestine. p. 1020

applied ecology Application of ecological theory and principles to management of natural resources. p. 1107

aquatic succession A process in which debris from rivers and runoff accumulates in a body of fresh water, causing it to fill in at the margins. p. 1163

aqueous humour A clear fluid that fills the space between the cornea and the lens of the eye. p. 916

archenteron The central endoderm-lined cavity of an embryo at the gastrula stage, which forms the primitive gut. p. 825

arteriole A branch from a small artery at the point where it reaches the organ it supplies. p. 787

artery A vessel that conducts blood away from the heart at relatively high pressure. p. 777

asexual reproduction Any mode of reproduction in which a single individual gives rise to offspring without fusion of gametes, that is, without genetic input from another individual. *See also* vegetative reproduction. p. 799

assimilation efficiency The ratio of the energy absorbed from consumed food to the total energy content of the food. p. 1178

association area One of several areas surrounding the sensory and motor areas of the cerebral cortex that integrate information from the sensory areas, formulate responses, and pass them on to the primary motor area. p. 933

astrocyte A star-shaped glial cell that provides support to neurons in the vertebrate central nervous system. p. 878

atrioventricular node (AV node) A region of the heart wall that receives signals from the sinoatrial node and conducts them to the ventricle. p. 787

atrioventricular valve (AV valve) A valve composed of endocardium and connective tissue between each atrium and ventricle that prevents backflow of blood from the ventricle to the atrium during emptying of the heart. p. 784

autoimmune reaction The production of antibodies against molecules of the body. p. 1097

autonomic nervous system A subdivision of the peripheral nervous system that controls largely involuntary processes, including digestion, secretion by sweat glands, circulation of the blood, many functions of the reproductive and excretory systems, and contraction of smooth muscles in all parts of the body. p. 899

axial skeleton The bones comprising the head and trunk of a vertebrate: the cranium, vertebral column, ribs, and sternum (breastbone). p. 952

axon The single elongated extension of a neuron that conducts signals away from the cell body to another neuron or an effector. p. 877

axon hillock A junction with the cell body of a neuron from which the axon arises. p. 878

axon terminal A branch at the tip of an axon that ends as a small, buttonlike swelling. p. 878

background extinction rate The average rate of extinction of taxa through time. p. 1203

B cell A lymphocyte that recognizes antigens in the body. p. 1087

bacteroid A rod-shaped or branched bacterium in the root nodules of nitrogen-fixing plants. p. 1008

basal lamina A membrane secreted at the inner surface of epithelial cells. p. 760

basal nucleus (plural, basal nuclei) One of several greymatter centres that surround the thalamus on both sides of the brain and moderate voluntary movements directed by motor centres in the cerebrum. p. 932

basement membrane A membrane at the inner surface of epithelia in vertebrates. It consists of the basal lamina and a layer of connective tissue. p. 760

basilar membrane A stiff structural element within the cochlea. p. 913

basophil A type of leukocyte that is induced to secrete histamine by allergens. p. 1098

Batesian mimicry The form of defence in which a palatable or harmless species resembles an unpalatable or poisonous one. p. 1142

bile A mixture of substances including bile salts, cholesterol, and bilirubin that is made in the liver, stored in the gallbladder, and used in the digestion of fats. p. 1011

biodiversity The richness of living systems as reflected in genetic variability within and among species, the number of species living on Earth, and the variety of communities and ecosystems. p. 1201

biological magnification The increasing concentration of nondegradable poisons in the tissues of animals at higher trophic levels. p. 1174

biomass The dry weight of biological material per unit area or volume of habitat. p. 1176

bipolar cell A type of neuron in the retina of the eye that connects the rods and cones with the ganglion cells. p. 919

blastocoel A fluid-filled cavity in the blastula embryo. p. 825

blastocyst An embryonic stage in mammals; a single cell–layered hollow ball of about 120 cells with a fluid-filled -blastocoel in which a dense mass of cells is localized to one side. p. 835

blastodisc A disclike layer of cells at the surface of the yolk produced by early cleavage divisions. p. 829

blastomere A small cell formed during cleavage of the embryo. p. 825

blastula The hollow ball of cells that is the result of cleavage divisions in an early embryo. p. 825

blood–brain barrier A specialized arrangement of capillaries in the brain that prevents most substances dissolved in the blood from entering the cerebrospinal fluid and thus protects the brain and spinal cord from viruses, bacteria, and toxic substances that may circulate in the blood. p. 930

bolus The food mass after chewing. p. 1012

bone The densest form of connective tissue, in which living cells secrete the mineralized matrix of collagen and calcium salts that surrounds them; forms the skeleton. p. 764

Bowman's capsule An infolded region at the proximal end of a nephron that cups around the glomerulus and collects the water and solutes filtered out of the blood. p. 1060

brain A single, organized collection of nervous tissue in an organism's head that forms the control centre of the nervous system and major sensory structures. p. 895

brain hormone (BH) A peptide hormone secreted by neurosecretory neurons in the brain of insects. p. 873

brain stem A stalklike structure formed by the pons and medulla, along with the midbrain, which connects the forebrain with the spinal cord. p. 930

bronchiole One of the small, branching airways in the lungs that lead into the alveoli. p. 1040

bronchus (plural, bronchi) An airway that leads from the trachea to the lungs. p. 1040

brown adipose tissue A specialized tissue in which the most intense heat generation by nonshivering thermogenesis takes place. p. 1073

budding A mode of asexual reproduction in which a new individual grows and develops while attached to the parent. p. 799

bulbourethral gland One of two pea-sized glands on either side of the prostate gland that secrete a mucous fluid that is added to semen. p. 813

bulk feeder An animal that consumes sizable food items whole or in large chunks. p. 1010

cadherin (calcium-dependent adhesion molecules) A cell surface protein responsible for selective cell adhesions that require calcium ions to set up adhesions. p. 842

calcitonin A nontropic peptide hormone that lowers the level of Ca^{2+} in the blood by inhibiting the ongoing dissolution of calcium from bone. p. 866

canines Pointed, conical teeth of a mammal, located between the incisors and the first premolars, that are specialized for biting and piercing. p. 974

capillary The smallest diameter blood vessel, with a wall that is one cell thick, which forms highly branched networks well adapted for diffusion of substances. p. 777

carapace A protective outer covering that extends backward behind the head on the dorsal side of an animal, such as the shell of a turtle or lobster. p. 969

carbon cycle The global circulation of carbon atoms, especially via the processes of photosynthesis and -respiration. p. 1186

cardiac cycle The systole–diastole sequence of the heart. p. 784

cardiac muscle The contractile tissue of the heart. p. 765

carotid body A small cluster of chemoreceptors and supporting cells located near the bifurcation of the carotid artery that measures changes in the composition of arterial blood flowing through it. p. 1049

carrying capacity The maximum size of a population that an environment can support indefinitely. p. 1120

cartilage A tissue composed of sparsely distributed chondrocytes surrounded by networks of collagen fibres embedded in a tough but elastic matrix of the glycoprotein. p. 764

catecholamine Any of a class of compounds derived from the amino acid tyrosine that circulates in the bloodstream, including epinephrine and norepinephrine. p. 867

cation A positively charged ion. p. 945

cation exchange Replacement of one cation with another, as on a soil particle. p. 1005

CD4+ T cell A type of T cell in the lymphatic system that has CD4 receptors on its surface. This type of T cell binds to an antigen-presenting cell in antibody-mediated immunity. p. 1091

CD8+ T cell A type of T cell in the lymphatic system that has CD8 receptors on its surface. This type of T cell binds to an antigen-presenting cell in cell-mediated immunity. p. 1096

cecum A blind pouch formed at the junction of the large and small intestine. p. 1020

cell body The portion of the neuron containing genetic material and cellular organelles. p. 877

cell lineage Cell derivation from the undifferentiated tissues of the embryo. p. 845

cell-mediated immunity An adaptive immune response in which a subclass of T cells—cytotoxic T cells—becomes activated and, with other cells of the immune system, attacks host cells infected by pathogens, particularly those infected by a virus. p. 1088

cellular blastoderm p. 846

central canal The central portion of the vertebral column in which the spinal cord is found. p. 897

cerebellum The portion of the brain that receives sensory input from receptors in muscles and joints, from balance receptors in the inner ear, and from the receptors of touch, vision, and hearing. p. 931

cerebral cortex A thin outer shell of grey matter covering a thick core of white matter within each hemisphere of the brain; the part of the forebrain responsible for information processing and learning. p. 930

cerebrospinal fluid Fluid that circulates through the central canal of the spinal cord and the ventricles of the brain, cushioning the brain and spinal cord from jarring movements and impacts, as well as nourishing the CNS and protecting it from toxic substances. p. 929

cervix The lower end of the uterus. p. 771

character displacement The phenomenon in which allopatric populations are morphologically similar and use similar resources, but sympatric populations are morphologically different and use different resources; may also apply to characters influencing mate choice. p. 1148

chemokine A protein secreted by activated macrophages that attracts other cells, such as neutrophils. p. 1083

chemoreceptor A sensory receptor that detects specific molecules or chemical conditions such as acidity. p. 885

chlorosis An abnormal yellowing of plant tissues due to lack of chlorophyll; a sign of nutrient deficiency or infection by a pathogen. p. 998

chondrocyte A cartilage-producing cell. p. 764

chorion In an amniote egg, an extraembryonic membrane that surrounds the embryo and yolk sac completely and exchanges oxygen and carbon dioxide with the environment; becomes part of the placenta in mammals. p. 830

chorionic villus (plural, villi) One of many treelike extensions from the chorion, which greatly increase the surface area of the chorion. p. 837

chylomicron A small triglyceride droplet covered by a protein coat. p. 1018

chyme Digested content of the stomach released for further digestion in the small intestine. p. 1017

ciliary body A fine ligament in the eye that anchors the lens to a surrounding layer of connective tissue and muscle. p. 917

circulatory system An organ system consisting of a fluid, a heart, and vessels for moving important molecules, and often cells, from one tissue to another. p. 775

circumcision Removal of the prepuce for religious, cultural, or hygienic reasons. p. 813

class II major histocompatibility complex (MHC) A collection of proteins that present antigens on the cell surface of an antigen-presenting cell in an antibody-mediated immune response. p. 1091

classical conditioning A type of learning in which an animal develops a mental association between two phenomena that are usually unrelated. p. 965

cleavage Mitotic cell divisions of the zygote that produce a blastula from a fertilized ovum. p. 825

climax community A relatively stable, late successional stage in which the dominant vegetation replaces itself and persists until an environmental disturbance eliminates it, allowing other species to invade. p. 1163

clitoris The structure at the junction of the labia minora in front of the vulva, homologous to the penis in the male. p. 809

clonal expansion The proliferation of the activated CD4 T cell by cell division to produce a clone of cells. p. 1091

clonal selection The process by which a lymphocyte is specifically selected for cloning when it encounters a foreign antigen from among a randomly generated, enormous diversity of lymphocytes with receptors that specifically recognize the antigen. p. 1092

closed circulatory system A circulatory system in which the fluid, blood, is confined in blood vessels and is distinct from the interstitial fluid. p. 776

clumped dispersion A pattern of distribution in which individuals in a population are grouped together. p. 1109

cochlea A snail-shaped structure (in vertebrates) in the inner ear containing the organ of hearing. p. 913

coevolution The evolution of genetically based, reciprocal adaptations in two or more species that interact closely in the same ecological setting. p. 1137

cohort A group of individuals of similar age. p. 1113

collagen Fibrous glycoprotein—very rich in -carbohydrates—embedded in a network of proteoglycans. p. 762

collecting duct A location where urine leaving individual nephrons is processed further. p. 1059

commensalism A symbiotic interaction in which one species benefits and the other is unaffected. pp. 1081, 1148

community ecology The ecological discipline that examines groups of populations occurring together in one area. p. 1108

compass orientation A wayfinding mechanism that allows animals to move in a particular direction, often over a specific distance or for a prescribed length of time. p. 977

competitive exclusion principle The ecological principle stating that populations of two or more species cannot coexist indefinitely if they rely on the same limiting resources and exploit them in the same way. p. 1147

complement system A nonspecific defence mechanism activated by invading pathogens, made up of more than 30 interacting soluble plasma proteins circulating in the blood and interstitial fluid. p. 1083

compound eye The eye of most insects and some crustaceans, composed of many-faceted, light-sensitive units called ommatidia fitted closely together, each with its own refractive system and each forming a portion of an image. p. 915

conduction The flow of heat between atoms or molecules in direct contact. pp. 887, 1067

cone In the vertebrate eye, a photoreceptor in the retina that is specialized for detection of different wavelengths (colours). In cone-bearing plants, a cluster of sporophylls. p. 917

conformational change Alteration in the three-dimensional shape of a protein. p. 943

connective tissue Tissue with cells scattered through an extracellular matrix; forms layers in and around body structures that support other body tissues, transmit - mechanical and other forces, and in some cases act as - filters. p. 761

consciousness Awareness of oneself, one's identity, and one's surroundings, with understanding of the signifi-cance and likely consequences of events. p. 935

consumer An organism that consumes other organisms in a community or ecosystem. p. 1156

convection The transfer of heat from a body to a fluid, such as air or water, that passes over its surface. p. 1067

cornea The transparent layer that forms the front wall of the eye, covering the iris. p. 915

corpus callosum A structure formed of thick axon bun-dles that connect the two cerebral hemispheres and coordinate their functions. p. 933

corpus luteum Cells remaining at the surface of the ovary during the luteal phase; the structure acts as an endocrine gland, secreting several hormones: estrogens, large quan-tities of progesterone, and inhibin. p. 810

cortical granule A secretory vesicle just under the plasma membrane of an egg cell. p. 805

cortisol The major glucocorticoid steroid hormone secreted by the adrenal cortex, which increases blood glucose by promoting breakdown of proteins and fats. p. 868

countercurrent exchange A mechanism in which the water flowing over the gills moves in a direction opposite to the flow of blood under the respiratory surface (can also apply to transfer of heat). p. 1038

crassulacean acid metabolism (CAM) A biochemical vari-ation of photosynthesis that was discovered in a member of the plant family Crassulaceae. Carbon dioxide is taken up and stored during the night to allow the stomata to remain closed during the daytime, decreasing water loss. p. 156

critical period A restricted stage of development early in life during which an animal has the capacity to respond to specific environmental stimuli. p. 965

crop Of birds, an enlargement of the digestive tube where the digestive contents are stored and mixed with lubri-cating mucus. p. 823

cupula In certain mechanoceptors, a gelatinous structure with stereocilia extending into it that moves with pressure changes in the surrounding water; movement of the cupula bends the stereocilia, which triggers release of neurotransmitters. p. 908

cytokine A molecule secreted by one cell type that binds to receptors on other cells and, through signal transduc-tion pathways, triggers a response. In innate immunity, cytokines are secreted by activated macrophages. p. 1082

cytoplasmic determinants The mRNA and proteins stored in the egg cytoplasm that direct the first stages of animal development in the period before genes of the zygote become active. p. 824

cytotoxic T cell A T lymphocyte that functions in cell-mediated immunity to kill body cells infected by viruses or transformed by cancer. p. 1096

daily torpor A period of inactivity and lowered metabolic rate that allows an endotherm to conserve energy when environmental temperatures are low. p. 1074

demographic transition model A graphic depiction of the historical relationship between a country's economic development and its birth and death rates. p. 1129

demography The statistical study of the processes that change a population's size and density through time. p. 1112

dendrite The branched extension of the nerve cell body that receives signals from other nerve cells. p. 877

dendritic cell A type of phagocyte, so called because it has many surface projections that resemble dendrites of neurons, that engulfs a bacterium in infected tissue by phagocytosis. p. 1091

denitrification A metabolic process in which certain - bacteria convert nitrites or nitrates into nitrous oxide and then into molecular nitrogen, which enters the atmosphere. p. 1192

density-dependent Description of environmental factors for which the strength of their effect on a population varies with the population's density. p. 1122

density-independent Description of environmental factors for which the strength of their effect on a - population does not vary with the population's density. p. 1124

depolarized State of the membrane (which was polarized at rest) as the membrane potential becomes less negative. p. 882

deposit feeder An animal that consumes particles of organic matter from the solid substrate on which it lives. p. 1010

dermis The skin layer below the epidermis; it is packed with connective tissue fibres such as collagen, which resist compression, tearing, or puncture of the skin. p. 1071

desert A sparsely vegetated biome that forms where rain-fall averages less than 25 cm per year. p. 1176

determination Mechanism in which the developmental fate of a cell is set. p. 827

diabetes mellitus A disease that results from problems with insulin production or action. p. 870

diastole The period of relaxation and filling of the heart between contractions. p. 784

differentiation Follows determination and involves the establishment of a cell-specific developmental program in the cells. Differentiation results in cell types with clearly defined structures and functions. p. 827

direct neurotransmitter A neurotransmitter that binds directly to a ligand-gated ion channel in the postsynaptic membrane, opening or closing the channel gate and altering the flow of a specific ion or ions in the postsynaptic cell. p. 890

disclimax community An ecological community in which regular disturbance inhibits successional change. p. 1166

dispersion The spatial distribution of individuals within a population's geographic range. p. 1109

dissociation The separation of water to produce hydrogen ions and hydroxide ions. p. 1046

distal convoluted tubule The tubule in the human nephron that drains urine into a collecting duct that leads to the renal pelvis. p. 1060

disulfide linkage Linkage that occurs when two sulfhydryl groups interact during a linking reaction. p. 1088

domestication Selective breeding of other species to increase desirable characteristics in progeny. p. 1229

dominance hierarchy A social system in which the behaviour of each individual is constrained by that individual's status in a highly structured social ranking. p. 985

dorsal lip of the blastopore A crescent-shaped depression rotated clockwise 90° on the embryo surface that marks the region derived from the grey crescent, to which cells from the animal pole move as gastrulation begins. p. 828

duodenum A short region of the small intestine where secretions from the pancreas and liver enter a common duct. p. 1014

ecdysone A steroid hormone that controls cuticle formation in insects and crustaceans and possibly nematodes. p. 858

echolocation A behaviour in which animal compares echoes of sounds it produced to the original signals. Differences between pulses and echoes allow location of obstacles and prey. p. 904

ecological community An assemblage of species living in the same place. p. 1108

ecological efficiency The ratio of net productivity at one trophic level to net productivity at the trophic level below it. p. 1178

ecological niche The resources a population uses and the environmental conditions it requires over its lifetime. p. 1147

ecological pyramid A diagram illustrating the effects of energy transfer from one trophic level to the next. p. 1180

ecosystem ecology An ecological discipline that explores the cycling of nutrients and the flow of energy between the biotic components of an ecological community and the abiotic environment. p. 1108

ecotone A wide transition zone between adjacent communities. p. 1152

ectotherm An animal that obtains its body heat primarily from the external environment. p. 1067

effector In signal transduction, a plasma membrane–associated enzyme, activated by a G protein, that generates one or more second messengers. In homeostatic feedback, the system that returns the condition to the set point if it has strayed away. p. 769

effector T cell A cell involved in effecting—bringing about—the specific immune response to an antigen. p. 1091

efferent arteriole The arteriole that receives blood from the glomerulus. p. 1063

efferent neuron A neuron that carries the signals indicating a response away from the interneuron networks to the effectors. p. 878

eggs Nonmotile gametes. p. 800

elastin A rubbery protein in some connective tissues that adds elasticity to the extracellular matrix. It is able to return to its original shape after being stretched, bent, or compressed. p. 762

electrical signalling A means of animal communication in which a signaller emits an electric discharge that can be received by another individual. p. 973

electrical synapse A mechanical and electrically conductive link between two abutting neurons that is formed at the gap junction. p. 880

electrocardiogram (ECG) Graphic representation of the electrical activity within the heart, detected by electrodes placed on the body. p. 787

electrochemical gradient A difference in chemical - concentration and electric potential across a membrane. p. 881

electroreceptor A specialized sensory receptor that detects electrical fields. p. 927

emigration The movement of individuals out of a population. p. 1112

endocrine gland Any of several ductless secretory organs that secrete hormones into the blood or extracellular fluid. pp. 760, 855

endocrine system The system of glands that release their secretions (hormones) directly into the circulatory system. p. 855

endoderm The innermost of the three primary germ layers of an embryo, which develops into the gastrointestinal tract and, in some animals, the respiratory organs. p. 825

endoparasite A parasite that lives in the internal organs of its host organism. p. 1150

endorphin One of a group of small proteins occurring naturally in the brain and around nerve endings that bind to opiate receptors and thus can raise the pain threshold. p. 864

endoskeleton A supportive internal body structure, such as bones, that provides support. p. 951

endotherm An animal that obtains most of its body heat from internal physiological sources. p. 1067

energy budget The total amount of energy that an organism can accumulate and use to fuel its activities. p. 1114

enzymatic hydrolysis A process in which chemical bonds are broken by the addition of H^+ and OH^-, the components of a molecule of water. p. 1010

eosinophil A type of leukocyte that targets extracellular parasites too large for phagocytosis in the inflammatory response. p. 1083

epiblast The top layer of the blastodisc. p. 829

epidermis A complex tissue that covers an organism's body in a single continuous layer or sometimes in multiple layers of tightly packed cells. p. 1071

epididymis A coiled storage tubule attached to the - surface of each testis. p. 813

epiglottis A flaplike valve at the top of the trachea. p. 1013

epinephrine A nontropic amine hormone secreted by the adrenal medulla. p. 867

epiphyte A plant that grows independently on other plants and obtains nutrients and water from the air. p. 1025

epithelial tissue Tissue formed of sheetlike layers of cells that are usually joined tightly together, with little extracellular matrix material between them. They protect body surfaces from invasion by bacteria and viruses and secrete or absorb substances. p. 759

epitope The small region of an antigen molecule to which BCRs or TCRs bind. p. 1088

equilibrium theory of island biogeography An hypothesis suggesting that the number of species on an island is governed by a give and take between the immigration of new species to the island and the extinction of species already there. p. 1136

erythrocyte A red blood cell that contains hemoglobin, a protein that transports O_2 in blood. p. 780

erythropoietin (EPO) A hormone that stimulates stem cells in bone marrow to increase erythrocyte production. p. 781

essential element Any of a number of elements required by living organisms to ensure normal reproduction, growth, development, and maintenance. p. 996

essential fatty acid Any fatty acid that the body cannot synthesize but needs for normal metabolism. p. 1001

essential mineral Any inorganic element such as calcium, iron, or magnesium that is required in the diet of an animal. p. 999

estivation Seasonal torpor in an animal that occurs in summer. p. 1075

estradiol A form of estrogen. p. 869

estrogen Any of the group of female sex hormones. p. 868

estuary A coastal habitat where tidal seawater mixes with fresh water from rivers, streams, and runoff. p. 1050

ethology A discipline that focuses on how animals behave. p. 965

eusocial A form of social organization, observed in some insect species, in which numerous related individuals—a large percentage of them sterile female workers—live and work together in a colony for the reproductive benefit of a single queen and her mate(s). p. 987

eustachian tube A duct leading from the air-filled middle ear to the throat that protects the eardrum from damage caused by changes in environmental atmospheric pressure. p. 913

evaporation Heat transfer through the energy required to change a liquid to a gas. p. 1067

excitatory postsynaptic potential (EPSP) The change in membrane potential caused when a neurotransmitter opens a ligand-gated Na^+ channel and Na^+ enters the cell, making it more likely that the postsynaptic neuron will generate an action potential. p. 894

exocrine gland A gland that is connected to the epithelium by a duct and that empties its secretion at the epithelial surface. p. 760

exoskeleton A hard external covering of an animal's body that blocks the passage of water and provides support and protection. p. 950

exploitative competition Form of competition in which two or more individuals or populations use the same limiting resources. p. 1143

exponential model of population growth Model that describes unlimited population growth. p. 1118

external fertilization The process in which sperm and eggs are shed into the surrounding water, occurring in most aquatic invertebrates, bony fishes, and amphibians. p. 803

external gill A gill that extends out from the body and lacks a protective covering. p. 1037

extracellular fluid The fluid occupying the spaces between cells in multicellular animals. p. 768

extraembryonic membrane A primary tissue layer extended outside the embryo that conducts nutrients from the yolk to the embryo, exchanges gases with the environment outside the egg, or stores metabolic wastes removed from the embryo. p. 830

facilitation hypothesis A hypothesis that explains ecological succession, suggesting that species modify the local environment in ways that make it less suitable for themselves but more suitable for colonization by species typical of the next successional stage. p. 1136

family planning program A program that educates people about ways to produce an optimal family size on an economically feasible schedule. p. 1130

fast block to polyspermy The barrier set up by the wave of depolarization triggered when sperm and egg fuse, making it impossible for other sperm to enter the egg. p. 805

fast muscle fibre A muscle fibre that contracts relatively quickly and powerfully. p. 947

fate map Mapping of adult or larval structures onto the region of the embryo from which each structure developed. p. 845

fat-soluble vitamin A vitamin that dissolves in liquid fat or fatty oils, in addition to water. p. 1002

fertilization The fusion of the nuclei of an egg and sperm cell, which initiates development of a new individual. pp. 800, 1050

fetus A developing human from the eighth week of gestation onward, at which point the major organs and organ systems have formed. p. 835

fibrin A protein necessary for blood clotting; fibrin forms a weblike mesh that traps platelets and red blood cells and holds a clot together. p. 783

fibrinogen A plasma protein that plays a central role in the blood-clotting mechanism. p. 780

fibroblast The type of cell that secretes most of the collagen and other proteins in the loose connective tissue. p. 762

fibronectin A class of glycoproteins that aids in the attachment of cells to the extracellular matrix and helps hold the cells in position. p. 762

fibrous connective tissue Tissue in which fibroblasts are sparsely distributed among dense masses of collagen and elastin fibres that are lined up in highly ordered, parallel bundles, producing maximum tensile strength and elasticity. p. 763

filtration The nonselective movement of some water and a number of solutes—ions and small molecules, but not large molecules such as proteins—into the proximal end of the renal tubules through spaces between cells. p. 1053

fission The mode of asexual reproduction in which the parent separates into two or more offspring of approximately equal size. p. 799

fixed action pattern A highly stereotyped instinctive behaviour; when triggered by a specific cue, it is performed over and over in almost exactly the same way. p. 962

fluid feeder An animal that obtains nourishment by ingesting liquids that contain organic molecules in solution. p. 1009

follicle cell A cell that grows from ovarian tissue and nourishes the developing egg. p. 803

follicle-stimulating hormone (FSH) The pituitary hormone that stimulates oocytes in the ovaries to continue meiosis and become follicles. During follicle enlargement, FSH interacts with luteinizing hormone to stimulate follicular cells to secrete estrogens. p. 864

forebrain The largest division of the brain, which includes the cerebral cortex and basal ganglia. It is credited with the highest intellectual functions. p. 898

foreskin A loose fold of skin that covers the glans of the penis. p. 814

founder cells p. 845

fovea The small region of the retina around which cones are concentrated in mammals and birds with eyes specialized for daytime vision. p. 917

fragmentation A type of vegetative reproduction in plants in which cells or a piece of the parent break off and then develop into new individuals. p.799

fundamental niche The range of conditions and resources that a population can possibly tolerate and use. p. 1147

gallbladder The organ that stores bile between meals, when no digestion is occurring. p. 1018

gametogenesis The formation of male and female gametes. p. 800

ganglion cell A type of neuron in the retina of the eye that receives visual information from photoreceptors via various intermediate cells such as bipolar cells, amacrine cells, and horizontal cells. p. 919

gap gene In *Drosophila* embryonic development, the first activated set of segmentation genes that progressively subdivide the embryo into regions, determining the segments of the embryo and the adult. p. 847

gastric juice A substance secreted by the stomach that contains the digestive enzyme pepsin. p. 937

gastrula The developmental stage resulting when the cells of the blastula migrate and divide once cleavage is complete. p. 825

gastrulation The second major process of early development in most animals, which produces an embryo with three distinct primary tissue layers. p. 825

generalized compartment model A model used to describe nutrient cycling in which two criteria—organic versus inorganic nutrients and available versus unavailable nutrients—define four compartments where nutrients accumulate. p. 1185

generation time The average time between the birth of an organism and the birth of its offspring. p. 1112

geographic range The overall spatial boundaries within which a population lives. p. 1108

germ cell An animal cell that is set aside early in embryonic development and gives rise to the gametes. pp. 801, 830

gizzard The part of the digestive tube that grinds ingested material into fine particles by muscular contractions of the wall. p. 1010

gland A cell or group of cells that produces and releases substances nearby, in another part of the body, or to the outside. p. 760

glans A soft, caplike structure at the end of the penis, containing most of the nerve endings producing erotic sensations. p. 813

glial cell A nonneuronal cell contained in the nervous tissue that physically supports and provides nutrients to neurons, provides electrical insulation between them, and scavenges cellular debris and foreign matter. pp. 766, 878

globulin A plasma protein that transports lipids (including cholesterol) and fat-soluble vitamins; a specialized subgroup of globulins, the immunoglobulins, constitute antibodies and other molecules contributing to the immune response. p. 780

glomerulus A ball of blood capillaries surrounded by Bowman's capsule in the human nephron. p. 1060

glucagon A pancreatic hormone with effects opposite to those of insulin: it stimulates glycogen, fat, and protein degradation. p. 870

glucocorticoid A steroid hormone secreted by the adrenal cortex that helps maintain the blood concentration of glucose and other fuel molecules. p. 867

Golgi tendon organ A proprioceptor of tendons. p. 910

gonad A specialized gamete-producing organ in which the germ cells collect. Gonads are the primary source of sex hormones in vertebrates: ovaries in the female and testes in the male. p. 868

gonadotropin-releasing hormone (GnRH) A tropic-hormone secreted by the hypothalamus that causes the pituitary to make luteinizing hormone (LH) and -follicle-stimulating hormone (FSH). p. 869

gonadotropin A hormone that regulates the activity of the gonads (ovaries and testes). p. 864

G protein. p. 858

graded potential A change in membrane potential that does not necessarily trigger an action potential. p. 894

greater vestibular gland One of two glands located slightly below and to the left and right of the opening of the vagina in women. They secrete mucus to provide lubrication, especially when the woman is sexually aroused. p. 809

greenhouse effect A phenomenon in which certain gases foster the accumulation of heat in the lower atmosphere, maintaining warm temperatures on Earth. p. 1190

grey crescent A crescent-shaped region of the underlying cytoplasm at the side opposite the point of sperm entry exposed after fertilization when the pigmented layer of cytoplasm rotates toward the site of sperm entry. p. 828

grey matter Areas of densely packed nerve cell bodies and dendrites in the brain and spinal cord. p. 929

gross primary productivity The rate at which producers convert solar energy into chemical energy. p. 1176

growth factor Any of a large group of peptide hormones that regulates the division and differentiation of many cell types in the body. p. 857

growth hormone (GH) A hormone that stimulates cell division, protein synthesis, and bone growth in children and adolescents, thereby causing body growth. p. 864

habitat The specific environment in which a population lives, as characterized by its biotic and abiotic features. p. 1108

habituation The learned loss of responsiveness to stimuli. p. 965

haplodiploidy A pattern of sex determination in insects in which females are diploid and males are haploid. p. 987

harvesting efficiency The ratio of the energy content of food consumed compared with the energy content of food available. p. 1178

heavy chain The heavier of the two types of polypeptide chains that are found in immunoglobulin and antibody molecules. p. 1089

helper T cell A clonal cell that assists with the activation of B cells. p. 1091

hepatic portal vein The blood vessel that leads to capillary networks in the liver. p. 1020

herbivory The interaction between herbivorous animals and the plants they eat. p. 1138

hermaphroditism The mechanism in which both mature egg-producing and mature sperm-producing tissue are present in the same individual. p. 807

hibernation Extended torpor during winter. p. 1075

hindbrain The lower area of the brain that includes the brain stem, medulla oblongata, and pons. p. 898

homeodomain An encoded transcription factor of each protein that binds to a region in the promoters of the genes whose transcription it regulates. p. 849

homeostasis A steady internal condition maintained by responses that compensate for changes in the external environment. pp. 756, 1051

homeostatic mechanism Any process or activity responsible for homeostasis. p. 756

homeotic gene Any of the family of genes that determines the structure of body parts during embryonic development. p. 849

horizon A noticeable layer of soil, such as topsoil, with a distinct texture and composition that varies with soil type. p. 1004

horizontal cell A type of neuron that forms lateral connections among photoreceptor cells in the retina of the eye. p. 918

human chorionic gonadotropin (hCG) A hormone that keeps the corpus luteum in the ovary from breaking down. p. 817

humus The organic component of soil remaining after decomposition of plants and animals, animal droppings, and other organic matter. p. 1004

hybridoma A B cell that has been induced to fuse with a cancerous lymphocyte called a myeloma cell, forming a single, composite cell. p. 1088

hydrogeologic cycle The global cycling of water between the ocean, the atmosphere, land, freshwater ecosystems, and living organisms. p. 1186

hydroponic culture A method of growing plants not in soil but with the roots bathed in a solution that contains water and mineral nutrients. p. 996

hydrostatic skeleton A structure consisting of muscles and fluid that, by themselves, provide support for the animal or part of the animal; no rigid support, such as a bone, is involved. p. 949

hymen A thin flap of tissue that partially covers the opening of the vagina. p. 809

hyperpolarized The condition of a neuron when its membrane potential is more negative than the resting value. p. 882

hypertension Commonly called high blood pressure, a medical condition in which blood pressure is chronically elevated above normal values. p. 787

hyperthermia The condition resulting when the heat gain of the body is too great to be counteracted. p. 1074

hypoblast The bottom layer of a blastodisc. p. 829

hypodermis The innermost layer of the skin that contains larger blood vessels and additional reinforcing connective tissue. p. 1071

hypothalamus The portion of the brain that contains centres regulating basic homeostatic functions of the body and contributing to the release of hormones. p. 932

hypothermia A condition in which the core temperature falls below normal for a prolonged period. p. 1073

immigration Movement of organisms into a population. p. 1112

immune privilege The situation in which certain sites in the body tolerate the presence of an antigen without mounting an inflammatory immune response. These sites include the brain, eyes, and testicles. p. 1096

immune response The defensive reactions of the immune system. p. 1081

immune system The combined defences, innate and acquired, a body uses to eliminate infections. p. 1080

immunoglobulin A specific protein substance produced by plasma cells to aid in fighting infection. p. 780

immunological memory The capacity of the immune system to respond more rapidly and vigorously to the second contact with a specific antigen than to the primary contact. p. 1094

immunological tolerance The process that protects the body's own molecules from attack by the immune system. p. 1097

incus The second of the three sound-conducting middle ear bones in vertebrates, located between the malleus and the stapes. p. 912

indirect neurotransmitter A neurotransmitter that acts as a first messenger, binding to a G protein–coupled receptor in the postsynaptic membrane, which activates the receptor and triggers generation of a second messenger such as cyclic AMP or other processes. p. 890

induction A mechanism in which one group of cells (the inducer cells) causes or influences another nearby group of cells (the responder cells) to follow a particular developmental pathway. p. 826

infection thread In the formation of root nodules on nitrogen-fixing plants, the tube formed by the plasma membrane of root hair cells as bacteria enter the cell. p. 1008

inflammation The heat, pain, redness, and swelling that occur at the site of an infection. p. 1082

inhibin A peptide that, in females, is an inhibitor of FSH secretion from the pituitary, thereby diminishing the signal for follicular growth. In males, inhibin inhibits FSH secretion from the pituitary, thereby decreasing spermatogenesis. p. 810

inhibiting hormone (IH) A hormone released by the hypothalamus that inhibits the secretion of a particular anterior pituitary hormone. p. 862

inhibition hypothesis A hypothesis suggesting that new species are prevented from occupying a community by whatever species are already present. p. 1136

inhibitory postsynaptic potential (IPSP) A change in membrane potential caused when hyperpolarization occurs, pushing the neuron farther from threshold. p. 894

innate immunity A nonspecific line of defence against pathogens that includes inflammation, which creates internal conditions that inhibit or kill many pathogens, and specialized cells that engulf or kill pathogens or infected body cells. p. 1080

inner cell mass The dense mass of cells within the blastocyst that will become the embryo. p. 935

inner ear That part of the ear, particularly the cochlea, that converts mechanical vibrations (sound) into neural messages that are sent to the brain. p. 913

insight learning A phenomenon in which animals can solve problems without apparent trial-and-error attempts at the solution. p. 965

instinctive behaviour A genetically "programmed" response that appears in complete and functional form the first time it is used. p. 962

insulin A hormone secreted by beta cells in the islets, acting mainly on cells of nonworking skeletal muscles, liver cells, and adipose tissue (fat) to lower blood glucose, fatty acid, and amino acid levels and promote the storage of those molecules. pp. 869, 1021

insulin-like growth factor (IGF) A peptide that directly stimulates growth processes. p. 864

integration The sorting and interpretation of neural messages and the determination of the appropriate response(s). p. 877

integrator In homeostatic feedback, the control centre that compares a detected environmental change with a set point. p. 769

integument Skin. p. 1070

interference competition Form of competition in which individuals fight over resources or otherwise harm each other directly. p. 1143

interferon A cytokine produced by infected host cells affected by viral dsRNA, which acts on both the infected cell that produces it, an autocrine effect, and neighbouring uninfected cells, a paracrine effect. p. 1085

intermediate disturbance hypothesis Hypothesis proposing that species richness is greatest in communities that experience fairly frequent disturbances of moderate intensity. p. 1161

internal fertilization The process in which sperm are released by the male close to or inside the entrance of the reproductive tract of the female. p. 804

internal gill A gill located within the body that has a cover providing physical protection for the gills. Water must be brought to internal gills. p. 1037

interneuron A neuron that integrates information to formulate an appropriate response. p. 878

interspecific competition The competition for resources between species. p. 1143

interstitial fluid The fluid occupying the spaces between cells in multicellular animals. p. 768

intraspecific competition The dependence of two or more individuals in a population on the same limiting resource. p. 1121

intrinsic rate of increase The maximum possible per capita population growth rate in a population living under ideal conditions. p. 1119

involution The process by which cells migrate into the blastopore. p. 828

iris Of the eye, the coloured muscular membrane that lies behind the cornea and in front of the lens, which by opening or closing determines the size of the pupil and hence the amount of light entering the eye. p. 915

islets of Langerhans Endocrine cells that secrete the -peptide hormones insulin and glucagon into the bloodstream. p. 869

juvenile hormones A family of fatty acid hormones that govern metamorphosis and reproduction in insects and crustaceans. p. 872

ketone Molecule in which the carbonyl group is linked to a carbon atom in the interior of a carbon chain. p. 870

keystone species A species that has a greater effect on community structure than its numbers might suggest. p. 1158

kin selection Altruistic behaviour to close relatives, allowing them to produce proportionately more surviving copies of the altruist's genes than the altruist might otherwise have produced on its own. p. 985

kinesis A change in the rate of movement or the frequency of turning movements in response to environmental stimuli. p. 975

K-selected species Long-lived, slow reproducing species that thrive in more stable environments. p. 1125

labia majora A pair of fleshy, fat-padded folds that partially cover the labia minora. p. 809

labia minora Two folds of tissue that run from front to rear on either side of the opening to the vagina. p. 809

larynx The voice box. p. 1040

lateral geniculate nuclei Clusters of neurons located in the thalamus that receive visual information from the optic nerves and send it on to the visual cortex. p. 920

lateral inhibition Visual processing in which lateral movement of signals from a rod or cone proceeds to a horizontal cell and continues to bipolar cells with which the horizontal cell makes inhibitory connections, serving both to sharpen the edges of objects and enhance contrast in an image. p. 919

lateral-line system The complex of mechanoreceptors along the sides of some fishes and aquatic amphibians that detect vibrations in the water. p. 908

lateralization A phenomenon in which some brain functions are more localized in one of the two hemispheres. p. 935

leaching The process by which soluble materials in soil are washed into a lower layer of soil or are dissolved and carried away by water. p. 1005

learned behaviour A response of an animal that is dependent on having a particular kind of experience during development. p. 962

learning A process in which experiences stored in memory change the behavioural responses of an animal. p. 935

leghemoglobin An iron-containing, red-pigmented protein produced in root nodules during the symbiotic association between *Bradyrhizobium* or *Rhizobium* and legumes. p. 1008

lek A display ground where males each possess a small territory from which they court attentive females. p. 981

lens The transparent, biconvex intraocular tissue that helps bring rays of light to a focus on the retina. p. 915

leukocyte A white blood cell, which eliminates dead and dying cells from the body, removes cellular debris, and participates in defending the body against invading organisms. p. 783

Leydig cell A cell that produces the male sex hormones. p. 813

life history The lifetime pattern of growth, maturation, and reproduction that is characteristic of a population or species. p. 1114

life table A chart that summarizes the demographic characteristics of a population. p. 1113

ligament A fibrous connective tissue that connects bones to each other at a joint. p. 763

ligand-gated ion channel A channel that opens or closes when a specific chemical, such as a neurotransmitter, binds to the channel. p. 890

light chain The lighter of the two types of polypeptide chains found in immunoglobulin and antibody molecules. p. 1088

limbic system A functional network formed by parts of the thalamus, hypothalamus, and basal nuclei, along with other nearby grey-matter centres—the amygdala, hippocampus, and olfactory bulbs—sometimes called the "emotional brain." p. 932

limiting nutrient An element in short supply within an ecosystem, the shortage of which limits productivity. p. 1176

logistic model of population growth Model of population growth that assumes that a population's per capita growth rate decreases as the population gets larger. p. 1120

long-term memory Memory that stores information from days to years or even for life. p. 935

long-term potentiation A long-lasting increase in the strength of synaptic connections in activated neural pathways following brief periods of repeated stimulation. p. 935

loop of Henle In mammals, a U-shaped bend of the proximal convoluted tubule. p. 1060

loose connective tissue A tissue formed of sparsely distributed cells surrounded by a more or less open network of collagen and other glycoprotein fibres. p. 762

luteinizing hormone (LH) A hormone secreted by the pituitary that stimulates the growth and maturation of eggs in females and the secretion of testosterone in males. p. 864

lymph The interstitial fluid picked up by the lymphatic system. p. 791

lymph node One of many small, bean-shaped organs spaced along the lymph vessels that contain macrophages and other leukocytes that attack invading disease organisms. p. 793

lymphatic system An accessory system of vessels and organs that helps balance the fluid content of the blood and surrounding tissues and participates in the body's defences against invading disease organisms. p. 791

lymphocyte A leukocyte that carries out most of its activities in the tissues and organs of the lymphatic system. Lymphocytes play major roles in immune responses. p. 781

macronutrient In humans, a mineral required in amounts ranging from 50 mg to more than 1 g per day. In plants, a nutrient needed in large amounts for the normal growth and development. p. 995

macrophage A phagocyte that takes part in nonspecific defences and adaptive immunity. p. 1082

magnetoreceptor A receptor found in some animals that navigate long distances that allows them to detect and use Earth's magnetic field as a source of directional information. p. 904

major histocompatibility complex A large cluster of genes encoding the MHC proteins. p. 1091

malleus The outermost of the sound-conducting bones of the middle ear in vertebrates. p. 912

malnutrition A condition resulting from a diet that lacks one or more essential nutrients. p. 1000

marsupium An external pouch on the abdomen of many female marsupials, containing the mammary glands, and within which the young continue to develop after birth. p. 807

mass extinctions The disappearance of a large number of species in a relatively short period of geologic time. p. 1203

mast cell A type of cell dispersed through connective tissue that releases histamine when activated by the death of cells, caused by a pathogen at an infection site. p. 1083

maternal-effect gene One of a class of genes that regulate the expression of other genes expressed by the mother during oogenesis and that control the polarity of the egg and, therefore, of the embryo. p. 847

mating systems The social systems describing how males and females pair up. p. 981

mechanoreceptor A sensory receptor that detects mechanical energy, such as changes in pressure, body position, or acceleration. The auditory receptors in the ears are examples of mechanoreceptors. p. 885

meiosis The division of diploid cells to haploid progeny, consisting of two sequential rounds of nuclear and cellular division. p. 800

melanocyte-stimulating hormone (MSH) A hormone secreted by the anterior pituitary that controls the degree of pigmentation in melanocytes. p. 864

melanotic encapsulation The mechanism by which hemocytes move toward and form a capsule around pathogens that are too big to phagocytose. The capsule may then be melanized by the deposition of phenolic compounds that further isolate the pathogen. p. 1082

melatonin A peptide hormone secreted by the pineal gland that helps maintain daily biorhythms. p. 871

membrane attack complexes An abnormal activation of the complement protein) portion of the blood, forming a cascade reaction that brings blood proteins together, binds them to the cell wall, and then inserts them through the cell membrane. p. 1085

memory The storage and retrieval of a sensory or motor experience or a thought. p. 935

memory B cell In antibody-mediated immunity, a long-lived cell expressing an antibody on its surface that can bind to a specific antigen. A memory B cell is activated the next time the antigen is encountered, producing a rapid secondary immune response. p. 1092

memory cell An activated lymphocyte that circulates in the blood and lymph, ready to initiate a rapid immune response on subsequent exposure to the same antigen. p. 1088

memory helper T cell In cell-mediated immunity, a long-lived cell differentiated from a helper T cell, which remains in an inactive state in the lymphatic system after an immune reaction has run its course and ready to be activated on subsequent exposure to the same antigen. p. 1094

meninges Three layers of connective tissue that surround and protect the spinal cord and brain. p. 929

menstrual cycle A cycle of approximately 1 month in the human female during which an egg is released from an ovary and the uterus is prepared to receive the fertilized egg; if fertilization does not occur, the endometrium breaks down, which releases blood and tissue breakdown products from the uterus to the outside through the vagina. p. 810

mesenteries Sheets of loose connective tissue, covered on both surfaces with epithelial cells, which suspend the abdominal organs in the coelom and provide lubricated, smooth surfaces that prevent chafing or abrasion between adjacent structures as the body moves. p. 763

mesoderm The middle layer of the three primary germ layers of an animal embryo, from which the muscular, skeletal, vascular, and connective tissues develop. p. 825

microclimate The abiotic conditions immediately surrounding an organism. p. 1163

micronutrient Any mineral required by an organism only in trace amounts. p. 995

midbrain The uppermost of the three segments of the brain stem, serving primarily as an intermediary between the rest of the brain and the spinal cord. p. 898

migration The predictable seasonal movement of animals from the area where they are born to a distant and initially unfamiliar destination, returning to their birth site later. p. 977

mimic The species in Batesian mimicry that resembles the model. p. 1142

mimicry A form of defence in which one species evolves an appearance resembling that of another. p. 1142

mineralocorticoid A steroid hormone secreted by the adrenal cortex that regulates the levels of Na and K in the blood and extracellular fluid. p. 868

model The species in Batesian mimicry that is resembled by the mimic. p. 1142

monoclonal antibody An antibody that reacts only against the same segment (epitope) of a single antigen. p. 1097

monocyte A type of leukocyte that enters damaged tissue from the bloodstream through the endothelial wall of the blood vessel. p. 1082

monogamy A mating system in which one male and one female form a long-term association. p. 981

morula The first stage of animal development, a solid ball or layer of blastomeres. p. 825

motor neuron An efferent neuron that carries signals to skeletal muscle. p. 878

motor unit A block of muscle fibres that is controlled by branches of the axon of a single efferent neuron. p. 946

moult-inhibiting hormone (MIH) A peptide neurohormone secreted by cells in the eyestalks (extensions of the brain leading to the eyes). p. 872

mucosa The lining of the gut that contains epithelial and glandular cells. p. 1012

Müllerian duct The bipotential primitive duct associated with the gonads that leads to a cloaca. p. 839

Müllerian mimicry A form of defence in which two or more unpalatable species share a similar appearance. p. 1142

muscle fibre A bundle of elongated, cylindrical cells that make up skeletal muscle. pp. 765, 941

muscle spindle A stretch receptor in muscle; a bundle of small, specialized muscle cells wrapped with the dendrites of afferent neurons and enclosed in connective tissue. p. 910

muscle tissue Cells that have the ability to contract (shorten) forcibly. p. 764

muscle twitch A single, weak contraction of a muscle fibre. p. 944

muscularis The muscular coat of a hollow organ or tubular structure. p. 1012

mutualism A symbiotic interaction between species in which both partners benefit. pp. 1081, 1148

mycorrhiza A mutualistic symbiosis in which fungal hyphae associate intimately with plant roots. p. 1006

myoblast An undifferentiated muscle cell. p. 846

myofibril A cylindrical contractile element about 1 m in diameter that runs lengthwise inside the muscle fibre cell. p. 941

myogenic heart A heart that maintains its contraction rhythm with no requirement for signals from the nervous system. p. 786

myoglobin An oxygen-storing protein closely related to hemoglobin. p. 947

natural killer (NK) cell A type of lymphocyte that destroys pathogen infected cells. p. 1084

navigation A wayfinding mechanism in which an animal moves toward a specific destination, using both a compass and a "mental map" of where it is in relation to the destination. p. 977

negative feedback The primary mechanism of homeostasis, in which a stimulus—a change in the external or internal environment—triggers a response that compensates for the environmental change. p. 769

negative pressure breathing Muscular contractions that expand the lungs, lowering the pressure of the air in the lungs and causing air to be pulled inward. p. 1039

nephron A specialized excretory tubule that contributes to osmoregulation and carries out excretion, found in all vertebrates. p. 1057

nerve A bundle of axons enclosed in connective tissue and all following the same pathway. p. 897

nerve cord A bundle of nerves that extends from the central ganglia to the rest of the body, connected to smaller nerves. p. 897

nerve net A simple nervous system that coordinates responses to stimuli but has no central control organ or brain. p. 895

nervous tissue Tissue that contains neurons, which serve as lines of communication and control between body parts. p. 766

net primary productivity The chemical energy remaining in an ecosystem after a producer's cellular respiration is deducted. p. 1176

neural crest A band of cells that arises early in the embryonic development of vertebrates near the region where the neural tube pinches off from the ectoderm; later, the cells migrate and develop into unique structures. p. 831

neural plate Ectoderm thickened and flattened into a longitudinal band, induced by notochord cells. p. 831

neural signalling The process by which an animal responds appropriately to a stimulus. p. 877

neural tube A hollow tube in vertebrate embryos that develops into the brain, spinal cord, spinal nerves, and spinal column. p. 897

neurogenic heart A heart that beats under the control of signals from the nervous system. p. 786

neuromuscular junction The junction between a nerve fibre and the muscle it supplies. p. 942

neuron An electrically active cell of the nervous system responsible for controlling behaviour and body functions. pp. 766, 856, 877

neuronal circuit The connection between axon terminals of one neuron and the dendrites or cell body of a second neuron. p. 878

neuropile The region of a ganglion in which branching axons and dendrites make interconnections. pp. 897, 902

neurosecretory neuron A neuron that releases a neurohormone into the circulatory system when appropriately stimulated. p. 855

neurotransmitter A chemical released by an axon terminal at a chemical synapse. p. 880

neurulation The process in vertebrates by which organogenesis begins with development of the nervous system from ectoderm. p. 831

neutrophil A type of phagocytic leukocyte that attaches to blood vessel walls in massive numbers when attracted to the infection site by chemokines. p. 1083

nitrification A metabolic process in which certain soil bacteria convert ammonia or ammonium ions into nitrites that are then converted by other bacteria to nitrates, a form usable by plants. pp. 1007, 1192

nitrogen cycle A biogeochemical cycle that moves nitrogen between the huge atmospheric pool of gaseous molecular nitrogen and several much smaller pools of nitrogen-containing compounds in soils, marine and freshwater ecosystems, and living organisms. p. 1188

nitrogen fixation A metabolic process in which certain bacteria and cyanobacteria convert molecular nitrogen into ammonia and ammonium ions, forms usable by plants. p. 1188

nociceptor A sensory receptor that detects tissue damage or noxious chemicals; their activity registers as pain. p. 885

node of Ranvier The gap between two Schwann cells, which exposes the axon membrane directly to extracellular fluids. p. 879

nonshivering thermogenesis The generation of heat by oxidative mechanisms in nonmuscle tissue throughout the body. p. 1073

norepinephrine A nontropic amine hormone secreted by the adrenal medulla. p. 867

ocellus (plural, ocelli) The simplest eye, which detects light but does not form an image. p. 915

olfactory bulb A grey-matter centre that relays inputs from odour receptors to both the cerebral cortex and the limbic system. p. 932

oligodendrocyte A type of glial cell that populates the CNS and is responsible for producing myelin. p. 879

oligotrophic lake A lake that is poor in nutrients and organic matter but rich in oxygen. p. 1176

omnivore An animal that feeds at several trophic levels, consuming plants, animals, and other sources of organic matter. p. 1000

oogenesis The process of producing eggs. p. 802

oogonium (plural, oogonia) A cell that enters meiosis and gives rise to gametes, produced by mitotic divisions of the germ cells in females. p. 801

open circulatory system An arrangement of internal transport in some invertebrates in which the vascular fluid, hemolymph, is released into sinuses, bathing organs directly, and is not always retained within vessels. p. 775

operant conditioning A form of associative learning in which animals learn to link a voluntary activity, an operant, with its favourable consequences, the reinforcement. p. 965

opsin One of several different proteins that bond covalently with the light-absorbing pigment of rods and cones (retinal). p. 918

optic chiasm Location just behind the eyes where the optic nerves converge before entering the base of the brain, a portion of each optic nerve crossing over to the opposite side. p. 920

optimal foraging theory A set of mathematical models that predict the diet choices of animals as they encounter a range of potential food items. p. 1139

organ Two or more different tissues integrated into a structure that carries out a specific function. p. 758

organ of corti An organ within the cochlear duct that contains the sensory hair cells detecting sound vibrations transmitted to the inner ear. p. 913

organ system The coordinated activities of two or more organs to carry out a major body function such as movement, digestion, or reproduction. p. 758

organismal ecology An ecological discipline in which researchers study the genetic, biochemical, physiological, morphological, and behavioural adaptations of organisms to their abiotic environments. p. 1108

organogenesis The development of the major organ systems, giving rise to a free-living individual with the body organization characteristic of its species. p. 825

osmoconformer An animal in which the osmolarity of the cellular and extracellular solutions matches the osmolarity of the environment. p. 1052

osmolality A measure of the osmotic concentration of a solution. It is measured in osmoles (the number of solute molecules and ions) per kilogram of solvent. p. 1052

osmoregulator An animal that uses control mechanisms to keep the osmolarity of cellular and extracellular fluids the same but at levels that may differ from the osmolarity of the surroundings. p. 1052

osteoblast A cell that produces the collagen and mineral of bone. p. 764

osteoclast A cell that removes bone minerals and recycles them through the bloodstream. p. 764

osteocyte A mature bone cell. p. 764

osteon The structural unit of bone, consisting of a minute central canal surrounded by osteocytes embedded in concentric layers of mineral matter. p. 764

otolith One of many small crystals of calcium carbonate embedded in the otolithic membrane of the hair cells. p. 910

outer ear The external structure of the ear, consisting of the pinna and meatus. p. 912

ova (ovum) *See* ovum. p. 802

ovarian cycle The cyclic events in the ovary leading to ovulation. p. 810

ovary In animals, the female gonad, which produces female gametes and reproductive hormones. In flowering plants, the enlarged base of a carpel in which one or more ovules develop into seeds. p. 869

overnutrition The condition caused by excessive intake of specific nutrients. p. 999

oviduct The tube through which the egg moves from the ovary to the outside of the body. p. 803

oviparous Referring to animals that lay eggs containing the nutrients needed for development of the embryo outside the mother's body. p. 805

ovoviviparous Referring to animals in which fertilized eggs are retained within the body and the embryo develops using nutrients provided by the egg; eggs hatch inside the mother. p. 805

ovulation The process in which oocytes are released into the oviducts as immature eggs. p. 809

ovum A female sex cell, or egg. p. 802

oxytocin A hormone that stimulates the ejection of milk from the mammary glands of a nursing mother. p. 865

pacemaker cell A specialized cardiac muscle cell in the upper wall of the right atrium that sets the rate of contraction in the heart. p. 786

pair-rule genes In *Drosophila* embryonic development, the set of segmentation regulatory genes activated by gap genes that divide the embryo into units of two segments each. p. 848

pancreas A mixed gland composed of an exocrine portion that secretes digestive enzymes into the small intestine and an endocrine portion, the islets of Langerhans, that secretes insulin and glucagon. p. 869

parasitism A symbiotic interaction in which one species, the parasite, uses another, the host, in a way that is harmful to the host. p. 1150

parasitoid An insect species in which a female lays eggs in the larva or pupa of another insect species, and her young consume the tissues of the living host. p. 1103

parasympathetic division The division of the autonomic nervous system that predominates during quiet, low-stress situations, such as while relaxing. p. 901

parathyroid gland One of a pair of glands that produce parathyroid hormone (PTH) (found only in tetrapod vertebrates). p. 866

parathyroid hormone (pTH) The hormone secreted by the parathyroid glands in response to a fall in blood Ca^{2+} levels. p. 866

parental investment The time and energy devoted to the production and rearing of offspring. p. 822

parthenogenesis A mode of asexual reproduction in which animals produce offspring by the growth and development of an egg without fertilization. p. 799

partial pressure The individual pressure exerted by each gas within a mixture of gases. p. 1033

parturition The process of giving birth. p. 838

passive immunity The acquisition of antibodies as a result of direct transfer from another person. p. 1095

passive parental care The amount of energy invested in offspring—in the form of the energy stored in eggs or seeds or energy transferred to developing young through a placenta—before they are born. p. 1115

pattern formation The arrangement of organs and body structures in their proper three-dimensional - relationships. p. 846

per capita growth rate The difference between the per capita birth rate and the per capita death rate of a population. p. 1119

perfusion The flow of blood or other body fluids on the internal side of the respiratory surface. p. 1035

peripheral nervous system (pNS) All nerve roots and nerves (motor and sensory) that supply the muscles of the body and transmit information about sensation (including pain) to the central nervous system. p. 865

peristalsis The rippling motion of muscles in the intestine or other tubular organs characterized by the alternate contraction and relaxation of the muscles that propel the contents onward. p. 1012

peritubular capillary A capillary of the network surrounding the glomerulus. p. 1060

pharynx The throat. In some invertebrates, a protrusible tube used to bring food into the mouth for passage to the gastrovascular cavity; in mammals, the common pathway for air entering the larynx and food entering the esophagus. p. 1040

phosphorus cycle A biogeochemical cycle in which weathering and erosion carry phosphate ions from rocks to soil and into streams and rivers, which eventually transport them to the ocean, where they are slowly incorporated into rocks. p. 1194

photopigment Light-absorbing pigment. p. 918

photopsin One of three photopigments in which retinal is combined with different opsins. p. 920

photoreceptor A sensory receptor that detects the energy of light. p. 885

physiology The study of the functions of organisms—the physicochemical processes of organisms. p. 757

piloting A wayfinding mechanism in which animals use familiar landmarks to guide their journey. p. 977

pineal gland A light-sensitive, melatonin-secreting gland that regulates some biological rhythms. p. 870

pinna The external structure of the outer ear, which concentrates and focuses sound waves. p. 912

placenta A specialized temporary organ that connects the embryo and fetus with the uterus in mammals, mediating the delivery of oxygen and nutrients. Analagous structures occur in other animals. p. 805

plasma The clear, yellowish fluid portion of the blood in which cells are suspended. Plasma consists of water, glucose and other sugars, amino acids, plasma -proteins, dissolved gases, ions, lipids, vitamins, -hormones and other signal molecules, and metabolic wastes. pp. 768, 780

plasma cell A large antibody-producing cell that develops from B cells. p. 1092

platelet An oval or rounded cell fragment enclosed in its own plasma membrane, which is found in the blood; they are produced in red bone marrow by the division of stem cells and contain enzymes and other factors that take part in blood clotting. p. 783

pleura The double layer of epithelial tissue covering the lungs. p. 1041

polarity The unequal distribution of yolk and other components in a mature egg. p. 825

polyandry A polygamous mating system in which one female mates with multiple males. p. 981

polygamy A mating system in which either males or females may have many mating partners. p. 981

polygyny A polygamous mating system in which one male mates with many females. p. 981

population density The number of individuals per unit area or per unit volume of habitat. p. 1108

population ecology The ecological discipline that focuses on how a population's size and other characteristics change in space and time. p. 1108

population size The number of individuals in a population at a specified time. p. 1108

positive feedback A mechanism that intensifies or adds to a change in internal or external environmental condition. p. 771

positive pressure breathing A gulping or swallowing motion that forces air into the lungs. p. 1038

posterior pituitary The neural portion of the pituitary, which stores and releases two hormones made by the hypothalamus, antidiuretic hormone and oxytocin. p. 862

postsynaptic cell The neuron or the surface of an effector after a synapse that receives the signal from the presynaptic cell. p. 880

postsynaptic membrane The plasma membrane of the postsynaptic cell. p. 890

predation The interaction between predatory animals and the animal prey they consume. p. 1138

prepuce Foreskin; a loose fold of skin that covers the glans of the penis. p. 814

presynaptic cell The neuron with an axon terminal on one side of the synapse that transmits the signal across the -synapse to the dendrite or cell body of the postsynaptic cell. p. 880

presynaptic membrane The plasma membrane of the axon terminal of a presynaptic cell, which releases neurotransmitter molecules into the synapse in response to the arrival of an action potential. p. 890

primary cell layers The ectoderm, mesoderm, and endoderm layers that form the embryonic tissues. p. 825

primary consumer A herbivore, a member of the second trophic level. p. 999

primary immune response The response of the immune system to the first challenge by an antigen. p. 1094

primary motor area The area of the cerebral cortex that runs in a band just in front of the primary somatosensory area and is responsible for voluntary movement. p. 933

primary somatosensory area The area of the cerebral cortex that runs in a band across the parietal lobes of the brain and registers information on touch, pain, temperature, and pressure. p. 933

primary succession Predictable change in species composition of an ecological community that develops on bare ground. p. 1136

primitive groove In the development of birds, the sunken midline of the primitive streak that acts as a conduit for migrating cells to move into the blastocoel. p. 830

primitive streak In the development of birds, the thickened region of the embryo produced by cells of the epiblast streaming toward the midline of the blastodisc. p. 829

production efficiency The ratio of the energy content of new tissue produced to the energy assimilated from food. p. 1179

progesterone A female sex hormone that stimulates growth of the uterine lining and inhibits contractions of the uterus. p. 869

progestin A class of sex hormones synthesized by the gonads of vertebrates and active predominantly in females. p. 868

prolactin (pRL) A peptide hormone secreted by the anterior pituitary that stimulates breast development and milk secretion in mammals. p. 839

promiscuity A mating system in which individuals do not form close pair bonds, and both males and females mate with multiple partners. p. 981

propagation In animal nervous systems, the concept that the action potential does not need further trigger events to keep going. p. 887

proprioceptor A mechanoreceptor that detects stimuli used in the CNS to maintain body balance and equilibrium and to monitor the position of the head and limbs. p. 907

prostaglandin One of a group of local regulators derived from fatty acids that are involved in paracrine and autocrine regulation. p. 812

prostate gland An accessory sex gland in males that adds a thin, milky fluid to the semen and adjusts the pH of the semen to the level of acidity best tolerated by sperm. p. 813

protonephridium The simplest form of invertebrate excretory tubule. p. 1053

proximal convoluted tubule The tubule between the Bowman's capsule and the loop of Henle in the nephron of the kidney, which carries and processes the filtrate. p. 1060

pulmonary circuit The circuit of the cardiovascular system that supplies the lungs. p. 776

pupil The dark centre in the middle of the iris through which light passes to the back of the eye. p. 915

pyramid of biomass A diagram that illustrates differences in standing crop biomass in a series of trophic levels. p. 1180

pyramid of energy A diagram that illustrates the amount of energy that flows through a series of trophic levels. p. 1180

pyramid of numbers A diagram that illustrates the number of individual organisms present in a series of trophic levels. p. 1181

radiation The transfer of heat energy as electromagnetic radiation. p. 1067

random dispersion A pattern of distribution in which the individuals in a population are distributed unpredictably in their habitat. p. 1111

rapid eye movement (REM) sleep The period during deep sleep when the delta wave **pattern is replaced by rapid,** irregular beta waves characteristic of the waking state. The person's heartbeat and breathing rate increase, the limbs twitch, and the eyes move rapidly behind the closed eyelids. p. 936

reabsorption The process in which some molecules (e.g, glucose and amino acids) and ions are transported by the transport epithelium back into the body fluid (animals with open circulatory systems) or into the blood in capillaries surrounding the tubules (animals with closed circulatory systems) as the filtered solution moves through the excretory tubule. p. 859

realized niche The range of conditions and resources that a population actually uses in nature. p. 1147

reception In signal transduction, the binding of a signal molecule with a specific receptor in a target cell. p. 877

reciprocal altruism Form of altruistic behaviour in which individuals help nonrelatives if they are likely to return the favour in the future. p. 986

rectum The final segment of the large intestine. p. 1020

reflex A programmed movement that takes place without conscious effort, such as the sudden withdrawal of a hand from a hot surface. p. 792

refractory period A period that begins at the peak of an action potential and lasts a few milliseconds, during which the threshold required for generation of an action potential is much higher than normal. p. 883

reinforcement The enhancement of reproductive isolation that had begun to develop while populations were geographically separated. p. 965

releasing hormone (RH) A peptide neurohormone that controls the secretion of hormones from the anterior pituitary. p. 862

renal artery An artery that carries bodily fluids into the kidney. p. 1059

renal cortex The outer region of the mammalian kidney that surrounds the renal medulla. p. 1059

renal medulla The inner region of the mammalian kidney. p. 1059

renal pelvis The central cavity in the kidney where urine drains from collecting ducts. p. 1059

renal vein The vein that routes filtered blood away from the kidney. p. 1059

reproductive strategy A set of behaviours that lead to reproductive success. p. 799

residual volume The air that remains in lungs after exhalation. p. 1043

resource partitioning The use of different resources or the use of resources in different ways by species living in the same place. p. 1148

respiratory medium The environmental source of O_2 and the "sink" for released CO_2. For aquatic animals, the respiratory medium is water; for terrestrial animals, it is air. p. 1035

respiratory surface A layer of epithelial cells that provides the interface between the body and the respiratory medium. p. 1034

response In signal transduction, the last stage in which the transduced signal causes the cell to change according to the signal and to the receptors on the cell. In the nervous system, the output resulting from the integration of neural messages. p. 877

resting potential A steady negative membrane potential exhibited by the membrane of a neuron that is not -stimulated—that is, not conducting an impulse. p. 881

reticular formation A complex network of interconnected neurons that runs through the length of the brain stem, connecting to the thalamus at the anterior end and to the spinal cord at the posterior end. p. 898

retina A light-sensitive membrane lining the posterior part of the inside of the eye. p. 915

rhodopsin The retinal–opsin photopigment. p. 918

rod In the vertebrate eye, a type of photoreceptor in the retina that is specialized for detection of light at low intensities. p. 917

root nodule A localized swelling on a root in which symbiotic nitrogen-fixing bacteria reside. p. 1007

round window A thin membrane that faces the middle ear. p. 913

r-selected species A short-lived species adapted to function well in a rapidly changing environment. p. 1125

saccule A fluid-filled chamber in the vestibular apparatus that provides information about the position of the head with respect to gravity (up versus down), as well as changes in the rate of linear movement of the body. p. 908

salivary amylase A substance that hydrolyzes starches to the disaccharide maltose. p. 1012

salivary gland A gland that secretes saliva through a duct on the inside of the cheek or under the tongue; the saliva lubricates food and begins digestion. p. 1014

salt marsh A tidal wetland dominated by emergent grasses and reeds. p. 1233

saltatory conduction A mechanism that allows small-diameter axons to conduct impulses rapidly. p. 888

sarcomere The basic unit of contraction in a myofibril. p. 942

Schwann cell A type of glial cell in the PNS that wraps nerve fibres with myelin and also secretes regulatory factors. p. 879

scrotum The baglike sac in which the testes are suspended in many mammals. p. 812

secondary consumer A carnivore that feeds on herbivores, a member of the third trophic level. p. 999

secondary immune response The rapid immune response that occurs during the second (and subsequent) encounters of the immune system of a mammal with a specific antigen. p. 1091

secondary productivity Energy stored in new consumer biomass as energy is transferred from producers to consumers. p. 1178

secondary succession Predictable changes in species composition in an ecological community that develops after existing vegetation is destroyed or disrupted by an environmental disturbance. p. 1136

segment polarity genes In *Drosophila* embryonic development, the set of segmentation regulatory genes activated by pair-rule genes that set the boundaries and anterior–posterior axis of each segment in the embryo. p. 848

segmentation genes Genes that work sequentially, progressively subdividing the embryo into regions, determining the segments of the embryo and the adult. p. 847

selective cell adhesion A mechanism in which cells make and break specific connections to other cells or to the extracellular matrix. p. 826

semicircular canal A part of the vestibular apparatus that detects rotational (spinning) motions. p. 908

semilunar valve (SL valve) A flap of endocardium and connective tissue reinforced by fibres that prevent the valve from turning inside out. p. 784

seminal vesicle A vesicle that secretes seminal fluid. p. 813

seminiferous tubule One of the tiny tubes in the testes where sperm cells are produced, grow, and mature. p. 812

sensitization Increased responsiveness to mild stimuli after experiencing a strong stimulus; one of the simplest forms of memory. p. 936

sensor A tissue or organ that detects a change in an external or internal factor such as pH, temperature, or the concentration of a molecule such as glucose. p. 769

sensory adaptation A condition in which the effect of a stimulus is reduced if it continues at a constant level. p. 906

sensory hair cell A hair cell that sends impulses along the auditory nerve to the brain when alternating changes of pressure agitate the basilar membrane on which the organ of Corti rests, moving the hair cells. p. 907

sensory neuron A neuron that transmits stimuli collected by their sensory receptors to interneurons. p. 878

sensory receptor (transducer) A receptor formed by the dendrites of afferent neurons or by specialized receptor cells making synapses with afferent neurons that pick up information about the external and internal environments of the animal. p. 884

sensory transduction The conversion of a stimulus into a change in membrane potential. p. 884

sequential hermaphroditism The form of hermaphroditism in which individuals change from one sex to the other. p. 807

serosa The serous membrane: a thin membrane lining the closed cavities of the body; has two layers with a space between that is filled with serous fluid. p. 1013

Sertoli cell One of the supportive cells that completely surrounds developing spermatocytes in the seminiferous tubules. Follicle-stimulating hormone stimulates Sertoli cells to secrete a protein and other molecules that are required for spermatogenesis. p. 813

set point The level at which the condition controlled by a homeostatic pathway is to be maintained. p. 769

sex ratio The relative proportions of males and females in a population. p. 1112

sexual reproduction The mode of reproduction in which male and female parents produce offspring through the union of egg and sperm generated by meiosis. p. 799

short-term memory Memory that stores information for seconds. p. 935

sign stimulus A simple cue that triggers a fixed action pattern. p. 962

simulation modelling An analytical method in which researchers gather detailed information about a system and then create a series of mathematical equations that predict how the components of the system interact and respond to change. p. 1196

simultaneous hermaphroditism A form of hermaphroditism in which individuals develop functional ovaries and testes at the same time. p. 807

single-lens eye An eye type that works by changing the amount of light allowed to enter into the eye and by focusing this incoming light with a lens. p. 915

sinoatrial node (SA node) The region of the heart that controls the rate and timing of cardiac muscle cell contraction. p. 786

skeletal muscle A muscle that connects to bones of the skeleton, typically made up of long and cylindrical cells that contain many nuclei. p. 765

slow block to polyspermy The process in which enzymes released from cortical granules alter the egg coats within minutes after fertilization so that no other sperm can attach and penetrate to the egg. p. 805

slow muscle fibre A muscle fibre that contracts relatively slowly and with low intensity. p. 947

smooth muscle A relatively small and spindle-shaped muscle cell in which actin and myosin molecules are arranged in a loose network rather than in bundles. p. 765

soil solution A combination of water and dissolved substances that coats soil particles and partially fills pore spaces. p. 1004

somatic cell Any of the cells of an organism's body other than reproductive cells. p. 801

somatic nervous system A subdivision of the peripheral nervous system controlling body movements that are primarily conscious and voluntary. p. 899

somites Paired blocks of mesoderm cells along the vertebrate body axis that form during early vertebrate development and differentiate into dermal skin, bone, and muscle. p. 832

spatial summation The summation of EPSPs produced by firing of different presynaptic neurons. p. 894

species composition The particular combination of species that occupy a site. p. 1156

species diversity A community characteristic defined by species richness and the relative abundance of species. p. 1136

species richness The number of species that live within an ecological community. p. 1136

sperm Motile gamete. p. 800

spermatocyte A developing gamete that becomes a spermatid at the end of meiosis. p. 813

spermatogenesis The process of producing sperm. p. 802

spermatogonium (plural, spermatogonia) A cell that enters meiosis and gives rise to gametes, produced by mitotic divisions of the germ cells in males. p. 801

spermatozoon (plural, spermatozoa) Also called sperm; a haploid cell that develops into a mature sperm cell when meiosis is complete. p. 802

sphincter A powerful ring of smooth muscle that forms a valve between major regions of the digestive tract. p. 788

spinal cord A column of nervous tissue located within the vertebral column and directly connected to the brain. p. 897

spinal nerve A nerve that carries signals between the spinal cord and the body trunk and limbs. p. 929

spiracle An opening in the chitinous exoskeleton of an insect through which air enters and leaves the tracheal system. p. 1036

standing crop biomass The total dry weight of plants present in an ecosystem at a given time. p. 1176

stapes The smallest of three sound-conducting bones in the middle ear of tetrapod vertebrates. p. 912

statocyst A mechanoreceptor in invertebrates that senses gravity and motion using statoliths. p. 907

stereocilia Microvilli covering the surface of hair cells clustered in the base of neuromasts. p. 908

stretch receptor A proprioceptor in the muscles and tendons of vertebrates that detects the position and movement of the limbs. p. 790

submucosa A thick layer of elastic connective tissue that contains neuron networks and blood and lymph vessels. p. 1012

subsoil The region of soil beneath topsoil, which contains relatively little organic matter. p. 1004

succession The change from one community type to another. p. 1161

survivorship curve Graphic display of the rate of survival of individuals over a species' life span. p. 1113

suspension (filter) feeder An animal that ingests small food items suspended in water. p. 1009

sympathetic division Division of the autonomic nervous system that predominates in situations involving stress, danger, excitement, or strenuous physical activity. p. 901

sympatric Occupying the same spaces at the same time. p. 4450

synapse A site where a neuron makes a communicating connection with another neuron or an effector such as a muscle fibre or gland. p. 879

systemic circuit In amphibians, the branch of a double blood circuit that receives oxygenated blood and provides the blood supply for most of the tissues and cells of a body. p. 778

systole The period of contraction and emptying of the heart. p. 784

T cell A lymphocyte produced by the division of stem cells in the bone marrow and then released into the blood and carried to the thymus. T cells participate in adaptive immunity. p. 1087

T (transverse) tubule The tubule that passes in a transverse manner from the sarcolemma across a myofibril of striated muscle. p. 942

tactile signal A means of animal communication in which the signaller uses touch to convey a message to the signal receiver. p. 973

taiga *See* boreal forest. p. 1177

taxis A behavioural response that is directed either toward or away from a specific stimulus. p. 975

T-cell receptor (TCR) A receptor that covers the plasma membrane of a T cell, specific for a particular antigen. p. 1088

temperate deciduous forest A forested biome found at low to middle altitudes at temperate latitudes, with warm summers, cold winters, and annual precipitation between 75 and 250 cm. p. 1154

temperate grassland A nonforested biome that stretches across the interiors of most continents, where winters are cold and snowy and summers are warm and fairly dry. p. 1177

temporal summation The summation of several EPSPs produced by successive firing of a single presynaptic neuron over a short period of time. p. 894

tendon A type of fibrous connective tissue that attaches muscles to bones. p. 763

territory A plot of habitat, defended by an individual male or a breeding pair of animals, within which the territory holders have exclusive access to food and other necessary resources. p. 960

tertiary consumer A carnivore that feeds on other carnivores, a member of the fourth trophic level. p. 1156

testis (plural, testes) The male gonad. In male vertebrates, they secrete androgens and steroid hormones that stimulate and control the development and maintenance of male reproductive systems. pp. 801, 868

testosterone A hormone produced by the testes, responsible for the development of male secondary sex characteristics and the functioning of the male reproductive organs. p. 813

tetanus A situation in which a muscle fibre cannot relax between stimuli, and twitch summation produces a peak level of continuous contraction. p. 946

thalamus A major switchboard of the brain that receives sensory information and relays it to the regions of the cerebral cortex concerned with motor responses to sensory information of that type. p. 932

thermal acclimatization A set of physiological changes in ectotherms in response to seasonal shifts in environmental temperature, allowing the animals to attain good physiological performance at both winter and summer temperatures. p. 1070

thermoreceptor A sensory receptor that detects the flow of heat energy. p. 885

thick filament A type of filament in striated muscle - composed of myosin molecules; they interact with thin filaments to shorten muscle fibres during contraction. p. 941

thin filament A type of filament in striated muscle composed of actin, tropomyosin, and troponin molecules; they interact with thick filaments to shorten muscle fibres during contraction. p. 941

threshold potential In signal conduction by neurons, the membrane potential at which the action potential fires. p. 882

thyroid gland A gland located beneath the voice box (larynx) that secretes hormones regulating growth and metabolism. p. 865

thyroid-stimulating hormone (TSH) A hormone that stimulates the thyroid gland to grow in size and secrete thyroid hormones. p. 864

thyroxine (T4) The main hormone of the thyroid gland, responsible for controlling the rate of metabolism in the body. p. 865

tidal volume The volume of air entering and leaving the lungs during inhalation and exhalation. p. 1042

time lag The delayed response of organisms to changes in environmental conditions. p. 1121

tolerance hypothesis Hypothesis asserting that ecological succession proceeds because competitively superior species replace competitively inferior ones. p. 1136

torpor A sleeplike state produced when a lowered set point greatly reduces the energy required to maintain body temperature, accompanied by reductions in metabolic, nervous, and physical activity. p. 1074

trace element An element that occurs in organisms in very small quantities (0.01%); in nutrition, a mineral required by organisms only in small amounts. p. 1001

trachea In insects, an extensively branched, air-conducting tube formed by invagination of the outer epidermis of the animal and reinforced by rings of chitin. In vertebrates, the windpipe, which branches into the bronchi. p. 1040

transmission In neural signalling, the sending of a message along a neuron and then to another neuron or to a muscle or gland. p. 877

transport epithelium A layer of cells with specialized transport proteins in their plasma membranes. p. 1053

triiodothyronine (T3) A hormone secreted by the thyroid gland that regulates metabolism. p. 865

trimester A division of human gestation, three months in length. p. 835

trophic cascade The effects of predator–prey interactions that reverberate through other population interactions at two or more trophic levels in an ecosystem. p. 1183

trophic level A position in a food chain or web that defines the feeding habits of organisms. p. 1000

trophoblast The outer single layer of cells of the blastocyst. p. 835

tropic hormone A hormone that regulates hormone secretion by another endocrine gland. p. 863

tropical deciduous forest A tropical forest biome that occurs where winter drought reduces photosynthesis and most trees drop their leaves seasonally. p. 1177

turnover rate The rate at which one generation of producers in an ecosystem is replaced by the next. p. 1181

tympanum A thin membrane in the auditory canal that vibrates back and forth when struck by sound waves. p. 911

umbilicus Navel; the scar left when the short length of umbilical cord still attached to the infant after birth dries and shrivels within a few days. p. 837

undernutrition A condition in animals in which intake of organic fuels is inadequate or whose assimilation of such fuels is abnormal. p. 1000

unicellular organism Individual consisting of a single cell. p. 1003

uniform dispersion A pattern of distribution in which the individuals in a population are evenly spaced in their habitat. p. 827

ureter The tube through which urine flows from the renal pelvis to the urinary bladder. p. 1059

urethra The tube through which urine leaves the bladder. In most animals, the urethra opens to the outside. p. 1059

urinary bladder A storage sac located outside the kidneys. p. 1059

uterine cycle The menstrual cycle. p. 810

uterus A specialized saclike organ, in which the embryo develops in viviparous animals. p. 805

utricle A fluid-filled chamber of the vestibular apparatus that provides information about the position of the head with respect to gravity (up versus down), as well as changes in the rate of linear movement of the body. p. 908

vaccination The process of administering a weakened form of a pathogen to patients as a means of giving them immunity to subsequent infection, and disease, caused by that pathogen. p. 1080

vas deferens (plural, vasa deferentia) The tube through which sperm travel from the epididymis to the urethra in the male reproductive system. p. 813

vegetal pole The end of the egg opposite the animal pole, which typically gives rise to internal structures such as the gut and the posterior end of the embryo. p. 825

vein In a plant, a vascular bundle that forms part of the branching network of conducting and supporting tissues in a leaf or other expanded plant organ. In an animal, a vessel that carries the blood back to the heart. p. 777

ventilation The flow of the respiratory medium (air or water, depending on the animal) over the respiratory surface. p. 1035

ventricle In the brain, an irregularly shaped cavity containing cerebrospinal fluid. In the heart, a chamber that pumps blood out of the heart. p. 897

venule A capillary that merges into the small veins leaving an organ. p. 787

vestibular apparatus The specialized sensory structure of the inner ear of most terrestrial vertebrates that is responsible for perceiving the position and motion of the head and, therefore, for maintaining equilibrium and for coordinating head and body movements. p. 908

visual signal A means of communication in which animals use facial expressions or body language to send messages to other individuals. p. 972

vital capacity The maximum tidal volume of air that an individual can inhale and exhale. p. 1043

vitamin An organic molecule required in small quantities that the animal cannot synthesize for itself. p. 1000

vitamin D A steroidlike molecule that increases the absorption of Ca^{2+} and phosphates from ingested food by promoting the synthesis of a calcium-binding protein in the intestine; it also increases the release of Ca^{2+} from bone in response to PTH. p. 866

vitelline coat A gel-like matrix of proteins, glycoproteins, or polysaccharides immediately outside the plasma membrane of an egg cell. p. 803

vitreous humour The jellylike substance that fills the main chamber of the eye, between the lens and the retina. p. 916

viviparous Referring to animals that retain the embryo within the mother's body and nourish it during at least early embryo development. p. 805

voltage-gated ion channel A membrane-embedded protein that opens and closes as the membrane potential changes. p. 883

vulva The external female sex organs. p. 809

watershed An area of land from which precipitation drains into a single stream or river. p. 1187

water-soluble vitamin A vitamin with a high proportion of oxygen and nitrogen able to form hydrogen bonds with water. p. 1002

white matter The myelinated axons that surround the grey matter of the central nervous system. p. 929

Wolffian duct A bipotential primitive duct associated with the gonads that leads to a cloaca. p. 839

yolk The portion of an egg that serves as the main energy source for the embryo. p. 824

yolk sac In an amniote egg, an extraembryonic membrane that encloses the yolk. p. 830

zero population growth A circumstance in which the birth rate of a population equals the death rate. p. 1119

zona pellucida A gel-like matrix of proteins, glycoproteins, or polysaccharides immediately outside the plasma membrane of the egg cell. p. 803

Appendix A
Answers to Self-Test Questions

Chapter 31

1. a 2. b 3. e 4. a 5. d 6. b 7. d 8. c 9. d 10. c, e

Chapter 32

1. a, b, c, d, e 2. d 3. b 4. d 5. a, d, e 6. d 7. e 8. a, b, c, d 9. b, d 10. d

Chapter 33

1. a, d 2. d 3. a, c 4. d 5. d 6. d 7. b 8. a 9. c 10. b

Chapter 34

1. d 2. d 3. b 4. c 5. d 6. d 7. d 8. b 9. c 10. b

Chapter 35

1. a 2. c 3. e 4. c 5. a 6. d 7. a, b, c, d 8. b, c 9. a 10. c

Chapter 36

1. b, c, d, e 2. a, c, d 3. a, c 4. a, c 5. e 6. b 7. c, d 8. a 9. c 10. b

Chapter 37

1. a 2. d 3. b, d 4. c 5. e 6. a, b, c, d, e 7. d 8. b, d 9. a, b 10. b

Chapter 38

1. d 2. d 3. e 4. e 5. a, b 6. c 7. a, b 8. a 9. e 10. e

Chapter 39

1. b 2. c 3. a 4. b 5. d 6. c 7. d 8. b 9. c 10. b

Chapter 40

1. a 2. a 3. b 4. d 5. c 6. a 7. d 8. b, c 9. e 10. c

Chapter 41

1. b, c 2. a 3. a, b, c 4. d 5. a, c, e 6. a, b, d 7. a 8. b 9. e 10. a, e

Chapter 42

1. a 2. d 3. c 4. a, c, d, e 5. a 6. c 7. b 8. b 9. b 10. b

Chapter 43

1. a 2. c 3. b 4. e 5. e 6. d 7. b 8. c 9. a 10. d

Chapter 44

1. a 2. b 3. b 4. c 5. a 6. a 7. a 8. d 9. d 10. a

Chapter 45

1. c 2. b 3. a 4. a 5. b 6. d 7. b 8. d 9. c 10. b

Chapter 46

1. d 2. c 3. a 4. d 5. d 6. a 7. c 8. d 9. c 10. a

Chapter 47

1. d 2. c 3. d 4. c 5. b 6. b 7. a 8. b 9. b 10. b

Chapter 48

1. c 2. d 3. b 4. b 5. c 6. d 7. b 8. b 9. b 10. b

Index

Brain (*continued*)
cerebral hemispheres, 930, 934
comparison of structures, 899i
evolution of, 897–899, 899i
forebrain, 898, 930
gustatory centres, 922
hindbrain, 898, 930
hippocampus, 935
hypothalamus, 860i, 861i, 862, 863i, 898, 925, **932**
limbic system, **932**
lobes of the cerebrum, 932, 933i
long-term memory, 935–936
medulla, 930
midbrain, 898, 930
motor area, **933**, 934i
olfactory system, 923
pons, 930
primary somatosensory area, **933**, 934i
sensory integration, 930–931
sensory region, 833
short-term memory, 935–936
thalamus, 898, 920, **932**
of vertebrates, 898
Brain stem, **930**, 931
Brassica (genus), 1244–1245
Breeding frequency, 1115–1116
Briggs, Robert, 844
Broca's area, 933
Bronchi, **1040**
Bronchioles, **1040**
Budding, **799**, 800i
Bulbourethral glands, **814**
Bulk feeders, 1009i, **1010**
Bushbabies (*Galago senegalensis*), 961

Cadherins (calcium-dependent adhesion molecules), **842**
Caecilians (*Boulengerula taitanus*), 823, 823i
Caenorhabditis elegans, 845, 845i
Caffeine, 1248
Calcitonin, **866**, 867i
Calcium-dependent adhesion molecules, **842**
Calvaria trees, extinction of, 1204–1205
Canadian polar bear populations, status of, 1219t
Cancer
of the breast, 816
cells, death of, 1079i
T cells killed by, 1096
Capillaries, **777**, 784, 788–789, 789i
Carbohydrates, enzymatic digestion
of, 1019, 1019t
Carbon, backbone of life, 1186–1188
Carbon cycle, **1186–1188**, 1188i, 1190
Carbon dioxide (CO_2)
diffusion of, 1045–1047
partial pressure of, 1044i
transfer of, 1032–1033, 1046i
Cardiac cycle, 786–788, 787i
Cardiac muscle, **765**, 765i
Cardio (word), 776
Caretta caretta, 928
Carnivore teeth, tetracycline rings in, 1107i
Carotid arteries, 1043

Carrying capacity, **1120**, 1228
Cartilage, 763i, 764
Catecholamines, **867**
Cation exchange, **1005**
Cats, domestic
domestication of, 1246–1247, 1247i
as invasive species, 1207
Cattle, domestication of, 1234–1235, 1235i, 1242
$CD4^+$ T cell, **1091**
$CD8^+$ T cell, **1096**
Cecum, 1020
CED-3, 850
CED-4, 850
CED-9, 850
Cell adhesion molecules (CAMs), **842**
Cell body, **877**, 878
Cell-death genes, **831**, 834, 850–851, 850i
Cell lineage, **845**, 845i
Cell-mediated immunity, 1088, 1095–1096, 1095i
Cell signalling, 855–856, 856i
Cellular blastoderm, **846**
Cellular respiration
oxidative phosphorylation, 947
Cellulose, 1015
Central nervous system, 929–935
brain, 930–931
cerebrospinal fluid, **929**
grey matter, **929**, 930
meninges, **929**
spinal cord, 929–930
of vertebrates, 898–899
white matter, 929–930, 929i
Central neural integration, 928–929
Central pattern generator (CPG), 956
Cephalization, 896–897
Cephalopod mollusc, 915, 915i, 936
Cerebellum, 930
Cerebral cortex, 922, **930**, 932–934
Cerebral hemispheres, 930, 934
Cerebrospinal fluid, **929**
Chaenophryne longiceps (anglerfish), 1026–1027, 1026i
Character displacement, **1148**
Cheatgrass (*Bromus tectorum*), 1210
Chemical defence, 1141–1142
Chemical synapses, **880**, 881i, 895i
Chemicals, plants as source of, 1248–1249
Chemokines, **1083**
Chemoreceptors, **885**, 921–924
Child abuse, evolutionary analysis of, 989
Chili peppers, domestication of, 1241
Chimpanzees (*Pan troglodytes*), 961, 988–989
Chitin, 951
Chitosans, 951
Chlorosis, 1000
Cholecystokinin (*CCK*), 1021i, 1022
Chondrocytes, **764**
Chorion, **830**
Chorionic villi, **837**
Cimicidae, 806
Circulatory systems. *See* Animal circulatory
systems
Circumcision, **814**

Glucose, 864
  GIP secretion, 1022
  stress and, 872
Glucose-dependent insulinotrophic peptide (GIP), 1022
Glycogen, 864, 867
Goitre, 866
Golgi tendon organs, **910**, 911i
Gonadal development, of fetus, 839
Gonadotropin-releasing, hormone (GnRH), 810, 811, 814,
  869, 968
Gonadotropins, **864**
Gonads, **868**–869
Gould, James L., 975
Grapes, domestication of, 1239
Great Barrier Reef, 797
Greater vestibular glands, **809**
Greenhouse effect, **1190**
Green revolution, 1228
Grey matter, **929**, 930
Gross primary productivity, **1176**
Growth factors, 761, **857**
Growth hormones (GH), 858, **864**
Guano, **1195**
Gulls, population of, 1106i
Guppies, 808
  life histories of, 1116–1117, 1116i, 1117i
Gurdon, John B., 844
Gustatory centres, 922

Habitats, **1108**
  protecting, 1220–1221
Habituation, **965**
Haeckel, Ernst, 1107
Hall, Brian K., 833
Halteres, 908
Hamilton, William D., 985
Handicap hypothesis, 983
Harvesting efficiency, **1178**
Hearing, in animal sensory systems, 911–913
Heart, 783–787
  aorta, 784
  atria, 783–784, 786
  atrioventricular (AV) valves, **784**
  blood circulation, 783–784
  coronary circulation, 784
  electric current, 774–775
  evolution of, 778–779
  mammalian, 783–784, 783i
  myogenic, 786
  neurogenic, 786
  semilunar (SL) valves, **784**
  superior vena cava, 784
  ventricles, 783, 783i, 784, 786
  of vertebrates, 779i, 783–784
Heartbeat, 784, 786, 790–791
Heartburn, 1014
Heinrich, Bernd, 974, 975
Helper T cells, **1091**
Heme, 782
Hemlock, 1248
Hemocytes, 780
Hemoglobin, 781, 782, 1044–1045, 1048

Hemoglobin–O$_2$ equilibrium curve, 1044, 1045i
Herbivorous snails, 1160
Herbivory, **1138**
Hermaphroditism, 807–808, 807i
Herrmann, Esther, 988
Hibernation, **1075**
High altitudes, survival at, 1047, 1048
Hindbrain, **898**
Hochachka, Peter, 1047
Holtfreter, Johannes, 842, 843
Homeodomain, 849
Homeostasis, 756, 768–772
  factors of internal environment, 769
  negative feedback control systems, 769–771, 771i
  positive feedback mechanisms, 771–772
  of terrestrial organisms, 1051
  thermostat, 769–771, 771i
Homeostatic mechanisms, **756**
Homeotic genes, 849
Homer-Dixon, Thomas, 1242–1243
Höner, O.P., 988
Honeybees
  domestic, 1235
  self-sacrificing behaviour, 987
Horizons, **1004**
Hormones, **855**
  adrenal cortex, 860i, 867–868
  adrenal medulla, 860, 861t, **867**
  adrenocorticotropic hormone, **864**, 868
  amine, 856–857
  and animal behaviour, 967–968
  antidiuretic hormone, **865**
  and biological rhythms, 870–871
  body processes, 857–858
  cardiac output and arteriole diameter, 791
  circulation of, **855**
  digestive processes, 1021i, 1022
  endocrine systems, 855–856, 871–873
  endorphins, 865
  and external genitalia, 840
  fatty acids, 857, 872
  feedback pathways, 857–858, 857i, 865, 867
  follicle-stimulating hormone, **864**
  fuel molecules, regulation of, 858
  gonads, **868**–869
  growth, 858, **864**
  hydrophilic, 858
  hydrophobic, 858–859, 859i
  hypothalamus-pituitary complex,
    862–865, 863i
  inhibiting, **862**, 863
  and local regulators, 856–857
  luteinizing hormone, 864
  mechanisms of hormone action, 858–862
  melanocyte-stimulating, **864**
  melatonin, 860, **871**
  neurohormone, 855–856
  oxytocin, **865**
  pancreas, 860i, 862t, **869**–870
  parathyroid, 866–867, 867i
  peptide, 857, 872
  pineal gland, 860i, **870**–871

Species
  conservation of, 1213–1215, 1216–1220, 1221–1225
  exploiting other, 1250
Species diversity, 1154, 1154i
Species richness variations, **1167**–1169, 1171
Spemann, Hans, 842
Sperm, **800**, 812–817
Spines and armour, 1141, 1141i
Spike initiation zone, **877**, 894
Spinal cord, 929–930
Spiracles, **1036**
Sp-opsin4, 916
Spotted hyena (*Crocuta crocuta*), 840
Sp-pax6, 916
Squash, domestication of, 1241, 1241i
Standing crop biomass, **1176**
Stapes, **912**
Starfishes (Asteroidea), 1101
Statocysts, **907**, 908i
Statoliths, 908
Stem cells, 761, 781
  blood cell origins in, 1085i
Stereocilia, **908**
Steroid hormones, 857
  glucocorticoids, **867**, 868, 868i
  mineralocorticoids, **868**
Stimulus, **769**
Stomach, 1013i, 1016–1017
Storey, Ken, 1070
Stress on systems and species, 1223
Stress response, 869i, 872
Stretch receptors, 910, 911i
Striated muscle, 941–**942**, 947–948
Stutchbury, Bridget J., 1169
Submucosa, **1012**, 1014i
Succession, **1161**–1166
Summation, **894**, 894i
Superior vena cava, 784
Survivorship curves, **1113–1114**, 1114i
Suspension (filter) feeders, **1009**, 1009i
Swallowing reflex, 1014, 1016i
Symbiosis, 1148–1149
Sympathetic division, **901**
Sympathetic system, 790
Synapse, **779**–780
Synaptic cleft, **880**
Synaptic vesicles, 891
Synovial joint, 954, 954i
Systemic circuit, of blood vessels, 784, 784i
Systole, **784**
Systolic blood pressure, 787

Tactile signals, **973**
Tailless, 847
Taipoxin, 1144–1145, 1144i
Target cells, 859–860
Tartaglia, Louis, 1025
Taste receptors, 922
Taxis, **975**
T-cell receptors (TCRs), **1088**, 1088i

T cells
  activation of, 1090–1091, 1090i
  antigens cleared by, 1087
  cancer cells killed by, 1079i
Tears, content of, 1042
Telencephalon, 898
Teleosts
  kidney function in, 1058i
  water conservation of, 1057–1058
Temperate zones, biodiversity in, 1136
Temperature variations, response to, 1070
Temporal summation, **894**
Terrestrial animals, lungs in, 1038–1040
Terrestrial environments, 1051
Territorial behaviour, 976–977
Testes, 860i, **868**
Testosterone, **813**, 857, 868, 976
Tetrahymena, 872
Tetrapod vertebrates, 910
  respiration in, 1038
Thalamus, 898, 920, **932**
Therian mammals, 806, 809
Thermal acclimatization, **1070**
Thermoreception, 925
Thermoreceptors, **885**, 1070–1071, 1072
Thermoregulation, 1066–1076, 1072i
3a-hydroxy-4-pregen-20-one (3aP), 816
Threonine, 1002
Threshold potential, **882**
Thrips population, rise and fall of, 1124i
Thymus, 1087
Thyroid gland, 860i, 861t, **865**–866
Thyroid hormones, 856–857
Thyroid-releasing hormone (TRH), 857
Thyroid-stimulating hormone (TSH), 857, **864**
Thyroxine (T_4), 858, 860, **865**–866
Tidal volume, 1042–1043
Tight junction, 758–759, 759i
Time lag, **1121**–1122
Tinbergen, Niko, 978
Tissues. *See* Animal tissues
Tobacco, domestication of, 1249i
Tobacco hornworm (*Manduca sexta*), 854
Tolerance hypothesis, **1165–1166**
Tomatoes (*Solanum lycopersicum*), 1239–1241
Tongues, 922, 923i, 924, 1014
Torpor, **1074**
Townes, P.L., 842, 843
Toxins
  as defence, 1141–1142
  resistance to, 1250
Trachea, **1040**
  lining of, 1032i
Tracheal system in insects, 1036–1037
Transducers. *See* Sensory receptors
Transmission, neural signalling, **877**–878
Transport epithelium, **1053**
Transport in animals, 774–793
  blood, 780–783
  blood flow and pressure, 790–791
  blood vessels, 787–790